INSTRUCTOR'S RESOURCE MANUAL
Lyn Riverstone

Mathematics

for Elementary Teachers

A CONTEMPORARY APPROACH

Tenth Edition

Gary L. Musser
Oregon State University

Blake E. Peterson
Brigham Young University

William F. Burger

PUBLISHER	Laurie Rosatone
ACQUISITIONS EDITOR	Jen Brady
ASSISTANT CONTENT EDITOR	Jacqueline Sinacori
SENIOR CONTENT MANAGER	Karoline Luciano
SENIOR PRODUCTION EDITOR	Kerry Weinstein

Founded in 1807, John Wiley & Sons, Inc. has been a valued source of knowledge and understanding for more than 200 years, helping people around the world meet their needs and fulfill their aspirations. Our company is built on a foundation of principles that include responsibility to the communities we serve and where we live and work. In 2008, we launched a Corporate Citizenship Initiative, a global effort to address the environmental, social, economic, and ethical challenges we face in our business. Among the issues we are addressing are carbon impact, paper specifications and procurement, ethical conduct within our business and among our vendors, and community and charitable support. For more information, please visit our website: www.wiley.com/go/citizenship.

ISBN 978-1-118-67924-1

10 9 8 7 6 5 4 3 2 1

TABLE OF CONTENTS

Preface

This manual has been prepared to assist you in using our text. There are several elements in this manual.

Philosophy: In this section, rationale is provided for the selection and organization of the material. You may want to read through this section in its entirety to obtain an overview of the text before reading the rest of this manual.

Chapter Commentaries: Specific suggestions on a section-by-section basis are provided.

Chapter Learning Objectives: A list of expectations, or learning objectives, is provided for each chapter. In stating learning objectives, we have opted for higher-level cognition on Bloom's taxonomy.   These lists might be reproduced and distributed to students at the first meeting of the term. In addition to helping the students with their studying and review, the expectations may be useful organizer as you prepare and teach for your classes.

When Will I Teach This Topic?:   Often students will ask "Where will I teach this topic."   This section provides the approximate grade levels (according to the Common Core Standards) where the material they are studying is likely to appear in a school mathematics series.

Exercise Maps: In this edition of the textbook, the Exercise/Problem Sets have been updated.   Not only have some new exercises and problems been added, some of the problems from the ninth edition have been deleted or renumbered.   The Exercise Map is provided to help you match up both the Part A and Part B Exercise/Problem Sets from the ninth and tenth editions.

Answers to Exercise/Problem Sets - Part B: Instead of providing answers to selected problems for all the odd problems, we make it convenient for you and your students by having answers to *all* of the part A portions in the text and *all* of part B in this manual.   If you collect assignments, the part B sets can allow for some originality by the students.   On the other hand, the part B answers can be removed or copied from this manual and placed in a learning center or library to allow students who want to work additional problems to have access to answers, thus freeing your office hours to work with students on diagnosed difficulties.

Answers for Guide to Problem Solving: The supplement entitled **Guide to Problem Solving** authored by the late Don Miller who taught at St. Cloud State University, artfully walks through all 21 strategies that are introduced in the text and can serve as an excellent source of problems to supplement your discussions of problem solving. Guide to Problem Solving contains answers for the odd-numbered problems whereas this section contains answers for the even-numbered problems. We make copies of these to share with our students.

Many resources and supplements for students and the instructor are available from Wiley on the web and for sale as described in the Preface of our textbook.

We would like this text and its supplements to provide the most effective resources possible for college teachers and their students. Thus, any comments that you can share with us will be appreciated and will permit us to adjust future editions to be as complete and error-free as possible. Please send your suggestions to Gary or Blake at the following addresses:

Gary L. Musser   Blake E. Peterson
1100 Emerald Tint Ct.   Brigham Young University
Las Vegas, NV 89144   Provo, UT 84602-6563
glmusser@cox.net   peterson@mathed.byu.edu
                                                                   FAX: 801-422-0511

E-mail or faxes are also welcome.

Philosophy

In writing this text we had two important commitments to balance, one to mathematics and one to elementary/middle school teachers. As experienced mathematicians can appreciate, this is a delicate task. After you see why we took the paths that we did, it may be easier for you to follow our development in its entirety. Also, making our rationale apparent may make it easier for you to adapt the material to fit your particular approach.

Because of research findings and our own experience over many years, we decided to let abstract mathematics naturally evolve from the physical world when introducing new topics. Many students who enter our courses are not operating effectively with abstractions, and these students find our concrete-pictorial-abstract approach particularly valuable. In addition to this dimension, we also like to emphasize the distinction between routine exercises and more challenging problem solving experiences. Thus, we adopted a taxonomy comprised of five cognitive levels. Finally, to help our students better conceptualize what we were trying to accomplish, we organized our content, representational levels, and cognitive taxonomy into a 3-dimensional Mathematics Learning Cube.

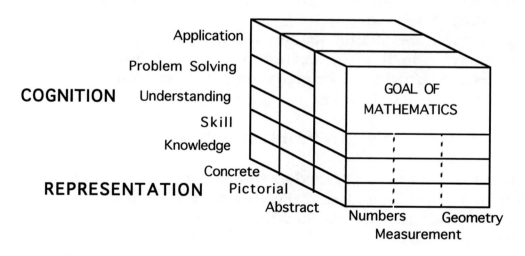

It is our hope that our students will carry this model with them after they study from this text and use this, or a similar model, when they teach. We reinforce the cognitive dimension of our cube in two ways. First, our exercise/problem sets separate practice exercises from problems that require a creative step. Unfortunately, it is impossible to make a perfect dichotomy to fit all students since problems to some students may be exercises to others; conversely, some students may find some exercises to be problems. However, we believe that it is important to try to make such a distinction to keep students attentive to incorporating more problem solving in their own future classrooms. Second, we have included many problems related to the mathematical thinking of children. These problems are called Analyzing Student Thinking problems and are found at the end of each exercise/problem set. Third, we have organized the chapter tests into four cognitive levels to help model testing designed to insure coverage of these various levels of sophistication.

We believe that our mathematical development has integrity throughout and that it is imperative that our students see the significant logical connections inherent in a sound, mathematical approach. Thus, to balance the demands of intuition and relevance on one hand and the importance of mathematical structure on the other, our approach is to introduce nearly all topics in a concrete, informal fashion (especially early in the text). Then, we gently guide students to abstract mathematical concepts so that they will be able to appreciate how the elementary/ middle school curriculum fits together into a meaningful whole rather than simply being a collection of disparate facts.

In the remainder of this section we discuss our development chapter-by-chapter. In the next section, we have additional chapter commentaries that provide more ideas for the classroom.

Chapter 1 - Introduction to Problem Solving

Problem solving is recognized as one the most important goals of mathematics. We have found Polya's four-step process to be helpful to our students, *especially* when a rich source of strategies (heuristics) is available. A valuable tool for solving a broad range of problems is algebra, so we introduce variables and basic methods of solving algebraic equations in this chapter. After some basic concepts are introduced in this chapter, margin notes are included throughout the text highlighting places where algebraic thinking is used.

We cover this chapter and selected strategies throughout the text when we teach our one-year sequence for elementary teachers.

Then, we have a one-quarter course, "Problem Solving for Teachers," where junior/senior level students use the "Problem Solving Study Guide" supplement to have a more in-depth discussion devoted to problem solving. Some instructors may wish to augment this chapter by including an introduction to logic (see Topic 1).

Chapter 2 - Sets, Whole Numbers, and Numeration

Here we introduce the set concepts required to develop all the major ideas in the remainder of the text. We like to cover bases other than ten in this chapter so that we can use them to illustrate algorithms in Chapter 4.

Chapter 3 - Whole Numbers: Operations and Properties

Operations and their properties are covered in this chapter and techniques of computation are covered in Chapter 4. We separate these topics into two chapters rather than integrating them for three reasons. First, the separation allows us to have Chapter 3 focus on the underlying conceptual meanings of the operations before moving on to the derived algorithms. Second, this dichotomy helps to clarify the fact that algorithms are separate from (although based on) the algebraic structure of the whole number system. Third, this separation allows for the broadening of the discussion of algorithms to three modes of computation: mental, electronic (calculators or computers), and written (our common algorithms and alternatives).

In this chapter our emphasis is on the algebraic structure of the whole numbers and the conceptual meaning of the operations with an eye towards how properties are useful in performing calculations. The thinking strategies approach to learning the basic facts is one important use of properties. Research has confirmed that this approach is effective with slow learners and we have had similar success working with individual students of all abilities.

Chapter 4 - Whole Number Computations - Mental, Electronic, and Written

As the chapter title suggests, we believe that students should consider performing computations mentally first (either exactly in simple cases or using estimations in more complex cases), using a calculator second (facility with a computer is also desirable), and using traditional paper-and-pencil algorithms last. Although we develop all the standard algorithms, we do not ask our students to "multiply two seven digit numbers" or "divide a seven digit number by a three digit number." Our reason for including so many nontraditional algorithms in the text and problem sets is that students find them fascinating and, through these algorithms, they can see more vividly that operations and algorithms are not synonymous. Thus, for example, since addition is *not* the addition *algorithm,* it *is* okay to adopt a combination of mental methods together with calculator techniques as an acceptable mode of calculation. Also, showing our students more algorithms helps them to support the various student developed algorithms. Our informal test to measure the effectiveness of an algorithm is to consider efficiency and accuracy when it is applied. In most cases, the mental method/calculator approach wins hands down against written algorithms. One final comment regarding division. Most of our students say that the last time that they used the long division algorithm was when they computed their gas mileage. But with onboard computers in many new cars, even this need is vanishing.

Chapter 5 - Number Theory

The chapter on number theory allows us to accomplish several objectives. First, we develop the content (factoring, GCF, and LCM) sufficient to make the work with fractions go smoothly. Second, the tests for divisibility give us a chance to make some simple proofs so that the tests aren't merely a collection of rules. Third, using some of the examples in our Focus On, we can share the notion of unsolved problems with our students at an understandable, relevant level. Mention is made of the 1995 proof of Fermat's Last Theorem in the Focus On.

Chapter 6 - Fractions

Deciding how to develop the real number system after discussing the whole numbers poses an interesting dilemma. First, one could take the whole numbers - integers - rationals - reals approach. On the surface, this sequence may be appealing due to its efficiency. However, this approach deprives the students of seeing numbers grow out of the physical world, much the way *our* students will be teaching. Thus we took the whole numbers - fractions - integers - rationals - reals approach (the sequence from school mathematics), where first fractions (and hence reciprocals) are motivated via models and next integers (with opposites) are introduced. Then the rationals are generated using fractions and integers. We have found this approach to be the most effective, *relevant* direction to take with elementary teachers and we believe that our coverage is as efficient (in terms of time) as the other approach. Note that, to save time, we defer discussing fraction order relations involving addition and multiplication until rational numbers. However, we do bring them up in the chapter on integers because of the influence of negative numbers.

Chapter 7 - Decimals, Ratio, Proportion, and Percent

We like to view (repeating) decimals and percents as another numeration system for the fractions. Although our work with ratio and proportion is restricted to decimals, we state that this treatment can be used with other number systems (such as the reals which are covered later).

Chapter 8 - Integers

We introduce integers by extending whole number concepts using both a set model (black/red chips) and a measurement model (the integer number line). Our formal definitions of the operations are motivated by the models and patterns. Although there are many ways to define integer addition and multiplication, our approach is to use as definitions the rules that most people use when performing operations on positive and negative numbers mentally.

Chapter 9 - Rational Numbers and Real Numbers, and Algebra

Our treatment of the rational numbers is brisk since the foundation for this material was laid in the chapters on fractions and integers. Real numbers are viewed as the set of all (repeating) decimals *and* as points of a "complete" number line. We like to cover rational exponents so that students can see that whole number and integer exponents can be usefully generalized. Because of their importance in problem solving, we extend the study of solving equations introduced in Chapter 1 to include inequalities and equations with real numbers. Chapter 9 was expanded to include relations and functions to enhance the coverage of algebra. After the real numbers are available, functions and their graphs are studied. Since more and more students are coming to class with graphics calculators, section 9.3, together with the Graphics Calculator webmodule on the website www.wiley.com/college/musser/, can be used to help students see the power of these devices.

Chapter 10 - Statistics

This chapter precedes the chapter on probability because of the topic's high priority in school mathematics and its importance in the everyday world of students and teachers. This also allows for early coverage in shorter courses, as soon as real numbers are developed. In section 10.1 we introduce Four Steps of Statistical Problem Solving. They are 1) Formulate Questions, 2) Collect Data, 3) Organize and Display Data, and 4) Analyze and Interpret Data. We briefly discuss the meaning of each of these steps and then spend the rest of the section focusing on Step 3 - various ways of organizing and representing data.

In section 10.2, the most commonly used measures of central tendency and dispersion are discussed, again from a teacher's point of view. We find this particularly useful for students who have not had a course on tests and measurement. The discussion of distributions is geometrical, illustrating the generalization of histograms, rather than delving into probability density functions. Section 10.3 focuses on potential misuses of statistics either in graphs or in sampling bias.

Chapter 11 - Probability

Probability is perhaps the most difficult and misunderstood topic in school mathematics. We suspect that this is due to its abstract nature, particularly the elusiveness of concrete interpretations of probability itself (not just experiments) and its reliance on set theory, ratio concepts, and counting techniques. Because of this, we have developed the major concepts and results about probability assuming no prior background.

Section 11.1 discusses experimental probability and the need for well chosen, albeit arbitrary, theoretical probability. We discuss the case of equally likely outcomes and use simple experiments to motivate the properties of probability. We deliberately avoid any discussion of probability axioms per se; such a treatment is far too abstract for the elementary or middle school classroom. We apply some of the set theory from Chapter 2 as a means of defining the concepts of experiment, sample space, outcome, event, and so on. Examples are chosen to illustrate the central ideas, but not to involve complicated counting techniques.

In section 11.2, we discuss methods for computing probabilities in experiments whose sample spaces may be cumbersome to list. For example, Pascal's triangle is used to enumerate outcomes in binomial experiments. Tree diagrams are introduced as a means of representing the outcomes of experiments involving several stages. Then, probability tree diagrams provide a method for assigning probabilities to the outcomes of such experiments and for computing probabilities of compound events in such experiments.

In section 11.3, we present more sophisticated counting techniques, that is, those using permutations and combinations explicitly. We find the fundamental counting property sufficient for our needs. Again, our main interest is in developing a fundamental understanding of probability and its applications and not in developing skills in counting. Thus, section 11.3 uses these counting techniques to determine the size of a sample space or the number of desired outcomes without having to list the entire set.

Section 11.4 addresses four probability concepts that may be included as time permits. First, the power of simulation is discussed as a simple means of approximating probabilities in highly complex experiments. Expected value is presented to give a glimpse of how probability is applied in establishing payoffs, admission fees, insurance premiums, service contract fees, and so on. Odds are presented as an application of ratios and as an alternate method of representing probability. Finally, conditional probability is introduced to show a generalization of probability, since probabilities in real-life situations are conditional probabilities. For example, insurance rates are set based on carefully researched conditional probabilities. (Some people claim that this is a form of discrimination, which, of course, it is, by definition!)

Chapter 12 - Geometric Shapes

For several reasons, we have chosen to organize the geometry material based on the van Hiele model of development. First, we find it pedagogically advantageous to start with visual experiences and move toward more formal results as we have done with number concepts. Our students have a wide variety of background experiences in geometry (including none), so we need to provide basic conceptual foundations. Second, many students have had unpleasant experiences with geometry in high school, which can be summarized as "too much formalism too soon." As a result, many of our students are apprehensive about studying geometry. By discussing the van Hiele model, we are able to identify the source of many of the difficulties that our students have had. This understanding leads to a sort of healing process and a revived sense of self-esteem. Finally, our students become sensitized to the challenges that elementary and middle school students face when studying geometry and realize that the solution is *not* to delay geometry until high school. Rather, a careful development of geometric concepts throughout the elementary and middle school years is called for - again, much as is done with number concepts.

Chapter 12 was changed in this edition to more closely follow the van Hiele model. In section 12.1, we describe the five van Hiele levels and incorporate an informal introduction to basic two-dimensional shapes at van Hiele level 0 of Recognition. Sorting and construction-type activities are presented as ways to help students reasoning at Level 0 to develop holistic thinking. Section 12.1 moves on to van Hiele level 1 by analyzing shapes, we use investigations with paper folding, tracing, and on a square lattice. As a means for exploring properties among the component parts of these shapes, we introduce the concept of symmetry. We are able to establish properties of shapes based on plausible observations, which we verify more formally in later sections. (The plausible observations are, of course, postulates at this point, but we purposely avoid any formal discussion about the role of postulates in geometry. This directly parallels our approach with number systems and their properties.) In section 12.3 we approach two-dimensional geometry at the level of relationships. Through the use of Venn diagram and paper-folding activities, we motivate more abstract definitions of geometric shapes. In keeping with the van Hiele model, a formal approach to plane geometry is introduced next, in Section 12.4, where we list our basic assumptions, and establish several fundamental results about points, lines, angles, and polygons. In section 12.5 we include a discussion about tessellations as an application of regular polygons and for esthetic reasons. In section 12.6, we describe three dimensional shapes and their properties, delaying measure of volume and surface area until Chapter 13.

Chapter 13 - Measurement

The organization of this chapter was also inspired by the van Hiele model, although we don't refer to it explicitly here. Informal measurement, using natural units, is discussed initially to illustrate holistic thinking in measurement. Once the system of natural units is standardized to the English system, the properties of the system can be discussed, culminating in the properties of an (abstract) ideal system. It is interesting to note that Thomas Jefferson had designed a system of measurement units of weights and measures with all the advantages of an ideal system. Jefferson's system was not adopted and now the metric system flourishes nearly everywhere instead.

In section 13.1, we have provided separate discussions of length, area, volume, weight (English), mass (metric), and temperature in the two systems of units since many of our students do not have a good intuitive understanding of all of these concepts. Yet, they likely will teach them. We include a discussion of dimensional analysis as a problem-solving tool in applied problems and as a procedure for converting among various units.

In sections 13.2, we study measurement as a deductive mathematical process, based on arbitrary units of length and area. (Tessellations of the plane and space are the basis of area and volume measurement.) We derive area formulas for various polygons and circles, based on the area of a rectangle. We give a proof of the Pythagorean theorem based on the areas of squares and right triangles. President Garfield's proof, using the area of a trapezoid, appears in the problem set. (Also, a transformational proof appears in Chapter 16 as a Mathematical Morsel.) In section 13.3 we derive surface area formulas based on previous results. We rely on the connections observed by Archimedes to find the surface area of a sphere. In section 13.4 we derive volume formulas for prisms, cylinders, pyramids, and cones. The formula for the volume of a sphere is done first using the 'Archimedes connection', then more formally using Cavalieri's principle.

Chapter 14 - Geometry Using Triangle Congruence and Similarity

This is the first of three chapters (Chapters 14, 15, and 16), each presenting a specific approach to problem solving in geometry. The three chapters are independent of each other, except that sections 14.1 and 14.2 are prerequisite for sections 16.2 and 16.3. Thus, any or all of the three approaches may be covered. The last section of each of these three chapters may be omitted with no loss of continuity. On the other hand, each provides a nice capstone to its chapter if you can't cover all chapters. If there is time to cover these sections in their entirety, an alternate coverage scheme would be to cover these final sections at the end of your course *after* all three approaches have been introduced to the students.

In section 14.1, the triangle congruence properties are developed and used to justify several classical geometric constructions. In so doing, we are reasoning at van Hiele level two; that is, from the congruence conditions, we can deductively verify the construction procedures. We find this mode of reasoning to be a challenge to many of our students, particularly to those who prefer to reason holistically, that is, on the basis of the construction diagram alone. In order to build our students' skill in using deductive reasoning, we have tried to keep to verifications of only a few major steps at first. In the remainder of section 14.1, we investigate the construction of regular polygons and the consequences of Gauss's theorem.

In section 14.2, we investigate triangle similarity properties and several applications of them. Geometric constructions are covered in sections 14.3 and 14.4. In section 14.5, we apply the triangle congruence and similarity properties in solving geometric problems. In so doing, we verify, at van Hiele level two and three, several results about quadrilaterals that we observed at level one in Chapter 12.

Chapter 15 - Geometry Using Coordinates

We introduce coordinates as a powerful problem solving tool in geometry. In section 15.1 we discuss slope and distance in the coordinate plane, then in section 15.2 we discuss equations of lines and circles, and the geometry of simultaneous linear equations. Finally, in section 15.3, we solve several problems using coordinates. Some students who have experienced difficulties with triangle congruence and similarity prefer a computational approach using coordinates much like some high school students prefer algebra to geometry. Our intention is to show the value of knowing several approaches to solving problems in geometry. Our students, who are expected to have taken three years of college preparatory math, tend to do very well in this chapter.

Chapter 16 - Geometry Using Transformations

In this chapter we present an approach to Euclidean geometry via isometries and similitudes. Our purpose is two-fold: (1) to present an alternative to "synthetic" Euclidean geometry via the triangle congruence and similarity conditions of Chapter 14 and (2) to present an *additional* approach to that of Chapter 14 or 15 that can be applied when advantageous.

In section 16.1, transformations as rigid motions (translation, rotation, reflection, glide-reflection) and similitudes are defined informally. (Note the special notation of directed line segment and directed angle.) Symmetry in the plane is analyzed using transformations, as are Escher-type tessellations. Our goal is to give an overview of transformation geometry, particularly for shorter courses that may not have time for all of the problem solving in section 16.3. Section 16.1 can be done anytime after sections 12.1 and 12.2.

Congruence and similarity of polygons are treated more formally in Section 16.2. We apply several results of sections 14.1 and 14.2 to verify that translations, rotations, reflections, and glide-reflections are isometries. We give a plausible argument that there are no other isometries in the plane. Thus, we can characterize all isometries in the plane and characterize congruence of shapes in general. We also verify properties of size transformations and similitudes, and characterize similarity of shapes in general by means of similitudes. This reasoning borders on level three reasoning since we are investigating the structure of geometry itself; thus, the material must be approached with care and patience. Alternatively, it could be saved for a separate geometry course for preservice teachers.

In section 16.3 we use a transformation approach to problem solving in geometry. For example, we verify the midsegment theorem in a triangle (Example 16.16) by means of size transformations. This result is verified in each of Chapters 14, 15, and 16, using the approach of that particular chapter.

Epilogue - An Eclectic Approach to Geometry

Since we have used this approach so successively in our classes, we decided to formalize it in the book. Talking about using a variety of approaches to geometry is one thing, but providing students with examples and mixed problems is powerful. Students freely express how much they enjoy seeing geometry in this light.

Chapter Commentaries

Chapter 1 - Introduction to Problem Solving

Polya's Four Steps: We find that a careful discussion of Polya's Four Steps is helpful initially. Then we reinforce each step throughout the chapter as we introduce new strategies through problems.

Problem Solving Strategies: Most of our students are initially weak in problem solving, mainly due to lack of practice and knowing where to start. In a survey of research studies, it was concluded that strategies are helpful in problem solving; we find that a toolbox of problem solving strategies gives many students a place to start. Unfortunately, even knowing a list of *strategies* is still not sufficient to produce excellent problem solvers. To take this idea one step further, we have included *clues* to assist students in selecting an appropriate strategy. In the main, these clues were generated by students solving problems from our First Edition. As a further aid for the students, hints and additional hints and written out solutions for all part A problems are provided in the *Hints and Solutions Manual for Part A Problems*. This combination of problems, Polya's four steps, strategies, clues, hints, and solutions is a powerful resource to help students develop their problem solving abilities.

Introduction to Algebra: One of the strategies introduced in this chapter is "Use a Variable". When using this strategy, it is important for students to understand what variables are. Since variables are most often used in some form of an equation, strategies for solving equations containing variables are also discussed. In this chapter, the introduction of algebra is done a basic level and then further developed in chapter 9 after all of the number systems have been introduced.

Chapter 2 - Sets, Whole Numbers, and Numeration

Sets and Operations on Sets: We cover set theory briskly so that we can devote more time to the many other key concepts in the elementary curriculum.

Numbers and Numerals: It is instructive for students to observe the various ways that we use "numbers": "cardinal" numbers to represent how many, "ordinal" numbers to represent an ordering, and "identification" numbers to serve as names.

Numeration Systems: Our emphasis is on the various attributes of numeration systems such as grouping, additivity, multiplicativity, place value, and so on. Also, the Roman and the Mayan systems show how numeration systems evolve; in the case of the Roman system, they extended their additive system to include the subtractive and the multiplicative attributes, and the Mayans changed from a base twenty system to one based on 18×20 due to their calendar. The Babylonian system provides an early example of a place value system as well as an introduction to the notion of a place holder. Our students enjoy a discussion on naming Hindu-Arabic numerals since, although the names are familiar to us, they can be confusing for children. In particular, our students like to rename the numbers 11,12,..., 19 to be "onety-one, onety-two,..., onety-nine" to conform to the way we name 21, 22, 23, and so on.

Ordering Whole Numbers: Although we acknowledge the counting chant and number line as a way children may order numbers (in an ordinal sense), we emphasize the set method for understanding ordering whole numbers (in the cardinal sense). Ordering whole numbers using addition is covered in Chapter 3.

Physical Representations of Whole Numbers: We like our students to be familiar with a variety of representations such as multibase pieces and a chip abacus so that they will carry the philosophy of introducing mathematics at the concrete level to their students. Low-cost representations can easily be made or can be found in the materials cards in our Student Activity Manual.

Nondecimal Numeration Systems: We cover this topic so that we may introduce various algorithms in Chapter 4 in an unfamiliar setting for our students, namely using a nondecimal base. This approach gives our students much more insight into how one might better teach algorithms in base ten. Although this section and the coverage of other bases is optional, we recommend its coverage keeping in mind that its usefulness is in providing students with a different point of view when studying various other number concepts in the text.

Chapter 3 - Whole Numbers: Operations and Properties

Addition: Addition is introduced using physical models and then properties are drawn out of the models. Algorithms are studied in the next chapter to make clear the separation between operations and properties, and algorithms. On the other hand, we want to emphasize as much mental mathematics as possible. Thus, we include the thinking strategies approach for learning the basic facts in this chapter. The thinking strategies lead nicely into mental math techniques that are introduced in Chapter 4.

Subtraction: We believe that students should see subtraction in various forms: take-away and missing addend, and both of these with comparison. Also, it is critical to show students how to use addition to get subtraction facts by combining the addition facts with the missing addend approach.

Multiplication: As with addition and subtraction, we introduce multiplication through models. Properties evolve from viewing appropriate models.

Division: With division, as well as with all four operations, it is important that the focus be on the underlying meaning of the operation, which is why the ideas of sharing and measurement division are introduced. The development of multiplication and division closely parallels that of addition and subtraction with division being defined using the missing factor approach in place of the missing addend approach. Students appreciate the diagram in Figure 3.33, which shows the interrelationships among the four operations.

Ordering Whole Numbers Using Addition: With addition now available, we can define the most mathematically useful form of order, namely, $a < b$ if and only if $a + n = b$ for some nonzero n. Then one can discuss theorems such as "If $a < b$, then $a + c < b + c$" time permitting.

Exponents: Exponents and resulting "rules" are introduced as shortcuts for multiplication. Note that the definition of exponent must be restated in the case $a^1 = a$ if one does not permit a "factor" to appear alone. After exponents are introduced, the order of operations is discussed along with the pneumonic device "**P**lease **E**xcuse **M**e **D**ear **A**unt **S**ally". (Order of operations is also mentioned in the calculator section in the next chapter.)

Chapter 4 - Whole Number Computation—Mental, Electronic, and Written

Mental Math: Because of the need to move away from excessive work with written algorithms toward more emphasis on mental math and calculators for calculations, we begin this chapter on computation with a thorough treatment of mental math. Techniques developed in this subsection arise from properties of whole numbers and were the techniques that were observed in children who were effective mental calculators.

Computational Estimation: The techniques introduced in this subsection, which are commonly used in K-8 mathematics text series, were observed by researchers in children who were good estimators. The notion of rounding to compatible numbers is an especially powerful estimation technique.

Using a Calculator: We have found that although many students use calculators, they are not aware of many of the functions available on a scientific calculator. This subsection contains an introduction to several calculator keys. Uses of other specialized keys, such as fractions, change-of-sign, and so on, are introduced when their corresponding mathematical concepts are developed. We encourage students to get *fraction* scientific calculators (if not graphics calculators).

Written Algorithms for Whole Number Addition: We have several objectives in this chapter. First and foremost, we want students to realize that algorithms are step-by-step procedures to obtain answers. Second, since our customary algorithms will likely continue to be taught (but probably used less) for many years to come, they can be presented more effectively to students by using concrete models before moving to symbolic place value representations. Third, there are (have been) many algorithms for the four basic operations and that we are using one of each *among many*. Fourth, it is appropriate for students to use any correct algorithm. Our students like the "left-to-right" mental addition method since it allows them to focus on *understanding* the process rather that having to always follow the *rule* "always add starting on the right." Left-to-right mental methods lead quite naturally into left-to-right written algorithms.

Written Algorithms for Whole Number Subtraction: One of our favorite subtraction algorithms is the "subtract-from-the-base" method, which is easily motivated using multibase pieces. It is much like the standard "borrowing" method except that the exchanges are not made; thus, one only needs to know how to subtract from the base rather than know all the usual subtraction facts. For example, to find 35 - 17, we view this problem as (25 + 10) - (10 + 7), or (20 - 10) + (10 - 7 + 5) instead of the usual (20 + 15) - (10 + 7) = (20 - 10) + (15 - 7). Students see the value of this alternative algorithm when we actually have a race in class *in different bases* by having volunteers use this method against the rest of the class using the standard algorithm. Invariably, students find this algorithm easier since they only need to know how to subtract from the base and add.

Written Algorithms for Whole Number Multiplication: Students find the transition from the intermediate algorithms to the standard algorithms very helpful. Although the expanded multiplication technique involving more digits than available on a typical calculator display may not be used often, it does illustrate how to use mental math, a calculator, and understanding of mathematics to extend even what a calculator can do.

Written Algorithms for Whole Number Division: Here, again, a succession of intermediate algorithms, in addition to a concrete example with base-ten blocks, helps students better understand the long division algorithm and to appreciate just how difficult teaching this algorithm will be.

Algorithms in Base Five: This section affords students an opportunity to test various algorithms in unfamiliar situations. Students find many nontraditional algorithms more to their liking when doing computations in other bases. This gives us another chance to discuss the role and evaluation of algorithms. Notice that students will find that trying a long division problem in another base can be a humbling experience since they cannot perform the necessary prerequisite mental computations nor estimate in other bases.

Chapter 5 - Number Theory

Primes and Composites: The definitions of prime and composite numbers using numbers of factors provide a nice partition of the counting numbers, namely, 1 (one factor), primes (exactly two factors), and composites (more than two factors).

Tests for Divisibility: The proofs of the tests for divisibility are accessible to students; moreover, the students appreciate understanding why the various tests work in the ways that they do. Also, these proofs provide a convenient place to discuss logical terms such as biconditional and converse (at least informally).

Counting Factors: This is a nice technique that is usually overlooked. One of its applications is to serve as a check to see if one has found *all* the factors of a number. The table provides a nice visual proof of why this technique works.

Greatest Common Factor: In most instances, the prime factorization method is preferred by students. Our focus is on the GCF as a concept to be used in simplifying fractions. Also, we have included the Euclidean algorithm which, when combined with a calculator, can be used to find the GCFs of larger numbers more easily.

Least Common Multiple: Here, again, students prefer the prime factorization approach because of its efficiency. Also, finding the LCM by first finding the GCF and using the relationship GCF(a,b)LCM(a,b) = ab is nice. Students will likely have a difficult time with the infinitude of primes proof the first time through. But, after applying it to several other primes, such as 3, 5, 7, and so on, and to one composite, say 4, they catch on and appreciate the proof.

Chapter 6 - Fractions

The Concept of Fraction: This was one of the toughest parts of the text to compose since there are two distinct notions that we need to get across (numeral and number), yet we didn't want to carry around the excess baggage of two names (fraction and fractional number) or equivalence classes of ordered pairs of whole numbers. We hope that your students will understand the many facets of the concept of a fraction as a numeral/number after working through this section. We decided to try to hit this issue head on instead of glossing over it as is done so often. Our definition of fraction equality is the usual cross multiplication definition, which naturally flows from models.

Ordering Fractions: Fractions are ordered using common denominators first since students find this approach to be a natural extension of whole number ordering. Then, the usual cross multiplication test for inequality is then derived. Density is introduced via the interesting theorem "if $\dfrac{a}{b} < \dfrac{c}{d}$, then $\dfrac{a}{b} < \dfrac{a+c}{b+d} < \dfrac{c}{d}$." This result surprises students and provides an opportunity to reinforce the fact that $\dfrac{a}{b} + \dfrac{c}{d} \neq \dfrac{a+c}{b+d}$ in general.

Addition and its Properties: Here, again, the definitions of addition and subtraction flow from work with models. Then we try to emphasize how properties of fraction addition are consequences of similar whole number properties.

Subtraction: Subtraction is motivated from models similar to addition.

Multiplication and its Properties: The definition of fraction multiplication evolves first as an extension of whole number multiplication; finally, a model is used to motivate the general definition.

Division: Our introduction of fraction division is novel, though not from a long-term historical perspective as can be seen in the Focus On. We try to enlighten students who have no *feeling* for fraction division, only a *rule* to invert and multiply. (How can such students possibly motivate this concept to children - in fact, most teachers don't; they just teach it as a rule much as stories are passed on from generation to generation.) Once, just after we had completed this unit, an excellent, mature, returning student confided that he was relieved to know that the operation of fraction division *existed*; he had always thought that there were only *three* fraction operations (no one ever used division since it was always changed to multiplication). Although many of our students may leave us with the "invert and multiply" rule still their predominant way of viewing fraction division, they do know that division is a legitimate operation and that it is multifaceted.

Mental Math and Estimation: Techniques introduced in Chapter 4 are extended to fractions. This approach reinforces the earlier work with whole numbers.

Chapter 7 - Decimals, Ratio, Proportion, and Percent

Decimals: Decimals are introduced as a natural extension of whole numbers using the number line and a hundreds square. Also, the fractions with terminating decimals are characterized.

Mental Math and Estimation: The techniques developed in Chapter 4 are extended to decimals. In addition, a new technique, using fraction equivalents, is introduced. Research found that skilled mental estimators would often convert decimals to convenient fractions and compatible numbers to estimate products.

Algorithms for Operations with Decimals: The key idea in this section is that computations involving decimals can be done by temporarily suppressing the decimal points *mentally*, performing the corresponding whole number algorithm, and then correctly inserting a decimal point in the answer. Multiplying decimals is a good place to apply rounding techniques and to do approximate calculations.

Classifying Repeating Decimals: This subsection allows us to completely describe the fractions in terms of their decimal representations.

Ratio: The work in ratios parallels the work with fractions *except* that numerators and denominators aren't restricted to whole numbers. Notice that ratios may have zero "denominators" (e.g. the ratio of men to women on an NFL football team). However, we restrict our study to ratios that have nonzero 'denominators'.

Proportion: Paying close attention to respective units is a key to success in solving proportions. The mental technique of scaling up/down is included to encourage mental math when solving proportions.

Converting Percents: Developing skill in converting among fractions, decimals, and percents is a prerequisite to solving percent problems mentally.

Mental Math and Estimation: The powerful mental technique of using fraction equivalents is introduced. This allows students to estimate answers as they do more formal percent calculations, perhaps using calculators.

Solving Percent Problems: Applied problems involving percent are solved using both the proportion and the equation methods. Work with calculators is especially relevant here, although one needs to watch for the different ways that various calculators handle percent.

Chapter 8 - Integers

Integers and the Integer Number Line: The set of integers and their opposites are introduced using both a black/red chip model and the integer number line. Note that the term opposite will be synonymous with additive inverse once that concept has been introduced.

Addition and its Properties: We have observed that students find the black/red chip model to be very helpful when learning integer operations. Addition is viewed as a natural extension of whole number addition when using colored chips.

Subtraction: Subtraction is demystified when using the chip model since the take-away approach naturally leads to the adding the opposite approach. Again, in the spirit of extending number systems, subtraction is shown to have an equivalent missing addend version. The two methods of whole number subtraction are extended to integer subtraction. In addition, the add-the-opposite approach is developed using models. Students profit from seeing that these three approaches to subtraction are equivalent. The mathematical morsel at the end of this section can be generalized to any finite collection of integers.

Multiplication and Its Properties: We motivate the definition of multiplication using patterns. However, one could use the chip model for this purpose as illustrated in exercises 4 and 5 of Exercise/Problem Set 8.2 - Part A. The results that $(-a)b = -ab$ and $(-a)(-b) = ab$ deserve special attention since most students view them simply as statements about the product of a negative and a positive, and the product of two negatives respectively. However, these are more general statements involving *additive inverses*.

Division: Just as with whole number division, integer division is viewed using the missing factor approach. We omit division with remainder due to its lack of application.

Negative Integers and Scientific Notation: Since decimals and the set of integers with its operations have been introduced, this is a natural place to study integer exponents and scientific notation.

Ordering Integers: Ordering integers is introduced as an extension of whole number ordering. Care must be taken to distinguish integer ordering, though, when multiplying both sides of an inequality by a negative (integer).

Chapter 9 - Rational Numbers and Real Numbers, with Algebra

Rational Numbers - An Extension of Fractions and Integers: Here we take a more formal approach than in earlier chapters. For example, our definition of equality is the familiar cross-multiplication definition (which extends a similar property in the fractions chapter). Also, our definition of addition is the general case involving unlike denominators. Since the rational numbers extend both the fractions and integers, this section can be covered at a brisk pace. The major "new" result is $-\dfrac{a}{b} = \dfrac{-a}{b} = \dfrac{a}{-b}$.

Ordering Rational Numbers: The material in this subsection ties together similar ideas in the fractions and integers.

Real Numbers- An Extension of Rational Numbers: There are several proofs to show that there is no rational number whose square is two - the one we selected can be easily generalized thus displaying the power of abstraction in mathematical reasoning. Figure 9.7, which shows the subset relationships among the number systems through the reals, is useful in helping students see the big picture.

Rational Exponents: Our students appreciate seeing how the definitions of fraction and rational exponents unfold. Although we did not include an extensive discussion of properties of radicals, they are developed in the problem set.

Algebra: In chapter 1, we had students solve equations using intuitive or "natural" methods such as guess and test, cover-up, and work backward. In this chapter, we use balance scale models to illustrate how to solve equations using the various properties of equality. Rules for solving inequalities are then developed abstractly by reasoning from the corresponding order properties. The equations and inequalities use rational numbers further extending what was introduced in chapter 1.

Relations and Functions: We use arrow diagrams to introduce relations and to illustrate relations that are reflexive, symmetric, and transitive. The notion of equivalence relation is covered since this concept appears in the studies of congruence and similarity among other areas. Understanding the concept of function is often difficult for students, so we carefully develop the definition and then have students explore a variety of function representations, concrete to abstract, including: arrow diagrams, tables, function machines, sets of ordered pairs, graphs, and geometric transformations.

Functions and their Graphs: A variety of functions such as linear, quadratic, cubic, and step functions and their graphs are studied. This is a great place to bring a graphics calculator to class to show how useful these powerful calculators are (*and* at an affordable price).

Chapter 10 - Statistics

Statistical Problem Solving: We believe that introducing our students to statistics as a problem-solving process, organized into Polya-like 4 steps, helps them to make important connections among the processes of (1) formulating statistical questions; (2) collecting data that may be used to answer those questions; (3) organizing and displaying the collected data; and (4) analyzing the data and interpreting it to answer those questions.

Organizing Information: We find that our students are especially interested in educational examples. Charts and graphs from *USA_Today* or similar news publications provide a variety of examples. *The Statistical Abstract of the United States* and various almanacs are excellent sources` of data for graphs and tables.

Measuring Central Tendency: Notice how box and whisker plots incorporate central tendency *and* dispersion.

Measuring Dispersion: Interpreting the variance and standard deviation of a collection of data can be a challenge. For large, roughly normally distributed collections, the standard deviation is about one-fourth of the range. Also, if $\bar{x}$ is the mean and s is the standard deviation, then for such collections, the intervals $\bar{x} \pm s$ and $\bar{x} \pm 2s$ capture about 68% and 95% of the data, respectively.

The fact that the mean and the standard deviation are the two parameters determining the shape of a normal distribution helps our students appreciate their prominence in statistics. The use of z-scores and percentiles allows for direct comparison of performances on several exams or other measurements. That is, z-scores and percentiles indicate relative positions within distributions (in standard deviation units.)

Deceptive Statistics: Since statistical information continues to be an influential factor in society, we used the last section to focus on the potential misuses of statistics. An understanding of these misuses should help your students and their future students become better consumers and citizens.

Chapter 11 - Probability

Simple Experiments: We find that a careful discussion of events using set theory is very useful before any assignment of probabilities.

Computing Probabilities in Simple Experiments: We have found that an informal treatment of the meaning of probability, say using relative frequency, is essential at the start. Examples from games, sports, medicine, and science are very useful.

Tree Diagrams and Counting Techniques: The relationship between outcomes in binomial experiments and Pascal's triangle can be explained using diagrams such as in Figures 11.20, 11.21, and 11.22. We have found that representing multistep experiments with probability tree diagrams is a very effective way of computing probabilities.

Probability Tree Diagrams: The additive property of probability tree diagrams is a direct application of the probability of a union of disjoint events. The multiplicative property of probability tree diagrams follows from multiplication of fractions. These two properties can be applied to equally likely and unequally likely outcomes, and to multistage experiments.

Extended Counting Techniques and Computing Probabilities: Since listing a large sample space can be unreasonable, advanced counting techniques are introduced to be used to determine the number of elements in a sample space or event. These numbers are then used to compute a probability.

Simulation: With the widespread availability of computers (and scientific calculators with random number generators), simulation of experiments provides a powerful approach to approximating probabilities. Simulations using numbered chips, dice, or random digit tables are alternatives to computer simulations.

Expected Value: In experiments with numerical sample spaces, expected value can be used to describe the most likely value, or the "weighted average." This couples nicely with simulation of complex experiments.

Odds: Odds are most naturally explained in the case of equally likely outcomes, but can easily be generalized.

Conditional Probability: An initial discussion of sample spaces "reduced" to reflect a given condition (with corresponding adjustments in probabilities) can be generalized to conditional probability as a ratio.

Chapter 12 Geometric Shapes

The van Hiele Theory: We find that our students are intrigued by the hierarchy of reasoning processes described by the van Hieles. We include a discussion of children's misconceptions about geometric shapes in part to help clear up some of our students' misconceptions. We are careful to point out that our approach to geometry will be at the lowest four levels, and not at the level of axiomatics. However, we do employ both informal and formal deduction.

Recognizing Geometric Shapes: We find that our students are generally weak in visualization skills and are challenged by the exercises and problems requiring them. Tables 12.1, 12.2, and 12.3 provide descriptions of basic geometric shapes as well as examples of the corresponding shapes found in the world around us.

Analyzing Geometric Shapes: We gradually build up a vocabulary for describing components of shapes and, consequently, various types of shapes.

Relationships Among Geometric Shapes: Relationships among classes of triangles are shown in Figure 12.37 and quadrilaterals are shown in Figure 12.38.

Symmetry: The tests for parallel and perpendicular line segments can be interpreted in Chapter 16 using reflections. We discuss only reflection and rotation symmetry here, leaving a discussion of more general transformations for Chapter 16.

Points and Lines in a Plane: We find that our students better understand the abstract nature of points, lines, and planes if we use an analogy to numbers; that is, we can represent the concepts with pictures (as with numbers and numerals), but the objects themselves exist only in our imaginations. The "protractor" device here is actually a fan of rays used to measure angles.

Angles: Several consequences of the parallel postulate (property 3 of points and lines) are developed and illustrated reasoning deductively.

Regular Polygons: From the angle sum in a triangle property, we are able to derive the measures of angles in regular *n*-gons.

Tessellations: Tessellations with triangles and quadrilaterals illustrate several major results (see the exercise/problem sets).

Tessellations with Regular Polygons: We are able to classify all of the regular tessellations based on our previous results about angle measures. (In the problem set, the semiregular tessellations are characterized.)

Circles: Circles are compared to regular polygons, an approach that we exploit in computing the area of a circle and the volumes and surface areas of cones and cylinders in Chapter 13.

Planes, Skew lines, and Dihedral Angles: We purposely avoid defining dihedral angles formed by half planes since the applications of interest to us involve polyhedra. The relationships between lines and planes are important when discussing polyhedra, also.

Polyhedra: Analogies between regular polyhedra and regular tessellations (semiregular polyhedra/tessellations) are useful.

Curved Shapes in Three Dimensions: We include a general definition of cylinder and cone, and determine their volumes in

Chapter 13. Three-dimensional symmetry is investigated in the problems.

Chapter 13 - Measurement

Nonstandard Units: Many students (and teachers) seem to confuse measurement and geometry, or think of measurement as linear measurement only. Thus, we discuss the *process* of measurement and bring in systems of units in a historical way.

Standard Units - The English and Metric Systems: We emphasize common metric prefixes (e.g., kilo-, centi-, milli-) and show the usefulness of "metric converters" such as in Figure 13.11. We find that the three "metric cubes" in Figure 13.22 are useful in illustrating the interrelatedness of metric units of length, volume, and mass. We like to distinguish between volume and capacity. A flat circular disk of clay has volume, but no capacity (it doesn't hold any water poured on it). However, if the clay is formed into a dish, its volume is the same and it now has capacity. Notice that there are different (though connected) units for volume and capacity in the English system (e.g., cubic units and quarts).

Dimensional Analysis: Our students need practice in estimation and approximation. Dimensional analysis gives us the opportunity to estimate first, then convert/compute. It also simplifies conversions within the English system, and, when necessary, between English and metric units.

Length: We include a brief discussion of distance on a line in part to show the relationship between order properties of the real numbers and betweenness.

Area: Our discussion of area occurs at van Hiele level two since we deduce area formulas from the area of a rectangle. It is important to point out that the area of a triangle is the product of the length of a base and its *corresponding* height, since there are *three* such pairs from which to choose.

The Pythagorean Theorem: Results about construction of irrational lengths follow immediately from the Pythagorean theorem. We can also illustrate algebraic results, such as $\sqrt{ab}$ =

$\sqrt{a} \cdot \sqrt{b}$, say on a square lattice, if one of a or b is a perfect square. The triangle inequality is useful in deciding whether three arbitrary lengths determine a triangle.

Surface Area and Volume: Our students benefit greatly from concrete experiences such as those in the Student Activity Manual. Students need practice in visualizing 'unfolded' shapes as well as the relationship between the area of the base of a right prism/cylinder and its volume. This has been one of the most difficult geometry units for our students, in part, we think, due to a lack of concrete background experiences. We urge a careful intuitive approach at first. Table 13.11 shows analogies in the volumes and surface areas of prisms/cylinders and pyramids/cones.

Chapter 14 - Geometry Using Triangle Congruence and Similarity

Congruence: We have found that many students prefer to think of triangle congruence informally ("same size and shape") rather than as a relationship (literally an equivalence relation) between triangles whose vertices are made to correspond in a suitable way. Thus, we encourage our students to extend their reasoning beyond holistic thinking. We motivate the triangle congruence properties through analytical reasoning in specific cases. (For more concrete approaches, see the Student Activity Manual.) Then we apply the congruence conditions to short verifications of properties of polygons.

Similarity: We find that students need some review of ratio and proportion in order to understand the proportionality of the sides in similar triangles.

Geometric Constructions: We have deliberately separated the construction procedures from their justifications in order to emphasize the deductive verifications using triangle congruence. We find that students benefit from practice in simply learning the procedures. You may wish to discuss only a few of the justifications, as time permits.

Constructing Regular n-gons: Our students are intrigued by the interplay between Gauss's classification of constructible regular *n*-gons and the unsolved problem of the existence of more Fermat primes. In our courses, we discuss some consequences about the constructibility of certain angles, e.g. as central angles or vertex angles in regular *n*-gons.

Geometric Problem Solving Using Triangle Congruence and Similarity: Several classical results, illustrated in Chapter 12, are verified here. Example 14.15, the converse of the Pythagorean theorem, actually uses the Pythagorean theorem! Many of the results of this section can be investigated inductively using exploration software before searching for deductive verifications.

Chapter 15 - Geometry Using Coordinates

Coordinates: If coordinates were not studied in section 9.3, the first few pages of that section could be covered here.

Distance: The midpoint formula can also be verified using triangle congruence (or similarity) if you prefer.

Slope: An analogy to the grade of a road or the pitch of a roof is helpful in understanding slope as a ratio. We have purposely kept the derivations of slope properties independent of Chapter 14. If you've discussed Chapter 14, you may wish to use triangle congruence or similarity properties in verifying the slopes of parallel lines property. We establish only the slope-intercept form of the equation of a nonvertical line to keep our treatment as lean as possible (others are found in the problem set, though). As enrichment, you may wish to discuss the geometry of other forms of a line.

Simultaneous Equations: We will apply results of this section in section 15.3 when establishing the concurrence of the medians and of the altitudes in a triangle.

Equations of Circles: We develop equations of circles to show that curves other than lines have analytical characterizations. You may wish to discuss other curves, such as the remaining conic sections. (See the problems in 15.2B.) We also apply the equation of a circle in finding the circumscribed circle of a triangle.

Geometric Problem Solving Using Coordinates: Example 15.8 is much more difficult using only triangle congruence or similarity. Results about the medians and altitudes of triangles can be motivated by constructions or exploration software.

Chapter 16 - Geometry Using Transformations

Transformations: Construction or drawing activities in addition to the use of a dynamic geometry software package are helpful for many of our students in developing an intuitive feeling for transformations. See the Student Activity Manual.

Symmetry: Tessellations, wallpaper, flooring, and clothing are sources of symmetric patterns. Miras are very useful for investigating reflection symmetry.

Making Escher-Type Patterns: There are several books available from Dale Seymour Publications and Creative Publications on tessellations and Escher-type patterns that our students enjoy.

Congruence: We present a special case of the verification that reflections preserve distance to avoid overwhelming the students with too much detail. The classification of isometries can be convincingly demonstrated with construction activities, as a more concrete approach.

Similarity: The development parallels that of congruence via size transformations.

Geometric Problem Solving Using Transformations: Example 16.12 is an alternative to an approach using congruence. (The latter technically involves betweenness considerations.) Several interesting applications of half-turns appear. An argument based on area of parallelograms also suffices.

Epilogue - An Eclectic Approach to Geometry

Enjoy this section - your students will too! Proving the midsegment theorem using three approaches—synthetic, coordinate, and transformation—opens students' eyes to the value of multiple approaches to geometry. Give students a chance to vote on their favorite approach and discuss the pros and cons of each method. This is a great capstone to the study of geometry.

Chapter Learning Objectives

Chapter 1 - Introduction to Problem Solving

Students are expected to be able to:

1-1   Distinguish between solving a problem and solving an exercise in mathematics.

1-2   Solve problems using Polya's 4-step problem-solving process:
       understand the problem   carry out the plan
       devise a plan   look back

1-3   Apply the process illustrated in the following diagram for formulating and solving mathematical problems.

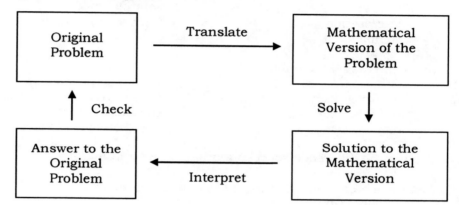

1-4   Use the following problem-solving strategies:
       guess and test   look for a pattern
       draw a picture   make a list
       use a variable   solve a simpler problem

1-5   Identify "clues" in the statements of problems that are helpful for selecting an appropriate problem-solving strategy.

1-6   Apply these terms when using algebra:
       equation
       solution
       solve

Chapter 2 - Sets, Whole Numbers, and Numeration

Students are expected to be able to:

2-1   Demonstrate understanding of the concepts of:
        set   equal sets
        element of a set   empty set

2-2   Use set-builder notation to denote sets.

2-3   Formalize the meaning of whole number using the concept of equivalent sets (one-to-one correspondence.)

2-4   Determine whether a given set is finite or infinite.

2-5   Construct a new set from two or more sets using the operations of:
        union   set difference
        intersection   Cartesian product
        complement

2-6   Use Venn diagrams to illustrate:
        subset   the union of two sets
        proper subset   the intersection of two sets
        universal set   the complement of a set
        disjoint sets   the difference of two sets

2-7   Explain the difference between a number and a numeral.

2-8   Distinguish between the three uses of whole numbers:
        cardinal number
        ordinal number
        identification number

2-9   Explain what is meant by the number of elements in a finite set.

2-10   Use sets and a whole-number line to describe the relations of less than and greater than for whole numbers.

2-11   Express whole numbers using these numeration systems:
        Egyptian   Mayan
        Roman   Hindu-Arabic
        Babylonian

2-12   Compare the attributes (additive, subtractive, multiplicative, positional, place value) of the following numeration systems:
        tally   Babylonian
        Egyptian   Mayan
        Roman   Hindu-Arabic

2-13   Explain what is meant by the base of the Hindu-Arabic numeration system.

2-14   Express a Hindu-Arabic numeral in any base in expanded notation and convert from expanded form to the numeral represented.

2-15   Describe the naming procedure for Hindu-Arabic numerals.

2-16   Convert a numeral from any base to base 10 and vice versa.

Chapter 3 - Whole Numbers: Operations and Properties

Students are expected to be able to:

3-1   Use a set model and a measurement model to represent addition and subtraction of whole numbers.

3-2   Demonstrate knowledge of the properties of whole number addition:
        closure   associativity
        commutativity   identity

and verify that subtraction has none of these properties.

3-3   Apply the following thinking strategies to learn basic addition facts in other bases and to simplify computations:
        commutativity   counting on by 1 and 2
        doubles   associativity
        adding zero   combinations to 10
        adding 10   doubles +/- 1 and +/- 2

3-4   Use the take-away and missing-addend approaches to define subtraction of whole numbers and apply comparison to each of the above approaches.

3-5   Use the missing-addend approach and four-fact families to relate addition and subtraction.

3-6   Use the repeated-addition, rectangular-array, and Cartesian-product approaches, in combination with a set model and a measurement model, to represent multiplication of whole numbers.

3-7   Demonstrate knowledge of the properties for multiplication of whole numbers and the distributive property of multiplication over addition (and subtraction) and verify that division of whole numbers has none of these properties.

3-8   Apply the following thinking strategies for learning basic multiplication facts and simplifying computations:
        commutativity   multiplication by 5
        multiplication by zero   multiplication by 9
        multiplication by 1   associativity
        multiplication by 2   distributivity

3-9   Differentiate between sharing and measurement division.

3-10   Use the missing-factor and the repeated-subtraction approaches to define division of whole numbers, including division problems involving zero.

3-11   Use the missing-factor approach and four-fact families to relate multiplication and division and illustrate the division algorithm using a number line model.

3-12   Use the operation of addition to define less than and greater than with whole numbers.

3-13 Demonstrate knowledge of the following properties of less than:
 transitivity
 property of less than and addition
 property of less than and multiplication.

3-14 Define whole number exponents using repeated multiplication.

3-15 Provide a proof for each of the following theorems about whole-number exponents, where a and b are whole numbers, and m and n are non-zero whole numbers:
 (a) $a^m \cdot a^n = a^{m+n}$
 (b) $a^m \cdot b^m = (ab)^m$
 (c) $(a^m)^n = a^{mn}$; $a^m \div a^n = a^{m-n}$, if $m \geq n$; $a^0 = 1$ for all nonzero whole numbers a
 (d) 0^0 is undefined

3-16 Apply the order of operations to evaluate arithmetic expressions.

Chapter 4 - Whole Number Computations—Mental, Electronic, and Written

Students are expected to be able to:

4-1   Apply the problem-solving strategy "use indirect reasoning."

4-2   Identify and apply the following mental math techniques:
         use properties
         compatible numbers
         compensation (additive, equal additions, and multiplicative)
         left-to-right methods
         multiply by powers of 10
         multiply by special factors

4-3   Identify and apply the following computational estimation techniques: front-
         end estimation (range, one- and two-column), and rounding (up, down,
         truncate, round a 5 up, to the nearest even, to compatible numbers).

4-4   Distinguish between arithmetic and algebraic logic on calculators by listing the
         mathematical convention for order of operations.

4-5   Use the following keys on a calculator (in addition to the usual number keys):
         parentheses keys   exponent keys
         constant function keys   memory keys

4-6   Interpret scientific notation as it appears on scientific calculators.

4-7   Model the standard written algorithms for addition, subtraction, multiplication
         and division using concrete models (multibase pieces and chip abacus).

4-8   Justify the standard written algorithms for addition, subtraction,
         multiplication and division using place value and properties.

4-9   Compute sums and products with (a) intermediate algorithms for addition and
         multiplication that lead to the standard algorithms and (b) the lattice methods
         for addition and multiplication.

4-10   Use nontraditional algorithms for subtraction.

4-11   Explain long-division algorithms (including the scaffold method) that lead to
         the standard algorithm.

4-12   Use a calculator to perform division with remainders.

4-13   Compute sums and products in bases 2 through 12 with (a) intermediate
         algorithms for addition and multiplication and (b) the lattice methods for
         addition and multiplication.

4-14   Compute differences in bases 2 through 12 with (a) the standard subtraction
         algorithm and (b) subtract from the base.

4-15   Compute quotients in bases 2 through 12 with (a) the scaffold method and (b)
         the standard long-division algorithm.

Chapter 5 - Number Theory

Students are expected to be able to:

5-1   Apply the problem-solving strategy "use properties of numbers."

5-2   Use the sieve of Eratosthenes to find prime numbers.

5-3   Use a factor tree to write the prime factorization of a given composite number.

5-4   Apply the fundamental theorem of arithmetic.

5-5   Apply each of the following terms:
    divides   factor
    divisor   is divisible by
    multiple

5-6   Use tests for divisibility (by 2, 3, 4, 5, 6, 8, 9, 10, 11, and 12), together with the Prime Factor Test, to determine whether a given number is prime or composite.

5-7   Use the exponents in the prime factorization of a number to count its factors.

5-8   Use (a) the set intersection method, (b) the prime factorization method, and (c) the Euclidean algorithm to find the greatest common factor of a given pair of numbers.

5-9   Use (a) the set intersection method, (b) the prime factorization method, and (c) the build-up method find the least common multiple of a given pair of numbers.

5-10   Relate the GCF and LCM of any two numbers to the product of the numbers.

Chapter 6 - Fractions

Students are expected to be able to:

6-1   Apply the problem-solving strategy "solve an equivalent problem."

6-2   Illustrate fractions that represent parts of a whole (numerals) which are written as pairs of whole numbers and a relative amount (numbers).

6-3   Apply the following terms
        numerator   mixed number
        denominator   complex fraction
        improper fraction

6-4   Use cross multiplication to determine which of two given fractions is greater or whether the two fractions are equal.

6-5   Express a fraction in simplest form (lowest terms).

6-6   Use concrete models show how to motivate the definitions of addition and subtraction of fractions.

6-7   Compute sums and differences of given pairs of fractions.

6-8   Apply the following properties of addition of fractions and determine which hold for subtraction of fractions:
        closure   associativity
        commutativity   identity

6-9   Use the following mental math/estimation techniques for adding and subtracting fractions:
        properties
        additive compensation
        equal-additions method of subtraction
        range estimation
        rounding to compatible numbers
        front-end with adjustment
        rounding to the nearest 1/2 or whole

6-10   Use concrete models show how to motivate the definitions of multiplication and division of fractions.

6-11   Compute products of given pairs of fractions.

6-12   Use the three equivalent approaches to find the quotient of two given fractions:
        common-denominator approach
        divided-the-numerators-and-denominators approach
        invert-the-divisor-and-multiply approach

6-13   Apply the following properties of multiplication of fractions and determine which hold for division of fractions:

      closure   identity
      commutativity   inverse
      associativity

and apply the distributive property of fraction multiplication over addition (and subtraction).

6-14   Use the following mental math/estimation techniques for multiplying and dividing fractions:

      properties
      compatible numbers
      range estimation
      rounding to the nearest 1/2 or whole

Chapter 7 - Decimals, Ratio, Proportion, and Percent

Students are expected to be able to:

7-1   Apply the problem-solving strategy "work backward."

7-2   Use a hundreds square and number line to represent decimals.

7-3   Write a given decimal numeral in expanded form.

7-4   Translate decimal numerals into their word names and vice versa.

7-5   Characterize the fractions with terminating decimal representations.

7-6   Order decimals in four ways:
          using a hundreds square
          using a number line
          comparing the numbers in fraction form
          comparing place values in decimal form

7-7   Use the following mental math/estimation techniques for adding and
          multiplying decimals:
          properties   range estimation
          compatible (decimal) numbers   rounding
          compensation   front-end with adjustment
          fraction equivalents

7-8   Justify the "moving the decimal point" when multiplying or dividing by a power
          of 10.

7-9   Compute sums, differences, products, and quotients of numbers in decimal
          form (a) using the standard algorithms and (b) using a calculator.

7-10   Use scientific notation to represent decimal numbers.

7-11   Convert any given fraction to its decimal form and any given repeating decimal
          to its fraction form.

7-12   Classify repeating decimals and characterize the fractions that have repeating,
          nonterminating decimal representations.

7-13   Use ratios to make (a) part-to-part and (b) part-to-whole comparisons of the
          relative sizes of two quantities.

7-14   Interpret the units of a ratio as a rate.

7-15   Solve proportions using (a) cross multiplication and (b) scaling up (or down).

7-16   Use 10-by-10 grids to represent n% (n percent).

7-17   Convert between the fraction, decimal and percent form of a given number.

7-18   Use the following mental math/estimation techniques for finding/estimating the percent of a number:

fraction equivalents   compensation
compatible numbers   rounding

7-19   Solve percent problems using the following approaches: (a) grid approach, (b) proportion approach, and (c) equation approach.

7-20   Use a calculator to solve percent problems.

Chapter 8 - Integers

Students are expected to be able to:

8-1   Apply the problem-solving strategy "use cases."

8-2   Use (a) colored chips (a set model) and (b) the integer number line (a measurement model) to represent integers and to model addition and subtraction of integers.

8-3   Apply the following properties of integer addition and determine which hold for subtraction:
    closure   additive identity
    commutativity   additive inverse
    associativity

8-4   Apply the additive cancellation for integers and the opposite of the opposite for integers theorems.

8-5   Subtract given pairs of integers using each of these approaches:
    take-away
    adding the opposite
    missing addend

8-6   Motivate the definition for integer multiplication using: (a) repeated addition and (b) patterns.

8-7   Apply the following properties of integer multiplication and determine which hold for division of integers:
    closure   associativity
    commutativity   multiplicative identity

and apply the distributive property of integer multiplication over addition (and subtraction).

8-8   Use the following results to calculate products of integers:
    (a) $a(-1) = -a$
    (b) $-a(b) = -(ab) = a(-b)$
    (c) $-a(-b) = ab$.

8-9   Use the missing-factor approach to explain division of integers.

8-10   Use negative exponents and scientific notation.

8-11   Use (a) the number-line approach and (b) the addition approach to order a given set of integers.

8-12   Apply the following properties of less than (and greater than):
    transitivity
    less than and addition
    multiplication by a positive and by a negative

Chapter 9 - Rational Numbers and Real Numbers, with an Introduction to Algebra

Students are expected to be able to:

9-1   Apply the problem-solving strategy "solve an equation."

9-2   Apply the following properties of addition of rational numbers:
      closure   additive identity
      commutativity   additive inverse
      associativity

9-3   Apply the additive-cancellation-for-rational-numbers and the opposite-of-the-opposite-for-rational-numbers theorems.

9-4   Subtract given pairs of rational numbers using the adding-the-opposite and the missing-addend approaches.

9-5   Apply the following properties of multiplication of rational numbers:
      closure   identity
      commutativity   multiplicative inverse
      associativity

      and apply the distributive property of multiplication over addition (and subtraction).

9-6   Use the three equivalent approaches to find the quotient of two given rational numbers:
          common-denominator approach
          divide-the-numerators-and-denominators approach
          invert-the-divisor-and-multiply approach

9-7   Order rational numbers using the following approaches:
      the number line   addition
      common positive denominators   cross multiplication

9-8   Determine whether a given real number is rational or irrational.

9-9   Use the Pythagorean theorem to find the length of a line segment given on a square lattice and to construct irrational lengths.

9-10   Apply the definitions of the following terms:
      nth root
      unit fraction exponent
      rational exponent

      and apply properties of rational exponents.

9-11   Solve equations of the forms:
       (a) $x + a = b$
       (b) $ax + b = c$
       (c) $ax + b = cx + d$

and represent the solution process both concretely (using a balance scale model) and abstractly (using algebraic symbols.)

9-12   Solve inequalities using the following properties of order:
       (a) if $a < b$ and $b < c$, then $a < c$
       (b) if $a < b$, then $a + c < b + c$
       (c) if $a < b$ and $c > 0$, then $ac < bc$
       (d) if $a < b$ and $c < 0$, then $ac > bc$.

9-13   Use arrow diagrams to represent relations and determine whether a given arrow diagram represents a relation that is reflexive, symmetric, or transitive, and whether the relation is an equivalence relation.

9-14   Determine whether a given sequence is arithmetic, geometric, or otherwise; if arithmetic (geometric), find the common difference (ratio) and the nth term.

9-15   Use function notation to express a given relationship between two sets (the domain and codomain.)

9-16   Represent functions as:
    arrow diagrams   graphs
    tables   formulas
    function machines   geometric transformations
    ordered pairs

9-17   Plot points with given coordinates in the Cartesian coordinate system.

9-18   Construct and interpret graphs of the following kinds of functions:
    linear   cubic
    quadratic   step
    exponential

9-19   Apply the vertical line test to determine if a graph is the graph of a function.

Chapter 10 - Statistics

Students are expected to be able to:

10-1   Apply the problem-solving strategy "look for a formula."

10-2   Solve problems using the Four Steps of Statistical Problem Solving:
     Formulate Questions   Organize and Display Data
     Collect Data   Analyze and Interpret Data

10-3   Interpret the following types of graphs:
     line plots   line graphs
     stem and leaf plots   circle graphs
     bar graphs   pictographs
     histograms   scatterplots

10-4   Construct appropriate types of graphs for a given collection of data.

10-5   Identify clusters and gaps (if they exist) on stem and leaf plots.

10-6   Use the regression line for a scatterplot to identify outliers and make predictions.

10-7   Identify the population and the sample for a given data-gathering situation.

10-8   Describe sources of bias in sampling.

10-9   Determine the following measures of central tendency for given data:
     mode
     median
     mean

10-10 Calculate the lower quartile, upper quartile, and the interquartile range (IQR), and identify any outliers for a box and whisker plot.

10-11 Explain the meaning of the percentile rank of a value in a given set of data.

10-12 Determine the following measures of dispersion for a given data set, using written and calculator methods:
     range   standard deviation
     variance   the z-score of a particular data value

10-13 Give a geometric interpretation of the mode, median, and mean of a distribution and, for a normal distribution, the mean, standard deviation, and z-scores.

10-14 Describe any of the following misleading attributes of a given graph:
     scaling
     axis manipulation
     reversing the category order
     cropping
     three-dimensional effects
     exploding, deceptive pictorial embellishments
     using an inappropriate type of graph

Chapter 11 - Probability

Students are expected to be able to:

11-1 Apply the problem-solving strategy "do a simulation."

11-2 Apply each of the following terms: experiment, outcome, event, and sample space.

11-3 Determine experimental and theoretical probabilities for events with equally likely outcomes.

11-4 Apply the following properties of probability:
   (a) For any event A, $0 \leq P(A) \leq 1$.
   (b) $P(\emptyset) = 0$.
   (c) $P(S) = 1$ where S is the sample space.
   (d) For all events A and B, then $P(A \cup B) = P(A) + P(B) - P(A \cap B)P(A \cup B)$.
   (e) If $\overline{A}$ denotes the complement of event A, then $P(\overline{A}) = 1 - P(A)$.

11-5 Construct tree diagrams to represent the outcomes in a sample space.

11-6 Use the fundamental counting property to determine the number of outcomes in a sample space and in an event.

11-7 Distinguish between experiments that consist of drawing with replacement and those that consist of drawing without replacement and determine probabilities in such experiments.

11-8 Construct probability tree diagrams and apply the multiplicative and additive properties of probability to compute probabilities in complex experiments.

11-9 Apply Pascal's triangle to count outcomes in experiments that consist of a sequence of smaller identical experiments, each having two equally likely possibilities.

11-10 Compute the number of permutations or combinations of r objects chosen from n objects.

11-11 Relate the row entries of Pascal's triangle to the values of the corresponding combinations.

11-12 Use permutations and combinations to compute probabilities.

11-13 Use simulations to model complex experiments and compute experimental probabilities.

11-14 Compute expected values for experiments whose outcomes are real numbers.

11-15 Convert between the probability of an event and the odds in favor or against the event.

11-16 Compute conditional probabilities.

Chapter 12 - Geometric Shapes

Students are expected to be able to:

12-1   Apply the problem-solving strategy "use a model."

12-2   Identify the van Hiele level, Level 0 (Recognition), Level 1 (Analysis), or Level 2 (Relationships) at which a student is operating.

12-3   Characterize geometric figures in terms of their component parts and attributes:

line segments	quadrilaterals
angles	other polygons
various types of triangles	

12-4   Use paper folding, dot paper, or tracings to identify characteristics of triangles and quadrilaterals, including equal side lengths, parallel sides, or perpendicular sides.

12-5   Classify various types of triangles and quadrilaterals according to common properties and relationships among general types.

12-6   Use Venn diagrams to represent relationships among various types of triangles and quadrilaterals.

12-7   Illustrate properties of triangles and quadrilaterals, including reflection and rotation symmetries, using paper folding or tracings.

12-8   Use models to represent the abstract concepts of plane, point, and line, and demonstrate the properties of lines in the plane and the distance between points.

12-9   Use a protractor to determine the measure of a given angle.

12-10 Apply formal definitions of the following geometric figures:

line segment	reflex angle
parallel lines	adjacent angles
perpendicular lines	vertical angles
angle	supplementary angles
acute angle	complementary angles
right angle	right triangle
obtuse angle	acute triangle
straight angle	obtuse triangle

12-11 Apply the corresponding angles property, the alternate interior angles property, and the angle sum in a triangle property.

12-12 Determine the measures of the following types of angles in a regular polygon:
central angle
vertex angle
exterior angle

12-13 Use tessellations to illustrate properties of arbitrary triangles and quadrilaterals.

12-14 Analyze tessellations composed of polygons, particularly those involving regular polygons.

12-15 Apply the definitions of the following terms:
    circle   radius
    center   diameter

12-16 Use paper folding to investigate properties of circles, including symmetry.

12-17 Describe pairs of lines and planes in three dimensional space according to the following relationships:
    parallel   perpendicular
    intersecting   skew

12-18 Determine the measure of a dihedral angle.

12-19 Apply the definitions of the following families of polyhedra:
    prisms (right and oblique)   regular polyhedra
    pyramids (right and oblique)   semiregular polyhedra

12-20 Illustrate Euler's formula for polyhedra.

12-21 Apply the definitions of the following curved shapes in three dimensions:
    cylinders (right and oblique)
    cones (right and oblique)
    spheres

Chapter 13 - Measurement

Students are expected to be able to:

13-1   Apply the problem-solving strategy "use dimensional analysis."

13-2   Use both non-standard and standard units and the three steps of the
        measurement process to measure:

length	capacity
area	weight
volume	temperature

13-3   Convert between units of measure within the English system, within the
        metric system, and from the English system to the metric system (and vice
        versa).

13-4   Work with the following metric prefixes:

milli-	deka-
centi-	hecto-
deci-	kilo-

13-5   Find the perimeter of geometric figures, including polygons and circles.

13-6   Apply formulas to find areas of the following geometric figures:

rectangle	parallelogram
square	trapezoid
triangle	circle

13-7   Verify the Pythagorean theorem, both informally (using a visual "proof") and
        formally (using algebra.)

13-8   Apply the Pythagorean theorem to determine lengths.

13-9   Use the triangle inequality to determine whether a given set of lengths could
        be used to form a triangle.

13-10   Justify formulas to find the surface area of the following three-dimensional
        figures:

prism	cone
cylinder	sphere
pyramid	

13-11   Apply formulas to find the surface area of the following three-dimensional
        figures:

prism	cone
cylinder	sphere
pyramid	

13-12   Justify formulas to find the volume of the following three-dimensional figures:

prism	cone
cylinder	sphere
pyramid	

13-13 Apply formulas to find the volume of the following three-dimensional figures:

      prism   cone

      cylinder   sphere

      pyramid

Chapter 14 - Geometry Using Triangle Congruence and Similarity

Students are expected to be able to:

14-1 Apply the problem-solving strategy "identify subgoals."

14-2 Establish a correspondence between two triangles to determine if they are congruent.

14-3 Apply the Side-Angle-Side (SAS), Angle-Side-Angle (ASA), and Side-Side-Side (SSS) congruence properties.

14-4 Establish a correspondence between two triangles to determine if they are similar.

14-5 Apply the Side-Angle-Side (SAS), Angle-Angle (AA), and Side-Side-Side (SSS) similarity properties.

14-6 Use similar triangles to solve application problems involving indirect measurement.

14-7 Perform the following basic compass and straightedge constructions:
   (a) copy a line segment
   (b) copy an angle
   (c) construct the perpendicular bisector of a line segment
   (d) bisect an angle
   (e) construct the line perpendicular to a given line through a specified point on the line
   (f) construct the line perpendicular to a given line through a specified point not on the line
   (g) construct the line parallel to a given line through a specified point not on the line.

14-8 Use triangle congruence properties and other results to justify each of the basic constructions (a)-(g) above.

14-9 Locate the circumcenter, centroid, incenter, and orthocenter for any given triangle using a compass and straightedge.

14-10 Use compass and straightedge to construct:
   (a) the circumscribed circle of a triangle
   (b) the inscribed circle of a triangle
   (c) an equilateral triangle with a given side

14-11 Use Gauss's theorem to determine which regular n-gons can be constructed using a compass and straightedge.

Chapter 15 - Geometry Using Coordinates

Students are expected to be able to:

15-1   Apply the problem-solving strategy "use coordinates."

15-2   Use the coordinate distance formula to:
      (a) find the distance between any two points and
      (b) determine whether three given points are collinear.

15-3   Use the midpoint formula to find the midpoint of a given line segment.

15-4   Use the slope formula:
      (a) to determine the slope (if it exists) of a line with two given points
      (b) and apply the concept of slope to determine whether three given
           points are collinear.

15-5   Apply the slopes of parallel lines theorem and the slopes of perpendicular lines theorem.

15-6   Determine the slope-intercept form of the equation of the line:
      (a) containing a given pair of points
      (b) containing a given point and having a given slope

15-7   Solve pairs of simultaneous equations and interpret the solution(s) geometrically.

15-8   Determine the equation of a circle given its center and radius and vice versa.

15-9   Use coordinate geometry to verify properties of triangles and quadrilaterals.

15-10   Use equations of lines and circles to illustrate geometric constructions in the coordinate plane.

Chapter 16 - Geometry Using Transformations

Students are expected to be able to:

16-1   Apply the problem-solving strategy "use symmetry."

16-2   Use dot paper, paper folding, tracings, and compass/straightedge to locate the image of a given point, line segment, angle, triangle, and quadrilateral under any of the following transformations:
        isometries (translation, reflection, rotation, or glide reflection)
        size transformation
        similitude

16-3   Describe an isometry that will map a given point to another given point, and a line segment, angle, triangle, or quadrilateral to a another given congruent figure.

16-4   Describe a similitude that will move a given triangle to a given similar triangle.

16-5   Determine whether a given tessellation of the plane has any the following types of symmetry:
        translation
        rotation
        reflection
        glide reflection

16-6   Verify the properties of isometries theorem.

16-7   Apply the triangle congruence and isometries theorem and the congruent polygons theorem to determine whether two given triangles or polygons are congruent.

When Will I Teach This?

The shaded regions in the following scope and sequence chart indicate when topics in *Mathematics for Elementary Teachers - A Contemporary Approach* may be covered in the typical K-8 curriculum. Topics are introduced at the conceptual level in earlier grades. Then students develop skills and facility with problem solving and application in later grades.

Chapter	Topic	K	1	2	3	4	5	6	7	8
1	Problem Solving									
2	Whole Number Concepts									
	Numeration									
3	Whole Number Operations									
4	Whole Number Computation									
5	Number Theory									
6	Fractions									
7	Decimals									
	Ratio and Proportion									
	Percent									
8	Integers									
9	Rational Numbers									
	Real Numbers									
	Solving Equations									
10	Statistics									
11	Probability									
12	Geometric Shapes									
13	Measurement									
14	Geometry – Congruence & Similarity									
15	Geometry – Coordinates									
16	Geometry - Transformations									

Exercise/Problem Sets Map for the Tenth Edition

The following Exercise/Problem Sets Map describes changes from the ninth edition. Except where noted, problems in Part A remained Part A problems, and Part B remained Part B.

CHAPTER 1		17	17	4	4	16	16	14	14
Section 1.1A		18	18	5	5	17	17	15	15
10th ed.	9th ed.	19	19	6	6	18	New	16	16
1	1	20	20	7	7	19	19	17	17
2	2	21	21	8	8	20	20	18	New
3	3	22	22	9	9	21	21	19	19
4	4	23	23	10	10	22	22	20	20
5	5	24	24	11	11	23	23	21	21
6	6	25	25	12	12	24	24	22	22
7	7	26	26	13	13	25	25	23	23
8	8	27	27	14	14	26	26	24	24
9	9	28	28	15	15	27	27	25	25
10	10	29	29	16	16	28	28	26	26
11	11	30	30	17	17	29	29	27	27
12	12	31	31	18	18	30	30	28	28
13	13	32	32	19	19	31	31	29	29
14	14	**Section 1.2A**		20	20	32	32	30	30
15	15	1	1	21	21	33	33	31	31
16	16	2	2	22	22	34	34	32	32
17	17	3	3	23	23	35	35	33	33
18	18	4	4	24	24	36	36	34	34
19	19	5	5	25	25	37	37	35	35
20	20	6	6	26	26	38	38	36	36
21	21	7	7	27	27	39	39	37	37
22	22	8	8	28	28	40	40	38	38
23	23	9	9	29	29	41	41	39	39
24	24	10	10	**CHAPTER 2**		42	42	40	40
Section 1.1B		11	11	**Section 2.1A**		43	43	41	41
1	1	12	12	10th ed.	9th ed.	44	44	42	42
2	2	13	13	1	New	**Section 2.1B**		43	43
3	3	14	14	2	2	1	New	44	44
4	4	15	15	3	3	2	New	45	45
5	5	16	16	4	4	3	3	46	46
6	6	17	17	5	5	4	4	47	47
7	7	18	18	6	6	5	New	48	48
8	8	19	19	7	7	6	New	**Section 2.2A**	
9	9	20	20	8	8	7	7	1	1
10	10	21	21	9	9	8	New	2	New
11	11	22	22	10	10	9	9	3	3
12	12	23	23	11	11	10	New	4	4
13	13	**Section 1.2B**		12	12	11	11	5	5
14	14	1	1	13	13	12	12	6	6
15	15	2	2	14	14	13	13	7	7
16	16	3	3	15	15	14	14	8	8

9	9	11	11	32	32	22	22	10	
10	10	12	12	33	33	23	23	11	10
11	11	13	13	34	34	24	24	12	11
12	New	14	14	35	35	25	25	12	12
13	13	15	15	36	36	26	26	14	13
14	14	16	16	37	37	27	27	15	14
15	15	17	17	38	38	28	28	16	15
16	16	18	18	**Section 3.1A**		29	29	17	16
17	17	19	19	10th ed.	9th ed.	30	30	18	17
18	18	20	20	1	1	**Section 3.2A**		19	18
19	19	21	21	2	2	1	New	20	19
20	20	22	22	3	3	2	2	21	20
21	21	23	23	4	4	3	3	22	21
Section 2.2B		24	24	5	5	4	4	23	22
1	1	25	25	6	6	5	5	24	23
2	New	26	26	7	7	6	6	25	24
3	3	27	27	8	8	7	7	26	25
4	4	28	28	9	9	8	8	27	26
5	5	29	29	10	10	9	9	28	27
6	New	30	30	11	11	10	10	29	28
7	7	**Section 2.3B**		12	12	11	11	30	29
8	8	1	1	13	13	12	12	31	30
9	9	2	2	14	14	13	13	32	31
10	10	3	3	15	15	14	14	33	32
11	11	4	4	16	16	15	New	34	33
12	12	5	5	17	17	16	16	35	34
13	13	6	6	18	18	17	17	36	35
14	14	7	7	19	19	18	18	37	36
15	15	8	8	20	20	19	19	38	37
16	16	9	9	21	21	20	20	39	38
17	17	10	10	**Section 3.1B**		21	21	40	39
18	18	11	11	1	1	22	22		
19	19	12	12	2	2	23	23	**Section 3.3A**	
20	20	13	13	3	3	24	24	1	1
21	21	14	New	4	4	25	25	2	2
22	22	15	15	5	5	26	26	3	3
23	23	16	16	6	6	27	27	4	4
24	24	17	17	7	7	28	28	5	5
25	25	18	18	8	8	29	29	6	6
26	26	19	19	9	9	30	30	7	7
27	27	20	20	10	10	31	31	8	8
Section 2.3A		21	21	11	11	32	32	9	9
1	1	22	22	12	12	**Section 3.2B**		10	10
2	2	23	23	13	13	1	1	11	11
3	3	24	24	14	14	2	2	12	12
4	4	25	25	15	15	3	3	13	13
5	5	26	26	16	16	4	4	14	14
6	6	27	27	17	17	5	5	15	15
7	7	28	28	18	18	6	6	16	16
8	8	29	29	19	19	7	7	17	17
9	9	30	30	20	20	8	8	18	18
10	10	31	31	21	21	9	9	19	19

20	20	14	14	24	24	26	26	32	32
21	21	15	15	25	25	27	27	33	33
22	22	16	16	26	26	28	28	34	34
23	23	17	17	27	27	29	29	35	36
Section 3.3B		18	18	28	28	30	30	36	36
1	1	19	19	29	29	31	31	37	37
2	2	20	20	30	30	32	32	38	38
3	3	21	21	31	31	33	33	39	39
4	4	22	22	32	32	34	34	40	40
5	5	23	23	33	33	35	35	41	41
6	6	24	24	34	34	36	36	42	42
7	7	25	25	35	35	37	37	43	43
8	8	26	26	36	36	38	38	44	44
9	9	27	27	37	37	39	39	45	45
10	10	28	28	38	38	40	40	47	47
11	11	29	29	39	39	41	41	48	48
12	12	30	30	40	40	42	42	49	49
13	13	31	31	41	41	43	43	50	50
14	14	32	32	42	42	44	44	51	51
15	15	33	33	43	43	45	45	52	52
16	16	34	34	44	44	**Section 4.2B**		53	53
17	17	35	35	45	45	1	1	54	54
18	18	36	36	46	46	2	2	**Section 4.3A**	
19	19	37	37	47	47	3	3	1	1
20	20	38	38	48	48	4	4	2	2
21	21	39	39	49	49	5	5	3	3
22	22	40	40	**Section 4.2A**		6	6	4	4
23	23	41	41	1	1	7	7	5	5
24	24	**Section 4.1B**		2	2	8	8	6	6
25	25	1	1	3	3	9	9	7	7
26	26	2	2	4	4	10	10	8	8
27	27	3	3	5	5	11	11	9	9
28	28	4	New	6	6	12	12	10	10
29	29	5	5	7	7	13	13	11	11
30	30	6	6	8	8	14	14	12	12
31	31	7	7	9	9	15	15	13	13
CHAPTER 4		8	8	10	10	16	16	14	New
Section 4.1A		9	9	11	11	17	17	15	15
10th ed.	**9th ed.**	10	10	12	12	18	18	16	16
1	1	11	11	13	13	19	19	17	17
2	2	12	12	14	14	20	20	18	18
3	3	13	13	15	15	21	21	19	19
4	4	14	14	16	16	22	22	20	20
5	5	15	15	17	17	23	23	21	21
6	6	16	16	18	18	24	24	22	22
7	7	17	17	19	19	25	25	23	23
8	8	18	18	20	20	26	26	24	24
9	9	19	19	21	21	27	27	**Section 4.3B**	
10	10	20	20	22	22	28	28	1	1
11	11	21	21	23	23	29	29	2	2
12	12	22	22	24	24	30	30	3	3
13	13	23	23	25	25	31	31	4	4

10th	9th	10th	9th	10th	9th	10th	9th	10th	9th
5	5	26	26	29	29	26	26	42	43
6	6	27	27	30	30	27	27	43	43
7	7	28	28	31	31	28	28	**Section 6.1A**	
8	8	29	29	32	32	29	29	10th ed.	9th ed.
9	9	30	30	33	33	30	30	1	1
10	10	31	31	34	34	31	31	2	2
11	11	32	32	35	35	32	32	3	3
12	12	33	33	36	36	33	33	4	4
13	13	34	34	37	37	34	34	5	5
14	14	35	35	38	38	35	35	6	6
15	15	36	36	39	39	**Section 5.2B**		7	7
16	16	37	37	40	40	1	1	8	8
17	17	38	38	41	41	2	2	9	9
18	18	39	39	42	42	3	3	10	10
19	19	40	40	43	43	4	4	11	11
20	20	41	41	44	44	5	5	12	12
21	21	42	42	45	45	6	New	13	13
22	22	43	43	46	46	7	7	14	14
23	23	44	44	47	47	8	8	15	15
24	24	45	45	48	48	9	9	16	16
25	25	46	46	49	New	10	10	17	17
26	26	47	47	50	49	11	11	18	18
27	27	48	New	51	50	12	12	19	19
28	28	**Section 5.1B**		52	51	13	13	20	20
CHAPTER 5		1	1	53	52	14	14	21	21
Section 5.1A		2	2	54	53	15	15	22	22
10th ed.	9th ed.	3	3	**Section 5.2A**		16	16	23	23
1	1	4	4	1	1	17	17	24	24
2	2	5	5	2	2	18	18	25	25
3	3	6	11	3	3	19	19	26	26
4	4	7	6	4	4	20	20	27	27
5	5	8	7	5	5	21	21	28	28
6	6	9	8	6	6	22	22	29	29
7	7	10	New	7	7	23	23	30	30
8	8	11	10	8	8	24	24	31	31
9	9	12	12	9	9	25	25	**Section 6.1B**	
10	10	13	13	10	10	26	26	1	1
11	11	14	14	11	11	27	27	2	2
12	12	15	15	12	12	28	28	3	3
13	13	16	16	13	13	29	29	4	4
14	14	17	17	14	14	30	30	5	5
15	15	18	18	15	15	31	31	6	6
16	16	19	19	16	16	32	32	7	7
17	17	20	20	17	17	33	33	8	8
18	18	21	21	18	18	34	34	9	9
19	19	22	22	19	19	35	35	10	10
20	20	23	23	20	20	36	36	11	11
21	21	24	24	21	21	37	37	12	12
22	22	25	25	22	22	38	38	13	13
23	23	26	26	23	23	39	39	14	14
24	24	27	27	24	24	40	40	15	15
25	25	28	28	25	25	41	41	16	16

17	17	29	29	5	5	15	15	15	15
18	18	30	30	6	6	16	16	16	16
19	19	31	31	7	7	17	17	17	New
20	20	32	32	8	New	18	New	18	18
21	21	33	33	9	New	19	19	19	19
22	22	**Section 6.2B**		10	10	20	20	20	20
23	23	1	New	11	11	21	21	**Section 7.1B**	
24	24	2	2	12	12	22	22	1	1
25	25	3	3	13	13	23	23	2	2
26	26	4	4	14	14	24	24	3	3
27	27	5	5	18	18	28	28	4	New
28	28	6	6	16	16	26	26	5	5
29	29	7	7	17	17	27	27	6	6
30	30	8	8	18	18	28	28	7	7
31	31	9	9	19	19	29	29	8	8
32	32	10	10	20	20	30	30	9	9
33	33	11	11	21	21	31	31	10	10
34	34	12	12	22	22	32	32	11	11
35	35	13	13	23	23	33	33	12	12
36	36	14	14	24	24	34	34	13	13
37	37	15	15	25	25	35	35	14	14
38	38	16	16	26	26	36	36	15	15
39	39	17	17	27	27	37	37	16	16
Section 6.2A		18	18	28	New	38	38	17	New
1	1	19	19	29	29	39	39	18	18
2	2	20	20	30	30	40	40	19	19
3	3	21	21	31	31	41	41	20	20
4	4	22	22	32	32	42	42	21	21
5	5	23	23	33	33	43	43	22	22
6	New	24	24	34	34	44	44	23	23
7	7	25	25	35	35	45	45	24	24
8	8	26	26	36	36	46	46	25	25
9	9	27	27	37	37	47	47	26	26
10	10	28	28	38	38	48	48	27	27
11	New	29	29	39	39	49	49	**Section 7.2A**	
12	12	30	30	40	40	**CHAPTER 7**		1	1
13	13	31	31	41	41	**Section 7.1A**		2	2
14	14	32	32	**Section 6.3B**		10th ed.	9th ed.	3	3
15	15	33	33	1	1	1	1	4	4
16	16	34	34	2	2	2	2	5	5
17	17	35	35	3	3	3	New	6	6
18	18	35	35	4	4	4	4	7	7
19	19	36	36	5	5	5	5	8	8
20	20	37	37	6	6	6	6	9	9
21	21	38	38	7	7	7	7	10	10
22	22	39	39	8	New	8	8	11	11
23	23	40	40	9	New	9	9	12	12
24	24	**Section 6.3A**		10	10	10	10	13	13
25	25	1	1	11	11	11	11	14	14
26	26	2	2	12	12	12	12	15	15
27	27	3	3	13	13	13	13	16	16
28	28	4	4	14	14	14	14	17	17

18	18	35	35	11	11	22	22	29	29
19	19	36	36	12	12	23	23	30	30
20	20	37	37	13	13	24	24	31	31
21	21	38	38	14	14	25	25	32	32
22	22	39	39	15	15	28	28	39	39
23	23	40	40	16	16	27	27	34	34
24	24	41	41	17	17	28	28	35	35
25	25	**Section 7.3A**		18	18	29	29	36	36
26	26	1	1, 7.4B	19	19	30	30	37	37
27	27	2	2	20	20	31	31	38	38
28	28	3	3	21	21	32	32	39	39
29	29	4	4	22	22	33	33	40	40
30	30	5	5	23	23	34	34	41	41
31	31	6	6	24	24	35	35	42	42
32	32	7	7	25	25	36	36	43	43
33	33	8	8	26	26	37	37	44	44
34	34	9	9	27	27	38	38	45	45
Section 7.2B		10	10	28	28	39	39	46	46
1	1	11	11	29	29	40	40	47	47
2	2	12	12	30	30	41	41	48	48
3	3	13	13	31	31	42	42	49	49
4	4	14	14	32	32	43	43	50	50
5	5	15	New	33	33	44	44	51	51
6	6	16	16	34	34	**Section 7.4B**		**CHAPTER 8**	
7	7	17	17	35	35	1	1	**Section 8.1A**	
8	8	18	18	36	36	2	2	10th ed.	9th ed.
9	9	19	19	37	37	3	3	1	New
10	10	20	20	38	38	4	4	2	2
11	11	21	21	39	39	5	5	3	3
12	12	22	22	40	40	6	6	4	New
13	13	23	23	**Section 7.4A**		7	7	5	5
14	14	24	24	1	1	8	8	6	6
15	15	25	25	2	2	9	9	7	7
16	16	26	26	3	3	10	10	8	8
17	17	27	27	4	4	11	11	9	9, 8.1B
18	18	28	28	5	5	12	12	10	10
19	19	29	29	6	6	13	13	11	11
20	20	30	30	7	7	14	14	12	12
21	21	31	31	8	8	15	15	13	13
22	22	32	32	9	9	16	16	14	14
23	23	33	33	10	10	17	17	15	15
24	24	**Section 7.3B**		11	11	18	18	16	New
25	25	1	1, 7.4A	12	12	19	19	17	17
26	26	2	2	13	13	20	20	18	18
27	27	3	3	14	14	21	21	19	19
28	28	4	4	15	15	22	22	20	20
29	29	5	5	16	16	23	23	21	21
30	30	6	6	17	17	24	24	22	22
31	31	7	7	18	18	25	25	23	23
32	32	8	8	19	19	26	26	24	24
33	33	9	9	20	20	27	27	25	25
34	34	10	10	21	21	28	28	26	26

27	27	15	15	29	29	34	34	47	47
28	28	16	16	30	30	35	35	48	48
Section 8.1B		17	17	31	31	36	36	**Section 9.2A**	
1	New	18	18	32	32	37	37	1	1
2	New	19	19	33	33	38	38	2	2
3	3	20	20	34	34	**Section 9.1B**		3	3
4	New	21	21	35	35	1	New	4	4
5	5	22	22	36	36	2	New	5	5
6	6	23	23	37	37	3	3	6	7
7	7	24	24	38	38	4	4	7	8
8	8	25	25	39	39	5	5	8	9
9	9, 8.1A	26	26	40	40	6	6	9	10
10	10	27	27	41	41	7	7	10	6
11	11	28	28	42	42	8	New	11	11
12	12	29	29	43	43	9	9	12	12
13	13	30	30	44	44	10	10	13	13
14	14	31	31	**CHAPTER 9**		11	11	14	14
15	15	32	32	**Section 9.1A**		12	12	15	15
16	16	33	33	**10th ed.**	**9th ed.**	13	13	16	16
17	17	34	34	1	1	14	14	17	New
18	18	35	35	2	New	15	15	18	18
19	19	36	36	3	3	16	16	19	19
20	20	37	37	4	4	17	17	20	New
21	21	**Section 8.2B**		5	5	18	19	21	21
22	22	1	1	6	6	19	19	22	22
23	23	2	2	7	7	20	20	23	23
24	24	3	3	8	8	21	21	24	24
25	25	4	4	9	9	22	22	25	25
26	26	5	5	10	10	23	23	26	26
27	27	6	6	11	11	24	New	27	27
28	28	7	7	12	12	25	25	28	28
29	29	8	8	13	13	26	26	29	29
30	30	9	9	14	14	27	27	30	30
31	31	10	10	15	15	28	28	31	31
32	32	11	11	16	16	29	29	32	32
33	33	12	12	17	17	30	30	33	33
34	34	13	13	18	18	31	31	34	34
Section 8.2A		14	14	19	19	32	32	35	35
1	1	15	15	20	20	33	33	36	36
2	2	16	16	21	21	34	34	37	37
3	3	17	17	22	New	36	36	38	38
4	4	18	18	23	23	36	36	39	39
5	5	19	19	24	24	37	37	40	40
6	6	20	20	25	25	38	38	**Section 9.2B**	
7	7	21	21	26	26	39	39	1	1
8	8	22	22	27	27	40	40	2	2
9	9	23	23	28	28	41	41	3	3
10	10	24	24	29	29	42	42	4	4
11	11	25	25	30	30	43	43	5	5
12	12	26	26	31	31	44	44	6	7
13	13	27	27	32	32	45	45	7	8
14	14	28	28	33	33	46	46	8	9

9	10	13	13	35	35	25	25	13	10
10	6	14	14	**Section 9.4A**		26	26	14	New
11	11	15	15	1	1	27	27	15	12
12	12	16	16	2	2	28	28	16	13
13	New	17	17	3	3	29	29	17	14
14	14	18	18	4	4	30	30	18	15
15	15	19	19	5	5	31	31	19	16
16	16	20	20	6	6	**CHAPTER 10**		20	17
17	New	21	21	7	7	**Section 10.1A**		21	18
18	18	22	22	8	8	10th ed.	9th ed.	22	New
19	19	23	23	9	9	1	New	23	New
20	20	24	24	10	10	2	13	24	New
21	21	25	25	11	11	3	14	25	New
22	22	26	26	12	12	4	1	26	New
23	23	27	27	13	13	5	2	27	New
24	24	28	28	14	14	6	3	28	25
25	25	29	29	15	15	7	4	29	New
26	26	**Section 9.3B**		16	16	8	5	30	27
27	27	1	1	17	17	9	6	31	28
28	28	2	2	18	18	10	7	32	29
29	29	3	3	19	19	11	8	33	30
30	30	4	4	20	20	12	9	34	31
31	31	5	5	21	21	13	10	35	32
32	32	6	6	22	22	14	11	36	33
33	33	7	7	23	23	15	12	37	34
34	34	8	8	24	24	16	13	38	35
35	35	9	9	25	25	17	14	39	36
36	36	10	10	**Section 9.4B**		18	15	**Section 10.2A**	
37	37	11	11	1	1	19	16	1	1
38	38	12	12	2	2	20	17	2	2
39	39	13	13	3	3	21	18	3	3
40	40	14	15	4	4	22	19	4	4
41	41	15	14	5	5	23	20	5	5
42	42	16	16	6	6	24	21	6	6
43	43	17	17	7	7	25	22	7	7
44	44	18	18	8	8	26	23	8	8
45	45	19	19	9	9	27	24	9	9
46	46	20	20	10	10	28	25	10	New
47	47	21	21	11	11	29	26	11	New
Section 9.3A		22	22	12	12	**Section 10.1B**		12	12
1	1	23	23	13	13	1	New	13	13
2	2	24	24	14	14	2	13	14	14
3	3	25	25	15	15	3	14	15	15
4	4	26	26	16	16	4	1	16	New
5	5	27	27	17	17	5	2	17	New
6	6	28	28	18	18	6	3	18	16
7	7	29	29	19	19	7	4	19	17
8	8	30	30	20	20	8	5	20	18
9	9	31	31	21	21	9	6	21	19
10	10	32	32	22	22	10	7	22	20
11	11	33	33	23	23	11	8	23	21
12	12	34	34	24	24	12	9	24	22

10th ed.	9th ed.
25	23
26	24
27	25
28	26
29	27
30	28
Section 10.2B	
1	1
2	2
3	3
4	4
5	5
6	6
7	7
8	8
9	9
10	New
11	New
12	12
13	13
14	14
15	15
16	New
17	New
18	16
19	17
20	New
21	19
22	20
23	New
24	22
25	23
26	24
27	26
28	27
29	28
30	29
31	30
32	31
33	32
34	33
35	34
36	35
37	36
Section 10.3A	
1	1
2	New
3	3
4	New
5	New
6	New
7	New

10th ed.	9th ed.
8	New
9	New
10	10
11	11
12	12
13	13
14	15
15	New
16	New
17	18
18	New
19	20
20	21
Section 10.3B	
1	New
2	2
3	New
4	New
5	New
6	6
7	7
8	New
9	New
10	10
11	11
12	12
13	New
14	15
15	16
16	17
17	New
18	19
19	20
20	21
21	22
22	23
23	24
24	25
25	26
26	27
CHAPTER 11	
Section 11.1A	
10th ed.	9th ed.
1	1
2	2
3	3
4	4
5	5
6	6
7	7
8	8
9	9

10th ed.	9th ed.
10	10
11	11
12	12
13	13
14	14
15	15
16	16
17	17
18	18
19	19
20	20
21	21
22	22
23	23
24	24
Section 11.1B	
1	1
2	2
3	3
4	4
5	5
6	6
7	7
8	8
9	9
10	10
11	11
12	12
13	13
14	14
15	15
16	16
17	17
18	18
19	19
20	20
21	21
22	22
23	23
24	24
25	25
26	26
27	27
28	28
29	29
30	30
31	31
32	32
Section 11.2A	
1	1
2	2
3	3

10th ed.	9th ed.
4	4
5	5
6	6
7	7
8	8
9	9
10	10
11	11
12	12
13	13
14	14
15	15
16	16
17	17
18	18
19	20
20	21
21	22
22	23
23	24
24	25
25	26
Section 11.2B	
1	1
2	2
3	3
4	4
5	5
6	6
7	7
8	8
9	9
10	10
11	11
12	12
13	New
14	14
15	15
16	16
17	17
18	18
19	19
20	20
21	21
22	22
23	23
24	24
25	25
26	26
27	27
28	28
29	29

10th ed.	9th ed.
30	30
31	31
32	32
33	33
34	34
Section 11.3A	
1	1
2	2
3	3
4	4
5	5
6	6
7	7
8	8
9	9
10	10
11	New
12	12
13	13
14	14
15	15
16	16
17	17
18	18
19	19
20	20
21	21
22	22
23	23
24	24
25	25
26	26
27	27
28	28
Section 11.3B	
1	1
2	2
3	3
4	4
5	5
6	6
7	7
8	8
9	9
10	10
11	11
12	New
13	13
14	14
15	15
16	16
17	17

18	18
19	19
20	20
21	21
22	22
23	23
24	24
25	25
26	26
27	27
28	28
29	29
30	30
31	31
32	32
33	33
34	34
35	35
Section 11.4A	
1	1
2	2
3	3
4	4
5	5
6	6
7	7
8	8
9	9
10	10
11	11
12	12
13	13
14	14
15	15
16	16
17	17
18	18
19	19
20	20
21	21
22	22
23	23
24	24
25	25
26	26
27	27
28	28
29	29
30	30
Section 11.4B	
1	1
2	2

3	3
4	4
5	5
6	6
7	7
8	8
9	9
10	10
11	11
12	12
13	13
14	14
15	15
16	16
17	17
18	18
19	19
20	20
21	21
22	22
23	23
24	24
25	25
26	26
27	27
28	28
29	29
30	30
31	31
32	32
33	33
34	34
35	35
36	36
CHAPTER 12	
Section 12.1A	
10th ed.	9th ed.
1	1
2	2
3	3
4	New
5	4
6	5
7	6
8	8
9	12
10	13
11	14
12	15
13	16
14	17
15	18

16	19
17	20
18	22
Section 12.1B	
1	1
2	2
3	3
4	New
5	4
6	5
7	6
8	8
9	12
10	13
11	14
12	15
13	New
14	17
15	20
16	21
17	22
18	23
19	24
20	26
21	28
Section 12.2A	
1	7
2	8
3	9
4	10
5	7,12.1
6	9,12.1
7	10,12.1
8	11,12.1
9	23,12.1
10	New
11	New
12	New
13	6
14	13
15	14
Section 12.2B	
1	7
2	8
3	9
4	10
5	7,12.1
6	9,12.1
7	10,12.1
8	11,12.1
9	18,12.1
10	New

11	New
12	11
13	12
14	6
15	20,12.1A
16	25,12.1
17	17
18	27
19	21
20	29,12.1
21	22
22	30,12.1
Section 12.3A	12.2A
1	1
2	2
3	3
4	4
5	New
6	New
7	11
8	12
9	15
10	20,12.3
Section 12.3B	12.2B
1	1
2	2
3	3
4	4
5	New
6	New
7	13
8	14
9	15
10	22,12.3
11	23,12.3
12	24,12.3
13	16
14	18
15	19
16	20
Section 12.4A	12.3A
1	1
2	2
3	3
4	4
5	5
6	6
7	7
8	8

9	9
10	10
11	11
12	12
13	13
14	14
15	15
16	16
17	17
18	18
19	19
20	21
21	22
Section 12.4B	12.3B
1	1
2	2
3	3
4	4
5	5
6	6
7	7
8	8
9	9
10	10
11	11
12	12
13	13
14	14
15	15
16	16
17	17
18	18
19	19
20	20
21	21
22	25
23	26
24	27
25	28
26	29
27	30
Section 12.5A	
1	1
2	2
3	3
4	4
5	5
6	6
7	7
8	8

9	9	28	28	9	9	23	23	40	40
10	10	29	29	10	10	24	24	41	41
11	11	30	30	11	11	25	25	**Section 13.2A**	
12	12	31	31	12	12	26	26	1	1
13	13	32	32	13	13	27	27	2	New
14	14	33	33	14	14	28	28	3	3
15	15	34	34	15	15	29	29	4	New
16	16	35	35	16	16	21	21	5	5
17	17	36	36	17	17	31	31	6	6
18	18	37	37	18	18	32	32	7	7
19	19	38	38	19	19	33	33	8	8
20	20	39	39	20	20	34	34	9	9
21	21	**Section 12.6A**		21	21	**Section 13.1B**		10	10
22	22		**12.5A**	22	22	1	1	11	11
23	23	1	1	23	23	2	2	12	12
24	24	2	2	24	24	3	3	13	13
25	25	3	3	25	25	4	4	14	14
26	26	4	4	26	26	5	5	15	15
27	27	5	5	27	27	6	6	16	16
28	28	6	6	28	28	7	7	17	17
29	29	7	7	29	29	8	8	18	18
30	30	8	8	30	30	9	9	19	19
31	31	9	9	31	31	10	10	20	20
Section 12.5B		10	10	32	32	11	11	21	21
	12.4B	11	New	33	33	12	12	22	22
1	1	12	12	34	34	13	13	23	23
2	2	13	13	35	35	14	14	24	24
3	3	14	14	**CHAPTER 13**		15	15	25	25
4	4	15	15	**Section 13.1A**		16	16	26	26
5	5	16	16	**10th ed.**	**9th ed.**	17	17	27	27
6	6	17	17	1	1	18	18	28	28
7	7	18	18	2	2	19	19	29	29
8	8	19	19	3	3	20	20	30	30
9	9	20	20	4	4	21	21	31	31
10	10	21	21	5	5	22	22	32	32
11	11	22	22	6	6	23	23	33	33
12	12	23	23	7	7	24	24	34	34
13	13	24	24	8	8	25	25	35	35
14	14	25	25	9	9	26	26	36	36
15	15	26	26	10	10	27	27	37	37
16	16	27	27	11	11	28	28	38	38
17	17	28	28	12	12	29	29	39	39
18	18	**Section 12.6B**		13	13	30	30	40	40
19	19		**12.5B**	14	14	31	31	41	41
20	20	1	1	15	15	32	32	42	42
21	21	2	2	16	16	33	33	43	43
22	22	3	3	17	17	34	34	44	44
23	23	4	4	18	18	35	35	45	45
24	24	5	5	19	19	36	36	46	46
25	25	6	6	20	20	37	37	47	47
26	26	7	7	21	21	38	38	**Section 13.2B**	
27	27	8	8	22	22	39	39	1	1

2	2	54	54	**Section 13.4A**		19	19	11	11
3	3	55	55	1	1	20	20	12	12
4	4	56	56	2	2	21	21	13	13
5	5	**Section 13.3A**		3	3	22	22	14	14
6	6	1	1	4	4	23	23	15	15
7	7	2	2	5	5	24	24	16	16
8	8	3	3	6	6	25	25	17	17
9	9	4	4	7	7	26	26	18	18
10	10	5	5	8	8	27	27	19	19
11	11	6	6	9	9	28	28	20	20
12	12	7	7	10	10	29	29	21	21
13	13	8	8	11	11	30	30	22	22
14	14	9	9	12	12	31	31	23	23
15	15	10	10	13	13	32	32	24	24
16	16	11	11	14	14	33	33	25	25
17	17	12	12	15	15	34	34	**Section 14.2A**	
18	18	13	13	16	16	35	35	1	1
19	19	14	14	17	17	36	36	2	2
20	20	15	15	18	18	37	37	3	3
21	21	16	16	19	19	38	38	4	4
22	22	17	17	20	20	**CHAPTER 14**		5	5
23	23	18	18	21	21	**Section 14.1A**		6	6
24	24	19	19	22	22	1	1	7	7
25	25	20	20	23	23	2	2	8	8
26	26	**Section 13.3B**		24	24	3	3	9	9
27	27	1	1	25	25	4	4	10	10
28	28	2	2	26	26	5	5	11	11
29	29	3	3	27	27	6	6	12	12
30	30	4	4	28	28	7	7	13	13
31	31	5	5	29	29	8	8	14	14
32	32	6	6	30	30	9	9	15	15
33	33	7	7	31	31	10	10	16	16
34	34	8	8	32	32	11	11	17	17
35	35	9	9	**Section 13.4B**		12	12	18	18
36	36	10	10	1	1	13	13	19	19
37	37	11	11	2	2	14	14	20	20
38	38	12	12	3	3	15	15	21	21
39	39	13	13	4	4	16	16	22	22
40	40	14	14	5	5	17	17	23	23
41	41	15	15	6	6	18	18	24	24
42	42	16	16	7	7	19	19	**Section 14.2B**	
43	43	17	17	8	8	**Section 14.1B**		1	1
44	44	18	18	9	9	1	1	2	2
45	45	19	19	10	10	2	2	3	3
46	46	20	20	11	11	3	3	4	4
47	47	21	21	12	12	4	4	5	5
48	48	22	22	13	13	5	5	6	6
49	49	23	23	14	14	6	6	7	7
50	50	24	24	15	15	7	7	8	8
51	51	25	25	16	16	8	8	9	9
52	52	26	26	17	17	9	9	10	10
53	53	27	27	18	18	10	10	11	11

12	12	10	10	11	11	17	18	21	21
13	13	11	11	12	12	18	19	22	22
14	14	12	12	13	13	19	20	23	23
15	15	13	13	14	14	20	21	24	24
16	16	14	14	15	15	21	22	25	25
17	17	15	15	16	16	**CHAPTER 15**		26	26
18	18	16	16	17	17	**Section 15.1A**		27	27
19	19	17	17	18	18	**10th ed.**	**9th ed.**	28	28
20	20	18	18	19	19	1	1	29	29
21	21	19	19	20	20	2	2	30	30
22	22	20	20	21	21	3	3	31	31
23	23	21	21	22	22	4	4	**Section 15.2A**	
24	24	22	22	23	23	5	5	1	New
25	25	23	23	24	24	6	6	2	New
26	26	24	24	25	25	7	7	3	New
27	27	25	25	26	26	8	8	4	4
28	28	26	26	27	27	9	9	5	New
29	29	27	27	**Section 14.5A**		10	10	6	6
30	30	28	28	1	1	11	11	7	7
31	31	29	29	2	2	12	12	8	8
Section 14.3A		**Section 14.4A**		3	3	13	13	9	9
1	1	1	1	4	4	14	14	10	10
2	2	2	2	5	5 14.5B	15	15	11	New
3	3	3	3	6	6	16	16	12	12
4	4	4	4	7	7	17	17	13	13
5	5	5	5	8	8	18	18	14	14
6	6	6	6	9	5	19	19	15	15
7	7	7	7	10	9	20	20	16	16
8	8	8	8	11	10	21	21	17	17
9	9	9	9	12	11	22	22	18	18
10	10	10	10	13	12	23	23	19	19
11	11	11	11	14	13	**Section 15.1B**		20	20
12	12	12	12	15	14	1	1	21	21
13	13	13	13	16	15	2	2	22	22
14	14	14	14	17	16	3	3	23	23
15	15	15	15	**Section 14.5B**		4	4	24	24
16	16	16	16	1	1	5	5	25	25
17	17	17	17	2	2	6	6	26	26
18	18	18	18	3	3	7	7	27	27
19	19	19	19	4	4	8	8	28	28
20	20	20	20	5	6	9	9	29	29
21	21	**Section 14.4B**		6	7	10	10	30	30
Section 14.3B		1	1	7	8	11	11	31	31
1	1	2	2	8	9	12	12	**Section 15.2B**	
2	2	3	3	9	10	13	13	1	New
3	3	4	4	10	12	14	14	2	New
4	4	5	5	11	11	15	15	3	New
5	5	6	6	12	13	16	16	4	4
6	6	7	7	13	14	17	17	5	New
7	7	8	8	14	15	18	18	6	6
8	8	9	9	15	16	19	19	7	7
9	9	10	10	16	17	20	20	8	9

9	8
10	10
11	New
12	12
13	13
14	14
15	15
16	16
17	17
18	18
19	19
20	20
21	21
22	22
23	23
24	24
25	25
26	26
27	27
28	28
29	29
30	30
31	31
32	32
33	33
34	34
35	35
36	36
37	37
38	38
Section 15.3A	
1	1
2	2
3	3
4	4
5	5
6	6
7	7
8	8
9	9
10	10
11	11
12	12
13	13
14	14
15	15
16	16
17	17
18	18
19	19
20	20
21	21

Section 15.3B	
1	1
2	2
3	3
4	4
5	5
6	6
7	7
8	8
9	9
10	10
11	11
12	12
13	13
14	14
15	15
16	16
17	17
18	18
19	19
20	20
21	21
22	22
23	23
24	24
25	25
26	26
27	27
28	28
CHAPTER 16	
Section 16.1A	
10th ed.	9th ed.
1	1
2	2
3	3
4	4
5	5
6	6
7	7
8	8
9	9
10	10
11	11
12	12
13	13
14	14
15	15
16	16
17	17
18	18
19	19
20	20

21	21
22	22
23	23
24	24
25	25
26	26
27	27
28	28
29	29
30	30
31	31
32	32
33	33
Section 16.1B	
1	1
2	2
3	3
4	4
5	5
6	6
7	7
8	8
9	9
10	10
11	11
12	12
13	13
14	14
15	15
16	16
17	17
18	18
19	19
20	20
21	21
22	22
23	23
24	24
25	25
26	26
27	27
28	28
29	29
30	30
31	31
32	32
33	33
34	34
35	35
36	36
37	37
38	38

39	39
40	40
41	41
Section 16.2A	
1	1
2	2
3	3
4	4
5	5
6	6
7	7
8	8
9	9
10	10
11	11
12	12
13	13
14	14
15	15
16	16
17	17
18	18
19	19
20	20
21	21
22	22
23	23
24	24
25	25
Section 16.2B	
1	1
2	2
3	3
4	4
5	5
6	6
7	7
8	8
9	9
10	10
11	11
12	12
13	13
14	14
15	15
16	16
17	17
18	18
19	19
20	20
21	21
22	22

23	23
24	24
25	25
26	26
27	27
28	28
29	29
30	30
31	31
32	32
Section 16.3A	
1	1
2	2
3	3
4	4
5	5
6	6
7	7
8	8
9	9
10	10
11	11
12	12
13	13
14	14
15	15
Section 16.3B	
1	5
2	6
3	7
4	1
5	4
6	3
7	2
8	14
9	8
10	9
11	10
12	15
13	11
14	12
15	15
16	16
17	17
18	18
19	19
20	20
21	21

ANSWERS TO EXERCISE/PROBLEM SETS, PART B

Chapter 1

Section 1.1

1. 41,312,432

2. Same number. Let x be your number. The $[([(5x + 8) \times 4 + 9] \times 5) - 105] \div 100 - 1 = [(20x + 32 + 9) \times 5 - 105] \div 100 - 1 = [(100x + 205) - 105] \div 100 - 1 = x$.

3. 15 items

4. Here 12 toothpicks form 5 squares. Remove some to solve the rest of the problem.

5. 78 and 79

6. For example, place 10 in the center. Then place numbers across from each other whose sum is 20.

7. $(6 + 6) \times 6 - 6 = 66$

8. 2520 feet

9. Product must be even since one page must have an even number on it.

10. 2 spares

11. 11 pieces

12. 3 moves

13. Pat: $68.54, Chris: $32.46

14. $2178 \times 4 = 8712$

15. $n + (n + 1) + (n + 2) + (n + 3) = 4n + 6$, thus the sum of four consecutive counting numbers is even since $4n + 6 = 2(2n + 3)$.

16. Bill

17. Top row: 4 10 6
    Bottom row: 11 16 5

18. Baseball - 0.35 pounds
    Football - 0.9 pounds
    Soccer ball - 1 pound

19. The answer will always be 5.
    Proof: $[(n + n + 1 + 9) \div 2] - n = [(2n + 10) \div 2] - n = n + 5 - n = 5$.

20. In the fifth row, the 3 should be 33.

21. 12 triangles

22. 18 and 22 are impossible. There are multiple possibilities for 19, 20, and 21.

23.

24.

25. Solve the equation $3n - 3 = 87$ to obtain $n = 30$ or 30 dots on each side.

26. Since y is divided by 5 and then 12 is added to that quotient to obtain 23, working backward, we should subtract 12 from 23 and then multiply that difference by 5.

Analyzing Student Thinking

27. Ask Wesley to test a few guesses to see what he can learn about possible solutions. Guess and test is a good way to get started, but since the solution is not a whole number, it will probably be more time consuming than solving the equation using algebra.

28. Rosemary, the Guess and Test strategy is useful because it can help you gain a better understanding of the problem and give you a good idea of what the answer is.

29. Ceclia, drawing a picture can help you gain a better understanding of problems involving physical situations. Use it when you are not sure what the problem is asking or when no solution method is obvious to you.

30. Damian, these equations are the same: one uses a box to represent a number and the other uses a letter (variable) to represent a number. We don't usually introduce students to variables until they are older.

31. Byron, let's represent the sum of three consecutive odd numbers using a variable:
$n + (n + 2) + (n + 4) = 3n + 6 = 96$
Solving this equation for n, the first of the three consecutive odd numbers, we get $n = 30$, an even number. This shows us that our equation has no solution.

32. Vance and Joule, both of your methods are valid and each one has its advantages. Drawing a picture and guessing and testing are powerful strategies that can help you gain a better understanding of a problem, and often can help you to develop an equation. In many cases, using an equation is more efficient than guess and test, and it is a good way to look back at your solution after using guess and test.

Section 1.2

1. (a) 26   (b) $\dfrac{5}{4}$
   (c) 486   (d) 2347

2. (a)   (b)

3. (a)

Rectangular Number	Number of Dots in Shape
1	$2 = 1 \cdot 2$
2	$6 = 2 \cdot 3$
3	$12 = 3 \cdot 4$
4	$20 = 4 \cdot 5$
5	$30 = 5 \cdot 6$
6	$42 = 6 \cdot 7$

(b)

(c) 110 dots
(d) 19th number
(e) $n(n + 1)$
(f) The nth rectangular number is twice the nth triangular number.

4. (a)

Pentagonal Number	Number of Dots in Shape
1	1
2	5
3	12
4	22
5	35

(b)

(c) 117 dots
(d) No, the 11th has 176 dots and the 12th has 210 dots.
(e) $1 + 4 + 7 + \ldots + [n + n + (n - 2)]$
$$= \frac{n(3n - 1)}{2}$$

5. (a) $12 \to 5 \to 25 \to 29 \to 85 \to 89 \to 145 \to 42 \to 20 \to 4 \to 16 \to 37 \to 58 \to 89 \to$ (a loop begins here)

    $13 \to 10 \to 1$ etc.

    $19 \to 82 \to 68 \to 100 \to 1 \to 1 \to$ etc.

    $21 \to 5 \to 25 \to$ (see 12 above)

    $127 \to 54 \to 41 \to 17 \to 50 \to 25 \to$ (see 12 above)

    (b) The cycle eventually ends when you reach the number 1 or the numbers cycle and 4 is the smallest number obtained. For 13 and 19, the process ends with a 1.
    (c) $111 \to 3 \to 9 \to 81 \to 65 \to 61 \to 37 \to 58 \to 89 \to 145 \to 42 \to 20 \to 4 \to 16 \to 37 \to 58 \to 89 \to$ (a loop begins here)

6. 35

7. $1 + 49 = 50$ and $25 + 25 = 50$

8. 220

9. (a) $16 \times 10 = 160$
    (b) $10,000 \times 199 = 1,990,000$

10. $1 + 1 + 2 + 3 + \ldots + 144 = 377 - 1 = 376$

11. (a) Every third term is even, or a term is even if the number of the term is a multiple of 3.

(b) Fibonacci numbers that are even: F_{51}, F_{150}, F_{300}
    Odd: F_{38}, F_{200}
(c) Every fourth term is divisible by 3, or a term is divisible by 3 if the number of the term is a multiple of 4.
(d) Fibonacci numbers that are multiples of 3: F_{48}, F_{196}, F_{1000}
    Not multiples of 3: F_{75}, F_{379}

12. 609

13. (a) 3, 7, 15
    (b) Example: To move 4 disks from the left post to the center post, the top 3 disks must first be moved to the right post. To move those three disks to the right posts, the top two disks must first be moved to the center post. To move the top two disks to the center post, the top disk must first be moved to the right post. This general reasoning allows one to move the disks in the fewest number of moves.
    (c) 63 moves

14. (a) $25 = 10 + 15$
    $26 = 10 + 15 + 1$
    $27 = 21 + 6$
    $28 = 28$
    $29 = 28 + 1$
    $30 = 21 + 3 + 6$
    $31 = 21 + 10$
    $32 = 21 + 10 + 1$
    $33 = 15 + 15 + 3$
    $34 = 28 + 6$
    $35 = 28 + 6 + 1$
    (b) $74 = 36 + 28 + 10$
    $81 = 66 + 15$
    $90 = 66 + 21 + 3$

15. (a) Products are both equal to 30.
    (b) Products of alternate numbers are always the same.

16. 18, 20, 22, 24, 26, 28, 30

17. (a)

Step 5

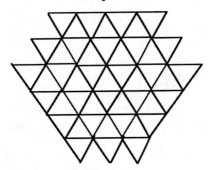

Step 6

(b)

Step	Number of Unit Triangles
1	1
2	4
3	10
4	19
5	31
6	46

(c) 64
(d) 136, 571, 3676

18. 13

19. (a) 27   (b) 13   (c) 3^{n-1}
     (d) For $n \geq 2$, $3^{n-2} + 3^{n-3} + \ldots + 1$

20. (a) 900   (b) 148   (c) 859

21. (a) 18, 29, 47
     (b) 60, 111, 189

22. A seven can be formed in six different ways, so seven is likeliest to appear.

23. The key idea here is that once the frog jumps out, it won't slip back down the two feet. It will make it out of a five-foot well in three days and out of a twenty-foot well in 18 days. This is an example of the Solve a Simpler Problem strategy.

Analyzing Student Thinking

24. Both students extended the pattern in a way that makes sense—there is more than one correct answer.

     To find each term after the initial 2 in the pattern, Marietta multiplied the previous term by 2: $4 = 2 \times 2$, $8 = 4 \times 2$, $16 = 8 \times 2$, $32 = 16 \times 2$, ...

     while Pascuel added successive even numbers to the previous term, starting with the initial 2:

     $4 = 2 + \underline{2}$, $8 = 4 + \underline{4}$, $14 = 8 + \underline{6}$, $22 = 14 + \underline{8}$, ...

25. Eula, to apply the solve a simpler problem strategy, reduce the sum to something that is more manageable, such as $1 + 3$, then look at $1 + 3 + 5$, then $1 + 3 + 5 + 7$, etc. Look for a pattern in each of these sums that you can generalize to the original problem.

26. Mickey, try listing these systematically by keeping one of the numbers fixed and listing all the possibilities for the second die. For example, list all the possibilities where you roll a 1 on the first die: (1, 1), (1, 2), (1, 3), (1, 4), and then list all the possibilities where you roll a 2 on the first die, etc.

27. Bridgette, notice that the differences between numbers increase by 2 each time.

     3, 5, 9, 15, 23
      ⌄ ⌄ ⌄ ⌄
      2 4 6 8

Following this pattern, the next two numbers would be 33 and 45.

28. Jeremy, the rectangle given in the original problem is divided into 5 sections by 3 sections. Both of these numbers are odd, so it makes sense for the simpler problem to involve a rectangle divided similarly, such as this one that is divided into 3 sections by 1 section:

29. Janell, yes, the strategies you used are frequently used together.

Chapter 2

Section 2.1

1. (a) {9, 10, 11,...}
   (b) {3, 4, 5, ..., 10}
   (c) {1, 3, 5, 7, ..., 99}
   (d) { } or Ø

2. (a) Not equal   (b) Equal
   (c) Not equal   (d) Equal
   (e) Not equal   (f) Not equal
   (g) Equal

3. (a) F (b) F (c) T (d) T (e) T

4. $1 \to x$ $1 \to y$ $1 \to z$
   $2 \to y$ $2 \to z$ $2 \to w$
   $3 \to z$ $3 \to w$ $3 \to x$
   $4 \to w$ $4 \to x$ $4 \to y$
   There are many other correct correspondences.

5. (a) Equivalent   (b) Equivalent
   (c) Equivalent   (d) Equivalent
   (e) Equivalent

6. (a) Not equal   (b) Equal
   (c) Equal   (d) Equal

7. { }, {O}, {△}, {□}, {O,△}, {△,□ },
   {O ,□}, {O,△,□ }
   All but the last one.

8. { }, (w), (x), (y), (z), {w, x}, {w, y},
   {w, z}, {x, y}, {x, z}, {y, z}, {w, x, y},
   {w, x, z}, {w, y, z}, {x, y, z}

9. (a) ∈   (b) ⊆ or ⊂
   (c) ⊄ , ~   (d) ∈
   (e) ⊆ , ~, =   (f) ⊆ or ⊂

10. (a) Finite; 10   (b) Infinite
    (c) Finite; 25
    (d) Finite; the number of sides of the polygon

11. (a) Match to {4, 6, 8, ..., $n + 2$, ...}
    (b) Match to
       {51, 52, 53, 54, ..., $n + 1$, ...}

12. (a) F (b) T (c) F (d) T (e) T
    (f) T

13. (a) T   (b) T (c) F

14. (a) True   (b) False
    (c) True   (d) False

15. (a)

(b)

(c)

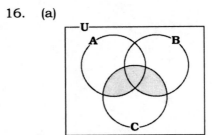

$(S - T) \bigcap (T - S) = Ø$

16. (a)

(b)

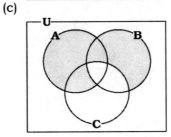

(c)

17. (a) $[A - (B ∪ C)] ∪ [(B ∪ C) - A]$

(b) (B - C) ∪ (A - C) ∪ (B ∩ C)

(c) (A ∪ C) - (B ∩ C)

18. (a)

(b)

(c)

19. (a)

(b)

(c)

(d)

(e)

(f)

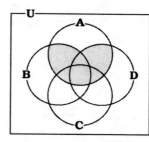

20. (a) {a, b, c, d, e, f, g}

(b) {c, d, e}

(c) {a, e, f}   (d) {a, b, c, d, e, f}

21. (a) Students who are either sophomores or orchestra members

(b) Sophomores who belong to orchestra

(c) Sophomores who do not belong to orchestra

(d) Orchestra members who are not sophomores

22. (a) {h, i, j}   (b) {3,10,13}

(c) {bicycles}

(d) {0,2,4,6,8,10}

23. (a) B   (b) ∅   (c) ∅

24. (a) {a, b ,c, d, e, f}   (b) {c}

(c) {a, b, c, x, y, z}   (d) ∅

(e) {c, d, e, f, x, y, z}   (f) ∅

(g) {x, y, z}

25. (a) {50, 55, 60, 65, 70, 75, 80}
     (b) {60, 70, 80}   (c) {60, 70, 80}
     (d) {60, 70, 80}   (e) {50} (f) {50}

26. (a) Yes, because $X \cap Y \subseteq X \cup Y$
     (b) No, because x may be an
         element of $X - Y$ or $Y - X$.

27. (a) $\overline{A \cap B} = \overline{A} \cup \overline{B} =$
         {2, 6, 10, 12, 14}
         Yes, the sets are the same.
     (b) $\overline{A \cap B}$ and $\overline{A} \cup \overline{B}$ are both
         represented by:

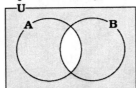

         Yes, the diagrams are the
         same.

28. (a) {(*a*, 1), (*b*, 1), (*c*, 1)}
     (b) {(1, *p*), (1, *q*), (1, *r*), (2, *p*), (2, *q*),
         (2, *r*)}
     (c) {(*p*, 1), (*p*, 2), (*q*, 1), (*q*, 2), (*r*, 1),
         (*r*, 2)}
     (d) {(*a*, 1)}

29. (a) 4 (b) 8 (c) 21

30. (a) {*a*} × {*b*}   (b) {1} × {1, 2}
     (c) {*d*} × {*e*, *f*, *g*}   (d) {3, 4} × {5, 6}
     (e) {*g*} × {*v*, *w*, *x*, *y*, *z*}
     (f) {1, 2} × {3, 4, 5}
     (g) {512} × {10, 11, 122, 205, 197,
         20, 21}
     (h) { } × { }

31. (a) X = {*b*, *c*} , Y = {*c*}
     (b) X = {2, 5} , Y = {1, 2, 3}

32. (a) F (b) F (c) F (d) T

33. (a) 2 (b) 24 (c) 720
     (d) $m (m - 1)(m - 2) \cdots (2)(1)$

34. (a) *A, B* not disjoint
     (b) not possible
     (c) *E, F* disjoint
     (d) *G* and *K* are empty sets.

35. 105

36. Rays whose endpoints are the
     center of the circle produce a 1-1
     correspondence between the circle
     and the triangle.

37. Rays whose endpoints are some
     point P in the interior of the
     triangle produce a 1-1
     correspondence between the circle
     and the triangle.

38. $13 \times 12 \times 11 \times \cdots \times 1$

39. (a) 16   (b) 25   (c) 2

40. (a) 7 cars (b) 23 cars (c) 16 cars

41. Since A is a proper subset of B, all
     its elements are elements of B.
     Since it is a *proper* subset, there
     must be at least one element of B
     which is not in A. Therefore, B
     must have at least 24 elements.

Analyzing Student Thinking

42. Jake is correct. If two sets are
     equal, they have the *same*
     elements. Therefore, they have
     the same *number* of elements, and
     are equivalent. Kaylee is
     incorrect, however. If two sets are
     equivalent, it means they have the
     same *number* of elements, not the
     same elements. Therefore, they
     could be, but are not necessarily,
     equal.

43. Yes, Tonia is correct. Any 3-
     element set has 8 subsets; 7 of
     these are proper subsets (do not
     include the whole 3-element set)
     and 7 are non-empty subsets (do
     not include the empty set).

44. Amanda is partially correct. While
     it is true that the first set (the
     counting numbers) *does* contain
     an infinite number of numbers
     that the second set (the even
     counting numbers) does not, she
     is incorrect in saying that the sets
     cannot be matched. The two sets

can be matched like this: $n \leftrightarrow 2n$.

45. LaNae is incorrect. $A \cup B$ has the same number of elements as both A and B in the case that $A \cup B = A = B$.

46. Marshall is incorrect. $A \cap B$ has the same number of elements as both A and B in the case that $A \cap B \, A = B$,

47. Michael is incorrect; for example, let $A = \{1, 3, 5, ...\}$ and $B = \{2, 4, 6, ...\}$. Then, $A \cap B = \varnothing$, a finite set.

48. DeDee, to find the set $A - B$, we remove from A any elements that are also in B. We can do this whether B is a subset of A or not.

Section 2.2

1. Answers will vary but here are three examples.
   (a) A total of 45 students attended a meeting.
   (b) Bob was the 45th customer to enter the store.
   (c) Katy wore number 45 on her softball jersey.

2. (a) Identification (b) Ordinal
   (c) Cardinal

3. (a) Cannot be used because the sets do not match.
   (b) Cannot be used; the sets are equivalent but we don't begin counting elements with 0.
   (c) Should be used; it is an equivalent set using consecutive counting numbers beginning with 1.

4. Number. A numeral is a symbo; a number is an idea.

5. 9 is greater than 4.
   (i) use the counting chat: 9 comes after 4.
   (ii) use the number line: 9 is to the right of 4.

(iii) use sets: A set with 4 elements can be matched with a proper subset of a set with 9 elements.

6. (a) >   (b) <   (c) <

7. (a)
   (b)

8. (a) LXXIX   (b) MMMLIV

9. (a)
   (b)

10. (a)   (b)

11. (a) 14,405   (b) 432
    (c) 1247   (d) 72,022

12. (a) , CXX
    (b)
    (c)
        CIIXXX ,
    (d) ,
        DCCXXVI,

13. Yes, Roman numerals form such a system because the position of the symbols matters but the value of the symbol is not multiplied by a place value.

14. 1989

15. (a) All 9's
     (b) 9876543210 or 98765432
         (depending on size of
         calculator display)

16. (a) 80: 八十 19: 十九   52: 五十二

     400: 四百   603: 六百三

     6031: 六千三十

     (b) Yes. Yes. Yes.

17. (1) If A and B are in the same
         row, then B is taller than the
         rest of the row and A.
     (2) If A and B are in the same
         column, then A is shorter
         than the rest of the column
         and B.
     (3) If they are in different rows
         and columns, let C be in the
         same column as A and same
         row as B. Since A is shortest
         in its column, A < C. Since B
         is tallest in its row, C < B.
         Thus, A < C < B.

18. (a) 124,797
     (b) 8,724,640,224

19. Eiffel Tower: 984 feet
     Great Pyramid of Giza: 480 feet
     Big Ben: 316 feet
     Statue of Liberty: 305 feet
     Leaning Tower of Pisa: 179 feet

20. Impossible. There are 32 white
     squares and 30 dark squares. But
     each domino covers a white and a
     dark square.

Analyzing Student Thinking

21. No, Tammie is not correct. Let $A =$
     $\{a\}$ and $B = \{b, c\}$. Then
     $n(A) = 1 \le 2 = n(B)$, but A is not a
     subset of B.

22. A child first learns to say the
     counting chant before they have
     an understanding of the concept
     of number.

23. Anthony, the tally system is easy
     for small numbers, but for larger
     numbers it is cumbersome—for
     example, which is easier, writing
     the numeral 100, or writing our
     100 tally marks?

24. Misti is correct—it would require 9
     of the numerals for a hundred, 9
     of the numerals for ten, and 9 of
     the numerals for one, or 27
     numerals.

25. Shalonda, to say that a
     numeration system is additive,
     subtractive or multiplicative, we
     are describing properties of the
     system, not which operations can
     be done in that system. To say
     that the Roman Numeration
     System is additive means that the
     total value of a numeral is found
     by adding the values of the
     individual numerals, like XI = 10 +
     1 = 11. When we say that this
     system is subtractive, we mean
     that the value of some numerals is
     found by subtracting a smaller
     numeral to the left of a larger one,
     as in 10 − 1 = 9. The Roman
     Numeration System is also
     multiplicative since we can
     indicate 1000 times a number by
     writing a bar above the numeral,
     as in $\overline{X} = 1000 \times 10 = 10,000$. You
     can do division in the Roman
     system. However, division is not
     used to represent numerals in the
     Roman system.

26. Natalie, this symbol serves as a
     placeholder in the Babylonian
     System, much like a zero in our
     own system, but the Babylonians
     did not recognize the value of this
     symbol as zero.

27. Bianca, the Mayan System does
     have a symbol to represent zero,
     it's ⊕ .

Section 2.3

1. (a) $4 \times 100 + 0 \times 10 + 9 \times 1$
    (b) $7 \times 1000 + 0 \times 100 + 9 \times 10 + 4 \times 1$
    (c) $7 \times 100 + 4 \times 10 + 6 \times 1$
    (d) $8 \times 100,000 + 4 \times 10,000 + 1 \times 1$

2. (a) 3075   (b) 70,600
    (c) 603,009   (d) 60,900,000

3. (a) Thousand
    (b) Ten
    (c) One

4. Seven, Eight, Nine, Ten

5. (a) Thirty-two million ninety
        thousand forty seven
    (b) Four hundred one billion two
        million, five hundred sixty
        thousand three hundred.
    (c) Ninety eight quadrillion

6. (a) 27,069,014
    (b) 12,000,070,003,005

7. It is multiplicative because each
    digit is multiplied by its place
    value. It is additive because the
    various products are added
    together to the find the value of
    the number.

8. 2121_{three}

9. (a)
    (b)
    (c)
    (d) 112_{four}, 221_{four}, 122_{four}
    (e) The first digit is multiplied by
        the place value and in different
        bases the place value is
        different. Thus a 2 could be
        $2 \cdot 9$ or $2 \cdot 16$, depending on the
        base.

10. 1, 2, 1, 3

11. With bundles of sticks:
    (a) 3 bundles of ten, 8 units
    (b) 5 bundles of six, 2 units
    (c) 1 bundle of one hundred
        twenty five, 3 bundles of five,
        2 units

    With a chip abacus:
    (a)

hundreds	tens	ones
	● ● ●	● ● ● / ● ● ● / ● ●

    (b)

100_{six}	10_{six}	1
	● ● ● / ● ●	● ●

    (c)

1000_{five}	100_{five}	10_{five}	1
●		● ● ●	● ●

12. (a) 120_{eight} (b) 140_{six}
    (c) 1010_{three}

13. Base 26; 675

14. The only digits in base three are 0,
    1, and 2, so we can't have a digit
    of 4.

15. (a) True   (b) False
    (c) True

16. (a) 1 2 3 10 11 12 13 20 21
        22 23 30 31 32 33 100
        101 102 103 110
    (b) 127

    (c) 1 2 3 4 5 10 11 12 13 14
        15 20 21 22 23 24 25 30
        31 32 33 34 35 40 41 42
        43 44 45 50 51 52 53 54
        55 100

(d) 1000_{nine}

17. (a) $22_{three} = 2(3) + 2(1)$

(b) $212_{three} = 2(3^2) + 1(3) + 2(1)$

(c) $12110_{three} = 1(3^4) + 2(3^3) + 1(3^2) + 1(3) + 0(1)$

18. (a) 111111_{two}

(b) 1000000_{two}
1000001_{two}
1000010_{two}

19. $99 = 10200_{three}$
$100 = 10201_{three}$

20. (a) ET_{twelve} (b) 1001000_{two}

(c) 347_{eight}

21. (a) 97   (b) 1572   (c) 45

22. (a) 164   (b) 16,910

23. (a) 11_{eight} (b) 66_{eight}

(c) 252_{eight} (d) 57_{eight}

A shortcut is to mark off the base-two numeral in groups of three digits and then to express each group as a base eight digit.

24. (a) 7_{nine} (b) 60_{nine}
(c) 750_{nine}

25. (a) Eight   (b) Eleven   (c) Six

26. None. Since the base number is always greater than any of the digits, if a is less than b (so that a_b makes sense), then b is greater than a (and b_a is incorrect notation).

27. One possibility is onety-one, onety-two, onety-three, onety-nine.

28. 1234

29. 36

30. (a) The numbers are placed on the cards according to their base 2 representations. Since 6 =

110_2 , it appears on the "4" card and "2" card.

(b) The numbers 1-15 can be expressed in base 2 using 4 digits, so 4 cards each containing 8 numbers will suffice. The "1" card will contain the numbers 1,3,5,7,9,11,13,15, the "2" card will contain 2,3,6,7,10,11,14,15, etc.

31. (a) In base 2, any number from 1 to 31 can be represented in terms of 1's, 2's, 4's, 8's, and 16's. For example, 13 = 11101_2, or 13 = 8 + 4 + 0 + 1

(b) 1, 3, 9, 27 will do it.

32. Base 2 is used in computers because the 0 and 1 can be simply represented by "off" and "on"; all numbers we type into the computer are converted to base 2, operated on in that base, then translated back into base 10 for output. Base 16 is also used in computers.

Analyzing Student Thinking

33. Jason, by studying other systems and bases, it helps us to better understand our own base-10 system.

34. Brandi, the chip abacus is a model that helps us to visualize the place-value aspects of our numeration system.

35. Jamie is not correct; the numeral 512 ought to be read "five hundred twelve," without the word "and." We say, "and" to indicate a decimal point.

36. Juan, your idea is very clever. Since 'onety' could mean '1 ten' just like 'forty' means '4 tens', 'onety-three' makes a lot of sense as a name for 13.

37. Gladys, numerals in base two require lots of zeros and ones. Another possibility is that base ten was commonly used because we had ten digits on our two hands.

38. Riann is incorrect; "one million" is a base 10 numeral name. We'd read this numeral in base 2 as "one zero zero zero zero zero, base 2."

Chapter 3

Section 3.1

1. Set model:

   Number line model:

   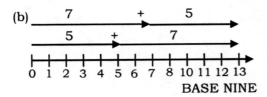

2. (b) and (c). Part (a) is false since g is common to both.

3. (a) Yes. All are multiples of 3 and the sum of two multiples of 3 is a multiple of 3.
   (b) No. $1 + 1 = 2$ and $2 \notin \{1\}$.
   (c) No. $1 + 5 = 6$ and $6 \notin \{1, 5, 9, \ldots\}$
   (d) Yes. All are multiples of 4 greater than 4.
   (e) No. $1 + 16 = 17$ and 17 is not greater than 17.

4. (a) 0, identity
   (b) 5, commutative
   (c) 3, associative
   (d) 6, commutative
   (e) 4, commutative
   (f) Whole, closure

5. (a) (BASE FIVE)
   (b) (BASE NINE)

6. By commutativity and associativity, they're equal.

7. (a) $(94 + 6) + (27 + 13) = 100 + 40 = 140$
      Associative and commutative
   (b) $(5 + 25) + (13 + 47) + 31 = 30 + 60 + 31 = 121$
      Associative and commutative

8. (a)

+	0	1	2	3	4	5
0	0	1	2	3	4	5
1	1	2	3	4	5	10
2	2	3	4	5	10	11
3	3	4	5	10	11	12
4	4	5	10	11	12	13
5	5	10	11	12	13	14

   (b) (i) $5_{six} + ? = 13_{six}; 4_{six}$
       (ii) $4_{six} + ? = 5_{six}; 1_{six}$
       (iii) $4_{six} + ? = 12_{six}; 4_{six}$
       (iv) $2_{six} + ? = 10_{six}; 4_{six}$

9. (a) $3_{six} + 2_{six} = 5_{six}$,
      $5_{six} - 3_{six} = 2_{six}$,
      $5_{six} - 2_{six} = 3_{six}$.
   (b) $5_{six} + 2_{six} = 11_{six}$,
      $2_{six} + 5_{six} = 11_{six}$,
      $11_{six} - 2_{six} = 5_{six}$.

10. (a) $x = 279 + 156$
    (b) $279 = x + 156$
    (c) $279 = x + 156$

11. (a) $7 - 3$, set model, comparison approach.
    (b) $8 - 3$, set model, missing-addend approach.
    (c) $6 - 2$, measurement model, take-away approach

12. (a) $x = 0$ (b) $x = y$
    (c) $z = 0, x \geq y$
       None are true for all.

13. (a) Set, missing addend, comparison, $200 + x = 362$

(b) Measurement, missing addend, no comparison, $114 + x = 250$

(c) Set, missing addend, no comparison, $105 + x = 1095$

14. (a) Mike needs to dig a 9-foot long trench. He's already dug 5 feet of the trench. How much more does he have left to dig?

   (b) Marta and Julio are making Valentine's cards. Marta has made 9 cards and Julio has made 5 cards. How many more cards has Marta made?

   (c)

   (d) Marta's Cards   Julio's Cards

15. (a) For example, 6, 19, 12, 15, 18, 21

   (b) Since 24 is the sum of eight 3's.

16. 5, 10, 15, ...

17. (a)

   (b)

(c) Let a, b, c and d represent the entries in the four squares. Then all four sums described are equal to $a + b + c + d$.

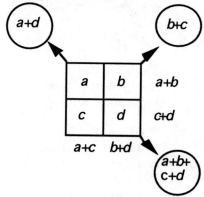

18. One possibility is shown.

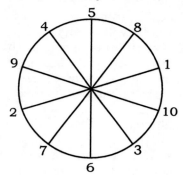

19.

16	2	3	13
5	11	10	8
9	7	6	12
4	14	15	1

20.

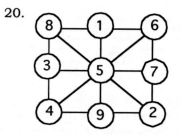

21. The sums along all lines are equal to 90. The sums of opposite triangles are equal.

22.   Yes. Consider a pan balance where $a + c$ chips on one pan balance $b + c$ chips on the other pan. Remove c chips from each pan and observe that they still balance.

Analyzing Student Thinking

23.   Show Kaitlyn two sets A and B that are *not* disjoint, and ask her to find the sum $n(A) + n(B)$.

24.   No, because Enrique is not considering the case that a number can be "linked" to itself. Consider the set {0, 1}. This set is not closed since $1 + 1 = 2$ and 2 is not an element of {0, 1}.

25.   By using thinking strategies, Monique will be able to figure out any addition facts she might forget. Also, with thinking strategies, she won't have as many facts to remember. Thinking strategies can be extended to multidigit numbers.

26.   Yes, Theresa can use a number line model to illustrate the properties of whole number addition. For instance, for the commutative property, she could compare the following two illustrations:

27.   Severino's technique uses the associative and commutative properties of addition and the fact that zero is the additive identity:

$27 + 36 =$
$27 + 36 + 0 =$

$27 + 36 + (3 - 3) =$
$(27 + 3) + 36 - 3 =$
$(30 + 36) - 3 = 66 - 3 = 63$

Patricia's technique uses the commutative and associative properties of addition:

$27 + 36 =$
$(20 + 7) + (30 + 6) =$
$(20 + 30) + (6 + 1 + 6) =$
$50 + (6 + 6) + 1 =$
$50 + (12 + 1) =$
$50 + 13 = 63$

28.   Remind Kayla that $7 + 3 = 10$ in a *base 10* system since this is 1 long (ten) and 0 ones. Then, ask Kayla, "In base eight, how many units make up a long?" Suggest that she draw a picture of the numerals using base 8 blocks.

29.   Tell Chandler that Conner used the missing addend approach; Connor found what number of girls must be added to the 9 boys to get the total number of 21 students.

30.   This picture helps me visualize the different approaches to subtraction (take-away and missing addend), the models I can use to illustrate each one (set and measurement), and whether I can apply comparison to each of these.

Section 3.2

1.   (a) 2×4 (b) 4×2 (c) 7×3

2.   (a)

   (b)

(c)

(d)

6   12   18   24

(e)

	e	f	g	h	i	j
a	(a,e)	(a,f)	(a,g)	(a,h)	(a,i)	(a,j)
b	(b,e)	(b,f)	(b,g)	(b,h)	(b,i)	(b,j)
c	(c,e)	(c,f)	(c,g)	(c,h)	(c,i)	(c,j)
d	(d,e)	(d,f)	(d,g)	(d,h)	(d,i)	(d,j)

3. (a) Cartesian product since the set of possibilities is {small, medium, large} × {cola, diet cola, lemon-lime, root beer, orange}: $x = 3 \cdot 5$
    (b) Rectangular array approach, since students form an array of 72 rows and 4 columns: $n = 72 \cdot 4$
    (c) Repeated addition, since the bill could be found by adding 70¢ + 70¢ + ... +70¢ where the sum has 25 terms: $c = 25 \cdot 70$

4. (a) 39 + 39 + 39 + 39 = 156
    (b) 231 + 231 + 231 = 693
    (c) 172 + 172 + 172 + 172 + 172 = 860
    (d) 843 + 843 + 843 + 843 + 843 + 843 = 5058

5. (a) (i) No. 2 + 1 = 3   (ii) Yes
    (b) (i) No. 4 + 3 = 7; (ii) Yes

6. (a) Distributive over subtraction
    (b) Associative
    (c) Multiplicative by 0
    (d) Distributive over addition

7. (a) $3 \cdot 29 + 3 \cdot 30 + 3 \cdot 6$
    (b) $5x - 5(2y)$
    (c) $(3 + 6 - 4)a$
    (d) $(x + 3)(x + 2)$
    (e) $37 \cdot 60 - 37 \cdot 22$

8. (a) 14(20 - 1)   (b) 25(40 - 2)
    (c) 35(100 - 2)   (d) 27(1000 - 1)

9. (a) 463 × 16 + 463
    (b) 463 × 15 + 463 × 2
    (c) 463 × 16 + 10 × 16 + 463 + 10

10. (a) 8 × 85 = (8 × 5) 17 = 40 × 17 = 680
    (b) 12(125) = 3 (4 × 125) = 3 × 500 = 1500

11. (a)

×	0	1	2	3	4	5	6	7
0	0	0	0	0	0	0	0	0
1	0	1	2	3	4	5	6	7
2	0	2	4	6	10	12	14	16
3	0	3	6	11	14	17	22	25
4	0	4	10	14	20	24	30	34
5	0	5	12	17	24	31	36	43
6	0	6	14	22	30	36	44	52
7	0	7	16	25	34	43	52	61

    (b) (i) $61_{eight} = 7_{eight} \times$?; 7_{eight}
        (ii) $17_{eight} = 3_{eight} \times$?; 5_{eight}
        (iii) $30_{eight} = 6_{eight} \times$?; 4_{eight}
        (iv) $16_{eight} = 2_{eight} \times$?; 7_{eight}
        (v) $44_{eight} = 6_{eight} \times$? 6_{eight}
        (vi) $25_{eight} = 7_{eight} \times$?; 3_{eight}

12. (a) Sharing. The 28 students are the groups, and the 60 cupcakes are broken into 28 groups to find out how many are in each group.
    (b) Measurement. The 2 cups is how much is in each group and the solution is the number of groups you can make from 6 cups.
    (c) Sharing. The 3 shirts is the number of groups and the $45 is divided among the groups. The solution is the amount of money in each group.

13. (a) Answers will vary. Kobe has 91 jelly beans and he eats 7 jelly beans every hour. How many hours until they are all gone?

(b) Answers will vary. Kobe has 91 jelly beans to give to 7 friends. How many jelly beans will each friend get?

14. (a) $24 = 12x$
    (b) $x = 27 \cdot 3$
    (c) $a = bx$

15. (a) 2, R = 1   (b) 0, R = 3
    (c) 7, R = 0   (d) 0, R = 1
    (e) 3, R = 0   (f) 0, R = 8

16. (a) 2, infinite
    (b) 12, infinite
    (c) 62, infinite
    (d) 23, infinite

17. None

18. 48

19. $21,000

20. $(2,348 + 7,652) \times 7,653,214 = (10,000)(7,653,214) = 76,532,140,000$

21. No. Consider {0, 1}.

22. No. Since division by zero is not permitted, zero cannot be in the set. If any two nonzero numbers are in a set, then a proper fraction results, hence not closed.

23. 333,333,333; 777,777,777; 999,999,999. Associativity for multiplication.

24. $7 + 7^2 + 7^3 + 7^4 = 2800$ (2801 if you count the man). Only 1; the speaker was going to St. Ives.

25. The number is divisible by 1001, which equals $7 \times 11 \times 13$. (Use place value to show this.)

26. $4913 = 17^3$, $5832 = 18^3$

27. The sequence of cubes.

28. Yes. The difference of n "twos" from $2n$ "ones" will be the square of n "threes."

29. (a) Dave   (b) Charlie

30. Since the sum of the ages equal to the house number does not provide a solution, there are two choices: 6,6,1 and 9,2,2. But there is an oldest child, so 9,2,2 is the answer.

31. Take a ball from the B/W box. If it's B, then the B/W box is B, the B box is W and the W is B/W. Argue similarly if the ball is W.

32. a or b must be 0. If both are nonzero, the product is nonzero.

Analyzing Student Thinking

33. There is a difference between these two approaches, but they are similar. With rectangular array approach, the product of $a \times b$ is the number of elements in a rectangular array with a rows and b columns. With the Cartesian product approach $a \times b$ is the number of ordered pairs that can be formed from a set with a elements and a set with b elements.

34. Phyllis is incorrect. The tree diagram approach can be used to model the product of any number of numbers. For example, to model the product of three numbers, $a \times b \times c$, draw a tree diagram with 3 sets of branches: a set of a branches and, for each of those a branches, draw b branches and, for each of those b branches, draw c branches. The total number of ends of the final branches will be $a \times b \times c$.

35. Maurice, this is a common misuse of the distributive property. The parentheses in the original problem indicate that we should first multiply 7 times 3 to get 21, then multiply 21 by 6, to obtain 126. The other problem will be 6 times as large, namely 756. Since the two answers are not the same,

we see that multiplication does not distribute over *multiplication*. The distributive property distributes multiplication over *addition* (or *subtraction*).

36. Yes, Taylor, applying the associative property of multiplication may help make this easier to compute mentally: $6(7 \times 3) = (6 \times 7) \times 3$. This equals 42 times 3, which equals 126.

37. Breanne, recall that the number 0 is the identity for *addition* since when we add 0 to any number, a, we get a. So, the identity for *multiplication* is a number that can be multiplied by any number, a, to get a. It's not 0 since 0 times a is 0, not a. The multiplicative identity is 1 since 1 times a is equal to a.

38. Olga, the distributive property could be used to break a multiplication problem down into two problems that are easier to compute mentally, as in this example:

$3 \times 14 = 3(10 + 4) =$

$3 \times 10 + 3 \times 4 =$

$30 + 12 = 42$

39. If we let a be any non-zero number, $a \div 0$ could only be equal to 0 if $0 \times 0 = a$. But $0 \times 0 = 0$, and a is not zero.

40. No, "4 divided by 12" is written $4 \div 12$ and leads to a fractional answer, whereas "4 divided into 12" is written $12 \div 4$ and is equal to 3.

Section 3.3

1. (a) 9   (b) 64

2. $29 < 44,\ 15 < 44,\ 44 > 29,\ 44 > 15$

3. Yes

4. (a) Yes   (b) Yes

5. (a) 4^7 (b) $3^6 \cdot 4^3$
   (c) $2x^3 y^2$ (d) $a^4 b^4$

6. $6^2 < 5^3 < 2^7 < 3^5$

7. (a) $10 \cdot a \cdot b \cdot b \cdot b \cdot b$
   (b) $2 \cdot x \cdot 2 \cdot x \cdot 2 \cdot x \cdot 2 \cdot x \cdot 2 \cdot x$
   (c) $2 \cdot x \cdot x \cdot x \cdot x \cdot x$

8. (a) x^9 (b) a^{12} (c) $(xy)^7$
   (d) 2^7 (e) 2^4 (f) 3^{23}

9. $7^{20} = \left(\left(7^2\right)^2\right)^5 = \left(\left(7^2\right)^5\right)^2 = \left(\left(7^5\right)^2\right)^2$

10. Sometimes true. If $b = m = 1$, then $a^n \cdot 1^1 = a^n$ and $a^{n \cdot 1} = a^n$.

11. (a) 12   (b) Any whole number
    (c) 7

12. (a) 2,203   (b) 31,226   (c) 2,304

13. (a) $2 \cdot 3(3 - 2) = 6$
    (b) $\dfrac{2 \cdot 3^3}{15 - 6} = \dfrac{2 \cdot 3^3}{3^2} = 6$
    (c) $25 - 16 + 4 = 13$
    (d) $32 - 2^4 \cdot 3^4 \div \left(2^3 \cdot 3^2\right)$
    $= 32 - 2 \cdot 9 = 14$

14. By agreement and because exponents can be thought of as repeated multiplication.

15. (a) $1 + 2 + 3 = 6,\ 1^3 + 2^3 + 3^3 = 36 = 6^2$
    (b) $1^3 + 2^3 + 3^3 + \ldots + n^3 = (1 + 2 + 3 + \ldots + n)^2$
    (c) $1^3 + 2^3 + 3^3 + \ldots + 10^3 = (1 + 2 + 3 + \ldots + 10)^2 = 55^2 = 3,025$

16. $\underline{4^{14}} = (2^2)^{14} = 2^{28} < 2^{30} = (2^3)^{10} = \underline{8^{10}} < \underline{9^{10}} = (3^2)^{10}$

$= 3\ ^{20} < \underline{3^{22}}$

17.   Approximately 80,530,000 mm or 80.5 km.

18.   (a) $2^7 = 128$ (b) 21
      (c) 1   (d) 7   (e) 7

19.   (a) 11   (b) 1,111
      (c) 111,111   (d) 11,111,111

20.   Using variables, this problem is equivalent to showing that $10a + b$ divides evenly into $(10a)^2 - b^2$, or that $x + y$ divides into $x^2 - y^2$. But $x^2 - y^2 = (x + y)(x - y)$. Thus $x + y$ divides into $x^2 - y^2$ exactly $x - y$ times.

21.   (a) $3 < 7$ and $3 \cdot 5 = 15 < 7 \cdot 5 = 35$.

      (b) $3 < 7$ and $3 \cdot 0 = 0\ </\ 7 \cdot 0 = 0$

      (c) Let $a < b$ and $c \neq 0$. By the Property of Less Than and Addition, $a + a + \cdots + a$ (c times) $< b + b + \cdots + b$ (c times). Thus, $ac < bc$.

      (d) If $a < b$ and c is a factor of a and b, then $a \div c < b \div c$.

22. $\dfrac{\overbrace{a \cdot a \cdots a}^{n} \cdot \overbrace{a \cdot a \cdots a}^{m-n}}{\underbrace{a \cdot a \cdots a}_{n}} = a^{m-n}$

Analyzing Student Thinking

23.   Brooke, the property of less than and addition is true for any whole numbers, a, b and c. However, for less than and subtraction, if $a < b$, then $a - c < b - c$, is only true for values of c that are less than a; otherwise $a - c$ is not a whole number (the whole numbers are not closed under subtraction).

24.   There is not a property of less than and division for whole numbers since the quotient of two whole numbers is not always a whole number (the whole numbers are not closed under division).

25.   Jarell, use the definition of whole-number exponents to write out the meaning of the product: $3^2 \cdot 3^4 = (3 \cdot 3) \cdot (3 \cdot 3 \cdot 3 \cdot 3)$. This is 6 factors of 3 or 3^6, not 6 factors of 9.

26.   Viridiana is incorrect. She has found two examples where the answers happen to be equal. We need only look at another example to see that the operations of addition and multiplication are not always the same; for instance, $2 + 3 = 5$ and $2 \cdot 3 = 6$.

27.   Abbi, notice that:
      $8^5 \div 2^2 = (2^3)^5 \div 2^2 = 2^{15} \div 2^2 = 2^{13} > 2^{12} = (2^2)^6 = 4^6 > 4^3$

28.   When Cho rewrote $(3^2)^2$ as $3^{(2^2)}$ she was correct, although this was probably due to luck since she also rewrote $(2^3)^2$ as $2^{(3^2)}$ and this can not be true: $(2^3)^2 = 2^6$ but $2^{(3^2)} = 2^9$. In general, $(a^b)^c = a^{(b^c)}$ is only true if $b \cdot c = b^c$.

29.   Ayumi is incorrect. Look at an example: $2^3 \cdot 3^2 = (2 \cdot 2 \cdot 2) \cdot (3 \cdot 3) = (8)(9) = 72$ but $(2 \cdot 3)^{3+2} = (6)^5 = 7776$.

30.   Gavin, check this with an example: $(4 + 3)^2 = (7)^2 = 49$, but $4^2 + 3^2 = 16 + 9 = 25$.

31.   Baily applied the exponent (<u>E</u>xcuse) before computing the difference within the parentheses (<u>P</u>lease). This is incorrect.

Chapter 4

Section 4.1

1. (a) 520 (b) 3700 (c) 137
   (d) 270

2. (a) 27 (b) 46 (c) 128
   (d) 263

3. (a) 598 (b) 301 (c) 321
   (d) 104

4. (a) 955 (b) 1900 (c) 3626
   (d) 248

5. (a) 12,800,000
   (b) 72,000,000
   (c) 1,400,000,000
   (d) 150,000,000,000
   (e) 480,000,000,000
   (f) 115,000,000,000,000

6. (a) 52 − 35: 52 − 30 = 22, 22 − 5 = 17
   (b) 173 − 96: 173 − 90 = 83, 83 − 6 = 77
   (c) 241 − 159: 241 − 100 = 141, 141 − 50 = 91, 91 − 9 = 82
   (d) 83 − 55: 83 − 50 = 33, 33 − 5 = 28

7. (a) 16 × 21 = 8 × 42 = 4 × 84 = 2 × 168 = 336
   (b) 4 × 72 = 2 × 144 = 288
   (c) 8 × 123 = 4 × 246 = 2 × 492 = 984
   (d) 16 × 211 = 8 × 422 = 4 × 844 = 2 × 1688 = 3376

8. Overestimate. For example, if her calculations show that houses with in seven miles are at risk, she should raise her estimate to ten miles to be safe.

9. (a) (i) 12,000
       (ii) 12,000 to 14,000
       (iii) 12,700 (iv) 12,800
   (b) (i) 5,000 (ii) 5,000 to 9,000
       (iii) 6,400 (iv) 6,800
   (c) (i) 10,000
       (ii) 10,000 to 50,000
       (iii) 17,000 (iv) 19,000

10. (a) 200,000 to 600,000
    (b) 40,000 to 100,000
    (c) 35,000,000 to 48,000,000

11. (a) 84 × 50 = 4,200
    (b) 5,600 ÷ 80 = 70
    (c) 2,400 ÷ 60 = 40
    (d) 80 × 80 = 6,400
    (e) 200 × 75 = 15,000
    (f) 6,300 ÷ 90 = 70

12. (a) 250 (b) 600 (c) 590
    (d) 4,200 (e) 7,000

13. (a) 2000 (b) 810,000
    (c) 720 (d) 216,000,000

14. (a) 52 × 40 = 2080 and
        50 × 38 = 3800/2 = 1900
    (b) 20 × 70 = 1400 and
        20 × 75 = 1500
    (c) 90 × 10 = 900 and
        90 × 11 = 990
    (d) 25 × 40 = 1000 and
        25 × 44 = 4400/4 = 1100

15. (a) <u>15</u>,000 to <u>24</u>,000 using range estimation
    (b) <u>50</u>,000 to <u>120</u>,000 using range estimation
    (c) <u>8</u>,000,000 to <u>27</u>,000,000 using range estimation

16. (a) 9 (b) 7

17. (a) 5^5 (b) 3^8 (c) 9^3 (d) 6^6

18. a. Multiply 14 and 39 with the calculator and then multiply by 100 = 20 × 5 mentally to get 54,600.
    b. Multiply 27 and 23 with the calculator and then multiply by 1000 = 40 × 25 mentally to get 621,000.
    c. Multiply 647 and 89 with the calculator and then multiply by 10000 = 50 × 200 mentally to get 575,830,000.
    d. Multiply 91 and 173 with the calculator and then multiply by 100 = 25 × 2 × 2 mentally to get 1,574,300.

19. (a) 489 R 21   (b) 2,593 R 100
     (c) 6,928 R 998   (d) 1,091 R 134

20. (a) Yes (b) Yes (c) No (d) No

21. True

22. All are true.

23. All

24. (a) 104,506   (b) 864
     (c) 31,753   (d) 161,590

25. (a) $136 \rightarrow 1^3 + 3^3 + 63^3 = 244 \rightarrow$
          $2^3 + 43^3 + 4^3 = 136$
     (b) $160 \rightarrow 1^3 + 6^3 + 0^3 = 217 \rightarrow$
          $2^3 + 1^3 + 7^3 = 352 \rightarrow$
          $3^3 + 5^3 + 2^3 = 160$
     (c) $919 \rightarrow 9^3 + 1^3 + 9^3 = 1,459$
          $\rightarrow 1^3 + 4^3 + 5^3 + 9^3 = 919$

26. 123,456,789

27. (a) 9,801
     (b) 998,00
     (c) 99,980,001

28. Row 1: 9
     Row 2: 7   4   2
     Row 3: 6
     Row 4: 362,880

29. 36×5
     (i) Special factor: $36 \times 5 =$
          $(36 \times 10) \div 2 = 180$.
     (ii) Multiplicative compensation:
          $36 \times 5 = (18 \times 2) \times 5 =$
          $18 \times (2 \times 5) = 180$.
     In (i) 360 was divided by 2 and in
     (ii) 36 was divided by 2 .

30. 27,777,777,555,555,556

31. Find $712 \cdot 864$, then affix 6 zeros
     at the end.

32. 777,777,776,222,222,223

33. $(299 + 20 + 20 + 2 + 1) \times (100 + 20 + 20 + 2 + 1)$

34. 1,234,321
     23,454,321
     12,345,654,321

35. 132, 264, 385, 594, 682, 396,
     407, 649, 836

36. 121,932,631,112,635,269

37. (a) 1,649; 3,136; 2,604
     (b) $(10a + c)(10b + c)$ should be
          $100(ab + c) + c^2$ where $a + b$
          = 10.
          Proof: $(10a + c)(10b + c)$
          $= (10a + c)10b + (10a + c)c$
          $= 100ab + 10bc + 10ac + c^2$
          $= 100ab + 10c(b + a) + c^2$
          $= 100ab + 100c + c^2$
          $= 100(ab + c) + c^2$
          (since $a + b = 10$)

38. (b) 678,947,368,421,052,631,588

39. (i) Identify the digit in the
          place to which you are
          rounding.
     (ii) If the digit(s) in the place(s) to
          the right is (are) a 5 (and all
          zeros) and the number in the
          place to which you are
          rounding is even, change the
          5 to a zero. If the number in
          the place to which you are
          rounding is odd, increase it by
          1 and change the 5 to a zero.
     (iii) If the digit(s) in the place(s) to
          the right is (are) a 5 (and
          something other than all
          zeros), add 1 to the digit in
          rounding and change all digits
          to its right to zeros.
     (iv) If the digit in the place to the
          right is a 4, change the 4 and
          all digits to its right to 0.

40. (a) 4   (b) 4   (c) 9   (d) 9

41. If the answer is odd, the odd
     number of coins is in the left
     hand. If even, the even number of
     coins is in the left hand.

Analyzing Student Thinking

42. Yes, Jessica's method is valid. By subtracting 30 instead of 28, she got a difference that was 2 less than the original. She compensated for this by adding 2 to the 54.

43. Kalil's method works if you start with an even number since 2 divides into it evenly. However, when dividing an odd number by 2, one obtains a decimal that must then be multiplied by 10. With whole numbers, affixing zeros is equivalent to multiplying by ten.

44. Kalil's method works fine with multiples of 5. For other numbers, we must divide by 10 after multiplying by 2.

45. Yes, since 125 ÷ 5 = (100 + 25) ÷ 5, and Paula used the fact that division distributes over addition *from the right*.

46. Alyssa, we can see that for the sum 158 + 547 the answer should be between 100 + 500 and 200+600, or 600 and 800, not 600 and 700. Also, notice that the sum is 600 + 58 + 47 which is greater than 700 since 58 + 47 is greater than 100.

47. Jared is not correct; for example, estimating 123 + 359 with one-column front-end estimation gives an estimate of 100 + 300 = 400, but with two-column front-end estimation it's 120 + 350 = 470. The two-column estimate is a *better* estimate because it is closer to the actual sum, 123 + 359 = 482.

48. A low estimate of the product is 3000 × 200 = 600,000, so Nicole's answer is much too small. She left off a digit when recording her answer; she wrote 89, 248, rather than 899, 248.

49. Kysha, finding this product is not possible using your calculator, since it is capable of displaying only numbers with 10 or fewer digits. If you use a more powerful calculator, or if you do the multiplication by hand, you will be able to compute the product. Here is one way to make the computation by hand easier: multiply 987 by 123 and affix 6 zeros at the end, then multiply 654 by 123 and affix 3 zeros at the end, then multiply 321 by 123. Then add these three numbers together to obtain the result.

Section 4.2

1. (a)

(b)

2. (a) S = Stick
   B = Bundle of 10 sticks
   H = Bundle of 10 bundles
   BBBBSSSSS + BBBBBSSSSS
   = BBBBBBBBBSSSSSSSSSSS
   = BBBBBBBBBBBS = HS

(b)

100	10	1

=101

3. Expanded form, commutative and associative properties of addition,

single-digit addition facts, expanded form, associative property of addition, distributive property of multiplication over addition, associative property and single-digit addition facts, place value.

4. (a) $4(100) + 7(10) + 8$
       $+ 2(100) + 6(10) + 9$
       $= 6(100) + 13(10) + 17$
       $= 7(100) + 4(10) + 7$

   (b) $1(1000) + 9(100) + 6(10) + 5$
       $+ 0(1000) + 8(100) + 5(10) + 7$
       $= 1(1000) + 17(100) + 11(10) + 12$
       $= 2(1000) + 8(100) + 2(10) + 2$

5. (a)
```
   347
+  679
    16
    11
     9
  1026
```
(b)
```
   3538
+   784
     12
     11
     12
      3
   4322
```

   (c) More efficient, but less meaningful without the zeros.

6. (a) 856   (b) 1763   (c) 535

7. (a) 1641   (b) 10,185

8. (a) Simple, requires more writing and crossing out numbers.
   (b) Fewer symbols, more complicated due to the carry.

9.   616   There are many other
     919   correct answers.
     898
     868
     686
     989

10. Estimate: The sum is greater than 80,000.

11. (a) B A C   (b) B C A
    (c) A B C   (d) C B A

12. (a)   (b)

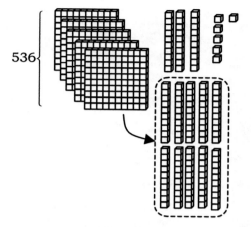

536

Exchange 1 flat for 10 longs.

536 take away 54 leaves 482.

625

Exchange 1 flat for 10 longs
and 1 long for 10 units.

625 take away 138 leaves 487.

13. (a)

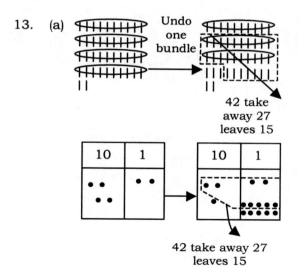

Undo
one
bundle

42 take
away 27
leaves 15

10	1

42 take away 27
leaves 15

(b)

Undo one
bundle of
100 and
one
bundle of
10.

324 take
away 68
leaves 256

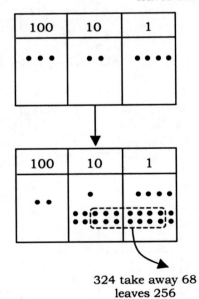

100	10	1
•••	••	••••

100	10	1
••	•	••••

324 take away 68
leaves 256

14.   10, 10, 11

15.   b, c, a

16.   (a)
$$4(100) + 5(10) + 5$$
$$-2(100) + 7(10) + 8$$
$$\overline{3(100) + 14(10) + 15}$$
$$-2(100) + 7(10) + 8$$
$$\overline{1(100) + 7(10) + 7}$$

(b)
$$5(100) + 0(10) + 3$$
$$-1(100) + 4(10) + 7$$
$$\overline{4(100) + 9(10) + 13}$$
$$-1(100) + 4(10) + 7$$
$$\overline{3(100) + 5(10) + 6}$$

(c)
$$3(1000) + 4(100) + 2(10) + 6$$
$$-0(1000) + 6(100) + 5(10) + 2$$
$$\overline{2(1000) + 13(100) + 12(10) + 6}$$
$$-0(1000) + 6(100) + 5(10) + 2$$
$$\overline{2(1000) + 7(100) + 7(10) + 4}$$

17.   (a) "29, 30, 40." Change is $12.
(b) "34, 35, 40, 60, 80, 100."
Change is $67.

18.   (a)
$$
\begin{array}{rr}
3479 & 3479 \\
-2175 & +\ 7824 \\
\hline
& 11303 \\
& +\qquad 1 \\
\hline
& 1304 \\
\end{array}
$$

(b)
$$
\begin{array}{r}
6,\ 0\ 0\ 2,\ 0\ 0\ 5 \\
-\ 4,\ 1\ 8\ 7,\ 2\ 6\ 9 \\
\end{array}
$$

$$
\begin{array}{r}
6,\ 0\ 0\ 2,\ 0\ 0\ 5 \\
+\ 5,\ 8\ 1\ 2,\ 7\ 3\ 0 \\
\hline
1\ 1,\ 8\ 1\ 4,\ 7\ 3\ 5 \\
+\qquad\qquad\qquad\ 1 \\
\hline
1,\ 8\ 1\ 4,\ 7\ 3\ 6 \\
\end{array}
$$

(c) The method with three-digit
numbers is the same except
the leading digit may be a zero.
If so, the answer is the two-
digit number that remains,
plus 1.

19. (a)

$$
\begin{array}{r}
{}^{1} \\
3476 \\
-\ 5\,{}^{6}\!\cancel{8}8 \\
\hline
18
\end{array}
\longrightarrow
\begin{array}{r}
{}^{1}\ {}^{1} \\
3476 \\
-\ 5\,{}^{6}\!\cancel{8}8 \\
\hline
2918
\end{array}
$$

(b)
$$
\begin{array}{r}
5\ {}^{1}0,\ {}^{1}0\ {}^{1}0\ {}^{1}4 \\
-\ {}^{4}\!3\ {}^{7}\!6,\ {}^{3}\!2\ {}^{9}\!8\ 9 \\
\hline
1\ \ 3,\ 7\ \ 1\ \ 5
\end{array}
$$

(c) Yes. Because the amount that is added to the minuend is added to the subtrahend, the difference remains the same.

20. (a)

(b)
$$
\begin{array}{r}
24 \\
\times\ 42 \\
\hline
8 \\
40 \\
160 \\
800 \\
\hline
1008
\end{array}
$$

(c) The product of the ones digits, 8, is represented by the unit blocks in (a); the product of the tens and ones digits, 40 and 160, by the longs; and the product of the hundreds digits, 800, by the flats.

21.

26

17

22. (a)

	20	3	
920	800	120	40
184	160	24	8
1004			

23 ⎫ 48

(b)

	30	4	
170	150	200	50
68	60	8	2
1768			

34 ⎫ 52

(c) The numbers within the grid are the same as the steps of the intermediate algorithm 1.

23. Expanded form, distributivity, expanded form, associativity of multiplication, place value, place value, addition

24. (a) 11,376   (b) 552,832

25. (a)
$$
\begin{array}{r}
276 \\
\times\ 43 \\
\hline
1104 \\
+\ 828 \\
\hline
11868
\end{array}
$$
   (b)
$$
\begin{array}{r}
768 \\
\times\ 891 \\
\hline
6144 \\
6912 \\
768 \\
\hline
684288
\end{array}
$$

26. (a)
~~44 × 83~~
~~22 × 166~~
11 × 332
5 × 664
~~2 × 1328~~
1 × 2656
3652

   (b)
31 × 54
15 × 108
7 × 216
3 × 432
1 × 864
1674

27. (a) Left Hand: 4 up, 1 down
       Right Hand: <u>1 up, 4 down</u>
       $(4 + 1) \times 10 + (4 \times 1)$
       = 54

   (b) Left Hand: 2 up, 3 down
       Right Hand: <u>4 up, 1 down</u>
       $(4 + 2) \times 10 + (3 \times 1)$
       = 63

(c) Left Hand: 3 up, 2 down
     Right Hand: 3 up, 2 down
                $(3 + 3) \times 10 + (2 \times 2)$
                      $= 64$

28. (a) $\cancel{1 \times 43}$

         2×86

         4×172

         $\underline{8 \times 344}$

         14×43

         $= (2 + 4 + 8) \times 43$

         $= 86 + 172 + 344 = 602$

     (b) 1×67

         $\cancel{2 \times 134}$

         4×268

         $\cancel{8 \times 536}$

         $\underline{16 \times 1072}$

         21×67

         $= (1 + 4 + 16) \times 67$

         $= 67 + 268 + 1072 = 1407$

     (c) 1×73

         2×146

         $\cancel{4 \times 292}$

         8×584

         $\cancel{16 \times 1168}$

         $\underline{32 \times 2336}$

         43×73

         $= (1 + 2 + 8 + 32) \times 73$

         $= 73 + 146 + 584 + 2336 = 3139$

     (d) Distributive property

29. (a)
```
    22) 749
       -660   30(22)
        89
       -66    3(22)
        23
       -22    1(22)
    1 + 34(22) = 749
```

(b)
```
   14) 3251
      -2800   200(14)
       451
      -280    20(14)
       171
      -140    10(14)
        31
       -28    2(14)
   3 + 232(14) = 3251
```

30. (a)
```
     63
    - 9
     54
    - 9
     45
    - 9
     36
    - 9
     27
    - 9
     18
    - 9
      9
    - 9
      0    63 ÷ 9 = 7
```

     (b) Repeated
          subtraction

31. (a) $39 - 3 - 3 - 3 - 3 - 3 - 3 - 3 - 3 - 3 - 3 - 3 - 3 - 3 = 0$ so
          $39 \div 3 = 13$.

     (b) $89 - 8 - 8 - 8 - 8 - 8 - 8 - 8 - 8 - 8 - 8 - 8 = 1$ so
          $89 \div 8 = 11$ r1.

     (c) $75 - 6 - 6 - 6 - 6 - 6 - 6 - 6 - 6 - 6 - 6 - 6 - 6 = 3$ so
          $75 \div 6 = 12$ r3.

     (d) Use the calculator to do repeated subtraction and count the number of times the divisor is subtracted.

32. (a) 18114 $\div$ 37 $=$ 489.56757

          $-$ 489 $=$ $\times$ 37 $=$ 21

          The quotient is 489 and the remainder is 21.

(b) $381271 \div 147 = 2593.680272$

$\boxed{-\ }2593 = \boxed{\times}147 = \boxed{100}$

The quotient is 2593 and the remainder is 100.

(c) $9346870 \div 349 = 26781.86246$

$\boxed{-\ }26781 = \boxed{\times}349 = \boxed{301}$

The quotient is 26781 and the remainder is 301.

(d) Yes, if a is divided by b, we have $a = bq + r$. This method finds $a - bq$, which is r.

33.

In 673, there is *one* group of 4 flats. The two remaining flats are exchanged for 20 longs.

In the remaining 273, there are *six* groups of 4 longs. The three remaining longs are exchanged for 30 units.

remainder

34. There is 1 flat in each of 3 groups and so there are 2 flats still to be divided (these will be grouped with the longs at the next step, making 22 longs).

35. Peter subtracted in the wrong order in 2 places. Jeff did not borrow properly. John did not need to borrow a second time in hundreds place.

36. 2, 3, 4, 5

37. (a) 631   (b) 37

38. (a) 10652 cents   (b) 10562 cents

39. (a) 12, 123, 1234, · · ·
    (b) 10 addends

40. The hundreds digit plus the ones digit is 9 and the middle digit is always 9.

41. Yes

42. All except 9.

43. Carol: 124   Steve: 96 Tracy: 44 r6

44. There is no extra dollar. 30 - 5 = 25. Also 3(9) - 2 = 25.

45. $x(x+2) + 1 = (x+1)^2$

Analyzing Student Thinking

46. We use a concrete model such as base-ten pieces to help students

develop a deeper understanding of the usual procedures, such as "carrying," involved in addition.

47. While it is fine for a student to use the lattice method, it is usually more efficient to use the standard algorithm.

48. 123 – 67 = (100 – 60) + 10 + (10 – 7) + 3 = (40) + 10 + (3) + 3 = 66. Some students may find the subtract-from-the-base algorithm easier and faster than the standard subtraction algorithm since they only need to know the addition facts and differences from 10.

49. Advantage: base ten blocks provide a concrete model as a first step in learning the standard multiplication algorithm, with intermediate multiplication algorithms assisting in the transition from the concrete model to the abstract standard algorithm. Disadvantage: the 4 sections of the rectangle formed by the base 10 blocks to represent a product correspond more closely to the subproducts in the intermediate multiplication algorithms than the standard algorithm; the complexity of the standard algorithm is difficult to model concretely.

50. Nicholas, we look at different algorithms for subtractions to help you better understand the process. If you want to focus on learning just one of these, you can choose the one that makes the most sense to you. The standard algorithm is usually the most efficient.

51. This case, discussed in Robert Davis's book, *Learning Mathematics: The Cognitive Science Approach to Mathematics Education*, involved a student who believed that you could not "borrow" from a zero place.

Therefore, each time she needed to borrow, she went directly to the 4 and borrowed from it without changing the zeros. She subtracted 7 from 15 and got 8, and she subtracted 3 from 10 and got 7. But both times she borrowed from the 4, which became a 3 and then a 2.

52. Natasha, the lattice method is very simple compared to the standard multiplication algorithm—simply multiply each pair of digits and add down the diagonals.

53. Yes, Andres's method will always work--he used expanded form and the distributive property.

54. Show Dylan a set of 6 flats, 2 longs, and 1 unit and ask him to share these among 3 groups. Each group will have 2 flats and 7 units, or 207.

Section 4.3

1. (a)

12_{seven} 6_{seven}

0 1 2 3 4 5 6 10 11 12 13 14 15 16 20 21 22
BASE SEVEN

(b)

4_{eight} 16_{eight}

0 1 2 3 4 5 6 7 10 11 12 13 14 15 16 17 20 21 22
BASE EIGHT

2. (a)

12_{five}

20_{five} 32_{five}

(b)

24_{five}

13_{five} 42_{five}

(c)

342_{five}

13_{five}

410_{five}

(d)

2134_{five}

1330_{five}

2314_{five}

3. (a) 131_{four} (b) 131_{eight}
   (c) 842_{nine}

4. (a) 154_{nine} (b) $1TT_{twelve}$

5. (a)

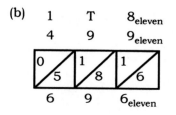

6. (a) 142_{twelve} (b) $18T_{eleven}$

7. (a)

(b)

8. (a)

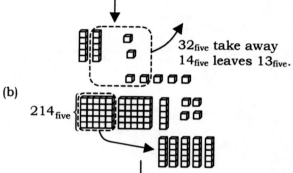

32_{five}

32_{five} take away
14_{five} leaves 13_{five}.

(b)

214_{five}

214_{five} take away
32_{five} leaves 122_{five}.

(c)

301_{five}

301_{five} take away
243_{five} leaves 3_{five}.

9.   (a) 44$_{\text{five}}$ (b) 155$_{\text{eight}}$
     (c) 11$_{\text{two}}$

10. (a) 6$_{\text{seven}}$ (b) 1E$_{\text{twelve}}$
     (c) 1$_{\text{eight}}$

11. 1001010$_{\text{two}}$ − 111001$_{\text{two}}$ =
     1001010$_{\text{two}}$ + 110$_{\text{two}}$
       − 1000000$_{\text{two}}$ + 1$_{\text{two}}$ =
     10001$_{\text{two}}$

12. (a)

     (b)

13. (a)

(b)

1044$_{\text{seven}}$ after exchanges

14. (a) 101011111$_{\text{two}}$ (b) 969$_{\text{twelve}}$
     (c) 65601$_{\text{seven}}$

15. (a)

     (b)

16. (a) 3$_{\text{five}}$ (b) 121$_{\text{six}}$
     (c) 143$_{\text{seven}}$

17. (a) 6$_{\text{seven}}$ (b) 8$_{\text{nine}}$
     (c) T$_{\text{twelve}}$

18.

Since there is not a group of size 11$_{\text{four}}$ cubes, the three cubes are exchanged for flats.

(continued on next page)

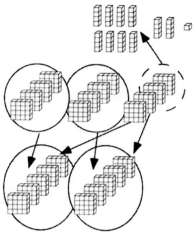

There are two groups of flats of size 11_{four}. The remaining two flats are exchanged for longs.

remainder

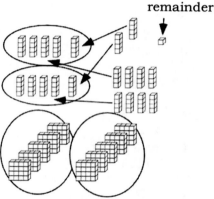

There are two groups of longs of size 11_{four} with no longs left over. There are no groups of units of size 11_{four}, but there is one unit remaining. Thus the quotient is 220_{four} with remainder 1.

19. eight

20. Betty has $6; Tom has $2.

21. 10

22. Assume n is even. Then n can be expressed as $2m$ where m is a whole number. Then $n^2 = (2m)^2 = 4m^2$ which is even. This contradicts the given information, so n must be odd.

Analyzing Student Thinking

23. Antolina, studying algorithms in other bases can help you understand the base ten algorithms better, as well as clarify the meanings of place value and regrouping. Plus, working with algorithms in other bases is just good exercise for your mind.

24. Ralph, go ahead and use the addition table—this will likely help you memorize it.

25. No, a base-four system uses only the digits 0, 1, 2, and 3, so we would not write the number 413_{four}.

26. Geoff, the standard algorithm involves just as many steps as the intermediate algorithm, the difference is that we record all of these steps on our paper when we use the intermediate algorithm. The standard algorithm requires you to do a lot of this work mentally. You may want to write out the steps until you are comfortable doing them in your head.

27. First, look at the student's work to see if you can identify the trouble he is having or ask him to explain what part he is having a hard time with. It may help to start with a model, such as the base 5 number line, showing how to use repeated subtraction to find a simple quotient. Then, demonstrate an intermediate algorithm, such as the scaffold method, and discuss the connections between this method and the standard algorithm.

28. Sherry, remember that 12_{six} in expanded form $1(6) + 2(1)$, or 8 in base 10. Thus, when you subtract 5_{six} from 12_{six}, you get 3_{six}.

Chapter 5

Section 5.1

1. Multiples of 2 in columns 2, 4, and 6; multiples of 3 in columns 3 and 6; multiples of 5 on diagonal; multiples of 7 on diagonals

2. (a) $2^6 \times 3$

  (b) $2^2 \times 5 \times 19$

  (c) $3^3 \times 59$

(d) $3 \times 29 \times 43$

3. (a) 3×13 (b) $3 \times 13 \times 29$
   (c) 5×11 (d) $5 \times 11 \times 17$
   (e) $11 \times 13 \times 23$ (f) $3 \times 13 \times 151$

4. (a) 7   (b) 10   (c) 3×18
   (d) $2 \times 5 \times 7$
   (e) $2^3 \times 3 \times 7^3 \times 13^5$
   (f) $2^2 \times 3^9 \times 5^6 \times 17^8$
   (g) $2^{17} \times 3^{16} \times 5^{86} \times 29^{37}$
   (h) 2×11
   (i) $p^2 q^8 r^6 s^2 t^{27}$
   (j) $(5 \times 3 + 2)$

5. 1, 2, 3, 4, 6, 8, 12, and 24

6. (a) False $2 \mid 18$ and $6 \mid 18$ but $12 \nmid 18$
   (b) False $6 \mid 4 \cdot 15$ but $6 \nmid 4$ and $6 \nmid 15$

7. (a) 114 ends in 4; $2 \times 57 = 114$
   (b) $3 + 3 + 6 = 12$ which is divisible by 3; $3 \times 112 = 336$ 112

8. (a) 3, 4, 9
   (b) 3, 9

9. (a) $9 + 5 + 4 = 18$, $4 + 1 + 2 = 7$, $18 - 7 = 11$. Since $18 \nmid 11$, $11 \nmid 945, 142$.
   (b) $6 + 2 + 4 + 1 = 13$, $2 + 7 + 5 = 14$, $14 - 13 = 1$. Since $11 \nmid 1$, $11 \nmid 6, 247, 251$.
   (c) $3 + 5 + 2 = 10$, $8 + 6 + 7 = 21$, $21 - 10 = 11$. Since $11 \mid 11$, $11 \mid 385, 627$.

10. (a)

$$
\begin{array}{rl}
2963 & \\
-\underline{15} & = 5 \times 3 \\
281 & \\
-\underline{5} & = 5 \times 1 \\
23 & \\
\end{array}
$$

$17 \mid 23$ so $17 \mid 2963$

(b)

$$37,142$$

$$- \quad 14 \quad = 7 \times 2$$

$$3,700$$

$$- \quad 0 \quad = 7 \times 0$$

$$370$$

$$- \quad 0 \quad = 7 \times 0$$

$$37$$

$17 | 37$ so $17 \nmid 37,142$

(c)

$$95,757,923$$

$$- \quad 15 \quad = 5 \times 3$$

$$9,575,777$$

$$- \quad 35 \quad = 5 \times 7$$

$$957,542$$

$$- \quad 10 \quad = 5 \times 2$$

$$95,744$$

$$- \quad 20 \quad = 5 \times 4$$

$$9,554$$

$$- \quad 20 \quad = 5 \times 4$$

$$935$$

$$- \quad 25 \quad = 5 \times 5$$

$$68$$

$17 | 68$ so $17 | 95,757,923$

11. (a) F. Try 24.
(b) F. Try 12.

12. (a) T. $8 | 608$ and
$3 | (3 + 2 + 5 + 6 + 8)$.
(b) F. $9 \nmid (1 + 3 + 7 + 5)$
(c) T. $40 | 800$
(d) T. $4 | 16$ and
$9 | (6+7+7+9+1+6)$

13. All are composite.
(a) even
(b) a multiple of 127
(c) a multiple of 3

14. 2, 3, 5, 7, 11, 13, 17, 19, 23. No other primes need to be checked.

15. (a) Yes   (b) No

16. Let $r = a \cdot 10^3 + b \cdot 10^2 + c \cdot 10 + d$ be any 4 digit number.
Rewrite:
$r = a(999+1) + b(99+1) + c(9+1) + d$

$= a \cdot 999 + a + b \cdot 99 + b + c9 + c + d$
$= (a \cdot 111 + b \cdot 11 + c)9 + (a + b + c + d)$
Since $9 | 9$ it also divides $(a \cdot 111 + b \cdot 11 + c) \cdot 9$. Thus, if $9 | (a + b + c + d)$, it is true that $9 | r$.

17. Observe that $4 | 10^n$ for $n \geq 2$ and that $8 | 10^n$ for $n \geq 3$. Then make a proof modifying the proof for divisibility by 2.

18. $9! - 8! + \ldots + 1! = 326981 = 79 \times 4139$

19. (a) 31, 37, 41, 43, 47, 53, 59
(b) 53, 59, 61, 67, 71 (and others)
(c) 101, 103, 107, 109 (and others)

20. Yes, we have checked all primes p such that $p^2 \leq 211$.

21. False. When $n = 41$, $n^2 - n + 41 = 41^2 - 41 + 41 = 41^2$, a composite.

22. $2^3 - 1 = 7$, a prime;
$2^5 - 1 = 31$, a prime;
$2^7 - 1 = 127$, a prime;
$2^{13} - 1 = 8191$, a prime.

23. Every number can be expressed as one of the following: $6n$, $6n + 1$, $6n + 2$, $6n + 3$, $6n - 2$, or $6n - 1$. But $6 | 6n$, $2 | (6n + 2)$, $3 | (6n + 3)$, and $2 | (6n - 2)$. Thus the only ones that could be primes are $6n + 1$ or $6n - 1$.

24. No, sum of two odd numbers is even. All evens, except 2, are composite.

25. Answers will vary.

26. 3,5,7 is the only prime triple. For suppose p, $p + 2$, $p + 4$ is another prime triple. Then p is not a multiple of 3, so (i) $p = 3k + 1$ or (ii) $p = 3k + 2$. If $p = 3k + 1$, then $p + 2 = 3k + 1 + 2 = 3k + 3$, which is a multiple of 3, hence not

prime. If $p = 3k + 2$, then $p + 4 = 3k + 2 + 4 = 3k + 6$, which again is a multiple of 3. Thus p, $p + 2$, and $p + 4$ can all be prime only when $p = 3$.

27. (a) $17 - 5$
     (b) $43 - 23$
     (c) $41 - 13$
     Note: Each part has many possible answers.

28. One possible solution:
     Row 1 - 67, 1,43;
     Row 2 13,37,61;
     Row 3 - 31, 73,7

29. No - according to Fundamental Theorem of Arithmetic, there is exactly one way to write any number as a product of prime

30. 16, 25

31. $2^3 \times 3 \times 5 \times 7 = 840$

32. $2^4 \times 3^2 \times 5^2 \times 7 \times 11 \times 13 \times 17 \times 19 \times 23$

33. 5. Proof: $n + (n+1) + (n+2) + (n+3) + (n+4) = 5n + 10 = 5(n + 2)$.

34. Yes; for example, consider a 4-digit number, n, in expanded form: $n = 1000a + 100b + 10c + d$. Reversing the digits and adding to n gives:
     $1000a + 100b + 10c + d$
     $\underline{1000d + 100c + 10b + a}$
     $1001a + 110b + 110c + 1001d$
     $= 11(91a + 10b + 10c + 91d)$, a multiple of 11. A similar argument can be made for an number with an even number of digits.

35. (a) 9
     (b) 99
     (c) 9

36. True. This can be proved using the test for divisibility by 3.

37. $16.22 or $5.11

38. (a) 2
     (b) 24
     (c) 248

39. 428571

40. 6 and 66 years old.

41. True. Let n = any whole number. Then
     $n + (n+1) + (n+2) + \ldots + [n+(m-2)] + [n+(m-1)] = mn + \dfrac{(m-1)m}{2} =$
     $m[n + \dfrac{(m-1)}{2}]$.

     Therefore (since m is odd, $n + m-1$ is a whole number) the m consecutive whole numbers beginning with n are divisible by m.

42. 349 at $1.73

43. (a) 9   (b) 10

44. Numbers that have a multiple of six 9s as digits.

45. 27,374,985

46. Yes

47. Let x and y be any two consecutive numbers in the Fibonacci sequence. Then, the next eight numbers are $x + y$, $x + 2y$, $2x + 3y$, $3x + 5y$, $5x + 8y$, $8x + 13y$, $13x + 21y$, and $21x + 34y$. The sum of these ten numbers is $55x + 88y$, a multiple of 11.

48. This table should be created on a spreadsheet.

n	p(n)	n	p(n)
1	43	11	173
2	47	12	197
3	53	13	223
4	61	14	251
5	71	15	281
6	83	16	313
7	97	17	347
8	113	18	383
9	131	19	421
10	151	20	461

49. Use 4 instead of 2.

Analyzing Student Thinking

50. Yes, Courtney, you can use the Sieve of Eratoshenes to find the composite numbers—if you followed the algorithm for finding primes, the composite numbers are all those that you crossed off.

51. No, the student is not correct; for example, 3 | (2 + 4), but 3 does not divide 2 or 4.

52. Yes, Christa is correct; since 10 = 9+1, 100 = 99+1, 1000 = 999+1 and so forth, each power of 10 is 1 more than a multiple of 9 as well as one more than a multiple of 3. Because of this similarity between powers of 10 and multiples of 3 or 9, the divisibility tests are also similar.

53. Yes, that's right, Brooklyn, you checked all the prime numbers whose square is less than or equal to 113.

54. $a \mid b$ is a statement about the relationship between the numbers a and b; for instance, to say that 4 divides 12, or 4 | 12, means there exists a whole number, namely 3, that can be multiplied by 4 to get 12. However, a/b is the quotient of the numbers a and b—it is equal to the answer you get when dividing a by b; for example, 12/4 = 3. It is true to say that, if $a \mid b$,then b/a is an integer.

55. Kelby, in your first example, 2 and 9 = 3 × 3 have no common factors, so their product divides 36. However, in your second example, 4 = 2 × 2 and 6 = 2 × 3 have a common factor of 2. Thus, the product of 4 × 6 = 24 = 2 × 2 × 2 × 3 has one more factor of 2 than does 36 = 2 × 2 × 3 × 3 and 24 does not divide 36. Notice that 12 is a number that is smaller than 24 but also a multiple of both 4 and 6. It does divide 36.

56. Lorena, 357 does happen to be divisible by 7 since 357 = 51 × 7, but your test for divisibility by 7 does not always work; for instance 27 has 7 as its last digit, but 27 is not divisible by 7.

57. No, 354 is not divisible by 4 or 6.

Section 5.2

1.   (a) 9   (b) 16   (c) 2016
   (d) 45
   (e) 24 factors: 1, 11, 11^2, 11^3, 11^4, 11^5, 13, 13^2, 13^3, 11×13, 11×13^2, 11×13^3, $11^2 \times 13$, $11^2 \times 13^2$, $11^2 \times 13^3$, $11^3 \times 13$, $11^3 \times 13^2$, $11^3 \times 13^3$, $11^4 \times 13$, $11^4 \times 13^2$, $11^4 \times 13^3$, $11^5 \times 13$, $11^5 \times 13^2$, $11^5 \times 13^3$

2.   (a) 120 = 2 × 2 × 2 × 3 × 5
   (b) 2, 3, 4 = 2 × 2, 5, 6 = 2 × 3, 8 = 2 × 2 × 2, 10 = 2 × 5, 12 = 2 × 2 × 3, etc.
   (c) Same factors, not used more times than in (a)
   (d) Prime factors of n are 11 and/or 13, not more than 5 factors of 11 and 3 factors of 13.

3.   (a) Factors of 24: {1, 2, 3, 4, 6, <u>8</u>, 12, 24}
   Factors of 16: (1, 2, 4, <u>8</u>, 16}
   GCF(24, 16) = 8
   (b) Factors of 48: {1, 2, 3, 4, 6, 8, 12, <u>16</u>, 24, 48}
   Factors of 64: {1, 2, 4, 8, <u>16</u>, 32, 64}
   GCF(48, 64) = 16
   (c) Factors of 54: {1, 2, 3, 6, 9, <u>18</u>, 27, 54}
   Factors of 72: {1, 2, 4, 3, 6, 8, 9, 12, <u>18</u>, 24, 36, 72}
   GCF(54, 72) = 18

4.   (a) 18   (b) 1   (c) 17

5.   (a) 6   (b) 111   (c) 3   (d) 1

6. (a) 22   (b) 9   (c) 2

7. (a) 2   (b) 6
    (c) 8   (d) 169

8. (a) check 2, 4
    (b) check 13
    (c) check 3, 11

9. (a) Multiples of 15: {15, 30, 45, 60, 90,...}
        Multiples of 18: {18, 36, 54, 72, 90, ...}
        LCM(15, 18) = 2 × 3² × 5 = 90
    (b) Multiples of 26: {26, 52, 78, ...}
        Multiples of 39: {39, 78, ...}
        LCM(26, 39) = 78
    (c) Multiples of 36: {36, 72, 108, 144, ...}
        Multiples of 45: {45, 90, 144, ...}
        LCM(36, 45) = 144

10. (a) 105   (b) 70
    (c) 300   (d) 910

11. (a) 357   (b) 1443   (c) 1125

12. (a) 1   (b) 2   (c) 69
    (d) 17   (e) $5^3 \cdot 7^3 \cdot 13^4$
    (f) $3^3 \cdot 7^2$

13. (a) 60   (b) 225
    (c) $3^4 \cdot 5^5 \cdot 7^6 \cdot 11^4$
    (d) $2^4 \cdot 3^8 \cdot 5^4 \cdot 11^3 \cdot 13^7$

14. (a) $1260 = 2^2 \cdot 3^2 \cdot 5 \cdot 7$
    (b) $59,400 = 2^3 \cdot 3^3 \cdot 5^2 \cdot 11$
    (c) $36,036 = 2^2 \cdot 3^2 \cdot 7 \cdot 11 \cdot 13$

15. (a) GCF(a, b) = 7; $a \cdot b = 4116$;
        LCM(a, b) = 4116 ÷ 7 = 588
    (b) $5^3 \cdot 7^4$
    (c) $a = 2^7 \cdot 5^5 \cdot 7^5 \cdot 11^4$, $b = 5^3 \cdot 7^4$
        and
        $a = 2^7 \cdot 5^3 \cdot 7^4$, $b = 5^4 \cdot 7^5 \cdot 11^4$

16. (a) (i)

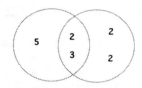

    (ii) GCF (30, 24) = 2·3
         LCM (30, 24) = 2·2·2·3·5
    (b) (i)

    (ii) GCF(4, 27) = 1
         LCM(4, 27) = 2·2·3·3·3
    (c) (i)

    (ii) GCF(18, 45) = 3·3
         LCM(18, 45) = 2·3·3·5

17. LCM(a, b) except when $a = b$, in which case they are equal.

18. (a) abundant   (b) perfect
    (c) abundant   (d) deficient

19. (a) No; 1648:
        1 + 2 + 4 + 8 + 16 + 103 + 206 + 412 + 824 = 1576
        1576:
        1 + 2 + 4 + 8 + 197 + 394 + 788 = 1394
    (b) Yes ; 2620:
        1 + 2 + 4 + 5 + 10 + 20 + 131 + 262 + 524 + 655 + 1310 = 2924
        2924:
        1 + 2 + 4 + 17 + 34 + 43 + 68 + 86 + 172 + 731 + 1462 = 2620
    (c) 18, 416

20. (a) No; 248:
        2 + 4 + 8 + 31 + 62 + 124 = 231
        231:
        3 + 7 + 11 + 21 + 33 + 77 = 152
    (b) Yes; 1050:

2 + 3 + 5 + 7 + 10 + 14 + 15 +
21 + 25 + 30 + 35 + 42 + 50 +
70 + 75 + 105 + 150 + 210 +
350 + 525 = 1925
1925:
5 + 7 + 11 + 25 + 35 + 55 + 77
+ 175 + 275 + 385 = 1050

(c) Yes; 1575:
3 + 5 + 7 + 9 + 15 + 21 + 25 +
35 + 45 + 63 + 75 + 105 + 175
+ 315 + 525 = 1648
1648:
2 + 4 + 8 + 16 + 103 + 206 +
412 + 824 = 1575

21. (a)

3:	1,3	2
4:	1,2,4	3
5:	1,5	2
6:	1,2,3,6	4
7:	1,7	2
8:	1,2,4,8	4
9:	1,3,9	3
10:	1,2,5,10	4
11:	1,11	2
12:	1,2,3,4,6,12	6
13:	1,13	2
14:	1,2,7,14	4
15:	1,3,5,15	4
16:	1,2,4,8,16	5

(b) prime numbers
(c) perfect square

22. (a) p
(b) p^2
(c) pq or p^3
(d) p^4
(e) p^5 or p^2q
(f) p^{11}, p^5q, p^3q^2, $p^2q\,r$

23. (a) b is a multiple of a
(b) a is a multiple of b
(c) both a and b are 1
(d) The only common factor of a and b is 1, i.e. GCF $(a, b) = 1$.

24. GCF$(x^2, y^2) = 1$. The prime factorizations of x and y share no primes. In x^2 and y^2 those same primes occur, just twice as often, so still none are common.

25. 496 is the sum of the cubes of 1,3,5, and 7. 8128 is the sum of the cubes of the odd numbers 1 through 15.

26. 5, 6

27. 136 miles

28. LCM(3, 4, 5) = 60 so 60 minutes after 11 was the first time all 3 dogs barked together again.

29. 90 since $90 = 2^1 \times 3^2 \times 5^1$, there are $(1+1)(2+1)(1+1) = 12$ factors.

30. 60 has 12 factors.

31. $23 \cdot 28 \cdot 33 = 21,252$

32. $494 \div 13 = 38$. $100a + 10b + a = 100a + 10(13 - a) + a = 91a + 10 \times 13 = (7a + 10)13$

33. $4 + 9 + 3 + 7 + 7 + 7 + 5 = 42$, $4,937,775 = 5 \times 5 \times 3 \times 65,837$, and $5 + 5 + 3 + 6 + 5 + 8 + 3 + 7 = 42$.

34. (a) 4
(b) 8
(c) $(\dfrac{m + n}{GCF(m, n)} - 1) \times GCF(m,n)$

35. $1729 = 12^3 + 1^3 = 10^3 + 9^3$

36. 377 and 233. Any pair of consecutive Fibonacci numbers beyond the 12th one. Other answers are possible.

Analyzing Student Thinking

37. No, Colby is not correct. In order to determine the number of factors, he needs to first write $8^3 9^4$ in its prime factorization form: $8^3 9^4 = 2^9 3^8$ has $(9+1)(8+1) = 90$ factors.

38. Eva, the LCM(a, b) is the smallest number that both a and b will divide. Thus, LCM$(a, b) \ge$ both a and b. However, the GCF(a, b) is the greatest number that divides both a and b; hence GCF$(a, b) \le$

both a and b. So, LCM$(a, b) \geq$ GCF(a, b).

39. LCD: least common denominator
    GCD: greatest common divisor

40. Ask Brett to consider the following whole numbers that have exactly three factors: 4, 9, 16, 25, 49, ... Can you see anything special about these numbers? They are all perfect squares.

41. Yes, he is correct in both cases. To write a fraction a/b in simplest form (i.e. "reduce" the fraction), one divides a and b by GCF(a, b). When finding a common denominator between two fractions, in order to add or subtract them, say, one usually uses the LCM of the denominators of the two fractions.

42. Both the Set Intersection method and the Prime Factorization method are important to learn. Using Set Intersection helps us to understand the meaning of the GCF, but it is more cumbersome to use this method. The Prime Factorization method is often more efficient to use.

43. Yes, the student is correct. This does not invalidate the theorem because, in the proof, it is assumed that p is the largest prime; 13 is clearly not the largest prime.

Chapter 6

Section 6.1

1. (a) 5/8   (b) 3/10
    (c) 4/5   (d) 5/12

2. (a) (i)

    (ii)

    (b) (i) ◯◯◯◯◯
            ◯◯◯◯◯

    (ii) ◯◯◯ ◯◯◯

         ◯◯◯

    (c) (i)

    (ii)

    (d) (i)

    0   1

    (ii)

    0   1   2   3

3. (a) △△△△△◯

    (b) △△◯◯◯◯◯◯

    (c) △△△◯

4. Yes. The shaded rectangles
    represent ½ and the shaded
    triangles represent ¼. Thus, the
    shaded region represents ¾.

5. (a) 9/40   (b) 5/40   (c) 7/40

6. (a) False, total days not the same
        for each month
    (b) True
    (c) False, each part (month) not
        equivalent size

7.

    The same amount is shaded in
    both figures.

8. (a) F   (b) F
    (c) T   (d) T

9. (a) and (d)

10. (a) 21/17   (b) 14/3
    (c) 5/7   (d) 29/2

11. (a) $5\dfrac{28}{111}$ (b) $62\dfrac{1}{3}$

12. (a) Since a 13th < an 11th < a 9th,
        $\dfrac{5}{13} < \dfrac{5}{11} < \dfrac{5}{9}$.
    (b) Since a 9th < an 8th < a 7th,
        $\dfrac{6}{7} < \dfrac{7}{8} < \dfrac{8}{9}$

13. (a) 7/13 < 14/25 < 4/7
    (b) 2/9 < 3/11 < 5/18 < 7/23

14. $\dfrac{ad+bc}{2bd}$ is midway between $\dfrac{a}{b}$ and
    $\dfrac{c}{d}$ since it is the average of the
    two.

15. Only fractions in (a) are equal.

In (b) $\dfrac{1516}{2312} < \dfrac{4196}{5202} < \dfrac{2653}{2890}$.

In (c) $\dfrac{516}{892} < \dfrac{1892}{3268} < \dfrac{1376}{2376}$

16. (a) $\dfrac{20}{230}, \dfrac{9}{100}$ (b) $\dfrac{4}{20}, \dfrac{20}{100}$

(c) $\dfrac{17}{230}, \dfrac{7}{100}$ (d) $\dfrac{7}{17}, \dfrac{41}{100}$

17. Both

18. Mr. Roberts's class

19. There are many correct possibilities. One is shown for each case.

(a)

(b)

(c)

(d)

(e)

20. (a) (i) $\dfrac{16}{64} = \dfrac{1}{4}$ (ii) $\dfrac{19}{95} = \dfrac{1}{5}$

(iii) $\dfrac{26}{65} = \dfrac{2}{5}$

(iv) $\dfrac{199}{995} = \dfrac{1}{5}$

(v) $\dfrac{26666}{66665} = \dfrac{2}{5}$

(b) Answers will vary here, but some examples are:

$\dfrac{1666}{6664}, \dfrac{2666666}{6666665}, \dfrac{1999}{9995}$

21. Yes, this process can continue. No, there is no smallest fraction greater than 0.

22. The size of the unit is different so comparison cannot be made.

23. (a) 672   (b) 11,193

24. Greater than - the fraction is always closer to one.

25. For example, 2001/6000, 2002/6000,..., 2999/6000

26. $80,000,000,000

27. 8/17

28. $2,800

29. Approximately 9.3 km

30. (a) In order, from nearest to farthest: Kelly, Janet, Cathy, Rose, Ann

(b) 2.5 K

31. (a)

(b)

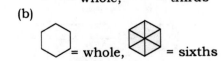

(c)

= whole,
=fourths

(d)

= whole,
= twelfths

32. These activities highlight that the wholes can be different shapes and the parts are always equal; and, most importantly, they provide a bridge from the concrete representation of a picture to the abstract representation of numerals.

Analyzing Student Thinking

33. David's statement is true since proper fractions are less than 1, while improper fractions are greater than 1.

34. It's true that multiplying the top and bottom of a fraction by the same number does not change the value of the fraction, by definition of fraction equality. However, adding the same number to the top and bottom of a fraction changes its value; for instance $\frac{1}{2} \neq \frac{1+2}{2+2} = \frac{3}{4}$.

35. Help Brandon find equal fractions with like denominators as follows: 3/4 = 15/20 and 3/5 = 12/20, so 13/20 or 14/20 would be between 3/4 and 3/5.

36. Rafael, to compare two fractions, first write them with a common denominator. Since $\frac{1}{4} = \frac{1 \cdot 2}{4 \cdot 2} = \frac{2}{8}$, we see the two fractions are actually equal.

37. Collin is correct in the case that the denominators of the two fractions are equal; for instance 4/5 is larger than 3/5 since 4 is larger than 3. However, if the two fractions do not have a common denominator, the one with the larger numerator may or may not be the larger fraction; for instance, 7/20 is not larger than 1/2, even though 7 is larger than 1.

38. Show the student that 3/2 would mean that the circle is divided into 2 equivalent parts, and 3 such parts are shaded—this requires two circles.

39. Hailey is incorrect; for example, $2 \times 3 < 1 \times 8$, but 2/3 is not less than 1/8. What we can say is: if $ab < cd$, then either $a/c < d/b$ or $a/d < c/b$.

Section 6.2

1. (a)

    $\frac{3}{4}$ $\frac{9}{12}$

    +   +

    $\frac{2}{3}$ $\frac{8}{12}$

    (b) $\frac{3}{4}$ + $\frac{2}{3}$ = $1\frac{5}{12}$

    0   1   2

    (c)

    =

    +

    +

    $\frac{9}{12}$ $\frac{8}{12}$

2. $\dfrac{5}{8} + \dfrac{1}{6} = \dfrac{15}{24} + \dfrac{4}{24} = \dfrac{19}{24}$

$\dfrac{5}{8} + \dfrac{1}{6} = \dfrac{30}{48} + \dfrac{8}{48} = \dfrac{38}{48} = \dfrac{19}{24}$

$\dfrac{5}{8} + \dfrac{1}{6} = \dfrac{45}{72} + \dfrac{12}{72} = \dfrac{57}{72} = \dfrac{19}{24}$

$\dfrac{5}{8} + \dfrac{1}{6} = \dfrac{90}{144} + \dfrac{24}{144} = \dfrac{114}{144} = \dfrac{19}{24}$

Other correct answers are possible.

3. (a)

$\dfrac{3}{4}$

$\dfrac{1}{3}$

Using the comparison approach, 5/12 are left.

(b)

$3\dfrac{1}{3}$

Take away $\dfrac{5}{6}$

leaves $2\dfrac{1}{2}$

4. (a) $\dfrac{5}{2^2 \times 3^3}$

(b) $\dfrac{(5^3 \times 29) + (3^2 \times 7)}{3^2 \times 5^3 \times 7^3 \times 29}$

(c) $\dfrac{(3^2 \times 13) + (5^3 \times 7^5)}{3^2 \times 5^4 \times 7^5 \times 13^3}$

(d) $\dfrac{11^5 + [17 \times 53^5 \times 67^4]}{11^5 \times 17^3 \times 53^5 \times 67^{13}}$

5. (a) $11\dfrac{2}{3}$

(b) $4\dfrac{3}{4}$

(c) $8\dfrac{1}{6}$

(d) $3\dfrac{2}{5}$

6. (a) $77/45 = 1\dfrac{32}{45}$

(b) $511/24 = 21\dfrac{7}{24}$

(c) $21\dfrac{22}{45}$

(d) $6\dfrac{1}{24}$

7. (a) $554/675$ (b) $149/156$

8. (a) $1\dfrac{29}{30}$ (b) $\dfrac{31}{36}$

9. (a) $5/12 + 4/12$

(b) $1/5 + 7/15$

(c) $1/3 + 5/12$

10. (a) (i) $3/8$ (ii) $1/24$
    (b) Associativity

11. (a) $1\dfrac{32}{45}$ (b) $6\dfrac{1}{24}$

12. (a) $1\dfrac{25}{126}$ (b) $\dfrac{73}{156}$

13. (a) $\dfrac{17}{30}$ (b) $\dfrac{18}{35}$

14. By cross multiplication: $\dfrac{2}{5} < \dfrac{5}{8}$
    since $2 \cdot 8 < 5 \cdot 5$.

    Using common denominators:
    $\dfrac{2}{5} < \dfrac{5}{8}$ since
    $\dfrac{2}{5} = \dfrac{2 \cdot 8}{5 \cdot 8} = \dfrac{16}{40} < \dfrac{25}{40} = \dfrac{5 \cdot 5}{8 \cdot 5} = \dfrac{5}{8}$

15. (a) $1\dfrac{5}{8}$

    (b) $3\dfrac{2}{15}$

    (c) $9\dfrac{2}{11}$

16. (a) $5\dfrac{4}{9} - 3 = 2\dfrac{4}{9}$

    (b) $9\dfrac{2}{6} - 3 = 6\dfrac{1}{3}$

    (c) $21\dfrac{5}{7} - 9 = 12\dfrac{5}{7}$

    (d) $5\dfrac{8}{11} - 3 = \dfrac{8}{11}$

17. (a) (i) 11 to 13   (ii) 12

    (b) (i) 1 to 2   (ii) $1\dfrac{1}{2}$

    (c) (i) 17 to 20   (ii) 18

18. (a) $6 + 6\dfrac{1}{2} = \dfrac{1}{2}$

    (b) $8 - 5\dfrac{1}{2} = 2\dfrac{1}{2}$

    (c) $8 + 2\dfrac{1}{2} + 7 = 17\dfrac{1}{2}$

19. $\sim 4 \cdot 6 = 24$

20. 8

21. 8

22. 52 bags

23. 45 minutes

24. $35' \dfrac{1}{2}''$

25. Amy: $2\dfrac{1}{2}$ Robert: $\dfrac{7}{15}$
    Review simpler problems, meaning of mixed numbers, use diagrams.

26. (a) $8^2 + 15^2 = 17^2$, 17

    (b) (i) $\dfrac{1}{7} + \dfrac{1}{9} = \dfrac{16}{63}$,
            $16^2 + 63^2 = 65^2$

        (ii) $\dfrac{1}{11} + \dfrac{1}{13} = \dfrac{24}{143}$,
             $24^2 + 143^2 = 145^2$

        (iii) $\dfrac{1}{19} + \dfrac{1}{21} = \dfrac{40}{399}$,
              $40^2 + 399^2 = 401^2$

    (c) The third number, c, is two more than the denominator of the sum.

    (d) $\dfrac{1}{2n-1} + \dfrac{1}{2n+1} = \dfrac{4n}{4n^2 - 1}$ and
        $(4n)^2 + (4n^2 - 1)^2 = (4n^2 + 1)^2$

27. 11/23

28. (a) 7/8, 15/16, 31/32,
    (b) 7   (c) 1

29. (a) 1/5 - 2/5 is not a fraction
    (b) 3/4 - 1/4 ≠ 1/4 - 3/4
    (c) (4/5 - 3/5) - 1/5 ≠ 4/5 - (3/5 - 1/5)

30. (a) $\dfrac{1}{6}$ $\dfrac{1}{30}$ $\dfrac{1}{60}$ $\dfrac{1}{60}$ $\dfrac{1}{30}$ $\dfrac{1}{6}$

    $\dfrac{1}{7}$ $\dfrac{1}{42}$ $\dfrac{1}{105}$ $\dfrac{1}{140}$ $\dfrac{1}{105}$ $\dfrac{1}{42}$ $\dfrac{1}{7}$

    (b) The first number in the nth row is $\dfrac{1}{n}$.

    (c) Each fraction in the triangle is the sum of the two fractions directly below it. For example,
    $\dfrac{1}{30} + \dfrac{1}{20} = \dfrac{1}{12}$.

31. (a) 5/12 - 1/3 = 1/12 and

11/12 - 1/3 = 7/12
(b) 6/12 - 1/6 = 1/3 and
     2/3 - 6/12 = 1/6

32. One way would be to use an area model for fraction addition.

33. This rearrangement is impossible.

Analyzing Student Thinking

34. Yes, Cristobal is correct—any common multiple of the denominators of the fractions will suffice as a common denominator; however, using the LCD often makes computations easier since the numbers involved will generally be smaller.

35. Ask Whitley to demonstrate her method. Chances are she is using a common denominator without being aware of it or she is using an invalid method.

36. You can change the fractions to improper fractions first, but it's not necessary. Another way is to write the fraction parts of the mixed numbers with a common denominator and then add the whole number parts and the fraction parts together:

$$3\frac{1}{4}+5\frac{2}{7}=3\frac{7}{28}+5\frac{8}{28}=8\frac{15}{28}.$$

37. Yes, Kalil applied the commutative and associative properties of fraction addition.

38. You might start by agreeing with the Marcos that in the real world the word *fraction* often means a small part. However, when we are writing numerical fractions, they can be quite large. For example, how big is 5/2? That's bigger than 1. 99/100 is a proper fraction, but it is much closer to 1 than to 1/2 or 0.

39. Show Brenda an example such as 1/2 and 1/3. In order to add or subtract these two fractions, we need to change them both to sixths so we can add the appropriate parts of the same-sized unit.

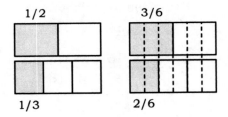

40. No, Marilyn needs to have the same unit (either both 8" or 12" inch pizzas). Also, saying 5/12 of a pizza does not refer to which size pizza, which is a problem. Another approach is to compute the area of the pizzas. If she ate 1/4 of the smaller pizza, she ate $1/4(8^2)$ = 16 square inches. If she ate 1/6 of the larger pizza, she ate $1/6(12^2)$ = 24 square inches. This is 16 + 24 = 40 square inches of pizza. The total amount of pizza is 64 + 144 = 208 square inches, and 40 is not 5/12(208).

Section 6.3

1. (a)

(b)

2. (a)

= 3/20

(b)

= 8/21

(c)

= 15/24

3. (a) $\dfrac{2}{3} \times \dfrac{4}{5} = \dfrac{8}{15}$

(b) $\dfrac{3}{4} \times \dfrac{7}{12} = \dfrac{21}{48}$

4. (a) 4/13   (b) 4/13

5. (a) 3/16, 5/8,   9/10, 7/5
    (b) 5/7,   10/9, 8/5,   16/3
    (c) They are reversed.

6. (a) Distributive
    (b) Associative
    (c) Commutative and Associative

7. (a) 4/15   (b) 3/5
    (c) 77/1,000,000
    (d) 8/9
    (e) 34/35   (f) 103/105
    (g) 26/35   (h) $41\dfrac{8}{35}$

8. (a) 3/4   (b) 3/10

9. (a) $31\dfrac{7}{20}$ (b) $104\dfrac{5}{24}$

    (c) $114\dfrac{32}{45}$

10. (a) Yes   (b) No

11. (a)

$2 \div \dfrac{2}{3} = 3$

(b)

$4 \div \dfrac{2}{5} = 10$

(c)

$1\dfrac{3}{4} \div \dfrac{1}{2} = 3\dfrac{1}{2}$

12. (a) $\dfrac{5}{6} \div \dfrac{1}{3} = 2\dfrac{1}{2}$ since $2\dfrac{1}{2}$ pieces of size 1/3 fit into 5/6.

1/3	1/3	1/3
5/6		

(b) $\dfrac{4}{3} \div \dfrac{2}{5} = 3\dfrac{1}{3}$ since $3\dfrac{1}{3}$ pieces of size 2/5 fit into 4/3.

2/5	2/5	2/5	2/5
4/3			

(c) $2\dfrac{1}{3} \div \dfrac{5}{6} = 2\dfrac{4}{5}$ since $2\dfrac{4}{5}$ pieces of size 5/6 fit into $2\dfrac{1}{3}$.

5/6	5/6	5/6
1	1	1/3

13. (a) $\dfrac{5}{8} \div \dfrac{3}{8} = \dfrac{5}{3}$

    (b) $\dfrac{12}{13} \div \dfrac{4}{13} = \dfrac{12}{4} = 3$

    (c) $\dfrac{13}{15} \div \dfrac{28}{30} = \dfrac{26}{30} \div \dfrac{28}{30} = \dfrac{26}{28} = \dfrac{13}{14}$

14. (a) $\dfrac{12}{15} \div \dfrac{4}{5} = \dfrac{3}{3} = 1$

    (b) $\dfrac{18}{24} \div \dfrac{9}{6} = \dfrac{2}{4} = \dfrac{1}{2}$

    (c) $\dfrac{30}{39} \div \dfrac{6}{13} = \dfrac{5}{3} = 1\dfrac{2}{3}$

    (d) $\dfrac{28}{33} \div \dfrac{14}{11} = \dfrac{2}{3}$

15. (a) $\dfrac{3}{4} \div \dfrac{6}{9} = \Box$ so

    $\dfrac{6}{9} \times \Box = \dfrac{3}{4}$

    $\dfrac{9}{6} \times \dfrac{6}{9} \times \Box = \dfrac{9}{6} \times \dfrac{3}{4}$

    $\Box = \dfrac{27}{24} = 1\dfrac{1}{8}$

    (b) $\dfrac{10}{7} \div \dfrac{8}{11} = \Box$ so

    $\dfrac{8}{11} \times \Box = \dfrac{10}{7}$

    $\dfrac{11}{8} \times \dfrac{8}{11} \times \Box = \dfrac{11}{8} \times \dfrac{10}{7}$

    $\Box = \dfrac{110}{56} = 1\dfrac{27}{28}$

    (c) $\dfrac{5}{6} \div \dfrac{2}{3} = \Box$ so

    $\dfrac{2}{3} \times \Box = \dfrac{5}{6}$

    $\dfrac{3}{2} \times \dfrac{2}{3} \times \Box = \dfrac{3}{2} \times \dfrac{5}{6}$

    $\Box = \dfrac{15}{12} = 1\dfrac{1}{4}$

16. (a) 4/3   (b) 2
    (c) 15/4   (d) 24/35

17. (a) 27/22   (b) 1700/9
    (c) 9/10

18. (a) 1/18   (b) 18

19. (a) $1\dfrac{77}{445}$ (b) $\dfrac{183}{328}$ (c) $1\dfrac{53}{156}$

20. (a) 1   (b) 88/217

21. (a) $52(1/2) = 26$

    (b) $\dfrac{5}{8} + \left(\dfrac{2}{5} + \dfrac{3}{5}\right) = \dfrac{5}{8} + 1 = 1\dfrac{5}{8}$

    (c) $\left(\dfrac{3}{7} \times \dfrac{7}{3}\right) \times \dfrac{1}{9} = 1 \times \dfrac{1}{9} = \dfrac{1}{9}$

    (d) $7 + 23\left(\dfrac{3}{7} + \dfrac{4}{7}\right) = 7 + 23(1) = 30$

22. (a) $20 \times 5\dfrac{1}{2} = 110$
    (b) $75 \div 25 = 3$
    (c) $56 \div 8 = 7$
    (d) $25 \times 4 = 6$

23. (a) 36   (b) 27

24. (a) $50 \times 246 = \dfrac{24,600}{2} = 12,300$

    (b) $84,602 \times 50$

    $= \dfrac{8,460,200}{2}$

    $= 4,230,100$

    (c) $75 \times 848 = \dfrac{3}{4} \times 84,800$

    $= 3 \times 21,200$

    $= 63,600$

    (d) $420 \times 75 = 42,000 \times \dfrac{3}{4}$

    $= 10,500 \times 3$

    $= 31,500$

25. (a) 15/14   (b) 5/2
    (c) 7/2   (d) 3/50

26. $\dfrac{2}{7} < \dfrac{2+3}{7+8} < \dfrac{3}{8}$ and

    $\dfrac{16}{56} < \dfrac{20}{56} < \dfrac{21}{56}$

27. 125.4 billion

28. 270 bottles

29. $4\frac{1}{2}$ yards, $2\frac{1}{4}$ yards

30. \$2100, \$3200

31. $1\frac{1}{3}$ pounds

32. \$0.50

33. 1/3

34. 3/4

35. Abigail: 4/12 = 1/3
    Harold: 24/20 = 6/5

36. (a) 96 eggs   (b) 12 days
    (c) 9 chickens

37. Top row: $2\frac{2}{3}$

    Second row: $2\frac{1}{2}$, $3\frac{1}{2}$, 1/4
    Third row: 1/2
    Bottom row: $15\frac{5}{9}$

38. $x + y = 18$ $xy = 40$
    $\frac{1}{x} + \frac{1}{y} = \frac{y+x}{xy}$
    $(x + y)^2 = x^2 + 2xy + y^2$
    (a) 18/40 = 9/20
    (b) $18^2 = x^2 + y^2 + 80$, thus
        $x^2 + y^2 = 244$.

39. (a) $6 + 1\frac{1}{5} = 6 \times 1\frac{1}{5}$

    $7 + 1\frac{1}{6} = 7 \times 1\frac{1}{6}$

    (b) Using a variable, check to see
        that $x + 1\frac{1}{x} = x \times 1\frac{1}{x}$.

40. (a) $\frac{a}{b} < \frac{c}{d}$ means for some

    nonzero $\frac{m}{n}$, $\frac{a}{b} + \frac{m}{n} = \frac{c}{d}$ and

$\frac{c}{d} < \frac{e}{f}$ means for some

nonzero $\frac{p}{q}$, $\frac{c}{d} + \frac{p}{q} = \frac{e}{f}$.

Replacing $\frac{c}{d}$ in the second

equation yields $(\frac{a}{b} + \frac{m}{n}) + \frac{p}{q}$

$= \frac{e}{f}$, or $\frac{a}{b} + (\frac{m}{n} + \frac{p}{q}) = \frac{e}{f}$,

where $\frac{m}{n} + \frac{p}{q}$ is a nonzero

fraction, so $\frac{a}{b} < \frac{e}{f}$ by the
alternative definition.

(b) $\frac{a}{b} < \frac{c}{d}$ means for some

nonzero $\frac{m}{n}$, $\frac{a}{b} + \frac{m}{n} = \frac{c}{d}$, so

$\frac{c}{d} + \frac{e}{f} = (\frac{a}{b} + \frac{m}{n}) + \frac{e}{f} =$

$(\frac{a}{b} + \frac{e}{f}) + \frac{m}{n}$. Thus

$\frac{a}{b} + \frac{e}{f} < \frac{c}{d} + \frac{e}{f}$, by the
alternative definition.

(c) As in parts (a) and (b), show

that $\frac{a}{b}\frac{e}{f} + \frac{m}{n}\frac{e}{f} = \frac{c}{d}\frac{e}{f}$, thus

$\frac{a}{b}\frac{e}{f} < \frac{c}{d}\frac{e}{f}$.

41. 60

42. (a) 2 3/4 + 5 7/8 = 2 + 3/4 + 5 +
    7/8 = 2 + 7/8 + 5 + 3/4 = 2
    7/8 + 5 3/4
    (b) (2 + 3/4) × (5 + 7/8) ≠
    (2 + 7/8) × (5 + 3/4)

Analyzing Student Thinking

43. Devonnie is not correct. To
    multiply fractions, you only need
    to multiply the numerators and
    multiply the denominators. You
    could find a common denominator
    when multiplying fractions, but
    this just makes unnecessary work.

44. Yes, Cameron simplified each fraction and then multiplied the fractions. Another way to do this problem is: multiply the fractions before simplifying, then simplify the product.

45.

= 15/28

46.

Start by drawing eight rectangles and divide each into four equal parts. Then shade three out of every four of the smaller rectangles. Count the number of groups of three smaller rectangles (each one represents 3/4). There are <u>ten</u> groups of size 3/4 in the 8 original rectangles, and another <u>two of the three parts</u> needed to make another group of size 3/4;

that is $8 \div \frac{3}{4} = 10\frac{2}{3}$.

47. Yes, this works except for the case when either of the divisors is zero.

48. Katrina, for $6 \div \frac{1}{2}$ the answer is 12 since there are 12 one-halves in 6 (two halves for each of the 6 units).

49. There is no one estimation method that is always preferred—the method you choose will depend, for instance, on how close to the actual answer you need your estimate to be.

Chapter 7

Section 7.1

1. (a) 70.05003   (b) 3000.89
   (c) 0.025001

2. (a) (i) $5(\frac{1}{10}) + 2(\frac{1}{100}) + 5(\frac{1}{1000})$

        (ii) $\frac{525}{1000}$

   (b) (i) $3 \times 10 + 4 + \frac{7}{1000}$

        (ii) $\frac{34007}{1000}$

   (c) (i) $5 + \frac{102}{100000}$

        (ii) $\frac{50102}{10000}$

3. (a) 0.000746
   (b) 746,000.000746
   (c) 746,000,000.746

4. (a) Seventy-eight billionths.
   (b) Seven thousand five hundred eighty-nine and twelve thousand three hundred forty-five hundred thousandths.
   (c) One hundred eighty-seven thousand two hundred thirteen and two thousand three hundred thousandths
   (d) Two and thirty-one hundred thousandths

5. Either it is read "point zero five nine" or "fifty-nine thousandths."

6. (a) and (c)

7. (a) R   (b) T, 4 places
   (c) T, 9 places   (d) T, 23 places
   Explanation: Highest power of 2 and/or 5.

8. (a) 3.078, 3.08, 3.087, 3.80
   (b) 8.0019929, 8.010019, 8.01002
   (c) 0.5, 0.5005, 0.505, 0.55

9. (a) 5/7, 10/13, 4/5
   (b) 4/11, 2/5, 3/7

(c) 7/13, 5/9, 11/18
(d) 17/29, 3/5, 11/18

10. (a) $\frac{1}{2} < \frac{5}{8} < \frac{17}{23}$

    (b) $\frac{2}{3} < \frac{3}{4} < \frac{13}{16}$

    (c) $\frac{8}{5} < \frac{50}{31} < \frac{26}{15}$

11. No

12. (a) Use the distributive property:
    7(3.4 + 6.6) = 7(10) = 70
    (b) Use equal additions method:
    (26.53 + 0.05) − (8.95 + 0.05) = 26.58 − 9 = 17.58
    (c) Convert to fractions:

    $0.491 + 10^2 = \frac{491}{1000} + 100$

    $= \frac{491}{1000} \times \frac{1}{100} = \frac{491}{100000} = 0.00491$

    (d) Use compensation:
    (5.89 + 0.11) + (6.27 − 0.11) = 6 + 6.16 = 12.16
    (e) Use the associative property:
    5.7 + (4.8 + 3.2) = 5.7 + 8 = 13.7
    (f) Move the decimal point three places to the right: 67,320
    (g) Use the commutative, associative, and identity properties:
    0.5 × (2 × 639) = (0.5 × 2) × 639
    $= 1 \times 639 = 639$
    (h) Use the associative and commutative properties:
    (6 × 12) × (0.5 × 12) = 72 + 6 = 78

13. (a) 230 × 1/10 = 23
    (b) 36 × 1/4 = 9
    (c) 82 × 1/2 = 41
    (d) 125 × 4/5 = 100
    (e) 175 × 1/5 = 35
    (f) 3/5 × 35 = 21

14. (a) 1264.16
    (b) 0.00000078752
    (c) 8.25×10^{27}
    (d) 8.25×10^{13}

15. (a) 30 × 3 = 90 to 40 × 4 = 160,
          35 × 4 = 140
     (b) 39
     (c) 60, 60 to 140
     (d) 10

16. (a) 125 ÷ 5 = 25
     (b) 90 × 8 = 720
     (c) 400 ÷ 5/4 = 320
     (d) 350 × 2/5 = 140
     (e) 1/4 × 48 = 1200
     (f) 3600 ÷ 3/5 = 3600 × 5/3 =
          6000

17. (a) 321.09   (b) 12.162
     (c) 4.0091   (d) 2.0
     (e) 2.00

18. (a) Change 1.4 to 0.6.
     (b) Magic

19. D = 5, O = 2, N = 6, A = 4, L = 8, G
     = 1, E = 9, R = 7, B = 3, T = 0

Analyzing Student Thinking

20. Joseph did not read the number
     correctly; the word "and" is used
     only for the decimal point.

21. Brigham, this method for
     determining whether or not a
     decimal will repeat works only if
     the fraction under consideration
     has been written in simplest form
     first. 42/150 can be simplified to
     7/25. The factors of the
     denominator, 25, are limited to 2's
     and 5's (in this case only 5's), so it
     is a terminating decimal, 0.28.

22. Mary Lou, we can see that 12/17
     is indeed a fraction since it is
     written in the form a/b, where a
     and b are whole numbers. Also,
     since the denominator has factors
     other than 2 and 5, it must have a
     repeating decimal representation—
     the repetend is longer than your
     calculator is capable of displaying.
     Doing the division by hand will
     give you the entire repetend but
     you might have to go out at least
     17 decimal places.

23. Camille, . 0.45 means 45/100 and
     0.5 = 0.50 means 50/100. Thus,
     6.45 < 6.50 since 45 < 50.

24. Caroline's method is incorrect;
     19.67472 is less than halfway
     between 19.67 and 19.68, so the
     nearest hundredth is 19.67.

25. It appears that Amir thinks the
     "round a 5 up" rule has a
     corresponding "round a 4 down"
     rule; an explanation similar to the
     one given to Caroline above could
     help him see why he is incorrect.

26. Merilee, since the denominator of
     2/3 has factors other than 2 and
     5, it must have a repeating
     decimal. If you divide 2 by 3 you
     get 0.6666..., but your calculator
     rounded the last 6 in the display
     to a 7 since the next digit is
     greater than 5 (it's a 6).

27. Alondra, recall that there are
     infinitely many fractions between
     any two fractions, and since
     decimals are fractions, there must
     be infinitely many decimals
     between 0.19 and 0.20; some
     examples are 0.191, 0.192, and
     0.1901.

Section 7.2

1. (a) 101.782   (b) 28.135
    (c) 0.2034   (d) 21.901

2. (a) 45.92   (b) 0.1248
    (c) 148   (d) 31.2

3. (a) 23,278.9504   (b) 390.009

4. (b) and (c)

5. (a) 8.6×10^2
    (b) 4.52×10^3
    (c) 2.6×10^7
    (d) 3.15×10^5
    (e) 1.084×10^9
    (f) 5.4×10^{13}

6. (a) 3.85×10^9 sec
    (b) 4.73×10^9 sec
    (c) 154,500,000,000 sec
        One hundred fifty-four billion
        five hundred million seconds

7. (a) 8.05×10^6
    (b) 6.278×10^{10}

8. (a) 5.9×10^{23} (b) 9.431×10^4
    (c) 8.3×10^4

9. (a) 3.468×10^{40} (b) 9.5×10^{14}
    (c) 4.6656×10^{55}

10. 19.522 kilometers

11. (a) 1.2×10^{14} kilograms
    (b) 2.48×10^{18} dollars
    (c) About 290,000 times.
    (d) About \$29,000 per person.
        Note: In 2001, we owed
        \$21,500 each – a 35%
        increase!

12. (a) $0.35\overline{0}$ (b) $0.1\overline{4}$
    (c) $0.4531\overline{596}$

13. (a) 0.317431743174
    (b) 0.317400000000
    (c) 0.115912311591

14. (a) 5/9
    (b) 78/99 = 26/33
    (c) 123/999 = 41/333
    (d) 123/990 = 41/330
    (e) 177/9900 = 59/3300
    (f) 123,333/999,000 =
        41,111/333,000

15. Not equal,
    $0.2\overline{525} = 0.25252525$ is smaller
    than $0.2525 = 0.2525525525$
    from the 100-thousandths place.

16. x, z, y

17. (a) 24.3, 27.5
    (b) 92.1984, 129.07776
    (c) 0.000555, 0.0005555
    (d) 9.6, 14.5

18. (e) $0.8\overline{3}$, $0.\overline{857142}$

18. (a) (i) 2 steps   (ii) 3 steps
        (iii) 1 step   (iv) 8 steps
    (b) Many answers are possible.
        One answer is 4.87.

19. (a) (i) 1/9   (ii) 1/99
        (iii) 1/999
        (iv) 1/9999
    (b) 1/999,999,999
    (c) $0.\overline{01}$

20. 1. Since $1/3 = 0.\overline{3}$, three times
    both sides of this equations yields
    $1 = 0.\overline{9}$.

21. (a) $a_{n+1} = a_n + 9/10^{n+1}$ and
        $1 = a_{n+1} + 1/10^{n+1}$
    (b) Since $1 = a_{100} + 1/10^{100}$,
        $1 - a_{100} = 1/10^{100}$.
        Therefore, $1 - a_n < 1/10^{100}$
        whenever $n > 100$.
    (c) Use idea in part (b).
    (d) Essentially $0.\overline{9}$ is greater than
        any number less than 1 and
        $0.\overline{9}$ does not exceed 1, hence
        $0.\overline{9} = 1$.

22. (a) $0.\overline{142857}$, $0.\overline{285714}$,
        etc. The repetends have 6
        digits and they share the same
        digits.
    (b) The repetends for 1/13, 3/13,
        4/13, 9/13, 10/13, 12/13
        use same digits and the rest
        use same digits. All have
        repetends with 6 digits.

23. $\dfrac{y}{10^n} + \dfrac{x}{99999} \cdot \dfrac{1}{10^n} = \dfrac{99999y + x}{(99999)(10^n)}$,
    where $0 \le y < 10^n$ and
    $1 \le x \le 99,998$

24. $999 \div 22 = 45$ with 9 remaining,
    so the 999th digit is 7.

25. (a) 1   (b) 7

26. After taking 1/2 of 16 1/2, the final correct step is to find 1/2 of 12, not 1/2 of 12 1/2.

27. (a) 28.6650 g   (b) 28.6749 g

28. (a) 257.6 mi   (b) 7.8 in.

29. $2528.24

30. $43.71

31. 55 mph

32. $3,750

33. $31.63

Analyzing Student Thinking

34. Bhumi simply lined up the numbers as if they were whole numbers, like this:

$$\begin{array}{r} 6.45 \\ \underline{2.3} \\ 6.68 \end{array}$$

To help her understand her misconception, you could have Bhumi write the numbers as fractions with denominator 100:

$$\frac{645}{100} + \frac{230}{100} = \frac{875}{100} = 8.75 .$$

35. Kaisha put the decimal point in the wrong place; $72 \times 35 = 2520$ and, since there are a total of two decimal places in the original problem (7.2×3.5), the final answer will have two also. Thus, 25.20 is the correct answer. Likely, Kaisha did not count the 0 when counting over two decimal places.

36. Yes, it appears Tyler used compensation to compute the product mentally (he divided and then multiplied by 0.01): 50×4.68 $= (50 \div 100) \times (4.68 \times 100)$ $= 0.5 \times 468 = 234$.

37. The student is incorrect since 0.33 is not equal to 1/3. The correct answer is $0.33 \times 24 = 7.92$, so the student's answer of 8 was a good estimate of the actual answer.

38. Show Henry that he needs to multiply by 1000 (since the repetend is 3 digits long) in order to get the numbers to line up for subtraction. If he does that, he will get $999n = 7445$, or $n = \dfrac{7445}{999}$.

39. Lauren could be correct since the ones could repeat indefinitely. Thus, one needs to ask Lauren what she was thinking. It appears that the pattern implied by the "..." is that, after each occurrence of a 2, the number of 1's increases by one and is then followed by a 2. If this is the case, the decimal never repeats.

40. Ask the student to tell you how she knows her claim is true. She might offer an argument such as the following: first, we know that every repeating decimal has a fraction representation. We also know the sum of two fractions is a fraction (closure property of fraction addition.) Thus, the sum of two repeating decimals must be a repeating decimal. Of course this is wrong, as can be seen in the sum of the two repeating decimals whose fraction forms are 1/3 and 2/3, since 1/3+2/3=1, a nonrepeating decimal.

41. Show Barry that he can multiply 1,275 by 3,987 on his calculator and then affix $10 + 6 = 16$ zeros at the end of the answer he gets. Additionally, show Barry how to enter the product on a scientific calculator, using scientific notation.

Section 7.3

1. (a) 5:6 (b) $\dfrac{5}{11}$

   (c) Cannot be determined
   (d) 15 boys

2. Each is an ordered pair. For example, (a) measures population density.

3. (a) 1/7 (b) 2/7 (c) 25/17

4. (a) No (b) No

5. (a) $\dfrac{32}{29}$ (b) $\dfrac{37}{86}$

   (c) Mandarin : Hindi/Urdu

   (d) $\dfrac{167}{500}$ (e) $\dfrac{507}{1000}$

6. (a) 2 1/2 (b) 1
   (c) 320 (d) 5.1

7. (a) 56 (b) 116.67

   (c) $\dfrac{2}{3}$ (d) 96

   (e) $\dfrac{30}{17}$ or ≈1.76 (f) $\dfrac{24}{11}$ or ≈ 2.18

8. $\dfrac{35 \text{ mi}}{87.5 \text{ mi}} = \dfrac{2 \text{ hrs}}{5 \text{ hrs}}$,

   $\dfrac{2 \text{ hrs}}{35 \text{ mi}} = \dfrac{5 \text{ hrs}}{87.5 \text{ mi}}$,

   $\dfrac{87.5 \text{mi}}{35 \text{mi}} = \dfrac{5 \text{ hrs}}{2 \text{ hrs}}$

9. (a) 26:6 = 52:12 = 104:24
   (b) 84:6 = 42:3 = 210:15
   (c) 40:12 = 10:3 = 30:9
   (d) 27.50:1.5 = 55:3 = 110:6
   (e) 750:12 = 250:4 = 1000:16

10. 88 kph

11. (a) 60 oz for 29 cents
    (b) $45 for 10 yards
    (c) 18 oz for 40 cents

12. Model *XL*

13. About 148 minutes

14. About 87 gallons.

15. About $2085

16. Just over 7 weeks.

17. (a) 105 miles, 350 miles, 35n miles
    (b) About 28 3/5 inches

18. 8572 seeds

19. About 2.3 miles

20. (a) 5 1/2 cups
    (b) 5 gallons
    (c) 6 liters
    (d) $2.71/lb

21. About 206.1 mph

22. (a) 134 (b) 70

23. (a) 6.48 runs
    (b) About 29 runs

24. (a) 11/32 inch
    (b) 29,500 miles

25. (a) A and C
    (b) 20 : 21
    (c) 12 : 11
    (d) No, adding using equivalent ratios does not give same result.

26. 6 inches

27. (a) F = 170 2/3, D = 576, A = 864, E = 1296, B = 1944
    (b) D = 288, E = 324, F = 341 1/3, G = 384, A = 432, B = 486
    (c) 1.125 = 9/8
    (d) 1.333 = 4/3

28. Ferne - 39
    Donna - 21
    Susan - 12

29. 54 feet

30. 31 eggs

31. No. Consider the following: Joleen bats 1 for 10 and Maureen bats 0 for 1. Then Joleen bats 1 for 1 and Maureen bats 1 for 2. At the end of the season, Joleen's

average is 1/11 and Maureen's is
1/3.

32.   4, 7, 28, $3n - 2$

33.   9:4

Analyzing Student Thinking

34.   Carlos, consider the following
      diagram that represents 3 parts oil
      (shaded) to 4 parts vinegar. Oil
      makes up 3/7 of the bottle of
      salad dressing, not 75%.

35.   Scott, a ratio of 5:4 means there
      will be 5 boys for every 4 girls in
      your class. So, there might be 5
      boys and 4 girls, but there also
      could be 10 boys and 8 girls, or 15
      boys and 12 girls.

36.   Yes, Ashlee is correct, provided
      $c \neq 0$. We can use cross-
      multiplication to show this. If
      $\frac{a}{b} = \frac{c}{d}$, then $ad = bc$. And, if $ad =$
      bc, then $\frac{a}{c} = \frac{b}{d}$.

37.   No; if 0.25 cm. = 12 miles, then
      100 cm. = 4800 miles, not 48
      miles.

38.   Micala does not understand that,
      to have the same flavor, she needs
      to keep the same ratio of OJ to
      water. Using 2 cans of OJ would
      require 6 cans of water, since 1:3
      = 2:6.

39.   Sabrina is incorrect; if 60% of the
      class is girls, then 40% is boys
      and that is a ratio of 6:4 or 3:2.

40.   The problem is mismatched units.
      The proportion needs to be
      $\frac{feet}{feet} = \frac{feet}{feet}$ or $\frac{inches}{inches} = \frac{feet}{feet}$ or
      $\frac{feet}{inches} = \frac{feet}{inches}$. This latter

proportion yields $\frac{4}{15} = \frac{tree}{144}$, or the
height of the tree is 38.4 feet.

Section 7.4

1.   (a) 44%, .44, 11/25
     (b) 97%, .97, 97/100
     (c) 124%, 1.24, $1\frac{6}{25}$

2. $\frac{6666}{10000}$, 0.6666; $\frac{3}{1000}$, 0.3%;
     0.025, 2.5%; $\frac{1}{20}$, 5%; $\frac{160}{100}$, 0.016;
     0.01, 1%; $\frac{1}{100000}$, 0.001%;
     $\frac{17}{200000}$, 0.000085

3.   (a) 400, 350, 25%, 250
     (b) $1.00, $15.00, $40.00
     (c) 0.06, 0.36, 0.03, 0.45

4.   (a) 98   (b) 61   (c) 50%
     (d) 1462   (e) 125%   (f) 142
     (g) 500   (h) 0.1%   (i) 350

5.   (a) 1.6   (b) 10   (c) 30
     (d) 150   (e) 6   (f) 44
     (g) 7.5   (h) 360

6.   (a) 90
     (b) 11
     (c) 3/4 × 320 = 240
     (d) 1/3 × 210 = 70
     (e) 2/5 × 250 = 100
     (f) 1/8 × 400 = 50
     (g) 2/3 × 660 = 440
     (h) 1/5 × 120 = 24

7.   (a) 1/5 × 35 = 7
     (b) 2/5 × 60 = 24
     (c) 1/4 × 60 = 15
     (d) 200% × 85 = 170
     (e) 15% × 42 = 6.3
     (f) 10% × 430 = 43
     (g) 1/2 × 26 = 13
     (h) 2/5 × 150 = 60

8.   (a) $1.65   (b) $2.25
     (c) $5.25   (d) $3.60

9. (a) What percent of 95 is 67?
   (b) 18.4 is 112% of what number?
   (c) What is $16\frac{2}{3}\%$ of $3\frac{1}{2}$?
   (d) 2.8 is what percent of 0.46?
   (e) 0.05% of what number is 4200?
   NOTE: Other answers are possible.

10. (a) 370.8   (b) 41.0%
    (c) 216.7%   (d) 350
    (e) 2400   (f) 75.6%

11. (a) 4400   (b) 22%
    (c) 1250   (d) 125
    (e) 650%

12. (a) 30.6   (b) 90.72
    (c) 190   (d) 62.5
    (e) $101.70   (f) $105.60

13. (a) $194.05   (b) $111.48
    (c) $1011.88   (d) $312.88

14. 68.75%
    Enter 80 as the whole and 55 as the part.

15. $12.91
    Guess and Test. By entering a value for the Whole and 70 for the Percent, we can add the Part and the Whole searching for a sum of $21.95. The best guess on the eManipulative is $12.90.

16. 66%

17. $11\frac{2}{3}\%$

18. $349.50

19. Rent, Utilities $2320, Tuition $2100, Food $1520, Other $660, Transportation $640, Clothes, Health $400, Books, Supplies $360

20. 36.1%

21. 150 games

22. (a) About 71%
    (b) About 99.6%

23. $1600

24. $7.80 to $12.00

25. (a) 12.1%   (b) 18.4%
    (c) No, gas consumption increased at a higher rate as the number of less efficient SUV's on the road increased.

26. $795

27. Both

28. (a) (i) $237.22   (ii) $799.56
        (iii) $187.74
    (b) $4505

29. 750%

30. 4% less

31. 49%

32. (a) $4515   (b) $174,418.61
    (c) $78,070.18
    (d) 202,272.73 pounds

33. At least 12 passes

34. They are equal.

35. 1 pencil, 9 erasers, 90 paper clips

36. Use Guess and Test; Tom = 7 and Carol = 13

37. 3. Cut open all of the links of one chain and use them to link the remaining chains together.

38. 1111

39. 20. Yes. $n \rightarrow n + 20 \rightarrow 10(n+20) \rightarrow 2(n + 20) \rightarrow n + 20 \rightarrow 20$

40. $133,156.49

41. (a) Investment (2) - at 6.1% compounded annually.
    (b) He must invest $3553.28 at the rate in (a).

42. (a) Net loss $5.50
    (b) Net loss $2.00
    (c) Strategy b

43. 15%

44. 45

Analyzing Student Thinking

45. That's incorrect, Martina. Notice that $\frac{60}{40}(\$27.88)=\$41.82$. Since you can't save more than the original price of the shirt, you have made an error.

46. No; 7/50 and 13/25 are easy, too, since 50 and 25 are divisors of 100:

    $7/50 = (7 \cdot 2)/(50 \cdot 2) = 14/100 = 14\%$
    $13/25 = (13 \cdot 4)/(25 \cdot 4) = 52/100 = 52\%$

47. Yes, because Bertrand set up a proportion of the form:

    $$\frac{percent}{100} = \frac{part}{whole}.$$

48. No; the student simply computed the amount of savings, a dollar amount, $199 – 159.20 = $39.80. To determine the percent saved, he could solve the following proportion:
    $$\frac{percent}{100} = \frac{part}{whole}$$
    $$\frac{x}{100} = \frac{39.80}{199}$$

49. No. The amount of money at the end of the first year is $1000 × 1.03 (that's 100% + 3% of $1000). Since the money is invested for 10 years, the total amount of money in the account with compound interest will be $1000 × $(1.03)^{10} =$ $1343.92.

50. No, since the selling price of the car after a 20% mark-up would be:

$17,888 × 1.20 = $21,465.60, but marking this down 20% would give a selling price of: $21465.60 ×0 .80 = $17,172.48, which is less than the dealer paid for the car.

51. Jerry took 35% of the sale price, rather than of the original price. Since you don't know the original price, you need to remember that if you saved 35% off the original price, you paid 65% of the original price. You can find the original price by dividing the sale price by 0.65. The original price was $210.77.

Chapter 8

Section 8.1

1. 556, -252 and -2.0 are the integers; 3/4, 556 and 1.1 are positive and -252 and -2.0 are negative.

2. (a) 1 (b) - 4 (c) 5 (d) - 5

3. (a) RRR

   (b) BBBBBB

4. (a) -56   (b) b
   (c) 1235   (d) $b - a$

5. (a) {-1, -2, -3, -4,...}
   (b) {1, 2, 3, 4,...}   (c) W

6. (a) BBBBRRRRRRR = -3

   (b) RRR RRRRR = -8

7. (a) 14 + (-6) = (8 + 6) + (-6) =
       8 + [6 + (-6)] = 8 + 0 = 8
   (b) 21 + (-41) = 21 + [(-21) + (-20)]
       = [21 + (-21)] + (-20) = 0 + -20
       = -20

8. 17. Top: 42; Second: 16 26;
   Middle: -6 22 4

9. (a) and (d) are true.

10. (a) Associative Property for Integer Addition
    (b) Additive Identity

11. (a) 3117   (b) 33

12. (a) -7   (b) -13

(c) 9   (d) -3

13. (a) Start with RRR and add 3 zero pairs to obtain BBBRRR RRR. Take away 6 reds to get BBBRRRRRR = 3
    (b) Start with 0 and add 4 zero pairs to obtain BBBBRRRR. Take away 4 red to get BBBBRRRR = 4

14. (a) -14   (b) 52
    (c) 14   (d) 6

15. (a) -231   (b) -56
    (c) 986   (d) -555

16. (a) opposite of negative five
    (b) Ten minus the opposite of negative two
    (c) opposite of p

17. (a) 3   (b) 7   (c) $-x$
    (d) $-x$ (e) x (f) x

18. (a) Gained 9 yards
    (b) Loss of 2 points
    (c) Gained $200

19. (b)

20. Philadelphia: 28   Cheyenne: 44
    Bismarck: 11

21. The result $-a$ represents "the opposite of a". Thus, when a is negative, $-a$ is positive.

22. 98 -28

23. (a) -8, 3   (b) -7, 4
    (c) 0, 8

24. Top: 9; Third 25 -15 14;
    Bottom: 33 -8 -7 21

25. (a) (i) 1 2 3 4 ...
        (ii) 1 2 3 4 . . .
             -1 -2 -3 -4. . .
              0 1 2 3 . . .
        (iii) . . . 6 4 2 0 1 3 5 . . .
              . . .-3 -2 -1 0 1 2 3 . . .

(b) These sets have same number of elements

26.

![square dissection puzzle with numbered regions: 50, 35, 27, 29, 25, 24, 33, 37, 42, and small circled numbers 8, 15, 17, 11, 19, 2, 6, 9, 7, 18, 16, 4]

27. Most people recognize that the word "unique" means "one of a kind." But in the phrase "*there is a unique integer*" there is also a guarantee that every integer has an additive inverse. So the phrase means that every integer has "at least one and at most one" additive inverse.

Analyzing Student Thinking

28. Yes, Jarell, theoretically we could continue indefinitely to create new representations for any integer. For instance, take a pair of one red and one black chip from a (theoretically) infinite pile of chips and add these to any collection of chips representing the integer to obtain a new representation of the integer.

29. No, Brandi is incorrect; integer addition has one property that whole-number addition does not: the Additive Inverse Property.

30. If the student subtracts the numbers as they stand, the problem will become 4 - (-6) which equals 10. This is incorrect. What was intended (but not said) was that one should find the difference between the two numbers, neglecting the minus

sign. Thus, 6 - 4 = 2, so the answer is -2.

31. Chandler, your answer is correct; now please explain why.

32. No; for example, 1 + (-2) = -1, a negative number.

33. The symbol $-n$ means "the opposite of n." So, the sign of $-n$ depends on the sign of n. If n is positive, say 5, its opposite is $-n = -(5) = -5$, a negative number. But, if n is negative, say -5, then its opposite is $-n = -(-5) = 5$, a positive number. And, if $n = 0$, then $-n = -(0) = 0$, which is neither a positive nor a negative number.

34. Yes. Each pair of one red and one black chip represents a zero and, since the integer is negative, there must be some red chips that are not paired with a black chip.

Section 8.2

1. (a)

(b)

(c)
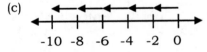

2. (a) -5 × (-1) = 5   -5 × (-2) = 10
       5 × (-3) = 15
   (b) -8 × (-1) = 8   -8 × (-2) = 16
       -8 × (-3) = 24
       Negative times negative equals positive

3. (a) -30   (b) 420
   (c) -230   (d) 0

4. (a) ƁƁƁƁ ƁƁƁƁ ƁƁƁƁ
       RRRR RRRR RRRR = -12

(b) RRRR RRRR = -8

(c) BBR̶R̶ = 2

5. Distributivity, additive inverse, multiplication by 0

6. (a) -6x - 12   (b) -5x + 55
    (c) -3x + 3y   (d) xa - xb
    (e) -xa + xb (f) x^2 - x - 6

7. (a) -1872   (b) 8134
    (c) 224,409   (d) -243,984

8. (a) -34   (b) 907

9. (a) 0   (b) 4   (c) 36

10. (a) -31   (b) 123
    (c) -58   (d) -1

11. No

12. (a) Negative   (b) Positive
    (c) Negative   (d) Positive
    (e) Positive   (f) Negative
    (g) Positive   (h) Negative

13. Always positive: c, d, e
    Always negative: f

14. (a) $\dfrac{1}{16}$ (b) $\dfrac{1}{32}$ (c) $\dfrac{1}{343}$

15. (a) $\dfrac{1}{729}$ (b) $\dfrac{1}{729}$ (c) 15,625
    (d) Yes

16. (a) $\dfrac{1}{512}$ (b) $\dfrac{1}{512}$ (c) $\dfrac{1}{50625}$
    (d) Yes

17. (a) 5^5 (b) 3^{16}
    (c) 4^5 or 2^{10} (d) $\dfrac{1}{6^4}$

18. (a) 0.000009
    (b) 0.000000000000126

19. (a) 6.91 × 10^{-7}
    (b) 3.048 × 10^{-13}
    (c) 8.071 × 10^{-20}

20. (a) 2.6936 × 10^{-20}
    (b) 4.4 × 10^{23}
    (c) 3.93 × 10^{-20}
    (d) 5.4 × 10^{-14}
    (e) 2.046 × 10^{-9}
    (f) 1.6 × 10^{-9}

21. (a) -7 + 4 = -3   (b) -6 + 11 = 5
    (c) -23 + 6 = -17

22. (a) <   (b) >   (c) >
    (d) >   (e) >   (f) >
    (g) =   (h) <

23. (a) <   (b) <

24. Second row: 8, 18
    Third row: -2
    Bottom row: 2, -2, -9
    Also,
    Second row: -8, -18
    Third row: 2
    Bottom row: -2, 2, -9

25. (a) -3, -2, and -1   (b)   No
    (c) -3

26. (a) No, no, yes (-1), no
    (b) Yes (0), no, no, yes (1)

27. (a) pq = -$|p||q|$
    (b) pq = $|p||q|$

28. (a) p/q = -$|p|/|q|$
    (b) p/q = $|p|/|q|$

29. No; -3 < -2, but $(-3)^2 > (-2)^2$.

30. Yes; $x < y$ means $y = x + p$ for some $p > 0$, $z - y = z - (x + p) = z - x - p$. Therefore, $z - y + p = z - x$ which means $z - y < z - x$.

31. 8.38 × 10^{-26} grams

32. 6.508 × 10^{-7} meter

33. (a) 1.1 × 10^{-22} kilograms
    (b) Approximately 1.62 × 10^{-27} kilograms.

34. (a) 2.31 × 10^6 corpuscles

(b) About 1.08×10^7 seconds or 125 days.

35. True. From problem 23 in part A, squares must be a multiple of 3 or one more than a multiple of 3. If neither x nor y is a multiple of 3, then $x^2 + y^2 = (3m + 1) + (3n + 1) = 3(m + n) + 2 = z^2$. But z^2 must be of the form $3r$ or $3r + 1$. Thus, one of x or y must be a multiple of 3.

36. 1806

37. If $(a - b)c = 0$, then $a - b = 0$ or $c = 0$. Because c was assumed to be nonzero, $a - b = 0$, or $a = b$.

Analyzing Student Thinking

38. Olga, the number $-xyz$ is not necessarily negative; this number has the opposite sign of the number xyz.

39. In general, this equation is false. If we multiply $(a + b)(a + b)$ using the distributive property, we get the answer $a^2 + 2ab + b^2$. So the problem becomes "When does $a^2 + b^2 = a^2 + 2ab + b^2$?" That reduces to "When does $2ab = 0$?" The Zero Divisors Property tells us that this is true when $a = 0$ or $b = 0$. So the conclusion is that the equation is rarely, but sometimes, true.

40. No; $-a \div -b = a/b$, and the sign of a/b can be positive, negative, or neither, depending on the signs of a and b.

41. Yes; $-a \div -b = \dfrac{-a}{-b} = \dfrac{(-1)a}{(-1)b} = \dfrac{a}{b}$.

42. No; multiplying by 10^{-7} would move the decimal point in 3.47 seven places to the left. Thus, there should only be six zeros between the decimal point and the

3 since .000000347 has the decimal point seven places to the left of 3.47.

43. Ask Tonya if she knows how to check her answer. Once she checks and sees that she is incorrect, remind her that the rule she is trying to apply to this problem states that "when you multiply or divide both sides of an inequality by a negative, reverse the inequality." But she was dividing both sides by 7, a positive, so the inequality remains unchanged.

44. Joe's calculator squared 7, then gave the opposite of that number, -49—this is the order of operations indicated by -7^2. Misha's calculator squared the opposite of 7, or $(-7)^2$.

Chapter 9

Section 9.1

1. (a) 7 and -3 are integers

    (b) $7\frac{1}{8} = \frac{57}{8}$ and 57 and 8 are

    integers.

    (c) $-3 = \frac{-3}{1}$; -3 and 1 are integers.

    (d) $0 = \frac{0}{1}$; 0 and 1 are integers

2. (a) I and Q (b) Q

3. -5/-6, - (-5/6), - (5/-6)

4. (a) True   (b) False

5. (a) -2/3   (b) 5/7
    (c) -4/9   (d) -8/9

6. (a) -1/2   (b) -41/36
    (c) -2/3   (d) 1/24

7. (a) 17/23   (b) 6/29

8. (a) 2/7   (b) 5/16

    (c) -4   (d) $-3\frac{1}{2}$

9. (a) -164/837   (b) -243/245

10. (a) F, I, N, Q (b) I and Q

11. (a) Identity property of rational
          number addition
     (b) Additive inverse property of
          rational number addition

12. (a) 2/3   (b) -33/28
     (c) 29/36   (d) -1

13. (a) -19/528   (b) 79/60

14. (a) None   (b) I and Q

15. (a) -2/7   (b) -1
     (c) 3/2   (d) -1/3

16. (a) 8/5   (b) 0
     (c) 5/6   (d) -23/27

17. (a) 1139/826   (b) 25/72

18. (a) F and Q (b) F, I, N, Q

19. (a) Associative property of rational
          number multiplication
     (b) Commutative property of
          rational number addition

20. (a) (i) $(-43)^2(-36)^3 =$
               $(1849)(-46,656) =$
               $-86,266,944$
          (ii) $(43)^2(36)^3 =$
               $(1849)(46,656) =$
               $86,266,944$. The final
               answer is negative since
               (neg.)$^{\text{even power}}$ (neg.)$^{\text{odd power}}$ =
               (pos.)(neg.) = neg.

     (b) (i) $\left(-\dfrac{18}{25}\right)\left(\dfrac{-45}{-91}\right)\left(\dfrac{28}{-81}\right) =$

               $\left(-\dfrac{-810}{-2275}\right)\left(\dfrac{28}{-81}\right) =$

               $\left(-\dfrac{-22680}{184275}\right) = \left(\dfrac{22680}{184275}\right)$

          (ii) $\left(\dfrac{18}{25}\right)\left(\dfrac{45}{91}\right)\left(\dfrac{28}{81}\right) =$

               $\left(\dfrac{810}{2275}\right)\left(\dfrac{28}{81}\right) = \left(\dfrac{22680}{184275}\right).$

               The final answer is positive
               since (neg.)(pos.)(neg.) =
               (neg.)(neg.) = pos.

21. (a) -4   (b) -3/5
     (c) 8/9   (d) 2/3

22. (a) -1207/627   (b) 9/5

23. (a) (i) $\dfrac{(-1111)(-23)(49)}{-77} =$

               $\dfrac{(25553)(49)}{-77} =$

               $\dfrac{1252097}{-77} = -16261$

          (ii) $\dfrac{(1111)(23)(49)}{77} =$

               $\dfrac{(25553)(49)}{77} =$

               $\dfrac{1252097}{77} = 16261$

The final answer is negative since

$$\frac{(neg.)(neg.)(pos.)}{neg.} =$$

$$\frac{(pos.)(pos.)}{neg.} =$$

$$\frac{pos.}{neg.} = neg.$$

(b) (i) $\dfrac{(-35)(-91)}{(-36)(-24)} \div \left(\dfrac{49}{-144}\right) =$

$\dfrac{3185}{-864} \div \left(\dfrac{49}{-144}\right) =$

$\dfrac{3185}{-864} \times \dfrac{-144}{49} =$

$\dfrac{-458640}{-42336} = \dfrac{458640}{42336}$

(ii) $\dfrac{(35)(91)}{(36)(24)} \div \left(\dfrac{49}{144}\right) =$

$\dfrac{3185}{864} \div \left(\dfrac{49}{144}\right) =$

$\dfrac{3185}{864} \times \dfrac{144}{49} = \dfrac{458640}{42336}$

The final answer is negative since

$$\frac{(neg.)(neg.)}{(neg.)(neg)} \div \left(\frac{pos.}{neg.}\right) =$$

$$\frac{(pos.)}{(pos.)} \div (neg.) =$$

$$(pos.) \div (neg.) = neg.$$

24. (a) >   (b) <
    (c) =   (d) <

25. (a) $\dfrac{475}{652} < \dfrac{-308}{-421}$

    (b) $\dfrac{372}{487} < \dfrac{-261}{319}$

26. (a) Property of Less Than and Addition
    (b) Property of Greater Than and Multiplication by a Negative

27. (a) $x < -18/35$ (b) $x > -43/35$

28. (a) $x < -5/2$ (b) $x < -35/16$

29. (a) $x > 5/2$ (b) $x < -56/15$

30. (a) $-113/217 < -163/314, -92/177$
    (b) $-545/522 < -812/779,$
        $-1357/1301$

31. There are many possible solutions
    (a) For example, $-11/9, -16/13,$
        and $-21/17$.
    (b) For example, $-2/21, -3/31,$
        and $-3/32$.

32. (a) $a/b + c/d = (ad + bc)/bd$

        (definition of addition) =
        $(bc + ad)/bd$ (commutativity of integer addition) =
        $bc/bd + ad/bd$ (definition of addition with a common denominator)
        $= c/d + a/b$ (simplification)
    (b) An argument similar to part (a)

33. (a) holds.
    (b) $3 - 1 \neq 1 - 3$
    (c) $(4 - 2) - 1 \neq 4 - (2 - 1)$
    (d) $a - 0 = a$, but $0 - a \neq a$.
    (e) There is no inverse since there is no identity.

34. Add $-a/b$ to both sides of the equation so that $0 = a/b + (-a/b)$. Thus, by definition, the opposite of $-a/b$ is a/b; in other words, $-(-a/b) = a/b$.

35. (a), (c), and (d) are true;
    (b) is false; $1/3 - 1/2 = -1/6$.

36. $(a/b)(c/d - e/f)$
    $= (a/b)[c/d + (-e/f)]$
    $= (a/b)(c/d) + (a/b)(-e/f)$
    $= (ac)/(bd) + (-ae)/(bf)$
    $= (ac)/(bd) - (ae)/(bf)$
    $= (a/b)(c/d) - (a/b)(e/f)$

37. For simplicity, assume that the denominators are positive. First get common denominators. Then $adf/bdf < cbf/bdf$ and $cbf/bdf < ebd/bdf$. Thus $adf < cdf$ and $cbf < ebd$. Therefore, $adf/bdf < ebd/bdf$, or $a/b < e/f$.

38. (a) $ad < bc$ and $ef > 0$. By Properties of Ordering Integers $adef < bcef$ and thus $a/b \times e/f < c/ \times e/f$ by the Cross Multiplication Property of Inequality.

    (b) Similar argument

39. If $\dfrac{a}{b} < \dfrac{c}{d}$ then $\dfrac{ad}{bd} < \dfrac{bc}{bd}$ so $ad < bc$. Thus, $ad + 1 \le bc$ and $2ad + 2 \le 2bc$, so $2ad + 1 < 2bc$. Hence

    $$\frac{ad}{bd} = \frac{2ad}{2bd} < \frac{2ad+1}{2bd} < \frac{2bc}{2bd} = \frac{bc}{bd} \text{ So}$$

    $\dfrac{e}{f} = \dfrac{2ad+1}{2bd}$ is one fraction that

    satisfies $\dfrac{a}{b} < \dfrac{e}{f} < \dfrac{c}{d}$.

40. Let n be an odd number, the first of the Pythagorean triple. Then n^2 is its square. Next, $(n^2 - 1)/2$ is the second number and $(n^2 - 1)/2 + 1$ is the third.
    $n^2 + [(n^2 - 1)/2]^2 =$
    $n^2 + (n^4 - 2n^2 + 1)/4 =$
    $(n^4 + 2n^2 + 1)/4$ and
    $[(n^2 - 1)/2 + 1]^2 = [(n^2 + 1)/2]^2 =$
    $(n^4 + 2n^2 + 1)/4$.

41. The sum $\dfrac{3}{7} + \dfrac{2}{5}$ is $\dfrac{3 \times 5 + 7 \times 2}{7 \times 5}$, or $\dfrac{29}{35}$, which has integers as its numerator and denominator and a nonzero denominator since both 7 and 5 are nonzero. Thus, $\dfrac{29}{35}$ satisfies the definition of a rational number.

Analyzing Student Thinking

42. Yes, Rock, fractions have the form a/b, where a and b are whole numbers. 2/3 fits this definition, but -2/3 does not since -2 is not a whole number. However, -2/3 does fit the definition of a rational number: a number of the form a/b, where a and b are integers.

43. Yes, Maria, 10/3 is the simplest form of the rational number. Karl is also correct, and he wrote his answer as a mixed number, where the fractional part is in simplest form.

44. Cody is incorrect. Rational-number addition has one property that fraction addition does not: the Additive Inverse Property.

45. Kelsey, let's write a fraction that is equivalent to -3/-4 = (-1)(3)/(-1)(4) = 3/4; this is a positive number. The quotient of two negative numbers is positive.

46. Yes. First, Pierce found a common denominator. To subtract two fractions with like denominators, just subtract their numerators: -45 – (-24) = -45 + 24 = -21. His answer of -21/216 is correct, though not in simplest form since the denominator he used, 216, is not the least possible common denominator, which is 72.

47. Marina is incorrect. It looks like she made a mistake in applying the distributive property. To apply this property, she'd need to do the following:
    2/5 × 1/7 – 2/5 × 3/7 =
    2/5 × (1/7 – 3/7) =
    2/5 × (-2/7) = -4/35.

48. Yes, Duncan is correct, $a/b \div c/d$ is equal to $(a \div c)/(b \div d)$. This method worked fine for computing the quotient of these two fractions since (-2) is a divisor of 12 and 7 is a divisor of 35. However, for instance, , the following computation is not as simply done using Duncan's method: 2/3 ÷ 3/4. The standard invert-and-multiply algorithm simplifies the problem.

Section 9.2

1. (a) Rational   (b) Irrational
    (c) Rational   (d) Irrational
    (e) Rational   (f) Irrational
    (g) Rational   (h) Irrational

2. The number 1.414 is a rational number approximately equal to $\sqrt{2}$.

3. (a) $\sqrt{10}$ (b) $\sqrt{13}$
    (c) $\sqrt{18} = 3\sqrt{2}$

4. (a) $\sqrt{8} = 2\sqrt{2}$
    (b) $\sqrt{9} = 3$
    (c)

5. (a) $x = \sqrt{13}$, $y = \sqrt{8} = 2$
    (b) $a = \sqrt{20} = 2\sqrt{5}$,
        $b = \sqrt{24} = 2\sqrt{6}$,
        $c = \sqrt{33}$

6. (a) 56   (b) 71

7. (a) $4\sqrt{3} - \sqrt{3} = (4-1)\sqrt{3} = 3\sqrt{3}$
        Distributive Property

    (b) $5\sqrt{7} + \left(\sqrt{35} + 7\sqrt{7}\right) =$
        $5\sqrt{7} + \left(\sqrt{5}\sqrt{7} + 7\sqrt{7}\right) =$
        $\left(12 + \sqrt{5}\right)\sqrt{7}$

        Distributive Property

    (c) $\sqrt{32} + \sqrt{50} =$
        $4\sqrt{2} + 5\sqrt{2} = 9\sqrt{2}$
        Distributive Property

8. (a) 6   (b) 9
    (c) 30   (d) 24

10. (a) $2\sqrt{10}$ (b) $4\sqrt{5}$
    (c) $6\sqrt{5}$

11. $0.876 < 0.8766876667... <$
    $0.8766 < 0.8\overline{76} <$
    $0.876787667788... <$
    $0.876787677876... < 0.8\overline{76}$

12. For example,
    0.577757777577777...

13. $\sqrt{5}$, $\sqrt{6}$, $\sqrt{7}$, 2.373373337... for example.

14. (a) $2.2^2 < 5 < 2.3^2$
        $2.23^2 < 5 < 2.24^2$
        $2.236^2 < 5 < 2.237^2$
        $\sqrt{5} \approx 2.24$
    (b) $4.3^2 < 19.1 < 4.4^2$
        $4.37^2 < 19.1 < 4.38^2$
        $4.370^2 < 19.1 < 4.371^2$
        $\sqrt{19.1} \approx 4.37$
    (c) $0.2^2 < 0.05 < 0.3^2$
        $0.22^2 < 0.05 < 0.23^2$
        $0.223^2 < 0.05 < 0.234^2$
        $\sqrt{0.05} \approx 0.22$
    (d) Because 0.05 and 5 differ by a factor of 100, $\sqrt{0.05}$ and $\sqrt{5}$ differ by a factor of 10.

15. $r_1 = 5$
    $s_1 = 24 \div 5 = 4.8$
    $r_2 = \dfrac{r_1 + s_1}{2} = 4.9$
    $s_2 = 24 \div 4.9 \approx 4.8979591$
    $r_3 \approx 4.8989795$
    $s_3 \approx 4.8989794$
    $r_3 - s_3 = 0.00000001$
    so $\sqrt{24} \approx 4.898979$

16. No.

17. (a) $0.5041 < 0.71$
    (b) $0.9604 < 0.98$
    (c) $1.1 < 1.21$

The squares of numbers
between 0 and 1 are smaller
than the number.

18. (a) 6   (b) 27   (c) 9
    (d) -8   (e) 27   (f) 729

19. (a) -2   (b) -6
    (c) Does not exist

20. (a) 1.5874 (rounded)
    (b) 2.1746 (rounded)
    (c) 344.061 (rounded)
    (d) 6.36 (rounded)

21. (a) $\sqrt[5]{7^2}$ (b) π to the $\sqrt{2}$ power

22. (a)

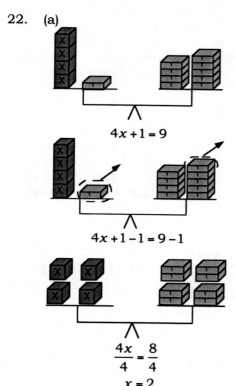

$$4x + 1 = 9$$

$$4x + 1 - 1 = 9 - 1$$

$$\frac{4x}{4} = \frac{8}{4}$$

$$x = 2$$

(b)

$$4x + 2 = 2x + 8$$

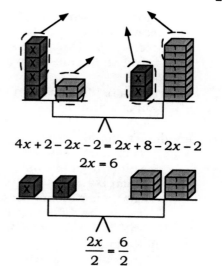

$$4x + 2 - 2x - 2 = 2x + 8 - 2x - 2$$

$$2x = 6$$

$$\frac{2x}{2} = \frac{6}{2}$$

$$x = 3$$

23. (a) $-4\sqrt{6}$ (b) $9\sqrt{3} + \sqrt{2}$
    (c) $\sqrt{3}$ (d) $-5/\pi$

24. (a) $x = -14$ (b) $x = 1/12$
    (c) $x = 13/3$ (d) $x = 3$
    (e) $x = 5$ (f) $x = 12$

25. (a) $x > 9/6 = 1.5$ (b) $x \geq -7/2$
    (c) $x \leq 4$ (d) $x < 5$

26. True. Reason, by analogy, from
    the proof that $\sqrt{2}$ is irrational.

27. Let $\sqrt{6} = a/b$. Then $6b^2 = a^2$ or
    $2 \times 3 \times b^2 = a^2$. If we consider
    the number of times the prime
    factor 2 occurs on both sides we
    arrive at a contradiction.

28. Assume it is rational. Simplify
    and then count factors of q on
    both sides.

29. Let $\sqrt[n]{2} = a/b$. Then $2b^n = a^n$. The
    prime factor 2 occurs a multiple
    of n times on the right, but 1
    more than a multiple of n times
    on the left. This is a contradiction
    of the Fundamental Theorem of
    Arithmetic

30. (a) Irrational. If $\sqrt[3]{p} = a/b$, the
    $b^3 \cdot p = a^3$ for integers a and b.
    But a^3 has a multiple of 3

factors of p whereas b^3p has one more than a multiple of 3 factors of p. This is contridiction since they are equal.

(b) Irrational. Justification is similar to that in (a).

31. (a) (i) Irrational. Proof: If $r + p$ is rational, say $r + p = t$ for some rational number t. Then $p = t - r$, which states that p is rational because $t - r$ is the difference of two rationals. A contradiction.

    (ii) Rational if $r = 0$.
    Irrational otherwise.

    (iii) Rational. $(\sqrt{2} + (-\sqrt{2}) = 0)$ or irrational $(\sqrt{2} + \sqrt{2} = 2\sqrt{2})$.

    (iv) Rational $(\sqrt{2} \times \sqrt{2} = 2)$ or irrational $(\sqrt{2} \times \sqrt{3} = \sqrt{6})$.

    (b) In (ii), $r = 0$ yields a rational number.

32. (a) $0.10110111... + 0.20220222... = 0.30330333...$

    (b) $0.10110111... + 0.01001000... = 0.11111111...$

    (c) $\sqrt{2} \times \sqrt{3} = \sqrt{6}$

    (d) $\sqrt{2} \times \sqrt{2} = 2$

33. (a) No   (b) No
    (c) No   (d) No

34. (a) They are equal.

    (b) $a + (1 - a)$ are the two numbers. Show that
    $$a^2 + (1 - a) = (1 - a)^2 + a.$$

35. (a) C = 261.63, C# = 277.19,
    D = 293.67, D# = 311.13,
    E = 329.63, F = 349.23,
    F# = 370.00, G = 392.00,
    B = 493.88, C = 523.25

    (b) Ratio is within 0.002 of 1.5

    (c) Within 0.002

36. Build the school at town A.

37. The sums are always the same.

38. 3 and 1/3, or -3 and -1/3

39. $47, $33, $13, $1
    There are other possible answers; for example, $282, $198, $78, $6.

40. 33

Analyzing Student Thinking

41. Sadi, to say the set of rational numbers is closed under addition means that the sum of two numbers inside that set (two rational numbers) will have a sum inside that set (also a rational number). It says nothing about the sum of two numbers outside the set, namely two irrationals. The following example shows the sum of two irrationals may be rational: 0.121121112... + 0.212212221... = 0.33333333...=1/3.

42. One way to explain would be to use the method for changing repeating decimals to fractions, but Ramona might be convinced by other methods as well. For example, if she agrees that 0.3333333... is equal to 1/3, then ask what 3 times 0.3333333... would be, and what 3 times 1/3 would be.

43. Lars is partially correct. It's true that, since $(-3)^2 = 9$, -3 is one of the two square roots of 9.

    However, the symbol $\sqrt{9}$ indicates the principal, or positive, square root of 9, so this is 3. To indicate the negative square root of 9, or -3, we'd write $-\sqrt{9}$.

44. Ian, a negative exponent indicates that it is applied to the reciprocal of the base: $27^{-5/3} = (1/27)^{5/3}$. Since the base, 27, is positive, so is its reciprocal.

45. Show Fatima any non-repeating, non-terminating decimal, such as 0.34334333433334...

46. Zachery, the negative exponent indicates that it is applied to the reciprocal of the base, not the reciprocal of the exponent itself.

47. 3-4-5, 5-12-13, 7-24-25, and 8-15-17 are four such examples.

Section 9.3

1. (a) {(a, t), (a, s), (i, t), (i, f), (i, s), (o, f), (o, s)}
    (b) {(a, b), (a, c), (c, a), (b, c), (c, b)}
    (c) {(8, 7), (8, 5), (8, 4), (8, 3), (8, 2), (8, 1), (6, 7), (6, 5), (6, 4), (6, 3), (6, 2), (6, 1), (4, 7), (4, 5), (4, 3), (4, 2), (4, 1), (7, 1), (5, 1), (3, 1), (2, 1)}
    (d) {(3, 6), (3, 9), (3, 12), (3, 15), (6, 12)}

2. (a)

    (b)

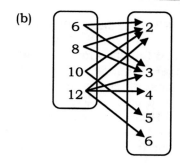

3. (a) "was the king of"
    (b) "is the square root of"

4. (a) transitive only
    (b) symmetric only
    (c) All. Equivalence relation.

5. (a) symmetric only
    (b) equivalence relation
    (c) reflexive only
    (d) symmetric only

6. (a) All. Equivalence relation. Every set in the partition has triangles of the same shape.
    (b) Reflexive and transitive
    (c) All. Equivalence relation. The partition contains 50 sets consisting of all people whose primary residence is in that state.

7. (a) Function.
    (b) Not a function. 1 has no image.
    (c) Not a function. 2 has two images.
    (d) Function.

8. (a) Function.
    (b) Not a function. Some cities have more than one zip code.
    (c) Function.
    (d) Not a function. Some pet owners have more than one pet.

9. (a) Not a function. Sue paired with both s and m.
    (b) Function.
    (c) Function.
    (d) Function.
    (e) Not a function. 2 paired with both 1 and 3; 3 paired with both 1 and 3.

10. (a) (0, 4), (1, 6), (2, 12)
         Range: {4, 6, 12}
     (b) (7, 81), (2, 16), (1, 9)
         Range: {9, 16, 81}
     (c) (2, 1), (3, 5)
         Range: {1, 5}

11. (a) 1000   (b) 18
     (c) 5, -5   (d) 3

12. (a) $f(x) = x + 3$ for $x \in \{1, 5, 8\}$
     $\{(1, 4)\ (5, 8)\ (8, 11)\}$

x	$f(x)$
1	4
5	8
8	11

   (b) $f(x) = \dfrac{1}{x}$ for $x \in \{\frac{1}{2}, 1, 3, 4\}$

   $\{(3, \frac{1}{3})\,, (4, \frac{1}{4})\,, (1, 1), (\frac{1}{2}, 2)\}$

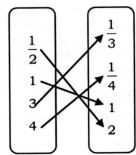

   (c) $f(x) = 3x$ for $x \in \{2, 4, 7\}$

n	$T(n)$
2	6
4	12
7	21

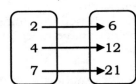

   (d) $\{(2, 1)\,, (3, 4)\,, (4, 9)\,, (5, 16)\}$

x	$f(x)$
2	1
3	4
4	9
5	16

13. (a) $\{1, 7\}$, $\{1, 2, 3, 4, 6, 12\}$
     (b) $(4, 2), (21, 19)$
     (c) $\{7, 8, 9, 10, \ldots\}$,
         $\{951, 952, 953, \ldots\}$
     (d) $\{3, 4, 5\}$, $\varnothing$

14. (a) $40
     (b) $59.35
     (c) $260.95

15. (a) 6, 11, 26, 10
     (b) One possibility:

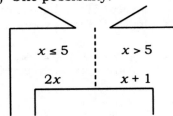

16. $f(0) = f(2) = -3$
     $f(-1) = f(3) = 0$
     $f(-2) = f(4) = 5$
     Answers will vary. This is not
     consistent with the definition of a
     function because it is 2 x-values
     mapping to 1 y-value. It would
     not be a function if there were 1 x-
     value mapping to 2 y-values.

17. (a) Geometric, 10, $5(10^{199})$
     (b) Geometric, 2, $8(2^{199})$
     (c) Arithmetic, 11, $199(11) + 12 = 2201$
     (d) Neither.

18. 5112

19. 153

20. (a) 27; 125; 1331   (b) 4; 6; 14

21. (a) $1102.50; $1276.28; $1628.89
     (b) 15 years

22. (a) $F(x) = 125(x + 10) + 295x$
             $= 420x + 1250$
     (b) $6,080 The total cost of the
         fencing is $6,080 when the
         cost of fencing for the sides
         and back is $11.50 per foot.
     (c) $18.45 per foot for the sides
         and back, $28.45 per foot for
         the front.

23. (a) $r = 3$
     (b) 4, 12, 36, 108, 324, 972,
         2916

24. (a)

x	$f(x)$
1	12
2	19
3	26
4	33
5	40
6	47
7	54
8	61

(b) Arithmetic, $a = 12$, $d = 7$
(c) $T(n) = 12 + (n - 1)7 = 7n + 5$
(d) $T(25) = 180$,
      $T(200) = 1405$
(e) Domain: $\{1,2,3,4, \ldots \}$
      Range: $\{12,19, 26, \ldots \}$

25. (a)

Year	Increase in Population	Population of Mexico
1990	0	88,300,000
1991	2,207,500	90,507,500
1992	2,262,688	92,770,188
1993	2,319,255	95,089,443
1994	2,377,236	97,466,679
1995	2,436,667	99,903,346
1996	2,497,584	102,400,930
1997	2,560,023	104,960,953
1998	2,624,024	107,584,977
1999	2,689,624	110,274,601
2000	2,756,866	113,031,466
2001	2,825,787	115,857,253
2002	2,896,431	118,753,683

(b) Geometric, $r = 1.025$
(c) 113,031,465
      127,884,728
(d) $P(n) = 88,300,000(1.025)^n$

26. 11

27. 6,210,001,000 is the only
      solution.

28. Two equations are equivalent if
      they have the same solution set.
      Let E_1 and E_2 represent two
      equations and E_1 be related to E_2
      if they have the same solution set.
      Then this relation is an
      equivalence relation.

Analyzing Student Thinking

29. Alfonso is incorrect. Since there is
      no common ratio (a number, r, by
      which each successive term in the
      sequence is multiplied) it is not a
      geometric sequence. A geometric
      sequence has the form a, ar, ar^2,
      ar^3, ar^4,...

30. Iris, since the rate is 75 cents per
      quarter mile and m is the number
      of miles traveled, the number of
      quarter miles traveled is $4m$.

31. Luke is correct; a graph of the
      three points shows that they are
      not in a straight line.

32. One possibility is: 1, 3, 9, 27, ...
      This is a geometric sequence with
      a common ratio of 3. Another
      possibility is: 1, 3, 6, 10, ... We
      first add 2, then add 3, then add
      4, and so on.
      Infinitely many answers are
      possible.

33. Nicha is incorrect; a relation is
      defined to be a set of ordered
      pairs, and this example fits that
      definition. However, her reasoning
      justifies that this relation is not a
      function.

34. Arielle, consider the relation "less
      than" on the set of real numbers—
      this relation is not reflexive since a
      number is not less than itself. As
      another example, for the set $A =$
      $\{1, 2, 3\}$, the relation $\{(1, 2), (2, 2),$
      $(1, 3)\}$ is not reflexive since the
      ordered pair $(1, 1)$ is not an
      element of the relation.

35. Hayden is incorrect. The definition of function requires that no first coordinate be paired with two different second coordinates. It is okay for elements in the domain of function to be paired to the same element in the range.

Section 9.4

1. (a) *x*-axis   (b) I   (c) II
    (d) *y*-axis   (e) III   (f) IV

2. (a) II   (b) I
    (c) I and IV

3. {(*x*, *y*) | 1 ≤ *x* ≤ 3 and -2 ≤ *y* ≤ 2}

4. (a)

x	0	1	-1	2	-2
f(x)	-2	1	-5	4	-8

    (b)

x	0	4	8	12	16
g(x)	9	6	3	0	-3

    (c)

x	0	1/2	1/4	1/6	1/12
c(x)	25	85	55	45	35

5. (a) (i)

    (ii)

    (iii)

    (iv)

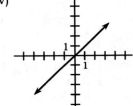

    (b) The constant term determines where the graph intersects the *x*-axis

6. (a) A straight line going up to the right that passes through the origin.
    (b) The value of *b* is where the line hits the *y*-axis. As *b* changes, the graph moves up or down with the same slope.

7. (a) (i)

(ii)

(iii)

(iv)

(b) Positive coefficients greater than one have the effect of narrowing the graph. Positive coefficients between 0 and 1 have the effect of broadening the graph. Multiplying by -1 has the effect of reflecting the graph in the *x*-axis. Thus the coefficient -3 would narrow the original graph and reflect it in the *x*-axis.

(c) The 5 makes the parabola in (i) 'narrower'. The 1/3 makes the parabola in (i) 'wider' and the 2 shifts it to the right 2 units.

8. (a) The parabola narrows.
    (b) A horizontal line.
    (c) The parabola opens down instead of up.

9. (a) (i)

Same in both cases.

(ii)

Same in both cases.

(iii)

Same in both cases.

(b) Their graphs are the same because they represent the same function.

10. (a) It's a lot steeper on the right.
     (b) It is a horizontal line $y=1$.
     (c) The graph decreases to the right.

11. (a)

x	-2	-1	0	1	2
$f(x)$	-2	2	0	-2	2

(b)

x	0	1	-1	2	-2
$f(x)$	-4	$-3\frac{1}{3}$	$-4\frac{2}{3}$	$1\frac{1}{3}$	$-9\frac{1}{3}$

12. (a) $1.92   (b) $3.12
     (c) $5.04   (d) $9.60
     (e) No;
     The sum of the costs of the individual calls is:

$$.24\|7.2+1\| + .24\|2.4+1\| + .24\|20.3+1\| =$$
$$.24\|8) + .24(13) + .24(21) = \|20.3+1\|$$

.24(8 + 13 + 21) = .24(42) = $10.08, but the cost of a single call would be:

$.24\|7.2 + 12.4 + 20.3 + 1\| =$

$.24\|39.9 + 1\| =$

.24(40) = $9.60

The difference is $.48 because 1 is added to each call duration, rather than adding 1 to the sum of all the call durations.

13. (a) (i) 3   (ii) -18
        (iii) -4   (iv) -1
    (b)

14. (a)

    (b)

    (c)

(d)

15. (a) linear   (b) step
    (c) quadratic   (d) exponential

16. (a) Function
        Domain: $-5 \leq x \leq 4$
        Range: $-2.5 \leq y \leq 4$
    (b) Not a function
    (c) Function
        Domain: All real numbers except 0
        Range: All real numbers except 0
    (d) Function
        Domain: $-4 \leq x < 2$ and
        $2 \leq x \leq 4$
        Range: $-3.5 < y \leq 3$

17. (a) (i) 1   (ii) 2   (iii) 3
    (b) Domain: $-2 \leq x \leq 6$
        Range: {1, 2, 3, 4}
    (c) $2 \leq x < 3$; none.
    (d) Step function

18. (a) Quadratic
    (b) A(4) ≈ 12.57
        A(12) ≈ 113.1

    (c)

    (d) The diameter, d, must be positive.

19. (a) The distance varies according to time.
    (b) D(8) = 1.5. D(8) is the number of miles to the lightning if 8 seconds have elapsed.
    (c) $D(t) = (3/16)t$

20. (a)

(b) About $342
(c) About 16.5 years
(d) About 11 years

21. (iii)

22. (a) $20 and $60
(b) $2000 to $2499.99
(c)

n	B
500	20
750	20
1000	40
1250	40
1500	60
1750	60
2000	80

(d) $B(n) = 20 \left\| n / 500 \right\|$

23. $T(n) = \dfrac{n}{4} + 4$

24. 1/3

Analyzing Student Thinking

25. Yes, Millicent, that's right. To see why this is true, look at a table for a general arithmetic sequence:

0	1	2	3
a	$a + d$	$a + 2d$	$a + 3d$

The nth term of the sequence is of the form $dn + a$; in other words, it's a linear function with slope d.

26. Each successive y value is increased by a multiple of 3 and the value of y can be expressed as $2(3^{x-1})$. Thus, the graph will be that of an exponential function.

27. If the common difference of the arithmetic sequence were negative, then the line would slope downward. For example, consider the sequence 6, 4, 2, 0, -2, . . . where the common difference is -2. If the common ratio of the geometric sequence were a positive fraction less than one, the curve would move downward; for example, consider the sequence 20, 10, 5, 2.5, 1.25, . . . where the common ratio is 0.5. As a point of interest, if the common ratio of a geometric sequence is negative, the graph does not proceed downward in an orderly fashion, but bounces back and forth between positive and negative values. For example, the sequence 20, -10, 5, -2.5, 1.25,... is geometric with common ratio -0.5.

28. Braxton, the difference between successive output values of a linear function will equal the slope value, as long as the difference in the input values is 1.

29. Yes, Cassidy, that everyday expression comes from the fact that exponential functions grow very quickly as the value of the input increases.

30. Mikaila is incorrect; for instance, her claim is not true for the function $f(x) = x^2$, since $f(-2) = 4$ and $-f(2) = -4$.

31. Yes, Easton, many functions have this property. For instance, any function of the form $f(x) = x^2 + c$ satisfies $f(x) = f(-x)$ since the

square of a number is equal to the
square of its opposite. Similarly,
functions of the form $f(x) = x^n + c$,
where n is even, have this
property. Such functions are said
to be "even."

Chapter 10

Section 10.1

1. (a) How many fans wear clothing in support of their team?
   (b) Estimate the percentage of fans wearing team clothing by using the percentage of fans wearing team clothing in a randomly selected sample of 5 to 10 sections at the stadium.

2. The population is the 1000 gold coins in the chest. The sample consists of the 20 coins taken from the top.

3. The population is all the students taking math classes. The sample consists of the 82 students who responded to the questionnaire.

4. (a) 45, 56, 64, 71, 73, 74, 76, 82, 83, 83, 84, 85, 87, 91, 92, 92, 92, 95, 96
   (b) 45, 96
   (c) 92
   (d)

   (e)

   (f)

5. (a) 12.|15 25 40 45 50 50 50 80 80 85
   (b)
   ```
   12.0|
   12.1| 5
   12.2| 5
   12.3|
   12.4| 0 5
   12.5| 0 0 0
   12.6|
   12.7|
   12.8| 0 0 5
   12.9|
   ```
   (c) The plot in part (b) since it shows the spread of the data better.

6. (a)

   (b)

7. (a)

Class 1		Class 2
	3	1
5 1	4	3 6 6
6 4	5	
5 5	6	5 7
8 7 7 6 6	7	4 5 6 8 9
9 6 6	8	2 4 5 7
4 3 0	9	2 8

   (b) It is difficult to determine which class is better in this case.

8. (a) Yes, no   (b) Yes, no
   (c) Vertical scale does not begin at 0

9. (a)

Chrysler New Yorker
Lincoln Mark VII
Cadillac DeVille
Oldsmobile Lss
Buick Riviera
Ford Taurus

50 100 150 200

(b) Look for the shortest bar, which means the best braking. It is the Lincoln Mark VII.

10. (a)

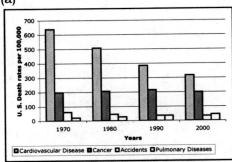

(b) Cardiovascular diseases and accidents

(c) Most resources should be targeted for cardiovascular diseases and cancer.

11. (a) $0, $21, $47.50, $112.50, $188.50, $275.50, $373.50, $481.50

(b)

(image of line graph: Tax (in dollars) vs. Income (in dollars))

12. (a) 108°   (b) 72°
    (c) 54°   (d) $1800, $600, $600

13. (a) (i)   29%   104°
        (ii) 38%   137°
        (iii) 15%   55°
        (iv) 18%   64°

(b)

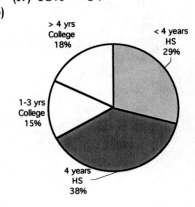

14. (a) About 110 million
    (b) About 233 million
    (c) About 305 million
    (d) The height of all of the bars would be cut in half.
    (e) The range from 5.3 million to about 308 million makes it difficult to have an amount for the symbol to represent.

15.   U.S. and Great Britain medal count for 2012 Summer Olympics

     Gold   Silver   Bronz

16. (a) and (c)

Dating Heights

(b) There are not any outliers.
(d) There is no change since there are no outliers.

17. (a) and (b)

Education vs. Income

(c) Answers may vary depending on the method used to sketch your regression line in part (b).

18. (a) and (b)

(c) It should look similar but may look slightly different depending on the strategy used to find it by hand.

19. (a) and (b)

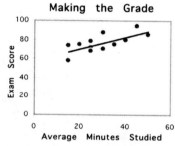

(c) It should look similar but may look slightly different depending on the strategy used to find it by hand.

20. (a) Approximately 1150
     (b) Approximately 1400

21. (a)

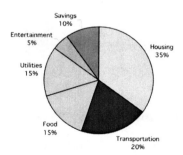

(b) The sector representing savings almost doubles and the rest of the sectors are smaller to accommodate it.

(c) $300

22. (a) Bar graph because it allows for comparison.
     (b) Bar graph:

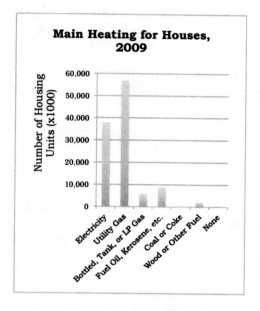

23. (a) Multiple circle because parts make up the whole population or multiple bar graphs for comparison.
     (b) Multiple bar graph:

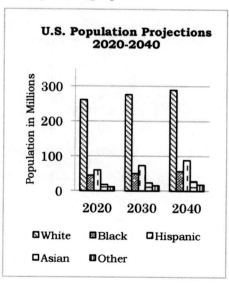

24. (a) Circle graph because values are parts of a whole or bar graph for comparison.
     (b) Circle graph:

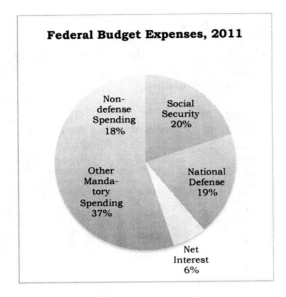

Federal Budget Expenses, 2011

25. (a) Line graph to show trend.
    (b)

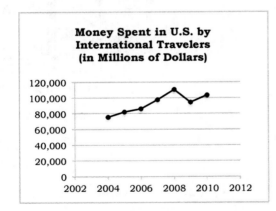

Percent of Population Age 65 and Over

26. (a) Pictograph, bar graph, or line graph to show trend and comparisons.
    (b) Line graph:

Money Spent in U.S. by International Travelers (in Millions of Dollars)

27. (a) Circle graph to show percentages
    (b) Circle graph:

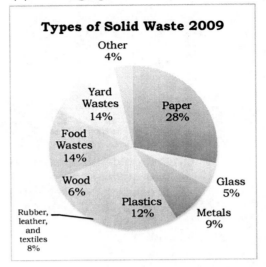

Types of Solid Waste 2009

28. (a) and (b)

Cars and Homes

    (c) About 9 home mortgages

29. About $195,000,000

30. (a) 298
    (b) 5010
    (c) $\dfrac{1}{101} - \dfrac{1}{102} = \dfrac{1}{10302}$

31. 102,564

Analyzing Student Thinking

32. Yes. It sounds like Angela made a histogram (a type of bar graph) where the stems represent the interval lengths and the number of

leaves show the frequency in each interval.

33. Ginger, a zig-zag or squiggle mark on the axis of a graph is used to show that part of the axis is not shown. It may be more convenient, or make for a more attractive graph, to do this. If you just crop the axis of your graph, but do not use the zig-zag to indicate this, you may deceive your reader.

34. No, Kevin has these two reversed. A circle graph is useful for showing relative amounts because it displays parts of a whole, while a line graph is useful for showing trends because it shows changes over time.

35. That's right, Chance. By comparing multiple circle graphs, one can see how relative amounts change.

36. Since line graphs are useful for showing changes over time, this type of graph is not appropriate for the categorized data Shawn collected. As Rosa suggests, a circle graph would work since each favorite color could be represented by one sector of the circle, showing the relative number of classmates with that favorite color.

37. Yes, Shawn, a bar chart would be an appropriate type of graph for this data, too, since it would allow you to make comparisons between the categories (each favorite color) by comparing the height of the bars (the number of classmates with that favorite color). However, neither a circle graph nor a bar chart would be "best". They are both okay.

38. No, Violet's method will not work since $60 + 70 + 30 + 50 + 90 = 300$, but the sum of the measures of the central angles of a full circle is 360 degrees.

39. Vince, a regression line is very useful: it can help you see a general trend in the points you've graphed, indicates a possible relationship between the two variables, and allows you to estimate the value of one of the variables, given the value of the other.

Section 10.2

1. (a) 0, 0, 0
   (b) 0, -0.5, no mode
   (c) 0, -0.05, no mode
   (d) $5 + \sqrt{2}$, $5 + \sqrt{2}$, no mode

2. (a) $\sqrt{2}/2$, $2\sqrt{2}$, $3\sqrt{2}$
   (b) π, π, $4 + \pi$
   (c) $\sqrt{3}/3 + \pi$, $(\sqrt{2} + \sqrt{3})/2 + \pi$, $\sqrt{3} + \pi$

3. 2.87

4. 26 students

5. No. $27 \times 70 = 21 \times 90$. Thus, 21 scores above ninety would yield a total that would exceed 27×70.

6. (a) {1, 3, 8, 9, 9}; answers may vary.
   (b) {1, 1, 5, 9, 9}; answers may vary.

7. (a) Lowest score = 50, lower quartile = 59, median = 73, upper quartile = 82, highest score = 97.
   (b) 20, 40, 60

8. (a)

3	00 00 05 05 08 09 11 14 18 24
	24 26 28 29 42 55 55 61 63 64
	73 73
4	17
5	11

(b) Class 2 performed better since most statistics except the lowest score are higher than their counterparts from Class 1.

9.   (a) The lower quartile: 21
   (b) The upper quartile: 42
   (c) The lower quartile: 25

10.   (a)

Stem	Leaves (x100)
6	4
7	8 8
8	1 2 2
9	1 2 2 3 3 4 5 9
10	1 1 1 1 1 4 5 6 8 8 8 9
11	2 3 4 5 5 6 7 8 9
12	0 2 5 9
13	1 3 4
14	1 3 4 6 6
15	5 7
16	0 1
17	
18	9

(b) There is a gap in the eighties. A cluster occurs around the hundreds.

(c) 18900 appears to be an outlier

(d) East:
Lowest value = 7800
Lower quartile = 10100
Median = 11800
Upper quartile = 14400
Highest value = 18900

West:
Lowest value = 6300
Lower quartile = 9100
Median = 10300
Upper quartile = 11500
Highest value = 15700

East has no outliers.
West has one outlier: 15700 (WY).

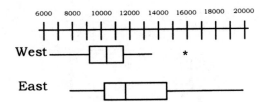

All measures for the east are higher than corresponding measures for the west.

11.   (a)

(b) Young's total of 511 is a mild outlier.

12.   (a) 0,0   (b) 59.3, 7.7
     (c) 11.7, 3.4   (d) 11.1, 3.3

13.   (a) $8; \sqrt{8}$ (b) $8; \sqrt{8}$ (c) $8; \sqrt{8}$
     (d) 16; 4. Adding/subtracting a constant amount does not change the variance or standard deviation.

14.   18, 18.5, 19, 2.6, 1.612

15.   .03, .38, -.66, -.84, -.31, .21, -1.01, -1.19, 1.26, 2.13

16.   7

17.   2nd percentile

18.   (a) Fiftieth Percentile
     (b)

z-SCORE	PERCENTILE
-2	2
-1	15 or 16
1	84 or 85
2	98

19.   A: test score >95
     B: 85 < test score ≤ 95
     C: 65 < test score ≤ 85
     D: 55 < test score ≤ 65
     F: test score ≤ 55

20.   (a) 57th percentile
     (b) 43%

21.   77%-78%

22.   65, 55, 75

23.   Approximately 113.4

24. 11 girls

25. 360/24 = 87.9 (to nearest tenth)

26. All the numbers are equal.

27. 63 (rounded to 2 places)

28. (a) No
    (b) Yes (if all scores are equal, then all z-scores are zero).

29. (a) 32.5   (b) 30; no.

30. (a) $s = 1.41$, $s_{n-1} = 1.58$ (to 2 places)

    (b) Yes, $s_{n-1} = \dfrac{\sqrt{n}}{n-1} \cdot s$

    whenever $s_{n-1} \neq 0 \neq s$

Analyzing Student Thinking

31. Amber, although the number 3.9 has a 3 in it, it is really much closer to 4 than 3, so that is more positive than neutral. More importantly, a median of 5 indicates that at least half of the class gave lavender a 5. A few negative votes have a more powerful effect on the mean than on the median, but these figures indicate the class is quite happy with the new color.

32. Spike, don't forget that the median is the middle number, when the data are written in order. So, the median is actually 7.5.

33. No. The median of a set with four numbers is the average of the middle two numbers.

34. No. A set with the mean = median = mode would have the average = middle number = most frequent number. {0, 4, 4, 8} is just such a set, with 4 = mean = median = mode.

35. By looking at a Bell curve, we can see that 47.5% of the data points have the z-scores between 0 and 2 but at most 2.5% of the data points have z-scores between 2 and 10.

36. Actually, Mckay, it's possible for a whisker to be shorter than the box, if the data in the middle half (represented by the box) are spread out and the data in the upper (or lower) quarter (represented by the whisker) are close together.

37. Whitney, consider the sets {0, 0, 0, 0, 10} and {0, 2, 5, 6, 10}. Both have a range of 10, but the spread in the data in each one is different, resulting in standard deviations that are not equal.

Section 10.3

1. (a)

    (b)

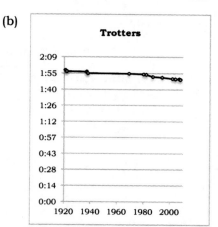

Putting the baseline at 1:50.0 as opposed to 0 makes the changes more dramatic.

2. (a)

(b) Use the graph in figure 10.24 to emphasize the decrease in profits. Use the graph in part (a) to de-emphasize the decrease. Both are accurate, but the choice of which to use depends on the feeling one wants to convey to the reader.

4.

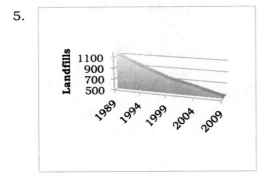

3. (a) Oil companies want the increase to appear less dramatic so the range of the vertical-axis is larger.

5.

(b) Consumer groups want the increase to appear more dramatic, so the range of the y-axis is small.

6.

7. Because of the perspective, sectors B and D appear to be significantly larger than sectors A and C.

8.

Karl Malone
13188 Attempts

Missed free throws 26%

Made free throws 74%

Shaquille O'Neal
11252 Attempts

Made free throws 53%

Missed free throws 47%

John Harlicek
6589 Attempts

Missed free throws 18%

Made free throws 82%

The number of free throws for each player appears to be the same when the graphs are the same size.

9.

10. If the length of the bars (lasagna noodles) is measured from the right side of the fork and we assume that the "less often" bar is accurate, then the "once/twice a month" bar should be about 15%, the "once/twice a week" bar should be about 35%, and the "three times a week" bar should be about 29%. If the length of the bars is measured from the left side of the fork, then the bars are even

less accurate at representing their corresponding percents.

11. No, the graph is not accurate. The radius has been tripled making the areas 9 times larger.

12. Exploding a sector; changing 3D perspective; incomplete labels; sectors don't add to 100%. Answers may vary.

13. (a) One possible source of bias is in the selection of the 5 items from each product line; those 5 might be made with special care or perhaps they were made at the start of the process when defects are more likely.

    (b) One source of bias in the samples is that the items produced at a specific time may have higher or lower quality than at other times of the day (due, say, to certain employees working on the production line at that time.)

    (c) One possible source of bias is in the selection of the 10 items from each product line; those 10 might be made with special care or perhaps they were made at the start of the process when defects are more likely.

14.

15.

16.

17. (a)

(b)

18. (a)

(b)

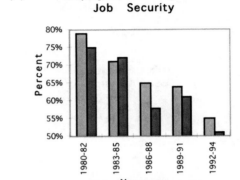

19. Population-all of the professor's students; Sample-the students in the selected class; Bias- (i) the professor selected the class, (ii) the students would be discouraged from writing their true feelings because of his presence.

20. Population-all of the student body; Sample-the students at the coffee house and the gym; Bias-the students at the coffee house are participating in a social activity and the students at the gym are participating in a sporting activity so they are likely to choose candidates Johnson and Jackson respectively.

Analyzing Student Thinking

21. Siope is correct. Depending on the situation, the vertical axis of a vertical bar graph can be cropped as long as there is some indication, like a "squiggle" mark, that the axis has been cropped.

22. Help Cesar convert the time he spends doing each activity into a percent by dividing by 24. As long as he accounts for all of the 24 hours, the percents will add up to 100 and a circle graph can be constructed.

23. No, when the length, width and height of a three-dimensional bar are doubled, the resulting bar is $2 \times 2 \times 2 = 8$ times greater in volume than the original.

24. Joel, there may be no intention to mislead. Nonetheless, it is important to be aware of the ways in which such a graph may be misleading, giving greater emphasis to differences among the data.

25. No, Otis, increasing only one dimension of the pencil icon by 3 times will result in a pencil that is 3 times larger than the original, representing 3 times the quantity represented by 1 pencil. That's accurate, not deceptive.

26. Anita, surveying only people at the park introduces a source of bias in your sample. In order to have a sample that is representative of the city's population, you need to include non-park users, too.

Chapter 11

Section 11.1

1. (a) Gift B or E
    (b) Gift A or C
    (c) No one

2. (a) {HH, HT, TH, TT]
    (b) {H1, H2, H3, H4, H5, H6, T1, T2, T3, T4, T5, T6}
    (c) {RG, RW, BG, BW}

3. (a) {R,G,B,Y,W}
    (b) {RR,RG,RB,RY,RW,GR,GG,GB, GY,GW,...,WR,WG,WB,WY,W} (25 pairs)
    (c) {RG,RB,RY,RW,GR,GB,GY,GW, BR,BG,BY,BW,YR,YG,YB,YW, WR,WG,WB,WY}

4. (a) {H1, H2, H3, H4, H5, H6, T1, T2, T3, T4, T5, T6}
    (b) {H1, H2, H3, H4, H5, H6}
    (c) {H3, T3}
    (d) {H2, T2, H4, T4, H6, T6}
    (e) {H5, H6}
    (f) {T1, T2, T3, T4, T5, T6, H5}

5. (a) C   (b) P   (c) I

6.
P	(H, P)	(T, P)
G	(H, G)	(T, G)
Y	(H, Y)	(T, Y)
	H	T

7. (a) 75/1000 = 0.075
    (b) 150/1000 = 0.15
    (c) 275/1000 = 0.275
    (d) 375/1000 = 0.375

8. (a) 1/2   (b) 11/12
    (c) 5/12   (d) 13/18
    (e) 5/18
    (f) In general, the answers for 500 rolls should be closer to the theoretical probability, but answers may vary.

9. (a) 0.5   (b) 0.25
    (c) 0.875   (d) 0.375
    (e) In general, the answers for 500 rolls should be closer to the theoretical probability, but answers may vary.

10. (a) 7/12   (b) 1   (c) 1/2

11. (a) 1/2   (b) 3/13
    (c) 10/13   (d) 3/26

12. (a) 37/75   (b) 64 times

13. (a) 7/22   (b) 3/22
    (c) 5/22   (d) 3/22
    (e) 15/22   (f) 9/22

14. (a) 5/9   (b) 27/38
    (c) 9/19   (d) 18/19

15. (a) 1/3   (b) 1/3
    (c) 1/3   (d) 1
    (e) 1/2, 1/8, 3/8, 1; yes.

16. (a) 1/6   (b) 5/6
    (c) 1/2   (d) 1/2
    (e) 2/3   (f) 1/3

17. (a) 7/13   (b) 3/4
    (c) 7/13   (d) 25/52

18. (a) 1/2   (b) 1/3   (c) 1/6
    (d) 1   (e) 7/12

19. (a) Either two or three heads appear; 1/2
    (b) Number of heads is not 2; 5/8
    (c) The second coin does not land tails; 1/2
    (d) Two heads appear, one of which is on second coin; 1/4

20. (a) The probability of getting a spade or a face card.
    (b) The probability of getting a jack, queen, or king of spades.
    (c) The probability of not getting a face card.

21. (a) Each state not equally likely, since populations not equal.
    (b) Intersection of two events is not empty set, so property 4 does not apply. Probability cannot be greater than 1.
    (c) Winning and losing are complementary events, but 1/2 + 1/3 ≠ 1.

22. (a) 1/3   (b) 2   (c) 4

23. (a) 6; 1/2   (b) 30;7/30
    (c) 20;1/20

24. $\dfrac{100^2 - \pi(40)^2}{100^2} \approx 0.497$

25. $91/216 \approx 0.42$

Analyzing Student Thinking

26. Although the probability of getting 50 heads out of 100 tosses is the most likely, the probability of getting 48 or 49 or 51 or 52 or other numbers close to 50 is slightly less, but very close to the probability of getting 50. Since these outcomes have similar probabilities, a different outcome could occur on each of a small number of trials.

27. Jimmer is incorrect, in general. However, if the spinner is divided from center into 3 pie shaped pieces of equal area, then he is correct.

28. Kyle is incorrect. There are 6 x 6 = 36 possible outcomes for rolling two dice. There are 11 outcomes which result in either a 1 on the blue die or a 3 on the red die: {(1, 1), (1, 2), (1, 3), (1, 4), (1, 5), (1, 6), (2, 3), (3, 3), (4, 3), (5, 3), (6, 3)} Thus, the probability of this event is 11/36.

29. No, Jaisha, since there are 6 outcomes for each of the two dice, there are 6 x 6 = 36 outcomes when two dice are tossed.

30. James, let's list the outcomes in the sample space: S = {HH, HT, TH, TT}. There are four outcomes: two heads, two tails, and two outcomes with a head and a tail. Thus, the probability of getting two heads is 1/4.

31. Jennifer and Karen are both mistakenly reasoning that the first 5 tosses affect the probability of the 6th toss. However, each toss of the coin has a 50% probability of landing on heads.

32. Jessa, any event that is sure to occur has a probability of 1. For instance, consider the event, "The coin will land heads or tails."

Section 11.2

1. (a)   (b)   (c)   (d)

2. (a)

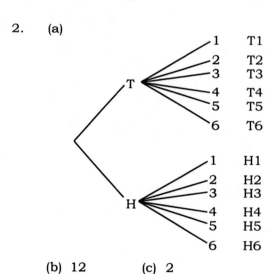

(b) 12   (c) 2
(d) 6   (e) 2 x 6 = 12

3.

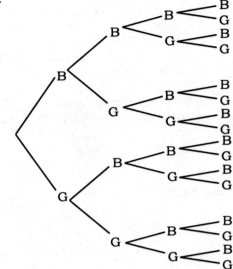

(d) 1 - 9/25 = 16/25

10. (a)

(b)

(c)

4.

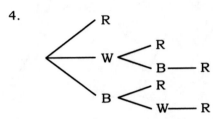

11.   (a), (b) and (c)

P(1H)=1/12

P(1T)=1/12

P(2H)=1/12

P(2T)=1/12
P(3H)=1/12

P(3T)=1/12

P(4H)=1/12

P(4T)=1/12
P(5H)=1/12

P(5T)=1/12

P(6H)=1/12

P(6T)=1/12

5.

H   1   H1
       2   H2
       3   H3
       4   H4
       5   H5
       6   H6

T   B   TB

       R   TR

       Y   TY

6.   20 ways

7.   36

8.   (a) R - 1/4, W - 1/4, B - 1/2
      (b) R - 1/5, W - 1/5, B - 3/5
      (c) R - 1/3, W - 1/6, B - 1/2

9.   (a) Y = 2/5, R = 3/5 appropriate
           for each branch
      (b) 4/25, 6/25
      (c) 4/25 + 6/25 + 6/25 = 16/25

(d) P(even and head)
     = P(2H) +P(4H) + P(6H)
     = 1/12 + 1/12 + 1/12 = 1/4

12. (a) and (b)

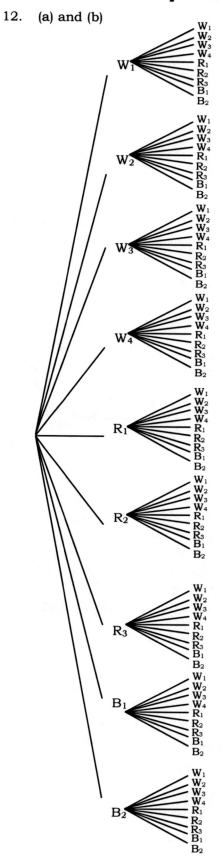

(c) Label each of the 9 branches in the first stage of the outcome tree with 1/9 and each of the 81 branches in the second stage with 1/9. The probability of each of the 81 outcomes is $1/9 \times 1/9 = 1/81$

(d) P(red and white) = $P(R_1W_1)$ + $P(R_1W_2)$ + $P(R_1W_3)$+ $P(R_1W_4)$ + $P(R_2W_1)$ + $P(R_2W_2)$ + $P(R_2W_3)$+ $P(R_2W_4)$ + $P(R_3W_1)$ + $P(R_3W_2)$ + $P(R_3W_3)$+ $P(R_3W_4)$ + = 12/81

13. (a)

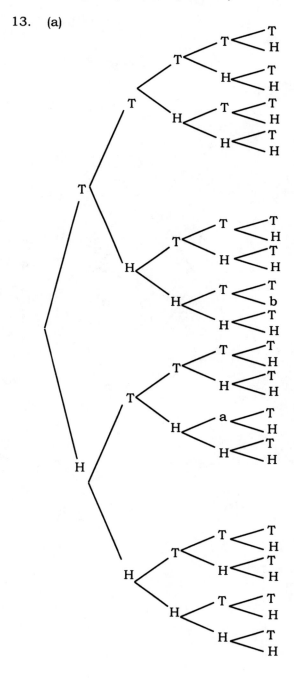

(b) 1, 5, 10, 10, 5, 1
(c) These are the same as the
     entries in the row 1, 5, 10, ...

14. (a) 10 × 10 × 10 × 10
          = 10,000
     (b) 10
     (c) 10/10,000 = 1/1000
     (d) 7/10,000

15. (a) 2 × 26 × 26 × 26 = 35,152
     (b) 1/35,152 ≈ 0.00003

16. (a) 8 × 3 × 2 × 5 = 240
     (b) 120
     (c) 1/2
     (d) 16/240 = 1/15

17. (a) 1, 5, 10, 10, 5, 1
     (b) 5
     (c) 10
     (d) 5/16, 1/2

18. (a)

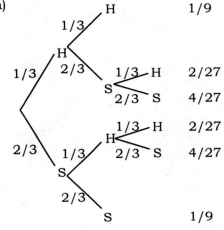

     (b) 1/9, 4/9   (c) 4/9
     (d) 2/27   (e) 20/27

19. (a)

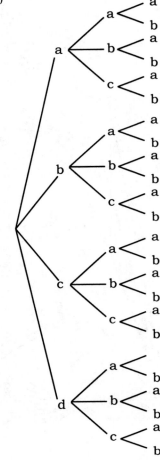

     (b) 24
     (c) 4 × 3 × 2 = 24, yes
     (d) 1/24

20. (a) $(0.343)^3 ≈ 0.04$
     (b) $(0.657)^3 ≈ 0.28$
     (c) 1 - 0.28 = 0.72
     (d) $3(0.343)(0.657)^2 ≈ 0.45$

21. (a)

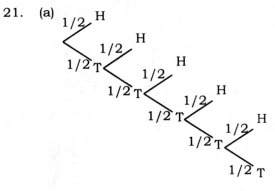

     (b) 1/2, 1/4, 1/8, 1/16

(c) 1/32

22. (a)

(b)   0.7

23. A = 3%, B = 16%, C = 31%,
D = 31%, E = 16%, F = 3%

24. If the prisoner places one white
ball in one box and the remaining
balls (9 white and 10 black) in the
other box, his chance of going free
would be (1 + 9/19)/2 = 0.737 or
73.7%.

25. Switch! For curtains *A*, *B*, and *C*,
suppose that the prize is behind *A*.
Here are the possibilities:

Choose *A* first. Then *B* or *C* is
shown. Stay wins, switch loses.

Choose *B* first. Then *C* is shown.
Stay loses, switch wins.

Choose *C* first. Then *B* is shown.
Stay loses, switch wins.

26. (a) 1/3   (b) 4/11

27. Let *a*, *b*, *a* + *b*, *a* + 2*b* be four
consecutive Fibonacci numbers.
Then $(a + b)^2 - b^2 = a^2 + 2ab$, and
$a(a + 2b) = a^2 + 2ab$. Thus, they
are always equal.

Analyzing Student Thinking

28. Maxwell, *or* means 'plus' only
when the two sets in question are
disjoint. In this example, you
counted one particular card,
namely the king of hearts, twice.
To adjust for that, P(king *or* heart)
= P(king) + P(heart) - P(king of
hearts). This equals 16/52, not
17/52. The 16 represents all of
the hearts plus the kings of

spades, clubs, and diamonds. In
general, we have to subtract the
items that are in the intersection
of the two sets in question
because we don't want them to be
counted twice, so P(A *or* B) = P(A) +
P(B) - P(A *and* B).

29. Parker, note that *for each* of the 52
possibilities on the first draw,
there are 52 possibilities on the
second draw. That means that
there are 52 × 52 ways to draw
two cards with replacement.

30. Megan, these two outcomes do not
have the same probability. For
drawing two aces in a row, the
probability is 4/52 × 3/51 since,
after drawing the first ace, there
are only three aces left in the
deck. However, the probability of
drawing an ace then a 2 is
4/52 × 4/51 since, after drawing
the ace first, there are still four 2s
left in the deck.

31. Matthew, Pascal's Triangle can be
used to compute only probability
problems involving two equally
likely outcomes. Since a die has
six equally likely outcomes,
Pascal's Triangle does not apply.

32. Nancy, since there is only 1 king
of hearts in a deck of cards, the
probability of drawing it is 1/52.

33. Riley has chosen the correct row of
Pascal's Triangle, but the entries
that correspond to the number of
ways to get 3 or 4 heads are 10
and 5:

1	5	10	10	5	1
(0H)	(1H)	(2H)	(3H)	(4H)	(5H)

P(3 or 4) = (10 + 5)/2^5 = 17/32

34. No. By the Fundamental
Counting Property, there are 2 × 2
× 2 × 2 = 16 possible outfits.

Section 11.3

1. (a) $\dfrac{20!}{5!} = 20 \cdot 19 \cdot 18 \cdot 17 \cdots 6$

    $= 20,274,183,401,472,000$

    (b) $(n+1)(n)(n-1)$

    (c) $\dfrac{57!}{55!} = 57 \cdot 56 = 3192$

2. (a) $m = 23$, $n = 4$

    (b) $m = 11$, $n = 2$

3. (a) $\dfrac{10!}{7!3!} = \dfrac{10 \cdot 9 \cdot 8}{3 \cdot 2 \cdot 1} = 120$

    (b)

    $\dfrac{23 \cdot 22 \cdot 21 \cdot 20 \cdot 19 \cdot 18 \cdot 17 \cdot 16 \cdot 15 \cdot 14}{10 \cdot 9 \cdot 8 \cdot 7 \cdot 6 \cdot 5 \cdot 4 \cdot 3 \cdot 2 \cdot 1}$

    $= 1,114,066$

    (c) $\dfrac{50 \cdot 49 \cdot 48 \cdot 47 \cdot 46}{5 \cdot 4 \cdot 3 \cdot 2 \cdot 1}$

    $= 2,118,760$

4. (a) $m = 16$, $n = 4$

    (b) $m = 33$, $n = 28$

5. (a) $_6P_2$ (b) $_{12}P_2$

6. (a) 90   (b) 45   (c) 45

    (d) 30   (e) 27

7. (a) 26^4

    (b) $26 \cdot 25 \cdot 24 \cdot 23 = 358,800$

    (c) 26^3

8. 8!

9. (a) $_{10}C_7 = 120$ (b) $_8C_5 = 56$

10. $_{11}C_7 = 330$

11. (a) 1, 20, 190, 1140

    (b) 1, 21, 210, 1330

    (c) $210 = 20 + 190$

    $1330 = 190 + 1140$

12. (a) 15/64

    (b) 20/64 = 5/16

    (c) 42/64 = 21/32

    (d) 63/64

13. $\dfrac{17!}{20!} = \dfrac{1}{6840}$

14. $\dfrac{_{16}C_3 \times _{13}C_5}{_{19}C_6 \times _{13}C_5} = \dfrac{20}{969}$

15. $\dfrac{7}{_{10}C_4} = \dfrac{1}{30}$

16. (a) $n = 9$ (b) $n = 12$

17. $\dfrac{12}{_{14}C_3 \times _{11}C_5} = \dfrac{1}{14014}$

18. $\dfrac{_4C_2 \times _4C_2}{_{52}C_5} = \dfrac{3}{216580}$

19. (a) $3 \cdot 13! = 18,681,062,4000$

    (b) $3(_{13}C_3 + _{13}C_2 + _{13}C_1 + _{13}C_0) = 1134$

20. $5,428,503,678,976$

    $\approx 5.4285 \times 10^{12}$

21. (a) 5!

    (b) $6! - 2 \times 5! = 4 \times 5! - 480$

22. $_{30}P_6 = 427,518,000$

23. $11! = 39,916,800$

24. 3 - Yes, 4 - Yes, 5 - No

25. (a) $(_4C_2 + _3C_2 + _2C_2)/_{10}C_2$

    $= (6 + 3 + 1)/45 = 2/9$

    (b) $(_4C_1 \times _6C_1)/_{10}C_2 = 24/45$

    $= 8/15$

    (c) $(_4C_1 \times _6C_1 + _4C_2 \times _6C_0)/_{10}C_2$

    $= (24 + 6)/45 = 2/3$

    (d) $(_4C_0 \times _6C_2/_{10}C_2 = 15/45$

    $= 1/3$

26. (a) $2 \times 6! = 1440$

    (b) $7! - 2 \times 6! = 3600$

    (c) $6 \times 5! = 720$

27. $12! = 479,001,600$

    $5! \times 4! \times 3! \times 6 = 103,680$

28. (a) $_8C_0 \times _6C_4 + _8C_1 \times _6C_3 +$

    $_8C_2 \times _6C_2 + _8C_3 \times _6C_1 +$

    $_8C_4 \times _6C_0 = 1265$

(b) $_8C_2 \times {}_8C_2 = 784$
(c) $_8C_4 = 70$
(d) $_6C_4 = 15$

Analyzing Student Thinking

29. Margaret is incorrect.
$$\frac{8!}{16!} =$$

$$\frac{8!}{16 \cdot 15 \cdot 14 \cdot 13 \cdot 12 \cdot 11 \cdot 10 \cdot 9 \cdot 8!} =$$

$$\frac{1}{16 \cdot 15 \cdot 14 \cdot 13 \cdot 12 \cdot 11 \cdot 10 \cdot 9} =$$

$$\frac{1}{518,918,400}$$

30. If permutations were used, then the order of selection would be taken into account. Lowell is correct because the order in which the committee members are selected does NOT matter, so combinations are the correct way to count the committees.

31. Since the order of selection matters in this situation, permutations are the correct way to solve this problem.

32. Brielle, Pascal's Triangle can be used to solve only probability problems involving two equally likely outcomes. Since there are 52 possible outcomes for drawing a card from a deck, Pascal's Triangle does not apply.

33. Lily's statement is correct only for the even-numbered rows. The odd-numbered rows of Pascal's Triangle have an even number of entries, and thus no middle number. Thus, Lily should have said, "the middle number of the nth row, where n is an even number, must be $_nC_{n/2}$."

34. Julio is incorrect. Since there are 6 different items that may be added to the sandwich or not (2 choices), there are $2^6 = 64$ possibilities. And for each of these

64, there are two choices of bread and only one choice of meat so there are only $64 \times 2 \times 1 = 128$ sandwich combinations.

35. Jeff, to compute this probability, we'd need to divide the number of outcomes with 5 "yea" and 4 "nay" votes by the total number of ways the 9 justices could vote. Since there are two possible votes for each justice, we could use the 9th row of Pascal's Triangle to get $126/2^9 = 63/256$. Note, however, that by using Pascal's Triangle, we have made the assumption that a vote of "yea" is equally likely to a "nay" vote. Since justices don't vote randomly, this is probably not a good assumption to make. You can see that computing the probability of a 5-4 majority is more complicated than you first thought.

Section 11.4

1. Answers will vary.

2. Answers may vary but should be around 7 packages.

3. (a) Answers will vary.
(b) The theoretical number is 21.74 or 22 pennies.

4. Step 1: Yes   Step 2: 2
Step 3: 44
(a) .88 (theoretical solution .63)

5. (a) Place pieces of paper corresponding to the chocolate candies in a bag. Draw out 2 pieces of paper and record the results.
(b) Answer should be near $\frac{150}{812} \approx 0.185$, but will vary.
(c) Place 5 ones, 7 twos, 8 threes, 5 fours, and 4 fives in the bin and draw 2. After 30 trials, the probability should be near 0.185.

6. Read the digits on the table and record numbers 1-6 as rolls. Ignore 0, 7, 8, 9. Starting on the top row, the first twenty rolls would be 1, 3, 1, 1, 2, 1, 2, 5, 2, 2, 3, 6, 5, 5, 2, 1, 6, 5, 2, 4.

7. 0.8

8. 4/5 (In long run such a sample will average just under one defective microscope.)

9. (a) $40,000   (b) $25
   (c) Scholarship A

10. Make $2,200

11. They are the same since they both reduce to 3:2.

12. (a) (i)   6:30 or 1:5
        (ii) 33:3 or 11:1
        (iii) 18:18 or 1:1
    (b) (i)   5:1   (ii) 1:11   (iii) 1:1

13. (a) 3:10   (b) 3:1
    (c) 1:51   (d) 10:3

14. (a) 3:5   (b) 7:1
    (c) 7:1   (d) 3:5

15. (a) 1:7, 7:1   (b) 2:3, 3:2

16. (a) 1/9   (b) 3/8   (c) 5/11

17. For example, the sum is...
    (a) not 8, 9, or 10
    (b) 6, 7, or 8
    (c) not 2.

18. (a) 10/21   (b) 1/3
    (c) 11/21   (d) 3/7
    (e) 3/10   (f) 5/11
    (g) 1/2   (h) 3/11
    (i) 3/7

19. (a) 1/4   (b) 1/5
    (c) 1/6   (d) 1/3

20. (a) 1/2, 3/4   (b) 1/2, 1/4

21. (a) 1/3   (b) 2/4 = 1/2
    (c) 3/5   (d) 1/2
    (e) 1   (f) 1/3

22. (a) 13/16   (b) 13/21
    (c) 15/16   (d) 5/14
    (e) 1   (f) 1/2

23. (a) and (b) Answers will vary.
    (c) 176/1024

24. Use a deck of 52 cards. Draw until 2 aces appear. Count and record the number of draws needed. Repeat n times, for your choice of n, say n = 100. Then compute the average number of draws needed. Theoretical expected value is 21.2.

25. Use slips of paper, numbered from 1 to 20. Call your number 1, for example. Draw 12 slips from a hat; this is the first jury. Replace all 12 slips and draw 12 slips again. This is the second jury. Repeat this n times, say n = 100. Count the number of times out of n that your number came up on one (or both) of the juries. It should be around 80% of the time. Theoretical probability = .84.

26. Switches should win about 2/3 of the time.

27. Answers will vary.

28. Click on the numbers 1, 2, 3, 4, 5, 6 to put in the box. Press Start. When each of the numbers 1-5 have been drawn, press Pause and record the number of draws. Repeat 100 times.

29. True. Let the row sum be m. Then the sum of all numbers must be the sum of three rows, or $3m$, a multiple of 3.

30. (a) Set the "Longest run in heads" to 4 and the "Probability of heads" to 0.5. Start tossing until you get 4 heads in a row and record how many tosses it took. Repeat this 20 times and average the number of tosses it took to get 4 heads in a row.
    (b) A reasonable answer would be around 25 to 30 tosses.

Analyzing Student Thinking

31. Sanchez is incorrect. Assuming his past batting record applies to future at bats, the odds that Swinging Sam will not get a hit on his next at bat are   P(no hit):P(hit) = 4/7:3/7 = 4:3.

32. No. The expected value may not necessarily be greater than $20. If the outcome "greater than $20" has a value of $25 and the outcome "less than $20" has a value of $1, then the expected value, which is $E = 25(3/4) + 1(1/4) = \$19$, would not be greater than $20.

33. Alfred, we must consider that some sums are more likely than others. Also, there are 36 possibilities when tossing two dice, not 11. If we list the outcomes with a prime sum, we can see there are 15 of them: (1, 1), (1, 2), (2, 1), (1, 4), (4, 1), (2, 3), (3, 2), (1, 6), (6, 1), (2, 5), (5, 2), (3, 4), (4, 3), (5, 6), (6, 5). Thus, the odds of tossing a prime sum are P(prime sum):P(not prime sum) = 15/36:21/36 = 15:21 = 5:7.

34. Josh is correct. Assuming that the five hits were counted as part of the .333, the odds of a hit on Julio's next at bat would be P(hit):P(no hit). That is, 0.333:0.667 or 1:2.

35. Jackson's answer is correct, but his reasoning is not. Since it is given that the card is red, we don't need to consider the two black suits. So, $P(\text{heart} \mid \text{red}) =$

$$\frac{P(\text{heart and red})}{P(\text{red})} = \frac{13/52}{26/52} = \frac{1}{2}$$

36. Luiza's statement is not always true. Consider the case when A and B are independent events:

$$P(A \mid B) = \frac{P(A \cap B)}{P(B)} = \frac{0}{P(B)} = 0.$$

Similarly, $P(B \mid A) = 0$ and $0 + 0$ is not equal to 1.

Chapter 12

Section 12.1

1. (a) Level 1
   (b) Level 0
   (c) Level 0

2. (a) None
   (b) 7
   (c) 2
   (d) Level 1

3. (a) {1, 2, 7} and {3, 4, 5, 6, 8, 9}.
      Shapes 1, 2, and 7 all have 4
      congruent sides and the rest of
      the shapes do not. Answers
      may vary.
   (b) {4, 6, 8, 9} and {1, 2, 3, 5, 7}.
      Shapes 1, 2, 3, 5, and 7 all
      have at least two parallel sides
      and the rest of the shapes do
      not. Answers may vary.
   (c) Level 1
   (d) Level 1

4. (a)

   (b)

(c)

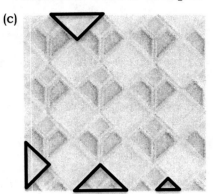

5. 9 rectangles

6. (a) 13   (b) 15   (c) 15

7.

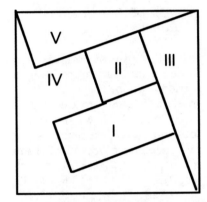

8. (a) *ABRI, IRGH, IBMG*
   (b) *RDFG*
   (c) *IDEG*
   (d) *ABI, IBR, BMR, IRG, IGH, GRM,
      DEF*
   (e) *ICG*
   (f) *JOPQ*

9. (a) (I)
   (b) (III)

10. Yes.

11. Lengths x and y are the same in
    each case.

12. (a) 3   (b) 4

13.

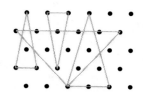

14. (a) 7: $\mathbf{3} \times 2^2 + \mathbf{4} \times 1^2 = 16$

    8: $\mathbf{1} \times 3^2 + \mathbf{3} \times 2^2 + \mathbf{4} \times 1^2$
    $= 25$

    9: $\mathbf{9} \times 1^2 = 9$

    $\mathbf{1} \times 4^2 + \mathbf{4} \times 2^2 + \mathbf{4} \times 1^2$
    $= 36$

    10: $\mathbf{2} \times 2^2 + \mathbf{8} \times 1^2 = 16$

    $\mathbf{1} \times 4^2 + \mathbf{9} \times 1^2 = 25$

    11: $\mathbf{1} \times 3^2 + \mathbf{2} \times 2^2 + \mathbf{8} \times 1^2$
    $= 25$

    $\mathbf{2} \times 3^2 + \mathbf{3} \times 2^2 + \mathbf{6} \times 1^2$
    $= 36$

    12: $\mathbf{1} \times 5^2 + \mathbf{11} \times 1^2 = 36$

    $\mathbf{3} \times 3^2 + \mathbf{9} \times 1^2 = 36$

    13: $\mathbf{1} \times 2^2 + \mathbf{12} \times 1^2 = 16$

    $\mathbf{4} \times 2^2 + \mathbf{9} \times 1^2 = 25$

    14: $\mathbf{1} \times 3^2 + \mathbf{1} \times 2^2 + \mathbf{12} \times 1^2$
    $= 25$

    $\mathbf{2} \times 3^2 + \mathbf{2} \times 2^2 + \mathbf{10} \times 1^2$
    $= 36$

    15: $\mathbf{7} \times 2^2 + \mathbf{8} \times 1^2 = 36$

    $\mathbf{1} \times 4^2 + \mathbf{2} \times 2^2 +$
    $\mathbf{12} \times 1^2 = 36$

    16: $\mathbf{16} \times 1^2 = 16$

    $\mathbf{3} \times 2^2 + \mathbf{13} \times 1^2 = 25$

    (b) See (a)

    (c) 9 and 16

15. (a)

(b)

16. (a)

(b)

Figures here show the fold line at the bottom. They could also be drawn with the fold line at the top.

17.

18.

Analyzing Student Thinking

19. These children's comments seem to reflect van Hiele Level 0, the visual level. Bernie does not recognize that straight sides are a property of triangles, and Chandra is visualizing a stereotypical triangle with slanted sides (which she calls "angles") and a horizontal base (which she calls "straight").

20. Level 0, because the orientation of the triangle on the page influenced Daniel's ability to recognize this as an isosceles triangle. Ask the student to investigate this triangle, as well as several other isosceles triangles with different orientations, constructed on a geoboard (or square dot paper). Because the geoboard can be turned and manipulated, this will help the student see that the orientation of a shape does not matter.

21. Carla seems to be at the initial level of Analysis, Level 1. Although she identifies the shape based on its general appearance (Level 0), this student's comments indicate that she notices the angles of the parallelogram are not the same as the angles of the rectangles she's seen. To help this student, emphasize that rectangles all have square corners.

Section 12.2

1. (a) Reflections over both diagonals, half turn rotation around the center of the square.
    (b) 1/2 turn around the center of the square.

2. (a) A,H,I,M,O,T,U,V,W,X,Y
    (b) B,C,D,E,H,I,K,O,X

3. (a) Rotation, 180° about center of circle.
    (b) Reflection, vertical line through center; rotation, 120° or 240° degrees about center of circle.
    (c) Reflection, vertical line.
    (d) Reflection, 12 lines through center; rotation, 30° and multiples.

4. (a)   (b)

    (c)   (d)

    (e)

5. (a) a, b, e, j
    (b) b, e, g, i, j
    (c) b, c, d, g, h, i, j
    (d) c, g, j

6. Yes. When the paper is folded so the ends of one line match, the ends of the other line also match.

7. No. When the paper is folded along one line the ends of the other line do not match.

8. (a) (i) $\overline{AC}$ and $\overline{BD}$
       (ii) $\overline{AD}$ and $\overline{BC}$, $\overline{AB}$ and $\overline{DC}$
       (iii) $\overline{AD}$ and $\overline{DC}$, $\overline{DC}$ and $\overline{CB}$, $\overline{BA}$ and $\overline{AD}$
       (iv) E, $\overline{AC}$
    (b) (i) $\overline{JL}$ and $\overline{IK}$
       (ii) $\overline{IJ}$ and $\overline{LK}$, $\overline{IL}$ and $\overline{JK}$
       (iii) $\overline{IL}$ and $\overline{LK}$, $\overline{LK}$ and $\overline{KJ}$, $\overline{KJ}$ and $\overline{JI}$
       (iv) M, $\overline{IK}$

9. Rotate 1/2 turn around the center, E. Then $\overline{AE}$ of the tracing coincides with $\overline{CE}$, and $\overline{BE}$ of the tracing coincides with $\overline{DE}$.

10. Fold one of the diagonals exactly onto itself so that the end points match up; crease the fold line.

Repeat this for the other diagonal. The two creases meet at the point of intersection of the diagonals.

11. Trace a square and its diagonals. Rotate the tracing until the traced diagonals lands on top of the other diagonal. These will match exactly, showing they are the same length.

12. (a) Fold on the dashed line.

(b) No, because the base angles of a non-isosceles trapezoid are not congruent.

13. Rotate 1/2 turn around the center.

14. Rhombi and kites both have perpendicular diagonals, and both have reflection symmetry. Rhombi have rotation symmetry, but kites do not. (Answers may vary.)

15. (a)

(b)

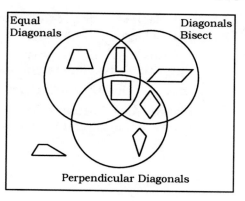

17. Yes, in general, Keith. However, if the kite is a rhombus, it will have two lines of symmetry.

18. Tell Janet to cut out a paper rectangle and then ask how she can fold the rectangle to show that the opposite sides are the same length.

19. No. The following figure has reflection symmetry, but not rotation symmetry.

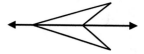

20. Beth is incorrect. Building a quadrilateral around any two perpendicular line segments, as Beth describes, may not result in a rhombus, as the following example illustrates:

In order for Beth's method to work, she'd need to use the fact that a rhombus has diagonals that bisect each other.

Analyzing Student Thinking

16. Yes; rhombi have perpendicular diagonals that bisect each other, and squares fit into all three categories. Yes; non-isosceles trapezoids do not fit into any of these categories. See the following Venn diagram.

21. No.

When we fold the parallelogram on the line, the bottom half of the parallelogram does not coincide with the top half, so this is not a line of symmetry.

22. Ask Becky to cut out the following parallelogram and fold it at point M so that $\overline{MA}$ lines up with $\overline{MC}$. Since these two line segments coincide, this shows that $\overline{BD}$ bisects $\overline{AC}$. Then ask Becky what she would need to do to show that $\overline{AC}$ bisects $\overline{BD}$.

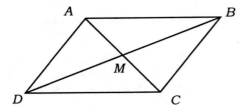

Section 12.3

1. Isosceles Triangles   Equilateral Triangles

2. Trapezoids   Rectangles

3. Kites   Rhombi

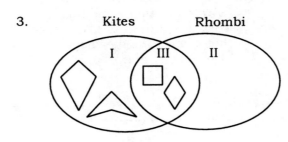

4. (a) (iii) Rectangles are inner set.
   (b) (ii) Note that the intersection is squares.
   (c) (iii) Squares inside rectangles.
   (d) (i)

5. (a) *ABI, RBI, RBM, RMG, RGI, HIG, FDE*
   (b) *OQJ*
   (c) *ICGH*   (d) *ACI*
   (e) *GMDF*   (f) *GMDE*
   (g) BIJ
   (Answers may vary.)

6. (a) kite
   (b) rectangle
   (c) isosceles trapezoid

7. m($\angle AOB$) = 83°, m($\angle BOC$) = 7°

8. m($\angle X$) = 123°

9. m($\angle 1$) = 47°, m($\angle 2$) = 47°, m($\angle 3$) = 106°, m($\angle 4$) = 133°

10. (a) No, there will always be at least one house not connected to one of the utilities.
    (b) Yes, one solution is shown next.

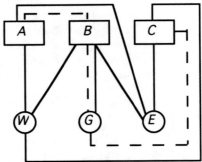

The problem stated above is related to a branch of mathematics called graph theory.

11. (a) Yes; by the Corresponding Angles Theorem and the Alternate Interior Angles Theorem, a parallelogram with one right angle must have four right angles—this is a rectangle.
    (b) No; for example, this quadrilateral has perpendicular diagonals, but is not a kite.

(c) Yes, by the Corresponding Angles Theorem and Alternate Interior Angles Theorem, a parallelogram with a pair of adjacent sides congruent must have four congruent sides—this is a rhombus.

Analyzing Student Thinking

12. Yes, Jonas, this is the case when the kite is also a rhombus

13. Gerald is incorrect. An isosceles triangle is defined to be a triangle with at least two sides the same length. Thus, an equilateral triangle is a special type of isosceles triangle.

14. No, Steve, because the definition of an isosceles trapezoid requires that the quadrilateral have exactly one pair of parallel sides; a rectangle has two pairs of parallel sides.

15. That's right, Elyse, since a square has 4 congruent sides, it fits the definition of a rhombus.

16. Bobby, some rectangles have a length that is different from the width, but the definition of rectangle does not require this. Whitney is right; a square fits the definition of rectangle since it has four right angles. Note however that we don't need to mention the parallel opposite sides since this is a *property* of rectangles, and not a requirement of the definition.

Section 12.4

1. (a) $\{L, M, N, R\}, \{Q, P, R\}, \{M, O, Q\}$
   (b) $\{\overleftrightarrow{LO}, \overleftrightarrow{MO}, \overleftrightarrow{NO}\}$
   $\{\overleftrightarrow{MN}, \overleftrightarrow{ON}, \overleftrightarrow{PN}\}$
   $\{\overleftrightarrow{OP}, \overleftrightarrow{QP}, \overleftrightarrow{NP}\}$

2. $\overline{AB}, \overline{AC}, \overline{AD}, \overline{AE}, \overline{AF}, \overline{BC}, \overline{BD}, \overline{BE}, \overline{BF}, \overline{CD}, \overline{CE}, \overline{CF}, \overline{DE}, \overline{DF}, \overline{EF}$

3. (a) $\angle LOM, \angle MON, \angle NOP, \angle NOQ, \angle POQ$
   (b) $\angle LOP, \angle LOQ, \angle MOP, \angle MOQ$
   (c) $\angle LON$
   (d) $\angle LOM$ and $\angle MON$
   $\angle MON$ and $\angle NOP$
   There are many others.

4. (a) 60°   (b) 30°   (c) 120°

5. (a) m($\angle C$) = 38°, m($\overline{AC}$) = 7 cm
   (b) m($\angle C$) = 55°,
   m($\overline{AC}$) = 6.4 cm
   Note: Answers will vary due to measurement error.

6. $\overline{AB}$ and $\overline{CB}$, $\overline{AD}$ and $\overline{CD}$, $\overline{AE}$ and $\overline{CE}$.
   $\angle ADE$ and $\angle CDE$,
   $\angle AED$ and $\angle CED$
   $\angle DAE$ and $\angle DCE$,
   $\angle EDA$ and $\angle EDC$,
   $\angle BAE$ and $\angle BCE$,
   $\angle BEA$ and $\angle BEC$,
   $\angle AEB$ and $\angle CEB$,
   $\angle ABE$ and $\angle CBE$,
   $\angle DAB$ and $\angle DCB$.

7. (a) $\angle LTO$ and $\angle XVO$
   $\angle MUN$ and $\angle XWV$
   $\angle NUX$ and $\angle VWQ$
   There are many others.
   (b) $\angle STX$ and $\angle XVO$
   $\angle NTX$ and $\angle XVW$
   $\angle NUX$ and $\angle XWR$
   $\angle TUX$ and $\angle XWV$

8. (a) Yes; 36 + 78 + 66 = 180.
   (b) No; 124 + 56 + 20 ≠ 180.
   (c) No; 90 + 74 + 18 ≠ 180.

9. (a) 28   (b) 5   (c) 8
   (d) 15 = 28 - (5 + 8)

10. (a) $\overline{AP}$ is the same length as $\overline{CP}$, so P is the midpoint of $\overline{AC}$.

(b) *P* is the midpoint of both diagonals.

(c) *P* is not the midpoint of either diagonal.

11. For example:

(a)

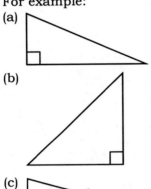

(b)

(c)

12. For example:

(a)

(b)

(c)

16. (a) *l* || *m* , given; m(∠3) = m(∠4), Alternate Interior Angles Property; m(∠3) = m(∠1), vertical angles have same measure; m(∠1) = m(∠4).

(b) m(∠3) = m(∠6), given; m(∠4) = m(∠6), vertical angles have the same measure; m(∠3) = m(∠4); *l* || *m*, Alternate Interior Angles Property.

17. (a) Equals 180°.

(b) m(∠1) + m(∠3) = 180°,   given; m(∠1) + m(∠2) = 180°, form straight angle; m(∠1) + m(∠3) = m(∠1) + m(∠2); m(∠3) = m(∠2), subtraction; *l* || *m*, Alternate Interior Angles Property

18. The sum of the measures of any two consecutive angles of a parallelogram is 180°. Any two opposite angles of a parallelogram are congruent.

19. m(∠*a*) = 62°, m(∠*b*) = 45°, m(∠*c*) = 79°, m(∠*d*) = 56°, and m(∠*e*) = 39°.

20. (a) *a* + *b* + *c* = 180° since the three angles form a straight angle.

(b) A rectangle with a base half as long as $\overline{AC}$.

(c) Yes, the results are the same.

21. 4 points → 6 lines
5 points → 10 lines
6 points → 15 lines

$$n \text{ points} \rightarrow \frac{n(n-1)}{2} \text{ lines}$$

Analyzing Student Thinking

22. Alora is correct. Her brother likely made the mistake of reading the measure of the exterior angle.

23. Yes, Kent. First, by the Vertical Angle Theorem, the lower two angles labeled 2 are congruent. By the Alternate

Interior Angles Theorem, the middle angles labeled 2 are congruent. Since the angle labeled 1 and the top angle labeled 2 form a straight angle, the sum of their measures is 180°. Thus, the measures of the original angles 1 and 2 add up to 180°.

24. In this context, the word "vertical" is an adjective derived from the word *vertex*. Vertical angles are a pair of angles formed by a pair of intersecting lines such that the only point the two angles have in common is their vertex, which is the point of intersection of the lines. The lines themselves don't have to be vertical.

25. Parallel lines may be defined differently. In one case, they are defined as TWO lines in a plane that do not intersect. However, there is a good reason to allow a line to be parallel to itself. Thus, this is allowed in one definition. Some books do define a trapezoid to be a quadrilateral with at least one pair of parallel lines. However, others choose to limit the definition to exactly one pair of parallel lines.

26. No, there are only four rays since $\overrightarrow{RS}$ and $\overrightarrow{RT}$ are the same ray, and $\overrightarrow{TR}$ and $\overrightarrow{TS}$ are the same ray.

27. A triangle cannot be both scalene and isosceles since a triangle cannot have 3 sides of different length *and* at least two sides the same length. Also, a triangle cannot be both right and obtuse since a triangle with a 90-degree angle cannot have another angle that is greater than 90 degrees. In general, only combinations that that do not conflict are possible.

Section 12.5

1. (a) *S, C*   (b) none
   (c) none   (c) *S*

2. (a) 720°   (b) 900°

3. ∠*AGH* and ∠*FGL* are exterior angles. ∠*LGH* and ∠*GHI* are vertex angles. ∠*GMH* and ∠*GML* are central angles. (Answers may vary.)

4. (a) 72°, 144°, 216°, 288°
   (b) 60°, 120°, 180°, 240°, 300°
   (c) 51.4°, 102.9°, 154.3°, 205,7°, 257.1°, 308.6°
   (d) 45°, 90°, 135°, 180°, 225°, 270°, 315°
   (e) $\dfrac{x \cdot 180°}{n}$, for $x = 1, \ldots, n-1$

5. (a) 122°
   (b) 68°, 112°
   (c) 115°, 115°, 120°, 120°

6. (a) 154.3°, 25.7°, 25.7°
   (b) 160°, 20°, 20°
   (c) 170°, 10°, 10°
   (d) 171.4°, 8.6°, 8.6°

7. 18 sides

8. (a) 12   (b) 15
   (c) 60

9. (a) 3   (b) 30
   (c) 24

10. (a) 20   (b) 10
    (c) 120

11. (a) 40°   (b) 24°
    (c) (180 − *x*)°

12. (a) 144°   (b) 60°
    (c) (180 − *a*)°

13. (a)

(b)

(b) Triangles

(c) Pentagons

14. E and D are midpoints of $\overline{AB}$ and $\overline{AC}$, respectively. Lines $\overleftrightarrow{ED}$ and $\overleftrightarrow{BC}$ do not meet in the tessellation (extended), so are parallel. Since ED = BF = FC, we have BC = 2ED.

15. $a_1/a_2 = b_1/b_2$. In this case $a_1/a_2 = 1/2$.

16. (a)

(b) No

17. (a) Kites

18. (a) (4, 8, 8)   (b) (4, 6, 12)
     (c) (3, 3, 3, 3, 6) (d) (3, 3, 4, 3, 4)
     (e) (3, 4, 6, 4)
     (f) (3, 3, 3, 3, 4, 4)
     (g) (3, 12, 12)   (h) (3, 6, 3, 6)

19. (a) (4, 4, 4, 4), (3, 3, 4, 12),
         (3, 3, 6, 6), (3, 4, 4, 6),
         (3, 4, 3, 12), (3, 6, 3, 6),
         (3, 4, 6, 4)
     (b) (3, 3, 3, 3, 6), (3, 3, 3, 4, 4),
         (3, 3, 4, 3, 4)
     (c) (3, 3, 3, 3, 3, 3)
     (d) no ways

20. Yes

21. No

22. (a) Pentagon: 1/5, 2/5, 3/5, 4/5 and 1 full turn around the center. Hexagon: 1/6, 1/3, 1/2, 2/3, 5/6, and 1 full turn around the center.
     (b) n.

23. (a)

(b)

24. (a)

(b) Sum of measures of vertex angles of a triangle is 180 degrees. Vertical angles have same measure.

25. $a = 45°$, $b = 45°$, $c = 65°$, $d = 80°$, $e = 30°$, $f = 70°$, $g = 20°$, $h = 55°$

26. Divide by 180, subtraction of fractions, addition property, division by 2 and distributivity.

27. (a) (3,7,42), (3,8,24), (3,9,18), (3,10,15), (3,12,12)
     (b) (4,5,20), (4,6,12), (4,8,8)
     (c) (5,5,10)
     (d) (6,6,6)
     (e) 10

28. (a) 5   (b) 10   (c) 5
     (d) (5,5,5), which does not surround point E
     (e) By putting triangle or Pentagon in the center, you get the same results except for (3,12,12).

29. (a) (4,4,4,4), (3,3,4,12), (3,3,6,6), (3,4,4,6)
     (b) (4,4,4,4)
     (c) (3,3,4,12), (3,4,3,12), (3,3,6,6), (3,4,4,6)
     (d) (3,6,3,6), (3,4,6,4)

30. (a) (3,3,3,3,6) and (3,3,3,4,4)
     (b) (3,3,3,3,6), (3,3,3,4,4), (3,3,4,3,4)
     (c) (3,3,3,3,3,3), regular
     (d) No, angle measure would have to be less than 60° (or have fewer sides than 2 then.)

31. (a) (i)   (ii)   (iii)   (iv)

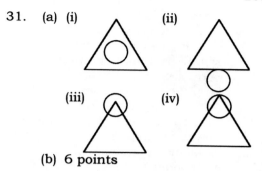

(b) 6 points

Analyzing Student Thinking

32. No. The sum of the measures of the four vertex angles of any quadrilateral is 360°. Thus, to tessellate a convex quadrilateral, surround each point by one copy of each vertex angle, matching the sides with the same length, as follows:

33. Tyrone, if you used regular pentagons (rather than a rough sketch) for your tessellation, you would be able to see there are gaps between the pentagons. This is because, since the angles of a regular pentagon measure 108°, when three pentagons are put together around a common vertex, these angles add up to 324°, not 360°.

34. This student is thinking about applying a formula that is appropriate for a *regular* pentagon where all five vertex angles are congruent. If the four angles are not all 108°, he needs to subtract the sum of the measures of the four angles from 540° to find the measure of the missing angle.

35. Yes. A regular octagon has 8 lines of symmetry. The first group used the 4 lines of symmetry that pass

through opposite vertices to form 8 congruent triangles, while the second group used the 4 lines of symmetry that pass through the midpoints of the opposite sides to form 8 congruent kites.

36. Clifton, you certainly can make a polygon with so many sides that it looks like a circle. In fact, the more sides you give the polygon, the more it resembles a circle. However, a circle is not a polygon since a polygon is made up of line segments and a circle is not.

37. Jackie is correct. For each vertex of a polygon, there are two exterior angles (one for each of the sides that meet at that vertex), as the following figure illustrates. The sum of the measures of all of these exterior angles is 720°.

38. Ask Marty and Heather to explain more about what they're thinking. What does he mean by "plane figure?" And which angles is he referring to: vertex angles? Which angles is Heather referring to: central angles? Ask these students to check their claims with a few such figures/angles.

39. First, give Jared 6 toothpicks and ask him if he can arrange them into a hexagon with different sized angles (he'll be able to form a convex hexagon like the one shown below).

It is also possible to make a hexagon that has equal angles and not equal sides; for example:

Section 12.6

1. (a) $\{\overline{BG}, \overline{CF}\}, \{\overline{CF}, \overline{DE}\}, \{\overline{BG}, \overline{DE}\}$
   (b) $\{\overline{DC}, \overline{GF}\}, \{\overline{AD}, \overline{GF}\}, \{\overline{EF}, \overline{BG}\},$
       $\{\overline{AB}, \overline{CF}\}$
       Other answers are possible.
   (c) Planes $DCFE$ and $BCFG$ with edge $\overline{CF}$. Other answers are possible.
   (d) Planes ADE and $CFED$ with edge $\overline{DE}$.

2. (a) $1/2$, $\sqrt{3}/2$
   (b) $\sqrt{3}/2$
   (c) $AE = DE = \sqrt{3}/2$, $AD = 1$

3. (a) Yes. 6 total faces – 2 triangles, 2 quadrilaterals, and 2 pentagons.
   (b) No. Faces are not polygons.
   (c) No. Not a single enclosed space.

4. (a) Triangular prism
   (b) Rectangular prism
   (c) Hexagonal prism

5. Prisms: (a) and (c); pyramid: (b)

6. (a) right triangular prism
   (b) regular tetrahedron
   (c) right rectangular prism
   (d)

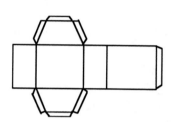

10. (a) Triangle: 4, 4, 8, 6;
         quadrilateral: 5, 5, 10, 8;
         pentagon: 6, 6, 12, 10;
         hexagon: 7, 7, 14, 12;
         n-gon: *n* + 1, *n* + 1, 2*n* + 2, 2*n*
     (b) Yes

11. (a) (i) 10, 12, 22, 20;
         (ii) 9, 9, 18, 16
     (b) Yes

12. Truncated icosahedron: 6-6-5
     Truncated dodecahedron: 10-10-3
     Cube octahedron: 4-4-3
     Small rhombicubahedrdon: 4-4-4-3
     On each polyhedron all vertex arrangements are the same, so they are all semiregular.

7.

8.

9. (a)   (b)

13. (a)   (b)

14. (a)   (b)

                 Parabola

     (c)

     Ellipse

15.

16.

17. (a) Either upper left or lower right.

182

(b) Either, depending on perspective.

18. 34

19. View (b). The tops in (a) and (c) should have a rectangle.

20. (a)

Base

Front

Right Side

(b) Base

Front

Right Side

21. Largest number = 19

2	3	2
2	2	2
2	2	2

Smallest number = 13

1	3	1
2	1	1
1	1	2

(Other base designs are possible.)

22. (a)

Sides	1	2	3	0
Cubes	0	0	8	0

(b)

Sides	1	2	3	0
Cubes	6	12	8	1

(c)

Sides	1	2	3	0
Cubes	24	24	8	8

(d)

Sides	1	2
Cubes	$6(n-2)^3$	$12(n-2)$

Sides	3	0
Cubes	8	$(n-2)^3$

23. They all are possible, for example (h)

24. Yes for all parts.

25. (a) 6   (b) 4
    (c) 6   (d) infinite number

26. (a) 3 of order 2 (through midpoints of nonintersecting edges); 4 of order 3 (through vertex and center of opposite face)
    (b) 5 of order 2 (through midpoint of edge and center of opposite face); 1 of order 5 (through centers of bases)

27. (a) 1   (b) Infinite   (c) Infinite

28. 6

Analyzing Student Thinking

29. Rene, you're right about planes in the 3-dimensional space and about lines in 2-dimensional space. However, when we talk

about lines in 3-dimensional space, we must consider that the two lines may be in different planes, in which case they may be neither intersecting, nor parallel; for example, a line on the ceiling where a wall meets the ceiling and a line on the floor that is perpendicular to the wall.

30. Mario, it can get a little confusing when we use the same term for two different objects. To clarify, you could call the "sides" of a polygon, "edges," and the "sides" of a polyhedron, "faces."

31. Cheryl, the word "right" used with a prism or pyramid refers to the axis being perpendicular to (forming a right angle with) the base, as opposed to an oblique polyhedron that leans. "Right triangular pyramid" would usually be taken to mean a pyramid that has a triangular base, but not necessarily a right triangular base. This makes one wonder if, to specify a right pyramid with a right triangular base, one would need to say a "right, right triangular pyramid."

32. No. There is a need for two different definitions because a circle is a 2-dimensional figure and a sphere is 3-dimensional. A circle is the set of points *in a plane* that are the same distance from its center, whereas a sphere is a set of points *in space* that are the same distance from its center.

33. Alicia, a non-isosceles trapezoid is an example of a polygon with no lines of symmetry. An oblique prism with such a trapezoid as its base would have no plane of symmetry.

34. Koji, there must be at least 3 regular polygons meeting at each vertex of a regular polyhedron. If we put 3 hexagons together, each with a 120° angle, the total would be 360°. The polyhedron would flatten out, making it impossible to form a solid.

35. Jesse, to see this one, it might help to imagine two walls; you can see these intersect in a line at the corner of the room. Now, imagine a third wall that comes out from the corner of the room, as the following drawing shows. These three walls intersect in a line.

Chapter 13 - Measurement

Section 13.1

1. (a) $1\frac{2}{3}$, $1\frac{1}{4}$, $\frac{1}{4}$
    (b) 12, 12,
    (c) Whether the pencil is mechanical or wood or old. Whether the fingers are fat or skinny.

2. (a) Waist, hips, length from neck to waist or to hemline, bust or chest, length of arm.
    (b) Length and width of foot, height of arch.
    (c) Height, weight, heartbeat, blood pressure.
    (d) Height, strength, height of jump, number of sit-ups in 1 minute.

3. (a) 220   (b) 320
    (c) 640   (d) 4492.125
    (e) 512,000   (f) 1
    (g) 126   (h) 48

4.

TABLESPOON	LIQUID OUNCE	CUP	PINT	QUART	GALLON
256	128	16	8	4	1
1024	512	64	32	16	4
384	192	24	12	6	1.5
64	32	4	2	1	.25

5.

SQUARE INCHES	SQUARE FEET	SQUARE YARDS
2592	18	2
6480	45	5
79056	549	61

6. (a) 205 m   (b) 72 m
    (c) 512 km

7. (a) 10 L   (b) 200 mL
    (c) 200 L

8. (a) 25 g   (b) 7 g
    (c) 1715 kg

9. (a) -5° C   (b) 39° C

10. (a) 10 cents   (b) 1 cent
    (c) $10   (d) $1000

11. "Mega" means one million times, so winnings are millions of dollars.

12. (a) 12 m   (b) 0.03569 km
    (c) 26,000,000 cm
    (d) 0.786 m
    (e) 38.4 cm   (f) 1200 cm
    (g) 1,345,000 cm (h) 0.019 km
    (i) 46,780 km   (j) 8.9 hm

13. (a) 10,000
    (b) four places to right
    (c) two places to the right
    (d) two places to the left.
    (e) are and hectare

14. (a) 2,000,000 cm³
    (b) 5,000,000,000 mm³
    (c) 16,000 cm³
    (d) 0.62 dm³
    (e) 0.056 m³
    (f) 1200 cm³

15. (a) 4750 mg
    (b) 0.057 hg
    (c) 32,000 mg

16. (a) 3.5 dL   (b) 0.56 L
    (c) 0.520 kL

17. (a) kg   (b) dm³, kg
    (c) mL, g

18. (a) 58°C   (b) 194°F
    (c) -22°F   (d) -88°C
    (e) -0.4°F

19. (a) 400 g/cm
    (b) 65 g/cm³
    (c) 0.972 ton/yd³
    (d) 98.2 mi/hr

20. (a) 48 farthings
    (b) 2 farthings

21. (a) 402.34 m   (b) 0.62 mi

22. (a) 750 mi/hr
    (b) 6,570,000 mi/yr

23. 1 jack = 1/8 james, 1/480 jennifers, 1/5760 jessicas;

1 james = 192 jills, 1/60 jennifers, 1/720 jessicas; 1 jennifer = 11,520 jills, 480 jacks, 1/12 jessicas; 1 jessica = 138,240 jills, 5760 jacks, 720 james

24. 261,100 watts

25. Approximately 85 ha

26. 89 kph (88.5 km/hr)
Note: most signs are reading 88 kph, which has us drive a little slower.

27. (a) 50 days   (b) 2.7 ft/hr

28. (a) 6,278,400,000 joules
(b) $88.39

29. -40° C = -40° F

30. (a) About 18 km/sec
(b) 5.4×10^9 km

31. 3.268 light years

32. This is impossible since the car has used up all the time required for the round trip by the time it reaches the first city.

33. (a) 1 hr/roll
(b) 18 rolls/hr or .055 hr/roll
(c) 2600 rolls

34. Surface area about 10243 m²; Volume about 68292 m³

Analyzing Student Thinking

35. Kimiko, standard units help in situations when we want to communicate our measurements to other people. Also, standard units are better when we need precise measurements, while nonstandard units are fine when the accuracy and precision are not important.

36. Jhoti, a square yard is a square that measures one yard (or 3 feet) on each side:

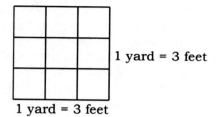

1 yard = 3 feet

Counting the number of square feet we see that 1 square yard = 9 square feet.

37. Monique is incorrect. She needs to multiply 43,560 by 14 to find the total area of the plot, 609,840 sq. feet. Then, she should take the square root to find the length of the side of the square plot, 780.92 ft.

38. Scotty is incorrect. The volume of topsoil ordered is 1 yd³ = 27 ft³ = $27 \times 12 \times 12 \times 12$ in³ = 46,656 in³. But Scotty would require $15 \times 24 \times 1/6$ = 60 ft³ = 60×12^3 in³ = 103,680 in³ of topsoil to cover his garden evenly to a depth of 2 inches.

39. Amy is incorrect. Imagine a square that measures 1 meter on each side (a m²). Then, each side measures 100 cm and there are 100 × 100 = 10,000 cm² in a m². In other words, 1 cm² = 1/10,000 = .0001 m². Similarly, it takes 100 × 100 × 100 = 1,000,000 cm³ to fill a cube that measures 1 m by 1 m by 1 m (a cubic meter), so 1 cm³ = 1/1,000,000 = .000001 m³.

40. Jeremy is incorrect 41°F = 5°C and 82°F = 28°C. Would that mean that in Celsius it was $5\frac{1}{2}$ times as hot as in the morning? Whether in Celsius or Fahrenheit, zero is not an absolute measure.

Therefore, this type of comparison, by a factor, does not apply here.

41. Kobe, there are many reasons. First, the metric system has all the features of an ideal system of units: portability, convertability, and interrelatedness, whereas the US system lacks convertability and interrrelatedness. In short, the metric system is a better system. Also, nearly every other country in the world uses the metric system. If the US were to make the switch, many international activities, including trade and communication, would be made easier.

Section 13.2

1. (a) $9/2 - \sqrt{3}$ (b) $3\sqrt{3}$
   (c) 7.96   (d) 6.03

2. (a) $q - p$
   (b) $\dfrac{q - p}{2}$
   (c) $p + \dfrac{q - p}{2} = \dfrac{p + q}{2}$
   (d) Yes
   (e) $\dfrac{-2.5 + 13.9}{2} = 5.7$

3. (a) -10.9   (b) -2.4

4. (a) $q - p$ (b) $\dfrac{2p + q}{3}$
   (c) $\dfrac{p + 2q}{3}$
   (d) $m = 2.9$, $n = 9.4$

5. (a) -10.2   (b) 11.1

6. (a) $P = 99.4$ units
   (b) $a = 7.6$ units
   (c) $b = 12$ units

7. 195.6 units

8. 90 units

9. (a) $r = 13.4/\pi$ units,

$d = 26.8/\pi$ units
(b) $d = 2\sqrt{15}$ units,
$c = 2\pi\sqrt{15}$ units
(c) $r = 9\pi$ units, $C = 18\pi^2$ units

10. (a) $A = 501.96$ sq. units
    (b) $a = 7.6$ units
    (c) $b = 12$ units

11. (a) $A = 25$ sq. units
    $P = 8 + 14\sqrt{2}$ units
    (b) $A = 20$ sq. units
    $P = 8 + 12\sqrt{2}$ units
    (c) $A = 22\dfrac{1}{2}$ sq. units
    $P = 14 + 14\sqrt{2}$ units
    (d) Figure (a) by $2\dfrac{1}{2}$

12. (a) 7 units   (b) $6\dfrac{1}{2}$ units
    (c) 8 units

13. 92 Pieces

14. (a) 8.2 km^2 (b) 60 m^2

15. 1292.94 sq. units

16. 418.86 sq. units

17. (a) $\sqrt{13}$, 4, $A_1 = 12$, $A_2 = 8$;
    5, 2, $A_1 = 6$, $A_2 = 8$
    (b) The statement is false since parallelograms with the same length sides had different areas.

18. (a) $(1/2)(2 + 6) = 4$ (b) 4
    (c) They are equal.

19. (a) 2   (b) 18   (c) 1:9

20. (a) $r = 15.2$ units,
    $d = 30.4$ units
    (b) $d = 2\sqrt{15}$ units,
    $A = 15\pi$ sq. units
    (c) $r = 9\pi$ units,
    $A = 81\pi^3$ sq. units

21. (a) $6\sqrt{7}$ sq. units

(b) 16 sq. units

22. (a) Hypotenuse of 2 by 1 right
         triangle
     (b) 4 × 1   (c) 3 × 3
     (d) 5 × 2

23. (a) $\sqrt{34}$ units   (b) 7 units

24. (a) Yes   (b) Yes   (c) No

25. (a) Acute

Right

Obtuse

b and *h* are the same on all
triangles to give equal areas.
(b) The perimeters are all
     different.
(c) There is no clear relationship.

26. No. If a parallelogram is very long
     and narrow, the perimeter will be
     large but the area will be small.

27. (a) Slant distance (13 ft) can be
         more easily measured than
         $6\sqrt{5}$ ft.
     (b) 3120 sq. ft.
     (c) 260 sheets
     (d) 120 sheets laid out in 15 rows
         by 8 rows. 10 sheets cut each
         into 2' by 3' pieces to be laid
         out end to end on top of
         others. 130 sheets for each
         half of the roof.

28. Approximately 25 meters

29. (a) $\sqrt{89} \approx 9.4$m   (b) $\sqrt{73} \approx 8.5$m
     (c) $\sqrt{34} \approx 5.8$m   (d) $\sqrt{98} \approx 9.9$m

30. (a) 16, 30, 34
     (b) 105, 208, 233
     (c) 715, 1428, 1597
     (d) 1, 1, 2, 3, 5, 8, 13, 21, 34, 55,
         89, 144, 233, 377, 610, 987,
         1597   Yes

31. (a) $\sqrt{3}$ units
     (b) $\sqrt{3}$ square units
     (c) $6\sqrt{3}$ square units

32. 250 square inches

33. A 4 × 4 and a 6 × 3 rectangle.

34. About 128 ft.

35. 40 posts

36. (a) Obtuse   (b) No
     (c) Acute   (d) Acute
     (e) Right   (f) No

37. (a) $\overline{RS} \| \overline{TU}$ since $\angle S$ and $\angle T$
         (interior angles on same side)
         are supplementary.
     (b) $(1/2)(a + b)(a + b)$
     (c) m ($\angle RVS$) + m($\angle RVU$) +
         m($\angle UVT$) = 180°, but
         m ($\angle RVS$) + 90° + m($\angle UVT$)
         = 180°, so m($\angle RVU$) = 90°.
     (d) $(1/2)ab + (1/2)c^2 + (1/2)ab$
     (e) $(1/2)(a + b)(a + b)$
         $= (1/2)ab + (1/2)c^2 + (1/2)ab$;
         $a^2 + 2ab + b^2 = 2ab + c^2$
         $a^2 + b^2 = c^2$.

38. (a) 63.7%   (b) 78.5%
     (c) Circular plug fits better into
         the square hole.

39. $x = 15$ units

40. Consider the possible ways of
     flattening out the room. The
     shortest distance between two
     points is given by a straight line.
     The shortest distance is 1133 cm
     or 11.33 m calculated as follows:

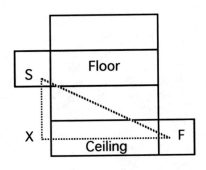

SX = 200 cm + 400 cm +
200 cm = 800 cm
XF = 1 cm + 800 cm + 1 cm
= 802 cm
SF = $\sqrt{(800)^2 + (802)^2}$ = 1132.8

41.   (a)

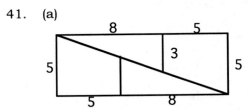

Area of square = 64 sq. units;
Area of rectangle = 65 sq.
units; yes.
(b) 169, 168, yes; 441, 442

42.   4 - π sq. units

43.   Area of equilateral triangle with
side 1 = $\sqrt{3}$ /4 sq. units. Area of
1/6 of circle is π /6 sq. units.
Area of half-petal (shaded) is
π /6 - $\sqrt{3}$ /4 sq. units. Total area
of the hexafoil is
12(π /6 - $\sqrt{3}$ /4) = 2 π - 3 $\sqrt{3}$ sq.
units.

44.   The shaded areas are equal. The
total area of the three smaller
circles is 36 π. The area of the
largest circle is 36 π. The
unshaded areas of overlap are

both subtracted from 36 π,
leaving the same amount
remaining.

45.   (a) About 7,954,550 mi
(b) About 318 times

46.   (a) No, the ratios area C: area B:
area A = 5:3:1, while the point
ratios are 4:2:1.
(b) Make the points 30, 18, 6.

47.   (a) 9$\sqrt{3}$ square units
(b) A = $\dfrac{s^2 \sqrt{3}}{4}$

48.   When P, Q, and R are collinear.

Analyzing Student Thinking

49.   Jordan, that formula works if you
have a *regular* n-gon. However, to
find the perimeter of a non-regular
n-gon, you'd need to find the sum
of the various lengths of the sides.

50.   Elise, the orientation of the base
does not matter. Each of the 3
sides of a triangle has a height
associated with it, and you may
use any of these to determine its
area.

51.   Ethan, the Pythagorean theorem
states, "the sum of the squares of
the lengths of the legs of a right
triangle is equal to the square of
the length of the hypotenuse."
Thus, when the hypotenuse has
length a and the legs have lengths
b and c, we have $b^2 + c^2 = a^2$.
Often students memorize the
Pythagorean theorem as $a^2 + b^2 = c^2$, but that assumes that the
hypotenuse has length c and the
legs have lengths a and b.

52.   Alayna is correct. The
circumference of a circle, $C = 2 \pi r$,
is a 1-dimensional measurement
and has the variable r to the first
power. The area of a circle, $A = \pi r^2$, is a 2-dimensional
measurement, and has the

variable r to the second power. This idea works with all figures, including the fact that formulas for volume would reflect 3-dimesionality.

53. Dana is correct in the first case, but not the second. The area of a square of side length s is $A = s^2$. Doubling the length of the side would give an area of $A = (2s)^2 = 4s^2$, 4 times the original area. However, when the side length is tripled, the new area would be $A = (3s)^2 = 9s^2$, 9 times the original area, not 6 times as Dana claimed.

54. Yes. When Carol got the answer 156 cm sq, she was done - that is the area. However, she took it one step further and squared 156. It seems she interpreted 156 cm² to mean $(156 \text{ cm})^2$, when in fact 156 cm² is simply an abbreviation for 156 square centimeters. That is, the unit of area is a square 1 cm by 1 cm.

55. Diana, you could choose any side for the base, as long as you use the altitude that corresponds to that base. If you want to use 10 as the length of the base, you'd need to know the length of the segment through point C and perpendicular to $\overline{AB}$, namely $\overline{CE}$.

56. No; for example, the following rectangles show that a rectangle with a larger perimeter may not have a larger area.

P = 9 units   P = 12 units
A = 5 sq. units   A = 5 sq. units

Section 13.3

1. (a) 1248.1 in²   (b) 186 m²

(c) 792 cm²   (d) 173 cm²

2. (a) SA = 60 + 30 × 20 = 660 sq. units
   (b) 254 sq. units

3. $864 + 432\sqrt{3}$ cm² or approximately 1612 cm²

4. (a) 792 cm²   (b) 173 cm²

5. (a) 766 cm²   (b) 866 cm²

6. (a) 122 sq. units
   (b) 450 sq. units

7. S = 564 sq. units

8. (a) 1206 sq. units
   (b) 4825 sq. units

9. 1923 in²

10. (a) 36π cm²
    (b) 610.09π cm²
    (c) 8.288 cm

11. 196π sq. units

12. Cube

13. 12 × 8 × 6 units

14. 8 units

15. (a) 72 square units
    (b) 272 square units
    (c) 1640 square units

16. (a) 4:25   (b) 4:25
    (c) 4 times original surface area

17. 347,538.7 ft²

18. Approximately 230 m²

19. (a) 384 sq. units
    (b) 192 sq. units

20. Each stripe covers 1/3 of the lateral surface area, so the red stripe covers about 2094 cm².

Analyzing Student Thinking

21. Carter is incorrect. He'd need to correct his statement in three ways: "If the bases of a *right* prism are *regular* hexagons, then the lateral surface area of the prism is six times the area of any of the *lateral* faces."

22. Amberly, notice that, if we use the distributive property to rewrite this expression for *S*, we get:
$S = 2\pi r(r + h) = 2\pi r^2 + 2\pi rh$. The r^2 and rh terms suggest this is a 2-dimensional measurement.

23. Tara, with the given perimeter of the base, you can find the length of one side of the base by dividing by the number of sides in the base. Then, use that, together with the known height to the apex, to apply the Pythagorean theorem and determine the slant height.

24. Kennedy is incorrect. Both of these measurements involve π since the lateral surface area of a right circular cylinder is the circumference of the base times the height of the cylinder, while the sum of the areas of the bases is the area of two circles. In fact, these two will be equal precisely when the height of the cylinder is equal to its radius so that $2\pi rh = 2\pi r^2$.

25. Mason, the surface area of the sphere quadruples when you double the radius since
$S = 4\pi(2r)^2 = 4\pi \cdot 4r^2 = 16\pi r^2$ is four times the surface area of the original sphere, $S = 4\pi r^2$.

26. Have Jalen roll up a rectangular piece of paper. It should look like a cylinder without its bases. Then when he unrolls it, he can see what the lateral surface looks like, namely a rectangle.

27. If Mark wants to use the same size circle for both cones, he can. In the following circle, the larger sector will make the fatter, shorter cone and the smaller sector will make the skinny, taller cone. The radius of the circle becomes the slant height for each cone.

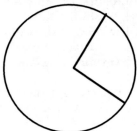

Section 13.4

1. (a) 2508 in³   (b) 148 m³
2. $320\sqrt{3}$ in³
3. 2160 m³
4. (a) 540π cm³   (b) 12.5π cm³
5. (a) About 1562 cm³
    (b) About 1951 cm³
6. (a) 40 cu. units
    (b) 70 cu. units
7. (a) 10 cu. units
    (b) 20 cu. units   (c) part (b)
8. (a) 18π cu. units
    (b) 96π cu. units
9. (a) triples
    (b) nine times larger
10. (a) 51 cu. units
    (b) 157 cu. units
11. About 27.11 cm³.
12. (a) Volume = 10 cu. units
    Surface Area = 36 sq. units
    (b) Volume = 11 cu. units

Surface Area = 38 sq. units
(c) Volume = 21 cu. units
     Surface Area = 64 sq. units

13. (a) 296 cm³   (b) 296 g

14. (a) All have volume 125,000 cm³.
     (b) A 15,000 cm²,
          B 17,500 cm²,
          C 19,500 cm²
     (c) No
     (d) Box A

15. (a) 120,000 cm³   (b) 31,000 cm²

16. (a) 3,072,000 cubic yards
     (b) 96,000 square yards

17. 4 trips

18. $h = 30/\pi \approx 9.55$ cm

19. $48.48

20. 6569 in³

21. (a) 48%   (b) 32.5%

22. $151\frac{2}{3}$ pounds

23. (a) New volume is 8 times
          the original.
     (b) New surface area is 4 the
          times original.

24. (a) 4:25   (b) 8:125
     (c) 8 times original volume

25. (a) $8\sqrt{2} \approx 11.31$ inches on a side
     (b) 63.66%

26. 192 cm³

27. Approximately 0.5 cm

28. $208/216 \approx 0.963$

29. 20.25 hours.

30. 160 ft

31. The one with the shorter side as
     height.

Analyzing Student Thinking

32. Yes. The surface area of a cube is
     equal to its volume precisely when
     $6s^2 = s^3$, which implies $s = 6$.

33. Yes. Since Nedra knew the area of
     the square base, she could
     determine the side length of the
     base. Then, using half this
     number and the slant height, she
     could apply the Pythagorean
     theorem to determine the altitude,
     which is all she needed for
     computing the volume.

34. Ask Carston to compare the
     volumes of two spheres, one with
     radius 1 unit and the other with
     radius 3 units. He should see
     that, in fact, the volume increases
     by a factor of 3^3.

35. Pedro is incorrect. Compare the
     volume of a cone, $V = \frac{1}{3}(\pi r^2)h$, to
     another that has had the radius
     doubled and the height tripled:
     $V = \frac{1}{3}\pi(2r)^2 \cdot (3h) = 4\pi r^2 h$. The
     new volume is 12 times larger
     than the original.

36. Suggest to Hester Ann that she
     could gain a better understanding
     of the problem by guessing and
     testing perfect cube numbers to
     see if any equal 56, the number of
     blocks. She'll find that fifty-six
     blocks cannot be made into a
     perfect cube. The nearest larger
     cube is 4^3 or 64. If the toy box is
     made so that 3" by 3" by 3" blocks
     can fit in it, then the 56 blocks
     will fit with room for 8 more later.
     The size of the box would be 12"
     on a side.

37. No. 1/3 of the surface area
     cannot be the volume since

surface area is a 2-dimensional
measurement and volume is 3-
dimensional.

38.   Yes, for instance: if the radius is
      10 cm and the height is $5/\pi$, the
      volume of the cylinder is 500 cm^3.

Chapter 14

Section 14.1

1. $\triangle BAC \cong \triangle FEG$, $\triangle BCA \cong \triangle FGE$, $\triangle CAB \cong \triangle GEF$, $\triangle CBA \cong \triangle GFE$

2. (a) EFD (b) ZYX

3. $\angle B \cong \angle H$, $\overline{BC} \cong \overline{HI}$ or
   $\angle A \cong \angle G$, $\overline{AC} \cong \overline{GI}$

4. (a) $\overline{GH} \cong \overline{ML}$ and $\overline{GI} \cong \overline{MN}$
   (b) $\angle H \cong \angle L$ and $\overline{HG} \cong \overline{LM}$ and $\overline{HI} \cong \overline{LN}$
   (c) $\angle I \cong \angle N$ and $\overline{IG} \cong \overline{NM}$ and $\overline{IH} \cong \overline{NL}$

5. $\angle A \cong \angle G$, $\angle B \cong \angle H$

6. (a) $\angle P \cong \angle S$, $\angle Q \cong \angle T$
   $\overline{QR} \cong \overline{TU}$, and m($\angle R$) = m($\angle U$) = 80°, so $\angle R \cong \angle U$.
   (b) Yes.
   (c) m($\angle R$) = 80° = m($\angle U$), so we can use $\angle R$, $\overline{RQ}$, $\angle Q$ and $\angle U$, $\overline{UT}$, and $\angle T$.

7. $\overline{BC} \cong \overline{HI}$, $\overline{CA} \cong \overline{IG}$

8. $\triangle ABC \cong \triangle FDE$ by SSS or SAS ($\angle C$ and $\angle F$ are right angles).

9. (a) SSS   (b) SAS   (c) ASA

10. Yes; m($\angle Y$)= 30°, m($\angle O$) = 80°, so $\triangle AMY \cong \triangle JON$ by ASA.

11. (a) $\overline{AB} \cong \overline{DE}$ (leg), $\angle B \cong \angle E$, $\overline{AC} \cong \overline{DF}$ (hypotenuse)
    (b) No
    (c) $BC = EF = \sqrt{8}$, so $\overline{BC} \cong \overline{EF}$
    (d) Yes; SAS.

12. (a) $\angle A \cong \angle X$, $\angle B \cong \angle Y$, $\angle C \cong \angle Z$

(b) No.
(c) No; $\triangle ABC$ and $\triangle XYZ$ would satisfy conditions for AAA, but are not congruent. This is a counter-example to the AAA property.

13.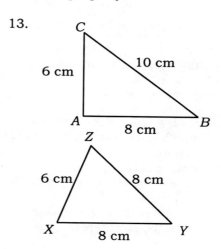

    m($\angle A$) = 90° > m($\angle X$)

14. Since the hexagon is regular, the length of hypotenuses (YZ) are all equal. The legs are given to be congruent. Therefore all the right triangles are congruent. From the original congruent vertex angles, angles congruent to $\angle Y$ and $\angle Z$ are removed, leaving angles of the same size.

15. (a) For example, have 3 pairs of congruent angles
    (b) For example, have 3 pairs of congruent angles and 1 pair of congruent non-corresponding sides
    (c) See the Mathematical Morsel at the end of Section 14.1

16. $\triangle ABC \cong \triangle WXY$ (by SAS congruence property); $\angle 1 \cong \angle 5$, $\angle 3 \cong \angle 7$, and $\overline{AC} \cong \overline{WY}$ (corresponding parts of congruent triangles); m($\angle A$) - m($\angle 3$) = m($\angle W$) - m($\angle 7$) so $\angle 4 \cong \angle 8$ and m($\angle C$) - m($\angle 1$) = m($\angle Y$) – m($\angle 5$) so $\angle 2 \cong \angle 6$; $\triangle ADC \cong \triangle WZY$ (by ASA congruence property);

$\overline{AD} \cong \overline{WZ}$, $\angle D \cong \angle Z$, $\overline{DC} \cong \overline{ZY}$ (corresponding parts of congruent triangles); so quad $ABCD \cong$ quad $WXYZ$.

17. $\overline{AB} \cong \overline{XY}$ (given), $\angle B \cong \angle Y$ (both right angles), $\overline{BC} \cong \overline{YZ}$ (Both have length $b = \sqrt{c^2 - a^2}$ by the Pythagorean Theorem) so $\triangle ABC \cong \triangle XYZ$ by the SAS congruence property

18. (a) Both a square and rhombus which is not a square could be drawn.
    (b) Both a rectangle and a parallelogram, which is not a rectangle could be drawn.
    (c) No, parts (a) and (b) have provided counterexamples.

Analyzing Student thinking

19. Yes. By the SSS Congruence Property, Danielle can prove that the two isosceles triangles formed by the diagonal of the rhombus are congruent. Hence, corresponding angles are congruent, so that, by the Alternate Interior Angles theorem, she can conclude that the opposite sides of the rhombus are parallel. In other words, a rhombus is a parallelogram.

20. Ask the student to indicate on his drawing which angles and side he's using when he applied the ASA Congruence Property. If he claims that the two pairs of non-right angles of the triangles are congruent, ask what property of rectangles he's using to justify that fact.

21. That's correct, Emily, since a rectangle is a parallelogram, the two pairs of alternate interior angles formed by the diagonal are congruent.

22. No, this is an example of SSA which is not sufficient to prove congruence, except in the case of a right triangle.

23. No. The congruence relationship $\triangle ABC \cong \triangle CAB$ means that $C \leftrightarrow A$, $A \leftrightarrow B$, and $B \leftrightarrow C$. Under these correspondences, the triangles are not congruent, since $\overline{AB}$ and $\overline{CA}$ don't necessarily have the same length. *But* we could say $\triangle ABC \cong \triangle BAC$ by SAS.

24. No. Notice that in one triangle the marked side is opposite the angle with two arcs and in the other triangle the marked side is opposite the angle with one arc. These are not corresponding sides. They could be congruent if the marked angles with one arc were congruent to the angles with two arcs. However, we cannot make that assumption.

25. Jose, the teacher's example had $\angle BAC \cong \angle DAC$ and $\angle BCA \cong \angle DCA$, so the two pairs of corresponding angles in the congruent triangles formed the angles $\angle A$ and $\angle C$, the bisected angles. However, for the parallelogram in your example, this is not the case; for instance $\angle EFH \cong \angle GHF$, but this pair of angles does not fit together to form either of the angles $\angle F$ or $\angle H$.

Section 14.2

1. (a) $\triangle LMN \sim \triangle OPQ$, by SAS similarity.
   (b) $\triangle RST \sim \triangle VWU$, by AA similarity.
   (c) Not similar. On one triangle, the 40° angle is between the proportional sides and on the other it is not.
   (d) $\triangle EFG \sim \triangle HJI$, by SSS similarity.

2. (a) $XY = \dfrac{27}{8}$ cm, $VW = \dfrac{128}{9}$ cm
   (b) $AB = 9$ in., $AC = 12$ in., $DC = 4$ in.

3. (a) $BC = \dfrac{65}{4}$ in., $AC = \dfrac{56}{9}$ in.
   (b) $RQ = 6$ in., $PT = 16$ in.

4. (a) False. Sides may be of different lengths.
   (b) False. Consider triangles whose angle measures are 80°, 80°, 20°, and 70°, 70°, 40°.
   (c) False. See part (a).
   (d) True. AA

5. $3/4 = 5/AD$, so $AD = 20/3$.

6. (a) $\triangle ABC \sim \triangle EDC$ by AA similarity because the vertical angles at C are congruent and both are right triangles.
   (b) 45'

7. 27 feet

8.

9.

10. $a = 13\ 1/3$ $b = 10$
    $c = 17\ 7/9$ $d = 42\ 7/9$

11. (a) No. If so, the two triangles would be similar. However, the sides are not proportional.
    (b) Yes. The triangles are similar by the SAS similarity property. Hence, by the corresponding angles property, the lines are parallel.

12. (a) bases 1:2, heights 1:2, areas 1:4
    (b) bases 3:4, heights 3:4, areas 9:16
    (c) lengths 1:3, widths 1:3, areas 1:9
    (d) The ratio of the areas is equal to the square of the ratios of the linear dimensions.

13. Yes. We can use either the AA or SAS similarity properties of triangles.

14. (a) Apply the alternate interior angles theorem and AA similarity property.
    (b) $a = 14$, $b = 60$

15.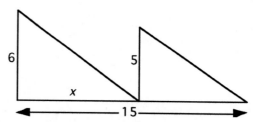

    $6/x = 5/(15-x)$, thus Tom's shadow is 90/11 ft and Carol's is 75/11 ft.

16. 25.86 ft

17. 6.53 feet

18. Assuming ACBD is a rectangle, we have $DC^2 = 50^2 + 70^2$, so $DC = 86$. But, $AB = DC$, so $AB \approx 86$ ft.

19. $AB = BC$ and $XY = YZ$ so $AB/BC = XY/YZ$ (equal 1) or $AB/XY = BC/YZ$ (interchanging means of the proportion). Since $\angle B \cong \angle Y$ and $AB/XY = BC/YZ$, $\triangle ABC \sim \triangle XYZ$ by the SAS similarity property. (Could also

prove using AA similarity property.)

20.   (a)

Area($\triangle ACD$) = 4 in^2
Area($\triangle BFC$) = 2.25 in^2
Area($\triangle AEB$) = 6.25 in^2
Therefore, Area($\triangle ACD$) +
Area($\triangle BFC$) = Area($\triangle AEB$)

(b)

Area($\triangle ACD$) = $5\sqrt{3}$ in^2
Area($\triangle BFC$) = $4\sqrt{3}$ in^2
Area($\triangle AEB$) = $9\sqrt{3}$ in^2
Therefore, Area($\triangle ACD$) +
Area($\triangle BFC$) = Area($\triangle AEB$).

(c)

Area of $ACDE$ = 18 cm^2
Area of $BHIC$ = 32 cm^2
Area of $AFGB$ = 50 cm^2
Therefore, Area($ACDE$) +

Area($BHIC$) = Area($AFGB$).

(d)

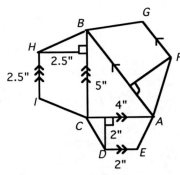

Area of $ACDE$ = 6 in^2
Area of $BHIC$ = 9.375 in^2
Area of $AFGB$ = 15.375 in^2
Therefore, Area($ACDE$) +
Area($BHIC$) = Area($AFGB$).

21. AB = 5/3, AE = 7/4, DE = 21/4

22.   Lines $\overleftrightarrow{A'B'}, \overleftrightarrow{B'C}, \overleftrightarrow{A'C'}$ form transversals. These can be used with pairs of parallel sides and corresponding angles to show that $\angle A \cong \angle A'$, $\angle B \cong \angle B'$, and $\angle C \cong \angle C'$. Thus the triangles are similar by AAA similarity.

23.   (a) 4.5   (b) 6.75

       (c) 10.125   (d) $3^n\left(\dfrac{1}{2^{n-1}}\right)$

24.   (a) 3/4   (b) 9/16

       (c) 27/64   (d) $\left(\dfrac{3}{4}\right)^{n-1}$

Analyzing Student Thinking

25.

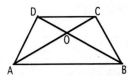

When the two diagonals of an isosceles trapezoid are drawn, there are actually 8 triangles formed. However, Selina is probably looking at the 4 non-overlapping triangles. $\triangle DOC$ ~ $\triangle BOA$ by AA, and $\triangle AOD \cong \triangle BOC$

by AAS (after proving $\triangle DAC \cong \triangle CBD$).

26. Yes, all 30°-60° triangles are right triangles since the sum of the measures of a triangle is 180°. Thus, Jade's claim is true by the AA Similarity Property.

27. Israel is correct. A 45° right triangle is a 45°-45°-90° triangle, and so is similar, by the AA Similarity Property, to all other such triangles.

28. Karli is correct. Each of the two smaller right triangles formed when $\overline{BD}$ is drawn share one angle with the original triangle $\triangle ABC$. Hence, by the AA Similarity Property, $\triangle ABC \sim \triangle ADB$ and $\triangle ABC \sim \triangle BDC$. Thus, all three triangles are similar.

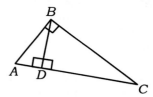

29. Brennan, similar triangles have the same shape, while congruent triangles have the same shape and the same size. Thus, congruent triangles meet the conditions required to be similar.

30. Edwardo, at noon the shadows may be too short (or nonexistent) for accurate measurement.

31. No, Barbara, these rectangles are not similar since $\frac{4}{6} \neq \frac{5}{8}$. If we solve the proportion $\frac{4}{6} = \frac{5}{x}$, we see that the long side of the new photo would need to be $x = 7.5$ in order to have a similar rectangle, so that there would be ½ inch of blank space on the enlargement, as shown in the figure below:

Section 14.3

1. Follow the steps of the *1. Copy a Line Segment* construction.

2. Follow the steps of the *2. Copy an Angle* construction.

3. Follow the steps of the *3. Construct a Perpendicular Bisector* construction.

4. Follow the steps of the *4. Bisect an Angle* construction.

5. Follow the steps of the *5. Construct a Perpendicular Line through a Point on a Line* construction.

6. Follow the steps of the *6. Construct a Perpendicular Line through a Point not on a Line* construction.

7. Follow the steps of the *7. Construct a Line Parallel to a Given Line through a Point not on the Line* construction.

8. (a) Follow the steps of the *5. Construct a Perpendicular Line through a Point on a Line* construction.
   (b) Follow the steps of the *6. Construct a Perpendicular Line through a Point not on a Line* construction.
   (c) Follow the steps of the *7. Construct a Line Parallel to a Given Line through a Point not on the Line* construction.
   (d) Follow the steps of the *7. Construct a Line Parallel to a Given Line through a Point not on the Line* construction.

9. (a) Follow the steps of the *5. Construct a Perpendicular Line through a Point on a Line* construction.
   (b) Follow the steps of the *7. Construct a Line Parallel to a Given Line through a Point not on the Line* construction.

(c) They are perpendicular to each other.

10. (a) Follow the steps of the *2. Copy an Angle* construction to copy the angle with measure $a°$ next to the angle with measure $b°$ as follows:

(b) Follow the steps of the *2. Copy an Angle* construction to copy the angle with measure $a°$ next to another copy of the angle with measure $a°$ as follows:

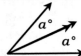

(c) Follow the steps of the *2. Copy an Angle* construction to copy the angle with measure $a°$ in the interior of the angle with measure $b°$ as follows:

(d) Follow the steps in *4. Bisect an Angle* construction to bisect the angle in part (a) above.

11. Construct the midpoint of each side using the *3. Construct a Perpendicular Bisector* construction. Connect these midpoints with the corresponding vertices on the opposite side of the triangle.

12. For each vertex of the triangle and it's opposite side, follow the steps of the *6. Construct a Perpendicular Line through a Point not on a Line* construction.

13. (a) Use constructions 2 and 1 to copy angles and side.

(b) Make copy of $\angle D$, copy length AB along both sides of the angle, and connect endpoints of two segments.

14. (b) By construction, $\overline{RS} \cong \overline{DE}$, $\overline{RT} \cong \overline{DF}$, and $\overline{ST} \cong \overline{EF}$. Thus, $\triangle RST \cong \triangle DEF$ by SSS congruence property.

15. $\triangle ADC \cong \triangle BDC$ by ASA so $\overline{AD} \cong \overline{BD}$.

16. (a) $RQ = 2a$, $\angle B \cong \angle Q$, $\angle C \cong \angle R$.
    (b) $\triangle ADC \sim \triangle PQR$ because all 3 corresponding pairs of angles are congruent and all 3 pairs of corresponding sides are proportional.
    (c) SAS similarity

17. They do in an equilateral triangle. In every isosceles triangle the perpendicular bisector of the base and the altitude to the base coincide.

18. This occurs when the triangle is isosceles and not equilateral.

19. (a) Construct right triangle with legs 3 and 1
    (b) Construct right triangle with legs 2 and 1 and hypotenuse $\sqrt{5}$, then construct right triangle with legs $\sqrt{5}$ and 1 .
    (c) Construct isosceles right triangle with legs $\sqrt{6}$ [see part (b)].
    (d) Construct right triangle with hypotenuse 4 and leg 1. The other leg will be $\sqrt{15}$.

20. $\triangle ABC \sim \triangle AQP$ by AA similarity and $\triangle ACD \sim \triangle APR$ by AA similarity. Therefore, $ABCD \sim AQPR$, since corresponding angles are congruent and corresponding sides are proportional

21. $\overline{AC} \cong \overline{BC}$ (equidistant), $\overline{AD} \cong \overline{BD}$ (midpoint) , $\overline{CD} \cong \overline{CD}$ (common

side), $\triangle ACD \cong \triangle BCD$ (SSS), $\angle ADC \cong \angle BDC$ (corresponding parts of congruent triangles), $\angle ADC$ and $\angle BDC$ are right angles (congruent and supplementary), $\overleftrightarrow{CD}$ is perpendicular bisector of $\overline{AB}$.

22. The line should be the perpendicular bisector of the segment $\overline{AB}$.

Analyzing Student Thinking

23. In an isosceles triangle, the altitude, median, and angle bisector from the *vertex* angle all lie on the same line. In Gwennette's case, she is looking at the altitude, median, and angle bisector from one of the two *base* angles, and the theorem does not hold there (unless the triangle is equilateral).

24. Yes, Tammy, it does make a difference. Changing the radius of the compass will, as you note, give you a perpendicular, but it won't bisect the line segment.

25. Ty, doing so will result in a rhombus *BPRQ*, which is a special type of kite. Therefore, the justification of this construction will be identical to the one following Figure 14.30. Hence, it is not necessary to choose point R so that $\overline{BP} \cong \overline{PR}$, but it works if you do so.

26. Yes, Bo, that is correct since $\overline{PA}$ and $\overline{QA}$ were constructed to each have length r as were $\overline{PA}$ and $\overline{PB}$.

27. Madison, the following construction would work: for example, swing an arc on one side of radius 1 and on the other side of radius 2. Draw the segment connecting the intersections, call it x. To copy the angle on another line segment, swing an arc of length 1 with center at one end point. Also swing an arc of length 2 from the same point. Put the point where the arc of length 1 intersects the line segment and swing an arc of length x until it hits the arc of length 2. By SSS the two congruent triangles will be formed.

28. Marlena is correct. When Latisha says, "the triangles won't match," she is probably referring to the orientation of the new triangle. Orientation may change, but the new triangle will be congruent no matter which side you start with, by SSS.

29. Glen, in the case of an obtuse triangle, only the altitude from the obtuse angle will be inside the triangle. The following figure shows how the altitude from an acute angle is outside the triangle.

Section 14.4

1. Construct perpendicular bisectors (Construction 3).

2.

3. (a) Inside
   (b) On the hypotenuse
   (c) Outside
   (d) Yes

4. (a) Inside   (b) Yes

5. Construct a circle with the center on one endpoint of the given segment and the radius point on the other endpoint. Construct another circle reversing the roles of the endpoints. Where the two circles intersect is the third point of the triangle.

This is similar to the compass and straightedge construction except the circles are replaced with compass arcs.

6.   (a) Dodecagon
     (b) 24-gon, 48-gon.

7.   (a) Decagon
     (b) 20-gon
     (c) 40-gon, 80-gon

8.   3, 4, 5, 6, 8, 10, 12, 15, 16, 17, 20, 24, 30, 32, 34, 40, 48, 51, 60, 64, 68, 80, 85, 96 (24 polygons).

9.   3, 5, 6, 7, 9, 10, 12, 13, 14, 15

10. (a) Use the same procedure except mark off four congruent segments on $\overline{AC}$.
     (b) Use construction 3 to find midpoint M of $\overline{AB}$. Then repeat construction 3 to bisect $\overline{AM}$ and $\overline{MB}$.

11.

$$\frac{\sqrt{5}}{1} = \frac{x}{2}$$

12. (a) Add together a right angle and 45°.
     (b) Subtract 60° from 135° angle.
     (c) Take central angle of regular pentagon.
     (d) Bisect 72° and add that 36° to 72° to get 108°.

13. (a) Construct triangle with sides 1 and 2.
     (c) $(\sqrt{5} - 1)/2$

14. Let P be equidistant from A and B. Then $AP = BP$. Let m be the line through the mid point M and P,

then $AM = BM$ and $PM = PM$ so $\triangle APM \cong \triangle BPM$ by SSS. Thus $\angle AMP \cong \angle BMP$ so m$\angle AMP = 90°$, which means that m is the perpendicular bisector of $\overline{AB}$. Therefore P is on the perpendicular bisector of $\overline{AB}$.

15. (c) It is the midpoint of the hypotenuse.

16. Yes

17. (c) $M_1M_3 = M_2M_4$ and $\overline{M_1M_3} \perp \overline{M_2M_4}$ (Aubel's theorem).

18. (a) About 26°   (b) $\dfrac{360°}{7}$
     (c) First double the angle to get one that measures $\dfrac{360°}{7}$. Then draw a circle so that $\dfrac{360°}{7}$ is a central angle whose sides intersect the circle at A and B. Set radius of compass to AB and mark off arcs around the circle. Connect points to get the regular heptagon.

19. Draw $\overline{AB} \perp \overline{XY}$ and $\overline{AC} \perp \overline{YZ}$. $\overline{AB} \cong \overline{AC}$, since A is equidistant from YX and YZ. $\overline{AY} \cong \overline{AY}$. Thus, $\triangle ABY \cong \triangle ACY$ by HL for right triangles. $\angle AYB \cong \angle AYC$, since they are corresponding parts of congruent triangles and therefore $\overrightarrow{YA}$ bisects $\angle XYZ$.

20. (a) QR
     (b) QS
     (c) Yes; $\angle RAQ \cong \angle SAQ$ (angle bisector), $\angle ARQ \cong \angle ASQ$ (both right angles), $\angle RQA \cong \angle SQA$ (third pair of angles of triangles are congruent if other 2 pairs are), $\overline{AQ} \cong \overline{AQ}$ so

$\triangle ARQ \cong \triangle ASQ$ by the ASA congruence property .

(d) $QR \cong QS$ because they are corresponding sides of congruent triangles.

(e) Refer to procedure of construction 9. Since Q is on line l, the bisector of $\angle CAB$, Q is equidistant from $\overline{AC}$ and $\overline{AB}$. Also Q is on line m, so Q is equidistant from $\overline{AC}$ and $\overline{BC}$. Hence, Q is equidistant from $\overline{AB}$, $\overline{BC}$, and $\overline{AC}$, the sides of $\triangle ABC$. Thus, Q is the incenter of $\triangle ABC$.

Analyzing Student Thinking

21. Rosanne, two are sufficient, assuming they are correct. If you want to check, constructing the third is recommended.

22. Mallory is incorrect in general, but her statement is true for acute triangles. The circumcenter of an obtuse triangle is always outside the triangle and the circumcenter of a right triangle will be on its hypotenuse.

23. An equilateral triangle has three 60° angles. If 6 equilateral triangles are gathered around a common vertex, the sum of the angles would be 360°. Furthermore, since all of Craig's triangles are congruent, the "radial" sides will match in length, the angles of the hexagon formed will be 120° (60°+ 60°), and the sides of the hexagon will all be equal in length. So Craig's method will work.

24. Samantha is incorrect. The centroid will always be inside becaue the medians of a triangle will always meet inside the triangle.

25. Chase is correct. This is true because the perpendicular bisectors of the sides of an equilateral triangle coincide with the bisectors of its angles.

26. Spencer is incorrect. The orthocenter is inside the triangle if the triangle is acute, outside for an obtuse triangle, and equal to the vertex of the right angle for a right triangle.

27. Roberto is correct. The diagonal of a rectangle is the hypotenuse of a right triangle, with legs being adjacent sides of the rectangle. Thus, if the sides of the rectangle are 1 unit by 2 units, the diagonal of rectangle has length $\sqrt{5}$ units, by the Pythagorean theorem.

Section 14.5

1. (a) For example, $\overline{AB} \cong \overline{AD}$, $\overline{BC} \cong \overline{DC}$.
   (b) $\overline{AC} \cong \overline{AC}$ (congruent to itself)
   (c) SSS
   (d) Corresponding parts of congruent triangles are congruent.
   (e) By definition of angle bisector.

2. (a) $\angle 2 \cong \angle 4$, $\angle 1 \cong \angle 3$
   (b) Yes; base angles of isosceles triangle
   (c) Yes; $\angle 1 \cong \angle 2 \cong \angle 3 \cong \angle 4$ from parts (a) and (b).

3. $\angle P \cong \angle Q$ since they are opposite the congruent sides $\overline{QR}$ and $\overline{PR}$. Further, $\angle Q \cong \angle R$ since they are opposite the congruent sides $\overline{PR}$ and $\overline{PQ}$. Thus, $\angle P \cong \angle Q \cong \angle R$.

4. $m(\angle A) + m(\angle D) = 180°$ (interior angles on same side of transversal are supplementary), $m(\angle D) = m(\angle C)$ (base angles congruent), so $m(\angle A) + m(\angle C) = 180°$ (substitution). Thus, $\angle A$ and $\angle C$ are supplementary. Similarly, $\angle B$ and $\angle D$ are supplementary

5. Since ∠ W and ∠ Z are supplementary (90° + 90° = 180°), $\overline{WX} \parallel \overline{ZY}$ (since interior angles on same side of transversal are supplementary). Similarly, ∠ W and ∠ X are supplementary and $\overline{WZ} \parallel \overline{XY}$. Therefore, WXYZ is a parallelogram since both pairs of opposite sides are parallel.

6. Since HIJK is a rectangle, it has 4 right angles. We need to show that it has four congruent sides. Since HIJK is a parallelogram, opposite sides are congruent; thus $\overline{HI} \cong \overline{JK}$ and $\overline{HK} \cong \overline{IJ}$. Combined with the given information $\overline{JK} \cong \overline{HI} \cong \overline{IJ} \cong \overline{HK}$. Therefore, HIJK is a square.

7. Construct $\overline{AB}$ with the length of the side. At A and B construct perpendiculars $\overline{AS}$ and $\overline{BT}$. With compass set the length of the diagonal mark an arc centered at A and intersecting $\overline{BT}$ (call intersection point C). Similarly, with the same compass setting, mark an arc centered at B intersecting $\overline{AS}$ (call intersection point D). ABCD is the desired rectangle.

8. Construct $\overline{AB}$ with length d, then construct the perpendicular bisector of $\overline{AB}$. Mark off C and D on the perpendicular diagonal using one half the length of d as the compass setting. Thus, ACBD is the desired square.

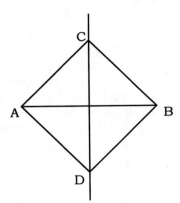

9. (a) A quadrilateral with diagonals that bisect each other is a parallelogram, and a parallelogram with perpendicular diagonals is a rhombus (shown in earlier problems).

    (b) Construct $\overline{AB}$ with length a, then construct the perpendicular bisector of $\overline{AB}$. Bisect the original segment of length b and mark off other vertices C and D on perpendicular diagonal using one half the length of b as the compass setting.

10. AD/CD = CD/DB (CD is geometric mean) and ∠ADC ≅ ∠CDB (both are right angles) so ΔADC ≅ ΔCDB (SAS similarity property). ∠A ≅ ∠DCB since they are corresponding angles of similar triangles. However, m(∠ACD) + m(∠A) = 90° (acute angles of right triangles are complementary) so m(∠ACD) + m(∠DCB) = 90° and ∠ACB is a right angle. Thus, ΔABC is a right triangle.

11. ∠D ≅ ∠F and ∠R ≅ ∠T (base angles of isosceles triangle are congruent). Since ∠D ≅ ∠R, it follows that ∠D ≅ ∠R. Hence, ΔDEF ~ ΔRST by AA similarity property.

12. (a) 36° (central angle of decagon), 72°, 72° (base angles of isosceles triangle)
    (b) 72°, 36°

(c) 36°, isosceles (since base angles are congruent)

(d) x, $1 - x$,

(e) $AC = AB = 1$, $BC = x$,
m($\angle A$) = 36°,
m($\angle B$) = m($\angle C$) = 72°
$BD = BC = x$, $CD = 1 - x$,
m($\angle B$) = 36°,
m($\angle C$) = m($\angle D$) = 72°
Yes (by the AA similarity property)

(f) BD, CD, x, $1 - x$

(g) $1 - x = x^2$ or $x = \dfrac{1 \pm \sqrt{5}}{2}$

(h) Yes, we can construct the length $\sqrt{5}$ then subtract length 1, and bisect it.

13. If $AC = A'C'$, then $\triangle ABC \cong \triangle A'B'C'$ by SAS. If not, let $AC = A'D'$. Then, $\triangle ABC \cong \triangle A'B'D'$ by SAS. Therefore, $\angle B \cong \angle A'B'D'$. But, from the given information, $\angle B \cong \angle B'$. Thus, $\angle B \cong \angle A'B'D'$, which is a contradiction.

14. $\triangle BAD \sim \triangle B'A'C'$ by SAS. Thus the sides of $\triangle BAD$ are proportional respectively to the sides of $\triangle B'A'C'$ which, by the given, are proportional respectively to the sides of $\triangle BAC$. Since $\triangle BAD$ and $\triangle BAC$ share the side $\overline{AB}$, the two triangles must be congruent by the SSS congruence property. Therefore, $\angle BAC \cong \angle BAD \cong \angle B'A'C'$. Thus, $\triangle BAC \sim \triangle B'A'C'$ by SAS similarity property.

Analyzing Student Thinking

15. Willard, while it may be obvious that a certain rhombus is a parallelogram, we cannot be sure from one example, or even many examples, that *every* rhombus is a parallelogram. A proof will help us see why this must be so.

16. No. The property that Victoria is trying to prove could be stated as follows: "In an isosceles triangle, the angle bisector of the vertex angle divides the opposite side into two congruent segments." What we have been "given" is an isosceles triangle and the angle bisector of the vertex angle. So Victoria can infer that, since she has an isosceles triangle, $PK = KC$. She can infer that since KI is an angle bisector, $\angle PKI \cong \angle CKI$. She cannot assume that $PI = IC$, because that is what she is trying to prove. She cannot assume that angles $\angle PIK$ and $\angle KIC$ are right angles, because it has not been "given." However, she can prove that $\triangle PIK \cong \triangle CIK$ by SAS. Therefore, $PI = IC$.

17. Charlotte, the congruence of opposite sides of a parallelogram is a direct consequence of the definition of parallelogram. The proof that diagonals bisect each other relies on this result, so cannot be used to prove it. Any attempt to do so would lead to circular reasoning. In general, a certain property of parallelograms must be proven before it is used in the proof of other properties.

18. Yes. Using SAS, the midquad forms two pairs of congruent triangles, as shown in the following figure. So the midquad of an isosceles trapezoid is a kite. It has also been proved that the midquad of any quadrilateral is a parallelogram. Thus, the opposite sides of the kite are congruent, making it a rhombus.

19. Braymen is correct. For a parallelogram to be a rectangle, congruent diagonals is sufficient— a known right angle is not necessary. There is enough given information to prove you have a rectangle. On the other hand, using Wenston's idea, it can also be shown that a parallelogram with one right angle is a rectangle.

In this case, known congruent diagonals is not needed for the proof.

20.   No. The following rectangle has a midquad that is not a square.

A square is the only quadrilateral that has a square for its midquad.

21.   If it has been *proved* that a rhombus has two pairs of parallel sides, then it can be concluded that a rhombus is a parallelogram. If Caesar is only saying that the rhombus and the parallelogram share a property, then he might believe that a rhombus is a parallelogram *and* a parallelogram is a rhombus. This is not true. A teacher needs to consider the various Van Hiele levels that might represent Caesar's perspective.

Chapter 15

Section 15.1

1. (a) $\sqrt{73}$ (b) 7

2. (a) $2\sqrt{5} + 4\sqrt{5} = 6\sqrt{5}$; yes
   (b) $\sqrt{212} + \sqrt{13.25} = \sqrt{331.25}$; yes

3. (a) (1, 7)   (b) (-9, 3)
   (c) (7, 5)   (d) (2, -5)

4. (a) $GH = 8$, $HI = \sqrt{32}$. Since $GH^2 = HI^2 + GI^2$, $\triangle GHI$ is a right triangle.
   (b) $LM = 2\sqrt{5}$, $MN = \sqrt{5}$, $LN = 5$. Since $LM^2 + MN^2 = LN^2$, $\triangle LMN$ is a right triangle.

5.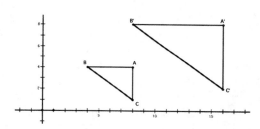

   (a) Double   (b) Same

6. (a) -5/7   (b) no slope

7. (a) Yes   (b) Yes

8. (a) Rises to the right
   (b) Vertical
   (c) Horizontal
   (d) Rises to the left

9. Not collinear

10. (a) No
    (b) Yes
    (c) No

11. (a) Top, bottom are horizontal,
    $\dfrac{2-(-2)}{4-1} = \dfrac{4}{3}$, $\dfrac{2-(-2)}{6-3} = \dfrac{4}{3}$, parallelogram

    (b) $\dfrac{10-(-5)}{-5-10} = -1$, $\dfrac{5-(-10)}{-10-5} = -1$, parallel; $\dfrac{10-5}{-5-(-10)} = 1$, $\dfrac{-5-(-10)}{10-5} = 1$, parallelogram

12. (a) Slope of $\overline{AB} = 1/6$, slope of $\overline{PQ} = -6$; $-6(1/6) = -1$.
    (b) Slope of $\overline{AB} = 1$, slope of $\overline{PQ} = -1$; $1(-1) = -1$.

13. (a) and (b) are right triangles.

14. All.

15. (a) False for both.
    (b) True for both.
    (c) False for both.
    (d) True for (ii) only.

16. (a) 3   (b) 2

17. (a) Scalene obtuse
    (b) Scalene acute

18. Trapezoid with right angles at A and B.

19. (a) (7,-9), (-3,15), or (13, -1)
    (b) Area = 56 square units in each case.

20. (a)

    (b) $B'(12,6)$, $C'(-6,6)$, $D'(-6,-6)$
    (c) perimeter of $A'B'C'D' = 3$(perimeter of $ABCD$)
    (d) area of $A'B'C'D' = 9$(area of $ABCD$)
    (e) $A'(2,-1)$, $B'(2,1)$, $C'(-1,1)$, $D'(-1,-1)$
    Perimeter of $A'B'C'D' =$

(1/2)(perimeter of *ABCD*)
area of *A'B'C'D'* =
(1/4)(area of *ABCD*)

21. (a) 792 ft
    (b) 28,512 ft (This is higher than any mountain in North America!)
    (c) Percent grade is the absolute value of the slope times 100.

22. Slope of $l = \dfrac{b}{a}$, slope of $m = -\dfrac{y}{b}$
    Hence $(b/a)(-y/b) = -1$, so $a = y$.
    Also, $OQ^2 + OP^2 = (b^2 + y^2) + (a^2 + b^2) = 2a^2 + 2b^2$, and $QP^2 = (a + b)^2 + (b - y)^2 = (a^2 + 2ab + b^2) + (b^2 - 2yb + b^2) = 2a^2 + 2b^2$
    $= OQ^2 + OP^2$. Thus, $\triangle OPQ$ is a right triangle, so $l \perp m$.

23. (a) All but Rio and Sydney.
    (b) Nome
    (c) No. All points in the contiguous United States are east of the 180° meridian.
    (d) 52° S
    (e) 106° E
    (f) 34° N 29° W

24. (a) (a, y, z)
    (b) $\sqrt{(y - b)^2 + (z - c)^2}$
    (c) $QR = |x - a|$
    (d) $PQ = \sqrt{QR^2 + PR^2} = \sqrt{(x - a)^2 + (y - b)^2 + (z - c)^2}$

Analyzing Student Thinking

25. Brayden, a vertical line has no slope since the ratio of its rise to run is $y/0$, which is undefined, while a horizontal line has zero slope since the ratio of rise to run is $0/x$ (x not zero).

26. The slope of a line is constant. A line cannot have more than one slope. Since $15/3 = (-1)(15)/(-1)(3) = -15/-3$, you both found the same number for the slope.

27. Both students are correct. The first student's method works because the slopes of perpendicular lines are negative reciprocals; if this is the case for the two shorter sides, she can conclude it's a right triangle. The second student's method works because the distance formula may be used to determine the lengths of the sides of the given triangle; if these satisfy the Pythagorean theorem, she can conclude it's a right triangle.

28. Two lines with slopes 4 and -4 will have the same "steepness," but the line with positive slope will rise from left to right, while the one with negative slope will fall from left to right.

29. Both students are correct. The first student's method works because three points P, Q, and R are collinear if the slopes of all the line segments they determine are the same. The second student's method works because, if the sum of the lengths of the two shortest line segments that the three points determine is equal to the length of the longest line segment, then the three points are collinear.

30. No. Janice did not follow the order of operations. The correct answer is $D = \sqrt{(9 - 3)^2 + (6 - 7)^2} = \sqrt{6^2 + (-1)^2} = \sqrt{36 + 1} = \sqrt{37}$.

31. The distance formula is
    $D = \sqrt{(x_2 - x_1)^2 + (y_2 - y_1)^2}$, so Janelle makes a good point about subtracting the y-values of the two points in the same order as the x-values. It turns out that Edmund will get the correct answer though because of the squaring. That is, $(7 - 6)^2 = (1)^2 = 1$ and $(6 - 7)^2 = (-1)^2 = 1$. Even though the order in which we subtract doesn't affect the answer in this instance, there

are other times when we need to pay attention to order; computing slope is an example of one such instance.

Section 15.2

1. (a) $(-2)7.5 = -15$ and $6(-3) + 3$
        $= -15$
    (b) $4(4) + 2 = 18$ and $3(6) = 18$
    (c) $x = 0$ is a vertical line containing all points with x-coordinate 0; $(0, 0)$ is one such point.
    (d) $y = -3$ is a horizontal line containing all points with y-coordinate -3; $(2, -3)$ is one such point.

2. There are three points given in each answer, however, there are infinitely many correct possibilities in each case.
    (a) $(4,0), (5,1), (6,2)$
    (b) $(3,0), (3,1), (3,-5)$
    (c) $(-1,0), (2,0), (7,0)$

3. (a) -3; 2
    (b) 5/2; -3
    (c) 0; -2

4. (a) $y = 1/4$, slope = 0, y-intercept $= 1/4$
    (b) $y = (3/4)x - 3$, y-intercept = -3

5. (a) $y = -2x + 5$
    (b) $y = 7/3x - 2$
    (c) $y = - (-3)x - 1/4$
    (d) $y = 1/2$

6. $(-2, 1), (-2, 0)$
    All such points must have x-coordinate -2.

7. (a)

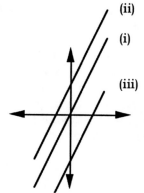

(ii)
(i)
(iii)

(b) They are parallel.
(c) They are the set of all lines in the plane parallel to the line $y = cx$. Each has slope c and y-intercept d, for a particular value of d.

8. (a) $y = -3x - 5$ (b) $x = -2$
    (c) $y = -x + 5$

9. (a) $(y - 1) = 4(x + 5)$
    (b) $(y - 6) = (-2/5)(x - 2)$

10. (a) $y = -x - 1$
    (b) $y = (-3/5)x - 19/5$

11. (a) $y = (1/2)x + 6$
    (b) $y = (-2/3)x - 22/3$

12. (a) (i) $y - 2 = -1/2(x + 5)$ or
            $y - 1 = - 1/2(x + 3)$
        (ii) $y = -1/2x - 1/2$
    (b) (i) $y - 7 = 0$
        (ii) $y = 7$

13. (a)   (b)

    (c)   (d)

14. (a) $(2, 2)$ (b) $(4, 8)$
    (c) No solution
    (d) $\{(x, y) \mid 3y = 5x + 1\}$

15. (a) $(3,2)$ (b) $(3,-4)$
    (c) No solution   (d) $(31/2, 3/2)$

16. (a) $(1,4)$ (b) $(1/2, 5/4)$

17. (a) $(5,0)$ (b) $(1,4)$
    (c) $(3,1)$

18. (a) No solution
    (b) Unique solution
    (c) Infinitely many solutions

19. (a) $(-3 + 1)^2 + (7 - 2)^2 = 4 + 25 = 29$

    (b) $(\sqrt{15})^2 + (-3 + 5)^2 = 5 + 4 = 9$

20. (a) $(2,-5)$, $r = 8$

    (b) $(-3,4)$, $r = 2\sqrt{5}$

21. (a) $(x + 1)^2 + (y + 2)^2 = 5$

    (b) $(x - 2)^2 + (y + 4)^2 = 41$

    (c) $(x - 1)^2 + (y - 4)^2 = 8$

22. (a) 0   (b) No solutions

23. $y = -3x + 5$

24. $y = 1/2x$, $y = -1/2x + 3$

25. $y = (-2/5)x + 29/10$

26. (a) $5.60; $13.10

    (b) $y = 0.5x + 0.6$

27. (a) $y = 0.65x + 350$

    (b) $y = x$

    (c) 1,000 items

28. (a)

    (b) If $x = 0$, there is no solution for y, and vice versa.

    (c) When $x > 0$ and near 0, y is very large. When $x < 0$ and near 0, y is very small.

29. (a)

    (b)

The graph in (b) is the reflection image of the graph in (a), in the x-axis.

30. (a)

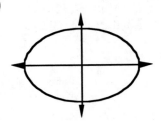

    (b)

The graph in (b) is a 90° rotation image of the graph in (a), around the origin.

31. $(x - 4/3)^2 + (y + 4/3)^2 = 425/9$

Analyzing Student Thinking

32. Stuart, to find another point, you need to use the fact that it is a horizontal line. Since the point (3, 4) is on the line, we know all the points on the line have a y-coordinate of 4. So, for example, (5, 4) is also on the line. Applying the slope formula with these two points gives a value of $m = 0$, and we see that the line's equation is $y = 4$. The slope of all horizontal lines is zero since the y-

coordinates of all the points on a horizontal line are the same.

33. Bethany, sketch a graph of the vertical line through the point (3, 4). Notice that this line does not cross the y-axis, so there is no y-intercept. Its equation is $x = 3$.

34. Jimmie, you can choose either point since both are points on the line. That is, both pairs of x- and y-values are solutions to the equation $y = (-1/4)x + b$, so you will get the same value of b, no matter which point you substitute.

35. No. Many students think that when they know x, their problems are over. However, geometrically, we are looking for the intersection of two lines. If the lines intersect in one point, we must find both coordinates, x and y.

36. No. The center is in the interior of the circle, not one of the points *on* the circle itself.

37. Cole, because you know the coordinates of the center and the coordinates of a point on the circle, you can use the distance formula to determine the radius.

38. The numbers on the coordinate axes are not evenly spaced.

Section 15.3

1. (a) $(-1, 5)$ (b) $(1, 4)$

2. (a) $(-1, -3\sqrt{3})$
   (b) $(-4, 6)$ and $(2, 6)$

3. $(a + b, c)$

4. (a) $(a + b, c)$
   (b) $b^2 + c^2 = a^2$ since $MP = MN = a$

5. (a) $(-5, 0), (5, 0), (5, 8), (-5, 8)$
   (b) $(-5, -4), (5, -4), (5, 4), (-5, 4)$

6. $AB = 1 - (-4) = 5$,
   $BC = \sqrt{(4-1)^2 + (3+1)^2} = 5$,
   $CD = 4 - (-1) = 5$,
   $DA = \sqrt{(-1+4)^2 + (3+1)^2} = 5$. Since $AB = BC = CD = DA$, $ABCD$ is a rhombus.

7. $\overline{AB} = \overline{BC} = \overline{CD} = \overline{AD} = \sqrt{17}$ and $\overline{AB} \perp \overline{BC}$ since the slope of $\overline{AB} = -1/4$ and the slope of $\overline{BC} = 4$.

8. The midpoint of $\overline{EG}$ is $(-3/2, -5/2)$ and the midpoint of $\overline{FH}$ is $(-3/2, -5/2)$. Since the diagonals meet at the midpoint of both, the diagonals are bisected.

9. (a) $y = -2x + 15$
   (b) $y = x - 12$
   (c) $x = 9$
   (d) $(9, -3)$; yes it lies on $x = 9$.
   (e) $\sqrt{90}$ for all three distances
   (f) circumcenter

10. The midpoint is $M(\frac{b}{2}, \frac{a}{2})$.

$$AM = \sqrt{\left(\frac{b}{2}\right)^2 + \left(\frac{a}{2}\right)^2} = \frac{1}{2}\sqrt{b^2 + a^2}$$

$$MB = \sqrt{\left(\frac{b}{2}\right)^2 + \left(\frac{a}{2}\right)^2} = \frac{1}{2}\sqrt{b^2 + a^2}$$

$$MC = \sqrt{\left(\frac{b}{2}\right)^2 + \left(\frac{a}{2}\right)^2} = \frac{1}{2}\sqrt{b^2 + a^2}$$

Thus, $AM = MB = MC$.

11. (a) $3\sqrt{53}; 2\sqrt{53}; 2/3$
    (b) $3\sqrt{29}; 2\sqrt{29}; 2/3$
    (c) $6\sqrt{5}; 4\sqrt{5}; 2/3$
    (d) On any median, 2/3 of the distance from the vertex point.

12. $b^2 + c^2 = a^2$;

Slope of $\overline{AC} = \dfrac{c}{b+a}$.

Slope of $\overline{BD} = \dfrac{c}{ba}$;

$\left(\dfrac{c}{b+a}\right)\left(\dfrac{c}{b-a}\right) = \dfrac{c^2}{b^2a^2} =$

$\dfrac{a^2b^2}{b^2a^2} = -1$. So $\overline{AC} \perp \overline{BD}$.

13. (a) Slope of $\overline{QG}=$ slope of $\overline{QM_2} = 2b/(2a - c)$ so that Q, G, and M_2 are collinear.

  (b) Slope of $\overline{RG}=$ slope of $\overline{RM_1} = b/(a - 2c)$ so that R, G, and M_1 are collinear.

14. (a) $QG = \sqrt{\left(a - \dfrac{a+c}{3}\right)^2 + \left(b - \dfrac{b}{3}\right)^2} =$

$\dfrac{\sqrt{(2a - c)^2 + (2b)^2}}{3}$

$GM_2 = \sqrt{\left(\dfrac{a+c}{3} - \dfrac{c}{2}\right)^2 + \left(\dfrac{b}{3}\right)^2} =$

$\dfrac{\sqrt{(2a - c)^2 + (2b)^2}}{6} = \dfrac{1}{2}QG$

Hence $QG{:}GM_2 = 2{:}1$

  (b) $RG = \sqrt{\left(c - \dfrac{a+c}{3}\right)^2 + \left(-\dfrac{b}{3}\right)^2} =$

$\dfrac{\sqrt{(2c - a)^2 + b^2}}{3}$

$GM_1 = \sqrt{\left(\dfrac{a+c}{3} - \dfrac{a}{2}\right)^2 + \left(\dfrac{b}{3} - \dfrac{b}{2}\right)^2} =$

$\dfrac{\sqrt{(2c - a)^2 + b^2}}{6} = \dfrac{1}{2}RG$

Hence $RG{:}GM_1 = 2{:}1$

15. (a) $(a/2, \sqrt{3}\,a/2)$
  (b) $x = a/2$, $x = a/2$, $x = a/2$, yes

  (c) Yes, $y = (\sqrt{3}/3)x$
  (d) Yes, $y = -(\sqrt{3}/3)x + (\sqrt{3}/3)a$
  (e) In an equilateral triangle, the median and altitude to a side is contained in the perpendicular bisector of that side.

16. (a) Let $A = (0, 0)$, $B = (m, n)$, $C = (p, q)$, $D = (r, s)$. Then $M = (p/2, q/2)$ and $N = ((m + r)/2, (n + s)/2)$. Also, $AB^2 = m^2 + n^2$, $BC^2 = (m - p)^2 + (n - q)^2$, $CD^2 = (p - r)^2 + (q - s)^2$, $DA^2 = r^2 + s^2$, etc.

  (b) If $ABCD$ is a parallelogram, then $N = M$. Thus, the sum of the squares of the sides of a parallelogram equals the sum of the squares of the diagonals.

17. Solution: Top--13, 2, 10, 3; Middle--5, 6, 9, 8; Bottom--4, 11, 1, 12 such that one side face has 13, 5, 4, 6 around it.

18. 24 3-point questions and 7 4-point questions.

19. Gold--16 g.; Silver--13 g.; Copper--15 g.

20. 66 and 82

21. 20

22. Yes, a 5 × 12 mat or a 6 × 8 mat.

Analyzing Student Thinking

23. No, Holly. Since you are trying to prove something is true for *any* quadrilateral, you don't want to make any assumption that would result in a special type of quadrilateral. For instance, if you tried to use only four letters by assuming the fourth vertex has coordinates (0, *d*), rather than (*d*, *e*), you'd have a kite.

24. Holly, first use the midpoint formula to determine the coordinates of the midpoints of each side of the given quadrilateral. Each pair of midpoints of consecutive sides determines a side of the new quadrilateral. To prove this is a parallelogram, you can show its opposite sides have the same slope, using the slope formula with the coordinates you found in the first step.

25. Yes, Molly, your vertices will work just fine. The proof of this result that is given in your book may be only slightly easier than the one with your chosen vertices only because all the coordinates are positive.

26. Jolene's choice of coordinates is fine, but she doesn't need three variables to name the vertices—two will suffice. Since the right angle is at the point $(a, 0)$, b must be equal to a, as the following figure illustrates:

27. Herbert is incorrect. The line through the midpoint of the hypotenuse and $(0, 0)$ bisects the hypotenuse, but will be perpendicular to the hypotenuse only in the case that $a = b$.

The perpendicular bisector, shown in the figure below, contains the point $(a/2, b/2)$ and has slope equal to the opposite reciprocal of the slope of the hypotenuse, $m = -(-b/a) = a/b$

Its equation is given by

$$y = (a/b)x + \left(\frac{b^2 - a^2}{2b} \right).$$

28. It can be *proved* that the diagonals of a rhombus bisect each other and are perpendicular to each other. Thus, *if* Shelley has this information from previous work, her placement and labeling are correct.

Chapter 16

Section 16.1

1. (a)

(b)

2.

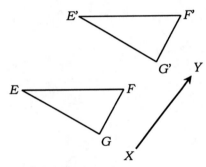

3. (a) $A'(1, 2)$, $B'(4, 3)$,
          $C'(6, 1)$, $D'(2, -2)$
     (b) $(x + 3, \ y - 1)$

4. Construct image of A, image of B,
     image of C and connect.

5. (a) 180°   (b) -20°

6. (a)

(b)

(c)

7.

8. (a)

(b)

9. (a)

   (b)

   (b)

16.

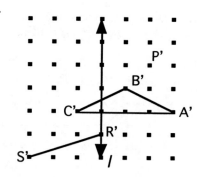

10. $A'(3, -1)$ $B'(6, -3)$ $C'(1, -4)$

11. (a) (5, -1)   (b) (3, 1)
    (c) (-4, 2)   (d) (-1, 3)
    (e) (-2, -5)   (f) $(y, -x)$

12. (a) (3, -2)   (b) (1, 3)
    (c) (-4, 5)

13. (a) $(y, -x)$ (b) $(-x, -y)$

14. Construct a perpendicular at O
    such that $AO = A'O$ as shown
    below. Repeat for points B and C
    to find B' and C' respectively.

15. (a)

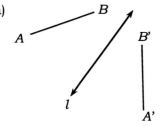

17. (b) (-2, 1) (-3, -5), (-6, 3)
    (c) $(-a, b)$

18. (a) Drop perpendiculars from A
    and B to line l. Then find A'
    and B' so $AX = XA'$ and $BY = YB'$.

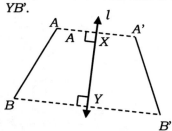

    (b) Repeat the construction in
    part (a) on points A, B, and C.
    Then connect A', B', and C'.

19. (a)

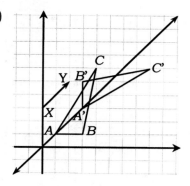

    (b) (3, 3), (3, 5), (8, 6)

(c) $(y + 2, x + 2)$

20. Construct lines, through A and B, parallel to $\overrightarrow{XY}$ and mark off the translation. Then construct perpendiculars to l through A' and B' to find reflection of the translated image.

21. (a) and (c). The original image $ABCDE$ is traversed clockwise as are the images for (a) and (c).

22. (a)

(b)

(c)

(d)

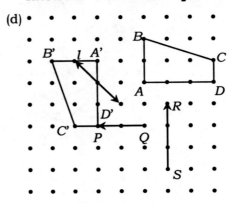

23. (a) Rotation (90°, 180°, 270°), Reflection (4 lines)
     (b) Rotation (90°, 180°, 270°),
     (c) Rotation 180°, Reflection (2 lines)
     (d) None

24. (a)   (b)

     (c)

25. (a)

     (b)

26. (a)

(b)

27. (a)

(b)

(c)

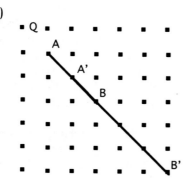

28. (a) $S_{P,1/2}$ Note: The scale has been changed so that the figure can fit this column.

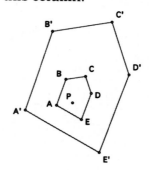

(b) $S_{P,3}$
Note: The scale has been changed so that the figure can fit this column.

29. (a) T_{XY}

(b) Not possible
(c) Not possible
(d) M_l followed by T_{XY}

30. (a) Not possible
(b) $R_{O,-90°}$

(c) Not possible
(d) M*l* followed by T*XY*

31. (a) None

(b) Rotation

(c) Glide reflection

32. (a)

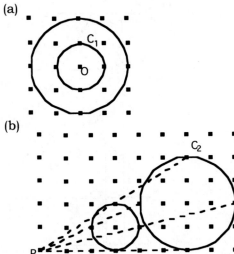

(b)

33. No, the location of the line of reflection does not affect the size and shape of the image. It only effects the location of the image

Analyzing Student Thinking

34. Yes. Although one can think of this as one slide or two slides, mathematicians tend to minimize and call it one. In this case the slide is $4\sqrt{2}$ units on a line 45° below the horizontal.

35. No since a flip reverses orientation, but a turn does not. Take a circle for example. A turn in the center and a flip across a diameter would look the same. However, if you labeled three points on the circle with letters and saw what happened to them under a 180-degree turn and a flip, you'd see they'd have reverse orientations.

36. No. Two reflections preserve orientation, but one reverses it. Thus, they are different.

37. No. Two glide reflections preserve orientation while one reverses it. Thus, they are different.

38. No. A motion that reverses orientation followed by a motion that reverses orientation ends up preserving orientation.

39. Yes.

$$OP'' = m \cdot OP' = m \cdot (k \cdot OP) = km \cdot OP$$
Thus, $S_{O,\,k}$ followed by $S_{O,\,m}$ is equal to $S_{O,\,km}$.

40. No. $S_{O,\,-k}$ is not defined since k must be a positive real number. However, if $S_{O,\,k}$ is followed by $S_{O,\,1/k}$, the result will be no transformation (or size transformation by a factor of 1), by #39 above.

41. Yes. Any similitude can be expressed as a size transformation followed by an isometry, and also as an isometry followed by a size transformation. Thus, a combination of two similitudes can be expressed as two size transformations followed by two isometries. Since two size transformations is a size transformation and two isometries is an isometry, we have a size transformation followed by an isometry. In other words, it's a similitude.

Section 16.2

1. (a) $A = (-3, 1)$, $B = (1, 2.5)$
   (b) $A' = (1, 6)$, $B' = (5, 7.5)$
   (c) $AB = \sqrt{(-3-1)^2 + (1-2.5)^2} = \sqrt{18.25}$. $A'B' = \sqrt{18.25}$, as well.

2. (a) $\sqrt{(c-a)^2 + (d-b)^2}$
   (b) $A' = (a + p,\ b + q)$, $B' = (c + p,\ d + q)$

   (c) $\sqrt{(c-a)^2 + (d-b)^2}$
   (d) Yes

3. (a) $A'(-1,\ -2)$, $B'(3,\ 0)$, $C'(0,\ 5)$
   (b) Yes, by SSS; $AB = A'B' = 2\sqrt{2}$ $AC = A'C' = \sqrt{50}$, $BC = B'C' = \sqrt{34}$
   (c) Yes, since $\triangle ABC \cong \triangle A'B'C'$, the corresponding angles are congruent.

4. $A' = (2, -3)$, $B' = (3, 1)$;
   $AB = \sqrt{1^2 + 4^2} = 17$,
   $A'B' = \sqrt{(-1)^2 + (-4)^2} = 17$,
   so $AB = A'B'$.

5. (a) $A = (4, 2)$ and $B = (-1, -3)$
   (b) $A' = (4, -2)$ and $B' = (-1, 3)$
   (c) $AB = \sqrt{(4+1)^2 + (2+3)^2} = 5\sqrt{2}$,
   $A'B' = \sqrt{(4+1)^2 + (-2-3)^2} = 5\sqrt{2}$

6. (a) $(-a, b)$
   (b) $AB = \sqrt{(a-c)^2 + (b-d)^2}$;
   $A' = (-a, b)$, $B' = (-c, d)$ and
   $A'B' = \sqrt{(-a+c)^2 + (b-d)^2} = \sqrt{(a-c)^2 + (b-d)^2}$

7. (a) $A'(2, -2)$, $B'(3, 1)$, $C'(-1, 4)$
   (b) Yes, by SSS; $AB = A'B' = \sqrt{10}$,
   $AC = A'C' = 3\sqrt{5}$,
   $BC = B'C' = 5$
   (c) Yes, since $\triangle ABC \cong \triangle A'B'C'$, the corresponding angles are congruent.

8. (a) $(-2, 1)$, $(2, 3)$
   (b) $(-2 + p,\ -1)$, $(2 + p,\ -3)$
   (c) $AB = \sqrt{(-2-2)^2 + (1-3)^2} = 2\sqrt{5}$
   $A'B' = \sqrt{[(-2+p)-(2+p)]^2 + (-1+3)^2} = 2\sqrt{5}$

9. (a) Reflection (b) Glide reflection
   (c) Rotation

10. (a) Rotation (b) Glide reflection

11. (a)

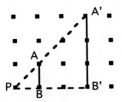

(b) $PA' = 3\sqrt{2}$, $PA = \sqrt{2}$, so $PA' = 3PA$

(c) $PB' = 3$, $PB = 1$, so $PB' = 3PB$

(d) 1, 3; $A'B' = 3AB$ (same scale factor)

12. (a) P is at lower right corner of lattice, $k = 2$

(b) $h = 1/2$

(c) They are reciprocals

13. (a) $T_{C_1C_2}$ followed by $S_{C_1,3/2}$ would map A_1 to A_2.

(b) Yes; the transformation $T_{C_1C_2}$ followed by $S_{C_1,r_2/r_1}$ maps one circle (center C_1, radius r_1) to a second circle (center C_2, radius r_2)

14. (a) For example, $S_{B,5/2}$ followed by $R_{C,-90°}$.

(b) For example, $S_{B,2/3}$ followed by a glide reflection.

(c) For example, $S_{B,2}$ followed by a glide reflection.

15. Since translations map lines to parallel lines, $p \parallel p'$ and $q \parallel q'$. Thus, since $p \parallel q$, we have that $p' \parallel q'$.

16. Since rotations preserve distances, $AB = A'B'$, $AC = A'C'$, and $BC = B'C'$. Since A, B, and C are collinear, $AB + BC = AC$. Therefore $A'B' + B'C' = AB + BC = AC = A'C'$ and A', B', and C' are collinear.

17. Since rotations preserve distance, $\overline{AB} \cong \overline{A'B'}$, $\overline{BC} \cong \overline{B'C'}$, and

$\overline{CA} \cong \overline{C'A'}$. Thus, $\triangle ABC \cong \triangle A'B'C'$. Therefore, $\angle BAC \cong \angle B'A'C'$ since they are corresponding parts of congruent triangles.

18. Since reflections preserve distance, $\overline{BP} \cong \overline{B'P'}$. Also, since l is the perpendicular bisector of $\overline{BB'}$, $\overline{BQ} \cong \overline{B'Q}$. Further, $\overline{PQ} \cong \overline{PQ}$ so $\triangle BPQ \cong \triangle B'PQ$ by the SSS congruence property. Therefore, $\angle BPQ \cong \angle B'PQ$ since they are corresponding angles of congruent triangles.

19. (a) Both are perpendicular to $\overline{AC}$ and therefore parallel.

(b) $M_l(A) = C$ since l is the perpendicular bisector of $\overline{AC}$. Then, $T_{CB}(C) = B$.

(c)

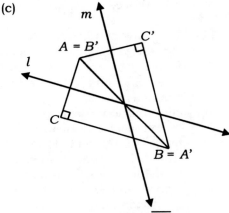

(d) At the midpoint of $\overline{AB}$. No.

20. $p \parallel q$ implies $\angle 1 \cong \angle 2$. Since an isometry preserves angle measure, $\angle 1 \cong \angle 3$ and $\angle 2 \cong \angle 4$. Thus, $\angle 3 \cong \angle 4$ and $p' \parallel q'$, by the corresponding angles property.

21. (a) One; the reflection line is the perpendicular bisector of $\overline{PQ}$.

(b) Infinitely many; reflect P to S in any line through the midpoint of $\overline{PQ}$, then translate T_{SQ}.

22. Construct ray $\overrightarrow{PB}$ and line through A' parallel to $\overline{AB}$. They intersect

at B'. In a like manner, draw ray $\overrightarrow{PC}$ and line through B' parallel to $\overline{BC}$. They intersect at C'. A similar procedure yields D'.

23. Construct line through P' parallel to $\overline{PR}$, and also the line through Q' parallel to $\overline{QR}$. These two lines will intersect at the point R'.

24. 1. $X' = X$ (by definition of reflection)
     2. Vertical angles, corresponding angles of $\triangle AXP$ and $\triangle A'X'P'$, vertical angles
     3. 180°, m($\angle A'X'B'$) = m($\angle A'X'B$) + m($\angle BX'Q$) + m($\angle QX'B'$) = $b + 2a = 180°$, yes
     4. Case (2) of reflection preserves distances: point X is on the reflection line.
     5. $AB = AX + XB$ (collinear with X between A and B) = $A'X' + X'B'$ (part 4) = $A'B'$ (collinear with X' between A' and B').

25. Yes it is a rotation around the intersection of the two lines of reflection. The angle of rotation is twice the angle between the intersecting lines

Analyzing Student Thinking

26. Racquel is correct. Isometries preserve the shape and size of the original figure. So the area of a triangle is preserved under an isometry.

27. Yes, Monica. We proved in problem #20 that isometries preserve parallel lines.

28. Yes, Thomas, in a size transformation angle measure is preserved, so parallel lines (and perpendicular lines) within a figure will retain their relationship after transformation. The same is not true for similitudes since they are combinations of size transformations and isometries (for example, a rotation).

29. Yes, Kristi, by the definition of congruence. Also, if the two shapes have the same orientation, then the transformation is translation or a rotation. If they have opposite orientations, then the transformation is either a reflection or a glide reflection.

30. Eli, a similitiude consists of a size transformation followed by an isometry. The similitude will preserve orientation, but if the isometry is a reflection or glide reflection, orientation is reversed.

31. Petra, congruent triangles are similar. Thus, any property of similitudes is also a property of isometries.

32. This depends on whether you count a glide-reflection as an isometry or as a combination of two isometries. Including it, there would be four isometries: translation, reflection, rotation and glide-reflection.

Section 16.3

1. (a) $H_C(H_B(H_A(H_C(H_B(H_A(P)))))) = P$
    (b) $H_C(H_B(H_A(H_C(H_B(H_A(Q)))))) = Q$
    (c) The combinations of six half turns, around the vertices of a triangle in succession, maps each point to itself.

2. Apply $T_{AA'}$ to $\triangle ABC$ first, for example. Let $B^* = T_{AA'}(B)$ and $C^* = T_{AA'}(C)$. Then the rotation with center A' and directed angle $\angle B^*A'B'$ (or $\angle C^*A'C'$) will map $\triangle A^*B^*C^*$ to $\triangle A'B'C'$.

3. $A^* = M_r(A)$, $B^* = M_r(B)$,

$C^* = M_r(C)$. Then $M_r(\triangle ABC) = \triangle A^*B^*C^*$ and $S_{O,1/2}(\triangle A^*B^*C^*) = \triangle A'B'C'$

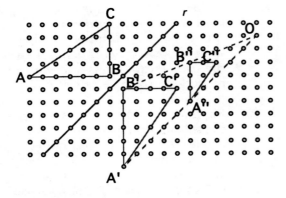

4.   All of them.

5. H_P; $R_{P,360°}$

6. M_{AI}, M_{BJ}, M_{CF}, M_{DG}, M_{EH},
      $R_{O,72°}$, $R_{O,144°}$, $R_{O,216°}$
      $R_{O,288°}$; $R_{O,360°}$

7. $R_{G,120°}$, $R_{G,240°}$, $R_{G,360°}$,
      M_{AF}, M_{BD}, M_{CE}

8.   Use $R_{B,90°}$ to map $\triangle ABD$ to $\triangle FBC$.
      Use $R_{C,-90°}$ to map $\triangle ACE$ to $\triangle KCB$.

9.   (a) $S_{A,2}(P) = B$, by definition.
            $S_{A,2}(R) = C$, by definition.
            $S_{A,2}(A) = A$, by definition.
            Hence, $S_{A,2}(\triangle APR) = \triangle ABC$.
            Other size transformations are
            possible.
      (b) $\overline{PR} \parallel \overline{BC}$ since the size
            transformation image of a line
            is parallel to the line. Hence,
            $\overline{PR} \parallel \overline{BQ}$. Similarly
            $\overline{RQ} \parallel \overline{PB}$ so $PBQR$ is a
            parallelogram.

10. $H_P(\overline{BC}) \parallel \overline{BC}$ and since
      $H_P(A) = C$, we must have that

$H_P(B)$ is on $\overline{AD}$. Similarly, $H_P(B)$ is on $\overline{CD}$ by considering $H_P(\overline{AB})$. Hence $H_P(B) = D$. Thus, P is the midpoint of $\overline{BD}$ also.

11. $M_l(A) = C$ and $M_l(C) = A$ by
      definition of M_l. Also,
      $M_l(B) = B$, so $M_l(\overline{AB}) = \overline{CB}$.
      Hence, $AB = BC$.

12.   Let $P = \overline{AC} \cap \overline{BD}$ as was shown
      earlier, $\overline{AC} \perp \overline{BD}$ and $\overline{AC}$ and
      $\overline{BD}$ are perpendicular bisectors of
      each other. Hence, $M_{AC}(B) = D$
      and $M_{BD}(A) = C$. Thus, M_{AC}
      followed by M_{BD} maps $ABCD$ to
      $CDAB$, i.e. M_{AC} followed by M_{BD}
      is equivalent to the half turn H_P.
      (See also problem 5.) Thus,
      $\overline{AB} \parallel \overline{CD}$ since a half turn maps
      a line to a line parallel to it.
      Similarly, $\overline{AD} \parallel \overline{CB}$.

13.   (a) $PA = PA' = PA''$. Also, PA' and r
            form an angle measuring
            $x°$, while PA'' and s form an
            angle measuring $y°$. Hence,
            $m(\angle APA') = 2x°$ and
            $m(\angle A'PA'') = 2y°$. Thus, $A'' = R_{P,2(x+y)}(A)$. Since A was
            arbitrary, and orientation is
            preserved, M_r followed by M_s
            is $R_{P,2(x+y)}$.
      (b)   Point P, the intersection of r
            and s, is the center of the
            rotation. The measure of the
            angle of the rotation is twice
            the measure of the angle
            between r and s.

14. (a)

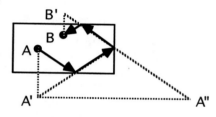

(b) Argument is similar to the billiard problem in set *A*.

15. $\dfrac{\pi - \sqrt{3}}{2}$

Analyzing Student Thinking

16. Annie is correct because an isosceles triangle has two congruent sides, so the triangle together with its reflection will have four congruent sides. Therefore, it is a rhombus by definition.

17. Chris is correct. He can use an isometry to move any figure to a congruent figure. Isometries are comprised of translations and rotations (which can be expressed as two reflections), a reflection, or a glide reflection (which can be expressed as three reflections).

18. Rueben is correct. A half turn is a 180° rotation. A reflection over a horizontal line followed by reflection over a vertical line is the same as a 180° rotation about the point of intersection of the two lines.

19. Eva is incorrect. Fold the parallelogram along the proposed line and notice that the two halves that result do not coincide.

20. If this were a reflection, angle measure would be preserved. However, the angle at top left is obtuse, and the angle at lower left is acute, so obviously one is not the image of the other under a reflection.

21. Jamie's path, as drawn, is not possible since when the ball hits a wooden board at the edge of the green, it must bounce away at an angle that equals the angle at which it approached the board. Jamie will need a more complicated path, which can be found by using reflections.

Epilogue

1. $\angle ABD \cong \angle CDB$ (alternate interior angle property with $\overline{AB} \parallel \overline{DC}$, $\overline{BD} \cong \overline{DB}$, so $\triangle ABD \cong \triangle CDB$ (by SAS congruence property), $\angle ADB \cong \angle CBD$ (corresponding parts of congruent triangles) so $\overline{AD} \parallel \overline{BC}$ (alternate interior angle property) and $ABCD$ is therefore a parallelogram.

2. (a) $M = \left(\dfrac{a}{2}, \dfrac{b}{2}\right)$ and $N = \left(\dfrac{c+d}{2}, \dfrac{b}{2}\right)$

    Hence, $MN = \dfrac{c+d-a}{2}$,

    $AB = d$, and $DC = c - a$.
    $AB + DC = d + c - a$ or $2MN$.

    Thus, $MN = \dfrac{1}{2}(AB + DC)$.

    Slopes of $\overline{AB}$ and $\overline{MN}$ are 0, thus $\overline{MN} \parallel \overline{AB}$.

3. (a) The diagonals, $\overline{AC}$ and $\overline{BD}$, *bisect* each other at point P. Hence, by the definition, $H_P(A) = C$ and $H_P(B) = D$.

    (b) $H_P(C) = A$ and $H_P(D) = B$, as well, so H_P maps the parallelogram onto itself. Notice that $H_P(\overline{AB}) = \overline{CD}$, etc. for the other sides, since an isometry maps a line segment to a line segment. The parallelogram rotates onto itself under a 180° rotation, hence has rotation symmetry.

4. $\overline{BE} \cong \overline{DE}$ and $\overline{AE} \cong \overline{CE} \cong$ (diagonals bisect each other). $\angle BEC \cong \angle DEA$ (vertical angles are congruent), so $\triangle BEC \cong \triangle DEA$ (SAS congruence property). Thus, $\angle BCE \cong \angle DAE$ (corresponding parts of congruent triangles) so $\overline{BC} \parallel \overline{AD}$ (alternate interior angle property). Similarly, $\angle BAE \cong \angle DCE$ and $\triangle BEA \cong \triangle DEC$ (SAS congruence property) so $\angle BAE$

$\cong \angle DCE$ (corresponding parts of congruent triangles) and $\overline{AB} \parallel \overline{DC}$ (alternate interior angle property). Since both pairs of opposite sides are parallel, $ABCD$ is a parallelogram.

5. Since $ABCD$ is a rhombus, $AB = AD$.

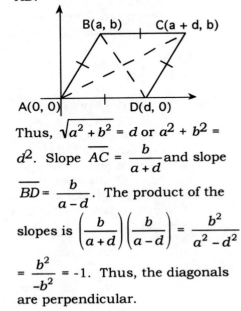

    Thus, $\sqrt{a^2 + b^2} = d$ or $a^2 + b^2 = d^2$. Slope $\overline{AC} = \dfrac{b}{a+d}$ and slope $\overline{BD} = \dfrac{b}{a-d}$. The product of the slopes is $\left(\dfrac{b}{a+d}\right)\left(\dfrac{b}{a-d}\right) = \dfrac{b^2}{a^2 - d^2}$

    $= \dfrac{b^2}{-b^2} = -1$. Thus, the diagonals are perpendicular.

6. $\overline{LP} \cong \overline{NP}$ and $\overline{MP} \cong \overline{OP}$ (diagonals of parallelogram bisect each other) and $\angle LPM \cong \angle NPM \cong \angle NPO \cong \angle LPO$ (diagonals are perpendicular), so $\triangle LPM \cong \triangle NPM \cong \triangle NPO \cong \triangle LPO$ (SAS congruence property). Therefore, $\overline{LM} \cong \overline{NM} \cong \overline{NO} \cong \overline{LO}$ (corresponding parts of congruent triangles) and $LMNO$ is a rhombus by definition.

7. Since $ABCD$ is a trapezoid, we have the following coordinates.

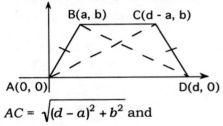

    $AC = \sqrt{(d-a)^2 + b^2}$ and

$BD = \sqrt{(d-a)^2 + (0-b)^2}$. Thus, $AC = BD$.

8. A parallelogram with perpendicular diagonals is a rhombus and thus has four congruent sides. Therefore, *HIJK* is a square.

Section T1 - Part B

1. (a) Roses are red and the sky is blue.
   (b) Roses are red and the sky is blue or turtles are green.
   (c) If the sky is blue, then roses are red and turtles are green.
   (d) Turtles are not green and turtles are green implies that roses are not red.

2.

p	q	$p \rightarrow q$	$\sim(p \wedge q)$	$p \wedge q$	$q \rightarrow p$
T	T	T	F	T	T
T	F	F	T	F	T
F	T	T	T	F	F
F	F	T	T	F	T

3. (a) T (b) F (c) T (d) T

4. $p \rightarrow q$ and $p \vee q$ have the same truth table.

5. (a) Hypotheses:
   All football players are introverts and Tony is a football player
   Conclusion:
   Tony is an introvert.
   (b) Hypotheses:
   Bob is taller than Jim and Jim is taller than Sue.
   Conclusion:
   Bob is taller than Sue.
   (c) Hypotheses:
   All penguins are elegant swimmers and no elegant swimmers fly.
   Conclusion:
   Penguins don't fly.

6. (c) and (e)

7. (a) Necessary
   (b) Sufficient
   (c) Sufficient

8. (a) T   (b) T
   (c) Unknown (d) T
   (e) F   (f) Unknown
   (g) T   (h) T
   (i) Unknown (j) F
   (k) T   (l) Unknown
   (m) Unknown (n) T (o) T

9. (a) $[(w \rightarrow t) \wedge t] \rightarrow w$ Invalid
   (b) $[(s \rightarrow l) \wedge \sim s] \rightarrow \sim l$ Invalid
   (c) $[(\sim s \rightarrow e) \wedge (w \rightarrow \sim e)] \rightarrow (w \rightarrow s)$ Valid
   (d) $[(m \wedge s) (j \rightarrow m)] \rightarrow j$ Invalid

10. (d), (e), and (f)

Section T2 - Part B

1. (a) 6 and 6
   (b) 6 and 6
   (c) 2 and 2
   (d) 4 and 4
   (e) Multiplication distributes over addition and subtraction in clock arithmetic.

2. (a) 1 and 1   (b) 0 and 0
   (c) 0 and 0
   (d) The exponent rule $a^m b^m = (ab)^m$ holds in clock arithmetic.

3. 1, 4, 5, 2, 3, 6

4. (a) 4 (b) 1 (c) 4 (d) 4
   (e) 3 (f) 2 (g) 0 (h) 0

5. (a) -17, -12, -7, -2, 3, 8, 13, 18
   (b) -17, -10, -3, 4, 11, 18
   (c) 2, 4, 8
   (d) 2, 3, . . . , 20

6. $3 \times 4 = 0$

7. (a) 0, 2, 4, 6
   (b) 0, 2, 4, 5, 6, 8
   (c) 0, 2, 3, 4, 6, 8, 9, 10
   For the 36-clock, 0, 2, 3, 4, 6, 8, 9, 10, 12, 14, 15, 16, 18, 20, 21, 22, 24, 26, 27, 28, 30, 32, 33, 34.

8. (a) 7 (b) 4 (c) 11 (d) 9
   In clock n, $n - 1$ is its own inverse.

9. a is the square root of b if $a^2 = b$.
   (a) 2   (b) 1, 3, 5, 7
   (c) 3   (d) 7
   Numbers may have zero or many square roots depending on the clock number.

10. Let 1 be positive. Then, if the sum of two positives is positive, 1 + 1 = 2, 2 + 1 = 3, 3 + 1 = 4, and 4 + 1 = 0 are all positive . Thus all numbers in the 5-clock are positive.

11. Multiplication is closed because addition is closed and multiplication can be viewed as repeated addition.

12. If $a \equiv b \bmod m$, then $m \mid (a - b)$. But then $m \mid (a - b)c$, or $m \mid (ac - bc)$. Thus, $ac \equiv bc \bmod m$.

13. $2 \times 3 \equiv 4 \times 3 \bmod 6$, but 2 is not congruent to 4 mod 6.

14. $7^2 \equiv 1 \bmod 8$. So $(7^2)^{50} \equiv 1^{50} \bmod 8$, or $7^{100} \equiv 1 \bmod 8$. Therefore, $7^{101} \equiv 7 \bmod 8$, so the remainder when 7^{101} is divided by 8 is 7.

Introduction to Graph Theory (on the Web)

1. (a) A = F = 2, B = C = 3, D = E = 1
   (b) B = C = E = F = 3, A = D = 2
   (c) A = B = E = F = G = H = 3, D = C = 4

2. (i) (a) A: B, F; B: A, C, F; C: B,D,E.
   (b) A: B,F; B: A, E, F; C: D,E,F.
   (c) A: B,D,F; B: A,C,G; C: B,D,H
   (ii) The degree of a vertex is the same as the number of vertices it is adjacent to.

3.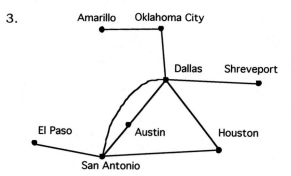

4. (a) Connected since there is a path from any vertex to any other vertex.
   (b) Not connected. For example, U does not have a path to X.
   (c) Connected since there is a path from any vertex to any other vertex.

5. (i) and (v) are equivalent; (ii) and (iii)are equivalent.

6. (a) (i) Yes, exactly two odd vertices
   (ii) Euler Path by Euler's Traversable Graph Theorem.
   (b) (i) No, four odd vertices.
   (ii) None
   (c) (i) Yes, all even vertices.
   (ii) Euler Circuit by Euler's Traversable Graph Theorem.
   (d) (I) Yes, exactly two odd vertices.
   (ii) Euler Path by Euler's Traversable Graph Theorem.

7. (a) Hamiltonian Path LMNOPQ
   (b) None, since the graph is not connected.
   (c) Hamiltonian Circuit ACDEBA

8. (a)

   (b)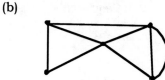

9. Since R + V = E +2, we have V = E + 2 – R, or V = 13 + 2 – 8 = 7.

10. (a) Hexagonal prism
    (b) Hexagonal pyramid
    (c) Pentagonal pyramid

11. Add 2 edges. For example HJ and LM. An Euler Circuit is NJINLMLKJHIKNHMN

12 (a)

or

(b)

or

13. (a)

(b)

(c)

14. (a) 1a: 12 1b: 16; 1c: 26; 4a: 14; 4b: 16; 4c: 16.
     (b) 1a: 6; 1b: 8; 1c: 13; 4a: 7; 4b: 8; 4c: 8
     (c) The sum of the degrees of the vertices is twice the number of edges.

15.

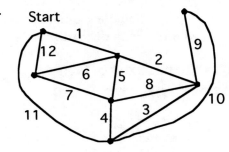

16. (a) 1a: 2; 1b: 2; 1c: 3.
     (b) 1a: BC, DE; 1b: AE, BC; 1c: AF, BF, EH.
     (c) 3; one edge for each pair of odd vertices.

17. Many solutions possible. Two are shown.

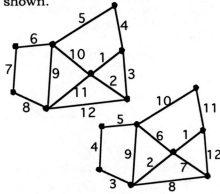

Answers To Even Numbered Problems In The PROBLEM SOLVING STUDY GUIDE

1. Guess and Test

1-B. 13 and 78

1-2. 53 and 32

1-4

2. Use a Variable

2-B.

$$n + 10$$
$$n \qquad n + 2$$
$$n + 8 \qquad n + 4 \qquad n + 6$$

2-2. Bruce was 52 years old in 1988.
He was born in 1936 = 44 × 44.
1988 - 1936 = 52.

2-4. 11 cows and 2 turkeys.
$4c + 2t = c + t + 35$
$3c + t = 35$

3. Draw a Picture

3-B. 30 seconds
2.5 seconds per floor
middle floor is 17
12 × 2.5 = 30

3-2. The fence will cost $2280.
120 posts and 120 sections

3-4. Jason will be halfway to his office
at 6:56 A.M.

4. Look for a Pattern

4-B (a) H 29 30 31
(b) R 69 70 71
(c) M 49 50 51
(d) P 61 26 63
(e) V 85 86 87

4-2. 18 girls and 12 boys
18 × 18 + 12 × 12 = 468

4-4. 99,225
99,225 = 315 × 315 = 9 × 11,025

5. Make a List

5-B The total number of coins cannot
be 18.
10 coins : 10 quarters
13 coins : 5 dimes and 8 quarters
16 coins : 10 dimes and 6
quarters
19 coins : 15 dimes and 4
quarters
22 coins : 20 dimes and 2
quarters
25 coins: 25 dimes

5-2. 36 ways; 3 pennies: 1 way,
4 pennies: 3 ways,
. . . , 10 pennies : 36 ways

5-4. Box Z: 9 marbles (X:18   Y:9)

6. Solve a Simpler Problem

6-B There are 864 dots on the 864
chips.

6-2. Largest 4-digit cube is $21^3 = 9261$.
9261 - 45 = 9216
Possible answers: 4 36 64
4 9 256   9 16 64

6-4. (a) $9,801 = 99^2$
(b) $27,000 = 30^3$
(c) $178 = 89 × 2$

7. Draw a Diagram

7-B Nine are red, not compact, and
have 4 doors.

7-2.   18 ways Ted, Amy, Bart

126	162	216	261	612
621	135	153	315	351
513	531	234	243	324
342	423	432		

7-4.   120 youth T-shirts, 80 adult

8.   Use Direct Reasoning

8-B   Ask either computer this question: What will the other computer answer if I ask it to tell   me which box contains $100?"

8-2.   There are 89 ways to get to the top step.
1 step stairway : 1 way
2 step stairway : 2 ways
3 step stairway : 3 ways
4 step stairway : 5 ways
. . . 10 step stairway : 89 ways

8-4.   The thousands digit is 8.
hundreds : 6
tens : 2
ones : 4

9.   Use Indirect Reasoning

9-B   Suppose that there is a triangle on the back side of card A. Then the statement on card A is true. This means that the statement on card B is also true. But this conclusion contradicts the fact that one statement is true and the other is false. Hence, the triangle must be on the back side of card B.

9-2.   (a) 1   (b) 2   (c) 6

9-4.   My vacation was 18 days, 13 with rain and 5 with no rain.

10.   Use Properties of Numbers

10-B   7,840

10-2.   There are 3 × 28 = 84 different triangles.

10-4.   Possible solutions:
Games/ 1 peg
Games/ 3 pegs
Games/ 4 pegs

Games/ 1 peg	Games/ 3 pegs	Games/ 4 pegs
5	14	1
6	11	3
7	8	5
8	5	7
9	2	9

11.   Solve an Equivalent Problem

11-B   There are 28 possible two-girl committees.

11-2.   Eight dogs
Cans/dogs/days:
5/4/1   40/32/1   40/8/4

11-4.   Suppose the chip under cup Z is not red. This means that Linda would have been able to guess the color of the chip under cup Y. Hence, the chip under cup Z must be red.

12.   Work Backward

12-B   Karen stated with $36.

12-2.   There are 92 girls.

12-4.   7/8
1/2 × 5/6 = 5/12
2/3 - 5/12 = 1/4
2 × 1/4 = 1/2
3/8 + 1/2 = 7/8

13.   Use Cases

13-B   Cody cannot place his cards as described in the problem. When the total in any two piles is even, the total in the other three piles must be odd and vice versa.

13-2.   7 children: 3 boys and 4 girls.

13-4.   Go second and then always make exactly the same move as your opponent.

14. Solve an Equation

14-B   Jeff's number is 8.
$100n + 100 = 900$
If you decrease the final result by 100 and then divide by 100, the answer will be the original number selected.

14-2.   16 red-odd chips, 75 blue-even chips

14-4.   40 members
$18x = 24(x - 10)$ yields $x = 40$

15. Look for a Formula

15-B $(1/2)^{30}$
$1 - 1/2 = 1/2$
$1 - 1/2 - 1/4 = 1/4$
$1 - 1/2 - 1/4 - 1/8 = 1/8 \ldots$

15-2.   16,800
$(1/3)n + (1/5)n + (1/6)n + (1/4)n + 42 = n$ implies $n = 840$
$0.05\,e = 840$
$e = 16,800$

15-4.   The snail will be 4 cm from the top.
$23/24 \times 96 = 92$
$96 - 92 = 4$

16. Do a Simulation

16-B   Answers will vary.

16-2.   Both cases have a probability of 3/8 that exactly two of the children will be girls.

16-4.   There were 240 chickens.
$x - 0.3x + 0.2x = 216$
$x = 240$

17. Use a Model

17-B   A model will show that Figure 1 cannot be separated as shown.

17-2.   The total value cannot be $3.
(a) 6 nickels + 4 dimes = $3.40
(b) 3 nickels + 7 dimes = $5.35

(d) 7 nickels + 6 dimes = $6.05

17-4.   One possible solution:
0 1 2 3 4 5   1 1 1 7 7 7

18. Use Dimensional Analysis

18-B   About 10.24 kilometers per liter

18-2.   1,200,000,301
The nth term is $9n - 2$. Hence, two more than any number in the sequence must be divisible by 9.

18-4.   20 20 0 0
20 12 8 0 → 20 0 8 12 →
18 0 8 14 → 18 8 0 14 →
18 8 8 6   → 20 8 6 6

19. Identify Subgoals

19-B   8400 ways = 6 × 20 × 70

19-2.   3 to 2
$7j + 3c = 81$
$j = (81 - 3c)/7$
Hence $c = 6$ and $j = 9$.
$j : c = 9 : 6 = 3 : 2$

19-4.   A tennis court, 36' by 78', has a perimeter of 228 feet.

20. Use Coordinates

20-B   Isosceles triangle: Two sides are 5 units long.
Right triangle: Two sides have slopes 4/3 and -3/4.
$(4/3 \times -3/4 = -1)$
The area of the triangle is 12.5 square units $(1/2 \times 5 \times 5)$.

20-2.   11 A. M. on Friday.
LCM(15, 28, 40) = 840 minutes = 14 hours

20-4.   If x and y are the lengths, cut the longer rope at a distance $(x + y)/3$ from one end.

21.   Use Symmetry

21-B.

21-2.   20,000
6/150 = 4%, estimate 4% tagged
4% p = 800
p = 20,000

21-4.   2,950 π square feet

CPSIA information can be obtained at www.ICGtesting.com
Printed in the USA
BVOW06s0503041214

377674BV00012B/133/P

9 781118 679241

ELEMENTARY STATISTICS

A BRIEF VERSION

Fifth Edition

Allan G. Bluman
Professor Emeritus
Community College of Allegheny County

Monterey Peninsula College
Statistics & Probability - MATH 16

Mc Graw Hill **Learning Solutions**

Boston   Burr Ridge, IL   Dubuque, IA   New York   San Francisco   St. Louis
Bangkok   Bogotá   Caracas   Lisbon   London   Madrid
Mexico City   Milan   New Delhi   Seoul   Singapore   Sydney   Taipei   Toronto

Elementary Statistics
A Brief Version, Fifth Edition
Monterey Peninsula College
Statistics & Probability - MATH 16

Copyright © 2010 by The McGraw-Hill Companies, Inc. All rights reserved. Printed in the United States of America. Except as permitted under the United States Copyright Act of 1976, no part of this publication may be reproduced or distributed in any form or by any means, or stored in a data base retrieval system, without prior written permission of the publisher.

This book is a McGraw-Hill Learning Solutions textbook and contains select material from *Elementary Statistics: A Brief Version*, Fifth Edition by Alan G. Bluman. Copyright © 2010, 2008, 2006, 2003 by The McGraw-Hill Companies, Inc. Reprinted with permission of the publisher. Many custom published texts are modified versions or adaptations of our best-selling textbooks. Some adaptations are printed in black and white to keep prices at a minimum, while others are in color.

2 3 4 5 6 7 8 9 0   DIG DIG   13 12

ISBN-13: 978-0-07-754554-3
ISBN-10: 0-07-754554-0
Part of
ISBN-13: 978-0-07-754795-0
ISBN-10: 0-07-754795-0

Learning Solutions Specialist: Kelly Casey
Production Editor: Pat Koch
Cover Design: Felicia Cornish
Printer/Binder: Digital Impressions

Brief Contents

Contents

Preface

Approach

Elementary Statistics: A Brief Version, Fifth Edition, is a shorter version of the popular text *Elementary Statistics: A Step by Step Approach,* Seventh Edition. This softcover edition includes all the features of the longer book, but it is designed for a course in which the time available limits the number of topics covered.

Elementary Statistics: A Brief Version was written as an aid in the beginning statistics course to students whose mathematical background is limited to basic algebra. The book follows a nontheoretical approach without formal proofs, explaining concepts intuitively and supporting them with abundant examples. The applications span a broad range of topics certain to appeal to the interests of students of diverse backgrounds and include problems in business, sports, health, architecture, education, entertainment, political science, psychology, history, criminal justice, the environment, transportation, physical sciences, demographics, eating habits, and travel and leisure.

About This Book

While a number of important changes have been made in the fifth edition, the learning system remains untouched and provides students with a useful framework in which to learn and apply concepts. Some of the retained features include the following:

- **Over 1200** exercises are located at the end of major sections within each chapter.

- **Hypothesis-Testing Summaries** are found at the end of Chapter 9 (z, t, χ^2, and F tests for testing means, proportions, and variances) and Chapter 11 (correlation, chi-square, and ANOVA), to show students the different types of hypotheses and the types of tests to use.

- A **Data Bank** listing various attributes (educational level, cholesterol level, gender, etc.) for 100 people and several additional data sets using real data are included and referenced in various exercises and projects throughout the book.

- An updated **reference card** containing the formulas and the z, t, χ^2, and PPMC tables is included with this textbook.

- End-of-chapter **Summaries, Important Terms,** and **Important Formulas** give students a concise summary of the chapter topics and provide a good source for quiz or test preparation.

- **Review Exercises** are found at the end of each chapter.

- Special sections called **Data Analysis** require students to work with a data set to perform various statistical tests or procedures and then summarize the results. The data are included in the Data Bank in Appendix D and can be downloaded from the book's website at www.mhhe.com/bluman.

- **Chapter Quizzes,** found at the end of each chapter, include multiple-choice, true/false, and completion questions along with exercises to test students' knowledge and comprehension of chapter content.

- The **Appendixes** provide students with an essential algebra review, an outline for report writing, extensive reference tables, a glossary, and answers to all quiz questions, all odd-numbered exercises, selected even-numbered exercises, and an alternate method for using the standard normal distribution.

- The **Applying the Concepts** feature is included in all sections and gives students an opportunity to think about the new concepts and apply them to hypothetical examples and scenarios similar to those found in newspapers, magazines, and radio and television news programs.

Changes in the Fifth Edition

This edition of *Elementary Statistics: A Brief Version* is updated and improved for students and instructors in the following ways:

- **Over 200** new exercises have been added, **most using real data,** and many exercises incorporate thought-provoking questions requiring students to interpret their results.
- Titles have been given to each application example and each exercise problem to emphasize their real-world relevance.
- Six new **Speaking of Statistics** topics have been included.
- An explanation of bar graphs has been added to Chapter 2 since bar graphs are one of the most commonly used graphs in statistics, and they are slightly different from Pareto charts.
- Over 30 examples have been replaced with new ones, the majority using real data.
- Two graphs have been added to the explanation of the chi-square distribution in Chapter 7 to help clarify the nature of the distribution and how the distribution is related to the chi-square table.
- The **Excel Technology Step by Step** boxes have been updated to reflect Microsoft Excel 2007.
- The shortcut formula for the standard deviation has been changed. The formula used now is $s = \sqrt{\dfrac{n(\Sigma X^2) - (\Sigma X)^2}{n(n-1)}}$, which is the one used in most other statistics books.

  It also avoids the complex fraction used in the other formula $s = \sqrt{\dfrac{\Sigma X^2 - [(\Sigma X)^2/n]}{n-1}}$.

  Many reviewers have stated that they like the first formula better than the second one.
- The cumulative standard normal distribution is used throughout the book.
- The null hypothesis is stated using the equals sign in all cases where appropriate.
- When σ or σ_1 and σ_2 are known, the z tests are used in hypothesis testing. When σ or σ_1 and σ_2 are unknown, the t tests are used in hypothesis testing.
- The F test for two variances is no longer used before the t test for the difference between two means when σ_1 and σ_2 are unknown.
- The **Data Projects** at the end of each chapter are all new and are specific to the areas of Business and Finance, Sports and Leisure, Technology, Health and Wellness, Politics and Economics, and Your Class.

Acknowledgments

It is important to acknowledge the many people whose contributions have gone into the Fifth Edition of *Elementary Statistics: A Brief Version*. Very special thanks are due to Jackie Miller of The Ohio State University for her provision of the Index of Applications, her exhaustive accuracy check of the page proofs, and her general availability and advice concerning all matters statistical. The Technology Step by Step sections were provided by Gerry Moultine of Northwood University (MINITAB), John Thomas of College of Lake County (Excel), and Michael Keller of St. Johns River Community College (TI-83 Plus and TI-84 Plus).

I would also like to thank Diane P. Cope for providing the new exercises, Kelly Jackson for writing the new Data Projects, and Sally Robinson for error checking, adding technology-accurate answers to the answer appendix, and writing the Solutions Manuals.

Finally, at McGraw-Hill Higher Education, thanks to John Osgood, Sponsoring Editor; Christina Lane, Developmental Editor; April Southwood, Senior Project Manager; Amber Bettcher, Digital Product Manager; and Sandra Schnee, Senior Media Project Manager.

Allan G. Bluman

Special thanks for their advice and recommendations for revisions found in the previous editions of the textbook go to:

Rosalie Abraham, *Florida Community College-North*

Stan Adamski, *Owens Community College*

Olcay Akman, *Illinois State University*

Anne Albert, *University of Findlay*

Patty G. Amick, *Greenville Technical College*

Raid Amin, *University of West Florida*

Trania Aquino, *Del Mar College*

Diana J. Asmus, *Greenville Technical College*

John J. Avioli, *Christopher Newport University*

Rona Axelrod, *Edison Community College*

Mark D. Baker, M.S., *Illinois State University*

Sivanandan Balakumar, *Lincoln University*

Naveen K. Bansal, *Marquette University*

Barb Barnet, *University of Wisconsin, Platteville*

Freda Bennett, *Massachusetts College of Liberal Arts*

Sr. Prof. Abraham Biggs, *Broward Community College*

Wes Black, *Illinois Valley Community College*

William L. Blubaugh, *University of Northern Colorado*

Matthew Bognar, *University of Iowa*

Andrea Boito, *Pennsylvania State University–Altoona*

Donna Brouillette, *Georgia Perimeter College*

Robert E. Buck, *Slippery Rock University*

Dean Burbank, *Gulf Coast Community College*

David Busekist, *Southeastern Louisiana University*

Christine Bush, *Palm Beach Community College–Palm Beach Gardens*

Ferry Butar Butar, *Sam Houston State University*

Carlos Canas, *Florida Memorial College*

Keri Catalfomo, *TriCounty Community College*

Lee R. Clendenning, *Berry College*

Sarah Trattler Clifton, *Southeastern Louisiana University*

James Condor, *Manatee Community College–Bradenton*

Diane Cope, *Washington & Jefferson College*

Gregory Daubenmire, *Las Positas College*

Jeff Edmunds, *University of Mary Washington*

Billy Edwards, *University of Tennessee at Chattanooga*

C. Wayne Ehler, *Ann Arundel Community College*

Melody E. Eldred, *State University College–Oneonta*

Abdul Elfessi, *University of Wisconsin–LaCrosse*

Hassan Elsalloukh, *University of Arkansas at Little Rock*

Thomas Fitzkee, *Francis Marion University*

Kevin Fox, *Shasta College*

Dr. Tom Fox, *Cleveland State Community College*

Leszek Gawarecki, *Kettering University*

Gholamhosse Gharehgozlo Hamedani, *Marquette University*

Kim Gilbert, *University of Georgia*

Joseph Glaz, *University of Connecticut*

Liliana Gonzalez, *University of Rhode Island–Kingston*

Dana Goodwin, *University of Central Arkansas*

Rebekah A. Griffith, *McNeese State University*

C. Richard Gumina, Jr., *Colorado State University*

Renu A. Gupta, *Louisiana State University–Alexandria*

Shawn Haghighi, *Lindenwood University*

Elizabeth Hamman, *Cypress College*

Dr. Willard J. Hannon, *Las Positas College*

Harold S. Hayford, *Pennsylvania State University–Altoona*

Robert L. Heiny, *University of Northern Colorado*

Todd Hendricks, *Georgia Perimeter College*

Shahryar Heydari, *Piedmont College*

Jada P. Hill, *Richland College*

Dr. James Hodge, *Mountain State University*

Helene Humphrey, *San Joaquin Delta College*

Patricia Humphrey, *Georgia Southern University*

Charles W. Johnson, *Collin County Community College–Plano*

Clarence Johnson, *Cuyahoga Community College*

Craig Johnson, *Brigham Young University—Idaho*

Jeffery C. Jones, *County College of Morris*

Anne M. Jowsey, *Niagara County Community College*

Anand Katiyar, *McNeese State University*

Brother Donald Kelly, *Marist College*

Dr. Susan Kelly, *University of Wisconsin–La Crosse*

Linda Kelly-Penny, *Midland College*

Michael Kent, *Borough of Manhattan Community College*

B. M. Golam Kibria, *Florida International University–Miami*

Hyun-Joo Kim, *Truman State University*

Jong Sung Kim, *Portland State University*

Joseph Kunicki, *University of Findlay*

Marie Langston, *Palm Beach Community College–Lakeworth*

Susan S. Lenker, *Central Michigan University*

Janna Liberant, *Rockland Community College SUNY*

Benny Lo, *DeVry University*

Jackie MacLaughlin, *Central Piedmont Community College*

Rich Marchand, *Slippery Rock University*

Steve Marsden, *Glendale College*

Chip Mason, *Belhaven College*

Judith McCrory, *Findlay University*

Michael McKenna, *Louisiana State University*

Lynnette Meslinsky, *Erie Community College*

Charles J. Miller, Jr., *Camden County College*

Ayrin C. Molefe, *University of Central Arkansas*

Carla A. Monticelli, *Camden County College*

Christina Morian, *Lincoln University*

Alfred K. Mulzet, *Florida Community College at Jacksonville*

Humberto Munoz, *Southern University and A&M College at Baton Rouge*

Miroslaw Mystkowski, *Gardner-Webb University*

Michael A. Nasab, *Long Beach City College*

Jeanne Osborne, *Middlesex County College*

Lindsay Packer, *College of Charleston*

Irene Palacios, *Grossmont College*

Elaine S. Paris, *Mercy College*

Samuel Park, *Long Island University–Brooklyn*

Chester Piascik, *Bryant University*

Suzie Pickle, *St. Petersburg College*

Robert H. Prince, *Berry College*

Leela Rakesh, *Central Michigan University*

Fernando Rincón, *Piedmont Technical College*

Aaron Robertson, *Colgate University*

Don R. Robinson, *Illinois State University*

Kathy Rogotzke, *North Iowa Area Community College–Mason City*

Deb Rumsey, *The Ohio State University*

Jason Samuels, *BMCC*

Salvatore Sciandra, *Niagara County Community College*

Carolyn Shealy, *Piedmont Technical College*

Dr. J. N. Singh, *Barry University*

George Smeltzer, *Pennsylvania State University–Abington*

Lynn Smith, *Gloucester County College*

Jeganathan Sriskandarajah, *Madison Area Technical College*

Diana Staats, *Dutchess Community College*

Richard Stevens, *University of Alaska–Fairbanks*

Dr. M. Jill Stewart, *Radford University*

Richard Stockbridge, *University of Wisconsin–Milwaukee*

Linda Sturges, *SUNY Maritime College*

Kagba Suaray, *California State University, Long Beach*

Gretchen I. Syhre, *Hawkeye Community College*

Martha Tapia, *Berry College*

Sherry Taylor, *Piedmont Technical College*

Klement Teixeira, *Borough of Manhattan Community College*

William Trunkhill, *Waubonsee Community College*

Jo Tucker, *Tarrant County College–SE*

Thomas Tunnell, *Illinois Valley Community College*

Diane Van Deusen, *Napa Valley College*

Christina Vertullo, *Marist College*

Dr. Mahbobeh Vezvaei, *Kent State University*

Tilaka N. Vijithakumara, *Illinois State University*

Cassandra L. Vincent, *Plattsburgh State University*

David Wallach, *Findlay University*

Cheng Wang, *Nova Southeastern University*

Barbara B. Ward, *Belmont University*

William D. Warde, *Oklahoma State University*

Brenda Weak, *Las Positas College*

Glenn Weber, *Christopher Newport University*

Daniel C. Weiner, *Boston University*

Jane-Marie Wright, *Suffolk County Community College*

Yibao Xu, *Borough of Manhattan Community College, CUNY*

Yi Ye, *University of North Florida*

Jill S. Yoder, *North Central Texas College*

Quinhong Zhang, *Northern Michigan University*

James Zimmer, *Chattanooga State*

Guided Tour: Features and Supplements

Each chapter begins with an **outline** and a list of **learning objectives.** The objectives are repeated at the beginning of each section to help students focus on the concepts presented within that section.

The outline and learning objectives are followed by a feature titled **Statistics Today,** in which a **real-life problem** shows students the relevance of the material in the chapter. This problem is subsequently solved near the end of the chapter by using the statistical techniques presented in the chapter.

CHAPTER 6

The Normal Distribution

Objectives

After completing this chapter, you should be able to

1. Identify distributions as symmetric or skewed.
2. Identify the properties of a normal distribution.
3. Find the area under the standard normal distribution, given various z values.
4. Find probabilities for a normally distributed variable by transforming it into a standard normal variable.
5. Find specific data values for given percentages, using the standard normal distribution.
6. Use the central limit theorem to solve problems involving sample means for large samples.
7. Use the normal approximation to compute probabilities for a binomial variable.

Outline

Introduction

6–1 **Normal Distributions**

6–2 **Applications of the Normal Distribution**

6–3 **The Central Limit Theorem**

6–4 **The Normal Approximation to the Binomial Distribution**

Summary

6–1

---

572   Chapter 11 Chi-Square and Analysis of Variance (ANOVA)

Statistics Today

Statistics and Heredity

An Austrian monk, Gregor Mendel (1822–1884), studied genetics, and his principles are the foundation for modern genetics. Mendel used his spare time to grow a variety of peas at the monastery. One of his many experiments involved crossbreeding peas that had smooth yellow seeds with peas that had wrinkled green seeds. He noticed that the results occurred with regularity. That is, some of the offspring had smooth yellow seeds, some had smooth green seeds, some had wrinkled yellow seeds, and some had wrinkled green seeds. Furthermore, after several experiments, the percentages of each type seemed to remain approximately the same. Mendel formulated his theory based on the assumption of dominant and recessive traits and tried to predict the results. He then crossbred his peas and examined 556 seeds over the next generation.

Finally, he compared the actual results with the theoretical results to see if his theory was correct. To do this, he used a "simple" chi-square test, which is explained in this chapter. See Statistics Today—Revisited at the end of this chapter.

Source: J. Hodges, Jr., D. Krech, and R. Crutchfield, *Stat Lab, An Empirical Introduction to Statistics* (New York: McGraw-Hill, 1975), pp. 228–229. Used with permission.

Introduction

The chi-square distribution was used in Chapters 7 and 8 to find a confidence interval for a variance or standard deviation and to test a hypothesis about a single variance or standard deviation.

It can also be used for tests concerning *frequency distributions*, such as "If a sample of buyers is given a choice of automobile colors, will each color be selected with the same frequency?" The chi-square distribution can be used to test the *independence* of

11–2

---

xvii

Over 200 **examples** with detailed solutions serve as models to help students solve problems on their own. Examples are solved by using a step by step explanation, and illustrations provide a clear display of results for students.

Two types of frequency distributions that are most often used are the *categorical frequency distribution* and the *grouped frequency distribution*. The procedures for constructing these distributions are shown now.

Categorical Frequency Distributions

The **categorical frequency distribution** is used for data that can be placed in specific categories, such as nominal- or ordinal-level data. For example, data such as political affiliation, religious affiliation, or major field of study would use categorical frequency distributions.

Example 2–1

Distribution of Blood Types

Twenty-five army inductees were given a blood test to determine their blood type. The data set is

A	B	B	AB	O
O	O	B	AB	B
B	B	O	O	A
O	B	O	A	O
AB	A	O	B	A

Construct a frequency distribution for the data.

Solution

Since the data are categorical, discrete classes can be used. There are four blood types: A, B, O, and AB. These types will be used as the classes for the distribution.

The procedure for constructing a frequency distribution for categorical data is given next.

Step 1 Make a table as shown.

A Class	B Tally	C Frequency	D Percent
A			
B			
O			
AB			

Step 2 Tally the data and place the results in column B.

Step 3 Count the tallies and place the results in column C.

Step 4 Find the percentage of values in each class by using the formula

$$\% = \frac{f}{n} \cdot 100\%$$

where f = frequency of the class and n = total number of values. For example, in the class of type A blood, the percentage is

$$\% = \frac{5}{25} \cdot 100\% = 20\%$$

Percentages are not normally part of a frequency distribution, but they can be added since they are used in certain types of graphs such as pie graphs. Also, the decimal equivalent of a percent is called a *relative frequency*.

Step 5 Find the totals for columns C (frequency) and D (percent). The completed table is shown.

Using this information, answer these questions.

1. What hypotheses would you use?
2. Is the sample considered small or large?
3. What assumption must be met before the hypothesis test can be conducted?
4. Which probability distribution would you use?
5. Would you select a one- or two-tailed test? Why?
6. What critical value(s) would you use?
7. Conduct a hypothesis test. Use $\sigma = 30.3$.
8. What is your decision?
9. What is your conclusion?
10. Write a brief statement summarizing your conclusion.
11. If you lived in a city whose population was about 50,000, how many automobile thefts per year would you expect to occur?

See page 465 for the answers.

Exercises 8–2

For Exercises 1 through 13, perform each of the following steps.

  a. State the hypotheses and identify the claim.
  b. Find the critical value(s).
  c. Compute the test value.
  d. Make the decision.
  e. Summarize the results.

Use diagrams to show the critical region (or regions), and use the traditional method of hypothesis testing unless otherwise specified.

1. **Walking with a Pedometer** An increase in walking has been shown to contribute to a healthier life-style. A sedentary American takes an average of 5000 steps per day (and 65% of Americans are overweight). A group of health-conscious employees of a large health care system volunteered to wear pedometers for a month to record their steps. It was found that a random sample of 40 walkers took an average of 5430 steps per day, and the population standard deviation is 600 steps. At $\alpha = 0.05$ can it be concluded that they walked more than the mean number of 5000 steps per day?
Source: www.msn.com/health

2. **Credit Card Debt** It has been reported that the average credit card debt for college seniors is $3262. The student senate at a large university feels that their seniors have a debt much less than this, so it conducts a study of 50 randomly selected seniors and finds that the average debt is $2995, and the population standard deviation is $1100. With $\alpha = 0.05$, is the student senate correct?
Source: USA TODAY.

3. **Revenue of Large Businesses** A researcher estimates that the average revenue of the largest businesses in the United States is greater than $24 billion. A sample of 50 companies is selected, and the revenues (in billions of dollars) are shown. At $\alpha = 0.05$, is there enough evidence to support the researcher's claim? $\sigma = 28.7$.

178	122	91	44	35
61	56	46	20	32
30	28	28	20	27
29	16	16	19	15
41	38	36	15	25
31	30	19	19	19
24	16	15	15	19
25	25	18	14	15
24	23	17	17	22
22	21	20	17	20

Source: New York Times Almanac.

4. **Salaries of Ph.D. Students** Full-time Ph.D. students receive an average salary of $12,837 according to the U.S. Department of Education. The dean of graduate studies at a large state university feels that Ph.D. students in his state earn more than this. He surveys 44 randomly selected students and finds their average salary is $14,445, and the population standard deviation is $1500. With $\alpha = 0.05$, is the dean correct?
Source: U.S. Department of Education/Chronicle of Higher Education.

5. **Health Care Expenses** The mean annual expenditure per 25- to 34-year-old consumer for health care is $1468. This includes health insurance, medical services, and drugs and medical supplies. Students at a large university took a survey, and it was found that for a sample of 60 students, the mean health care expense was $1520, and the population standard deviation is $198. Is there sufficient evidence at $\alpha = 0.01$ to conclude that their health care expenditure differs from the national average of $1468? Is the conclusion different at $\alpha = 0.05$?
Source: Time Almanac.

Numerous examples and exercises use **real data**. The icon shown here indicates that the data set for the exercise is available in a variety of file formats on the text's website and Data CD.

Numerous **Procedure Tables** summarize processes for students' quick reference. All use the step by step method.

The **Speaking of Statistics** sections invite students to think about poll results and other statistics-related news stories in another connection between statistics and the real world.

Historical Notes, Unusual Stats, and **Interesting Facts,** located in the margins, make statistics come alive for the reader.

Figure 2–2
Histogram for Example 2–4

Historical Note
Graphs originated when ancient astronomers drew the position of the stars in the heavens. Roman surveyors also used coordinates to locate landmarks on their maps.
The development of statistical graphs can be traced to William Playfair (1748–1819), an engineer and drafter who used graphs to present economic data pictorially.

Record High Temperatures

Step 2 Represent the frequency on the *y* axis and the class boundaries on the *x* axis.

Step 3 Using the frequencies as the heights, draw vertical bars for each class. See Figure 2–2.
As the histogram shows, the class with the greatest number of data values (18) is 109.5–114.5, followed by 13 for 114.5–119.5. The graph also has one peak with the data clustering around it.

The Frequency Polygon
Another way to represent the same data set is by using a frequency polygon.

The **frequency polygon** is a graph that displays the data by using lines that connect points plotted for the frequencies at the midpoints of the classes. The frequencies are represented by the heights of the points.

Example 2–5 shows the procedure for constructing a frequency polygon.

Example 2–5
Record High Temperatures
Using the frequency distribution given in Example 2–4, construct a frequency polygon.

Solution
Step 1 Find the midpoints of each class. Recall that midpoints are found by adding the upper and lower boundaries and dividing by 2:

$$\frac{99.5 + 104.5}{2} = 102 \qquad \frac{104.5 + 109.5}{2} = 107$$

and so on. The midpoints are

Class boundaries	Midpoints	Frequency
99.5–104.5	102	2
104.5–109.5	107	8
109.5–114.5	112	18
114.5–119.5	117	13
119.5–124.5	122	7
124.5–129.5	127	1
129.5–134.5	132	

2–19

Rules and definitions are set off for easy referencing by the student.

---

416   Chapter 8 Hypothesis Testing

Again, remember that nothing is being proved true or false. The statistician is only stating that there is or is not enough evidence to say that a claim is *probably* true or false. As noted previously, the only way to prove something would be to use the entire population under study, and usually this cannot be done, especially when the population is large.

P-Value Method for Hypothesis Testing
Statisticians usually test hypotheses at the common α levels of 0.05 or 0.01 and sometimes at 0.10. Recall that the choice of the level depends on the seriousness of the type I error. Besides listing an α value, many computer statistical packages give a *P*-value for hypothesis tests.

The **P-value** (or probability value) is the probability of getting a sample statistic (such as the mean) or a more extreme sample statistic in the direction of the alternative hypothesis when the null hypothesis is true.

In other words, the *P*-value is the actual area under the standard normal distribution curve (or other curve, depending on what statistical test is being used) representing the probability of a particular sample statistic or a more extreme sample statistic occurring if the null hypothesis is true.
For example, suppose that an alternative hypothesis is $H_1: \mu > 50$ and the mean of a sample is $\bar{X} = 52$. If the computer printed a *P*-value of 0.0356 for a statistical test, then the probability of getting a sample mean of 52 or greater is 0.0356 if the true population mean is 50 (for the given sample size and standard deviation). The relationship between the *P*-value and the α value can be explained in this manner. For $P = 0.0356$, the null hypothesis would be rejected at $\alpha = 0.05$ but not at $\alpha = 0.01$. See Figure 8–18.
When the hypothesis test is two-tailed, the area in one tail must be doubled. For a two-tailed test, if α is 0.05 and the area in one tail is 0.0356, the *P*-value will be 2(0.0356) = 0.0712. That is, the null hypothesis should not be rejected at $\alpha = 0.05$, since 0.0712 is greater than 0.05. In summary, then, if the *P*-value is less than α, reject the null hypothesis. If the *P*-value is greater than α, do not reject the null hypothesis.
The *P*-values for the *z* test can be found by using Table E in Appendix C. First find the area under the standard normal distribution curve corresponding to the *z* test value. For a left-tailed test, use the area given in the table; for a right-tailed test, use 1.0000 minus the area given in the table. To get the *P*-value for a two-tailed test, double the area you found in the tail. This procedure is shown in step 3 of Examples 8–6 and 8–7.
The *P*-value method for testing hypotheses differs from the traditional method somewhat. The steps for the *P*-value method are summarized next.

Critical Thinking sections at the end of each chapter challenge students to apply what they have learned to new situations. The problems presented are designed to deepen conceptual understanding and/or to extend topical coverage.

---

256   Chapter 4 Probability and Counting Rules

Critical Thinking Challenges

1. Con Man Game Consider this problem: A con man has 3 coins. One coin has been specially made and has a head on each side. A second coin has been specially made, and on each side it has a tail. Finally, a third coin has a head and a tail on it. All coins are of the same denomination. The con man places the 3 coins in his pocket, selects one, and shows you one side. It is heads. He is willing to bet you even money that it is the two-headed coin. His reasoning is that it can't be the two-tailed coin since a head is showing; therefore, there is a 50-50 chance of it being the two-headed coin. Would you take the bet? (*Hint:* See Exercise 1 in Data Projects.)

2. de Méré Dice Game Chevalier de Méré won money when he bet unsuspecting patrons that in 4 rolls of 1 die, he could get at least one 6, but he lost money when he bet that in 24 rolls of 2 dice, he could get at least a double 6. Using the probability rules, find the probability of each event and explain why he won the majority of the time on the first game but lost the majority of the time when playing the second game. (*Hint:* Find the probabilities of losing each game and subtract from 1.)

3. Classical Birthday Problem How many people do you think need to be in a room so that 2 people will have the same birthday (month and day)? You might think it is 366. This would, of course, guarantee it (excluding leap year), but how many people would need to be in a room so that there would be a 90% probability that 2 people were born on the same day? What about a 50% probability? Actually, the number is much smaller than you may think. For example, if you have 50 people in a room, the probability that 2 people will have the same birthday is 97%. If you have 23 people in a room, there is a 50% probability that 2 people were born on the same day! The problem can be solved by using the probability rules. It must be assumed that all birthdays are equally likely, but this assumption will have little effect on the answers. The way to find the answer is by using the complementary event rule as P/2 people having the same birthday) = 1 − P(all have different birthdays).

For example, suppose there were 3 people in the room. The probability that each had a different birthday would be

$$\frac{365}{365} \cdot \frac{364}{365} \cdot \frac{363}{365} = \frac{{}_{365}P_3}{365^3} = 0.992$$

Hence, the probability that at least 2 of the 3 people will have the same birthday will be

$$1 − 0.992 = 0.008$$

Hence, for *k* people, the formula is

P(at least 2 people have the same birthday)

$$= 1 − \frac{{}_{365}P_k}{365^k}$$

Using your calculator, complete the table and verify that for at least a 50% chance of 2 people having the same birthday, 23 or more people will be needed.

Number of people	Probability that at least 2 have the same birthday
1	0.000
2	0.003
5	0.027
10	
15	
20	
21	
22	
23	

4. We know that if the probability of an event happening is 100%, then the event is a certainty. Can it be concluded that if there is a 50% chance of contracting a communicable disease through contact with an infected person, there would be a 100% chance of contracting the disease if 2 contacts were made with the infected person? Explain your answer.

At the end of appropriate sections, **Technology Step by Step** boxes show students how to use MINITAB, the TI-83 Plus and TI-84 Plus graphing calculators, and Excel to solve the types of problems covered in the section. Instructions are presented in numbered steps, usually in the context of examples—including examples from the main part of the section. Numerous computer or calculator screens are displayed, showing intermediate steps as well as the final answer.

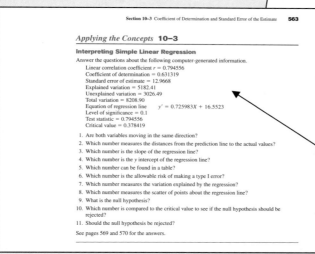

Applying the Concepts are exercises found at the end of each section to reinforce the concepts explained in the section. They give the student an opportunity to think about the concepts and apply them to hypothetical examples similar to real-life ones found in newspapers, magazines, and professional journals. Most contain open-ended questions—questions that require interpretation and may have more than one correct answer. These exercises can also be used as classroom discussion topics for instructors who like to use this type of teaching technique.

Data Projects, which appear at the end of each chapter, further challenge students' understanding and application of the material presented in the chapter. Many of these require the student to gather, analyze, and report on real data.

Experience Student Success!

ALEKS® ALEKS is a unique online math tool that uses adaptive questioning and artificial intelligence to correctly place, prepare, and remediate students . . . all in one product! Institutional case studies have shown that **ALEKS has improved pass rates by over 20% versus traditional online homework and by over 30% compared to using a text alone.**

By offering each student an individualized learning path, ALEKS directs students to work on the math topics that they are ready to learn. Also, to help students keep pace in their course, instructors can correlate ALEKS to their textbook or syllabus in seconds.

To learn more about how ALEKS can be used to boost student performance, please visit **www.aleks.com/highered/math** or contact your McGraw-Hill representative.

Easy Graphing Utility!
Students can answer graphing problems with ease!

ALEKS Pie
Each student is given their own individualized learning path.

Course Calendar
Instructors can schedule assignments and reminders for students.

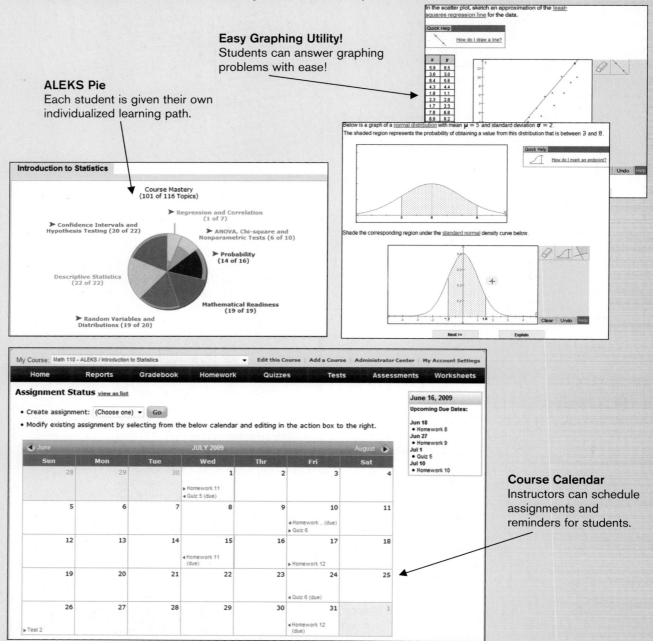

New ALEKS Instructor Module

Enhanced Functionality and Streamlined Interface Help to Save Instructor Time

ALEKS® The new ALEKS Instructor Module features enhanced functionality and streamlined interface based on research with ALEKS instructors and homework management instructors. Paired with powerful assignment driven features, textbook integration, and extensive content flexibility, the new ALEKS Instructor Module simplifies administrative tasks and makes ALEKS more powerful than ever.

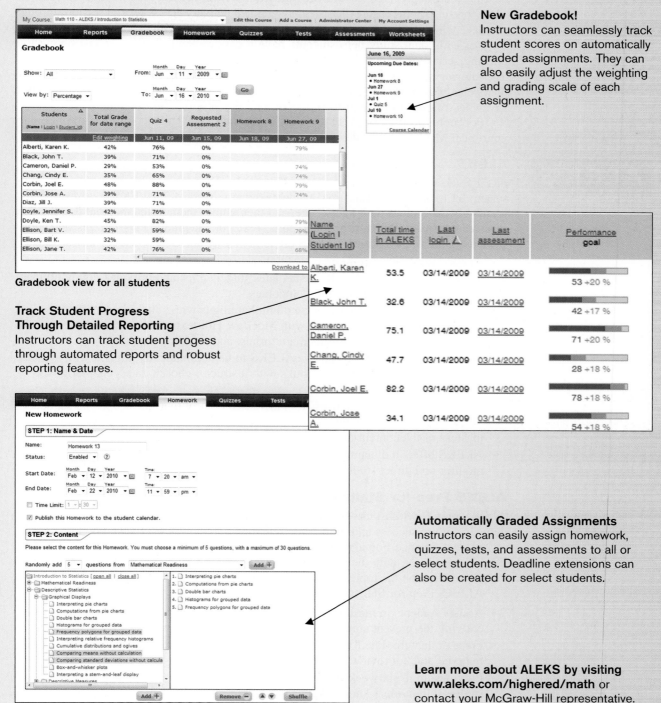

Gradebook view for all students

New Gradebook!
Instructors can seamlessly track student scores on automatically graded assignments. They can also easily adjust the weighting and grading scale of each assignment.

Track Student Progress Through Detailed Reporting
Instructors can track student progess through automated reports and robust reporting features.

Automatically Graded Assignments
Instructors can easily assign homework, quizzes, tests, and assessments to all or select students. Deadline extensions can also be created for select students.

Select topics for each assignment

Learn more about ALEKS by visiting www.aleks.com/highered/math or contact your McGraw-Hill representative.

Multimedia Supplements

MathZone—www.mhhe.com/bluman

McGraw-Hill's MathZone is a complete online homework system for mathematics and statistics. Instructors can assign textbook-specific content from over 40 McGraw-Hill titles as well as customize the level of feedback students receive, including the ability to have students show their work for any given exercise. Assignable content includes an array of videos and other multimedia along with algorithmic exercises, providing study tools for students with many different learning styles.

Within MathZone, a diagnostic assessment tool powered by ALEKS™ is available to measure student preparedness and provide detailed reporting and personalized remediation. MathZone also helps ensure consistent assignment delivery across several sections through a course administration function and makes sharing courses with other instructors easy.

For additional study help students have access to NetTutor™, a robust online live tutoring service that incorporates whiteboard technology to communicate mathematics. The tutoring schedules are built around peak homework times to best accommodate student schedules. Instructors can also take advantage of this whiteboard by setting up a Live Classroom for online office hours or a review session with students.

For more information, visit the book's website (www.mhhe.com/bluman) or contact your local McGraw-Hill sales representative (www.mhhe.com/rep).

ALEKS—www.aleks.com

ALEKS (**A**ssessment and **LE**arning in **K**nowledge **S**paces) is a dynamic online learning system for mathematics education, available over the Web 24/7. ALEKS assesses students, accurately determines their knowledge, and then guides them to the material that they are most ready to learn. With a variety of reports, Textbook Integration Plus, quizzes, and homework assignment capabilities, ALEKS offers flexibility and ease of use for instructors.

- ALEKS uses artificial intelligence to determine exactly what each student knows and is ready to learn. ALEKS remediates student gaps and provides highly efficient learning and improved learning outcomes.
- ALEKS is a comprehensive curriculum that aligns with syllabi or specified textbooks. Used in conjunction with McGraw-Hill texts, students also receive links to text-specific videos, multimedia tutorials, and textbook pages.
- Textbook Integration Plus allows ALEKS to be automatically aligned with syllabi or specified McGraw-Hill textbooks with instructor chosen dates, chapter goals, homework, and quizzes.
- ALEKS with AI-2 gives instructors increased control over the scope and sequence of student learning. Students using ALEKS demonstrate a steadily increasing mastery of the content of the course.
- ALEKS offers a dynamic classroom management system that enables instructors to monitor and direct student progress towards mastery of course objectives.

ALEKS Prep for Statistics

ALEKS prep for Statistics can be used during the beginning of the course to prepare students for future success and to increase retention and pass rates. Backed by two decades of National Science Foundation funded research, ALEKS interacts with students much like a human tutor, with the ability to precisely assess a student's preparedness and provide instruction on the topics the student is ready to learn.

ALEKS Prep for Statistics:

- Assists students in mastering core concepts that should have been learned prior to entering the present course.
- Frees up lecture time for instructors, allowing more time to focus on current course material and not review material.
- Provides up to six weeks of remediation and intelligent tutorial help to fill in students' individual knowledge gaps.

TEGRITY—http://tegritycampus.mhhe.com

Tegrity Campus is a service that makes class time available all the time by automatically capturing every lecture in a searchable format for students to review when they study and complete assignments. With a simple one-click start and stop process, you capture all computer screens and corresponding audio. Students replay any part of any class with easy-to-use browser-based viewing on a PC or Mac.

Educators know that the more students can see, hear, and experience class resources, the better they learn. With Tegrity Campus, students quickly recall key moments by using Tegrity Campus's unique search feature. This search helps students efficiently find what they need, when they need it across an entire semester of class recordings. Help turn all your students' study time into learning moments immediately supported by your lecture.

To learn more about Tegrity watch a 2 minute Flash demo at http://tegritycampus.mhhe.com

Electronic Textbook

CourseSmart is a new way for faculty to find and review eTextbooks. It's also a great option for students who are interested in accessing their course materials digitally and saving money. CourseSmart offers thousands of the most commonly adopted textbooks across hundreds of courses from a wide variety of higher education publishers. It is the only place for faculty to review and compare the full text of a textbook online, providing immediate access without the environmental impact of requesting a print exam copy. At CourseSmart, students can save up to 50% off the cost of a print book, reduce the impact on the environment, and gain access to powerful Web tools for learning including full text search, notes and highlighting, and e-mail tools for sharing notes between classmates. www.CourseSmart.com

MegaStat®

MegaStat® is a statistical add-in for Microsoft Excel, handcrafted by J. B. Orris of Butler University. When MegaStat is installed it appears as a menu item on the Excel menu bar and allows you to perform statistical analysis on data in an Excel workbook. ELEMENTARY STATISTICS: A BRIEF VERSION requires the use of this MegaStat add-in for Excel only for those Excel Technology Step by Step operations in the text that Excel would otherwise not have been able to perform. The MegaStat plug-in can be found at www.mhhe.com/bluman.

Computerized Test Bank (CTB) Online (instructors only)

The computerized test bank contains a variety of questions, including true/false, multiple-choice, short answer, and short problems requiring analysis and written answers. The testing material is coded by type of question and level of difficulty. The Brownstone Diploma® system enables you to efficiently select, add, and organize questions, such as by type of question or level of difficulty. It also allows for printing tests along with answer keys as well as editing the original questions, and it is available for Windows and Macintosh systems. Printable tests and a print version of the test bank can also be found on the website.

Lecture Videos

New lecture videos introduce concepts, definitions, theorems, formulas, and problem-solving procedures to help students better comprehend the topic at hand. These videos are closed-captioned for the hearing-impaired, are subtitled in Spanish, and meet the Americans with Disabilities Act Standards for Accessible Design. They can be found online at www.mhhe.com/bluman.

Exercise Videos

In these videos the instructor works through selected exercises, following the solution methodology employed in the text. Also included are tutorials for using the TI-83 Plus and TI-84 Plus calculators, Excel, and MINITAB, presented in an engaging format for students. These videos are closed-captioned for the hearing-impaired, are subtitled in

Spanish, and meet the Americans with Disabilities Act Standards for Accessible Design. They can be found online at www.mhhe.com/bluman.

NetTutor

NetTutor is a revolutionary system that enables students to interact with a live tutor over the Web by using NetTutor's Web-based, graphical chat capabilities. Students can also submit questions and receive answers, browse previously answered questions, and view previous live chat sessions. NetTutor can be accessed through MathZone.

MINITAB Student Release 14

The student version of MINITAB statistical software is available with copies of the text. Ask your McGraw-Hill representative for details.

SPSS Student Version for Windows

A student version of SPSS statistical software is available with copies of this text. Consult your McGraw-Hill representative for details.

Student Data Sets

Real-life data sets that can be used with specific exercises throughout the text are available for student use. These data files are located both on a Student Data CD that is packaged with all new textbooks as well as online at www.mhhe.com/bluman. The data files included are formatted in the following:

- Minitab 14 Portable (for Macintosh or Windows)
- TI-Graph Link files for TI-83 or TI-84
- Excel 2007 (for Windows or Macintosh)
- Comma-delimited ASCII
- SPSS for Windows

Print Supplements

Annotated Instructors Edition (instructors only)

The Annotated Instructor's Edition contains answers to all exercises and tests. The answers to most questions are printed in red next to each problem. Answers not appearing on the page can be found in the Answer Appendix at the end of the book.

Instructor Solutions Manual (instructors only)

By Sally Robinson of South Plains College, this manual includes worked-out solutions to all the exercises in the text and answers to all quiz questions. This manual can be found online at www.mhhe.com/bluman.

Student Solutions Manual

By Sally Robinson of South Plains College, this manual contains detailed solutions to all odd-numbered text problems and answers to all quiz questions.

MINITAB 14 Manual

This manual provides the student with how-to information on data and file management, conducting various statistical analyses, and creating presentation-style graphics while following each text chapter.

TI-83 Plus and TI-84 Plus Graphing Calculator Manual

This friendly, practical manual teaches students to learn about statistics and solve problems by using these calculators while following each text chapter.

Excel Manual

This workbook, specially designed to accompany the text, provides additional practice in applying the chapter concepts while using Excel.

CHAPTER **7**

Confidence Intervals and Sample Size

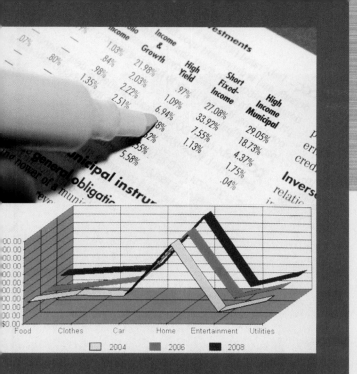

The Nature of Probability and Statistics

Objectives

After completing this chapter, you should be able to

1 Demonstrate knowledge of statistical terms.

2 Differentiate between the two branches of statistics.

3 Identify types of data.

4 Identify the measurement level for each variable.

5 Identify the four basic sampling techniques.

6 Explain the difference between an observational and an experimental study.

7 Explain how statistics can be used and misused.

8 Explain the importance of computers and calculators in statistics.

Outline

Are We Improving Our Diet?

Statistics Today

It has been determined that diets rich in fruits and vegetables are associated with a lower risk of chronic diseases such as cancer. Nutritionists recommend that Americans consume five or more servings of fruits and vegetables each day. Several researchers from the Division of Nutrition, the National Center for Chronic Disease Control and Prevention, the National Cancer Institute, and the National Institutes of Health decided to use statistical procedures to see how much progress is being made toward this goal.

The procedures they used and the results of the study will be explained in this chapter. See Statistics Today—Revisited at the end of this chapter.

Introduction

You may be familiar with probability and statistics through radio, television, newspapers, and magazines. For example, you may have read statements like the following found in newspapers.

Unusual Stats

Of people in the United States, 14% said that they feel happiest in June, and 14% said that they feel happiest in December.

- In Massachusetts, 36% of adults aged 25 and older have at least a bachelor's degree. (Source: U.S. Census Bureau.)
- In 1995 there were 926,621 bankruptcy filings, while in 2005 there were 2,078,415 bankruptcy filings. (Source: Administrative Office of the U.S. Courts, Washington, D.C.)
- Toddlers need an average of 13 hours of sleep per day.
- The average in-state college tuition and fees for 4-year public college is $5836. (Source: The College Board.)
- There is a 3.8% probability of selecting a briefcase containing $1 million on the television show "Deal or No Deal."
- The back-to-school student plans to spend, on average, $114.38 on electronics and computer-related items. (Source: National Retail Federation.)

Statistics is used in almost all fields of human endeavor. In sports, for example, a statistician may keep records of the number of yards a running back gains during a football game, or the number of hits a baseball player gets in a season. In other areas, such as public health, an administrator might be concerned with the number of residents who contract a new strain of flu virus during a certain year. In education, a researcher might want to know if new methods of teaching are better than old ones. These are only a few examples of how statistics can be used in various occupations.

Furthermore, statistics is used to analyze the results of surveys and as a tool in scientific research to make decisions based on controlled experiments. Other uses of statistics include operations research, quality control, estimation, and prediction.

Statistics is the science of conducting studies to collect, organize, summarize, analyze, and draw conclusions from data.

Students study statistics for several reasons:

1. Like professional people, you must be able to read and understand the various statistical studies performed in your fields. To have this understanding, you must be knowledgeable about the vocabulary, symbols, concepts, and statistical procedures used in these studies.

2. You may be called on to conduct research in your field, since statistical procedures are basic to research. To accomplish this, you must be able to design experiments; collect, organize, analyze, and summarize data; and possibly make reliable predictions or forecasts for future use. You must also be able to communicate the results of the study in your own words.

3. You can also use the knowledge gained from studying statistics to become better consumers and citizens. For example, you can make intelligent decisions about what products to purchase based on consumer studies, about government spending based on utilization studies, and so on.

These reasons can be considered the goals for studying statistics.

It is the purpose of this chapter to introduce the goals for studying statistics by answering questions such as the following:

What are the branches of statistics?

What are data?

How are samples selected?

1–1

Objective 1

Demonstrate knowledge of statistical terms.

Descriptive and Inferential Statistics

To gain knowledge about seemingly haphazard situations, statisticians collect information for *variables,* which describe the situation.

A **variable** is a characteristic or attribute that can assume different values.

Data are the values (measurements or observations) that the variables can assume. Variables whose values are determined by chance are called **random variables.**

Suppose that an insurance company studies its records over the past several years and determines that, on average, 3 out of every 100 automobiles the company insured were involved in accidents during a 1-year period. Although there is no way to predict the specific automobiles that will be involved in an accident (random occurrence), the company can adjust its rates accordingly, since the company knows the general pattern over the long run. (That is, on average, 3% of the insured automobiles will be involved in an accident each year.)

A collection of data values forms a **data set.** Each value in the data set is called a **data value** or a **datum.**

Objective 2

Differentiate between the two branches of statistics.

Data can be used in different ways. The body of knowledge called statistics is sometimes divided into two main areas, depending on how data are used. The two areas are

1. Descriptive statistics
2. Inferential statistics

Descriptive statistics consists of the collection, organization, summarization, and presentation of data.

In *descriptive statistics* the statistician tries to describe a situation. Consider the national census conducted by the U.S. government every 10 years. Results of this census give you the average age, income, and other characteristics of the U.S. population. To obtain this information, the Census Bureau must have some means to collect relevant data. Once data are collected, the bureau must organize and summarize them. Finally, the bureau needs a means of presenting the data in some meaningful form, such as charts, graphs, or tables.

The second area of statistics is called *inferential statistics.*

Inferential statistics consists of generalizing from samples to populations, performing estimations and hypothesis tests, determining relationships among variables, and making predictions.

Here, the statistician tries to make inferences from *samples* to *populations.* Inferential statistics uses **probability,** i.e., the chance of an event occurring. You may be familiar with the concepts of probability through various forms of gambling. If you play cards, dice, bingo, and lotteries, you win or lose according to the laws of probability. Probability theory is also used in the insurance industry and other areas.

It is important to distinguish between a sample and a population.

A **population** consists of all subjects (human or otherwise) that are being studied.

Most of the time, due to the expense, time, size of population, medical concerns, etc., it is not possible to use the entire population for a statistical study; therefore, researchers use samples.

A **sample** is a group of subjects selected from a population.

If the subjects of a sample are properly selected, most of the time they should possess the same or similar characteristics as the subjects in the population. The techniques used to properly select a sample will be explained in Section 1–3.

An area of inferential statistics called **hypothesis testing** is a decision-making process for evaluating claims about a population, based on information obtained from samples. For example, a researcher may wish to know if a new drug will reduce the number of heart attacks in men over 70 years of age. For this study, two groups of men over 70 would be selected. One group would be given the drug, and the other would be given a placebo (a substance with no medical benefits or harm). Later, the number of heart attacks occurring in each group of men would be counted, a statistical test would be run, and a decision would be made about the effectiveness of the drug.

Statisticians also use statistics to determine *relationships* among variables. For example, relationships were the focus of the most noted study in the 20th century, "Smoking and Health," published by the Surgeon General of the United States in 1964. He stated that after reviewing and evaluating the data, his group found a definite relationship between smoking and lung cancer. He did not say that cigarette smoking actually causes lung cancer, but that there is a relationship between smoking and lung cancer. This conclusion was based on a study done in 1958 by Hammond and Horn. In this study,

Statistics and the New Planet

In the summer of 2005, astronomers announced the discovery of a new planet in our solar system. This planet, as of this writing, has not yet been named; however, astronomers have dubbed it Xena. They also discovered that it has a moon that is larger than Pluto.[1] Xena is about 9 billion miles from the Sun. (Some sources say 10 billion.) Its diameter is about 4200 miles. Its surface temperature has been estimated at −400°F, and it takes 560 years to circle the Sun.

How does Xena compare to the other planets? Let's look at the statistics.

Planet	Diameter (miles)	Distance from the Sun (millions of miles)	Orbital period (days)	Mean temperature (°F)	Number of moons
Mercury	3,032	36	88	333	0
Venus	7,521	67.2	224.7	867	0
Earth	7,926	93	365.2	59	1
Mars	4,222	141.6	687	−85	2
Jupiter	88,846	483.8	4,331	−166	63
Saturn	74,897	890.8	10,747	−220	47
Uranus	31,763	1,784.8	30,589	−320	27
Neptune	30,775	2,793.1	59,800	−330	13
Pluto[1]	1,485	3,647.2	90,588	−375	1

Source: NASA.

[1]Some astronomers no longer consider Pluto a planet.

With these statistics, we can make some comparisons. For example, Xena is about the size of the planet Mars, but it is over 21 times the size of Pluto. (Compare the volumes.) It takes about twice as long to circle the Sun as Pluto. What other comparisons can you make?

187,783 men were observed over a period of 45 months. The death rate from lung cancer in this group of volunteers was 10 times as great for smokers as for nonsmokers.

Finally, by studying past and present data and conditions, statisticians try to make predictions based on this information. For example, a car dealer may look at past sales records for a specific month to decide what types of automobiles and how many of each type to order for that month next year.

Applying the Concepts 1–1

Attendance and Grades

Read the following on attendance and grades, and answer the questions.

A study conducted at Manatee Community College revealed that students who attended class 95 to 100% of the time usually received an A in the class. Students who attended class

80 to 90% of the time usually received a B or C in the class. Students who attended class less than 80% of the time usually received a D or an F or eventually withdrew from the class.

Based on this information, attendance and grades are related. The more you attend class, the more likely you will receive a higher grade. If you improve your attendance, your grades will probably improve. Many factors affect your grade in a course. One factor that you have considerable control over is attendance. You can increase your opportunities for learning by attending class more often.

1. What are the variables under study?
2. What are the data in the study?
3. Are descriptive, inferential, or both types of statistics used?
4. What is the population under study?
5. Was a sample collected? If so, from where?
6. From the information given, comment on the relationship between the variables.

See page 33 for the answers.

1–2   Variables and Types of Data

Objective 3

Identify types of data.

As stated in Section 1–1, statisticians gain information about a particular situation by collecting data for random variables. This section will explore in greater detail the nature of variables and types of data.

Variables can be classified as qualitative or quantitative. **Qualitative variables** are variables that can be placed into distinct categories, according to some characteristic or attribute. For example, if subjects are classified according to gender (male or female), then the variable *gender* is qualitative. Other examples of qualitative variables are religious preference and geographic locations.

Quantitative variables are numerical and can be ordered or ranked. For example, the variable *age* is numerical, and people can be ranked in order according to the value of their ages. Other examples of quantitative variables are heights, weights, and body temperatures.

Quantitative variables can be further classified into two groups: discrete and continuous. *Discrete variables* can be assigned values such as 0, 1, 2, 3 and are said to be countable. Examples of discrete variables are the number of children in a family, the number of students in a classroom, and the number of calls received by a switchboard operator each day for a month.

Discrete variables assume values that can be counted.

Continuous variables, by comparison, can assume an infinite number of values in an interval between any two specific values. Temperature, for example, is a continuous variable, since the variable can assume an infinite number of values between any two given temperatures.

Continuous variables can assume an infinite number of values between any two specific values. They are obtained by measuring. They often include fractions and decimals.

The classification of variables can be summarized as follows:

Since continuous data must be measured, answers must be rounded because of the limits of the measuring device. Usually, answers are rounded to the nearest given unit. For example, heights might be rounded to the nearest inch, weights to the nearest ounce, etc. Hence, a recorded height of 73 inches could mean any measure from 72.5 inches up to but not including 73.5 inches. Thus, the boundary of this measure is given as 72.5–73.5 inches. *Boundaries are written for convenience as 72.5–73.5 but are understood to mean all values up to but not including 73.5.* Actual data values of 73.5 would be rounded to 74 and would be included in a class with boundaries of 73.5 up to but not including 74.5, written as 73.5–74.5. As another example, if a recorded weight is 86 pounds, the exact boundaries are 85.5 up to but not including 86.5, written as 85.5–86.5 pounds. Table 1–1 helps to clarify this concept. The boundaries of a continuous variable are given in one additional decimal place and always end with the digit 5.

Table 1–1	Recorded Values and Boundaries	
Variable	**Recorded value**	**Boundaries**
Length	15 centimeters (cm)	14.5–15.5 cm
Temperature	86 degrees Fahrenheit (°F)	85.5–86.5°F
Time	0.43 second (sec)	0.425–0.435 sec
Mass	1.6 grams (g)	1.55–1.65 g

In addition to being classified as qualitative or quantitative, variables can be classified by how they are categorized, counted, or measured. For example, can the data be organized into specific categories, such as area of residence (rural, suburban, or urban)? Can the data values be ranked, such as first place, second place, etc.? Or are the values obtained from measurement, such as heights, IQs, or temperature? This type of classification—i.e., how variables are categorized, counted, or measured—uses **measurement scales,** and four common types of scales are used: nominal, ordinal, interval, and ratio.

Objective **4**

Identify the measurement level for each variable.

The first level of measurement is called the *nominal level* of measurement. A sample of college instructors classified according to subject taught (e.g., English, history, psychology, or mathematics) is an example of nominal-level measurement. Classifying survey subjects as male or female is another example of nominal-level measurement. No ranking or order can be placed on the data. Classifying residents according to zip codes is also an example of the nominal level of measurement. Even though numbers are assigned as zip codes, there is no meaningful order or ranking. Other examples of nominal-level data are political party (Democratic, Republican, Independent, etc.), religion (Christianity, Judaism, Islam, etc.), and marital status (single, married, divorced, widowed, separated).

The **nominal level of measurement** classifies data into mutually exclusive (nonoverlapping), exhausting categories in which no order or ranking can be imposed on the data.

The next level of measurement is called the *ordinal level.* Data measured at this level can be placed into categories, and these categories can be ordered, or ranked. For example, from student evaluations, guest speakers might be ranked as superior, average, or poor. Floats in a homecoming parade might be ranked as first place, second place, etc. *Note that precise measurement of differences in the ordinal level of measurement* does not *exist.* For instance, when people are classified according to their build (small, medium, or large), a large variation exists among the individuals in each class.

Unusual Stat

Sixty-three percent of us say we would rather hear the bad news first.

Other examples of ordinal data are letter grades (A, B, C, D, F).

> The **ordinal level of measurement** classifies data into categories that can be ranked; however, precise differences between the ranks do not exist.

The third level of measurement is called the *interval level.* This level differs from the ordinal level in that precise differences do exist between units. For example, many standardized psychological tests yield values measured on an interval scale. IQ is an example of such a variable. There is a meaningful difference of 1 point between an IQ of 109 and an IQ of 110. Temperature is another example of interval measurement, since there is a meaningful difference of 1°F between each unit, such as 72 and 73°F. *One property is lacking in the interval scale: There is no true zero.* For example, IQ tests do not measure people who have no intelligence. For temperature, 0°F does not mean no heat at all.

> The **interval level of measurement** ranks data, and precise differences between units of measure do exist; however, there is no meaningful zero.

The final level of measurement is called the *ratio level.* Examples of ratio scales are those used to measure height, weight, area, and number of phone calls received. Ratio scales have differences between units (1 inch, 1 pound, etc.) and a true zero. In addition, the ratio scale contains a true ratio between values. For example, if one person can lift 200 pounds and another can lift 100 pounds, then the ratio between them is 2 to 1. Put another way, the first person can lift twice as much as the second person.

> The **ratio level of measurement** possesses all the characteristics of interval measurement, and there exists a true zero. In addition, true ratios exist when the same variable is measured on two different members of the population.

There is not complete agreement among statisticians about the classification of data into one of the four categories. For example, some researchers classify IQ data as ratio data rather than interval. Also, data can be altered so that they fit into a different category. For instance, if the incomes of all professors of a college are classified into the three categories of low, average, and high, then a ratio variable becomes an ordinal variable. Table 1–2 gives some examples of each type of data.

Table 1–2   Examples of Measurement Scales

Nominal-level data	Ordinal-level data	Interval-level data	Ratio-level data
Zip code	Grade (A, B, C, D, F)	SAT score	Height
Gender (male, female)		IQ	Weight
Eye color (blue, brown, green, hazel)	Judging (first place, second place, etc.)	Temperature	Time
Political affiliation	Rating scale (poor, good, excellent)		Salary
Religious affiliation			Age
Major field (mathematics, computers, etc.)	Ranking of tennis players		
Nationality			

Applying the Concepts **1-2**

Safe Travel

Read the following information about the transportation industry and answer the questions.

Transportation Safety

The chart shows the number of job-related injuries for each of the transportation industries for 1998.

Industry	Number of injuries
Railroad	4520
Intercity bus	5100
Subway	6850
Trucking	7144
Airline	9950

1. What are the variables under study?

2. Categorize each variable as quantitative or qualitative.

3. Categorize each quantitative variable as discrete or continuous.

4. Identify the level of measurement for each variable.

5. The railroad is shown as the safest transportation industry. Does that mean railroads have fewer accidents than the other industries? Explain.

6. What factors other than safety influence a person's choice of transportation?

7. From the information given, comment on the relationship between the variables.

See page 33 for the answers.

1-3

Objective 5

Identify the four basic sampling techniques.

Data Collection and Sampling Techniques

In research, statisticians use data in many different ways. As stated previously, data can be used to describe situations or events. For example, a manufacturer might want to know something about the consumers who will be purchasing his product so he can plan an effective marketing strategy. In another situation, the management of a company might survey its employees to assess their needs in order to negotiate a new contract with the employees' union. Data can be used to determine whether the educational goals of a school district are being met. Finally, trends in various areas, such as the stock market, can be analyzed, enabling prospective buyers to make more intelligent decisions concerning what stocks to purchase. These examples illustrate a few situations where collecting data will help people make better decisions on courses of action.

Data can be collected in a variety of ways. One of the most common methods is through the use of surveys. Surveys can be done by using a variety of methods. Three of the most common methods are the telephone survey, the mailed questionnaire, and the personal interview.

Telephone surveys have an advantage over personal interview surveys in that they are less costly. Also, people may be more candid in their opinions since there is no face-to-face contact. A major drawback to the telephone survey is that some people in the population will not have phones or will not answer when the calls are made; hence, not all people have a chance of being surveyed. Also, many people now have unlisted numbers and cell phones, so they cannot be surveyed. Finally, even the tone of the voice of the interviewer might influence the response of the person who is being interviewed.

Mailed questionnaire surveys can be used to cover a wider geographic area than telephone surveys or personal interviews since mailed questionnaire surveys are less expensive to conduct. Also, respondents can remain anonymous if they desire. Disadvantages of mailed questionnaire surveys include a low number of responses and inappropriate

Historical Note

A pioneer in census taking was Pierre-Simon de Laplace. In 1780, he developed the Laplace method of estimating the population of a country. The principle behind his method was to take a census of a few selected communities and to determine the ratio of the population to the number of births in these communities. (Good birth records were kept.) This ratio would be used to multiply the number of births in the entire country to estimate the number of citizens in the country.

answers to questions. Another drawback is that some people may have difficulty reading or understanding the questions.

Personal interview surveys have the advantage of obtaining in-depth responses to questions from the person being interviewed. One disadvantage is that interviewers must be trained in asking questions and recording responses, which makes the personal interview survey more costly than the other two survey methods. Another disadvantage is that the interviewer may be biased in his or her selection of respondents.

Data can also be collected in other ways, such as *surveying records* or *direct observation* of situations.

As stated in Section 1–1, researchers use samples to collect data and information about a particular variable from a large population. Using samples saves time and money and in some cases enables the researcher to get more detailed information about a particular subject. Samples cannot be selected in haphazard ways because the information obtained might be biased. For example, interviewing people on a street corner during the day would not include responses from people working in offices at that time or from people attending school; hence, not all subjects in a particular population would have a chance of being selected.

To obtain samples that are unbiased—i.e., that give each subject in the population an equally likely chance of being selected—statisticians use four basic methods of sampling: random, systematic, stratified, and cluster sampling.

Random Sampling

Random samples are selected by using chance methods or random numbers. One such method is to number each subject in the population. Then place numbered cards in a bowl, mix them thoroughly, and select as many cards as needed. The subjects whose numbers are selected constitute the sample. Since it is difficult to mix the cards thoroughly, there is a chance of obtaining a biased sample. For this reason, statisticians use another method of obtaining numbers. They generate random numbers with a computer or calculator. Before the invention of computers, random numbers were obtained from tables.

Some two-digit random numbers are shown in Table 1–3. To select a random sample of, say, 15 subjects out of 85 subjects, it is necessary to number each subject from 01 to 85.

Commuting Times

This graph shows the highest average commuting times for cities with a population of 250,000 or more.

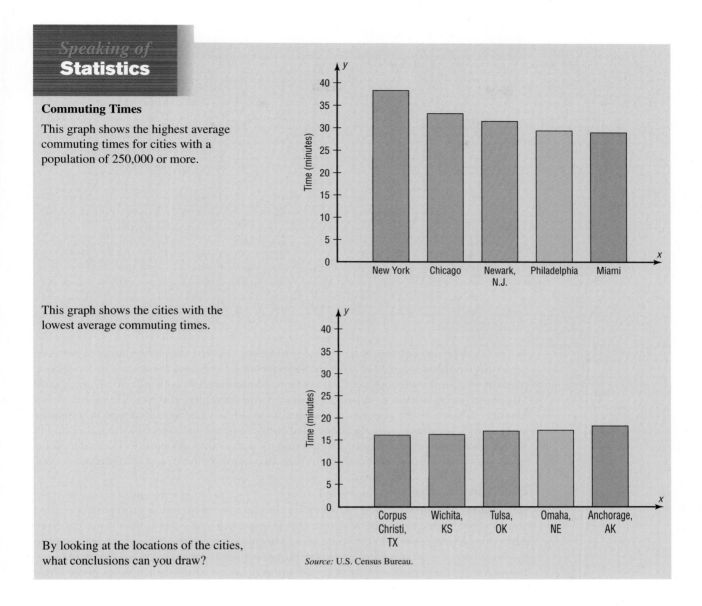

This graph shows the cities with the lowest average commuting times.

By looking at the locations of the cities, what conclusions can you draw?

Source: U.S. Census Bureau.

Then select a starting number by closing your eyes and placing your finger on a number in the table. (Although this may sound somewhat unusual, it enables us to find a starting number at random.) In this case suppose your finger landed on the number 12 in the second column. (It is the sixth number down from the top.) Then proceed downward until you have selected 15 different numbers between 01 and 85. When you reach the bottom of the column, go to the top of the next column. If you select a number greater than 85 or the number 00 or a duplicate number, just omit it. In our example, we will use the subjects numbered 12, 27, 75, 62, 57, 13, 31, 06, 16, 49, 46, 71, 53, 41, and 02.

Systematic Sampling

Researchers obtain **systematic samples** by numbering each subject of the population and then selecting every kth subject. For example, suppose there were 2000 subjects in the population and a sample of 50 subjects were needed. Since $2000 \div 50 = 40$, then $k = 40$,

Table 1–3	Random Numbers											
79	41	71	93	60	35	04	67	96	04	79	10	86
26	52	53	13	43	50	92	09	87	21	83	75	17
18	13	41	30	56	20	37	74	49	56	45	46	83
19	82	02	69	34	27	77	34	24	93	16	77	00
14	57	44	30	93	76	32	13	55	29	49	30	77
29	12	18	50	06	33	15	79	50	28	50	45	45
01	27	92	67	93	31	97	55	29	21	64	27	29
55	75	65	68	65	73	07	95	66	43	43	92	16
84	95	95	96	62	30	91	64	74	83	47	89	71
62	62	21	37	82	62	19	44	08	64	34	50	11
66	57	28	69	13	99	74	31	58	19	47	66	89
48	13	69	97	29	01	75	58	05	40	40	18	29
94	31	73	19	75	76	33	18	05	53	04	51	41
00	06	53	98	01	55	08	38	49	42	10	44	38
46	16	44	27	80	15	28	01	64	27	89	03	27
77	49	85	95	62	93	25	39	63	74	54	82	85
81	96	43	27	39	53	85	61	12	90	67	96	02
40	46	15	73	23	75	96	68	13	99	49	64	11

and every 40th subject would be selected; however, the first subject (numbered between 1 and 40) would be selected at random. Suppose subject 12 were the first subject selected; then the sample would consist of the subjects whose numbers were 12, 52, 92, etc., until 50 subjects were obtained. When using systematic sampling, you must be careful about how the subjects in the population are numbered. If subjects were arranged in a manner such as wife, husband, wife, husband, and every 40th subject were selected, the sample would consist of all husbands. Numbering is not always necessary. For example, a researcher may select every tenth item from an assembly line to test for defects.

Stratified Sampling

Researchers obtain **stratified samples** by dividing the population into groups (called strata) according to some characteristic that is important to the study, then sampling from each group. Samples within the strata should be randomly selected. For example, suppose the president of a two-year college wants to learn how students feel about a certain issue. Furthermore, the president wishes to see if the opinions of the first-year students differ from those of the second-year students. The president will select students from each group to use in the sample.

Cluster Sampling

Researchers also use **cluster samples.** Here the population is divided into groups called clusters by some means such as geographic area or schools in a large school district, etc. Then the researcher randomly selects some of these clusters and uses all members of the selected clusters as the subjects of the samples. Suppose a researcher wishes to survey apartment dwellers in a large city. If there are 10 apartment buildings in the city, the researcher can select at random 2 buildings from the 10 and interview all the residents of these buildings. Cluster sampling is used when the population is large or when it involves subjects residing in a large geographic area. For example, if one wanted to do a study involving the patients in the hospitals in New York City, it would be very costly and time-consuming to try to obtain a random sample of patients since they would be spread over a large area. Instead, a few hospitals could be selected at random, and the patients in these hospitals would be interviewed in a cluster.

The four basic sampling methods are summarized in Table 1–4.

istorical Note

In 1936, the *Literary Digest,* on the basis of a biased sample of its subscribers, predicted that Alf Landon would defeat Franklin D. Roosevelt in the upcoming presidential election. Roosevelt won by a landslide. The magazine ceased publication the following year.

Table 1–4	Summary of Sampling Methods
Random	Subjects are selected by random numbers.
Systematic	Subjects are selected by using every kth number after the first subject is randomly selected from 1 through k.
Stratified	Subjects are selected by dividing up the population into groups (strata), and subjects are randomly selected within groups.
Cluster	Subjects are selected by using an intact group that is representative of the population.

Other Sampling Methods

In addition to the four basic sampling methods, researchers use other methods to obtain samples. One such method is called a **convenience sample.** Here a researcher uses subjects that are convenient. For example, the researcher may interview subjects entering a local mall to determine the nature of their visit or perhaps what stores they will be patronizing. This sample is probably not representative of the general customers for several reasons. For one thing, it was probably taken at a specific time of day, so not all customers entering the mall have an equal chance of being selected since they were not there when the survey was being conducted. But convenience samples can be representative of the population. If the researcher investigates the characteristics of the population and determines that the sample is representative, then it can be used.

Applying the Concepts 1–3

American Culture and Drug Abuse

Assume you are a member of the Family Research Council and have become increasingly concerned about the drug use by professional sports players. You set up a plan and conduct a survey on how people believe the American culture (television, movies, magazines, and popular music) influences illegal drug use. Your survey consists of 2250 adults and adolescents from around the country. A consumer group petitions you for more information about your survey. Answer the following questions about your survey.

1. What type of survey did you use (phone, mail, or interview)?
2. What are the advantages and disadvantages of the surveying methods you did not use?
3. What type of scores did you use? Why?
4. Did you use a random method for deciding who would be in your sample?
5. Which of the methods (stratified, systematic, cluster, or convenience) did you use?
6. Why was that method more appropriate for this type of data collection?
7. If a convenience sample were obtained, consisting of only adolescents, how would the results of the study be affected?

See page 33 for the answers.

1–4

Objective 6

Explain the difference between an observational and an experimental study.

Observational and Experimental Studies

There are several different ways to classify statistical studies. This section explains two types of studies: *observational studies* and *experimental studies*.

In an **observational study,** the researcher merely observes what is happening or what has happened in the past and tries to draw conclusions based on these observations.

For example, data from the Motorcycle Industry Council (*USA TODAY*) stated that "Motorcycle owners are getting older and richer." Data were collected on the ages and incomes of motorcycle owners for the years 1980 and 1998 and then compared. The findings showed considerable differences in the ages and incomes of motorcycle owners for the two years.

In this study, the researcher merely observed what had happened to the motorcycle owners over a period of time. There was no type of research intervention.

In an **experimental study,** the researcher manipulates one of the variables and tries to determine how the manipulation influences other variables.

For example, a study conducted at Virginia Polytechnic Institute and presented in *Psychology Today* divided female undergraduate students into two groups and had the students perform as many sit-ups as possible in 90 sec. The first group was told only to "Do your best," while the second group was told to try to increase the actual number of sit-ups done each day by 10%. After four days, the subjects in the group who were given the vague instructions to "Do your best" averaged 43 sit-ups, while the group that was given the more specific instructions to increase the number of sit-ups by 10% averaged 56 sit-ups by the last day's session. The conclusion then was that athletes who were given specific goals performed better than those who were not given specific goals.

This study is an example of a statistical experiment since the researchers intervened in the study by manipulating one of the variables, namely, the type of instructions given to each group.

In a true experimental study, the subjects should be assigned to groups randomly. Also, the treatments should be assigned to the groups at random. In the sit-up study, the article did not mention whether the subjects were randomly assigned to the groups.

Sometimes when random assignment is not possible, researchers use intact groups. These types of studies are done quite often in education where already intact groups are available in the form of existing classrooms. When these groups are used, the study is said to be a **quasi-experimental study.** The treatments, though, should be assigned at random. Most articles do not state whether random assignment of subjects was used.

Statistical studies usually include one or more *independent variables* and one *dependent variable.*

The **independent variable** in an experimental study is the one that is being manipulated by the researcher. The independent variable is also called the **explanatory variable.** The resultant variable is called the **dependent variable** or the **outcome variable.**

The outcome variable is the variable that is studied to see if it has changed significantly due to the manipulation of the independent variable. For example, in the sit-up study, the researchers gave the groups two different types of instructions, general and specific. Hence, the independent variable is the type of instruction. The dependent variable, then, is the resultant variable, that is, the number of sit-ups each group was able to perform after four days of exercise. If the differences in the dependent or outcome variable are large and other factors are equal, these differences can be attributed to the manipulation of the independent variable. In this case, specific instructions were shown to increase athletic performance.

In the sit-up study, there were two groups. The group that received the special instruction is called the **treatment group** while the other is called the **control group.** The treatment group receives a specific treatment (in this case, instructions for improvement) while the control group does not.

Both types of statistical studies have advantages and disadvantages. Experimental studies have the advantage that the researcher can decide how to select subjects and how to assign them to specific groups. The researcher can also control or manipulate the independent variable. For example, in studies that require the subjects to consume a certain amount of medicine each day, the researcher can determine the precise dosages and, if necessary, vary the dosage for the groups.

There are several disadvantages to experimental studies. First, they may occur in unnatural settings, such as laboratories and special classrooms. This can lead to several problems. One such problem is that the results might not apply to the natural setting. The age-old question then is, "This mouthwash may kill 10,000 germs in a test tube, but how many germs will it kill in my mouth?"

Another disadvantage with an experimental study is the **Hawthorne effect.** This effect was discovered in 1924 in a study of workers at the Hawthorne plant of the Western Electric Company. In this study, researchers found that the subjects who knew they were participating in an experiment actually changed their behavior in ways that affected the results of the study.

Another problem is called *confounding of variables.*

A **confounding variable** is one that influences the dependent or outcome variable but was not separated from the independent variable.

Researchers try to control most variables in a study, but this is not possible in some studies. For example, subjects who are put on an exercise program might also improve their diet unbeknownst to the researcher and perhaps improve their health in other ways not due to exercise alone. Then diet becomes a confounding variable.

Observational studies also have advantages and disadvantages. One advantage of an observational study is that it usually occurs in a natural setting. For example, researchers can observe people's driving patterns on streets and highways in large cities. Another advantage of an observational study is that it can be done in situations where it would be unethical or downright dangerous to conduct an experiment. Using observational studies, researchers can study suicides, rapes, murders, etc. In addition, observational studies can be done using variables that cannot be manipulated by the researcher, such as drug users versus nondrug users and right-handedness versus left-handedness.

Observational studies have disadvantages, too. As mentioned previously, since the variables are not controlled by the researcher, a definite cause-and-effect situation cannot be shown since other factors may have had an effect on the results. Observational studies can be expensive and time-consuming. For example, if one wanted to study the habitat of lions in Africa, one would need a lot of time and money, and there would be a certain amount of danger involved. Finally, since the researcher may not be using his or her own measurements, the results could be subject to the inaccuracies of those who collected the data. For example, if the researchers were doing a study of events that occurred in the 1800s, they would have to rely on information and records obtained by others from a previous era. There is no way to ensure the accuracy of these records.

When you read the results of statistical studies, decide if the study was observational or experimental. Then see if the conclusion follows logically, based on the nature of these studies.

No matter what type of study is conducted, two studies on the same subject sometimes have conflicting conclusions. Why might this occur? An article entitled "Bottom Line: Is It Good for You?" (*USA TODAY Weekend*) states that in the 1960s studies suggested that margarine was better for the heart than butter since margarine contains less saturated fat and users had lower cholesterol levels. In a 1980 study, researchers found that butter was better than margarine since margarine contained trans-fatty acids, which are worse for the heart than butter's saturated fat. Then in a 1998 study, researchers found that margarine was better for a person's health. Now, what is to be believed? Should one use butter or margarine?

The answer here is that you must take a closer look at these studies. Actually, it is not a choice between butter or margarine that counts, but the type of margarine used. In the 1980s, studies showed that solid margarine contains trans-fatty acids, and scientists believe that they are worse for the heart than butter's saturated fat. In the 1998 study, liquid margarine was used. It is very low in trans-fatty acids, and hence it is more healthful than butter because trans-fatty acids have been shown to raise cholesterol. Hence, the conclusion is to use liquid margarine instead of solid margarine or butter.

Before decisions based on research studies are made, it is important to get all the facts and examine them in light of the particular situation.

Applying the Concepts **1–4**

Just a Pinch Between Your Cheek and Gum

As the evidence on the adverse effects of cigarette smoke grew, people tried many different ways to quit smoking. Some people tried chewing tobacco or, as it was called, smokeless tobacco. A small amount of tobacco was placed between the cheek and gum. Certain chemicals from the tobacco were absorbed into the bloodstream and gave the sensation of smoking cigarettes. This prompted studies on the adverse effects of smokeless tobacco. One study in particular used 40 university students as subjects. Twenty were given smokeless tobacco to chew, and twenty given a substance that looked and tasted like smokeless tobacco, but did not contain any of the harmful substances. The students were randomly assigned to one of the groups. The students' blood pressure and heart rate were measured before they started chewing and 20 minutes after they had been chewing. A significant increase in heart rate occurred in the group that chewed the smokeless tobacco. Answer the following questions.

1. What type of study was this (observational, quasi-experimental, or experimental)?
2. What are the independent and dependent variables?
3. Which was the treatment group?
4. Could the students' blood pressures be affected by knowing that they are part of a study?
5. List some possible confounding variables.
6. Do you think this is a good way to study the effect of smokeless tobacco?

See page 33 for the answers.

1–5 Uses and Misuses of Statistics

Objective 7

Explain how statistics can be used and misused.

As explained previously, statistical techniques can be used to describe data, compare two or more data sets, determine if a relationship exists between variables, test hypotheses, and make estimates about population characteristics. However, there is another aspect of statistics, and that is the misuse of statistical techniques to sell products that don't work properly, to attempt to prove something true that is really not true, or to get our attention by using statistics to evoke fear, shock, and outrage.

There are two sayings that have been around for a long time that illustrate this point:

"There are three types of lies—lies, damn lies, and statistics."

"Figures don't lie, but liars figure."

Just because we read or hear the results of a research study or an opinion poll in the media, this does not mean that these results are reliable or that they can be applied to any and all situations. For example, reporters sometimes leave out critical details such as the size of the sample used or how the research subjects were selected. Without this information, you cannot properly evaluate the research and properly interpret the conclusions of the study or survey.

It is the purpose of this section to show some ways that statistics can be misused. You should not infer that all research studies and surveys are suspect, but that there are many factors to consider when making decisions based on the results of research studies and surveys. Here are some ways that statistics can be misrepresented.

Suspect Samples

The first thing to consider is the sample that was used in the research study. Sometimes researchers use very small samples to obtain information. Several years ago, advertisements contained such statements as "Three out of four doctors surveyed recommend brand such and such." If only 4 doctors were surveyed, the results could have been obtained by chance alone; however, if 100 doctors were surveyed, the results might be quite different.

Not only is it important to have a sample size that is large enough, but also it is necessary to see how the subjects in the sample were selected. Studies using volunteers sometimes have a built-in bias. Volunteers generally do not represent the population at large. Sometimes they are recruited from a particular socioeconomic background, and sometimes unemployed people volunteer for research studies to get a stipend. Studies that require the subjects to spend several days or weeks in an environment other than their home or workplace automatically exclude people who are employed and cannot take time away from work. Sometimes only college students or retirees are used in studies. In the past, many studies have used only men, but have attempted to generalize the results to both men and women. Opinion polls that require a person to phone or mail in a response most often are not representative of the population in general, since only those with strong feelings for or against the issue usually call or respond by mail.

Another type of sample that may not be representative is the convenience sample. Educational studies sometimes use students in intact classrooms since it is convenient. Quite often, the students in these classrooms do not represent the student population of the entire school district.

When results are interpreted from studies using small samples, convenience samples, or volunteer samples, care should be used in generalizing the results to the entire population.

Ambiguous Averages

In Chapter 3, you will learn that there are four commonly used measures that are loosely called *averages*. They are the *mean, median, mode,* and *midrange.* For the same data set, these averages can differ markedly. People who know this can, without lying, select the one measure of average that lends the most evidence to support their position.

Changing the Subject

Another type of statistical distortion can occur when different values are used to represent the same data. For example, one political candidate who is running for reelection might say, "During my administration, expenditures increased a mere 3%." His opponent, who is trying to unseat him, might say, "During my opponent's administration, expenditures have increased a whopping $6,000,000." Here both figures are correct; however, expressing a 3% increase as $6,000,000 makes it sound like a very large increase. Here again, ask yourself, Which measure better represents the data?

Detached Statistics

A claim that uses a detached statistic is one in which no comparison is made. For example, you may hear a claim such as "Our brand of crackers has one-third fewer calories." Here, no comparison is made. One-third fewer calories than what? Another example is a claim that uses a detached statistic such as "Brand A aspirin works four times faster." Four times faster than what? When you see statements such as this, always ask yourself, Compared to what?

Implied Connections

Many claims attempt to imply connections between variables that may not actually exist. For example, consider the following statement: "Eating fish may help to reduce your cholesterol." Notice the words *may help*. There is no guarantee that eating fish will definitely help you reduce your cholesterol.

"Studies suggest that using our exercise machine will reduce your weight." Here the word *suggest* is used; and again, there is no guarantee that you will lose weight by using the exercise machine advertised.

Another claim might say, "Taking calcium will lower blood pressure in some people." Note the word *some* is used. You may not be included in the group of "some" people. Be careful when you draw conclusions from claims that use words such as *may, in some people,* and *might help.*

Misleading Graphs

Statistical graphs give a visual representation of data that enables viewers to analyze and interpret data more easily than by simply looking at numbers. In Chapter 2, you will see how some graphs are used to represent data. However, if graphs are drawn inappropriately, they can misrepresent the data and lead the reader to draw false conclusions. The misuse of graphs is also explained in Chapter 2.

Faulty Survey Questions

When analyzing the results of a survey using questionnaires, you should be sure that the questions are properly written since the way questions are phrased can often influence the way people answer them. For example, the responses to a question such as "Do you feel that the North Huntingdon School District should build a new football stadium?" might be answered differently than a question such as "Do you favor increasing school taxes so that the North Huntingdon School District can build a new football stadium?" Each question asks something a little different, and the responses could be radically different. When you read and interpret the results obtained from questionnaire surveys, watch out for some of these common mistakes made in the writing of the survey questions.

To restate the premise of this section, statistics, when used properly, can be beneficial in obtaining much information, but when used improperly, can lead to much misinformation. It is like your automobile. If you use your automobile to get to school or work or to go on a vacation, that's good. But if you use it to run over your neighbor's dog because it barks all night long and tears up your flower garden, that's not so good!

1–6 Computers and Calculators

Objective 8

Explain the importance of computers and calculators in statistics.

In the past, statistical calculations were done with pencil and paper. However, with the advent of calculators, numerical computations became much easier. Computers do all the numerical calculation. All one does is to enter the data into the computer and use the appropriate command; the computer will print the answer or display it on the screen. Now the TI-83 Plus or TI-84 Plus graphing calculator accomplishes the same thing.

There are many statistical packages available; this book uses MINITAB and Microsoft Excel. Instructions for using MINITAB, the TI-83 Plus or TI-84 Plus graphing calculator, and Excel have been placed at the end of each relevant section, in subsections entitled Technology Step by Step.

You should realize that the computer and calculator merely give numerical answers and save the time and effort of doing calculations by hand. You are still responsible for understanding and interpreting each statistical concept. In addition, you should realize that the results come from the data and do not appear magically on the computer. Doing calculations using the procedure tables will help you reinforce this idea.

The author has left it up to instructors to choose how much technology they will incorporate into the course.

Technology *Step by Step*

MINITAB
Step by Step

General Information

MINITAB statistical software provides a wide range of statistical analysis and graphing capabilities.

Take Note

In this text you will see captured screen images from computers running MINITAB Release 14. If you are using an earlier or later release of MINITAB, the screens you see on your computer may bear slight visual differences from the screens pictured in this text. **But don't be alarmed!** All the Step by Step operations described in this text, including the commands, the menu options, and the functionality, will work just fine on your computer.

Start the Program

1. Click the Windows XP Start Menu, then All Programs.
2. Click the MINITAB 14 folder and then click ▆ MINITAB 14 , the program icon. The program screen will look similar to the one shown here. You will see the Session Window, the Worksheet Window, and perhaps the Project Manager Window.
3. Click the Project Manager icon on the toolbar to bring the project manager to the front.

For Vista, click the start button, then "All Programs." Next click "MINITAB Solutions" and then "MINITAB Statistical Software English."

To use the program, data must be entered from the keyboard or from a file.

Entering Data in MINITAB

In MINITAB, all the data for one variable are stored in a column. Step by step instructions for entering these data follow.

Data

213   208   203   215   222

1. Click in row 1 of Worksheet 1***. This makes the worksheet the active window and puts the cursor in the first cell. The small data entry arrow in the upper left-hand corner of the worksheet should be pointing down. If it is not, click it to change the direction in which the cursor will move when you press the [Enter] key.

2. Type in each number, pressing [Enter] after each entry, including the last number typed.

3. *Optional:* Click in the space above row 1 to type in **Weight,** the column label.

Save a Worksheet File

4. Click on the **File Menu.** *Note:* This is *not* the same as clicking the disk icon ⊞ .

5. Click **Save Current Worksheet As . . .**

6. In the dialog box you will need to verify three items:

   a) Save in: Click on or type in the disk drive and directory where you will store your data. For a CD this would be **A:.**

   b) File Name: Type in the name of the file, such as **MyData.**

   c) Save as Type: The default here is MINITAB. An extension of mtw is added to the name.

   Click [Save]. The name of the worksheet will change from Worksheet 1*** to MyData.MTW.

Open the Databank File

The raw data are shown in Appendix D. There is a row for each person's data and a column for each variable. MINITAB data files comprised of data sets used in this book, including the

Databank, are available on the accompanying CD-ROM or at the Online Learning Center (www.mhhe.com/bluman). Here is how to get the data from a file into a worksheet.

1. Click **File>Open Worksheet.** A sequence of menu instructions will be shown this way.

   Note: This is *not* the same as clicking the file icon 📂. If the dialog box says Open Project instead of Open Worksheet, click [Cancel] and use the correct menu item. The Open Worksheet dialog box will be displayed.

2. You must check three items in this dialog box.

   a) The Look In: dialog box should show the directory where the file is located.

   b) Make sure the Files of Type: shows the correct type, MINITAB [*.mtw].

   c) Double-click the file name in the list box Databank.mtw. A dialog box may inform you that a copy of this file is about to be added to the project. Click on the checkbox if you do not want to see this warning again.

3. Click the [OK] button. The data will be copied into a second worksheet. Part of the worksheet is shown here.

	C1	C2	C3	C4	C5	C6	C7	C8	C9	C10	C11-T	C12-T
	ID-NUMBER	AGE	ED-LEVEL	SMOKING	EXERCISE	WEIGHT	SERUM	SYSTOLIC	IQ	SODIUM	GENDER	MARITAL-ST
1	1	27	2	1	1	120	193	126	118	136	F	M
2	2	18	1	0	1	145	210	120	105	137	M	S
3	3	32	2	0	0	118	196	128	115	135	F	M

   a) You may maximize the window and scroll if desired.

   b) C12-T Marital Status has a T appended to the label to indicate alphanumeric data. MyData.MTW is not erased or overwritten. Multiple worksheets can be available; however, only the active worksheet is available for analysis.

4. To switch between the worksheets, select **Window>MyData.MTW.**

5. Select **File>Exit** to quit. To save the project, click [Yes].

6. Type in the name of the file, **Chapter01.** The Data Window, the Session Window, and settings are all in one file called a project. Projects have an extension of mpj instead of mtw.

   Clicking the disk icon 💾 on the menu bar is the same as selecting **File>Save Project.**

   Clicking the file icon 📂 is the same as selecting **File>Open Project.**

7. Click [Save]. The mpj extension will be added to the name. The computer will return to the Windows desktop. The two worksheets, the Session Window results, and settings are saved in this project file. When a project file is opened, the program will start up right where you left off.

TI-83 Plus or TI-84 Plus
Step by Step

The TI-83 Plus or TI-84 Plus graphing calculator can be used for a variety of statistical graphs and tests.

General Information

To turn calculator on:
Press **ON** key.
To turn calculator off:
Press **2nd [OFF].**

To reset defaults only:

1. Press **2nd,** then **[MEM].**

2. Select **7,** then **2,** then **2.**

Optional. To reset settings on calculator and clear memory: (*Note:* This will clear all settings and programs in the calculator's memory.)
Press **2nd,** then **[MEM].** Then press **7,** then **1,** then **2.**
(Also, the contrast may need to be adjusted after this.)

To adjust contrast (if necessary):

Press **2nd.** Then press and hold ▲ to darken or ▼ to lighten contrast.

To clear screen:

Press **CLEAR.**

(*Note:* This will return you to the screen you were using.)

To display a menu:

Press appropriate menu key. Example: **STAT.**

To return to home screen:

Press **2nd,** then **[QUIT].**

To move around on the screens:

Use the arrow keys.

To select items on the menu:

Press the corresponding number or move the cursor to the item, using the arrow keys. Then press **ENTER.**

(*Note:* In some cases, you do not have to press **ENTER,** and in other cases you may need to press **ENTER** twice.)

Entering Data

To enter single-variable data (if necessary, clear the old list):

1. Press **STAT** to display the Edit menu.

2. Press **ENTER** to select 1:Edit.

3. Enter the data in L_1 and press **ENTER** after each value.

4. After all data values are entered, press **STAT** to get back to the Edit menu or **2nd [QUIT]** to end.

Example TI1–1

Enter the following data values in L_1: **213, 208, 203, 215, 222.**

To enter multiple-variable data:

The TI-83 Plus or TI-84 Plus will take up to six lists designated L_1, L_2, L_3, L_4, L_5, and L_6.

1. To enter more than one set of data values, complete the preceding steps. Then move the cursor to L_2 by pressing the ▶ key.

2. Repeat the steps in the preceding part.

Output

Editing Data

To correct a data value before pressing **ENTER,** use ◀ and retype the value and press **ENTER.**

To correct a data value in a list after pressing **ENTER,** move cursor to incorrect value in list and type in the correct value. Then press **ENTER.**

To delete a data value in a list:

Move cursor to value and press **DEL.**

To insert a data value in a list:

1. Move cursor to position where data value is to be inserted, then press **2nd [INS].**

2. Type data value; then press **ENTER.**

To clear a list:

1. Press **STAT,** then **4.**

2. Enter list to be cleared. Example: To clear L_1, press **2nd [L₁].** Then press **ENTER.**

   (*Note:* To clear several lists, follow step 1, but enter each list to be cleared, separating them with commas. To clear all lists at once, follow step 1 then press **ENTER.**)

Sorting Data

To sort the data in a list:

1. Enter the data in L_1.
2. Press **STAT 2** to get SortA to sort the list in ascending order.
3. Then press **2nd [L₁] ENTER.**

The calculator will display Done.

4. Press **STAT ENTER** to display sorted list.

   (*Note:* The SortD or **3** sorts the list in descending order.)

Example TI1–2

Sort in ascending order the data values entered in
Example TI1–1.

Output

L1	L2	L3	1
213	------	------	
208			
203			
215			
222			

L1(6)=

Excel
Step by Step

Excel's Analysis ToolPak Add-In

General Information

Microsoft Excel 2007 has two different ways to solve statistical problems. First, there are built-in functions, such as STDEV and CHITEST, available from the standard toolbar by clicking

Formulas, then selecting the Insert Function icon *fx*. Another feature of Excel that is useful for calculating multiple statistical measures and performing statistical tests for a set of data is the Data Analysis command found in the Analysis Tool-Pak Add-in.

To load the Analysis Tool-Pak:

Click the Microsoft Office button, then select Excel Options.

1. Click **Add-Ins,** and select **Add-ins** from the list of options on the left side of the options box.

2. Select the Analysis Tool-Pak, then click the **Go** button at the bottom of the options box.

3. After loading the Analysis Tool-Pak, the Data Analysis command is available in the Analysis group on the Data tab.

MegaStat

Later in this text you will encounter a few Excel Technology Step by Step operations that will require the use of the MegaStat Add-in for Excel. MegaStat can be downloaded from the CD that came with your textbook as well as from the text's Online Learning Center at www.mhhe.com/bluman.

1. Save the Zip file containing the MegaStat Excel Add-in file (MegaStat.xls) and the associated help file on your computer's hard drive.

2. After opening the Zip file, double-click the MegaStat Add-in file, then Extract the MegaStat program to your computer's hard drive. After extracting the file, you can load the MegaStat Add-in to Excel by double-clicking the MegaStat.xls file. When the Excel program opens to load the Add-in, choose the Enable Macros option.

3. After installation of the add-in, you will be able to access MegaStat by selecting the Add-ins tab on the Excel toolbar.

4. If MegaStat is not listed under Add-ins when you reopen the Excel program, then you can access MegaStat by double-clicking the MegaStat.xls file at any time.

Entering Data

1. Select a cell at the top of a column on an Excel worksheet where you want to enter data. When working with data values for a single variable, you will usually want to enter the values into a single column.

2. Type each data value and press **[Enter]** or **[Tab]** on your keyboard.

You can also add more worksheets to an Excel workbook by clicking the Insert Worksheet icon 🔲 located at the bottom of an open workbook.

Example XL1–1: Opening an existing Excel workbook/worksheet

1. Open the Microsoft Office Excel 2007 program.

2. Click the Microsoft Click Office button , then click the Open file function. The Open dialog box will be displayed.

3. In the Look in box, click the folder where the Excel workbook file is located.

4. Double-click the file name in the list box. The selected workbook file will be opened in Excel for editing.

Summary

The two major areas of statistics are descriptive and inferential. Descriptive statistics includes the collection, organization, summarization, and presentation of data. Inferential statistics includes making inferences from samples to populations, estimations and hypothesis testing, determining relationships, and making predictions. Inferential statistics is based on *probability theory.*

Since in most cases the populations under study are large, statisticians use subgroups called samples to get the necessary data for their studies. There are four basic methods used to obtain samples: random, systematic, stratified, and cluster.

Data can be classified as qualitative or quantitative. Quantitative data can be either discrete or continuous, depending on the values they can assume. Data can also be measured by various scales. The four basic levels of measurement are nominal, ordinal, interval, and ratio.

There are two basic types of statistical studies: observational studies and experimental studies. When conducting observational studies, researchers observe what is happening or what has happened and then draw conclusions based on these observations. They do not attempt to manipulate the variables in any way.

When conducting an experimental study, researchers manipulate one or more of the independent or explanatory variables and see how this manipulation influences the dependent or outcome variable.

Finally, the applications of statistics are many and varied. People encounter them in everyday life, such as in reading newspapers or magazines, listening to the radio, or watching television. Since statistics is used in almost every field of endeavor, the educated individual should be knowledgeable about the vocabulary, concepts, and procedures of statistics.

Today, computers and calculators are used extensively in statistics to facilitate the computations.

Unusual Stat

The chance that someone will attempt to burglarize your home in any given year is 1 in 20.

LAFF - A - DAY

"We've polled the entire populace, Your Majesty, and we've come up with exactly the results you ordered!"

Source: © 1993 King Features Syndicate, Inc. World Rights reserved. Reprinted with special permission of King Features Syndicate.

Important Terms

cluster sample 12

confounding variable 15

continuous variables 6

control group 14

convenience sample 13

data 3

data set 3

data value or datum 3

dependent variable 14

descriptive statistics 4

discrete variables 6

experimental study 14

explanatory variable 14

Hawthorne effect 15

hypothesis testing 4

independent variable 14

inferential statistics 4

interval level of measurement 8

measurement scales 7

nominal level of measurement 7

observational study 13

ordinal level of measurement 8

outcome variable 14

population 4

probability 4

qualitative variables 6

quantitative variables 6

quasi-experimental study 14

random sample 10

random variable 3

ratio level of measurement 8

sample 4

statistics 3

stratified sample 12

systematic sample 11

treatment group 14

variable 3

Review Exercises

Note: **All odd-numbered problems and even-numbered problems marked with "ans" are included in the answer section at the end of this book.**

1. Name and define the two areas of statistics.

2. What is probability? Name two areas where probability is used.

3. Suggest some ways statistics can be used in everyday life.

4. Explain the differences between a sample and a population.

5. Why are samples used in statistics?

6. **(ans)** In each of these statements, tell whether descriptive or inferential statistics have been used.

   a. In the year 2010, 148 million Americans will be enrolled in an HMO (Source: *USA TODAY*).
   b. Nine out of ten on-the-job fatalities are men (Source: *USA TODAY Weekend*).
   c. Expenditures for the cable industry were $5.66 billion in 1996 (Source: *USA TODAY*).
   d. The median household income for people aged 25–34 is $35,888 (Source: *USA TODAY*).
   e. Allergy therapy makes bees go away (Source: *Prevention*).
   f. Drinking decaffeinated coffee can raise cholesterol levels by 7% (Source: American Heart Association).

   g. The national average annual medicine expenditure per person is $1052 (Source: *The Greensburg Tribune Review*).
   h. Experts say that mortgage rates may soon hit bottom (Source: *USA TODAY*).

7. Classify each as nominal-level, ordinal-level, interval-level, or ratio-level measurement.

   a. Pages in the city of Cleveland telephone book.
   b. Rankings of tennis players.
   c. Weights of air conditioners.
   d. Temperatures inside 10 refrigerators.
   e. Salaries of the top five CEOs in the United States.
   f. Ratings of eight local plays (poor, fair, good, excellent).
   g. Times required for mechanics to do a tune-up.
   h. Ages of students in a classroom.
   i. Marital status of patients in a physician's office.
   j. Horsepower of tractor engines.

8. **(ans)** Classify each variable as qualitative or quantitative.

   a. Number of bicycles sold in 1 year by a large sporting goods store.
   b. Colors of baseball caps in a store.
   c. Times it takes to cut a lawn.
   d. Capacity in cubic feet of six truck beds.
   e. Classification of children in a day care center (infant, toddler, preschool).
   f. Weights of fish caught in Lake George.
   g. Marital status of faculty members in a large university.

9. Classify each variable as discrete or continuous.

    a. Number of doughnuts sold each day by Doughnut Heaven.
    b. Water temperatures of six swimming pools in Pittsburgh on a given day.
    c. Weights of cats in a pet shelter.
    d. Lifetime (in hours) of 12 flashlight batteries.
    e. Number of cheeseburgers sold each day by a hamburger stand on a college campus.
    f. Number of DVDs rented each day by a video store.
    g. Capacity (in gallons) of six reservoirs in Jefferson County.

10. Give the boundaries of each value.

    a. 42.8 miles.
    b. 1.6 milliliters.
    c. 5.36 ounces.
    d. 18 tons.
    e. 93.8 ounces.
    f. 40 inches.

11. Name and define the four basic sampling methods.

12. (ans) Classify each sample as random, systematic, stratified, or cluster.

    a. In a large school district, all teachers from two buildings are interviewed to determine whether they believe the students have less homework to do now than in previous years.
    b. Every seventh customer entering a shopping mall is asked to select her or his favorite store.
    c. Nursing supervisors are selected using random numbers to determine annual salaries.
    d. Every 100th hamburger manufactured is checked to determine its fat content.
    e. Mail carriers of a large city are divided into four groups according to gender (male or female) and according to whether they walk or ride on their routes. Then 10 are selected from each group and interviewed to determine whether they have been bitten by a dog in the last year.

13. Give three examples each of nominal, ordinal, interval, and ratio data.

14. For each of these statements, define a population and state how a sample might be obtained.

    a. The average cost of an airline meal is $4.55 (Source: *Everything Has Its Price,* Richard E. Donley, Simon and Schuster).
    b. More than 1 in 4 United States children have cholesterol levels of 180 milligrams or higher (Source: The American Health Foundation).
    c. Every 10 minutes, 2 people die in car crashes and 170 are injured (Source: National Safety Council estimates).

    d. When older people with mild to moderate hypertension were given mineral salt for 6 months, the average blood pressure reading dropped by 8 points systolic and 3 points diastolic (Source: *Prevention*).
    e. The average amount spent per gift for Mom on Mother's Day is $25.95 (Source: The Gallup Organization).

15. Select a newspaper or magazine article that involves a statistical study, and write a paper answering these questions.

    a. Is this study descriptive or inferential? Explain your answer.
    b. What are the variables used in the study? In your opinion, what level of measurement was used to obtain the data from the variables?
    c. Does the article define the population? If so, how is it defined? If not, how could it be defined?
    d. Does the article state the sample size and how the sample was obtained? If so, determine the size of the sample and explain how it was selected. If not, suggest a way it could have been obtained.
    e. Explain *in your own words* what procedure (survey, comparison of groups, etc.) might have been used to determine the study's conclusions.
    f. Do you agree or disagree with the conclusions? State your reasons.

16. Information from research studies is sometimes taken out of context. Explain why the claims of these studies might be suspect.

    a. The average salary of the graduates of the class of 1980 is $32,500.
    b. It is estimated that in Podunk there are 27,256 cats.
    c. Only 3% of the men surveyed read *Cosmopolitan* magazine.
    d. Based on a recent mail survey, 85% of the respondents favored gun control.
    e. A recent study showed that high school dropouts drink more coffee than students who graduated; therefore, coffee dulls the brain.
    f. Since most automobile accidents occur within 15 miles of a person's residence, it is safer to make long trips.

17. Identify each study as being either observational or experimental.

    a. Subjects were randomly assigned to two groups, and one group was given an herb and the other group a placebo. After 6 months, the numbers of respiratory tract infections each group had were compared.
    b. A researcher stood at a busy intersection to see if the color of the automobile that a person drives is related to running red lights.

c. A researcher finds that people who are more hostile have higher total cholesterol levels than those who are less hostile.

d. Subjects are randomly assigned to four groups. Each group is placed on one of four special diets—a low-fat diet, a high-fish diet, a combination of low-fat diet and high-fish diet, and a regular diet. After 6 months, the blood pressures of the groups are compared to see if diet has any effect on blood pressure.

18. Identify the independent variable(s) and the dependent variable for each of the studies in Exercise 17.

19. For each of the studies in Exercise 17, suggest possible confounding variables.

20. **Beneficial Bacteria** According to a pilot study of 20 people conducted at the University of Minnesota, daily doses of a compound called arabinogalactan over a period of 6 months resulted in a significant increase in the beneficial lactobacillus species of bacteria. Why can't it be concluded that the compound is beneficial for the majority of people?

21. Comment on the following statement, taken from a magazine advertisement: "In a recent clinical study, Brand ABC (actual brand will not be named) was proved to be 1950% better than creatine!"

22. In an ad for women, the following statement was made: "For every 100 women, 91 have taken the road less traveled." Comment on this statement.

23. In many ads for weight loss products, under the product claims and in small print, the following statement is made: "These results are not typical." What does this say about the product being advertised?

24. In an ad for moisturizing lotion, the following claim is made: ". . . it's the number 1 dermatologist-recommended brand." What is misleading about this claim?

25. An ad for an exercise product stated: "Using this product will burn 74% more calories." What is misleading about this statement?

26. "Vitamin E is a proven antioxidant and may help in fighting cancer and heart disease." Is there anything ambiguous about this claim? Explain.

27. "Just 1 capsule of Brand X can provide 24 hours of acid control." (Actual brand will not be named.) What needs to be more clearly defined in this statement?

28. ". . . Male children born to women who smoke during pregnancy run a risk of violent and criminal behavior that lasts well into adulthood." Can we infer that smoking during pregnancy is responsible for criminal behavior in people?

29. **Caffeine and Health** In the 1980s, a study linked coffee to a higher risk of heart disease and pancreatic cancer. In the early 1990s, studies showed that drinking coffee posed minimal health threats. However, in 1994, a study showed that pregnant women who drank 3 or more cups of tea daily may be at risk for spontaneous abortion. In 1998, a study claimed that women who drank more than a half-cup of caffeinated tea every day may actually increase their fertility. In 1998, a study showed that over a lifetime, a few extra cups of coffee a day can raise blood pressure, heart rate, and stress (Source: "Bottom Line: Is It Good for You? Or Bad?" by Monika Guttman, *USA TODAY Weekend*). Suggest some reasons why these studies appear to be conflicting.

Extending the Concepts

30. Find an article that describes a statistical study, and identify the study as observational or experimental.

31. For the article that you used in Exercise 30, identify the independent variable(s) and dependent variable for the study.

32. For the article that you selected in Exercise 30, suggest some confounding variables that may have an effect on the results of the study.

Statistics Today

Are We Improving Our Diet?—Revisited

Researchers selected a *sample* of 23,699 adults in the United States, using phone numbers selected at *random,* and conducted a *telephone survey.* All respondents were asked six questions:

1. How often do you drink juices such as orange, grapefruit, or tomato?
2. Not counting juice, how often do you eat fruit?
3. How often do you eat green salad?
4. How often do you eat potatoes (not including french fries, fried potatoes, or potato chips)?
5. How often do you eat carrots?
6. Not counting carrots, potatoes, or salad, how many servings of vegetables do you usually eat?

Researchers found that men consumed fewer servings of fruits and vegetables per day (3.3) than women (3.7). Only 20% of the population consumed the recommended 5 or more daily servings. In addition, they found that youths and less-educated people consumed an even lower amount than the average.

Based on this study, they recommend that greater educational efforts are needed to improve fruit and vegetable consumption by Americans and to provide environmental and institutional support to encourage increased consumption.

Source: Mary K. Serdula, M.D., et al., "Fruit and Vegetable Intake Among Adults in 16 States: Results of a Brief Telephone Survey," *American Journal of Public Health* 85, no. 2. Copyright by the American Public Health Association.

Chapter Quiz

Determine whether each statement is true or false. If the statement is false, explain why.

1. Probability is used as a basis for inferential statistics.

2. The height of President Lincoln is an example of a variable.

3. The highest level of measurement is the interval level.

4. When the population of college professors is divided into groups according to their rank (instructor, assistant professor, etc.) and then several are selected from each group to make up a sample, the sample is called a cluster sample.

5. The variable *age* is an example of a qualitative variable.

6. The weight of pumpkins is considered to be a continuous variable.

7. The boundary of a value such as 6 inches would be 5.9–6.1 inches.

Select the best answer.

8. The number of absences per year that a worker has is an example of what type of data?

   a. Nominal
   b. Qualitative
   c. Discrete
   d. Continuous

9. What are the boundaries of 25.6 ounces?

   a. 25–26 ounces
   b. 25.55–25.65 ounces
   c. 25.5–25.7 ounces
   d. 20–39 ounces

10. A researcher divided subjects into two groups according to gender and then selected members from each group for her sample. What sampling method was the researcher using?

    a. Cluster
    b. Random
    c. Systematic
    d. Stratified

11. Data that can be classified according to color are measured on what scale?

    a. Nominal
    b. Ratio
    c. Ordinal
    d. Interval

12. A study that involves no researcher intervention is called

    a. An experimental study.
    b. A noninvolvement study.
    c. An observational study.
    d. A quasi-experimental study.

13. A variable that interferes with other variables in the study is called

    a. A confounding variable.
    b. An explanatory variable.
    c. An outcome variable.
    d. An interfering variable.

Use the best answer to complete these statements.

14. Two major branches of statistics are _____ and _____.

15. Two uses of probability are _____ and _____.

16. The group of all subjects under study is called a(n) _____.

17. A group of subjects selected from the group of all subjects under study is called a(n) _____.

18. Three reasons why samples are used in statistics are
    a. _____ b. _____ c. _____.

19. The four basic sampling methods are
    a. _____ b. _____ c. _____ d. _____.

20. A study that uses intact groups when it is not possible to randomly assign participants to the groups is called a(n) _____ study.

21. In a research study, participants should be assigned to groups using _____ methods, if possible.

22. For each statement, decide whether descriptive or inferential statistics is used.

    a. The average life expectancy in New Zealand is 78.49 years. Source: *World Factbook 2004.*
    b. A diet high in fruits and vegetables will lower blood pressure. Source: Institute of Medicine.
    c. The total amount of estimated losses from hurricane Hugo was $4.2 billion. Source: Insurance Service Office.
    d. Researchers stated that the shape of a person's ears is related to the person's aggression. Source: *American Journal of Human Biology.*
    e. In 2013, the number of high school graduates will be 3.2 million students. Source: National Center for Education.

23. Classify each as nominal-level, ordinal-level, interval-level, or ratio-level measurement.

    a. Rating of movies as G, PG, and R.
    b. Number of candy bars sold on a fund drive.
    c. Classification of automobiles as subcompact, compact, standard, and luxury.
    d. Temperatures of hair dryers.
    e. Weights of suitcases on a commercial airline.

24. Classify each variable as discrete or continuous.

    a. Ages of people working in a large factory.
    b. Number of cups of coffee served at a restaurant.
    c. The amount of a drug injected into a guinea pig.
    d. The time it takes a student to drive to school.
    e. The number of gallons of milk sold each day at a grocery store.

25. Give the boundaries of each.

    a. 48 seconds.
    b. 0.56 centimeter.
    c. 9.1 quarts.
    d. 13.7 pounds.
    e. 7 feet.

Critical Thinking Challenges

1. **World's Busiest Airports** A study of the world's busiest airports was conducted by *Airports Council International.* Describe three variables that one could use to determine which airports are the busiest. What *units* would one use to measure these variables? Are these variables categorical, discrete, or continuous?

2. **Smoking and Criminal Behavior** The results of a study published in *Archives of General Psychiatry* stated that male children born to women who smoke during pregnancy run a risk of violent and criminal behavior that lasts into adulthood. The results of this study were challenged by some people in the media. Give several reasons why the results of this study would be challenged.

3. **Piano Lessons Improve Math Ability** The results of a study published in *Neurological Research* stated that second-graders who took piano lessons and played a computer math game more readily grasped math problems in fractions and proportions than a similar group who took an English class and played the same math game. What type of inferential study was this? Give several reasons why the piano lessons could improve a student's math ability.

4. **ACL Tears in Collegiate Soccer Players** A study of 2958 collegiate soccer players showed that in 46 anterior cruciate ligament (ACL) tears, 36 were in women. Calculate the percentages of tears for each gender.

   a. Can it be concluded that female athletes tear their knees more often than male athletes?
   b. Comment on how this study's conclusion might have been reached.

5. **Anger and Snap Judgments** Read the article entitled "Anger Can Cause Snap Judgments" and answer the following questions.

   a. Is the study experimental or observational?
   b. What is the independent variable?
   c. What is the dependent variable?
   d. Do you think the sample sizes are large enough to merit the conclusion?
   e. Based on the results of the study, what changes would you recommend to persons to help them reduce their anger?

6. **Hostile Children Fight Unemployment** Read the article entitled "Hostile Children Fight Unemployment" and answer the following questions.

   a. Is the study experimental or observational?
   b. What is the independent variable?
   c. What is the dependent variable?
   d. Suggest some confounding variables that may have influenced the results of the study.
   e. Identify the three groups of subjects used in the study.

ANGER CAN CAUSE SNAP JUDGMENTS

Anger can make a normally unbiased person act with prejudice, according to a forthcoming study in the journal *Psychological Science.*

Assistant psychology professors David DeSteno at Northeastern University in Boston and Nilanjana Dasgupta at the University of Massachusetts, Amherst, randomly divided 81 study participants into two groups and assigned them a writing task designed to induce angry, sad or neutral feelings. In a subsequent test to uncover nonconscious associations, angry subjects were quicker to connect negatively charged words—like war, death and vomit—with members of the opposite group—even though the groupings were completely arbitrary.

"These automatic responses guide our behavior when we're not paying attention," says DeSteno, and they can lead to discriminatory acts when there is pressure to make a quick decision. "If you're aware that your emotions might be coloring these gut reactions," he says, "you should take time to consider that possibility and adjust your actions accordingly."

—Eric Strand

Source: Reprinted with permission from *Psychology Today,* Copyright © (2004) Sussex Publishers, Inc.

UNEMPLOYMENT

Hostile Children Fight Unemployment

Aggressive children may be destined for later long-term unemployment. In a study that began in 1968, researchers at the University of Jyvaskyla in Finland examined about 300 participants at ages 8, 14, 27, and 36. They looked for aggressive behaviors like hurting other children, kicking objects when angry, or attacking others without reason.

Their results, published recently in the *International Journal of Behavioral Development*, suggest that children with low self-control of emotion —especially aggression—were significantly more prone to long-term unemployment. Children with behavioral inhibitions—such as passive and anxious behaviors—were also indirectly linked to unemployment

as they lacked the preliminary initiative needed for school success. And while unemployment rates were high in Finland during the last data collection, jobless participants who were aggressive as children were less likely to have a job two years later than their nonaggressive counterparts.

Ongoing unemployment can have serious psychological consequences, including depression, anxiety and stress. But lead researcher Lea Pulkkinen, Ph.D., a Jyvaskyla psychology professor, does have encouraging news for parents: Aggressive children with good social skills and child-centered parents were significantly less likely to be unemployed for more than two years as adults.

—*Tanya Zimbardo*

Source: Reprinted with permission from *Psychology Today,* Copyright © (2001) Sussex Publishers, Inc.

 ## Data Projects

1. **Business and Finance** Investigate the types of data that are collected regarding stock and bonds, for example, price, earnings ratios, and bond ratings. Find as many types of data as possible. For each, identify the level of measure as nominal, ordinal, interval, or ratio. For any quantitative data, also note if they are discrete or continuous.

2. **Sports and Leisure** Select a professional sport. Investigate the types of data that are collected about that sport, for example, in baseball, the level of play (A, AA, AAA, Major League), batting average, and home-run hits. For each, identify the level of measure as nominal, ordinal, interval, or ratio. For any quantitative data, also note if they are discrete or continuous.

3. **Technology** Music organization programs on computers and music players maintain information about a song, such as the writer, song length, genre, and your personal rating. Investigate the types of data collected about a song. For each, identify the level of measure as nominal, ordinal, interval, or ratio. For any quantitative data, also note if they are discrete or continuous.

4. **Health and Wellness** Think about the types of data that can be collected about your health and wellness, things such as blood type, cholesterol level, smoking status, and BMI. Find as many data items as you can. For each, identify the level of measure as nominal, ordinal, interval, or ratio. For any quantitative data, also note if they are discrete or continuous.

5. **Politics and Economics** Every 10 years since 1790, the federal government has conducted a census of U.S. residents. Investigate the types of data that were collected in the 2000 census. For each, identify the level of measure as nominal, ordinal, interval, or ratio. For any quantitative data, also note if they are discrete or continuous. Use the library or a genealogy website to find a census form from 1860. What types of data were collected? How do the types of data differ?

6. **Your Class** Your school probably has a database that contains information about each student, such as age, county of residence, credits earned, and ethnicity. Investigate the types of student data that your college collects and reports. For each, identify the level of measure as nominal, ordinal, interval, or ratio. For any quantitative data, also note if they are discrete or continuous.

Answers to Applying the Concepts

Section 1–1   Attendance and Grades

1. The variables are grades and attendance.

2. The data consist of specific grades and attendance numbers.

3. These are descriptive statistics; however, if an inference is made to all students, then that would be inferential statistics.

4. The population under study is students at Manatee Community College (MCC).

5. While not specified, we probably have data from a sample of MCC students.

6. Based on the data, it appears that, in general, the better your attendance the higher your grade.

Section 1–2   Safe Travel

1. The variables are industry and number of job-related injuries.

2. The type of industry is a qualitative variable, while the number of job-related injuries is quantitative.

3. The number of job-related injuries is discrete.

4. Type of industry is nominal, and the number of job-related injuries is ratio.

5. The railroads do show fewer job-related injuries; however, there may be other things to consider. For example, railroads employ fewer people than the other transportation industries in the study.

6. A person's choice of transportation might also be affected by convenience issues, cost, service, etc.

7. Answers will vary. One possible answer is that the railroads have the fewest job-related injuries, while the airline industry has the most job-related injuries (more than twice those of the railroad industry). The numbers of job-related injuries in the subway and trucking industries are fairly comparable.

Section 1–3   American Culture and Drug Abuse

Answers will vary, so this is one possible answer.

1. I used a telephone survey. The advantage to my survey method is that this was a relatively inexpensive survey method (although more expensive than using the mail) that could get a fairly sizable response. The disadvantage to my survey method is that I have not included anyone without a telephone. (*Note:* My survey used a random dialing method to include unlisted numbers and cell phone exchanges.)

2. A mail survey also would have been fairly inexpensive, but my response rate may have been much lower than what I got with my telephone survey. Interviewing would have allowed me to use follow-up questions and to clarify any questions of the respondents at the time of the interview. However, interviewing is very labor- and cost-intensive.

3. I used ordinal data on a scale of 1 to 5. The scores were 1 = strongly disagree, 2 = disagree, 3 = neutral, 4 = agree, 5 = strongly agree.

4. The random method that I used was a random dialing method.

5. To include people from each state, I used a stratified random sample, collecting data randomly from each of the area codes and telephone exchanges available.

6. This method allowed me to make sure that I had representation from each area of the United States.

7. Convenience samples may not be representative of the population, and a convenience sample of adolescents would probably differ greatly from the general population with regard to the influence of American culture on illegal drug use.

Section 1–4   Just a Pinch Between Your Cheek and Gum

1. This was an experiment, since the researchers imposed a treatment on each of the two groups involved in the study.

2. The independent variable is whether the participant chewed tobacco or not. The dependent variables are the students' blood pressures and heart rates.

3. The treatment group is the tobacco group—the other group was used as a control.

4. A student's blood pressure might not be affected by knowing that he or she was part of a study. However, if the student's blood pressure were affected by this knowledge, all the students (in both groups) would be affected similarly. This might be an example of the placebo effect.

5. Answers will vary. One possible answer is that confounding variables might include the way that the students chewed the tobacco, whether or not the students smoked (although this would hopefully have been evened out with the randomization), and that all the participants were university students.

6. Answers will vary. One possible answer is that the study design was fine, but that it cannot be generalized beyond the population of university students (or people around that age).

Frequency Distributions and Graphs

Objectives

After completing this chapter, you should be able to

1. Organize data using a frequency distribution.

2. Represent data in frequency distributions graphically using histograms, frequency polygons, and ogives.

3. Represent data using bar graphs, Pareto charts, time series graphs, and pie graphs.

4. Draw and interpret a stem and leaf plot.

5. Draw and interpret a scatter plot for a set of paired data.

Outline

Statistics Today

How Your Identity Can Be Stolen

Identity fraud is a big business today. The total amount of the fraud in 2006 was $56.6 billion. The average amount of the fraud for a victim is $6383, and the average time to correct the problem is 40 hours. The ways in which a person's identity can be stolen are presented in the following table:

Lost or stolen wallet, checkbook, or credit card	38%
Friends, acquaintances	15
Corrupt business employees	15
Computer viruses and hackers	9
Stolen mail or fraudulent change of address	8
Online purchases or transactions	4
Other methods	11

Source: Javelin Strategy & Research; Council of Better Business Bureau, Inc.

Looking at the numbers presented in a table does not have the same impact as presenting numbers in a well-drawn chart or graph. The article did not include any graphs. This chapter will show you how to construct appropriate graphs to represent data and help you to get your point across to your audience.

See Statistics Today—Revisited at the end of the chapter for some suggestions on how to represent the data graphically.

Introduction

When conducting a statistical study, the researcher must gather data for the particular variable under study. For example, if a researcher wishes to study the number of people who were bitten by poisonous snakes in a specific geographic area over the past several years, he or she has to gather the data from various doctors, hospitals, or health departments.

To describe situations, draw conclusions, or make inferences about events, the researcher must organize the data in some meaningful way. The most convenient method of organizing data is to construct a *frequency distribution*.

After organizing the data, the researcher must present them so they can be understood by those who will benefit from reading the study. The most useful method of presenting the data is by constructing *statistical charts* and *graphs*. There are many different types of charts and graphs, and each one has a specific purpose.

This chapter explains how to organize data by constructing frequency distributions and how to present the data by constructing charts and graphs. The charts and graphs illustrated here are histograms, frequency polygons, ogives, pie graphs, Pareto charts, and time series graphs. A graph that combines the characteristics of a frequency distribution and a histogram, called a stem and leaf plot, is also explained. Two other graphs, the stem and leaf plot and the scatter plot, are also included in this chapter.

2–1

Organizing Data

Wealthy People

Objective 1

Organize data using a frequency distribution.

 Suppose a researcher wished to do a study on the ages of the top 50 wealthiest people in the world. The researcher first would have to get the data on the ages of the people. In this case, these ages are listed in *Forbes Magazine*. When the data are in original form, they are called **raw data** and are listed next.

49	57	38	73	81
74	59	76	65	69
54	56	69	68	78
65	85	49	69	61
48	81	68	37	43
78	82	43	64	67
52	56	81	77	79
85	40	85	59	80
60	71	57	61	69
61	83	90	87	74

Since little information can be obtained from looking at raw data, the researcher organizes the data into what is called a *frequency distribution*. A frequency distribution consists of *classes* and their corresponding *frequencies*. Each raw data value is placed into a quantitative or qualitative category called a **class**. The **frequency** of a class then is the number of data values contained in a specific class. A frequency distribution is shown for the preceding data set.

Class limits	Tally	Frequency
35–41	///	3
42–48	///	3
49–55	////	4
56–62	卌 卌	10
63–69	卌 卌	10
70–76	卌	5
77–83	卌 卌	10
84–90	卌	5
		Total 50

Now some general observations can be made from looking at the frequency distribution. For example, it can be stated that the majority of the wealthy people in the study are over 55 years old.

A **frequency distribution** is the organization of raw data in table form, using classes and frequencies.

The classes in this distribution are 35–41, 42–48, etc. These values are called *class limits*. The data values 35, 36, 37, 38, 39, 40, 41 can be tallied in the first class; 42, 43, 44, 45, 46, 47, 48 in the second class; and so on.

Two types of frequency distributions that are most often used are the *categorical frequency distribution* and the *grouped frequency distribution.* The procedures for constructing these distributions are shown now.

Categorical Frequency Distributions

The **categorical frequency distribution** is used for data that can be placed in specific categories, such as nominal- or ordinal-level data. For example, data such as political affiliation, religious affiliation, or major field of study would use categorical frequency distributions.

Example 2–1	Distribution of Blood Types

Twenty-five army inductees were given a blood test to determine their blood type. The data set is

A	B	B	AB	O
O	O	B	AB	B
B	B	O	A	O
A	O	O	O	AB
AB	A	O	B	A

Construct a frequency distribution for the data.

Solution

Since the data are categorical, discrete classes can be used. There are four blood types: A, B, O, and AB. These types will be used as the classes for the distribution.

The procedure for constructing a frequency distribution for categorical data is given next.

Step 1 Make a table as shown.

A	B	C	D
Class	**Tally**	**Frequency**	**Percent**
A			
B			
O			
AB			

Step 2 Tally the data and place the results in column B.

Step 3 Count the tallies and place the results in column C.

Step 4 Find the percentage of values in each class by using the formula

$$\% = \frac{f}{n} \cdot 100\%$$

where f = frequency of the class and n = total number of values. For example, in the class of type A blood, the percentage is

$$\% = \frac{5}{25} \cdot 100\% = 20\%$$

Percentages are not normally part of a frequency distribution, but they can be added since they are used in certain types of graphs such as pie graphs. Also, the decimal equivalent of a percent is called a *relative frequency.*

Step 5 Find the totals for columns C (frequency) and D (percent). The completed table is shown.

A Class	B Tally	C Frequency	D Percent
A	丗	5	20
B	丗 //	7	28
O	丗 ////	9	36
AB	////	4	16
		Total 25	100

For the sample, more people have type O blood than any other type.

Grouped Frequency Distributions

When the range of the data is large, the data must be grouped into classes that are more than one unit in width, in what is called a **grouped frequency distribution.** For example, a distribution of the number of hours that boat batteries lasted is the following.

Class limits	Class boundaries	Tally	Frequency
24–30	23.5–30.5	///	3
31–37	30.5–37.5	/	1
38–44	37.5–44.5	丗	5
45–51	44.5–51.5	丗 ////	9
52–58	51.5–58.5	丗 /	6
59–65	58.5–65.5	/	1
			25

The procedure for constructing the preceding frequency distribution is given in Example 2–2; however, several things should be noted. In this distribution, the values 24 and 30 of the first class are called *class limits.* The **lower class limit** is 24; it represents the smallest data value that can be included in the class. The **upper class limit** is 30; it represents the largest data value that can be included in the class. The numbers in the second column are called **class boundaries.** These numbers are used to separate the classes so that there are no gaps in the frequency distribution. The gaps are due to the limits; for example, there is a gap between 30 and 31.

Students sometimes have difficulty finding class boundaries when given the class limits. The basic rule of thumb is that *the class limits should have the same decimal place value as the data, but the class boundaries should have one additional place value and end in a 5.* For example, if the values in the data set are whole numbers, such as 24, 32, and 18, the limits for a class might be 31–37, and the boundaries are 30.5–37.5. Find the boundaries by subtracting 0.5 from 31 (the lower class limit) and adding 0.5 to 37 (the upper class limit).

$$\text{Lower limit} - 0.5 = 31 - 0.5 = 30.5 = \text{lower boundary}$$
$$\text{Upper limit} + 0.5 = 37 + 0.5 = 37.5 = \text{upper boundary}$$

If the data are in tenths, such as 6.2, 7.8, and 12.6, the limits for a class hypothetically might be 7.8–8.8, and the boundaries for that class would be 7.75–8.85. Find these values by subtracting 0.05 from 7.8 and adding 0.05 to 8.8.

Finally, the **class width** for a class in a frequency distribution is found by subtracting the lower (or upper) class limit of one class from the lower (or upper) class limit of the next class. For example, the class width in the preceding distribution on the duration of boat batteries is 7, found from $31 - 24 = 7$.

The class width can also be found by subtracting the lower boundary from the upper boundary for any given class. In this case, $30.5 - 23.5 = 7$.

Note: Do not subtract the limits of a single class. It will result in an incorrect answer.

The researcher must decide how many classes to use and the width of each class. To construct a frequency distribution, follow these rules:

1. *There should be between 5 and 20 classes.* Although there is no hard-and-fast rule for the number of classes contained in a frequency distribution, it is of the utmost importance to have enough classes to present a clear description of the collected data.

2. *It is preferable but not absolutely necessary that the class width be an odd number.* This ensures that the midpoint of each class has the same place value as the data. The **class midpoint** X_m is obtained by adding the lower and upper boundaries and dividing by 2, or adding the lower and upper limits and dividing by 2:

$$X_m = \frac{\text{lower boundary} + \text{upper boundary}}{2}$$

or

$$X_m = \frac{\text{lower limit} + \text{upper limit}}{2}$$

For example, the midpoint of the first class in the example with boat batteries is

$$\frac{24 + 30}{2} = 27 \qquad \text{or} \qquad \frac{23.5 + 30.5}{2} = 27$$

The midpoint is the numeric location of the center of the class. Midpoints are necessary for graphing (see Section 2–2). If the class width is an even number, the midpoint is in tenths. For example, if the class width is 6 and the boundaries are 5.5 and 11.5, the midpoint is

$$\frac{5.5 + 11.5}{2} = \frac{17}{2} = 8.5$$

Rule 2 is only a suggestion, and it is not rigorously followed, especially when a computer is used to group data.

3. *The classes must be mutually exclusive.* Mutually exclusive classes have nonoverlapping class limits so that data cannot be placed into two classes. Many times, frequency distributions such as

Age
10–20
20–30
30–40
40–50

are found in the literature or in surveys. If a person is 40 years old, into which class should she or he be placed? A better way to construct a frequency distribution is to use classes such as

Age
10–20
21–31
32–42
43–53

4. *The classes must be continuous.* Even if there are no values in a class, the class must be included in the frequency distribution. There should be no gaps in a

frequency distribution. The only exception occurs when the class with a zero frequency is the first or last class. A class with a zero frequency at either end can be omitted without affecting the distribution.

5. *The classes must be exhaustive.* There should be enough classes to accommodate all the data.

6. *The classes must be equal in width.* This avoids a distorted view of the data.

   One exception occurs when a distribution has a class that is open-ended. That is, the class has no specific beginning value or no specific ending value. A frequency distribution with an open-ended class is called an **open-ended distribution.** Here are two examples of distributions with open-ended classes.

Age	Frequency		Minutes	Frequency
10–20	3		Below 110	16
21–31	6		110–114	24
32–42	4		115–119	38
43–53	10		120–124	14
54 and above	8		125–129	5

The frequency distribution for age is open-ended for the last class, which means that anybody who is 54 years or older will be tallied in the last class. The distribution for minutes is open-ended for the first class, meaning that any minute values below 110 will be tallied in that class.

Example 2–2 shows the procedure for constructing a grouped frequency distribution, i.e., when the classes contain more than one data value.

Example 2–2

Record High Temperatures

These data represent the record high temperatures in degrees Fahrenheit (°F) for each of the 50 states. Construct a grouped frequency distribution for the data using 7 classes.

112	100	127	120	134	118	105	110	109	112
110	118	117	116	118	122	114	114	105	109
107	112	114	115	118	117	118	122	106	110
116	108	110	121	113	120	119	111	104	111
120	113	120	117	105	110	118	112	114	114

Source: *The World Almanac and Book of Facts.*

Solution

The procedure for constructing a grouped frequency distribution for numerical data follows.

Step 1 Determine the classes.

Find the highest value and lowest value: $H = 134$ and $L = 100$.

Find the range: $R =$ highest value $-$ lowest value $= H - L$, so

$R = 134 - 100 = 34$

Select the number of classes desired (usually between 5 and 20). In this case, 7 is arbitrarily chosen.

Find the class width by dividing the range by the number of classes.

$$\text{Width} = \frac{R}{\text{number of classes}} = \frac{34}{7} = 4.9$$

Round the answer up to the nearest whole number if there is a remainder: $4.9 \approx 5$. (Rounding *up* is different from rounding *off*. A number is rounded up if there is any decimal remainder when dividing. For example, $85 \div 6 = 14.167$ and is rounded up to 15. Also, $53 \div 4 = 13.25$ and is rounded up to 14. Also, after dividing, if there is no remainder, you will need to add an extra class to accommodate all the data.)

Select a starting point for the lowest class limit. This can be the smallest data value or any convenient number less than the smallest data value. In this case, 100 is used. Add the width to the lowest score taken as the starting point to get the lower limit of the next class. Keep adding until there are 7 classes, as shown, 100, 105, 110, etc.

Subtract one unit from the lower limit of the second class to get the upper limit of the first class. Then add the width to each upper limit to get all the upper limits.

$$105 - 1 = 104$$

The first class is 100–104, the second class is 105–109, etc.

Find the class boundaries by subtracting 0.5 from each lower class limit and adding 0.5 to each upper class limit:

99.5–104.5, 104.5–109.5, etc.

Step 2   Tally the data.

Step 3   Find the numerical frequencies from the tallies.

The completed frequency distribution is

Class limits	Class boundaries	Tally	Frequency
100–104	99.5–104.5	//	2
105–109	104.5–109.5	⁷⁄ₕₕ ///	8
110–114	109.5–114.5	⁷⁄ₕₕ ⁷⁄ₕₕ ⁷⁄ₕₕ ///	18
115–119	114.5–119.5	⁷⁄ₕₕ ⁷⁄ₕₕ ///	13
120–124	119.5–124.5	⁷⁄ₕₕ //	7
125–129	124.5–129.5	/	1
130–134	129.5–134.5	/	1
			$n = \Sigma f = 50$

The frequency distribution shows that the class 109.5–114.5 contains the largest number of temperatures (18) followed by the class 114.5–119.5 with 13 temperatures. Hence, most of the temperatures (31) fall between 109.5 and 119.5°F.

Sometimes it is necessary to use a *cumulative frequency distribution*. A **cumulative frequency distribution** is a distribution that shows the number of data values less than or equal to a specific value (usually an upper boundary). The values are found by adding the frequencies of the classes less than or equal to the upper class boundary of a specific class. This gives an ascending cumulative frequency. In this example, the cumulative frequency for the first class is $0 + 2 = 2$; for the second class it is $0 + 2 + 8 = 10$; for the third class it is $0 + 2 + 8 + 18 = 28$. Naturally, a shorter way to do this would be to just add the cumulative frequency of the class below to the frequency of the given class. For example, the cumulative frequency for the number of data values less than 114.5 can be found by adding $10 + 18 = 28$. The cumulative frequency distribution for the data in this example is as follows:

	Cumulative frequency
Less than 99.5	0
Less than 104.5	2
Less than 109.5	10
Less than 114.5	28
Less than 119.5	41
Less than 124.5	48
Less than 129.5	49
Less than 134.5	50

Cumulative frequencies are used to show how many data values are accumulated up to and including a specific class. In Example 2–2, 28 of the total record high temperatures are less than or equal to 114°F. Forty-eight of the total record high temperatures are less than or equal to 124°F.

After the raw data have been organized into a frequency distribution, it will be analyzed by looking for peaks and extreme values. The peaks show which class or classes have the most data values compared to the other classes. Extreme values, called outliers, show large or small data values that are relative to other data values.

When the range of the data values is relatively small, a frequency distribution can be constructed using single data values for each class. This type of distribution is called an **ungrouped frequency distribution** and is shown next.

Example 2–3

MPGs for SUVs

The data shown here represent the number of miles per gallon (mpg) that 30 selected four-wheel-drive sports utility vehicles obtained in city driving. Construct a frequency distribution, and analyze the distribution.

12	17	12	14	16	18
16	18	12	16	17	15
15	16	12	15	16	16
12	14	15	12	15	15
19	13	16	18	16	14

Source: *Model Year Fuel Economy Guide.* United States Environmental Protection Agency.

Solution

Step 1 Determine the classes. Since the range of the data set is small ($19 - 12 = 7$), classes consisting of a single data value can be used. They are 12, 13, 14, 15, 16, 17, 18, 19.

Note: If the data are continuous, class boundaries can be used. Subtract 0.5 from each class value to get the lower class boundary, and add 0.5 to each class value to get the upper class boundary.

Step 2 Tally the data.

Step 3 Find the numerical frequencies from the tallies, and find the cumulative frequencies.

The completed ungrouped frequency distribution is

Class limits	Class boundaries	Tally	Frequency
12	11.5–12.5	⊤⊦⊦ /	6
13	12.5–13.5	/	1
14	13.5–14.5	///	3
15	14.5–15.5	⊤⊦⊦ /	6
16	15.5–16.5	⊤⊦⊦ ///	8
17	16.5–17.5	//	2
18	17.5–18.5	///	3
19	18.5–19.5	/	1

In this case, almost one-half (14) of the vehicles get 15 or 16 miles per gallon. The cumulative frequencies are

	Cumulative frequency
Less than 11.5	0
Less than 12.5	6
Less than 13.5	7
Less than 14.5	10
Less than 15.5	16
Less than 16.5	24
Less than 17.5	26
Less than 18.5	29
Less than 19.5	30

The steps for constructing a grouped frequency distribution are summarized in the following Procedure Table.

Procedure Table

Constructing a Grouped Frequency Distribution

Step 1 Determine the classes.

Find the highest and lowest values.

Find the range.

Select the number of classes desired.

Find the width by dividing the range by the number of classes and rounding up.

Select a starting point (usually the lowest value or any convenient number less than the lowest value); add the width to get the lower limits.

Find the upper class limits.

Find the boundaries.

Step 2 Tally the data.

Step 3 Find the numerical frequencies from the tallies, and find the cumulative frequencies.

When you are constructing a frequency distribution, the guidelines presented in this section should be followed. However, you can construct several different but correct frequency distributions for the same data by using a different class width, a different number of classes, or a different starting point.

Furthermore, the method shown here for constructing a frequency distribution is not unique, and there are other ways of constructing one. Slight variations exist, especially in computer packages. But regardless of what methods are used, classes should be mutually exclusive, continuous, exhaustive, and of equal width.

In summary, the different types of frequency distributions were shown in this section. The first type, shown in Example 2–1, is used when the data are categorical (nominal), such as blood type or political affiliation. This type is called a categorical frequency distribution. The second type of distribution is used when the range is large and classes several units in width are needed. This type is called a grouped frequency distribution and is shown in Example 2–2. Another type of distribution is used for numerical data and when the range of data is small, as shown in Example 2–3. Since each class is only one unit, this distribution is called an ungrouped frequency distribution.

All the different types of distributions are used in statistics and are helpful when one is organizing and presenting data.

The reasons for constructing a frequency distribution are as follows:

1. To organize the data in a meaningful, intelligible way.

2. To enable the reader to determine the nature or shape of the distribution.

3. To facilitate computational procedures for measures of average and spread (shown in Sections 3–1 and 3–2).

4. To enable the researcher to draw charts and graphs for the presentation of data (shown in Section 2–2).

5. To enable the reader to make comparisons among different data sets.

The factors used to analyze a frequency distribution are essentially the same as those used to analyze histograms and frequency polygons, which are shown in Section 2–2.

Applying the Concepts **2–1**

Ages of Presidents at Inauguration

The data represent the ages of our Presidents at the time they were first inaugurated.

57	61	57	57	58	57	61	54	68
51	49	64	50	48	65	52	56	46
54	49	50	47	55	55	54	42	51
56	55	54	51	60	62	43	55	56
61	52	69	64	46	54			

1. Were the data obtained from a population or a sample? Explain your answer.

2. What was the age of the oldest President?

3. What was the age of the youngest President?

4. Construct a frequency distribution for the data. (Use your own judgment as to the number of classes and class size.)

5. Are there any peaks in the distribution?

6. Identify any possible outliers.

7. Write a brief summary of the nature of the data as shown in the frequency distribution.

See page 108 for the answers.

Exercises 2–1

1. List five reasons for organizing data into a frequency distribution.

2. Name the three types of frequency distributions, and explain when each should be used.

3. Find the class boundaries, midpoints, and widths for each class.

    a. 12–18
    b. 56–74
    c. 695–705
    d. 13.6–14.7
    e. 2.15–3.93

4. How many classes should frequency distributions have? Why should the class width be an odd number?

5. Shown here are four frequency distributions. Each is incorrectly constructed. State the reason why.

    a.
Class	Frequency
27–32	1
33–38	0
39–44	6
45–49	4
50–55	2

    b.
Class	Frequency
5–9	1
9–13	2
13–17	5
17–20	6
20–24	3

    c.
Class	Frequency
123–127	3
128–132	7
138–142	2
143–147	19

    d.
Class	Frequency
9–13	1
14–19	6
20–25	2
26–28	5
29–32	9

6. What are open-ended frequency distributions? Why are they necessary?

7. **Trust in Internet Information** A survey was taken on how much trust people place in the information they read on the Internet. Construct a categorical frequency distribution for the data. A = trust in everything they read, M = trust in most of what they read, H = trust in about one-half of what they read, S = trust in a small portion of what they read. (Based on information from the *UCLA Internet Report.*)

M	M	M	A	H	M	S	M	H	M
S	M	M	M	M	A	M	M	A	M
M	M	H	M	M	M	H	M	H	M
A	M	M	M	H	M	M	M	M	M

8. **State Gasoline Tax** The state gas tax in cents per gallon for 25 states is given below. Construct a grouped frequency distribution and a cumulative frequency distribution with 5 classes.

7.5	16	23.5	17	22
21.5	19	20	27.1	20
22	20.7	17	28	20
23	18.5	25.3	24	31
14.5	25.9	18	30	31.5

Source: *The World Almanac and Book of Facts.*

9. **Weights of the NBA's Top 50 Players** Listed are the weights of the NBA's top 50 players. Construct a grouped frequency distribution and a cumulative frequency distribution with 8 classes. Analyze the results in terms of peaks, extreme values, etc.

240	210	220	260	250	195	230	270	325	225
165	295	205	230	250	210	220	210	230	202
250	265	230	210	240	245	225	180	175	215
215	235	245	250	215	210	195	240	240	225
260	210	190	260	230	190	210	230	185	260

Source: www.msn.foxsports.com

10. **Stories in the World's Tallest Buildings** The number of stories in each of the world's 30 tallest buildings is listed below. Construct a grouped frequency distribution and a cumulative frequency distribution with 7 classes.

88	88	110	88	80	69	102	78	70	55
79	85	80	100	60	90	77	55	75	55
54	60	75	64	105	56	71	70	65	72

Source: *New York Times Almanac.*

11. **GRE Scores at Top-Ranked Engineering Schools** The average quantitative GRE scores for the top 30 graduate schools of engineering are listed. Construct a grouped frequency distribution and a cumulative frequency distribution with 5 classes.

767	770	761	760	771	768	776	771	756	770
763	760	747	766	754	771	771	778	766	762
780	750	746	764	769	759	757	753	758	746

Source: *U.S. News & World Report Best Graduate Schools.*

12. Airline Passengers The number of passengers (in thousands) for the leading U.S. passenger airlines in 2004 is indicated below. Use the data to construct a grouped frequency distribution and a cumulative frequency distribution with a reasonable number of classes and comment on the shape of the distribution.

91,570	86,755	81,066	70,786	55,373	42,400
40,551	21,119	16,280	14,869	13,659	13,417
13,170	12,632	11,731	10,420	10,024	9,122
7,041	6,954	6,406	6,362	5,930	5,585
5,427					

Source: *The World Almanac and Book of Facts.*

13. Ages of Declaration of Independence Signers The ages of the signers of the Declaration of Independence are shown. (Age is approximate since only the birth year appeared in the source, and one has been omitted since his birth year is unknown.) Construct a grouped frequency distribution and a cumulative frequency distribution for the data using 7 classes. (The data for this exercise will be used for Exercise 5 in Section 2–2 and Exercise 23 in Section 3–1.)

41	54	47	40	39	35	50	37	49	42	70	32
44	52	39	50	40	30	34	69	39	45	33	42
44	63	60	27	42	34	50	42	52	38	36	45
35	43	48	46	31	27	55	63	46	33	60	62
35	46	45	34	53	50	50					

Source: *The Universal Almanac.*

14. Online Gambling Online computer gaming has become a popular leisure time activity. Fifty-six percent of the 117 million active gamers play games online. Below are listed the numbers of players playing a free online game at various times of the day. Construct a grouped frequency distribution and a cumulative frequency distribution with 6 classes.

3907	3629	3640	3839	3446	2313	2537	2037	3194
3739	3886	3698	3898	2101	1525	2311	3344	3647

Source: www.msn.tech.com

15. Presidential Vetoes The number of total vetoes exercised by the past 20 Presidents is listed below. Use the data to construct a grouped frequency distribution and a cumulative frequency distribution with 5 classes. What is challenging about this set of data?

44	39	37	21	31	170	44	632	30	78
42	6	250	43	44	82	50	181	66	37

Source: *World Almanac and Book of Facts.*

16. U.S. National Park Acreage The acreage of the 39 U.S. National Parks under 900,000 acres (in thousands of acres) is shown here. Construct a grouped frequency distribution and a cumulative frequency distribution for the data using 8 classes. (The data in this exercise will be used in Exercise 11 in Section 2–2.)

41	66	233	775	169
36	338	233	236	64
183	61	13	308	77
520	77	27	217	5
650	462	106	52	52
505	94	75	265	402
196	70	132	28	220
760	143	46	539	

Source: *The Universal Almanac.*

17. Heights of Alaskan Volcanoes The heights (in feet above sea level) of the major active volcanoes in Alaska are given here. Construct a grouped frequency distribution and a cumulative frequency distribution for the data using 10 classes. (The data in this exercise will be used in Exercise 9 in Section 3–1 and Exercise 17 in Section 3–2.)

4,265	3,545	4,025	7,050	11,413
3,490	5,370	4,885	5,030	6,830
4,450	5,775	3,945	7,545	8,450
3,995	10,140	6,050	10,265	6,965
150	8,185	7,295	2,015	5,055
5,315	2,945	6,720	3,465	1,980
2,560	4,450	2,759	9,430	
7,985	7,540	3,540	11,070	
5,710	885	8,960	7,015	

Source: *The Universal Almanac.*

18. Home Run Record Breakers During the 1998 baseball season, Mark McGwire and Sammy Sosa both broke Roger Maris's home run record of 61. The distances (in feet) for each home run follow. Construct a grouped frequency distribution and a cumulative frequency distribution for each player, using 8 classes. (The information in this exercise will be used for Exercise 12 in Section 2–2, Exercise 10 in Section 3–1, and Exercise 14 in Section 3–2.)

McGwire				Sosa			
306	370	370	430	371	350	430	420
420	340	460	410	430	434	370	420
440	410	380	360	440	410	420	460
350	527	380	550	400	430	410	370
478	420	390	420	370	410	380	340
425	370	480	390	350	420	410	415
430	388	423	410	430	380	380	366
360	410	450	350	500	380	390	400
450	430	461	430	364	430	450	440
470	440	400	390	365	420	350	420
510	430	450	452	400	380	380	400
420	380	470	398	370	420	360	368
409	385	369	460	430	433	388	440
390	510	500	450	414	482	364	370
470	430	458	380	400	405	433	390
430	341	385	410	480	480	434	344
420	380	400	440	410	420		
377	370						

Source: *USA TODAY.*

Extending the Concepts

19. JFK Assassination A researcher conducted a survey asking people if they believed more than one person was involved in the assassination of John F. Kennedy. The results were as follows: 73% said yes, 19% said no, and 9% had no opinion. Is there anything suspicious about the results?

Technology *Step by Step*

MINITAB
Step by Step

Make a Categorical Frequency Table (Qualitative or Discrete Data)

1. Type in all the blood types from Example 2–1 down **C1** of the worksheet.

    A B B AB O O O B AB B B B O A O A O O O AB AB A O B A

2. Click above row 1 and name the column **BloodType.**

3. Select **Stat>Tables>Tally Individual Values.**

    The cursor should be blinking in the Variables dialog box. If not, click inside the dialog box.

4. Double-click C1 in the Variables list.

5. Check the boxes for the statistics: Counts, Percents, and Cumulative percents.

6. Click [OK]. The results will be displayed in the Session Window as shown.

Tally for Discrete Variables: BloodType

BloodType	Count	Percent	CumPct
A	5	20.00	20.00
AB	4	16.00	36.00
B	7	28.00	64.00
O	9	36.00	100.00
N=	25		

Make a Grouped Frequency Distribution (Quantitative Variable)

1. Select **File>New>New Worksheet.** A new worksheet will be added to the project.

2. Type the data used in Example 2–2 into C1. Name the column **TEMPERATURES.**

3. Use the instructions in the textbook to determine the class limits.

    In the next step you will create a new column of data, converting the numeric variable to text categories that can be tallied.

4. Select **Data>Code>Numeric to Text.**

    a) The cursor should be blinking in Code data from columns. If not, click inside the box, then double-click C1 Temperatures in the list. Only quantitative variables will be shown in this list.

    b) Click in the Into columns: then type the name of the new column, **TempCodes.**

    c) Press [Tab] to move to the next dialog box.

    d) Type in the first interval **100:104.**

        Use a colon to indicate the interval from 100 to 104 with no spaces before or after the colon.

    e) Press [Tab] to move to the New: column, and type the text category **100–104.**

    f) Continue to tab to each dialog box, typing the interval and then the category until the last category has been entered.

The dialog box should look like the one shown.

Code - Numeric to Text	
Code data from columns:	
TEMPERATURES	
Into columns:	
TempCodes	
Original values (eg. 1:4 12):	**New:**
100:104	100 – 104
105:109	105 – 109
110:114	110 – 114
115:119	115 – 119
120:124	120 – 124
125:129	125 – 129
130:134	130 – 134
Select	
Help	OK Cancel

5. Click [OK]. In the worksheet, a new column of data will be created in the first empty column, C2. This new variable will contain the category for each value in C1. The column C2-T contains alphanumeric data.

6. Click **Stat>Tables>Tally Individual Values,** then double-click TempCodes in the Variables list.

   a) Check the boxes for the desired statistics, such as Counts, Percents, and Cumulative percents.

   b) Click [OK].

   The table will be displayed in the Session Window. Eighteen states have high temperatures between 110 and 114°F. Eighty-two percent of the states have record high temperatures less than or equal to 119°F.

Tally for Discrete Variables: TempCodes

TempCodes	Count	Percent	CumPct
100–104	2	4.00	4.00
105–109	8	16.00	20.00
110–114	18	36.00	56.00
115–119	13	26.00	82.00
120–124	7	14.00	96.00
125–129	1	2.00	98.00
130–134	1	2.00	100.00
N=	50		

7. Click **File>Save Project As** . . . , and type the name of the project file, **Ch2-2.** This will save the two worksheets and the Session Window.

Excel
Step by Step

Categorical Frequency Table (Qualitative or Discrete Data)

1. In an open workbook select cell A1 and type in all the blood types from Example 2–1 down column A.

2. Type in the variable name **Blood Type** in cell B1.

3. Select cell B2 and type in the four different blood types down the column.

4. Type in the name **Count** in cell C1.

5. Select cell C2. From the toolbar, select the Formulas tab on the toolbar.

6. Select the Insert Function icon f_x , then select the Statistical category in the Insert Function dialog box.

7. Select the Countif function from the function name list.

8. In the dialog box, type **A1:A25** in the **Range** box. Type in the blood type "A" in quotes in the **Criteria** box. The count or frequency of the number of data corresponding to the blood type should appear below the input. Repeat for the remaining blood types.

9. After all the data have been counted, select cell **C6** in the worksheet.

10. From the toolbar select Formulas, then AutoSum and type in C2:C5 to insert the total frequency into cell **C6**.

After entering data or a heading into a worksheet, you can change the width of a column to fit the input. To automatically change the width of a column to fit the data:

1. Select the column or columns that you want to change.

2. On the Home tab, in the Cells group, select Format.

3. Under Cell Size, click Autofit Column Width.

Making a Grouped Frequency Distribution (Quantitative Data)

1. Press **[Ctrl]-N** for a new workbook.

2. Enter the raw data from Example 2–2 in column **A**, one number per cell.

3. Enter the upper class boundaries in column **B**.

4. From the toolbar select the Data tab, then click Data Analysis.

5. In the Analysis Tools, select Histogram and click [OK].

6. In the Histogram dialog box, type **A1:A50** in the Input Range box and type **B1:B7** in the Bin Range box.

7. Select New Worksheet Ply, and check the Cumulative Percentage option. Click [OK].

8. You can change the label for the column containing the upper class boundaries and expand the width of the columns automatically after relabeling:

   Select the Home tab from the toolbar.

   Highlight the columns that you want to change.

   Select Format, then AutoFit Column Width.

Note: By leaving the Chart Output unchecked, a new worksheet will display the table only.

2–2

Objective 2

Represent data in frequency distributions graphically using histograms, frequency polygons, and ogives.

Histograms, Frequency Polygons, and Ogives

After you have organized the data into a frequency distribution, you can present them in graphical form. The purpose of graphs in statistics is to convey the data to the viewers in pictorial form. It is easier for most people to comprehend the meaning of data presented graphically than data presented numerically in tables or frequency distributions. This is especially true if the users have little or no statistical knowledge.

Statistical graphs can be used to describe the data set or to analyze it. Graphs are also useful in getting the audience's attention in a publication or a speaking presentation. They can be used to discuss an issue, reinforce a critical point, or summarize a data set. They can also be used to discover a trend or pattern in a situation over a period of time.

The three most commonly used graphs in research are

1. The histogram.
2. The frequency polygon.
3. The cumulative frequency graph, or ogive (pronounced o-jive).

An example of each type of graph is shown in Figure 2–1. The data for each graph are the distribution of the miles that 20 randomly selected runners ran during a given week.

The Histogram

> The **histogram** is a graph that displays the data by using contiguous vertical bars (unless the frequency of a class is 0) of various heights to represent the frequencies of the classes.

Example 2–4

Record High Temperatures

Construct a histogram to represent the data shown for the record high temperatures for each of the 50 states (see Example 2–2).

Class boundaries	Frequency
99.5–104.5	2
104.5–109.5	8
109.5–114.5	18
114.5–119.5	13
119.5–124.5	7
124.5–129.5	1
129.5–134.5	1

Solution

Step 1 Draw and label the x and y axes. The x axis is always the horizontal axis, and the y axis is always the vertical axis.

Figure 2–1

Examples of Commonly Used Graphs

(a) Histogram

(b) Frequency polygon

(c) Cumulative frequency graph

Figure 2–2

Histogram for
Example 2–4

Figure 2–2

Histogram for
Example 2–4

Step 2   Represent the frequency on the y axis and the class boundaries on the x axis.

Step 3   Using the frequencies as the heights, draw vertical bars for each class. See Figure 2–2.

   As the histogram shows, the class with the greatest number of data values (18) is 109.5–114.5, followed by 13 for 114.5–119.5. The graph also has one peak with the data clustering around it.

The Frequency Polygon

Another way to represent the same data set is by using a frequency polygon.

> The **frequency polygon** is a graph that displays the data by using lines that connect points plotted for the frequencies at the midpoints of the classes. The frequencies are represented by the heights of the points.

   Example 2–5 shows the procedure for constructing a frequency polygon.

Example 2–5

Record High Temperatures

Using the frequency distribution given in Example 2–4, construct a frequency polygon.

Solution

Step 1   Find the midpoints of each class. Recall that midpoints are found by adding the upper and lower boundaries and dividing by 2:

$$\frac{99.5 + 104.5}{2} = 102 \qquad \frac{104.5 + 109.5}{2} = 107$$

and so on. The midpoints are

Class boundaries	Midpoints	Frequency
99.5–104.5	102	2
104.5–109.5	107	8
109.5–114.5	112	18
114.5–119.5	117	13
119.5–124.5	122	7
124.5–129.5	127	1
129.5–134.5	132	1

Figure 2–3

Frequency Polygon for
Example 2–5

Step 2   Draw the *x* and *y* axes. Label the *x* axis with the midpoint of each class, and then use a suitable scale on the *y* axis for the frequencies.

Step 3   Using the midpoints for the *x* values and the frequencies as the *y* values, plot the points.

Step 4   Connect adjacent points with line segments. Draw a line back to the *x* axis at the beginning and end of the graph, at the same distance that the previous and next midpoints would be located, as shown in Figure 2–3.

The frequency polygon and the histogram are two different ways to represent the same data set. The choice of which one to use is left to the discretion of the researcher.

The Ogive

The third type of graph that can be used represents the cumulative frequencies for the classes. This type of graph is called the *cumulative frequency graph,* or *ogive.* The **cumulative frequency** is the sum of the frequencies accumulated up to the upper boundary of a class in the distribution.

The **ogive** is a graph that represents the cumulative frequencies for the classes in a frequency distribution.

Example 2–6 shows the procedure for constructing an ogive.

Example 2–6

Record High Temperatures

Construct an ogive for the frequency distribution described in Example 2–4.

Solution

Step 1   Find the cumulative frequency for each class.

	Cumulative frequency
Less than 99.5	0
Less than 104.5	2
Less than 109.5	10
Less than 114.5	28
Less than 119.5	41
Less than 124.5	48
Less than 129.5	49
Less than 134.5	50

Figure 2–4

Plotting the Cumulative Frequency for Example 2–6

Figure 2–5

Ogive for Example 2–6

Step 2   Draw the *x* and *y* axes. Label the *x* axis with the class boundaries. Use an appropriate scale for the *y* axis to represent the cumulative frequencies. (Depending on the numbers in the cumulative frequency columns, scales such as 0, 1, 2, 3, . . . , or 5, 10, 15, 20, . . . , or 1000, 2000, 3000, . . . can be used. Do *not* label the *y* axis with the numbers in the cumulative frequency column.) In this example, a scale of 0, 5, 10, 15, . . . will be used.

Step 3   Plot the cumulative frequency at each upper class boundary, as shown in Figure 2–4. Upper boundaries are used since the cumulative frequencies represent the number of data values accumulated up to the upper boundary of each class.

Step 4   Starting with the first upper class boundary, 104.5, connect adjacent points with line segments, as shown in Figure 2–5. Then extend the graph to the first lower class boundary, 99.5, on the *x* axis.

Cumulative frequency graphs are used to visually represent how many values are below a certain upper class boundary. For example, to find out how many record high temperatures are less than 114.5°F, locate 114.5°F on the *x* axis, draw a vertical line up until it intersects the graph, and then draw a horizontal line at that point to the *y* axis. The *y* axis value is 28, as shown in Figure 2–6.

Figure 2–6

Finding a Specific
Cumulative Frequency

The steps for drawing these three types of graphs are shown in the following Procedure Table.

Unusual Stat

Twenty-two percent of Americans sleep 6 hours a day or fewer.

Procedure Table

Constructing Statistical Graphs

Step 1   Draw and label the x and y axes.

Step 2   Choose a suitable scale for the frequencies or cumulative frequencies, and label it on the y axis.

Step 3   Represent the class boundaries for the histogram or ogive, or the midpoint for the frequency polygon, on the x axis.

Step 4   Plot the points and then draw the bars or lines.

Relative Frequency Graphs

The histogram, the frequency polygon, and the ogive shown previously were constructed by using frequencies in terms of the raw data. These distributions can be converted to distributions using *proportions* instead of raw data as frequencies. These types of graphs are called **relative frequency graphs.**

Graphs of relative frequencies instead of frequencies are used when the proportion of data values that fall into a given class is more important than the actual number of data values that fall into that class. For example, if you wanted to compare the age distribution of adults in Philadelphia, Pennsylvania, with the age distribution of adults of Erie, Pennsylvania, you would use relative frequency distributions. The reason is that since the population of Philadelphia is 1,478,002 and the population of Erie is 105,270, the bars using the actual data values for Philadelphia would be much taller than those for the same classes for Erie.

To convert a frequency into a proportion or relative frequency, divide the frequency for each class by the total of the frequencies. The sum of the relative frequencies will always be 1. These graphs are similar to the ones that use raw data as frequencies, but the values on the y axis are in terms of proportions. Example 2–7 shows the three types of relative frequency graphs.

| Example 2–7 | Miles Run per Week |

Construct a histogram, frequency polygon, and ogive using relative frequencies for the distribution (shown here) of the miles that 20 randomly selected runners ran during a given week.

Class boundaries	Frequency
5.5–10.5	1
10.5–15.5	2
15.5–20.5	3
20.5–25.5	5
25.5–30.5	4
30.5–35.5	3
35.5–40.5	2
	20

Solution

Step 1 Convert each frequency to a proportion or relative frequency by dividing the frequency for each class by the total number of observations.

For class 5.5–10.5, the relative frequency is $\frac{1}{20} = 0.05$; for class 10.5–15.5, the relative frequency is $\frac{2}{20} = 0.10$; for class 15.5–20.5, the relative frequency is $\frac{3}{20} = 0.15$; and so on.

Place these values in the column labeled Relative frequency.

Class boundaries	Midpoints	Relative frequency
5.5–10.5	8	0.05
10.5–15.5	13	0.10
15.5–20.5	18	0.15
20.5–25.5	23	0.25
25.5–30.5	28	0.20
30.5–35.5	33	0.15
35.5–40.5	38	0.10
		1.00

Step 2 Find the cumulative relative frequencies. To do this, add the frequency in each class to the total frequency of the preceding class. In this case, $0 + 0.05 = 0.05, 0.05 + 0.10 = 0.15, 0.15 + 0.15 = 0.30, 0.30 + 0.25 = 0.55$, etc. Place these values in the column labeled Cumulative relative frequency.

An alternative method would be to find the cumulative frequencies and then convert each one to a relative frequency.

	Cumulative frequency	Cumulative relative frequency
Less than 5.5	0	0.00
Less than 10.5	1	0.05
Less than 15.5	3	0.15
Less than 20.5	6	0.30
Less than 25.5	11	0.55
Less than 30.5	15	0.75
Less than 35.5	18	0.90
Less than 40.5	20	1.00

Step 3 Draw each graph as shown in Figure 2–7. For the histogram and ogive, use the class boundaries along the *x* axis. For the frequency polygon, use the midpoints on the *x* axis. The scale on the *y* axis uses proportions.

Figure 2–7

Graphs for
Example 2–7

(a) Histogram

(b) Frequency polygon

(c) Ogive

Distribution Shapes

When one is describing data, it is important to be able to recognize the shapes of the distribution values. In later chapters you will see that the shape of a distribution also determines the appropriate statistical methods used to analyze the data.

A distribution can have many shapes, and one method of analyzing a distribution is to draw a histogram or frequency polygon for the distribution. Several of the most common shapes are shown in Figure 2–8: *the bell-shaped or mound-shaped, the uniform-shaped, the J-shaped, the reverse J-shaped, the positively or right-skewed shape, the negatively or left-skewed shape, the bimodal-shaped, and the U-shaped.*

Distributions are most often not perfectly shaped, so it is not necessary to have an exact shape but rather to identify an overall pattern.

A *bell-shaped distribution* shown in Figure 2–8(a) has a single peak and tapers off at either end. It is approximately symmetric; i.e., it is roughly the same on both sides of a line running through the center.

Figure 2–8

Distribution Shapes

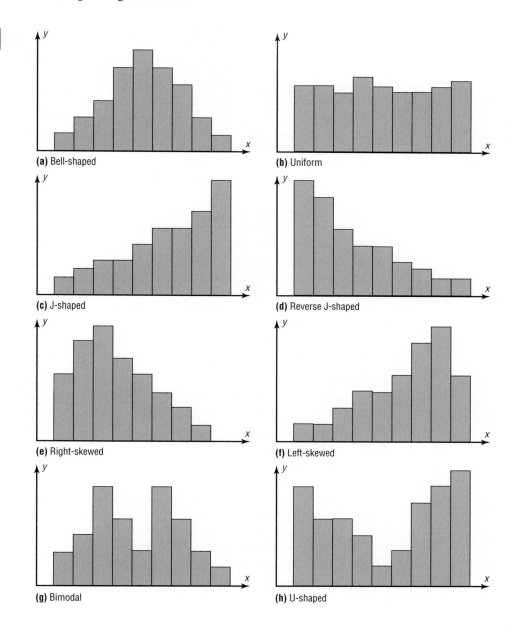

(a) Bell-shaped

(b) Uniform

(c) J-shaped

(d) Reverse J-shaped

(e) Right-skewed

(f) Left-skewed

(g) Bimodal

(h) U-shaped

A *uniform distribution* is basically flat or rectangular. See Figure 2–8(b).

A *J-shaped distribution* is shown in Figure 2–8(c), and it has a few data values on the left side and increases as one moves to the right. A *reverse J-shaped distribution* is the opposite of the J-shaped distribution. See Figure 2–8(d).

When the peak of a distribution is to the left and the data values taper off to the right, a distribution is said to be *positively or right-skewed*. See Figure 2–8(e). When the data values are clustered to the right and taper off to the left, a distribution is said to be *negatively or left-skewed*. See Figure 2–8(f). Skewness will be explained in detail in Chapter 3. Distributions with one peak, such as those shown in Figure 2–8(a), (e), and (f), are said to be *unimodal*. (The highest peak of a distribution indicates where the mode of the data values is. The mode is the data value that occurs more often than any other data value. Modes are explained in Chapter 3.) When a distribution has two peaks of the same height, it is said to be *bimodal*. See Figure 2–8(g). Finally, the graph shown in Figure 2–8(h) is a *U-shaped* distribution.

Distributions can have other shapes in addition to the ones shown here; however, these are some of the more common ones that you will encounter in analyzing data.

When you are analyzing histograms and frequency polygons, look at the shape of the curve. For example, does it have one peak or two peaks? Is it relatively flat, or is it U-shaped? Are the data values spread out on the graph, or are they clustered around the center? Are there data values in the extreme ends? These may be *outliers*. (See Section 3–3 for an explanation of outliers.) Are there any gaps in the histogram, or does the frequency polygon touch the *x* axis somewhere other than at the ends? Finally, are the data clustered at one end or the other, indicating a *skewed distribution*?

For example, the histogram for the record high temperatures shown in Figure 2–2 shows a single peaked distribution, with the class 109.5–114.5 containing the largest number of temperatures. The distribution has no gaps, and there are fewer temperatures in the highest class than in the lowest class.

Applying the Concepts **2–2**

Selling Real Estate

Assume you are a realtor in Bradenton, Florida. You have recently obtained a listing of the selling prices of the homes that have sold in that area in the last 6 months. You wish to organize that data so you will be able to provide potential buyers with useful information. Use the following data to create a histogram, frequency polygon, and cumulative frequency polygon.

142,000	127,000	99,600	162,000	89,000	93,000	99,500
73,800	135,000	119,500	67,900	156,300	104,500	108,650
123,000	91,000	205,000	110,000	156,300	104,000	133,900
179,000	112,000	147,000	321,550	87,900	88,400	180,000
159,400	205,300	144,400	163,000	96,000	81,000	131,000
114,000	119,600	93,000	123,000	187,000	96,000	80,000
231,000	189,500	177,600	83,400	77,000	132,300	166,000

1. What questions could be answered more easily by looking at the histogram rather than the listing of home prices?
2. What different questions could be answered more easily by looking at the frequency polygon rather than the listing of home prices?
3. What different questions could be answered more easily by looking at the cumulative frequency polygon rather than the listing of home prices?
4. Are there any extremely large or extremely small data values compared to the other data values?
5. Which graph displays these extremes the best?
6. Is the distribution skewed?

See page 108 for the answers.

Exercises 2–2

1. Do Students Need Summer Development? For 108 randomly selected college applicants, the following frequency distribution for entrance exam scores was obtained. Construct a histogram, frequency polygon, and ogive for the data. (The data for this exercise will be used for Exercise 13 in this section.)

Class limits	Frequency
90–98	6
99–107	22
108–116	43
117–125	28
126–134	9

Applicants who score above 107 need not enroll in a summer developmental program. In this group, how many students do not have to enroll in the developmental program?

2. Number of College Faculty The number of faculty listed for a variety of private colleges which offer only bachelor's degrees is listed below. Use these data to construct a frequency distribution with 7 classes, a histogram, a frequency polygon, and an ogive. Discuss the shape of this distribution. What proportion of schools have 180 or more faculty?

165	221	218	206	138	135	224	204
70	210	207	154	155	82	120	116
176	162	225	214	93	389	77	135
221	161	128	310				

Source: *World Almanac and Book of Facts.*

3. Counties, Divisions, or Parishes for 50 States The number of counties, divisions, or parishes for each of the 50 states is given below. Use the data to construct a grouped frequency distribution with 6 classes, a histogram, a frequency polygon, and an ogive. Analyze the distribution.

67	27	15	75	58	64	8	67	159	5
102	44	92	99	105	120	64	16	23	14
83	87	82	114	56	93	16	10	21	33
62	100	53	88	77	36	67	5	46	66
95	254	29	14	95	39	55	72	23	3

Source: *World Almanac and Book of Facts.*

4. NFL Salaries The salaries (in millions of dollars) for 31 NFL teams for a specific season are given in this frequency distribution.

Class limits	Frequency
39.9–42.8	2
42.9–45.8	2
45.9–48.8	5
48.9–51.8	5
51.9–54.8	12
54.9–57.8	5

Source: NFL.com

Construct a histogram, a frequency polygon, and an ogive for the data; and comment on the shape of the distribution.

5. Automobile Fuel Efficiency Thirty automobiles were tested for fuel efficiency, in miles per gallon (mpg). The following frequency distribution was obtained. Construct a histogram, a frequency polygon, and an ogive for the data.

Class boundaries	Frequency
7.5–12.5	3
12.5–17.5	5
17.5–22.5	15
22.5–27.5	5
27.5–32.5	2

6. Construct a frequency histogram, a frequency polygon, and an ogive for the data in Exercise 9 in Section 2–1. Analyze the results.

7. Air Quality Standards The number of days that selected U.S. metropolitan areas failed to meet acceptable air quality standards is shown below for 1998 and 2003. Construct grouped frequency distributions and a histogram for each set of data, and compare your results.

1998						2003					
43	76	51	14	0	10	10	11	14	20	15	6
20	0	5	17	67	25	17	0	5	19	127	4
38	0	56	8	0	9	31	5	88	1	1	16
14	5	37	14	95	20	14	19	20	9	138	22
23	12	33	0	3	45	13	10	20	20	20	12

Source: *World Almanac.*

8. How Quick Are Dogs? In a study of reaction times of dogs to a specific stimulus, an animal trainer obtained the following data, given in seconds. Construct a histogram, a frequency polygon, and an ogive for the data; analyze the results. (The histogram in this exercise will be used for Exercise 18 in this section, Exercise 16 in Section 3–1, and Exercise 26 in Section 3–2.)

Class limits	Frequency
2.3–2.9	10
3.0–3.6	12
3.7–4.3	6
4.4–5.0	8
5.1–5.7	4
5.8–6.4	2

9. Quality of Health Care The scores of health care quality as calculated by a professional risk management company are listed on the next page for selected states.

Use the data to construct a frequency distribution, a histogram, a frequency polygon, and an ogive.

118.2 114.6 113.1 111.9 110.0 108.8 108.3 107.7 107.0 106.7
105.3 103.7 103.2 102.8 101.6 99.8 98.1 96.6 95.7 93.6
92.5 91.0 90.0 87.1 83.1

Source: *New York Times Almanac.*

10. Making the Grade The frequency distributions shown indicate the percentages of public school students in fourth-grade reading and mathematics who performed at or above the required proficiency levels for the 50 states in the United States. Draw histograms for each, and decide if there is any difference in the performance of the students in the subjects.

Class	Reading frequency	Math frequency
17.5–22.5	7	5
22.5–27.5	6	9
27.5–32.5	14	11
32.5–37.5	19	16
37.5–42.5	3	8
42.5–47.5	1	1

Source: *National Center for Educational Statistics.*

11. Construct a histogram, a frequency polygon, and an ogive for the data in Exercise 16 in Section 2–1, and analyze the results.

12. For the data in Exercise 18 in Section 2–1, construct a histogram for the home run distances for each player and compare them. Are they basically the same, or are there any noticeable differences? Explain your answer.

13. For the data in Exercise 1 in this section, construct a histogram, a frequency polygon, and an ogive, using relative frequencies. What proportion of the applicants needs to enroll in the summer development program?

14. For the data for 2003 in Exercise 4 in this section, construct a histogram, a frequency polygon, and an ogive, using relative frequencies.

15. Cereal Calories The number of calories per serving for selected ready-to-eat cereals is listed here. Construct a frequency distribution using 7 classes. Draw

a histogram, a frequency polygon, and an ogive for the data, using relative frequencies. Describe the shape of the histogram.

130	190	140	80	100	120	220	220	110	100
210	130	100	90	210	120	200	120	180	120
190	210	120	200	130	180	260	270	100	160
190	240	80	120	90	190	200	210	190	180
115	210	110	225	190	130				

Source: *The Doctor's Pocket Calorie, Fat, and Carbohydrate Counter.*

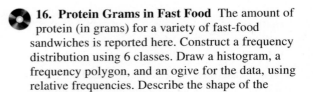 **16. Protein Grams in Fast Food** The amount of protein (in grams) for a variety of fast-food sandwiches is reported here. Construct a frequency distribution using 6 classes. Draw a histogram, a frequency polygon, and an ogive for the data, using relative frequencies. Describe the shape of the histogram.

23	30	20	27	44	26	35	20	29	29
25	15	18	27	19	22	12	26	34	15
27	35	26	43	35	14	24	12	23	31
40	35	38	57	22	42	24	21	27	33

Source: *The Doctor's Pocket Calorie, Fat, and Carbohydrate Counter.*

17. For the data for year 2003 in Exercise 7 in this section, construct a histogram, a frequency polygon, and an ogive, using relative frequencies.

18. How Quick Are Older Dogs? The animal trainer in Exercise 8 in this section selected another group of dogs who were much older than the first group and measured their reaction times to the same stimulus. Construct a histogram, a frequency polygon, and an ogive for the data.

Class limits	Frequency
2.3–2.9	1
3.0–3.6	3
3.7–4.3	4
4.4–5.0	16
5.1–5.7	14
5.8–6.4	4

Analyze the results and compare the histogram for this group with the one obtained in Exercise 8 in this section. Are there any differences in the histograms? (The data in this exercise will be used for Exercise 16 in Section 3–1 and Exercise 26 in Section 3–2.)

Extending the Concepts

19. Using the histogram shown here, do the following.

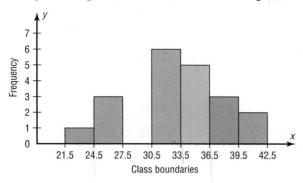

Class boundaries

a. Construct a frequency distribution; include class limits, class frequencies, midpoints, and cumulative frequencies.
b. Construct a frequency polygon.
c. Construct an ogive.

20. Using the results from Exercise 19, answer these questions.

a. How many values are in the class 27.5–30.5?
b. How many values fall between 24.5 and 36.5?
c. How many values are below 33.5?
d. How many values are above 30.5?

MINITAB
Step by Step

Construct a Histogram

1. Enter the data from Example 2–2, the high temperatures for the 50 states.

2. Select **Graph>Histogram.**

3. Select [Simple], then click [OK].

4. Click C1 TEMPERATURES in the Graph variables dialog box.

5. Click [Labels]. There are two tabs, Title/Footnote and Data Labels.

  a) Click in the box for Title, and type in Your Name and Course Section.

  b) Click [OK]. The Histogram dialog box is still open.

6. Click [OK]. A new graph window containing the histogram will open.

7. Click the **File** menu to print or save the graph.

8. Click **File>Exit.**

9. Save the project as **Ch2-3.mpj.**

TI-83 Plus or TI-84 Plus

Step by Step

Constructing a Histogram

To display the graphs on the screen, enter the appropriate values in the calculator, using the WINDOW menu. The default values are $X_{min} = -10$, $X_{max} = +10$, $Y_{min} = -10$, and $Y_{max} = +10$.

The X_{scl} changes the distance between the tick marks on the x axis and can be used to change the class width for the histogram.

To change the values in the WINDOW:

1. Press **WINDOW.**

2. Move the cursor to the value that needs to be changed. Then type in the desired value and press **ENTER.**

3. Continue until all values are appropriate.

4. Press **[2nd] [QUIT]** to leave the WINDOW menu.

To plot the histogram from raw data:

1. Enter the data in L$_1$.

2. Make sure WINDOW values are appropriate for the histogram.

3. Press **[2nd] [STAT PLOT] ENTER.**

4. Press **ENTER** to turn the plot on, if necessary.

5. Move cursor to the Histogram symbol and press **ENTER,** if necessary.

6. Make sure Xlist is L$_1$.

7. Make sure Freq is 1.

8. Press **GRAPH** to display the histogram.

9. To obtain the number of data values in each class, press the **TRACE** key, followed by ◄ or ► keys.

Input

Input

Output

Example TI2–1

Plot a histogram for the following data from Examples 2–2 and 2–4.

112	100	127	120	134	118	105	110	109	112
110	118	117	116	118	122	114	114	105	109
107	112	114	115	118	117	118	122	106	110
116	108	110	121	113	120	119	111	104	111
120	113	120	117	105	110	118	112	114	114

Press **TRACE** and use the arrow keys to determine the number of values in each group.

To graph a histogram from grouped data:

1. Enter the midpoints into L$_1$.

2. Enter the frequencies into L$_2$.

3. Make sure WINDOW values are appropriate for the histogram.

4. Press **[2nd] [STAT PLOT] ENTER.**

5. Press **ENTER** to turn the plot on, if necessary.

6. Move cursor to the histogram symbol, and press **ENTER,** if necessary.

7. Make sure Xlist is L$_1$.

8. Make sure Freq is L$_2$.

9. Press **GRAPH** to display the histogram.

Example TI2–2

Plot a histogram for the data from Examples 2–4 and 2–5.

Class boundaries	Midpoints	Frequency
99.5–104.5	102	2
104.5–109.5	107	8
109.5–114.5	112	18
114.5–119.5	117	13
119.5–124.5	122	7
124.5–129.5	127	1
129.5–134.5	132	1

Output

Output

Input

Input

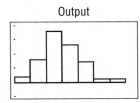

Output

To graph a frequency polygon from grouped data, follow the same steps as for the histogram except change the graph type from histogram (third graph) to a line graph (second graph).

To graph an ogive from grouped data, modify the procedure for the histogram as follows:

1. Enter the upper class boundaries into L_1.

2. Enter the cumulative frequencies into L_2.

3. Change the graph type from histogram (third graph) to line (second graph).

4. Change the Y_{max} from the WINDOW menu to the sample size.

Excel
Step by Step

Constructing a Histogram

1. Press **[Ctrl]-N** for a new workbook.

2. Enter the data from Example 2–2 in column A, one number per cell.

3. Enter the upper boundaries into column B.

4. From the toolbar, select the Data tab, then select Data Analysis.

5. In Data Analysis, select Histogram and click [OK].

6. In the Histogram dialog box, type **A1:A50** in the Input Range box and type **B1:B7** in the Bin Range box.

7. Select New Worksheet Ply and Chart Output. Click [OK].

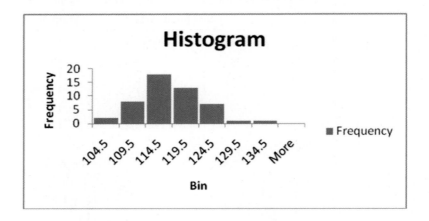

Editing the Histogram

To move the vertical bars of the histogram closer together:

1. Right-click one of the bars of the histogram, and select Format Data Series.

2. Move the Gap Width bar to the left to narrow the distance between bars.

To change the label for the horizontal axis:

1. Left-click the mouse over any region of the histogram.

2. Select the Chart Tools tab from the toolbar.

3. Select the Layout tab, Axis Titles and Primary Horizontal Axis Title.

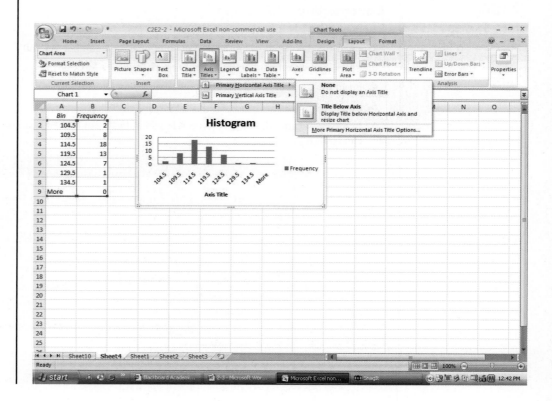

Once the Axis Title text box is selected, you can type in the name of the variable represented on the horizontal axis.

Constructing a Frequency Polygon

1. Press **[Ctrl]-N** for a new workbook.

2. Enter the midpoints of the data from Example 2–2 into column A. Enter the frequencies into column B.

	A	B
1	Midpoints	Frequencies
2	102	2
3	107	8
4	112	18
5	117	13
6	122	7
7	127	1
8	132	1

3. Highlight the Frequencies (including the label) from column B.

4. Select the Insert tab from the toolbar and the Line Chart option.

5. Select the 2-D line chart type.

We will need to edit the graph so that the midpoints are on the horizontal axis and the frequencies are on the vertical axis.

1. Right-click the mouse on any region of the graph.

2. Select the Select Data option.

3. Select Edit from the Horizontal Axis Labels and highlight the midpoints from column A, then click [OK].

4. Click [OK] on the Select Data Source box.

Inserting Labels on the Axes

1. Click the mouse on any region of the graph.

2. Select Chart Tools and then Layout on the toolbar.

3. Select Axis Titles to open the horizontal and vertical axis text boxes. Then manually type in labels for the axes.

Changing the Title

1. Select Chart Tools, Layout from the toolbar.

2. Select Chart Title.

3. Choose one of the options from the Chart Title menu and edit.

Constructing an Ogive

To create an ogive, you can use the upper class boundaries (horizontal axis) and cumulative frequencies (vertical axis) from the frequency distribution.

1. Type the upper class boundaries and cumulative frequencies into adjacent columns of an Excel worksheet.

2. Highlight the cumulative frequencies (including the label) and select the Insert tab from the toolbar.

3. Select Line Chart, then the 2-D Line option.

As with the frequency polygon, you can insert labels on the axes and a chart title for the ogive.

2–3   Other Types of Graphs

In addition to the histogram, the frequency polygon, and the ogive, several other types of graphs are often used in statistics. They are the bar graph, Pareto chart, time series graph, and pie graph. Figure 2–9 shows an example of each type of graph.

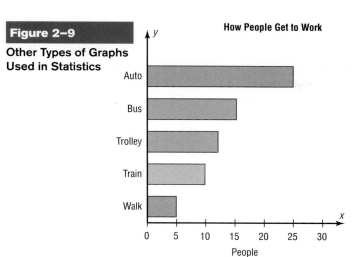

How People Get to Work

(a) Bar graph

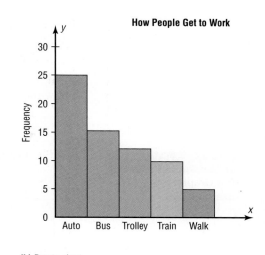

How People Get to Work

(b) Pareto chart

Figure 2–9

Other Types of Graphs Used in Statistics

Figure 2–9

Other Types of Graphs Used in Statistics

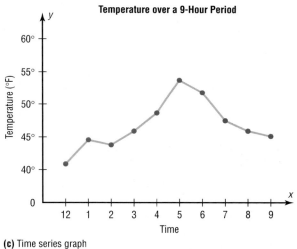

Temperature over a 9-Hour Period

(c) Time series graph

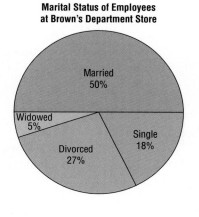

Marital Status of Employees at Brown's Department Store

(d) Pie graph

Objective 3

Represent data using bar graphs, Pareto charts, time series graphs, and pie graphs.

Bar Graphs

When the data are qualitative or categorical, bar graphs can be used to represent the data. A bar graph can be drawn using either horizontal or vertical bars.

> A **bar graph** represents the data by using vertical or horizontal bars whose heights or lengths represent the frequencies of the data.

Example 2–8

College Spending for First-Year Students

The table shows the average money spent by first-year college students. Draw a horizontal and vertical bar graph for the data.

Electronics	$728
Dorm decor	344
Clothing	141
Shoes	72

Source: The National Retail Federation.

Solution

1. Draw and label the *x* and *y* axes. For the horizontal bar graph place the frequency scale on the *x* axis, and for the vertical bar graph place the frequency scale on the *y* axis.
2. Draw the bars corresponding to the frequencies. See Figure 2–10.

Figure 2–10

Bar Graphs for
Example 2–8

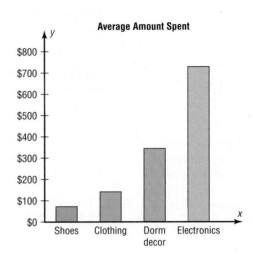

The graphs show that first-year college students spend the most on electronic equipment including computers.

Pareto Charts

When the variable displayed on the horizontal axis is qualitative or categorical, a *Pareto chart* can also be used to represent the data.

A **Pareto chart** is used to represent a frequency distribution for a categorical variable, and the frequencies are displayed by the heights of vertical bars, which are arranged in order from highest to lowest.

Example 2–9

Turnpike Costs

The table shown here is the average cost per mile for passenger vehicles on state turnpikes. Construct and analyze a Pareto chart for the data.

State	Number
Indiana	2.9¢
Oklahoma	4.3
Florida	6.0
Maine	3.8
Pennsylvania	5.8

Source: *Pittsburgh Tribune Review.*

Solution

Step 1   Arrange the data from the largest to smallest according to frequency.

State	Number
Florida	6.0¢
Pennsylvania	5.8
Oklahoma	4.3
Maine	3.8
Indiana	2.9

Step 2   Draw and label the x and y axes.

Step 3   Draw the bars corresponding to the frequencies. See Figure 2–11. The Pareto chart shows that Florida has the highest cost per mile. The cost is more than twice as high as the cost for Indiana.

Suggestions for Drawing Pareto Charts

1. Make the bars the same width.
2. Arrange the data from largest to smallest according to frequency.
3. Make the units that are used for the frequency equal in size.

When you analyze a Pareto chart, make comparisons by looking at the heights of the bars.

The Time Series Graph

When data are collected over a period of time, they can be represented by a time series graph.

Figure 2–11

Pareto Chart for
Example 2–9

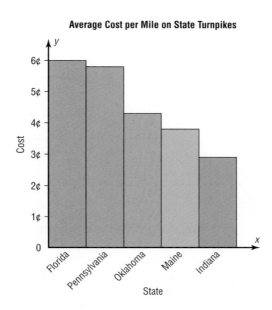

> A **time series graph** represents data that occur over a specific period of time.

Example 2–10 shows the procedure for constructing a time series graph.

Example 2–10

Arson Damage to Churches

The arson damage to churches for the years 2001 through 2005 is shown. Construct and analyze a time series graph for the data.

Year	Damage (in millions)
2001	$2.8
2002	3.3
2003	3.4
2004	5.0
2005	8.5

Source: U.S. Fire Administration.

Solution

Step 1 Draw and label the x and y axes.

Step 2 Label the x axis for years and the y axis for the damage.

Step 3 Plot each point according to the table.

Step 4 Draw line segments connecting adjacent points. Do not try to fit a smooth curve through the data points. See Figure 2–12. The graph shows a steady increase over the 5-year period.

Historical Note

Time series graphs are over 1000 years old. The first ones were used to chart the movements of the planets and the sun.

Figure 2–12

Time Series Graph for Example 2–10

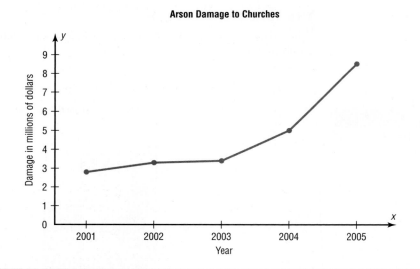

When you analyze a time series graph, look for a trend or pattern that occurs over the time period. For example, is the line ascending (indicating an increase over time) or descending (indicating a decrease over time)? Another thing to look for is the slope, or steepness, of the line. A line that is steep over a specific time period indicates a rapid increase or decrease over that period.

Figure 2–13

**Two Time Series
Graphs for Comparison**

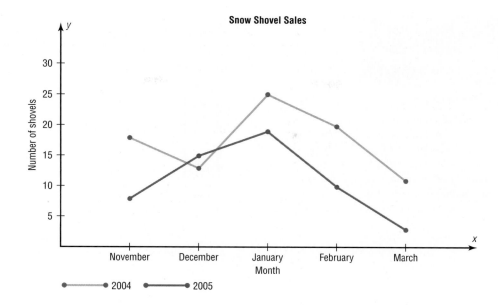

Two data sets can be compared on the same graph (called a *compound time series graph*) if two lines are used, as shown in Figure 2–13. This graph shows the number of snow shovels sold at a store for two seasons.

The Pie Graph

Pie graphs are used extensively in statistics. The purpose of the pie graph is to show the relationship of the parts to the whole by visually comparing the sizes of the sections. Percentages or proportions can be used. The variable is nominal or categorical.

A **pie graph** is a circle that is divided into sections or wedges according to the percentage of frequencies in each category of the distribution.

Example 2–11 shows the procedure for constructing a pie graph.

Example 2–11

Super Bowl Snack Foods

This frequency distribution shows the number of pounds of each snack food eaten during the Super Bowl. Construct a pie graph for the data.

Snack	Pounds (frequency)
Potato chips	11.2 million
Tortilla chips	8.2 million
Pretzels	4.3 million
Popcorn	3.8 million
Snack nuts	2.5 million
Total $n =$	30.0 million

Source: *USA TODAY Weekend.*

Speaking of
Statistics

Cell Phone Usage

The graph shows the estimated number (in millions) of cell phone subscribers since 1995. How do you think the growth will affect our way of living? For example, emergencies can be handled faster since people are using their cell phones to call 911.

Source: Cellular Telecommunications and Internet Association.

Solution

Step 1   Since there are 360° in a circle, the frequency for each class must be converted into a proportional part of the circle. This conversion is done by using the formula

$$\text{Degrees} = \frac{f}{n} \cdot 360°$$

where f = frequency for each class and n = sum of the frequencies. Hence, the following conversions are obtained. The degrees should sum to 360°.*

Potato chips	$\frac{11.2}{30} \cdot 360° = 134°$	
Tortilla chips	$\frac{8.2}{30} \cdot 360° = 98°$	
Pretzels	$\frac{4.3}{30} \cdot 360° = 52°$	
Popcorn	$\frac{3.8}{30} \cdot 360° = 46°$	
Snack nuts	$\frac{2.5}{30} \cdot 360° = 30°$	
Total	$\overline{360°}$	

Step 2   Each frequency must also be converted to a percentage. Recall from Example 2–1 that this conversion is done by using the formula

$$\% = \frac{f}{n} \cdot 100\%$$

Hence, the following percentages are obtained. The percentages should sum to 100%.†

Potato chips	$\frac{11.2}{30} \cdot 100\% = 37.3\%$	
Tortilla chips	$\frac{8.2}{30} \cdot 100\% = 27.3\%$	

Note: The degrees column does not always sum to 360° due to rounding.
†*Note:* The percent column does not always sum to 100% due to rounding.

Pretzels	$\dfrac{4.3}{30} \cdot 100\%$ =	14.3%
Popcorn	$\dfrac{3.8}{30} \cdot 100\%$ =	12.7%
Snack nuts	$\dfrac{2.5}{30} \cdot 100\%$ =	8.3%
Total		99.9%

Step 3   Next, using a protractor and a compass, draw the graph using the appropriate degree measures found in step 1, and label each section with the name and percentages, as shown in Figure 2–14.

Figure 2–14

Pie Graph for
Example 2–11

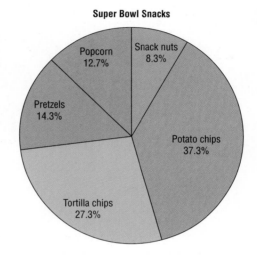

Super Bowl Snacks

Example 2–12   Construct a pie graph showing the blood types of the army inductees described in Example 2–1. The frequency distribution is repeated here.

Class	Frequency	Percent
A	5	20
B	7	28
O	9	36
AB	4	16
	25	100

Solution

Step 1   Find the number of degrees for each class, using the formula

$$\text{Degrees} = \frac{f}{n} \cdot 360°$$

For each class, then, the following results are obtained.

A $\dfrac{5}{25} \cdot 360° = 72°$

B $\dfrac{7}{25} \cdot 360° = 100.8°$

$$O \qquad \frac{9}{25} \cdot 360° = 129.6°$$

$$AB \qquad \frac{4}{25} \cdot 360° = 57.6°$$

Step 2 Find the percentages. (This was already done in Example 2–1.)

Step 3 Using a protractor, graph each section and write its name and corresponding percentage, as shown in Figure 2–15.

Figure 2–15

Pie Graph for
Example 2–12

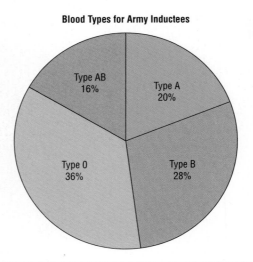

Blood Types for Army Inductees

The graph in Figure 2–15 shows that in this case the most common blood type is type O.

To analyze the nature of the data shown in the pie graph, look at the size of the sections in the pie graph. For example, are any sections relatively large compared to the rest?

Figure 2–15 shows that among the inductees, type O blood is more prevalent than any other type. People who have type AB blood are in the minority. More than twice as many people have type O blood as type AB.

Misleading Graphs

Graphs give a visual representation that enables readers to analyze and interpret data more easily than they could simply by looking at numbers. However, inappropriately drawn graphs can misrepresent the data and lead the reader to false conclusions. For example, a car manufacturer's ad stated that 98% of the vehicles it had sold in the past 10 years were still on the road. The ad then showed a graph similar to the one in Figure 2–16. The graph shows the percentage of the manufacturer's automobiles still on the road and the percentage of its competitors' automobiles still on the road. Is there a large difference? Not necessarily.

Notice the scale on the vertical axis in Figure 2–16. It has been cut off (or truncated) and starts at 95%. When the graph is redrawn using a scale that goes from 0 to 100%, as in Figure 2–17, there is hardly a noticeable difference in the percentages. Thus, changing the units at the starting point on the *y* axis can convey a very different visual representation of the data.

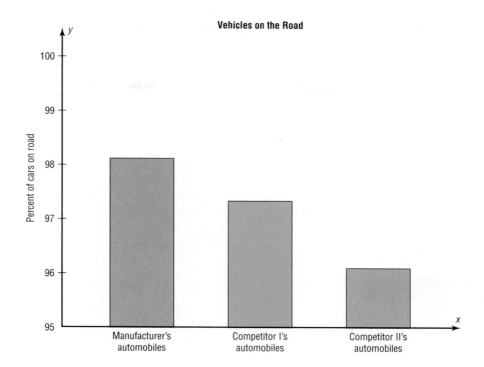

Figure 2–16

Graph of Automaker's Claim Using a Scale from 95 to 100%

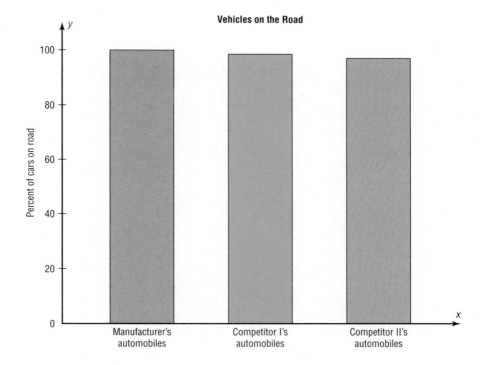

Figure 2–17

Graph in Figure 2–16 Redrawn Using a Scale from 0 to 100%

It is not wrong to truncate an axis of the graph; many times it is necessary to do so. However, the reader should be aware of this fact and interpret the graph accordingly. Do not be misled if an inappropriate impression is given.

Let us consider another example. The projected required fuel economy in miles per gallon for General Motors vehicles is shown. In this case, an increase from 21.9 to 23.2 miles per gallon is projected.

Year	2008	2009	2010	2011
Projected MPG	21.9	22.6	22.9	23.2

Source: National Highway Traffic Safety Administration.

When you examine the graph shown in Figure 2–18(a) using a scale of 0 to 25 miles per gallon, the graph shows a slight increase. However, when the scale is changed to 21

Figure 2–18

Projected Miles per Gallon

(a)

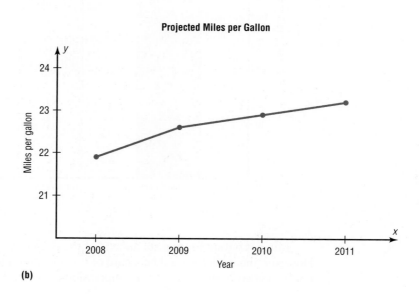

(b)

to 24 miles per gallon, the graph shows a much larger increase even though the data remain the same. See Figure 2–18(b). Again, by changing the units or starting point on the *y* axis, one can change the visual representation.

Another misleading graphing technique sometimes used involves exaggerating a one-dimensional increase by showing it in two dimensions. For example, the average cost of a 30-second Super Bowl commercial has increased from $42,000 in 1967 to $2.5 million in 2006 (Source: *USA TODAY*).

The increase shown by the graph in Figure 2–19(a) represents the change by a comparison of the heights of the two bars in one dimension. The same data are shown two-dimensionally with circles in Figure 2–19(b). Notice that the difference seems much larger because the eye is comparing the areas of the circles rather than the lengths of the diameters.

Note that it is not wrong to use the graphing techniques of truncating the scales or representing data by two-dimensional pictures. But when these techniques are used, the reader should be cautious of the conclusion drawn on the basis of the graphs.

Figure 2–19

Comparison of Costs for a 30-Second Super Bowl Commercial

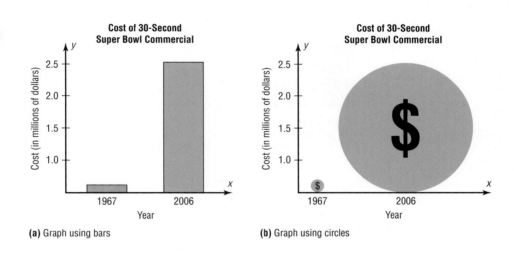

(a) Graph using bars   **(b)** Graph using circles

Another way to misrepresent data on a graph is by omitting labels or units on the axes of the graph. The graph shown in Figure 2–20 compares the cost of living, economic growth, population growth, etc., of four main geographic areas in the United States. However, since there are no numbers on the *y* axis, very little information can be gained from this graph, except a crude ranking of each factor. There is no way to decide the actual magnitude of the differences.

Figure 2–20

A Graph with No Units on the *y* Axis

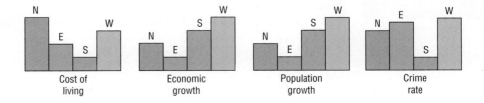

Finally, all graphs should contain a source for the information presented. The inclusion of a source for the data will enable you to check the reliability of the organization presenting the data. A summary of the types of graphs and their uses is shown in Figure 2–21.

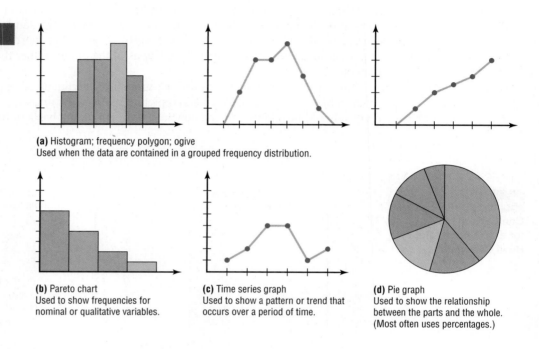

Figure 2–21

Summary of Graphs and Uses of Each

(a) Histogram; frequency polygon; ogive
Used when the data are contained in a grouped frequency distribution.

(b) Pareto chart
Used to show frequencies for nominal or qualitative variables.

(c) Time series graph
Used to show a pattern or trend that occurs over a period of time.

(d) Pie graph
Used to show the relationship between the parts and the whole. (Most often uses percentages.)

Stem and Leaf Plots

The stem and leaf plot is a method of organizing data and is a combination of sorting and graphing. It has the advantage over a grouped frequency distribution of retaining the actual data while showing them in graphical form.

Objective 4

Draw and interpret a stem and leaf plot.

> A **stem and leaf plot** is a data plot that uses part of the data value as the stem and part of the data value as the leaf to form groups or classes.

Example 2–13 shows the procedure for constructing a stem and leaf plot.

Example 2–13   At an outpatient testing center, the number of cardiograms performed each day for 20 days is shown. Construct a stem and leaf plot for the data.

25	31	20	32	13
14	43	02	57	23
36	32	33	32	44
32	52	44	51	45

How Much Paper Money Is in Circulation Today?

The Federal Reserve estimated that during a recent year, there were 22 billion bills in circulation. About 35% of them were $1 bills, 3% were $2 bills, 8% were $5 bills, 7% were $10 bills, 23% were $20 bills, 5% were $50 bills, and 19% were $100 bills. It costs about 3¢ to print each $1 bill.

The average life of a $1 bill is 22 months, a $10 bill 3 years, a $20 bill 4 years, a $50 bill 9 years, and a $100 bill 9 years. What type of graph would you use to represent the average lifetimes of the bills?

Solution

Step 1   Arrange the data in order:

02, 13, 14, 20, 23, 25, 31, 32, 32, 32,
32, 33, 36, 43, 44, 44, 45, 51, 52, 57

Note: Arranging the data in order is not essential and can be cumbersome when the data set is large; however, it is helpful in constructing a stem and leaf plot. The leaves in the final stem and leaf plot should be arranged in order.

Step 2   Separate the data according to the first digit, as shown.

02   13, 14   20, 23, 25   31, 32, 32, 32, 32, 33, 36
43, 44, 44, 45   51, 52, 57

Step 3   A display can be made by using the leading digit as the *stem* and the trailing digit as the *leaf.* For example, for the value 32, the leading digit, 3, is the stem and the trailing digit, 2, is the leaf. For the value 14, the 1 is the stem and the 4 is the leaf. Now a plot can be constructed as shown in Figure 2–22.

```
0 | 2
1 | 3 4
2 | 0 3 5
3 | 1 2 2 2 2 3 6
4 | 3 4 4 5
5 | 1 2 7
```

Leading digit (stem)	Trailing digit (leaf)
0	2
1	3 4
2	0 3 5
3	1 2 2 2 2 3 6
4	3 4 4 5
5	1 2 7

Figure 2–22 shows that the distribution peaks in the center and that there are no gaps in the data. For 7 of the 20 days, the number of patients receiving cardiograms was between 31 and 36. The plot also shows that the testing center treated from a minimum of 2 patients to a maximum of 57 patients in any one day.

If there are no data values in a class, you should write the stem number and leave the leaf row blank. Do not put a zero in the leaf row.

Example 2–14

An insurance company researcher conducted a survey on the number of car thefts in a large city for a period of 30 days last summer. The raw data are shown. Construct a stem and leaf plot by using classes 50–54, 55–59, 60–64, 65–69, 70–74, and 75–79.

52	62	51	50	69
58	77	66	53	57
75	56	55	67	73
79	59	68	65	72
57	51	63	69	75
65	53	78	66	55

Solution

Step 1 Arrange the data in order.

50, 51, 51, 52, 53, 53, 55, 55, 56, 57, 57, 58, 59, 62, 63,
65, 65, 66, 66, 67, 68, 69, 69, 72, 73, 75, 75, 77, 78, 79

Step 2 Separate the data according to the classes.

50, 51, 51, 52, 53, 53   55, 55, 56, 57, 57, 58, 59
62, 63   65, 65, 66, 66, 67, 68, 69, 69   72, 73
75, 75, 77, 78, 79

Step 3 Plot the data as shown here.

Leading digit (stem)	Trailing digit (leaf)
5	0 1 1 2 3 3
5	5 5 6 7 7 8 9
6	2 3
6	5 5 6 6 7 8 9 9
7	2 3
7	5 5 7 8 9

The graph for this plot is shown in Figure 2–23.

Figure 2–23

Stem and Leaf Plot for Example 2–14

5	0 1 1 2 3 3
5	5 5 6 7 7 8 9
6	2 3
6	5 5 6 6 7 8 9 9
7	2 3
7	5 5 7 8 9

When the data values are in the hundreds, such as 325, the stem is 32 and the leaf is 5. For example, the stem and leaf plot for the data values 325, 327, 330, 332, 335, 341, 345, and 347 looks like this.

32	5 7
33	0 2 5
34	1 5 7

When you analyze a stem and leaf plot, look for peaks and gaps in the distribution. See if the distribution is symmetric or skewed. Check the variability of the data by looking at the spread.

Interesting Fact

The average number of pencils and index cards David Letterman tosses over his shoulder during one show is 4.

Related distributions can be compared by using a back-to-back stem and leaf plot. The back-to-back stem and leaf plot uses the same digits for the stems of both distributions, but the digits that are used for the leaves are arranged in order out from the stems on both sides. Example 2–15 shows a back-to-back stem and leaf plot.

Example 2–15

The number of stories in two selected samples of tall buildings in Atlanta and Philadelphia is shown. Construct a back-to-back stem and leaf plot, and compare the distributions.

Atlanta					Philadelphia				
55	70	44	36	40	61	40	38	32	30
63	40	44	34	38	58	40	40	25	30
60	47	52	32	32	54	40	36	30	30
50	53	32	28	31	53	39	36	34	33
52	32	34	32	50	50	38	36	39	32
26	29								

Source: *The World Almanac and Book of Facts.*

Solution

Step 1 Arrange the data for both data sets in order.

Step 2 Construct a stem and leaf plot using the same digits as stems. Place the digits for the leaves for Atlanta on the left side of the stem and the digits for the leaves for Philadelphia on the right side, as shown. See Figure 2–24.

Figure 2–24

Back-to-Back Stem and Leaf Plot for Example 2–15

Atlanta		Philadelphia
9 8 6	2	5
8 6 4 4 2 2 2 2 2 1	3	0 0 0 0 2 2 3 4 6 6 6 8 8 9 9
7 4 4 0 0	4	0 0 0 0
5 3 2 2 0 0	5	0 3 4 8
3 0	6	1
0	7	

Step 3 Compare the distributions. The buildings in Atlanta have a large variation in the number of stories per building. Although both distributions are peaked in the 30- to 39-story class, Philadelphia has more buildings in this class. Atlanta has more buildings that have 40 or more stories than Philadelphia does.

Stem and leaf plots are part of the techniques called *exploratory data analysis*. More information on this topic is presented in Chapter 3.

Applying the Concepts **2–3**

Leading Cause of Death

The following shows approximations of the leading causes of death among men ages 25–44 years. The rates are per 100,000 men. Answer the following questions about the graph.

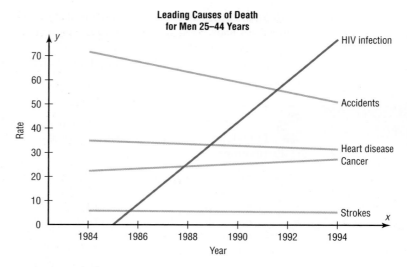

Leading Causes of Death for Men 25–44 Years

1. What are the variables in the graph?
2. Are the variables qualitative or quantitative?
3. Are the variables discrete or continuous?
4. What type of graph was used to display the data?
5. Could a Pareto chart be used to display the data?
6. Could a pie chart be used to display the data?
7. List some typical uses for the Pareto chart.
8. List some typical uses for the time series chart.

See page 108 for the answers.

Exercises 2–3

1. **Women's Softball Champions** The NCAA Women's Softball Division 1 Champions since 1982 are listed below. Use the data to construct a Pareto chart and a vertical bar graph.

'82 UCLA	'94 Arizona
'83 Texas A&M	'95 UCLA
'84 UCLA	'96 Arizona
'85 UCLA	'97 Arizona
'86 Cal St – Fullerton	'98 Fresno State
'87 Texas A&M	'99 UCLA
'88 UCLA	'00 Oklahoma
'89 UCLA	'01 Arizona
'90 UCLA	'02 California
'91 Arizona	'03 UCLA
'92 UCLA	'04 UCLA
'93 Arizona	'05 Michigan

Source: *New York Times Almanac.*

2. **Delegates Who Signed the Declaration of Independence** The state represented by each delegate who signed the Declaration of Independence is indicated. Organize the data in a Pareto chart and a vertical bar graph and comment on the results.

MA 5	PA 9	SC 4
NH 3	RI 2	CT 4
VA 7	NY 4	DE 3
MD 4	GA 3	
NJ 5	NC 3	

Source: *New York Times Almanac.*

3. **Internet Connections** The following data represent the estimated number (in millions) of computers connected to the Internet worldwide. Construct a Pareto chart and a horizontal bar graph for the data. Based on the data, suggest the best place to market appropriate Internet products.

Location	Number of computers
Homes	240
Small companies	102
Large companies	148
Government agencies	33
Schools	47

Source: IDC.

4. **Roller Coaster Mania** The World Roller Coaster Census Report lists the following number of roller

coasters on each continent. Represent the data graphically, using a Pareto chart and a horizontal bar graph.

Africa	17
Asia	315
Australia	22
Europe	413
North America	643
South America	45

Source: www.rcdb.com

5. World Energy Use The following percentages indicate the source of energy used worldwide. Construct a Pareto chart and a vertical bar graph for the energy used.

Petroleum	39.8%
Coal	23.2
Dry natural gas	22.4
Hydroelectric	7.0
Nuclear	6.4
Other (wind, solar, etc.)	1.2

Source: New York Times Almanac.

6. Airline Departures Draw a time series graph to represent the data for the number of airline departures (in millions) for the given years. Over the years, is the number of departures increasing, decreasing, or about the same?

Year	1996	1997	1998	1999	2000	2001	2002
Number of departures	7.9	9.9	10.5	10.9	11.0	9.8	10.1

Source: The World Almanac and Book of Facts.

7. Average Global Temperatures Represent these average global temperatures in a time series graph.

1900–09	56.5	1960–69	57.1
1910–19	56.6	1970–79	57.0
1920–29	56.7	1980–89	57.4
1930–39	57.0	1990–99	57.6
1940–49	57.1		
1950–59	57.1		

Source: World Almanac.

8. Nuclear Power Reactors Draw a time series graph for the data shown and comment on the trend. The data represent the number of active nuclear reactors.

Year	1992	1994	1996	1998	2000	2002
Number	109	109	109	104	104	104

Source: The World Almanac and Book of Facts.

9. Percentage of Voters in Presidential Elections Listed are the percentages of voters who voted in past Presidential elections since 1964. Illustrate the data with a time series graph. The day before the 2006 election, a website published a survey where 90% of the

respondents said they voted in the 2004 election. Give possible reasons for the discrepancy.

1964	95.83	1980	76.53	1996	65.97
1968	89.65	1984	74.63	2000	67.50
1972	79.85	1988	72.48	2004	64.0
1976	77.64	1992	78.04		

Source: New York Times Almanac.

10. Reasons We Travel The following data are based on a survey from American Travel Survey on why people travel. Construct a pie graph for the data and analyze the results.

Purpose	Number
Personal business	146
Visit friends or relatives	330
Work-related	225
Leisure	299

Source: USA TODAY.

11. Characteristics of the Population 65 and Over Two characteristics of the population aged 65 and over are shown below for 2004. Illustrate each characteristic with a pie graph.

Marital status		Educational attainment	
Never married	3.9%	Less than ninth grade	13.9%
Married	57.2	Completed 9–12 but	
Widowed	30.8	no diploma	13.0
Divorced	8.1	H.S. graduate	36.0
		Some college/	
		associates degree	18.4
		Bachelor's/advanced	
		degree	18.7

Source: New York Times Almanac.

12. Components of the Earth's Crust The following elements comprise the earth's crust, the outermost solid layer. Illustrate the composition of the earth's crust with a pie graph.

Oxygen	45.6%
Silicon	27.3
Aluminum	8.4
Iron	6.2
Calcium	4.7
Other	7.8

Source: New York Times Almanac.

13. Workers Switch Jobs In a recent survey, 3 in 10 people indicated that they are likely to leave their jobs when the economy improves. Of those surveyed, 34% indicated that they would make a career change, 29% want a new job in the same industry, 21% are going to start a business, and 16% are going to retire. Make a pie chart and a Pareto chart for the data. Which chart do you think better represents the data?

Source: National Survey Institute.

14. State which graph (Pareto chart, time series graph, or pie graph) would most appropriately represent the given situation.

    a. The number of students enrolled at a local college for each year during the last 5 years.

    b. The budget for the student activities department at a certain college for each year during the last 5 years.

    c. The means of transportation the students use to get to school.

    d. The percentage of votes each of the four candidates received in the last election.

    e. The record temperatures of a city for the last 30 years.

    f. The frequency of each type of crime committed in a city during the year.

15. Presidents' Ages at Inauguration The age at inauguration for each U.S. President is shown. Construct a stem and leaf plot and analyze the data.

57	54	52	55	51	56
61	68	56	55	54	61
57	51	46	54	51	52
57	49	54	42	60	69
58	64	49	51	62	64
57	48	50	56	43	46
61	65	47	55	55	54

Source: *New York Times Almanac.*

16. Calories in Salad Dressings A listing of calories per one ounce of selected salad dressings (not fat-free) is given below. Construct a stem and leaf plot for the data.

100	130	130	130	110	110	120	130	140	100
140	170	160	130	160	120	150	100	145	145
145	115	120	100	120	160	140	120	180	100
160	120	140	150	190	150	180	160		

17. Twenty Days of Plant Growth The growth (in centimeters) of two varieties of plant after 20 days is shown in this table. Construct a back-to-back stem and leaf plot for the data, and compare the distributions.

Variety 1				Variety 2			
20	12	39	38	18	45	62	59
41	43	51	52	53	25	13	57
59	55	53	59	42	55	56	38
50	58	35	38	41	36	50	62
23	32	43	53	45	55		

18. Math and Reading Achievement Scores The math and reading achievement scores from the National Assessment of Educational Progress for selected states are listed below. Construct a back-to-back stem and leaf plot with the data and compare the distributions.

Math					Reading				
52	66	69	62	61	65	76	76	66	67
63	57	59	59	55	71	70	70	66	61
55	59	74	72	73	61	69	78	76	77
68	76	73			77	77	80		

Source: *World Almanac.*

19. The sales of recorded music in 2004 by genre are listed below. Represent the data with an appropriate graph.

Rock	23.9		Jazz	2.7
Country	13.0		Classical	2.0
Rap/hip-hop	12.1		Oldies	1.4
R&B/urban	11.3		Soundtracks	1.1
Pop	10.0		New age	1.0
Religious	6.0		Other	8.9
Children's	2.8			

Source: *World Almanac.*

Extending the Concepts

20. Successful Space Launches The number of successful space launches by the United States and Japan for the years 1993–1997 is shown here. Construct a compound time series graph for the data. What comparison can be made regarding the launches?

Year	1993	1994	1995	1996	1997
United States	29	27	24	32	37
Japan	1	4	2	1	2

Source: *The World Almanac and Book of Facts.*

21. Meat Production Meat production for veal and lamb for the years 1960–2000 is shown here. (Data are in millions of pounds.) Construct a compound time series graph for the data. What comparison can be made regarding meat production?

Year	1960	1970	1980	1990	2000
Veal	1109	588	400	327	225
Lamb	769	551	318	358	234

Source: *The World Almanac and Book of Facts.*

22. Top 10 Airlines The top 10 airlines with the most aircraft are listed. Represent these data with an appropriate graph.

American	714		Continental	364
United	603		Southwest	327
Delta	600		British Airways	268
Northwest	424		American Eagle	245
U.S. Airways	384		Lufthansa (Ger.)	233

Source: *Top 10 of Everything.*

23. Nobel Prizes in Physiology or Medicine The top prize-winning countries for Nobel Prizes in Physiology or Medicine are listed here. Represent the data with an appropriate graph.

United States	80	Denmark	5
United Kingdom	24	Austria	4
Germany	16	Belgium	4
Sweden	8	Italy	3
France	7	Australia	3
Switzerland	6		

Source: *Top 10 of Everything.*

Source: Cartoon by Bradford Veley, Marquette, Michigan. Used with permission.

24. Cost of Milk The graph shows the increase in the price of a quart of milk. Why might the increase appear to be larger than it really is?

25. Boom in Number of Births The graph shows the projected boom (in millions) in the number of births. Cite several reasons why the graph might be misleading.

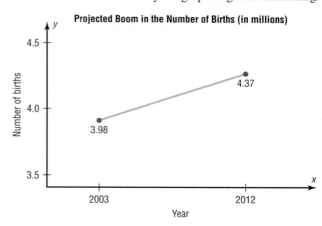

Technology *Step by Step*

MINITAB
Step by Step

Construct a Pie Chart

1. Enter the summary data for snack foods and frequencies from Example 2–11 into C1 and C2.

2. Name them **Snack** and **f.**
3. Select **Graph>Pie Chart.**
   a) Click the option for Chart summarized data.
   b) Press [Tab] to move to Categorical variable, then double-click C1 to select it.
   c) Press [Tab] to move to Summary variables, and select the column with the frequencies f.

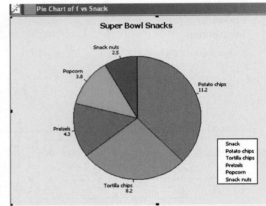

4. Click the [Labels] tab, then Titles/Footnotes.
   a) Type in the title: **Super Bowl Snacks.**
   b) Click the Slice Labels tab, then the options for Category name and Frequency.
   c) Click the option to Draw a line from label to slice.
   d) Click [OK] twice to create the chart.

Construct a Bar Chart

The procedure for constructing a bar chart is similar to that for the pie chart.

1. Select **Graph>Bar Chart.**
   a) Click on the drop-down list in Bars Represent: then select values from a table.
   b) Click on the Simple chart, then click [OK]. The dialog box will be similar to the Pie Chart Dialog Box.
2. Select the frequency column C2 f for Graph variables: and Snack for the Categorical variable.

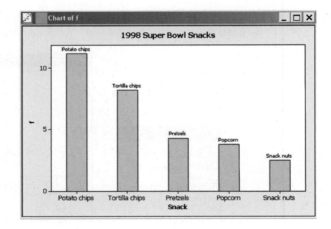

3. Click on [Labels], then type the title in the Titles/Footnote tab: **1998 Super Bowl Snacks.**

4. Click the tab for Data Labels, then click the option to Use labels from column: and select C1 Snacks.

5. Click [OK] twice.

Construct a Pareto Chart

Pareto charts are a quality control tool. They are similar to a bar chart with no gaps between the bars, and the bars are arranged by frequency.

1. Select **Stat>Quality Tools>Pareto.**

2. Click the option to Chart defects table.

3. Click in the box for the Labels in: and select Snack.

4. Click on the frequencies column C2 f.

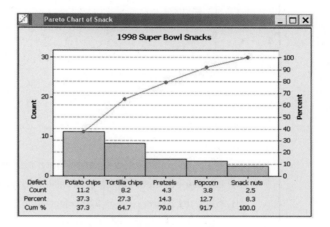

5. Click on [Options].

    a) Check the box for Cumulative percents.

    b) Type in the title, **1998 Super Bowl Snacks.**

6. Click [OK] twice. The chart is completed.

Construct a Time Series Plot

The data used are for the number of vehicles that used the Pennsylvania Turnpike.

Year	1999	2000	2001	2002	2003
Number	156.2	160.1	162.3	172.8	179.4

1. Add a blank worksheet to the project by selecting **File>New>New Worksheet.**

2. To enter the dates from 1999 to 2003 in C1, select **Calc>Make Patterned Data>Simple Set of Numbers.**

    a) Type **Year** in the text box for Store patterned data in.

    b) From first value: should be **1999.**

    c) To Last value: should be **2003.**

    d) In steps of should be **1** (for every other year). The last two boxes should be 1, the default value.

    e) Click [OK]. The sequence from 1999 to 2003 will be entered in C1 whose label will be Year.

3. Type **Vehicles (in millions)** for the label row above row 1 in C2.

4. Type **156.2** for the first number, then press [Enter]. Never enter the commas for large numbers!

5. Continue entering the value in each row of C2.

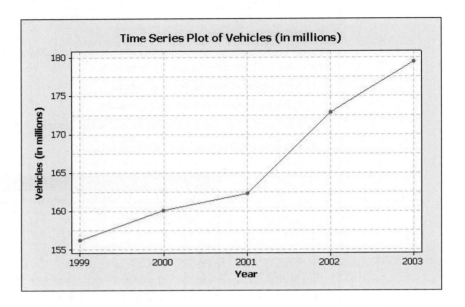

6. To make the graph, select **Graph>Time series plot,** then Simple, and press [OK].

   a) For Series select Vehicles (in millions), then click [Time/scale].

   b) Click the Stamp option and select Year for the Stamp column.

   c) Click the Gridlines tab and select all three boxes, Y major, Y minor, and X major.

   d) Click [OK] twice. A new window will open that contains the graph.

   e) To change the title, double-click the title in the graph window. A dialog box will open, allowing you to edit the text.

Construct a Stem and Leaf Plot

1. Type in the data for Example 2–14. Label the column **CarThefts.**

2. Select **STAT>EDA>Stem-and-Leaf.** This is the same as **Graph>Stem-and-Leaf.**

3. Double-click on C1 CarThefts in the column list.

4. Click in the Increment text box, and enter the class width of **5.**

5. Click [OK]. This character graph will be displayed in the session window.

Stem-and-Leaf Display: CarThefts
Stem-and-leaf of CarThefts   N = 30
Leaf Unit = 1.0

6	5	011233
13	5	5567789
15	6	23
15	6	55667899
7	7	23
5	7	55789

TI-83 Plus or TI-84 Plus
Step by Step

To graph a time series, follow the procedure for a frequency polygon from Section 2–2, using the following data for the number of outdoor drive-in theaters

Year	1988	1990	1992	1994	1996	1998	2000
Number	1497	910	870	859	826	750	637

Output

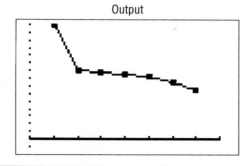

Excel
Step by Step

Constructing a Pie Chart

To make a pie chart:

1. Enter the blood types from Example 2–12 into column A of a new worksheet.

2. Enter the frequencies corresponding to each blood type in column B.

3. Highlight the data in columns A and B and select Insert from the toolbar, then select the Pie chart type.

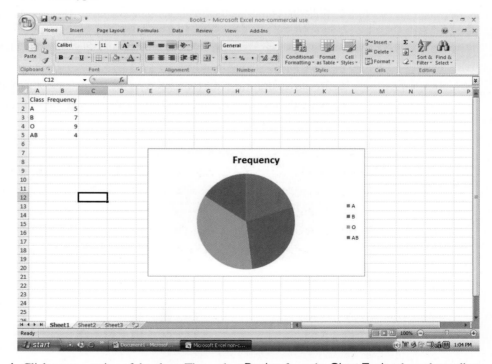

4. Click on any region of the chart. Then select Design from the Chart Tools tab on the toolbar.

5. Select Formulas from the chart Layouts tab on the toolbar.

6. To change the title of the chart, click on the current title of the chart.

7. When the text box containing the title is highlighted, click the mouse in the text box and change the title.

Constructing a Pareto Chart

To make a Pareto chart:

1. Enter the snack food categories from Example 2–11 into column A of a new worksheet.

2. Enter the corresponding frequencies in column B. The data should be entered in descending order according to frequency.

3. Highlight the data from columns A and B and select the Insert tab from the toolbar.

4. Select the Column Chart type.

5. To change the title of the chart, click on the current title of the chart.

6. When the text box containing the title is highlighted, click the mouse in the text box and change the title.

Constructing a Time Series Plot

To make a time series chart:

1. Enter the years 1999 through 2003 from Example 2–10 in column A of a new worksheet.
2. Enter the corresponding frequencies in column B.
3. Highlight the data from column B and select the Insert tab from the toolbar.
4. Select the Line chart type.

5. Right-click the mouse on any region of the graph.
6. Select the Select Data option.
7. Select Edit from the Horizontal Axis Labels and highlight the years from column A, then click [OK].
8. Click [OK] on the Select Data Source box.
9. Create a title for your chart, such as Number of Vehicles Using the Pennsylvania Turnpike Between 1999 and 2003. Right-click the mouse on any region of the chart. Select the Chart Tools tab from the toolbar, then Layout.
10. Select Chart Title and highlight the current title to change the title.
11. Select Axis Titles to change the horizontal and vertical axis labels.

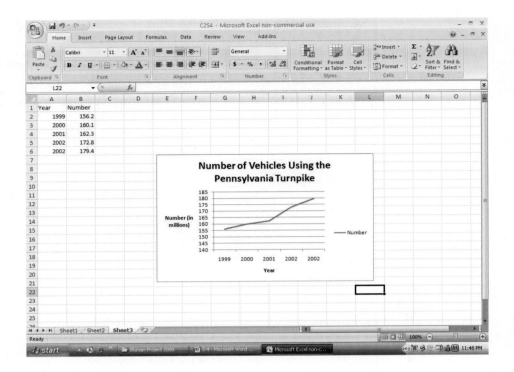

2–4 Paired Data and Scatter Plots

Objective 5

Draw and interpret a scatter plot for a set of paired data.

Many times researchers are interested in determining if a relationship between two variables exists. In order to accomplish this, the researcher collects data consisting of two measures that are paired with each other. For example, researchers have found that there is a relationship between the temperature and the chirping frequencies of crickets. As the temperature increases, so does the chirping frequency of the crickets.

To conduct this study, two measures are needed, the temperature and the chirping frequency of a cricket. These measures are paired in such a way that the first measured, temperature, called the *independent variable,* is designated as *x*, and the second variable, the number of chirps per second, called the *dependent variable,* is designated as *y*.

Once a set of order pairs (*x*, *y*) of data values is collected, a graph can be drawn to represent the data. This graph is called a *scatter plot* or *scatter diagram.*

A **scatter plot** is a graph of order pairs of data values that is used to determine if a relationship exists between the two variables.

Example 2–16 shows how to draw a scatter plot.

Example 2–16

Wet Bike Accidents A researcher is interested in determining if there is a relationship between the number of wet bike accidents and the number of wet bike fatalities. The data are for a 10-year period. Draw a scatter plot for the data.

No. of accidents, x	376	650	884	1162	1513	1650	2236	3002	4028	4010
No. of fatalities, y	5	20	20	28	26	34	35	56	68	55

Source: Personal Watercraft Industry Assoc., U.S. Coast Guard.

Solution

Step 1   Draw and label the x and y axes.

Step 2   Plot the points for pairs of data. The graph is shown in Figure 2–25.

Figure 2–25

Scatter Plot for the
Data in Example 2–16

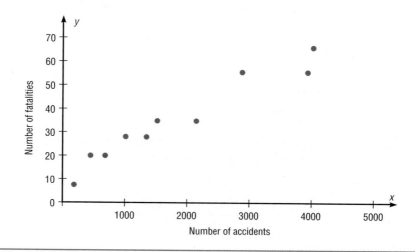

In the Technology Step by Step subsection at the end of this section, you will learn to construct this scatter plot using Excel and the same data.

Analyzing the Scatter Plot

There are several types of relationships that can exist between the x values and the y values. These relationships can be identified by looking at the pattern of the points on the graphs. The types of patterns and corresponding relationships are given next.

1. A **positive linear relationship** exists when the points fall approximately in an ascending straight line and both the x and y values increase at the same time [see Figure 2–26(a)]. The relationship then is that as the values for the x variable increase, the values for the y variable are increasing.

2. A **negative linear relationship** exists when the points fall approximately in a descending straight line from left to right [see Figure 2–26(b)]. The relationship then is that as the x values are increasing, the y values are decreasing, or vice versa.

3. A *nonlinear relationship* exists when the points fall in a curved line [see Figure 2–26(c)]. The relationship is described by the nature of the curve.

4. *No relationship* exists when there is no discernable pattern of the points [see Figure 2–26(d)].

Figure 2–26

Examples of Scatter Plots and Relationships

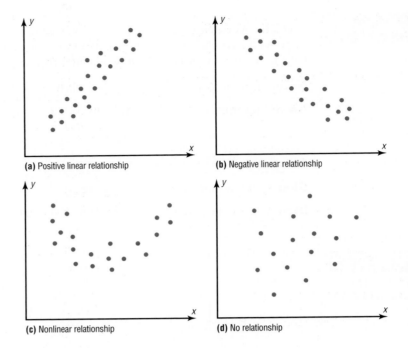

(a) Positive linear relationship

(b) Negative linear relationship

(c) Nonlinear relationship

(d) No relationship

The relationship between the variables in Example 2–16 appears to be a positive linear relationship. In other words, as the number of wet bike accidents increases, the number of deaths that occurred in these accidents has also been increasing.

More information on scatter plots, correlation, and regression can be found in Chapter 10.

Applying the Concepts **2–4**

Absences and Final Grades

Professor Bluman wanted to see if there was a relationship between the number of absences and the final grades of the students in STAT 101. A random sample of 7 students shows the following information:

Number of absences	6	2	15	9	12	5	8
Final grade (%)	82	86	43	74	58	90	78

Draw a scatter plot and answer each question.

1. Which variable is the independent variable?
2. Which variable is the dependent variable?
3. What type of relationship, if any, exists?
4. What can you conclude from the scatter plot?

See page 109 for the answers.

Exercises 2–4

These exercises involve drawing and analyzing scatter plots using the diagrams in Figure 2–21.

1. What is the name of the graph that is used to investigate whether or not two variables are related?

2. In relationship studies, what are the names of the two variables used?

3. Explain what is meant when two variables are positively related. What would the scatter plot look like?

4. Explain what is meant when two variables are negatively related. What would the scatter plot look like?

5. Heights of Tall Buildings The data represent the heights in feet and the number of stories of the tallest buildings in Pittsburgh. Draw a scatter plot for the data and describe the relationship.

(Source: *The World Almanac and Book of Facts.*)

Height, x	485	511	520	535	582	615	616	635	728	841
No. of Stories, y	40	37	41	42	38	45	31	40	54	64

6. Hours Spent Jogging A researcher wishes to determine whether the number of hours a person jogs per week is related to the person's age. Draw a scatter plot and comment on the nature of the relationship.

Age, x	34	22	48	56	62
Hours, y	5.5	7	3.5	3	1

7. Recreational Expenditures A study was conducted to determine if the amount a person spends per month on recreation is related to the person's income. Draw a scatter plot and comment on the nature of the relationship.

Income, x	$800	$1200	$1000	$900	$850	$907	$1100
Amount, y	$60	$200	$160	$135	$45	$90	$150

8. Employee Absences A researcher wishes to determine if there is a relationship between the number of days an employee missed a year and the person's age. Draw a scatter plot and comment on the nature of the relationship.

Age, x	22	30	25	35	65	50	27	53	42	58
Days missed, y	0	4	1	2	14	7	3	8	6	4

9. Statistics Final Exam Scores A statistics instructor wishes to determine if a relationship exists between the final exam score in Statistics 101 and the final exam scores of the same students who took Statistics 102. Draw a scatter plot and comment on the nature of the relationship.

Stat 101, x	87	92	68	72	95	78	83	98
Stat 102, y	83	88	70	74	90	74	83	99

10. Ages and Accidents of Drivers These data represent the ages of drivers and the number of accidents reported for each age group in Pennsylvania for a selected year. Draw a scatter plot and describe the nature of the relationship.

Source: PA Department of Transportation.

Age, x	16	17	18	19	20	21
No. of accidents, y	6605	8932	8506	7349	6458	5974

11. LPGA Golf Tournaments The data shown indicate the number of tournaments and the earnings in thousands of dollars of 10 randomly selected LPGA golfers. Draw a scatter plot for the data and determine the nature of the relationship.

Source: *USA Today.*

No. of tournaments, x	27	30	24	21	18	32	25	32	25	27
Earnings, y	$956	757	583	517	104	173	252	303	355	405

12. National Hockey League Games The data shown indicate the number of wins and the number of points scored for teams in the National Hockey League. Draw a scatter plot for the data and describe the nature of the relationship.

Source: *USA Today.*

No. of wins, x	10	9	6	5	4	12	11	8
No. of points, y	23	22	15	15	10	26	26	26
	7	5	9	8	6	6	4	
	21	16	12	19	16	16	11	

13. Absences and Final Grades An educator wants to see if there is a relationship between the number of absences a student has and his or her final grade in a course. Draw a scatter plot and comment on the nature of the relationship.

Number of absences, x	10	12	2	0	8	5
Final grade, y	70	65	96	94	75	82

14. Price of Cigarettes These data represent the average price of a pack of cigarettes and the state excise tax (in cents) for 20 randomly selected states. Draw a scatter diagram and describe the nature of the relationship.

Source: Tobacco Institute.

Ave. price, x	2.14	2.00	1.74	2.09	1.72	1.59	2.43
Excise tax, y	29	37	20	50	24	12	60
	1.84	1.99	1.89	1.68	2.45	2.17	1.69
	28	44	36	20	76	48	18
	1.63	1.65	1.76	1.77	1.82	1.90	
	17	18	21	31	33	41	

Technology *Step by Step*

MINITAB
Step by Step

Constructing a Scatter Plot

Example MT2–1

There are several ways to make scatterplots in MINITAB. The first makes a graph of text characters in the session window. This graph can be saved as a rich text file or copied and pasted into any text document.

1. Enter the data from Example 2–16 in C1 and C2 of the worksheet. Label the columns **FATALITIES** and **Accidents.**

2. Select **Graph>Character Graphs>Scatterplot.**

3. Click in the dialog box for Y variable: then double-click C2 FATALITIES in the list.

4. The cursor should be in the X Variable dialog box. Double-click Accidents in the list to select it for the X variable.

5. Click [Annotate] and enter an appropriate title such as **Number of Fatalities to Number of Accidents.**

6. Click [OK]. The graph will be displayed in the session window as shown.

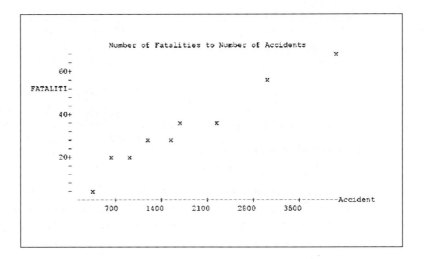

Example MT2–2

The same data are used.

1. Select **Graph>Plot.**

2. In the dialog box select FATALITIES for the Y variable and Accidents for the X variable.

3. Click the Annotation arrow then Title. Type in an appropriate title.

This figure shows the data in the worksheet and the high-resolution graph window. It is apparent from the scatter plot there is a positive relationship between fatalities and accidents.

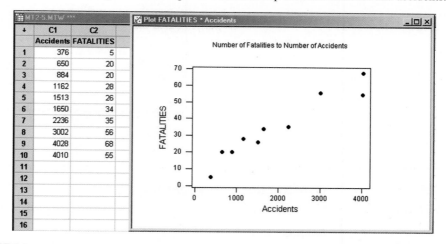

TI-83 Plus or TI-84 Plus

Step by Step

Constructing a Scatter Plot

To graph a scatter plot:

1. Enter the x values in L_1 and the y values in L_2.

2. Make sure the Window values are appropriate. Select an Xmin slightly less than the smallest x data value and an Xmax slightly larger than the largest x data value. Do the same for Ymin and Ymax. Also, you may need to adjust the Xscl and Yscl values, depending on the data.

3. Press **2nd [STAT PLOT] 1** for Plot 1.

4. Move the cursor to On and press ENTER on the **Plot 1** menu.

5. Move the cursor to the graphic that looks like a scatter plot next to Type (first graph) and press ENTER. Make sure the Xlist is L_1 and the Ylist is L_2.

6. Press GRAPH.

Example TI2–3

Draw a scatter plot for the data from Example 2–12.

x	376	650	884	1162	1513	1650	2236	3002	4028	4010
y	5	20	20	28	26	34	35	56	68	55

Input

Input

Output

Excel

Step by Step

Constructing a Scatter Plot

Excel has features that can be used to construct scatter plots for bivariate data.

Example 2–2

A researcher is interested in determining if there is a relationship between the number of wet bike accidents and the number of wet bike fatalities. The data are for a 10-year period. Draw a scatter plot for the data and compute the correlation coefficient.

Number of accidents, x	376	650	884	1162	1513	1650	2236	3002	4028	4010
Number of fatalities, y	5	20	20	28	26	34	35	56	68	55

Construct the scatter plot.

1. Enter the x values in column A and the corresponding y values in column B.
2. Click on the chart wizard icon.
3. Select chart type XY (Scatter) under the **Standard Types** tab. Click [Next>].
4. Select the y values (no label) for the Data Range. Then, select the **series** tab.

5. Select the *x* values (no label) for the X value range, press [Next>].

6. Select a title and label the axes, press Finish.

Scatter Plot

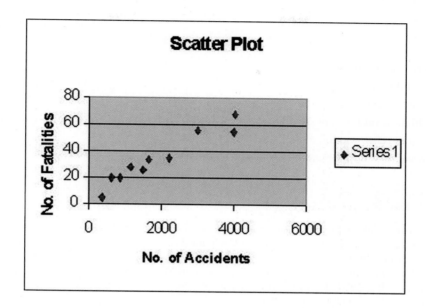

Summary

When data are collected, they are called raw data. Since very little knowledge can be obtained from raw data, they must be organized in some meaningful way. A frequency distribution using classes is the solution. Once a frequency distribution is constructed, the representation of the data by graphs is a simple task. The most commonly used graphs in research statistics are the histogram, frequency polygon, and ogive. Other graphs, such as the Pareto chart, time series graph, and pie graph, can also be used. Some of these graphs are seen frequently in newspapers, magazines, and various statistical reports.

A stem and leaf plot uses part of the data values as stems and part of the data values as leaves. This graph has the advantages of a frequency distribution and a histogram.

When the data are collected in pairs (i.e., each value *x* from one data set corresponds to a value *y* in the other data set), the relationship, if one exists, can be determined by looking at a scatter plot.

Important Terms

bar graph 69

categorical frequency distribution 38

class 37

class boundaries 39

class midpoint 40

class width 39

cumulative frequency 54

cumulative frequency distribution 42

frequency 37

frequency distribution 37

frequency polygon 53

grouped frequency distribution 39

histogram 51

lower class limit 39

negative linear relationship 95

ogive 54

open-ended distribution 41

Pareto chart 70

pie graph 73

positive linear relationship 95

raw data 37

relative frequency graph 56

scatter plot 94

stem and leaf plot 80

time series graph 72

ungrouped frequency distribution 43

upper class limit 39

Important Formulas

Formula for the percentage of values in each class:

$$\% = \frac{f}{n} \cdot 100\%$$

where

f = frequency of the class

n = total number of values

Formula for the range:

R = highest value − lowest value

Formula for the class width:

Class width = upper boundary − lower boundary

Formula for the class midpoint:

$$X_m = \frac{\text{lower boundary} + \text{upper boundary}}{2}$$

or

$$X_m = \frac{\text{lower limit} + \text{upper limit}}{2}$$

Formula for the degrees for each section of a pie graph:

$$\text{Degrees} = \frac{f}{n} \cdot 360°$$

Review Exercises

1. **How People Get Their News** The Brunswick Research Organization surveyed 50 randomly selected individuals and asked them the primary way they received the daily news. Their choices were via newspaper (N), television (T), radio (R), or Internet (I). Construct a categorical frequency distribution for the data and interpret the results. The data in this exercise will be used for Exercise 2 in this section.

N	N	T	T	T	I	R	R	I	T
I	N	R	R	I	N	N	I	T	N
I	R	T	T	T	T	N	R	R	I
R	R	I	N	T	R	T	I	I	T
T	I	N	T	T	I	R	N	R	T

2. Construct a pie graph for the data in Exercise 1, and analyze the results.

3. **Ball Sales** A sporting goods store kept a record of sales of five items for one randomly selected hour during a recent sale. Construct a frequency distribution for the data (B = baseballs, G = golf balls, T = tennis balls, S = soccer balls, F = footballs). (The data for this exercise will be used for Exercise 4 in this section.)

F	B	B	B	G	T	F
G	G	F	S	G	T	
F	T	T	T	S	T	
F	S	S	G	S	B	

4. Draw a pie graph for the data in Exercise 3 showing the sales of each item, and analyze the results.

5. **BUN Count** The blood urea nitrogen (BUN) count of 20 randomly selected patients is given here in milligrams per deciliter (mg/dl). Construct an ungrouped frequency distribution for the data. (The data for this exercise will be used for Exercise 6.)

17	18	13	14
12	17	11	20
13	18	19	17
14	16	17	12
16	15	19	22

6. Construct a histogram, a frequency polygon, and an ogive for the data in Exercise 5 in this section, and analyze the results.

7. The percentage (rounded to the nearest whole percent) of persons from each state completing 4 years or more of college is listed below. Organize the data into a grouped frequency distribution with 5 classes.

Percentage of persons completing 4 years of college

23	25	24	34	22	24	27	37	33	24
26	23	38	24	24	17	28	23	30	25
30	22	33	24	28	36	24	19	25	31
34	31	27	24	29	28	21	25	26	15
26	22	27	21	25	28	24	21	25	26

Source: *New York Times Almanac.*

8. Using the data in Exercise 7, construct a histogram, a frequency polygon, and an ogive.

9. **NFL Franchise Values** The data shown (in millions of dollars) are the values of the 30 National Football League franchises. Construct a frequency distribution for the data using 8 classes. (The data for this exercise will be used for Exercises 10 and 12 in this section.)

170	191	171	235	173	187	181	191
200	218	243	200	182	320	184	239
186	199	186	210	209	240	204	193
211	186	197	204	188	242		

Source: *Pittsburgh Post-Gazette.*

10. Construct a histogram, a frequency polygon, and an ogive for the data in Exercise 9 in this section, and analyze the results.

11. **Ages of the Vice Presidents at the Time of Their Death** The ages of the Vice Presidents of the United States at the time of their death are listed below. Use the data to construct a frequency distribution, histogram,

frequency polygon, and ogive, using relative frequencies. Use 6 classes.

90	83	80	73	70	51	68	79	70	71
72	74	67	54	81	66	62	63	68	57
66	96	78	55	60	66	57	71	60	85
76	98	77	88	78	81	64	66	77	70

Source: *New York Times Almanac.*

12. Construct a histogram, frequency polygon, and ogive by using relative frequencies for the data in Exercise 9 in this section.

13. **NBA Champions** The NBA Champions from 1985 on are listed below. Use the data to construct a Pareto chart and a vertical bar graph.

1985 Los Angeles	1996 Chicago
1986 Boston	1997 Chicago
1987 Los Angeles	1998 Chicago
1988 Detroit	1999 San Antonio
1989 Detroit	2000 Los Angeles
1990 Detroit	2001 Los Angeles
1991 Chicago	2002 Los Angeles
1992 Chicago	2003 San Antonio
1993 Chicago	2004 Detroit
1994 Houston	2005 San Antonio
1995 Houston	

Source: *World Almanac.*

14. **Trial-Ready Cases** Construct a Pareto chart and a horizontal bar graph for the number of trial-ready civil action and equity cases decided in less than 6 months for the selected counties in southwestern Pennsylvania.

County	Number of cases
Westmoreland	427
Washington	298
Green	151
Fayette	106
Somerset	87

Source: *Pittsburgh Tribune-Review.*

15. **Minimum Wage** The given data represent the federal minimum hourly wage in the years shown. Draw a time series graph to represent the data and analyze the results.

Year	Wage
1960	$1.00
1965	1.25
1970	1.60
1975	2.10
1980	3.10
1985	3.35
1990	3.80
1995	4.25
2000	5.15
2005	5.15

Source: *The World Almanac and Book of Facts.*

16. **Farm Data** Construct a time series graph for each set of data and analyze the results.

Year	No. of farms (millions)	Avg. size (acres)
1940	6.35	174
1950	5.65	213
1960	3.96	297
1970	2.95	374
1980	2.44	426
1990	2.15	460
2000	2.17	436

Source: *World Almanac.*

17. **Presidential Debates** The data show the number (in millions) of viewers who watched the first and second Presidential debates. Construct two time series graphs and compare the results.

Year	1992	1996	2000	2004
First debate	62.4	36.1	46.6	62.5
Second debate	69.9	36.3	37.6	46.7

Source: *Nielson Media Research.*

18. **Working Women** In a study of 100 women, the numbers shown here indicate the major reason why each woman surveyed worked outside the home. Construct a pie graph for the data and analyze the results.

Reason	Number of women
To support self/family	62
For extra money	18
For something different to do	12
Other	8

19. **Career Changes** A survey asked if people would like to spend the rest of their careers with their present employers. The results are shown. Construct a pie graph for the data and analyze the results.

Answer	Number of people
Yes	660
No	260
Undecided	80

20. **Museum Visitors** The number of visitors to the Railroad Museum during 24 randomly selected hours is shown here. Construct a stem and leaf plot for the data.

67	62	38	73	34	43	72	35
53	55	58	63	47	42	51	62
32	29	47	62	29	38	36	41

21. **Public Libraries** The numbers of public libraries in operation for selected states are listed below. Organize the data with a stem and leaf plot.

| 102 | 176 | 210 | 142 | 189 | 176 | 108 | 113 | 205 |
| 209 | 184 | 144 | 108 | 192 | 176 | | | |

Source: *World Almanac.*

22. Job Aptitude Test A special aptitude test is given to job applicants. The data shown here represent the scores of 30 applicants. Construct a stem and leaf plot for the data and summarize the results.

204	210	227	218	254
256	238	242	253	227
251	243	233	251	241
237	247	211	222	231
218	212	217	227	209
260	230	228	242	200

23. Television Ratings The data shown are the number of viewers (in millions) and the ratings of 15 television programs for a randomly selected week. Draw a scatter plot and describe the nature of the relationship.

Source: Neilsen Ratings.

No. of viewers, x	22.5	13.2	12.3	6.9	5.4	3.7	11.4	3.7
Ratings, y	14.6	9.2	8.1	4.9	4.0	2.4	8.0	2.5

	21.2	10.1	13.7	4	3.2	23.1	15
	14.4	11.3	9.5	3.0	2.2	16.2	10.6

24. Tutoring and Final Grades An educator wants to see how the number of hours of tutoring a student receives affects the final grade of the student. The data obtained follow. Draw a scatter plot and describe the nature of the relationship.

No. of hours, x	10	8	12	4	8	5
Final grade, y	83	91	92	71	82	75

Statistics Today

How Your Identity Can Be Stolen—Revisited

Data presented in numerical form do not convey an easy-to-interpret conclusion; however, when data are presented in graphical form, readers can see the visual impact of the numbers. In the case of identity fraud, the reader can see that most of the identity frauds are due to lost or stolen wallets, checkbooks, or credit cards, and very few identity frauds are caused by online purchases or transactions.

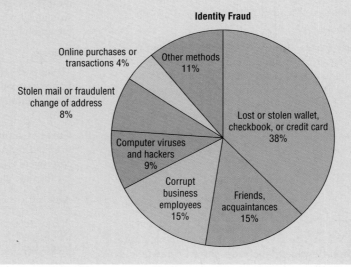

Data Analysis

A Data Bank is found in Appendix D, or on the World Wide Web by following links from
www.mhhe.com/math/stat/bluman

1. From the Data Bank located in Appendix D, choose one of the following variables: age, weight, cholesterol level, systolic pressure, IQ, or sodium level. Select at least 30 values. For these values, construct a grouped frequency distribution. Draw a histogram, frequency polygon, and ogive for the distribution. Describe briefly the shape of the distribution.

2. From the Data Bank, choose one of the following variables: educational level, smoking status, or exercise. Select at least 20 values. Construct an ungrouped frequency distribution for the data. For the distribution, draw a Pareto chart and describe briefly the nature of the chart.

3. From the Data Bank, select at least 30 subjects and construct a categorical distribution for their marital status. Draw a pie graph and describe briefly the findings.

4. Using the data from Data Set IV in Appendix D, construct a frequency distribution and draw a histogram. Describe briefly the shape of the distribution of the tallest buildings in New York City.

5. Using the data from Data Set XI in Appendix D, construct a frequency distribution and draw a frequency polygon. Describe briefly the shape of the distribution for the number of pages in statistics books.

6. Using the data from Data Set IX in Appendix D, divide the United States into four regions, as follows:

Northeast CT ME MA NH NJ NY PA RI VT

Midwest IL IN IA KS MI MN MS NE ND OH SD WI

South AL AR DE DC FL GA KY LA MD NC OK SC TN TX VA WV

West AK AZ CA CO HI ID MT NV NM OR UT WA WY

Find the total population for each region, and draw a Pareto chart and a pie graph for the data. Analyze the results. Explain which chart might be a better representation for the data.

7. Using the data from Data Set I in Appendix D, make a stem and leaf plot for the record low temperatures in the United States. Describe the nature of the plot.

Chapter Quiz

Determine whether each statement is true or false. If the statement is false, explain why.

1. In the construction of a frequency distribution, it is a good idea to have overlapping class limits, such as 10–20, 20–30, 30–40.

2. Histograms can be drawn by using vertical or horizontal bars.

3. It is not important to keep the width of each class the same in a frequency distribution.

4. Frequency distributions can aid the researcher in drawing charts and graphs.

5. The type of graph used to represent data is determined by the type of data collected and by the researcher's purpose.

6. In construction of a frequency polygon, the class limits are used for the *x* axis.

7. Data collected over a period of time can be graphed by using a pie graph.

Select the best answer.

8. What is another name for the ogive?

   a. Histogram
   b. Frequency polygon
   c. Cumulative frequency graph
   d. Pareto chart

9. What are the boundaries for 8.6–8.8?

   a. 8–9
   b. 8.5–8.9
   c. 8.55–8.85
   d. 8.65–8.75

10. What graph should be used to show the relationship between the parts and the whole?

    a. Histogram
    b. Pie graph

    c. Pareto chart
    d. Ogive

11. Except for rounding errors, relative frequencies should add up to what sum?

    a. 0
    b. 1
    c. 50
    d. 100

Complete these statements with the best answers.

12. The three types of frequency distributions are _____, _____, and _____.

13. In a frequency distribution, the number of classes should be between _____ and _____.

14. Data such as blood types (A, B, AB, O) can be organized into a(n) _____ frequency distribution.

15. Data collected over a period of time can be graphed using a(n) _____ graph.

16. A statistical device used in exploratory data analysis that is a combination of a frequency distribution and a histogram is called a(n) _____.

17. On a Pareto chart, the frequencies should be represented on the _____ axis.

18. **Housing Arrangements** A questionnaire on housing arrangements showed this information obtained from 25 respondents. Construct a frequency distribution for the data (H = house, A = apartment, M = mobile home, C = condominium).

    | H | C | H | M | H | A | C | A | M |
    | C | M | C | A | M | A | C | C | M |
    | C | C | H | A | H | H | M |

19. Construct a pie graph for the data in Problem 18.

 20. **Items Purchased at a Convenience Store** When 30 randomly selected customers left a convenience

store, each was asked the number of items he or she purchased. Construct an ungrouped frequency distribution for the data.

2	9	4	3	6
6	2	8	6	5
7	5	3	8	6
6	2	3	2	4
6	9	9	8	9
4	2	1	7	4

21. Construct a histogram, a frequency polygon, and an ogive for the data in Problem 20.

22. Murders in Selected Cities For a recent year, the number of murders in 25 selected cities is shown. Construct a frequency distribution using 9 classes, and analyze the nature of the data in terms of shape, extreme values, etc. (The information in this exercise will be used for Exercise 23 in this section.)

248	348	74	514	597
270	71	226	41	39
366	73	241	46	34
149	68	73	63	65
109	598	278	69	27

Source: *Pittsburgh Tribune Review.*

23. Construct a histogram, frequency polygon, and ogive for the data in Problem 22. Analyze the histogram.

24. Recycled Trash Construct a Pareto chart and a horizontal bar graph for the number of tons (in millions) of trash recycled per year by Americans based on an Environmental Protection Agency study.

Type	Amount
Paper	320.0
Iron/steel	292.0
Aluminum	276.0
Yard waste	242.4
Glass	196.0
Plastics	41.6

Source: *USA TODAY.*

25. Trespasser Fatalities The data show the number of fatal trespasser casualties on railroad property in the United States. Draw a time series graph and explain any trend.

Year	1998	1999	2000	2001
Number	536	463	511	540

Source: Federal Railroad Administration.

26. Museum Visitors The number of visitors to the Historic Museum for 25 randomly selected hours is shown. Construct a stem and leaf plot for the data.

15	53	48	19	38
86	63	98	79	38
62	89	67	39	26
28	35	54	88	76
31	47	53	41	68

27. Travel and Sales A sales manager wishes to determine if there is a relationship between the number of miles her representatives travel and the amount of their monthly sales (in hundreds of dollars). Draw a scatter plot for the data and determine the nature of the relationship.

Miles traveled, x	50	250	120	300	200
Sales, y	$25	175	100	210	150

Critical Thinking Challenges

1. Water Usage The graph shows the average number of gallons of water a person uses for various activities. Can you see anything misleading about the way the graph is drawn?

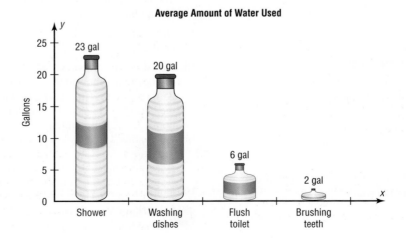

Average Amount of Water Used

2. **The Great Lakes** Shown are various statistics about the Great Lakes. Using appropriate graphs (your choice) and summary statements, write a report analyzing the data.

	Superior	Michigan	Huron	Erie	Ontario
Length (miles)	350	307	206	241	193
Breadth (miles)	160	118	183	57	53
Depth (feet)	1,330	923	750	210	802
Volume (cubic miles)	2,900	1,180	850	116	393
Area (square miles)	31,700	22,300	23,000	9,910	7,550
Shoreline (U.S., miles)	863	1,400	580	431	300

Source: *The World Almanac and Book of Facts.*

3. **Teacher Strikes** In Pennsylvania there were more teacher strikes in 2004 than there were in all other states combined. Because of the disruptions, state legislators want to pass a bill outlawing teacher strikes and submitting contract disputes to binding arbitration. The graph shows the number of teacher strikes in Pennsylvania for the school years 1992 to 2004. Use the graph to answer these questions.

a. In what year did the largest number of strikes occur? How many were there?

b. In what year(s) did the smallest number of teacher strikes occur? How many were there?

c. In what year was the average duration of the strikes the longest? What was it?

d. In what year was the average duration of the strikes the shortest? What was it?

e. In what year was the number of teacher strikes the same as the average duration of the strikes?

f. Find the difference in the number of strikes for the school years 1992–1993 and 2004–2005.

g. Do you think teacher strikes should be outlawed? Justify your conclusions.

Teacher Strikes in Pennsylvania

Source: Pennsylvania School Boards Associations.

Data Projects

Where appropriate, use MINITAB, the TI-83 Plus, the TI-84 Plus, Excel, or a computer program of your choice to complete the following exercises.

1. **Business and Finance** Consider the 30 stocks listed as the Dow Jones Industrials. For each, find their earnings per share. Randomly select 30 stocks traded on the NASDAQ. For each, find their earnings per share. Create a frequency table with 5 categories for each data set. Sketch a histogram for each. How do the two data sets compare?

2. **Sports and Leisure** Use systematic sampling to create a sample of 25 National League and 25 American League baseball players from the most recently completed season. Find the number of home runs for each player. Create a frequency table with 5 categories for each data set. Sketch a histogram for each. How do the two leagues compare?

3. **Technology** Randomly select 50 songs from your music player or music organization program. Find the length (in seconds) for each song. Use these data to create a frequency table with 6 categories. Sketch a frequency polygon for the frequency table. Is the shape of the distribution of times uniform, skewed, or bell-shaped? Also note the genre of each song. Create a Pareto chart showing the frequencies of the various categories. Finally, note the year each song was released. Create a pie chart organized by decade to show the percentage of songs from various time periods.

4. **Health and Wellness** Use information from the Red Cross to create a pie chart depicting the percentages of Americans with various blood types. Also find information about blood donations and the percentage of each type donated. How do the charts compare? Why is the collection of type O blood so important?

5. **Politics and Economics** Consider the U.S. Electoral College System. For each of the 50 states, determine the number of delegates received. Create a frequency table with 8 classes. Is this distribution uniform, skewed, or bell-shaped?

6. **Your Class** Have each person in class take his or her pulse and determine the heart rate (beats in one minute). Use the data to create a frequency table with 6 classes. Then have everyone in the class do 25 jumping jacks and immediately take the pulse again after the activity. Create a frequency table for those data as well. Compare the two results. Are they similarly distributed? How does the range of scores compare?

Answers to Applying the Concepts

Section 2–1 Ages of Presidents at Inauguration

1. The data were obtained from the population of all Presidents at the time this text was written.

2. The oldest inauguration age was 69 years old.

3. The youngest inauguration age was 42 years old.

4. Answers will vary. One possible answer is

Age at inauguration	Frequency
42–45	2
46–49	6
50–53	7
54–57	16
58–61	5
62–65	4
66–69	2

5. Answers will vary. For the frequency distribution given in Exercise 4, there is a peak for the 54–57 bin.

6. Answers will vary. This frequency distribution shows no outliers. However, if we had split our frequency into 14 bins instead of 7, then the ages 42, 43, 68, and 69 might appear as outliers.

7. Answers will vary. The data appear to be unimodal and fairly symmetric, centering on 55 years of age.

Section 2–2 Selling Real Estate

1. A histogram of the data gives price ranges and the counts of homes in each price range. We can also talk about how the data are distributed by looking at a histogram.

2. A frequency polygon shows increases or decreases in the number of home prices around values.

3. A cumulative frequency polygon shows the number of homes sold at or below a given price.

4. The house that sold for $321,550 is an extreme value in this data set.

5. Answers will vary. One possible answer is that the histogram displays the outlier well since there is a gap in the prices of the homes sold.

6. The distribution of the data is skewed to the right.

Section 2–3 Leading Cause of Death

1. The variables in the graph are the year, cause of death, and rate of death per 100,000 men.

2. The cause of death is qualitative, while the year and death rates are quantitative.

3. Year is a discrete variable, and death rate is continuous. Since cause of death is qualitative, it is neither discrete nor continuous.

4. A line graph was used to display the data.

5. No, a Pareto chart could not be used to display the data, since we can only have one quantitative variable and one categorical variable in a Pareto chart.

6. We cannot use a pie chart for the same reasons as given for the Pareto chart.

7. A Pareto chart is typically used to show a categorical variable listed from the highest-frequency category to the category with the lowest frequency.

8. A time series chart is used to see trends in the data. It can also be used for forecasting and predicting.

Section 2–4   Absences and Final Grades

1. The number of absences can be considered to be the independent variable.

2. The final grade can be considered to be the dependent variable.

3. The scatter plot shows that there is a somewhat linear negative relationship between the variables.

4. It can be concluded in general that more classes missed are associated with lower grades, and fewer classes missed are associated with higher grades.

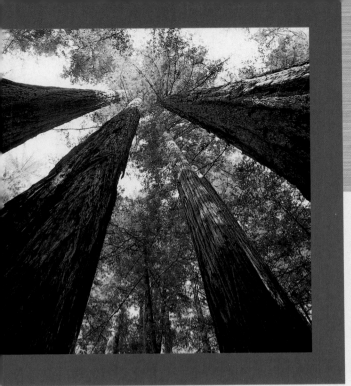

Data Description

Objectives

After completing this chapter, you should be able to

1 Summarize data, using measures of central tendency, such as the mean, median, mode, and midrange.

2 Describe data, using measures of variation, such as the range, variance, and standard deviation.

3 Identify the position of a data value in a data set, using various measures of position, such as percentiles, deciles, and quartiles.

4 Use the techniques of exploratory data analysis, including boxplots and five-number summaries, to discover various aspects of data.

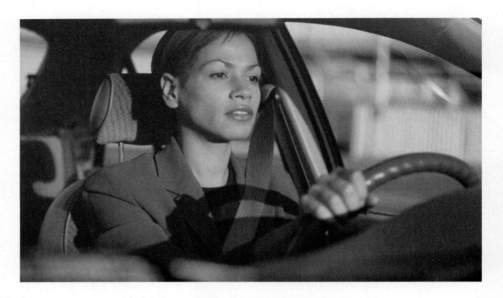

Statistics Today

How Long Are You Delayed by Road Congestion?

No matter where you live, at one time or another, you have been stuck in traffic. To see whether there are more traffic delays in some cities than in others, statisticians make comparisons using descriptive statistics. A statistical study by the Texas Transportation Institute found that a driver is delayed by road congestion an average of 36 hours per year. To see how selected cities compare to this average, see Statistics Today—Revisited at the end of the chapter.

This chapter will show you how to obtain and interpret descriptive statistics such as measures of average, measures of variation, and measures of position.

Introduction

Chapter 2 showed how you can gain useful information from raw data by organizing them into a frequency distribution and then presenting the data by using various graphs. This chapter shows the statistical methods that can be used to summarize data. The most familiar of these methods is the finding of averages.

For example, you may read that the average speed of a car crossing midtown Manhattan during the day is 5.3 miles per hour or that the average number of minutes an American father of a 4-year-old spends alone with his child each day is 42.[1]

In the book *American Averages* by Mike Feinsilber and William B. Meed, the authors state:

> *"Average" when you stop to think of it is a funny concept. Although it describes all of us it describes none of us. . . . While none of us wants to be the average American, we all want to know about him or her.*

The authors go on to give examples of averages:

> *The average American man is five feet, nine inches tall; the average woman is five feet, 3.6 inches.*
> *The average American is sick in bed seven days a year missing five days of work.*
> *On the average day, 24 million people receive animal bites.*
> *By his or her 70th birthday, the average American will have eaten 14 steers, 1050 chickens, 3.5 lambs, and 25.2 hogs.[2]*

Interesting Fact

A person has on average 1460 dreams in 1 year.

---

[1]"Harper's Index," *Harper's* magazine.

[2]Mike Feinsilber and William B. Meed, *American Averages* (New York: Bantam Doubleday Dell).

In these examples, the word *average* is ambiguous, since several different methods can be used to obtain an average. Loosely stated, the average means the center of the distribution or the most typical case. Measures of average are also called *measures of central tendency* and include the *mean, median, mode,* and *midrange.*

Knowing the average of a data set is not enough to describe the data set entirely. Even though a shoe store owner knows that the average size of a man's shoe is size 10, she would not be in business very long if she ordered only size 10 shoes.

As this example shows, in addition to knowing the average, you must know how the data values are dispersed. That is, do the data values cluster around the mean, or are they spread more evenly throughout the distribution? The measures that determine the spread of the data values are called *measures of variation,* or *measures of dispersion.* These measures include the *range, variance,* and *standard deviation.*

Finally, another set of measures is necessary to describe data. These measures are called *measures of position.* They tell where a specific data value falls within the data set or its relative position in comparison with other data values. The most common position measures are *percentiles, deciles,* and *quartiles.* These measures are used extensively in psychology and education. Sometimes they are referred to as *norms.*

The measures of central tendency, variation, and position explained in this chapter are part of what is called *traditional statistics.*

Section 3–4 shows the techniques of what is called *exploratory data analysis.* These techniques include the *boxplot* and the *five-number summary.* They can be used to explore data to see what they show (as opposed to the traditional techniques, which are used to confirm conjectures about the data).

3–1   Measures of Central Tendency

Chapter 1 stated that statisticians use samples taken from populations; however, when populations are small, it is not necessary to use samples since the entire population can be used to gain information. For example, suppose an insurance manager wanted to know the average weekly sales of all the company's representatives. If the company employed a large number of salespeople, say, nationwide, he would have to use a sample and make

Objective

Summarize data, using measures of central tendency, such as the mean, median, mode, and midrange.

an inference to the entire sales force. But if the company had only a few salespeople, say, only 87 agents, he would be able to use all representatives' sales for a randomly chosen week and thus use the entire population.

Measures found by using all the data values in the population are called *parameters.* Measures obtained by using the data values from samples are called *statistics;* hence, the average of the sales from a sample of representatives is a *statistic,* and the average of sales obtained from the entire population is a *parameter.*

A **statistic** is a characteristic or measure obtained by using the data values from a sample.

A **parameter** is a characteristic or measure obtained by using all the data values from a specific population.

These concepts as well as the symbols used to represent them will be explained in detail in this chapter.

General Rounding Rule In statistics the basic rounding rule is that when computations are done in the calculation, rounding should not be done until the final answer is calculated. When rounding is done in the intermediate steps, it tends to increase the difference between that answer and the exact one. But in the textbook and solutions manual, it is not practical to show long decimals in the intermediate calculations; hence, the values in the examples are carried out to enough places (usually three or four) to obtain the same answer that a calculator would give after rounding on the last step.

The Mean

The *mean,* also known as the *arithmetic average,* is found by adding the values of the data and dividing by the total number of values. For example, the mean of 3, 2, 6, 5, and 4 is found by adding $3 + 2 + 6 + 5 + 4 = 20$ and dividing by 5; hence, the mean of the data is $20 \div 5 = 4$. The values of the data are represented by X's. In this data set, $X_1 = 3$, $X_2 = 2$, $X_3 = 6$, $X_4 = 5$, and $X_5 = 4$. To show a sum of the total X values, the symbol Σ (the capital Greek letter sigma) is used, and ΣX means to find the sum of the X values in the data set. The summation notation is explained in Appendix A.

The **mean** is the sum of the values, divided by the total number of values. The symbol $\overline{X}$ represents the sample mean.

$$\overline{X} = \frac{X_1 + X_2 + X_3 + \cdots + X_n}{n} = \frac{\Sigma X}{n}$$

where n represents the total number of values in the sample.

For a population, the Greek letter μ (mu) is used for the mean.

$$\mu = \frac{X_1 + X_2 + X_3 + \cdots + X_N}{N} = \frac{\Sigma X}{N}$$

where N represents the total number of values in the population.

In statistics, Greek letters are used to denote parameters, and Roman letters are used to denote statistics. Assume that the data are obtained from samples unless otherwise specified.

Example 3–1

Days Off per Year

 The data represent the number of days off per year for a sample of individuals selected from nine different countries. Find the mean.

20, 26, 40, 36, 23, 42, 35, 24, 30

Source: World Tourism Organization.

Solution

$$\overline{X} = \frac{\Sigma X}{n} = \frac{20 + 26 + 40 + 36 + 23 + 42 + 35 + 24 + 30}{9} = \frac{276}{9} = 30.7 \text{ days}$$

Hence, the mean of the number of days off is 30.7 days.

| **Example 3–2** | **Area Boat Registrations** |

The data shown represent the number of boat registrations for six counties in southwestern Pennsylvania. Find the mean.

| 3782 | 6367 | 9002 | 4208 | 6843 | 11,008 |

Source: Pennsylvania Fish and Boat Commission.

Solution

$$\overline{X} = \frac{\Sigma X}{n} = \frac{3782 + 6367 + 9002 + 4208 + 6843 + 11,008}{6} = \frac{41,210}{6} = 6868.3$$

The mean for the six county boat registrations is 6868.3.

The mean, in most cases, is not an actual data value.

Rounding Rule for the Mean The mean should be rounded to one more decimal place than occurs in the raw data. For example, if the raw data are given in whole numbers, the mean should be rounded to the nearest tenth. If the data are given in tenths, the mean should be rounded to the nearest hundredth, and so on.

The procedure for finding the mean for grouped data uses the midpoints of the classes. This procedure is shown next.

| **Example 3–3** | **Miles Run per Week** |

Using the frequency distribution for Example 2–7, find the mean. The data represent the number of miles run during one week for a sample of 20 runners.

Solution

The procedure for finding the mean for grouped data is given here.

Step 1 Make a table as shown.

A Class	B Frequency f	C Midpoint X_m	D $f \cdot X_m$
5.5–10.5	1		
10.5–15.5	2		
15.5–20.5	3		
20.5–25.5	5		
25.5–30.5	4		
30.5–35.5	3		
35.5–40.5	2		
	$n = 20$		

Step 2 Find the midpoints of each class and enter them in column C.

$$X_m = \frac{5.5 + 10.5}{2} = 8 \qquad \frac{10.5 + 15.5}{2} = 13 \qquad \text{etc.}$$

Step 3 For each class, multiply the frequency by the midpoint, as shown, and place the product in column D.

$$1 \cdot 8 = 8 \qquad 2 \cdot 13 = 26 \qquad \text{etc.}$$

The completed table is shown here.

A Class	B Frequency f	C Midpoint X_m	D $f \cdot X_m$
5.5–10.5	1	8	8
10.5–15.5	2	13	26
15.5–20.5	3	18	54
20.5–25.5	5	23	115
25.5–30.5	4	28	112
30.5–35.5	3	33	99
35.5–40.5	2	38	76
	$n = 20$		$\Sigma f \cdot X_m = 490$

Step 4 Find the sum of column D.

Step 5 Divide the sum by n to get the mean.

$$\overline{X} = \frac{\Sigma f \cdot X_m}{n} = \frac{490}{20} = 24.5 \text{ miles}$$

Unusual Stat

A person looks, on average, at about 14 homes before he or she buys one.

The procedure for finding the mean for grouped data assumes that the mean of all the raw data values in each class is equal to the midpoint of the class. In reality, this is not true, since the average of the raw data values in each class usually will not be exactly equal to the midpoint. However, using this procedure will give an acceptable approximation of the mean, since some values fall above the midpoint and other values fall below the midpoint for each class, and the midpoint represents an estimate of all values in the class.

The steps for finding the mean for grouped data are summarized in the next Procedure Table.

Procedure Table

Finding the Mean for Grouped Data

Step 1 Make a table as shown.

A Class	B Frequency f	C Midpoint X_m	D $f \cdot X_m$

Step 2 Find the midpoints of each class and place them in column C.

Step 3 Multiply the frequency by the midpoint for each class, and place the product in column D.

Step 4 Find the sum of column D.

Step 5 Divide the sum obtained in column D by the sum of the frequencies obtained in column B.

The formula for the mean is

$$\overline{X} = \frac{\Sigma f \cdot X_m}{n}$$

[*Note:* The symbols $\Sigma f \cdot X_m$ mean to find the sum of the product of the frequency (f) and the midpoint (X_m) for each class.]

Statistics

Ages of the Top 50 Wealthiest People

The histogram shows the ages of the top 50 wealthiest individuals according to *Forbes Magazine* for a recent year. The mean age is 66.04 years. The median age is 68 years. Explain why these two statistics are not enough to adequately describe the data.

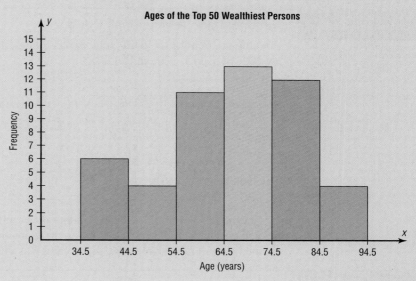

The Median

An article recently reported that the median income for college professors was $43,250. This measure of central tendency means that one-half of all the professors surveyed earned more than $43,250, and one-half earned less than $43,250.

The *median* is the halfway point in a data set. Before you can find this point, the data must be arranged in order. When the data set is ordered, it is called a **data array.** The median either will be a specific value in the data set or will fall between two values, as shown in Examples 3–4 through 3–8.

The **median** is the midpoint of the data array. The symbol for the median is MD.

Steps in computing the median of a data array

Step 1   Arrange the data in order.

Step 2   Select the middle point.

Example 3–4	**Hotel Rooms**

The number of rooms in the seven hotels in downtown Pittsburgh is 713, 300, 618, 595, 311, 401, and 292. Find the median.

Source: Interstate Hotels Corporation.

Solution

Step 1   Arrange the data in order.

292, 300, 311, 401, 595, 618, 713

Step 2   Select the middle value.

292, 300, 311, 401, 595, 618, 713

↑

Median

Hence, the median is 401 rooms.

Example 3–5	**National Park Vehicle Pass Costs**

Find the median for the daily vehicle pass charge for five U.S. National Parks. The costs are $25, $15, $15, $20, and $15.

Source: National Park Service.

Solution

$15 $15 $15 $20 $25

↑

Median

The median cost is $15.

Examples 3–4 and 3–5 each had an odd number of values in the data set; hence, the median was an actual data value. When there are an even number of values in the data set, the median will fall between two given values, as illustrated in Examples 3–6, 3–7, and 3–8.

Example 3–6	**Tornadoes in the United States**

The number of tornadoes that have occurred in the United States over an 8-year period follows. Find the median.

684, 764, 656, 702, 856, 1133, 1132, 1303

Source: *The Universal Almanac.*

Solution

656, 684, 702, 764, 856, 1132, 1133, 1303

↑

Median

Since the middle point falls halfway between 764 and 856, find the median MD by adding the two values and dividing by 2.

$$\text{MD} = \frac{764 + 856}{2} = \frac{1620}{2} = 810$$

The median number of tornadoes is 810.

Example 3–7	Cloudy Days

 The number of cloudy days for the top 10 cloudiest cities is shown. Find the median.

209, 223, 211, 227, 213, 240, 240, 211, 229, 212

Source: National Climatic Data Center.

Solution

Arrange the data in order.

209, 211, 211, 212, 213, 223, 227, 229, 240, 240
$$\uparrow$$
Median

$$MD = \frac{213 + 223}{2} = 218$$

Hence, the median is 218 days.

Example 3–8	Magazines Purchased

 Six customers purchased these numbers of magazines: 1, 7, 3, 2, 3, 4. Find the median.

Solution

$$1, 2, 3, 3, 4, 7 \qquad MD = \frac{3 + 3}{2} = 3$$
$$\uparrow$$
Median

Hence, the median number of magazines purchased is 3.

The Mode

The third measure of average is called the *mode.* The mode is the value that occurs most often in the data set. It is sometimes said to be the most typical case.

> The value that occurs most often in a data set is called the **mode.**

A data set that has only one value that occurs with the greatest frequency is said to be **unimodal.**

If a data set has two values that occur with the same greatest frequency, both values are considered to be the mode and the data set is said to be **bimodal.** If a data set has more than two values that occur with the same greatest frequency, each value is used as the mode, and the data set is said to be **multimodal.** When no data value occurs more than once, the data set is said to have *no mode.* A data set can have more than one mode or no mode at all. These situations will be shown in some of the examples that follow.

Example 3–9	NFL Signing Bonuses

 Find the mode of the signing bonuses of eight NFL players for a specific year. The bonuses in millions of dollars are

18.0, 14.0, 34.5, 10, 11.3, 10, 12.4, 10

Source: *USA TODAY.*

Solution

It is helpful to arrange the data in order although it is not necessary.

    10, 10, 10, 11.3, 12.4, 14.0, 18.0, 34.5

Since $10 million occurred 3 times—a frequency larger than any other number—the mode is $10 million.

Example 3–10

Coal Employees in Pennsylvania

 Find the mode for the number of coal employees per county for 10 selected counties in southwestern Pennsylvania.

    110, 731, 1031, 84, 20, 118, 1162, 1977, 103, 752

Source: *Pittsburgh Tribune-Review.*

Solution

Since each value occurs only once, there is no mode.
    Note: Do not say that the mode is zero. That would be incorrect, because in some data, such as temperature, zero can be an actual value.

Example 3–11

Licensed Nuclear Reactors

The data show the number of licensed nuclear reactors in the United States for a recent 15-year period. Find the mode.

Source: *The World Almanac and Book of Facts.*

104	104	104	104	104
107	109	109	109	110
109	111	112	111	109

Solution

Since the values 104 and 109 both occur 5 times, the modes are 104 and 109. The data set is said to be bimodal.

The mode for grouped data is the modal class. The **modal class** is the class with the largest frequency.

Example 3–12

Miles Run per Week

Find the modal class for the frequency distribution of miles that 20 runners ran in one week, used in Example 2–7.

Class	Frequency
5.5–10.5	1
10.5–15.5	2
15.5–20.5	3
20.5–25.5	5 ← Modal class
25.5–30.5	4
30.5–35.5	3
35.5–40.5	2

Solution

The modal class is 20.5–25.5, since it has the largest frequency. Sometimes the midpoint of the class is used rather than the boundaries; hence, the mode could also be given as 23 miles per week.

The mode is the only measure of central tendency that can be used in finding the most typical case when the data are nominal or categorical.

Example 3–13

Student Majors

A survey showed this distribution for the number of students enrolled in each field. Find the mode.

Business	1425
Liberal arts	878
Computer science	632
Education	471
General studies	95

Solution

Since the category with the highest frequency is business, the most typical case is a business major.

An extremely high or extremely low data value in a data set can have a striking effect on the mean of the data set. These extreme values are called *outliers*. This is one reason why when analyzing a frequency distribution, you should be aware of any of these values. For the data set shown in Example 3–14, the mean, median, and mode can be quite different because of extreme values. A method for identifying outliers is given in Section 3–3.

Example 3–14

Salaries of Personnel

A small company consists of the owner, the manager, the salesperson, and two technicians, all of whose annual salaries are listed here. (Assume that this is the entire population.)

Staff	Salary
Owner	$50,000
Manager	20,000
Salesperson	12,000
Technician	9,000
Technician	9,000

Find the mean, median, and mode.

Solution

$$\mu = \frac{\Sigma X}{N} = \frac{50,000 + 20,000 + 12,000 + 9000 + 9000}{5} = \$20,000$$

Hence, the mean is $20,000, the median is $12,000, and the mode is $9,000.

In Example 3–14, the mean is much higher than the median or the mode. This is so because the extremely high salary of the owner tends to raise the value of the mean. In this and similar situations, the median should be used as the measure of central tendency.

The Midrange

The *midrange* is a rough estimate of the middle. It is found by adding the lowest and highest values in the data set and dividing by 2. It is a very rough estimate of the average and can be affected by one extremely high or low value.

The **midrange** is defined as the sum of the lowest and highest values in the data set, divided by 2. The symbol MR is used for the midrange.

$$MR = \frac{\text{lowest value} + \text{highest value}}{2}$$

Example 3–15

Water-Line Breaks

 In the last two winter seasons, the city of Brownsville, Minnesota, reported these numbers of water-line breaks per month. Find the midrange.

2, 3, 6, 8, 4, 1

Solution

$$MR = \frac{1 + 8}{2} = \frac{9}{2} = 4.5$$

Hence, the midrange is 4.5.

If the data set contains one extremely large value or one extremely small value, a higher or lower midrange value will result and may not be a typical description of the middle.

Example 3–16

NFL Signing Bonuses

Find the midrange of data for the NFL signing bonuses in Example 3–9. The bonuses in millions of dollars are

18.0, 14.0, 34.5, 10, 11.3, 10, 12.4, 10

Solution

The smallest bonus is $10 million and the largest bonus is $34.5 million.

$$MR = \frac{10 + 34.5}{2} = \frac{44.5}{2} = \$22.25 \text{ million}$$

Notice that this amount is larger than seven of the eight amounts and is not typical of the average of the bonuses. The reason is that there is one very high bonus, namely, $34.5 million.

In statistics, several measures can be used for an average. The most common measures are the mean, median, mode, and midrange. Each has its own specific purpose and use. Exercises 39 through 41 show examples of other averages, such as the harmonic mean, the geometric mean, and the quadratic mean. Their applications are limited to specific areas, as shown in the exercises.

The Weighted Mean

Sometimes, you must find the mean of a data set in which not all values are equally represented. Consider the case of finding the average cost of a gallon of gasoline for three taxis. Suppose the drivers buy gasoline at three different service stations at a cost of \$3.22, \$3.53, and \$3.63 per gallon. You might try to find the average by using the formula

$$\overline{X} = \frac{\Sigma X}{n}$$

$$= \frac{3.22 + 3.53 + 3.63}{3} = \frac{10.38}{3} = \$3.46$$

But not all drivers purchased the same number of gallons. Hence, to find the true average cost per gallon, you must take into consideration the number of gallons each driver purchased.

The type of mean that considers an additional factor is called the *weighted mean,* and it is used when the values are not all equally represented.

Find the **weighted mean** of a variable X by multiplying each value by its corresponding weight and dividing the sum of the products by the sum of the weights.

$$\overline{X} = \frac{w_1 X_1 + w_2 X_2 + \cdots + w_n X_n}{w_1 + w_2 + \cdots + w_n} = \frac{\Sigma w X}{\Sigma w}$$

where $w_1, w_2, \ldots, w_n$ are the weights and $X_1, X_2, \ldots, X_n$ are the values.

Example 3–17 shows how the weighted mean is used to compute a grade point average. Since courses vary in their credit value, the number of credits must be used as weights.

Example 3–17

Grade Point Average

A student received an A in English Composition I (3 credits), a C in Introduction to Psychology (3 credits), a B in Biology I (4 credits), and a D in Physical Education (2 credits). Assuming A = 4 grade points, B = 3 grade points, C = 2 grade points, D = 1 grade point, and F = 0 grade points, find the student's grade point average.

Solution

Course	Credits (w)	Grade (X)
English Composition I	3	A (4 points)
Introduction to Psychology	3	C (2 points)
Biology I	4	B (3 points)
Physical Education	2	D (1 point)

$$\overline{X} = \frac{\Sigma w X}{\Sigma w} = \frac{3 \cdot 4 + 3 \cdot 2 + 4 \cdot 3 + 2 \cdot 1}{3 + 3 + 4 + 2} = \frac{32}{12} = 2.7$$

The grade point average is 2.7.

Table 3–1 summarizes the measures of central tendency.

Table 3–1	Summary of Measures of Central Tendency	
Measure	**Definition**	**Symbol(s)**
Mean	Sum of values, divided by total number of values	$\mu, \overline{X}$
Median	Middle point in data set that has been ordered	MD
Mode	Most frequent data value	None
Midrange	Lowest value plus highest value, divided by 2	MR

Researchers and statisticians must know which measure of central tendency is being used and when to use each measure of central tendency. The properties and uses of the four measures of central tendency are summarized next.

Properties and Uses of Central Tendency

The Mean
1. The mean is found by using all the values of the data.
2. The mean varies less than the median or mode when samples are taken from the same population and all three measures are computed for these samples.
3. The mean is used in computing other statistics, such as the variance.
4. The mean for the data set is unique and not necessarily one of the data values.
5. The mean cannot be computed for the data in a frequency distribution that has an open-ended class.
6. The mean is affected by extremely high or low values, called outliers, and may not be the appropriate average to use in these situations.

The Median
1. The median is used to find the center or middle value of a data set.
2. The median is used when it is necessary to find out whether the data values fall into the upper half or lower half of the distribution.
3. The median is used for an open-ended distribution.
4. The median is affected less than the mean by extremely high or extremely low values.

The Mode
1. The mode is used when the most typical case is desired.
2. The mode is the easiest average to compute.
3. The mode can be used when the data are nominal, such as religious preference, gender, or political affiliation.
4. The mode is not always unique. A data set can have more than one mode, or the mode may not exist for a data set.

The Midrange
1. The midrange is easy to compute.
2. The midrange gives the midpoint.
3. The midrange is affected by extremely high or low values in a data set.

Figure 3–1

Types of Distributions

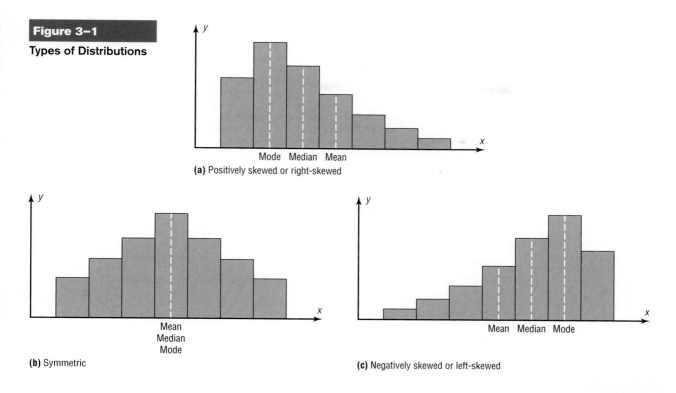

(a) Positively skewed or right-skewed

(b) Symmetric

(c) Negatively skewed or left-skewed

Distribution Shapes

Frequency distributions can assume many shapes. The three most important shapes are positively skewed, symmetric, and negatively skewed. Figure 3–1 shows histograms of each.

In a **positively skewed** or **right-skewed distribution,** the majority of the data values fall to the left of the mean and cluster at the lower end of the distribution; the "tail" is to the right. Also, the mean is to the right of the median, and the mode is to the left of the median.

For example, if an instructor gave an examination and most of the students did poorly, their scores would tend to cluster on the left side of the distribution. A few high scores would constitute the tail of the distribution, which would be on the right side. Another example of a positively skewed distribution is the incomes of the population of the United States. Most of the incomes cluster about the low end of the distribution; those with high incomes are in the minority and are in the tail at the right of the distribution.

In a **symmetric distribution,** the data values are evenly distributed on both sides of the mean. In addition, when the distribution is unimodal, the mean, median, and mode are the same and are at the center of the distribution. Examples of symmetric distributions are IQ scores and heights of adult males.

When the majority of the data values fall to the right of the mean and cluster at the upper end of the distribution, with the tail to the left, the distribution is said to be **negatively skewed** or **left-skewed.** Also, the mean is to the left of the median, and the mode is to the right of the median. As an example, a negatively skewed distribution results if the majority of students score very high on an instructor's examination. These scores will tend to cluster to the right of the distribution.

When a distribution is extremely skewed, the value of the mean will be pulled toward the tail, but the majority of the data values will be greater than the mean or less than the mean (depending on which way the data are skewed); hence, the median rather than the mean is a more appropriate measure of central tendency. An extremely skewed distribution can also affect other statistics.

A measure of skewness for a distribution is discussed in Exercise 48 in Section 3–2.

Applying the Concepts **3–1**

Teacher Salaries

The following data represent salaries (in dollars) from a school district in Greenwood, South Carolina.

10,000	11,000	11,000	12,500	14,300	17,500
18,000	16,600	19,200	21,560	16,400	107,000

1. First, assume you work for the school board in Greenwood and do not wish to raise taxes to increase salaries. Compute the mean, median, and mode, and decide which one would best support your position to not raise salaries.
2. Second, assume you work for the teachers' union and want a raise for the teachers. Use the best measure of central tendency to support your position.
3. Explain how outliers can be used to support one or the other position.
4. If the salaries represented every teacher in the school district, would the averages be parameters or statistics?
5. Which measure of central tendency can be misleading when a data set contains outliers?
6. When you are comparing the measures of central tendency, does the distribution display any skewness? Explain.

See page 188 for the answers.

Exercises 3–1

For Exercises 1 through 8, find (*a*) the mean, (*b*) the median, (*c*) the mode, and (*d*) the midrange.

1. **Grade Point Averages** The average undergraduate grade point average (GPA) for the 25 top-ranked medical schools is listed below.

3.80	3.77	3.70	3.74	3.70
3.86	3.76	3.68	3.67	3.57
3.83	3.70	3.80	3.74	3.67
3.78	3.74	3.73	3.65	3.66
3.75	3.64	3.78	3.73	3.64

Source: *U.S. News & World Report Best Graduate Schools.*

2. **Heights of the Highest Waterfalls** The heights (in feet) of the 20 highest waterfalls in the world are shown here. (*Note:* The height of Niagara Falls is 182 feet!)

3212 2800 2625 2540 2499 2425 2307 2151 2123 2000
1904 1841 1650 1612 1536 1388 1215 1198 1182 1170

Source: *New York Times Almanac.*

3. **High Temperatures** The reported high temperatures (in degrees Fahrenheit) for selected world cities on an October day are shown below. Which measure of central tendency do you think best describes these data?

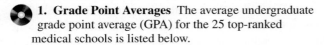

62 72 66 79 83 61 62 85 72 64 74 71
42 38 91 66 77 90 74 63 64 68 42

Source: www.accuweather.com

4. **Observers in the Frogwatch Program** The number of observers in the Frogwatch USA program (a wildlife conservation program dedicated to helping conserve frogs and toads) for the top 10 states with the most observers is 484, 483, 422, 396, 378, 352, 338, 331, 318, and 302. The top 10 states with the most active watchers list these numbers of visits: 634, 464, 406, 267, 219, 194, 191, 150, 130, and 114. Compare the measures of central tendency for these two groups of data.

Source: www.nwf.org/frogwatch

5. **Expenditures per Pupil for Selected States** The expenditures per pupil for selected states are listed below. Based on these data, what do you think of the claim that the average expenditure per pupil in the United States exceeds $10,000?

6,300	11,847	8,319	9,344	9,870
10,460	7,491	7,552	12,568	8,632
7,552	12,568	8,632	11,057	10,454
8,109				

Source: *New York Times Almanac.*

6. **Earnings of Nonliving Celebrities** *Forbes* magazine prints an annual Top-Earning Nonliving Celebrities list (based on royalties and estate earnings). Find the measures of central tendency for these data and comment on the skewness. Figures represent millions of dollars.

Kurt Cobain	50	Ray Charles	10
Elvis Presley	42	Marilyn Monroe	8
Charles M. Schulz	35	Johnny Cash	8
John Lennon	24	J.R.R. Tolkien	7
Albert Einstein	20	George Harrison	7
Andy Warhol	19	Bob Marley	7
Theodore Geisel (Dr. Seuss)	10		

Source: articles.moneycentral.msn.com

7. Earthquake Strengths Twelve major earthquakes had Richter magnitudes shown here.

7.0, 6.2, 7.7, 8.0, 6.4, 6.2,
7.2, 5.4, 6.4, 6.5, 7.2, 5.4

Which would you consider the best measure of average?

Source: *The Universal Almanac.*

8. Top-Paid CEOs The data shown are the total compensation (in millions of dollars) for the 50 top-paid CEOs for a recent year. Compare the averages, and state which one you think is the best measure.

17.5	18.0	36.8	31.7	31.7
17.3	24.3	47.7	38.5	17.0
23.7	16.5	25.1	17.4	18.0
37.6	19.7	21.4	28.6	21.6
19.3	20.0	16.9	25.2	19.8
25.0	17.2	20.4	20.1	29.1
19.1	25.2	23.2	25.9	24.0
41.7	24.0	16.8	26.8	31.4
16.9	17.2	24.1	35.2	19.1
22.9	18.2	25.4	35.4	25.5

Source: *USA TODAY.*

9. Find the (*a*) mean, (*b*) median, (*c*) mode, and (*d*) midrange for the data in Exercise 17 in Section 2–1. Is the distribution symmetric or skewed? Use the individual data values.

10. Find the (*a*) mean, (*b*) median, (*c*) mode, and (*d*) midrange for the distances of the home runs for McGwire and Sosa, using the data in Exercise 18 in Section 2–1.

   Compare the means. Decide if the means are approximately equal or if one of the players is hitting longer home runs. Use the individual data values.

11. Populations of Selected Cities Populations for towns and cities of 5000 or more (based on the 2004 figures) in the 15XXX zip code area are listed here for two different years. Find the mean, median, mode, and midrange for each set of data. What do your findings suggest?

2004			1990		
11,270	8,825	7,439	13,374	9,200	8,133
8,220	5,132	8,395	9,278	4,768	9,135
5,463	8,174	5,044	6,113	9,656	5,784
8,739	5,282	7,869	9,229	21,923	8,286
6,199	5,307	10,493	10,687	5,319	9,126
10,309	14,925	8,397	11,221	15,174	9,901
9,964	14,849	5,094	10,823	15,864	5,445
14,340	5,707	6,672	14,292	5,748	6,961

Source: *World Almanac.*

For Exercises 12 through 21, find the (*a*) mean and (*b*) modal class.

12. Exam Scores For 108 randomly selected college students, this exam score frequency distribution was obtained. (The data in this exercise will be used in Exercise 18 in Section 3–2.)

Class limits	Frequency
90–98	6
99–107	22
108–116	43
117–125	28
126–134	9

13. Hourly Compensation for Production Workers The hourly compensation costs (in U.S. dollars) for production workers in selected countries are represented below. Find the mean and modal class.

Class	Frequency
2.48–7.48	7
7.49–12.49	3
12.50–17.50	1
17.51–22.51	7
22.52–27.52	5
27.53–32.53	5

Compare the mean of these grouped data to the U.S. mean of $21.97.

Source: *New York Times Almanac.*

14. Automobile Fuel Efficiency Thirty automobiles were tested for fuel efficiency (in miles per gallon). This frequency distribution was obtained. (The data in this exercise will be used in Exercise 20 in Section 3–2.)

Class boundaries	Frequency
7.5–12.5	3
12.5–17.5	5
17.5–22.5	15
22.5–27.5	5
27.5–32.5	2

15. Percentage of Foreign-Born People The percentage of foreign-born population for each of the 50 states is represented below. Find the mean and modal class. Do you think the mean is the best average for this set of data? Explain.

Percentage	Frequency
0.8–4.4	26
4.5–8.1	11
8.2–11.8	4
11.9–15.5	5
15.6–19.2	2
19.3–22.9	1
23.0–26.6	1

Source: *World Almanac.*

16. Find the mean and modal class for each set of data in Exercises 8 and 18 in Section 2–2. Is the average about the same for both sets of data?

17. Percentage of College-Educated Population over 25 Below are the percentages of the population over 25 years of age who have completed 4 years of college or more for the 50 states and the District of Columbia. Find the mean and modal class.

Percentage	Frequency
15.2–19.6	3
19.7–24.1	15
24.2–28.6	19
28.7–33.1	6
33.2–37.6	7
37.7–42.1	0
42.2–46.6	1

Source: *New York Times Almanac.*

18. Net Worth of Corporations These data represent the net worth (in millions of dollars) of 45 national corporations.

Class limits	Frequency
10–20	2
21–31	8
32–42	15
43–53	7
54–64	10
65–75	3

19. Cost per Load of Laundry Detergents The cost per load (in cents) of 35 laundry detergents tested by a consumer organization is shown. (The data in this exercise will be used for Exercise 19 in Section 3–2.)

Class limits	Frequency
13–19	2
20–26	7
27–33	12
34–40	5
41–47	6
48–54	1
55–61	0
62–68	2

20. Commissions Earned This frequency distribution represents the commission earned (in dollars) by 100 salespeople employed at several branches of a large chain store.

Class limits	Frequency
150–158	5
159–167	16
168–176	20
177–185	21
186–194	20
195–203	15
204–212	3

21. Copier Service Calls This frequency distribution represents the data obtained from a sample of 75 copying machine service technicians. The values represent the days between service calls for various copying machines.

Class boundaries	Frequency
15.5–18.5	14
18.5–21.5	12
21.5–24.5	18
24.5–27.5	10
27.5–30.5	15
30.5–33.5	6

22. Use the data from Exercise 14 in Section 2–1 and find the mean and modal class.

23. Find the mean and modal class for the data in Exercise 13 in Section 2–1.

24. Use the data from Exercise 3 in Section 2–2 and find the mean and modal class.

25. Enrollments for Selected Independent Religiously Controlled 4-Year Colleges Listed below are the enrollments for selected independent religiously controlled 4-year colleges which offer bachelor's degrees only. Construct a grouped frequency distribution with six classes and find the mean and modal class.

1013 1867 1268 1666 2309 1231 3005 2895 2166 1136
1532 1461 1750 1069 1723 1827 1155 1714 2391 2155
1412 1688 2471 1759 3008 2511 2577 1082 1067 1062
1319 1037 2400

Source: *World Almanac.*

26. Find the weighted mean price of three models of automobiles sold. The number and price of each model sold are shown in this list.

Model	Number	Price
A	8	$10,000
B	10	12,000
C	12	8,000

27. Fat Grams Using the weighted mean, find the average number of grams of fat per ounce of meat or fish that a person would consume over a 5-day period if he ate these:

Meat or fish	Fat (g/oz)
3 oz fried shrimp	3.33
3 oz veal cutlet (broiled)	3.00
2 oz roast beef (lean)	2.50
2.5 oz fried chicken drumstick	4.40
4 oz tuna (canned in oil)	1.75

Source: *The World Almanac and Book of Facts.*

28. Diet Cola Preference A recent survey of a new diet cola reported the following percentages of people who liked the taste. Find the weighted mean of the percentages.

Area	% Favored	Number surveyed
1	40	1000
2	30	3000
3	50	800

29. Costs of Helicopters The costs of three models of helicopters are shown here. Find the weighted mean of the costs of the models.

Model	Number sold	Cost
Sunscraper	9	$427,000
Skycoaster	6	365,000
High-flyer	12	725,000

30. Final Grade An instructor grades exams, 20%; term paper, 30%; final exam, 50%. A student had grades of 83, 72, and 90, respectively, for exams, term paper, and final exam. Find the student's final average. Use the weighted mean.

31. Final Grade Another instructor gives four 1-hour exams and one final exam, which counts as two 1-hour exams. Find a student's grade if she received 62, 83, 97, and 90 on the 1-hour exams and 82 on the final exam.

32. For these situations, state which measure of central tendency—mean, median, or mode—should be used.

 a. The most typical case is desired.

 b. The distribution is open-ended.

 c. There is an extreme value in the data set.

 d. The data are categorical.

 e. Further statistical computations will be needed.

 f. The values are to be divided into two approximately equal groups, one group containing the larger values and one containing the smaller values.

33. Describe which measure of central tendency—mean, median, or mode—was probably used in each situation.

 a. One-half of the factory workers make more than $5.37 per hour, and one-half make less than $5.37 per hour.

 b. The average number of children per family in the Plaza Heights Complex is 1.8.

 c. Most people prefer red convertibles over any other color.

 d. The average person cuts the lawn once a week.

 e. The most common fear today is fear of speaking in public.

 f. The average age of college professors is 42.3 years.

34. What types of symbols are used to represent sample statistics? Give an example. What types of symbols are used to represent population parameters? Give an example.

35. A local fast-food company claims that the average salary of its employees is $13.23 per hour. An employee states that most employees make minimum wage. If both are being truthful, how could both be correct?

Extending the Concepts

36. If the mean of five values is 64, find the sum of the values.

37. If the mean of five values is 8.2 and four of the values are 6, 10, 7, and 12, find the fifth value.

38. Find the mean of 10, 20, 30, 40, and 50.

 a. Add 10 to each value and find the mean.

 b. Subtract 10 from each value and find the mean.

 c. Multiply each value by 10 and find the mean.

 d. Divide each value by 10 and find the mean.

 e. Make a general statement about each situation.

39. The *harmonic mean* (HM) is defined as the number of values divided by the sum of the reciprocals of each value. The formula is

$$HM = \frac{n}{\Sigma(1/X)}$$

For example, the harmonic mean of 1, 4, 5, and 2 is

$$HM = \frac{4}{1/1 + 1/4 + 1/5 + 1/2} = 2.05$$

This mean is useful for finding the average speed. Suppose a person drove 100 miles at 40 miles per hour and returned driving 50 miles per hour. The average miles per hour is *not* 45 miles per hour, which is found by adding 40 and 50 and dividing by 2. The average is found as shown.

Since

Time = distance ÷ rate

then

Time 1 = $\frac{100}{40}$ = 2.5 hours to make the trip

Time 2 = $\frac{100}{50}$ = 2 hours to return

Hence, the total time is 4.5 hours, and the total miles driven are 200. Now, the average speed is

$$Rate = \frac{distance}{time} = \frac{200}{4.5} = 44.44 \text{ miles per hour}$$

This value can also be found by using the harmonic mean formula

$$HM = \frac{2}{1/40 + 1/50} = 44.44$$

Using the harmonic mean, find each of these.

a. A salesperson drives 300 miles round trip at 30 miles per hour going to Chicago and 45 miles per hour returning home. Find the average miles per hour.

b. A bus driver drives the 50 miles to West Chester at 40 miles per hour and returns driving 25 miles per hour. Find the average miles per hour.

c. A carpenter buys $500 worth of nails at $50 per pound and $500 worth of nails at $10 per pound. Find the average cost of 1 pound of nails.

40. The *geometric mean* (GM) is defined as the *n*th root of the product of *n* values. The formula is

$$GM = \sqrt[n]{(X_1)(X_2)(X_3) \cdots (X_n)}$$

The geometric mean of 4 and 16 is

$$GM = \sqrt{(4)(16)} = \sqrt{64} = 8$$

The geometric mean of 1, 3, and 9 is

$$GM = \sqrt[3]{(1)(3)(9)} = \sqrt[3]{27} = 3$$

The geometric mean is useful in finding the average of percentages, ratios, indexes, or growth rates. For example, if a person receives a 20% raise after 1 year of service and a 10% raise after the second year of service, the average percentage raise per year is not 15 but 14.89%, as shown.

$$GM = \sqrt{(1.2)(1.1)} = 1.1489$$

or

$$GM = \sqrt{(120)(110)} = 114.89\%$$

His salary is 120% at the end of the first year and 110% at the end of the second year. This is equivalent to an average of 14.89%, since 114.89% − 100% = 14.89%.

This answer can also be shown by assuming that the person makes $10,000 to start and receives two raises of 20 and 10%.

Raise 1 = 10,000 · 20% = $2000
Raise 2 = 12,000 · 10% = $1200

His total salary raise is $3200. This total is equivalent to

$10,000 · 14.89% = $1489.00
$11,489 · 14.89% = $\underline{1710.71}$
$3199.71 ≈ $3200

Find the geometric mean of each of these.

a. The growth rates of the Living Life Insurance Corporation for the past 3 years were 35, 24, and 18%.

b. A person received these percentage raises in salary over a 4-year period: 8, 6, 4, and 5%.

c. A stock increased each year for 5 years at these percentages: 10, 8, 12, 9, and 3%.

d. The price increases, in percentages, for the cost of food in a specific geographic region for the past 3 years were 1, 3, and 5.5%.

41. A useful mean in the physical sciences (such as voltage) is the *quadratic mean* (QM), which is found by taking the square root of the average of the squares of each value. The formula is

$$QM = \sqrt{\frac{\sum X^2}{n}}$$

The quadratic mean of 3, 5, 6, and 10 is

$$QM = \sqrt{\frac{3^2 + 5^2 + 6^2 + 10^2}{4}}$$
$$= \sqrt{42.5} = 6.52$$

Find the quadratic mean of 8, 6, 3, 5, and 4.

42. An approximate median can be found for data that have been grouped into a frequency distribution. First it is necessary to find the median class. This is the class that contains the median value. That is the *n*/2 data value. Then it is assumed that the data values are evenly distributed throughout the median class. The formula is

$$MD = \frac{n/2 - cf}{f}(w) + L_m$$

where   *n* = sum of frequencies
cf = cumulative frequency of class immediately preceding the median class
w = width of median class
f = frequency of median class
L_m = lower boundary of median class

Using this formula, find the median for data in the frequency distribution of Exercise 15.

Technology *Step by Step*

Excel
Step by Step

Finding Measures of Central Tendency

Example XL3–1

Find the mean, mode, and median of the data from Example 3–11. The data represent the population of licensed nuclear reactors in the United States for a recent 15-year period.

104	104	104	104	104
107	109	109	109	110
109	111	112	111	109

1. On an Excel worksheet enter the numbers in cells A2–A16. Enter a label for the variable in cell A1.

On the same worksheet as the data:

2. Compute the mean of the data: key in **=AVERAGE(A2:A16)** in a blank cell.

3. Compute the mode of the data: key in **=MODE(A2:A16)** in a blank cell.

4. Compute the median of the data: key in **=MEDIAN(A2:A16)** in a blank cell.

These and other statistical functions can also be accessed without typing them into the worksheet directly.

1. Select the Formulas tab from the toolbar and select the Insert Function Icon f_x.

2. Select the Statistical category for statistical functions.

3. Scroll to find the appropriate function and click [OK].

	A	B	C
1	Number of Reactors		
2	104	107.7333	mean
3	104	104	mode
4	104	109	median
5	104		
6	104		
7	107		
8	109		
9	109		
10	109		
11	110		
12	109		
13	111		
14	112		
15	111		
16	109		

3–2   Measures of Variation

In statistics, to describe the data set accurately, statisticians must know more than the measures of central tendency. Consider Example 3–18.

Example 3–18

Objective 2

Describe data, using measures of variation, such as the range, variance, and standard deviation.

Comparison of Outdoor Paint

A testing lab wishes to test two experimental brands of outdoor paint to see how long each will last before fading. The testing lab makes 6 gallons of each paint to test. Since different chemical agents are added to each group and only six cans are involved, these two groups constitute two small populations. The results (in months) are shown. Find the mean of each group.

Brand A	Brand B
10	35
60	45
50	30
30	35
40	40
20	25

Solution

The mean for brand A is

$$\mu = \frac{\Sigma X}{N} = \frac{210}{6} = 35 \text{ months}$$

The mean for brand B is

$$\mu = \frac{\Sigma X}{N} = \frac{210}{6} = 35 \text{ months}$$

Since the means are equal in Example 3–18, you might conclude that both brands of paint last equally well. However, when the data sets are examined graphically, a somewhat different conclusion might be drawn. See Figure 3–2.

As Figure 3–2 shows, even though the means are the same for both brands, the spread, or variation, is quite different. Figure 3–2 shows that brand B performs more consistently; it is less variable. For the spread or variability of a data set, three measures are commonly used: *range, variance,* and *standard deviation.* Each measure will be discussed in this section.

Range

The range is the simplest of the three measures and is defined now.

> The **range** is the highest value minus the lowest value. The symbol R is used for the range.
>
> R = highest value − lowest value

Figure 3–2

Examining Data Sets Graphically

Variation of paint (in months)

(a) Brand A

Variation of paint (in months)

(b) Brand B

| **Example 3–19** | Comparison of Outdoor Paint |

Find the ranges for the paints in Example 3–18.

Solution

For brand A, the range is

$$R = 60 - 10 = 50 \text{ months}$$

For brand B, the range is

$$R = 45 - 25 = 20 \text{ months}$$

Make sure the range is given as a single number.

The range for brand A shows that 50 months separate the largest data value from the smallest data value. For brand B, 20 months separate the largest data value from the smallest data value, which is less than one-half of brand A's range.

One extremely high or one extremely low data value can affect the range markedly, as shown in Example 3–20.

| **Example 3–20** | Employee Salaries |

 The salaries for the staff of the XYZ Manufacturing Co. are shown here. Find the range.

Staff	Salary
Owner	$100,000
Manager	40,000
Sales representative	30,000
Workers	25,000
	15,000
	18,000

Solution

The range is $R = \$100,000 - \$15,000 = \$85,000$.

Since the owner's salary is included in the data for Example 3–20, the range is a large number. To have a more meaningful statistic to measure the variability, statisticians use measures called the *variance* and *standard deviation*.

Population Variance and Standard Deviation

Before the variance and standard deviation are defined formally, the computational procedure will be shown, since the definition is derived from the procedure.

Rounding Rule for the Standard Deviation The rounding rule for the standard deviation is the same as that for the mean. The final answer should be rounded to one more decimal place than that of the original data.

| **Example 3–21** | Comparison of Outdoor Paint |

 Find the variance and standard deviation for the data set for brand A paint in Example 3–18.

10, 60, 50, 30, 40, 20

Solution

Step 1   Find the mean for the data.

$$\mu = \frac{\Sigma X}{N} = \frac{10 + 60 + 50 + 30 + 40 + 20}{6} = \frac{210}{6} = 35$$

Step 2   Subtract the mean from each data value.

$$10 - 35 = -25 \qquad 50 - 35 = +15 \qquad 40 - 35 = +5$$
$$60 - 35 = +25 \qquad 30 - 35 = -5 \qquad 20 - 35 = -15$$

Step 3   Square each result.

$$(-25)^2 = 625 \qquad (+15)^2 = 225 \qquad (+5)^2 = 25$$
$$(+25)^2 = 625 \qquad (-5)^2 = 25 \qquad (-15)^2 = 225$$

Step 4   Find the sum of the squares.

$$625 + 625 + 225 + 25 + 25 + 225 = 1750$$

Step 5   Divide the sum by N to get the variance.

$$\text{Variance} = 1750 \div 6 = 291.7$$

Step 6   Take the square root of the variance to get the standard deviation. Hence, the standard deviation equals $\sqrt{291.7}$, or 17.1. It is helpful to make a table.

A Values X	B $X - \mu$	C $(X - \mu)^2$
10	−25	625
60	+25	625
50	+15	225
30	−5	25
40	+5	25
20	−15	225
		1750

Column A contains the raw data X. Column B contains the differences $X - \mu$ obtained in step 2. Column C contains the squares of the differences obtained in step 3.

The preceding computational procedure reveals several things. First, the square root of the variance gives the standard deviation; and vice versa, squaring the standard deviation gives the variance. Second, the variance is actually the average of the square of the distance that each value is from the mean. Therefore, if the values are near the mean, the variance will be small. In contrast, if the values are far from the mean, the variance will be large.

You might wonder why the squared distances are used instead of the actual distances. One reason is that the sum of the distances will always be zero. To verify this result for a specific case, add the values in column B of the table in Example 3–21. When each value is squared, the negative signs are eliminated.

Finally, why is it necessary to take the square root? The reason is that since the distances were squared, the units of the resultant numbers are the squares of the units of the original raw data. Finding the square root of the variance puts the standard deviation in the same units as the raw data.

When you are finding the square root, always use its positive or principal value, since the variance and standard deviation of a data set can never be negative.

The **variance** is the average of the squares of the distance each value is from the mean. The symbol for the population variance is σ^2 (σ is the Greek lowercase letter sigma). The formula for the population variance is

$$\sigma^2 = \frac{\Sigma(X - \mu)^2}{N}$$

where

X = individual value
μ = population mean
N = population size

The **standard deviation** is the square root of the variance. The symbol for the population standard deviation is σ.

The corresponding formula for the population standard deviation is

$$\sigma = \sqrt{\sigma^2} = \sqrt{\frac{\Sigma(X - \mu)^2}{N}}$$

Example 3–22

Comparison of Outdoor Paint

Find the variance and standard deviation for brand B paint data in Example 3–18. The months were

35, 45, 30, 35, 40, 25

Solution

Step 1 Find the mean.

$$\mu = \frac{\Sigma X}{N} = \frac{35 + 45 + 30 + 35 + 40 + 25}{6} = \frac{210}{6} = 35$$

Step 2 Subtract the mean from each value, and place the result in column B of the table.

Step 3 Square each result and place the squares in column C of the table.

A X	B $X - \mu$	C $(X - \mu)^2$
35	0	0
45	10	100
30	−5	25
35	0	0
40	5	25
25	−10	100

Step 4 Find the sum of the squares in column C.

$$\Sigma(X - \mu)^2 = 0 + 100 + 25 + 0 + 25 + 100 = 250$$

Step 5 Divide the sum by N to get the variance.

$$\sigma^2 = \frac{\Sigma(X - \mu)^2}{N} = \frac{250}{6} = 41.7$$

Step 6 Take the square root to get the standard deviation.

$$\sigma = \sqrt{\frac{\Sigma(X - \mu)^2}{N}} = \sqrt{41.7} = 6.5$$

Hence, the standard deviation is 6.5.

Interesting Fact

Each person receives on average 598 pieces of mail per year.

Since the standard deviation of brand A is 17.1 (see Example 3–21) and the standard deviation of brand B is 6.5, the data are more variable for brand A. *In summary, when the means are equal, the larger the variance or standard deviation is, the more variable the data are.*

Sample Variance and Standard Deviation

When computing the variance for a sample, one might expect the following expression to be used:

$$\frac{\Sigma(X - \overline{X})^2}{n}$$

where $\overline{X}$ is the sample mean and n is the sample size. *This formula is not usually used, however, since in most cases the purpose of calculating the statistic is to estimate the corresponding parameter.* For example, the sample mean $\overline{X}$ is used to estimate the population mean μ. The expression

$$\frac{\Sigma(X - \overline{X})^2}{n}$$

does not give the best estimate of the population variance because when the population is large and the sample is small (usually less than 30), the variance computed by this formula usually underestimates the population variance. Therefore, instead of dividing by n, find the variance of the sample by dividing by $n - 1$, giving a slightly larger value and an *unbiased* estimate of the population variance.

The formula for the sample variance, denoted by s^2, is

$$s^2 = \frac{\Sigma(X - \overline{X})^2}{n - 1}$$

where

$\overline{X}$ = sample mean

n = sample size

To find the standard deviation of a sample, you must take the square root of the sample variance, which was found by using the preceding formula.

Formula for the Sample Standard Deviation

The standard deviation of a sample (denoted by s) is

$$s = \sqrt{s^2} = \sqrt{\frac{\Sigma(X - \overline{X})^2}{n - 1}}$$

where

X = individual value

$\overline{X}$ = sample mean

n = sample size

Shortcut formulas for computing the variance and standard deviation are presented next and will be used in the remainder of the chapter and in the exercises. These formulas are mathematically equivalent to the preceding formulas and do not involve using the mean. They save time when repeated subtracting and squaring occur in the original formulas. They are also more accurate when the mean has been rounded.

Shortcut or Computational Formulas for s^2 and s

The shortcut formulas for computing the variance and standard deviation for data obtained from samples are as follows.

Variance	Standard deviation

$$s^2 = \frac{n(\Sigma X^2) - (\Sigma X)^2}{n(n - 1)} \qquad s = \sqrt{\frac{n(\Sigma X^2) - (\Sigma X)^2}{n(n - 1)}}$$

Examples 3–23 and 3–24 explain how to use the shortcut formulas.

Example 3–23

European Auto Sales

Find the sample variance and standard deviation for the amount of European auto sales for a sample of 6 years shown. The data are in millions of dollars.

11.2, 11.9, 12.0, 12.8, 13.4, 14.3

Source: *USA TODAY.*

Solution

Step 1 Find the sum of the values.

$$\Sigma X = 11.2 + 11.9 + 12.0 + 12.8 + 13.4 + 14.3 = 75.6$$

Step 2 Square each value and find the sum.

$$\Sigma X^2 = 11.2^2 + 11.9^2 + 12.0^2 + 12.8^2 + 13.4^2 + 14.3^2 = 958.94$$

Step 3 Substitute in the formulas and solve.

$$s^2 = \frac{n(\Sigma X^2) - (\Sigma X)^2}{n(n - 1)}$$

$$= \frac{6(958.94) - 75.6^2}{6(6 - 1)}$$

$$= \frac{5753.64 - 5715.36}{6(5)}$$

$$= \frac{38.28}{30}$$

$$= 1.276$$

The variance is 1.28 rounded.

$$s = \sqrt{1.28} = 1.13$$

Hence, the sample standard deviation is 1.13.

Note that ΣX^2 is not the same as $(\Sigma X)^2$. The notation ΣX^2 means to square the values first, then sum; $(\Sigma X)^2$ means to sum the values first, then square the sum.

Variance and Standard Deviation for Grouped Data

The procedure for finding the variance and standard deviation for grouped data is similar to that for finding the mean for grouped data, and it uses the midpoints of each class.

Example 3–24

Miles Run per Week

Find the variance and the standard deviation for the frequency distribution of the data in Example 2–7. The data represent the number of miles that 20 runners ran during one week.

Class	Frequency	Midpoint
5.5–10.5	1	8
10.5–15.5	2	13
15.5–20.5	3	18
20.5–25.5	5	23
25.5–30.5	4	28
30.5–35.5	3	33
35.5–40.5	2	38

Solution

Step 1 Make a table as shown, and find the midpoint of each class.

A Class	B Frequency f	C Midpoint X_m	D $f \cdot X_m$	E $f \cdot X_m^2$
5.5–10.5	1	8		
10.5–15.5	2	13		
15.5–20.5	3	18		
20.5–25.5	5	23		
25.5–30.5	4	28		
30.5–35.5	3	33		
35.5–40.5	2	38		

Step 2 Multiply the frequency by the midpoint for each class, and place the products in column D.

$$1 \cdot 8 = 8 \qquad 2 \cdot 13 = 26 \qquad \ldots \qquad 2 \cdot 38 = 76$$

Step 3 Multiply the frequency by the square of the midpoint, and place the products in column E.

$$1 \cdot 8^2 = 64 \qquad 2 \cdot 13^2 = 338 \qquad \ldots \qquad 2 \cdot 38^2 = 2888$$

Step 4 Find the sums of columns B, D, and E. The sum of column B is n, the sum of column D is $\Sigma f \cdot X_m$, and the sum of column E is $\Sigma f \cdot X_m^2$. The completed table is shown.

A Class	B Frequency	C Midpoint	D $f \cdot X_m$	E $f \cdot X_m^2$
5.5–10.5	1	8	8	64
10.5–15.5	2	13	26	338
15.5–20.5	3	18	54	972
20.5–25.5	5	23	115	2,645
25.5–30.5	4	28	112	3,136
30.5–35.5	3	33	99	3,267
35.5–40.5	2	38	76	2,888
	$n = 20$		$\Sigma f \cdot X_m = 490$	$\Sigma f \cdot X_m^2 = 13,310$

Step 5　Substitute in the formula and solve for s^2 to get the variance.

$$s^2 = \frac{n(\Sigma f \cdot X_m^2) - (\Sigma f \cdot X_m)^2}{n(n-1)}$$
$$= \frac{20(13,310) - 490^2}{20(20-1)}$$
$$= \frac{266,200 - 240,100}{20(19)}$$
$$= \frac{26,100}{380}$$
$$= 68.7$$

Step 6　Take the square root to get the standard deviation.

$$s = \sqrt{68.7} = 8.3$$

Be sure to use the number found in the sum of column B (i.e., the sum of the frequencies) for n. Do not use the number of classes.

The steps for finding the variance and standard deviation for grouped data are summarized in this Procedure Table.

Procedure Table

Finding the Sample Variance and Standard Deviation for Grouped Data

Step 1　Make a table as shown, and find the midpoint of each class.

A Class	B Frequency	C Midpoint	D $f \cdot X_m$	E $f \cdot X_m^2$

Step 2　Multiply the frequency by the midpoint for each class, and place the products in column D.

Step 3　Multiply the frequency by the square of the midpoint, and place the products in column E.

Step 4　Find the sums of columns B, D, and E. (The sum of column B is n. The sum of column D is $\Sigma f \cdot X_m$. The sum of column E is $\Sigma f \cdot X_m^2$.)

Step 5　Substitute in the formula and solve to get the variance.

$$s^2 = \frac{n(\Sigma f \cdot X_m^2) - (\Sigma f \cdot X_m)^2}{n(n-1)}$$

Step 6　Take the square root to get the standard deviation.

$\mathcal{U}$*nusual Stat*

The average number of times that a man cries in a month is 1.4.

The three measures of variation are summarized in Table 3–2.

Table 3–2	**Summary of Measures of Variation**	
Measure	**Definition**	**Symbol(s)**
Range	Distance between highest value and lowest value	R
Variance	Average of the squares of the distance that each value is from the mean	σ^2, s^2
Standard deviation	Square root of the variance	σ, s

Uses of the Variance and Standard Deviation

1. As previously stated, variances and standard deviations can be used to determine the spread of the data. If the variance or standard deviation is large, the data are more dispersed. This information is useful in comparing two (or more) data sets to determine which is more (most) variable.
2. The measures of variance and standard deviation are used to determine the consistency of a variable. For example, in the manufacture of fittings, such as nuts and bolts, the variation in the diameters must be small, or the parts will not fit together.
3. The variance and standard deviation are used to determine the number of data values that fall within a specified interval in a distribution. For example, Chebyshev's theorem (explained later) shows that, for any distribution, at least 75% of the data values will fall within 2 standard deviations of the mean.
4. Finally, the variance and standard deviation are used quite often in inferential statistics. These uses will be shown in later chapters of this textbook.

Coefficient of Variation

Whenever two samples have the same units of measure, the variance and standard deviation for each can be compared directly. For example, suppose an automobile dealer wanted to compare the standard deviation of miles driven for the cars she received as trade-ins on new cars. She found that for a specific year, the standard deviation for Buicks was 422 miles and the standard deviation for Cadillacs was 350 miles. She could say that the variation in mileage was greater in the Buicks. But what if a manager wanted to compare the standard deviations of two different variables, such as the number of sales per salesperson over a 3-month period and the commissions made by these salespeople?

A statistic that allows you to compare standard deviations when the units are different, as in this example, is called the *coefficient of variation*.

The **coefficient of variation,** denoted by CVar, is the standard deviation divided by the mean. The result is expressed as a percentage.

For samples,

$$\text{CVar} = \frac{s}{\overline{X}} \cdot 100\%$$

For populations,

$$\text{CVar} = \frac{\sigma}{\mu} \cdot 100\%$$

Example 3–25

Sales of Automobiles

The mean of the number of sales of cars over a 3-month period is 87, and the standard deviation is 5. The mean of the commissions is $5225, and the standard deviation is $773. Compare the variations of the two.

Solution

The coefficients of variation are

$$\text{CVar} = \frac{s}{\overline{X}} = \frac{5}{87} \cdot 100\% = 5.7\% \qquad \text{sales}$$

$$\text{CVar} = \frac{773}{5225} \cdot 100\% = 14.8\% \qquad \text{commissions}$$

Since the coefficient of variation is larger for commissions, the commissions are more variable than the sales.

| Example 3–26 | Pages in Women's Fitness Magazines |

The mean for the number of pages of a sample of women's fitness magazines is 132, with a variance of 23; the mean for the number of advertisements of a sample of women's fitness magazines is 182, with a variance of 62. Compare the variations.

Solution

The coefficients of variation are

$$\text{CVar} = \frac{\sqrt{23}}{132} \cdot 100\% = 3.6\% \qquad \text{pages}$$

$$\text{CVar} = \frac{\sqrt{62}}{182} \cdot 100\% = 4.3\% \qquad \text{advertisements}$$

The number of advertisements is more variable than the number of pages since the coefficient of variation is larger for advertisements.

Range Rule of Thumb

The range can be used to approximate the standard deviation. The approximation is called the **range rule of thumb.**

The Range Rule of Thumb

A rough estimate of the standard deviation is

$$s \approx \frac{\text{range}}{4}$$

In other words, if the range is divided by 4, an approximate value for the standard deviation is obtained. For example, the standard deviation for the data set 5, 8, 8, 9, 10, 12, and 13 is 2.7, and the range is $13 - 5 = 8$. The range rule of thumb is $s \approx 2$. The range rule of thumb in this case underestimates the standard deviation somewhat; however, it is in the ballpark.

A note of caution should be mentioned here. The range rule of thumb is only an *approximation* and should be used when the distribution of data values is unimodal and roughly symmetric.

The range rule of thumb can be used to estimate the largest and smallest data values of a data set. The smallest data value will be approximately 2 standard deviations below the mean, and the largest data value will be approximately 2 standard deviations above the mean of the data set. The mean for the previous data set is 9.3; hence,

$$\text{Smallest data value} = \overline{X} - 2s = 9.3 - 2(2.8) = 3.7$$

$$\text{Largest data value} = \overline{X} + 2s = 9.3 + 2(2.8) = 14.9$$

Notice that the smallest data value was 5, and the largest data value was 13. Again, these are rough approximations. For many data sets, almost all data values will fall within 2 standard deviations of the mean. Better approximations can be obtained by using Chebyshev's theorem and the empirical rule. These are explained next.

Chebyshev's Theorem

As stated previously, the variance and standard deviation of a variable can be used to determine the spread, or dispersion, of a variable. That is, the larger the variance or standard deviation, the more the data values are dispersed. For example, if two variables measured in the same units have the same mean, say, 70, and the first variable has a standard deviation of 1.5 while the second variable has a standard deviation of 10, then the data for the second variable will be more spread out than the data for the first variable. *Chebyshev's theorem,* developed by the Russian mathematician Chebyshev (1821–1894), specifies the proportions of the spread in terms of the standard deviation.

Chebyshev's theorem   The proportion of values from a data set that will fall within k standard deviations of the mean will be at least $1 - 1/k^2$, where k is a number greater than 1 (k is not necessarily an integer).

This theorem states that at least three-fourths, or 75%, of the data values will fall within 2 standard deviations of the mean of the data set. This result is found by substituting $k = 2$ in the expression.

$$1 - \frac{1}{k^2} \qquad \text{or} \qquad 1 - \frac{1}{2^2} = 1 - \frac{1}{4} = \frac{3}{4} = 75\%$$

For the example in which variable 1 has a mean of 70 and a standard deviation of 1.5, at least three-fourths, or 75%, of the data values fall between 67 and 73. These values are found by adding 2 standard deviations to the mean and subtracting 2 standard deviations from the mean, as shown:

$$70 + 2(1.5) = 70 + 3 = 73$$

and

$$70 - 2(1.5) = 70 - 3 = 67$$

For variable 2, at least three-fourths, or 75%, of the data values fall between 50 and 90. Again, these values are found by adding and subtracting, respectively, 2 standard deviations to and from the mean.

$$70 + 2(10) = 70 + 20 = 90$$

and

$$70 - 2(10) = 70 - 20 = 50$$

Furthermore, the theorem states that at least eight-ninths, or 88.89%, of the data values will fall within 3 standard deviations of the mean. This result is found by letting $k = 3$ and substituting in the expression.

$$1 - \frac{1}{k^2} \qquad \text{or} \qquad 1 - \frac{1}{3^2} = 1 - \frac{1}{9} = \frac{8}{9} = 88.89\%$$

For variable 1, at least eight-ninths, or 88.89%, of the data values fall between 65.5 and 74.5, since

$$70 + 3(1.5) = 70 + 4.5 = 74.5$$

and

$$70 - 3(1.5) = 70 - 4.5 = 65.5$$

For variable 2, at least eight-ninths, or 88.89%, of the data values fall between 40 and 100.

Figure 3–3

Chebyshev's Theorem

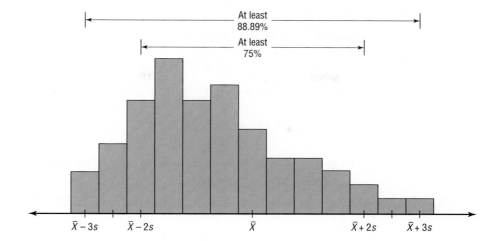

This theorem can be applied to any distribution regardless of its shape (see Figure 3–3).

Examples 3–27 and 3–28 illustrate the application of Chebyshev's theorem.

Example 3–27

Prices of Homes

The mean price of houses in a certain neighborhood is $50,000, and the standard deviation is $10,000. Find the price range for which at least 75% of the houses will sell.

Solution

Chebyshev's theorem states that three-fourths, or 75%, of the data values will fall within 2 standard deviations of the mean. Thus,

$$\$50,000 + 2(\$10,000) = \$50,000 + \$20,000 = \$70,000$$

and

$$\$50,000 - 2(\$10,000) = \$50,000 - \$20,000 = \$30,000$$

Hence, at least 75% of all homes sold in the area will have a price range from $30,000 to $70,000.

Chebyshev's theorem can be used to find the minimum percentage of data values that will fall between any two given values. The procedure is shown in Example 3–28.

Example 3–28

Travel Allowances

A survey of local companies found that the mean amount of travel allowance for executives was $0.25 per mile. The standard deviation was $0.02. Using Chebyshev's theorem, find the minimum percentage of the data values that will fall between $0.20 and $0.30.

Solution

Step 1   Subtract the mean from the larger value.

$$\$0.30 - \$0.25 = \$0.05$$

Step 2   Divide the difference by the standard deviation to get k.

$$k = \frac{0.05}{0.02} = 2.5$$

Step 3   Use Chebyshev's theorem to find the percentage.

$$1 - \frac{1}{k^2} = 1 - \frac{1}{2.5^2} = 1 - \frac{1}{6.25} = 1 - 0.16 = 0.84 \quad \text{or} \quad 84\%$$

Hence, at least 84% of the data values will fall between $0.20 and $0.30.

The Empirical (Normal) Rule

Chebyshev's theorem applies to any distribution regardless of its shape. However, when a distribution is *bell-shaped* (or what is called *normal*), the following statements, which make up the **empirical rule,** are true.

Approximately 68% of the data values will fall within 1 standard deviation of the mean.

Approximately 95% of the data values will fall within 2 standard deviations of the mean.

Approximately 99.7% of the data values will fall within 3 standard deviations of the mean.

For example, suppose that the scores on a national achievement exam have a mean of 480 and a standard deviation of 90. If these scores are normally distributed, then approximately 68% will fall between 390 and 570 ($480 + 90 = 570$ and $480 - 90 = 390$). Approximately 95% of the scores will fall between 300 and 660 ($480 + 2 \cdot 90 = 660$ and $480 - 2 \cdot 90 = 300$). Approximately 99.7% will fall between 210 and 750 ($480 + 3 \cdot 90 = 750$ and $480 - 3 \cdot 90 = 210$). See Figure 3–4. (The empirical rule is explained in greater detail in Chapter 6.)

Figure 3–4

The Empirical Rule

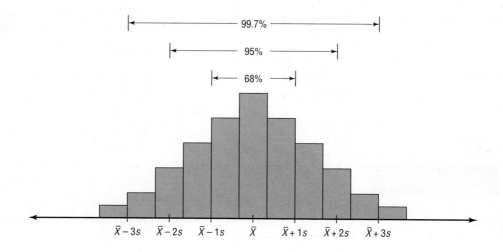

Applying the Concepts 3–2

Blood Pressure

The table lists means and standard deviations. The mean is the number before the plus/minus, and the standard deviation is the number after the plus/minus. The results are from a study attempting to find the average blood pressure of older adults. Use the results to answer the questions.

	Normotensive		Hypertensive	
	Men $(n = 1200)$	**Women** $(n = 1400)$	**Men** $(n = 1100)$	**Women** $(n = 1300)$
Age	55 ± 10	55 ± 10	60 ± 10	64 ± 10
Blood pressure (mm Hg)				
Systolic	123 ± 9	121 ± 11	153 ± 17	156 ± 20
Diastolic	78 ± 7	76 ± 7	91 ± 10	88 ± 10

1. Apply Chebyshev's theorem to the systolic blood pressure of normotensive men. At least how many of the men in the study fall within 1 standard deviation of the mean?

2. At least how many of those men in the study fall within 2 standard deviations of the mean?

Assume that blood pressure is normally distributed among older adults. Answer the following questions, using the empirical rule instead of Chebyshev's theorem.

3. Give ranges for the diastolic blood pressure (normotensive and hypertensive) of older women.

4. Do the normotensive, male, systolic blood pressure ranges overlap with the hypertensive, male, systolic blood pressure ranges?

See page 188 for the answers.

Exercises 3–2

1. What is the relationship between the variance and the standard deviation?

2. Why might the range *not* be the best estimate of variability?

3. What are the symbols used to represent the population variance and standard deviation?

4. What are the symbols used to represent the sample variance and standard deviation?

5. Why is the unbiased estimator of variance used?

6. The three data sets have the same mean and range, but is the variation the same? Prove your answer by computing the standard deviation. Assume the data were obtained from samples.

 a. 5, 7, 9, 11, 13, 15, 17
 b. 5, 6, 7, 11, 15, 16, 17
 c. 5, 5, 5, 11, 17, 17, 17

For Exercises 7–13, find the range, variance, and standard deviation. Assume the data represent samples, and use the shortcut formula for the unbiased estimator to compute the variance and standard deviation.

7. **Police Calls in Schools** The number of incidents in which police were needed for a sample of 10 schools in Allegheny County is 7, 37, 3, 8, 48, 11, 6, 0, 10, 3. Are the data consistent or do they vary? Explain your answer.

 Source: U.S. Department of Education.

8. **Cigarette Taxes** The increases (in cents) in cigarette taxes for 17 states in a 6-month period are

 60, 20, 40, 40, 45, 12, 34, 51, 30, 70, 42, 31, 69, 32, 8, 18, 50

 Use the range rule of thumb to estimate the standard deviation. Compare the estimate to the actual standard deviation.

 Source: Federation of Tax Administrators.

9. Precipitation and High Temperatures The normal daily high temperatures (in degrees Fahrenheit) in January for 10 selected cities are as follows.

50, 37, 29, 54, 30, 61, 47, 38, 34, 61

The normal monthly precipitation (in inches) for these same 10 cities is listed here.

4.8, 2.6, 1.5, 1.8, 1.8, 3.3, 5.1, 1.1, 1.8, 2.5

Which set is more variable?

Source: *New York Times Almanac.*

10. Size of U.S. States The total surface area (in square miles) for each of six selected Eastern states is listed here.

28,995	PA	37,534	FL
31,361	NY	27,087	VA
20,966	ME	37,741	GA

The total surface area for each of six selected Western states is listed (in square miles).

72,964	AZ	70,763	NV
101,510	CA	62,161	OR
66,625	CO	54,339	UT

Which set is more variable?

Source: *New York Times Almanac.*

11. Stories in the Tallest Buildings The number of stories in the 13 tallest buildings for two different cities is listed below. Which set of data is more variable?

Houston: 75, 71, 64, 56, 53, 55, 47, 55, 52, 50, 50, 50, 47

Pittsburgh: 64, 54, 40, 32, 46, 44, 42, 41, 40, 40, 34, 32, 30

Source: *World Almanac.*

12. Starting Teachers' Salaries Starting teacher salaries (in equivalent U.S. dollars) for upper secondary education in selected countries are listed below. Which set of data is more variable? (The U.S. average starting salary at this time was $29,641.)

Europe		Asia	
Sweden	$48,704	Korea	$26,852
Germany	41,441	Japan	23,493
Spain	32,679	India	18,247
Finland	32,136	Malaysia	13,647
Denmark	30,384	Philippines	9,857
Netherlands	29,326	Thailand	5,862
Scotland	27,789		

Source: *World Almanac.*

13. The average age of U.S. astronaut candidates in the past has been 34, but candidates have ranged in age from 26 to 46. Use the range rule of thumb to estimate the standard deviation of the applicants' ages.

Source: www.nasa.gov

14. Home Runs Find the range, variance, and standard deviation for the distances of the home runs for

McGwire and Sosa, using the data in Exercise 18 in Section 2–1. Compare the ranges and standard deviations. Decide which is more variable or if the variability is about the same. (Use individual data.)

15. Use the data for Exercise 11 in Section 3–1. Find the range, variance, and standard deviation for each set of data. Which set of data is more variable?

16. Deficient Bridges in U.S. States The Federal Highway Administration reported the number of deficient bridges in each state. Find the range, variance, and standard deviation.

15,458	1,055	5,008	3,598	8,984
1,337	4,132	10,618	17,361	6,081
6,482	25,090	12,681	16,286	18,832
12,470	17,842	16,601	4,587	47,196
23,205	25,213	23,017	27,768	2,686
7,768	25,825	4,962	22,704	2,694
4,131	13,144	15,582	7,279	12,613
810	13,350	1,208	22,242	7,477
10,902	2,343	2,333	2,979	6,578
14,318	4,773	6,252	734	13,220

Source: *USA TODAY.*

17. Find the range, variance, and standard deviation for the data in Exercise 17 of Section 2–1.

For Exercises 18 through 27, find the variance and standard deviation.

18. Baseball Team Batting Averages Team batting averages for major league baseball in 2005 are represented below. Find the variance and standard deviation for each league. Compare the results.

NL		AL	
0.252–0.256	4	0.256–0.261	2
0.257–0.261	6	0.262–0.267	5
0.262–0.266	1	0.268–0.273	4
0.267–0.271	4	0.274–0.279	2
0.272–0.276	1	0.280–0.285	1

Source: *World Almanac.*

19. Cost per Load of Laundry Detergents The costs per load (in cents) of 35 laundry detergents tested by a consumer organization are shown here.

Class limits	Frequency
13–19	2
20–26	7
27–33	12
34–40	5
41–47	6
48–54	1
55–61	0
62–68	2

20. **Automotive Fuel Efficiency** Thirty automobiles were tested for fuel efficiency (in miles per gallon). This frequency distribution was obtained.

Class boundaries	Frequency
7.5–12.5	3
12.5–17.5	5
17.5–22.5	15
22.5–27.5	5
27.5–32.5	2

21. **Murders in Cities** The data show the number of murders in 25 selected cities.

Class limits	Frequency
34–96	13
97–159	2
160–222	0
223–285	5
286–348	1
349–411	1
412–474	0
475–537	1
538–600	2

22. **Reaction Times** In a study of reaction times to a specific stimulus, a psychologist recorded these data (in seconds).

Class limits	Frequency
2.1–2.7	12
2.8–3.4	13
3.5–4.1	7
4.2–4.8	5
4.9–5.5	2
5.6–6.2	1

23. **Lightbulb Lifetimes** Eighty randomly selected lightbulbs were tested to determine their lifetimes (in hours). This frequency distribution was obtained.

Class boundaries	Frequency
52.5–63.5	6
63.5–74.5	12
74.5–85.5	25
85.5–96.5	18
96.5–107.5	14
107.5–118.5	5

24. **Murder Rates** The data represent the murder rate per 100,000 individuals in a sample of selected cities in the United States.

Class	Frequency
5–11	8
12–18	5
19–25	7
26–32	1
33–39	1
40–46	3

Source: FBI and U.S. Census Bureau.

25. **Battery Lives** Eighty randomly selected batteries were tested to determine their lifetimes (in hours). The following frequency distribution was obtained.

Class boundaries	Frequency
62.5–73.5	5
73.5–84.5	14
84.5–95.5	18
95.5–106.5	25
106.5–117.5	12
117.5–128.5	6

Can it be concluded that the lifetimes of these brands of batteries are consistent?

26. Find the variance and standard deviation for the two distributions in Exercises 8 and 18 in Section 2–2. Compare the variation of the data sets. Decide if one data set is more variable than the other.

27. **Word Processor Repairs** This frequency distribution represents the data obtained from a sample of word processor repairers. The values are the days between service calls on 80 machines.

Class boundaries	Frequency
25.5–28.5	5
28.5–31.5	9
31.5–34.5	32
34.5–37.5	20
37.5–40.5	12
40.5–43.5	2

28. **Exam Scores** The average score of the students in one calculus class is 110, with a standard deviation of 5; the average score of students in a statistics class is 106, with a standard deviation of 4. Which class is more variable in terms of scores?

29. **Suspension Bridges** The lengths (in feet) of the main span of the longest suspension bridges in the United States and the rest of the world are shown below. Which set of data is more variable?

United States: 4205, 4200, 3800, 3500, 3478, 2800, 2800, 2310
World: 6570, 5538, 5328, 4888, 4626, 4544, 4518, 3970

Source: *World Almanac.*

30. **Exam Scores** The average score on an English final examination was 85, with a standard deviation of 5; the average score on a history final exam was 110, with a standard deviation of 8. Which class was more variable?

31. **Ages of Accountants** The average age of the accountants at Three Rivers Corp. is 26 years, with a standard deviation of 6 years; the average salary of the accountants is $31,000, with a standard deviation of $4000. Compare the variations of age and income.

32. Using Chebyshev's theorem, solve these problems for a distribution with a mean of 80 and a standard deviation of 10.

  a. At least what percentage of values will fall between 60 and 100?

  b. At least what percentage of values will fall between 65 and 95?

33. The mean of a distribution is 20 and the standard deviation is 2. Use Chebyshev's theorem.

  a. At least what percentage of the values will fall between 10 and 30?

  b. At least what percentage of the values will fall between 12 and 28?

34. In a distribution of 160 values with a mean of 72, at least 120 fall within the interval 67–77. Approximately what percentage of values should fall in the interval 62–82? Use Chebyshev's theorem.

35. Calories The average number of calories in a regular-size bagel is 240. If the standard deviation is 38 calories, find the range in which at least 75% of the data will lie. Use Chebyshev's theorem.

36. Time Spent Online Americans spend an average of 3 hours per day online. If the standard deviation is 32 minutes, find the range in which at least 88.89% of the data will lie. Use Chebyshev's theorem.

Source: www.cs.cmu.edu

37. Solid Waste Production The average college student produces 640 pounds of solid waste each year including 500 disposable cups and 320 pounds of paper. If the standard deviation is approximately 85 pounds, within what weight limits will at least 88.89% of all students' garbage lie?

Source: Environmental Sustainability Committee, www.esc.mtu.edu

38. Sale Price of Homes The average sale price of new one-family houses in the United States for 2003 was $246,300. Find the range of values in which at least 75% of the sale prices will lie if the standard deviation is $48,500.

Source: *New York Times Almanac.*

39. Trials to Learn a Maze The average of the number of trials it took a sample of mice to learn to traverse a maze was 12. The standard deviation was 3. Using Chebyshev's theorem, find the minimum percentage of data values that will fall in the range of 4 to 20 trials.

40. Farm Sizes The average farm in the United States in 2004 contained 443 acres. The standard deviation is 42 acres. Use Chebyshev's theorem to find the minimum percentage of data values that will fall in the range of 338–548 acres.

Source: *World Almanac.*

41. Citrus Fruit Consumption The average U.S. yearly per capita consumption of citrus fruit is 26.8 pounds. Suppose that the distribution of fruit amounts consumed is bell-shaped with a standard deviation equal to 4.2 pounds. What percentage of Americans would you expect to consume more than 31 pounds of citrus fruit per year?

Source: USDA/Economic Research Service.

42. Work Hours for College Faculty The average full-time faculty member in a post-secondary degree-granting institution works an average of 53 hours per week.

  a. If we assume the standard deviation is 2.8 hours, what percentage of faculty members work more than 58.6 hours a week?

  b. If we assume a bell-shaped distribution, what percentage of faculty members work more than 58.6 hours a week?

Source: National Center for Education Statistics.

Extending the Concepts

43. Serum Cholesterol Levels For this data set, find the mean and standard deviation of the variable. The data represent the serum cholesterol levels of 30 individuals. Count the number of data values that fall within 2 standard deviations of the mean. Compare this with the number obtained from Chebyshev's theorem. Comment on the answer.

211	240	255	219	204
200	212	193	187	205
256	203	210	221	249
231	212	236	204	187
201	247	206	187	200
237	227	221	192	196

44. Ages of Consumers For this data set, find the mean and standard deviation of the variable. The data represent the ages of 30 customers who ordered a product advertised on television. Count the number of data values that fall within 2 standard deviations of the mean. Compare this with the number obtained from Chebyshev's theorem. Comment on the answer.

42	44	62	35	20
30	56	20	23	41
55	22	31	27	66
21	18	24	42	25
32	50	31	26	36
39	40	18	36	22

45. Using Chebyshev's theorem, complete the table to find the minimum percentage of data values that fall within k standard deviations of the mean.

k	1.5	2	2.5	3	3.5
Percent					

46. Use this data set: 10, 20, 30, 40, 50

   a. Find the standard deviation.

   b. Add 5 to each value, and then find the standard deviation.

   c. Subtract 5 from each value and find the standard deviation.

   d. Multiply each value by 5 and find the standard deviation.

   e. Divide each value by 5 and find the standard deviation.

   f. Generalize the results of parts *b* through *e*.

   g. Compare these results with those in Exercise 38 of Exercises 3–1.

 47. The mean deviation is found by using this formula:

$$\text{Mean deviation} = \frac{\Sigma|X - \overline{X}|}{n}$$

where

   X = value

   $\overline{X}$ = mean

   n = number of values

   $|\ |$ = absolute value

Find the mean deviation for these data.

5, 9, 10, 11, 11, 12, 15, 18, 20, 22

48. A measure to determine the skewness of a distribution is called the *Pearson coefficient of skewness*. The formula is

$$\text{Skewness} = \frac{3(\overline{X} - \text{MD})}{s}$$

The values of the coefficient usually range from -3 to $+3$. When the distribution is symmetric, the coefficient is zero; when the distribution is positively skewed, it is positive; and when the distribution is negatively skewed, it is negative.

   Using the formula, find the coefficient of skewness for each distribution, and describe the shape of the distribution.

   a. Mean = 10, median = 8, standard deviation = 3.

   b. Mean = 42, median = 45, standard deviation = 4.

   c. Mean = 18.6, median = 18.6, standard deviation = 1.5.

   d. Mean = 98, median = 97.6, standard deviation = 4.

49. All values of a data set must be within $s\sqrt{n - 1}$ of the mean. If a person collected 25 data values that had a mean of 50 and a standard deviation of 3 and you saw that one data value was 67, what would you conclude?

Technology *Step by Step*

Excel
Step by Step

Finding Measures of Variation
Example XL3–2

Find the variance, standard deviation, and range of the data from Example 3–23. The data represent the amount (in millions of dollars) of European auto sales for a sample of 6 years.

   11.2   11.9   12.0   12.8   13.4   14.3

   1. On an Excel worksheet enter the data in cells A2–A7. Enter a label for the variable in cell A1.

   2. For the sample variance, enter **=VAR(A2:A7)**.

   3. For the sample standard deviation, enter **=STDEV(A2:A7)**.

   4. For the range, compute the difference between the maximum and the minimum values by entering **=MAX(A2:A7) − MIN(A2:A7)**.

These and other statistical functions can also be accessed without typing them into the worksheet directly.

   1. Select the Formulas tab from the toolbar and select the Insert Function Icon .

   2. Select the Statistical category for statistical functions.

   3. Scroll to find the appropriate function and click [OK].

	A	B	C	D
1	Sales (in millions $)	1.276	variance	
2		11.2	1.129602	standard deviation	
3		11.9	3.1	range	
4		12			
5		12.8			
6		13.4			
7		14.3			
8					
9					

3–3

Objective 3

Identify the position of a data value in a data set, using various measures of position, such as percentiles, deciles, and quartiles.

Measures of Position

In addition to measures of central tendency and measures of variation, there are measures of position or location. These measures include standard scores, percentiles, deciles, and quartiles. They are used to locate the relative position of a data value in the data set. For example, if a value is located at the 80th percentile, it means that 80% of the values fall below it in the distribution and 20% of the values fall above it. The *median* is the value that corresponds to the 50th percentile, since one-half of the values fall below it and one-half of the values fall above it. This section discusses these measures of position.

Standard Scores

There is an old saying, "You can't compare apples and oranges." But with the use of statistics, it can be done to some extent. Suppose that a student scored 90 on a music test and 45 on an English exam. Direct comparison of raw scores is impossible, since the exams might not be equivalent in terms of number of questions, value of each question, and so on. However, a comparison of a relative standard similar to both can be made. This comparison uses the mean and standard deviation and is called a standard score or *z* score. (We also use *z* scores in later chapters.)

A standard score or *z* score tells how many standard deviations a data value is above or below the mean for a specific distribution of values. If a standard score is zero, then the data value is the same as the mean.

A **z score** or **standard score** for a value is obtained by subtracting the mean from the value and dividing the result by the standard deviation. The symbol for a standard score is *z*. The formula is

$$z = \frac{\text{value} - \text{mean}}{\text{standard deviation}}$$

For samples, the formula is

$$z = \frac{X - \overline{X}}{s}$$

For populations, the formula is

$$z = \frac{X - \mu}{\sigma}$$

The *z* score represents the number of standard deviations that a data value falls above or below the mean.

For the purpose of this section, it will be assumed that when we find *z* scores, the data were obtained from samples.

Example 3–29

Test Scores

A student scored 65 on a calculus test that had a mean of 50 and a standard deviation of 10; she scored 30 on a history test with a mean of 25 and a standard deviation of 5. Compare her relative positions on the two tests.

Solution

First, find the *z* scores. For calculus the *z* score is

$$z = \frac{X - \overline{X}}{s} = \frac{65 - 50}{10} = 1.5$$

For history the z score is

$$z = \frac{30 - 25}{5} = 1.0$$

Since the z score for calculus is larger, her relative position in the calculus class is higher than her relative position in the history class.

Note that if the z score is positive, the score is above the mean. If the z score is 0, the score is the same as the mean. And if the z score is negative, the score is below the mean.

Example 3–30   **Test Scores**

Find the z score for each test, and state which is higher.

Test A	$X = 38$	$\overline{X} = 40$	$s = 5$
Test B	$X = 94$	$\overline{X} = 100$	$s = 10$

Solution

For test A,

$$z = \frac{X - \overline{X}}{s} = \frac{38 - 40}{5} = -0.4$$

For test B,

$$z = \frac{94 - 100}{10} = -0.6$$

The score for test A is relatively higher than the score for test B.

When all data for a variable are transformed into z scores, the resulting distribution will have a mean of 0 and a standard deviation of 1. A z score, then, is actually the number of standard deviations each value is from the mean for a specific distribution. In Example 3–29, the calculus score of 65 was actually 1.5 standard deviations above the mean of 50. This will be explained in greater detail in Chapter 6.

Percentiles

Percentiles are position measures used in educational and health-related fields to indicate the position of an individual in a group.

Percentiles divide the data set into 100 equal groups.

In many situations, the graphs and tables showing the percentiles for various measures such as test scores, heights, or weights have already been completed. Table 3–3 shows the percentile ranks for scaled scores on the Test of English as a Foreign Language. If a student had a scaled score of 58 for section 1 (listening and comprehension), that student would have a percentile rank of 81. Hence, that student did better than 81% of the students who took section 1 of the exam.

Table 3–3	Percentile Ranks and Scaled Scores on the Test of English as a Foreign Language*				
Scaled score	Section 1: Listening comprehension	Section 2: Structure and written expression	Section 3: Vocabulary and reading comprehension	Total scaled score	Percentile rank
68	99	98			
66	98	96	98	660	99
64	96	94	96	640	97
62	92	90	93	620	94
60	87	84	88	600	89
→58	81	76	81	580	82
56	73	68	72	560	73
54	64	58	61	540	62
52	54	48	50	520	50
50	42	38	40	500	39
48	32	29	30	480	29
46	22	21	23	460	20
44	14	15	16	440	13
42	9	10	11	420	9
40	5	7	8	400	5
38	3	4	5	380	3
36	2	3	3	360	1
34	1	2	2	340	1
32		1	1	320	
30		1	1	300	
Mean	51.5	52.2	51.4	517	Mean
S.D.	7.1	7.9	7.5	68	S.D.

*Based on the total group of 1,178,193 examinees tested from July 1989 through June 1991.

Source: Reprinted by permission of Educational Testing Service, the copyright owner.

Figure 3–5 shows percentiles in graphical form of weights of girls from ages 2 to 18. To find the percentile rank of an 11-year-old who weighs 82 pounds, start at the 82-pound weight on the left axis and move horizontally to the right. Find 11 on the horizontal axis and move up vertically. The two lines meet at the 50th percentile curved line; hence, an 11-year-old girl who weighs 82 pounds is in the 50th percentile for her age group. If the lines do not meet exactly on one of the curved percentile lines, then the percentile rank must be approximated.

Percentiles are also used to compare an individual's test score with the national norm. For example, tests such as the National Educational Development Test (NEDT) are taken by students in ninth or tenth grade. A student's scores are compared with those of other students locally and nationally by using percentile ranks. A similar test for elementary school students is called the California Achievement Test.

Percentiles are not the same as percentages. That is, if a student gets 72 correct answers out of a possible 100, she obtains a percentage score of 72. There is no indication of her position with respect to the rest of the class. She could have scored the highest, the lowest, or somewhere in between. On the other hand, if a raw score of 72 corresponds to the 64th percentile, then she did better than 64% of the students in her class.

Figure 3–5

Weights of Girls by Age and Percentile Rankings

Source: Distributed by Mead Johnson Nutritional Division. Reprinted with permission.

Percentiles are symbolized by

$$P_1, P_2, P_3, \ldots, P_{99}$$

and divide the distribution into 100 groups.

Percentile graphs can be constructed as shown in Example 3–31. Percentile graphs use the same values as the cumulative relative frequency graphs described in Section 2–2, except that the proportions have been converted to percents.

| Example 3–31 | **Systolic Blood Pressure** |

The frequency distribution for the systolic blood pressure readings (in millimeters of mercury, mm Hg) of 200 randomly selected college students is shown here. Construct a percentile graph.

A Class boundaries	B Frequency	C Cumulative frequency	D Cumulative percent
89.5–104.5	24		
104.5–119.5	62		
119.5–134.5	72		
134.5–149.5	26		
149.5–164.5	12		
164.5–179.5	4		
	200		

Solution

Step 1   Find the cumulative frequencies and place them in column C.

Step 2   Find the cumulative percentages and place them in column D. To do this step, use the formula

$$\text{Cumulative \%} = \frac{\text{cumulative frequency}}{n} \cdot 100\%$$

For the first class,

$$\text{Cumulative \%} = \frac{24}{200} \cdot 100\% = 12\%$$

The completed table is shown here.

A Class boundaries	B Frequency	C Cumulative frequency	D Cumulative percent
89.5–104.5	24	24	12
104.5–119.5	62	86	43
119.5–134.5	72	158	79
134.5–149.5	26	184	92
149.5–164.5	12	196	98
164.5–179.5	4	200	100
	200		

Step 3   Graph the data, using class boundaries for the x axis and the percentages for the y axis, as shown in Figure 3–6.

Once a percentile graph has been constructed, one can find the approximate corresponding percentile ranks for given blood pressure values and find approximate blood pressure values for given percentile ranks.

For example, to find the percentile rank of a blood pressure reading of 130, find 130 on the x axis of Figure 3–6, and draw a vertical line to the graph. Then move horizontally to the value on the y axis. Note that a blood pressure of 130 corresponds to approximately the 70th percentile.

If the value that corresponds to the 40th percentile is desired, start on the y axis at 40 and draw a horizontal line to the graph. Then draw a vertical line to the x axis and read

Figure 3–6

Percentile Graph for Example 3–31

the value. In Figure 3–6, the 40th percentile corresponds to a value of approximately 118. Thus, if a person has a blood pressure of 118, he or she is at the 40th percentile.

Finding values and the corresponding percentile ranks by using a graph yields only approximate answers. Several mathematical methods exist for computing percentiles for data. These methods can be used to find the approximate percentile rank of a data value or to find a data value corresponding to a given percentile. When the data set is large (100 or more), these methods yield better results. Examples 3–32 through 3–35 show these methods.

Percentile Formula

The percentile corresponding to a given value X is computed by using the following formula:

$$\text{Percentile} = \frac{(\text{number of values below } X) + 0.5}{\text{total number of values}} \cdot 100$$

Example 3–32

Test Scores

A teacher gives a 20-point test to 10 students. The scores are shown here. Find the percentile rank of a score of 12.

18, 15, 12, 6, 8, 2, 3, 5, 20, 10

Solution

Arrange the data in order from lowest to highest.

2, 3, 5, 6, 8, 10, 12, 15, 18, 20

Then substitute into the formula.

$$\text{Percentile} = \frac{(\text{number of values below } X) + 0.5}{\text{total number of values}} \cdot 100\%$$

Since there are six values below a score of 12, the solution is

$$\text{Percentile} = \frac{6 + 0.5}{10} \cdot 100\% = 65\text{th percentile}$$

Thus, a student whose score was 12 did better than 65% of the class.

Note: One assumes that a score of 12 in Example 3–32, for instance, means theoretically any value between 11.5 and 12.5.

Example 3–33   **Test Scores**

Using the data in Example 3–32, find the percentile rank for a score of 6.

Solution

There are three values below 6. Thus

$$\text{Percentile} = \frac{3 + 0.5}{10} \cdot 100\% = 35\text{th percentile}$$

A student who scored 6 did better than 35% of the class.

Examples 3–34 amd 3–35 show a procedure for finding a value corresponding to a given percentile.

Example 3–34   **Test Scores**

Using the scores in Example 3–32, find the value corresponding to the 25th percentile.

Solution

Step 1   Arrange the data in order from lowest to highest.

2, 3, 5, 6, 8, 10, 12, 15, 18, 20

Step 2   Compute

$$c = \frac{n \cdot p}{100}$$

where
    n = total number of values
    p = percentile

Thus,

$$c = \frac{10 \cdot 25}{100} = 2.5$$

Step 3   If c is not a whole number, round it up to the next whole number; in this case, $c = 3$. (If c is a whole number, see Example 3–35.) Start at the lowest value and count over to the third value, which is 5. Hence, the value 5 corresponds to the 25th percentile.

Example 3–35   Using the data set in Example 3–32, find the value that corresponds to the 60th percentile.

Solution

Step 1   Arrange the data in order from smallest to largest.

2, 3, 5, 6, 8, 10, 12, 15, 18, 20

Step 2 Substitute in the formula.

$$c = \frac{n \cdot p}{100} = \frac{10 \cdot 60}{100} = 6$$

Step 3 If c is a whole number, use the value halfway between the c and $c + 1$ values when counting up from the lowest value—in this case, the 6th and 7th values.

2, 3, 5, 6, 8, 10, 12, 15, 18, 20

      6th value   7th value

The value halfway between 10 and 12 is 11. Find it by adding the two values and dividing by 2.

$$\frac{10 + 12}{2} = 11$$

Hence, 11 corresponds to the 60th percentile. Anyone scoring 11 would have done better than 60% of the class.

The steps for finding a value corresponding to a given percentile are summarized in this Procedure Table.

Procedure Table

Finding a Data Value Corresponding to a Given Percentile

Step 1 Arrange the data in order from lowest to highest.

Step 2 Substitute into the formula

$$c = \frac{n \cdot p}{100}$$

where
    n = total number of values
    p = percentile

Step 3A If c is not a whole number, round up to the next whole number. Starting at the lowest value, count over to the number that corresponds to the rounded-up value.

Step 3B If c is a whole number, use the value halfway between the cth and $(c + 1)$st values when counting up from the lowest value.

Quartiles and Deciles

Quartiles divide the distribution into four groups, separated by Q_1, Q_2, Q_3.

Note that Q_1 is the same as the 25th percentile; Q_2 is the same as the 50th percentile, or the median; Q_3 corresponds to the 75th percentile, as shown:

Quartiles can be computed by using the formula given for computing percentiles on page 156. For Q_1 use $p = 25$. For Q_2 use $p = 50$. For Q_3 use $p = 75$. However, an easier method for finding quartiles is found in this Procedure Table.

Procedure Table

Finding Data Values Corresponding to Q_1, Q_2, and Q_3

Step 1   Arrange the data in order from lowest to highest.

Step 2   Find the median of the data values. This is the value for Q_2.

Step 3   Find the median of the data values that fall below Q_2. This is the value for Q_1.

Step 4   Find the median of the data values that fall above Q_2. This is the value for Q_3.

Example 3–36 shows how to find the values of Q_1, Q_2, and Q_3.

Example 3–36   Find Q_1, Q_2, and Q_3 for the data set 15, 13, 6, 5, 12, 50, 22, 18.

Solution

Step 1   Arrange the data in order.

5, 6, 12, 13, 15, 18, 22, 50

Step 2   Find the median (Q_2).

5, 6, 12, 13, 15, 18, 22, 50
↑
MD

$$MD = \frac{13 + 15}{2} = 14$$

Step 3   Find the median of the data values less than 14.

5, 6, 12, 13
↑
Q_1

$$Q_1 = \frac{6 + 12}{2} = 9$$

So Q_1 is 9.

Step 4   Find the median of the data values greater than 14.

15, 18, 22, 50
↑
Q_3

$$Q_3 = \frac{18 + 22}{2} = 20$$

Here Q_3 is 20. Hence, $Q_1 = 9$, $Q_2 = 14$, and $Q_3 = 20$.

In addition to dividing the data set into four groups, quartiles can be used as a rough measurement of variability. The **interquartile range (IQR)** is defined as the difference between Q_1 and Q_3 and is the range of the middle 50% of the data.

The interquartile range is used to identify outliers, and it is also used as a measure of variability in exploratory data analysis, as shown in Section 3–4.

Deciles divide the distribution into 10 groups, as shown. They are denoted by D_1, D_2, etc.

Note that D_1 corresponds to P_{10}; D_2 corresponds to P_{20}; etc. Deciles can be found by using the formulas given for percentiles. Taken altogether then, these are the relationships among percentiles, deciles, and quartiles.

Deciles are denoted by $D_1, D_2, D_3, \ldots, D_9$, and they correspond to $P_{10}, P_{20}, P_{30}, \ldots, P_{90}$.

Quartiles are denoted by Q_1, Q_2, Q_3 and they correspond to P_{25}, P_{50}, P_{75}.

The median is the same as P_{50} or Q_2 or D_5.

The position measures are summarized in Table 3–4.

Table 3–4	Summary of Position Measures	
Measure	**Definition**	**Symbol(s)**
Standard score or z score	Number of standard deviations that a data value is above or below the mean	z
Percentile	Position in hundredths that a data value holds in the distribution	P_n
Decile	Position in tenths that a data value holds in the distribution	D_n
Quartile	Position in fourths that a data value holds in the distribution	Q_n

Outliers

A data set should be checked for extremely high or extremely low values. These values are called *outliers*.

An **outlier** is an extremely high or an extremely low data value when compared with the rest of the data values.

An outlier can strongly affect the mean and standard deviation of a variable. For example, suppose a researcher mistakenly recorded an extremely high data value. This value would then make the mean and standard deviation of the variable much larger than they really were. Outliers can have an effect on other statistics as well.

There are several ways to check a data set for outliers. One method is shown in this Procedure Table.

Procedure Table

Procedure for Identifying Outliers

Step 1   Arrange the data in order and find Q_1 and Q_3.

Step 2   Find the interquartile range: IQR = $Q_3 - Q_1$.

Step 3   Multiply the IQR by 1.5.

Step 4   Subtract the value obtained in step 3 from Q_1 and add the value to Q_3.

Step 5   Check the data set for any data value that is smaller than $Q_1 - 1.5(\text{IQR})$ or larger than $Q_3 + 1.5(\text{IQR})$.

This procedure is shown in Example 3–37.

Example 3–37

Check the following data set for outliers.

5, 6, 12, 13, 15, 18, 22, 50

Solution

The data value 50 is extremely suspect. These are the steps in checking for an outlier.

Step 1   Find Q_1 and Q_3. This was done in Example 3–36; Q_1 is 9 and Q_3 is 20.

Step 2   Find the interquartile range (IQR), which is $Q_3 - Q_1$.

$$\text{IQR} = Q_3 - Q_1 = 20 - 9 = 11$$

Step 3   Multiply this value by 1.5.

$$1.5(11) = 16.5$$

Step 4   Subtract the value obtained in step 3 from Q_1, and add the value obtained in step 3 to Q_3.

$$9 - 16.5 = -7.5 \qquad \text{and} \qquad 20 + 16.5 = 36.5$$

Step 5   Check the data set for any data values that fall outside the interval from -7.5 to 36.5. The value 50 is outside this interval; hence, it can be considered an outlier.

There are several reasons why outliers may occur. First, the data value may have resulted from a measurement or observational error. Perhaps the researcher measured the variable incorrectly. Second, the data value may have resulted from a recording error. That is, it may have been written or typed incorrectly. Third, the data value may have been obtained from a subject that is not in the defined population. For example, suppose test scores were obtained from a seventh-grade class, but a student in that class was actually in the sixth grade and had special permission to attend the class. This student might have scored extremely low on that particular exam on that day. Fourth, the data value might be a legitimate value that occurred by chance (although the probability is extremely small).

There are no hard-and-fast rules on what to do with outliers, nor is there complete agreement among statisticians on ways to identify them. Obviously, if they occurred as a result of an error, an attempt should be made to correct the error or else the data value should be omitted entirely. When they occur naturally by chance, the statistician must make a decision about whether to include them in the data set.

When a distribution is normal or bell-shaped, data values that are beyond 3 standard deviations of the mean can be considered suspected outliers.

Applying the Concepts **3–3**

Determining Dosages

In an attempt to determine necessary dosages of a new drug (HDL) used to control sepsis, assume you administer varying amounts of HDL to 40 mice. You create four groups and label them *low dosage, moderate dosage, large dosage,* and *very large dosage.* The dosages also vary within each group. After the mice are injected with the HDL and the sepsis bacteria, the time until the onset of sepsis is recorded. Your job as a statistician is to effectively communicate the results of the study.

1. Which measures of position could be used to help describe the data results?
2. If 40% of the mice in the top quartile survived after the injection, how many mice would that be?
3. What information can be given from using percentiles?
4. What information can be given from using quartiles?
5. What information can be given from using standard scores?

See page 188 for the answers.

Exercises 3–3

1. What is a *z* score?

2. Define *percentile rank.*

3. What is the difference between a percentage and a percentile?

4. Define *quartile.*

5. What is the relationship between quartiles and percentiles?

6. What is a decile?

7. How are deciles related to percentiles?

8. To which percentile, quartile, and decile does the median correspond?

9. **Vacation Days** If the average number of vacation days for a selection of various countries has a mean of 29.4 days and a standard deviation of 8.6, find the *z* scores for the average number of vacation days in each of these countries.

Canada	26 days
Italy	42 days
United States	13 days

Source: www.infoplease.com

10. **Age of Senators** The average age of senators in the 108th Congress was 59.5 years. If the standard deviation was 11.5 years, find the *z* scores corresponding to the oldest and youngest senators: Robert C. Byrd (D, WV), 86, and John Sununu (R, NH), 40.

Source: *CRS Report for Congress.*

11. **Exam Scores** A final examination for a psychology course has a mean of 84 and a standard deviation of 4. Find the corresponding *z* score for each raw score.

a.	87	*d.*	76
b.	79	*e.*	82
c.	93		

12. **Teacher's Salary** The average teacher's salary in a particular state is $54,166. If the standard deviation is

$10,200, find the salaries corresponding to the following z scores.

a. 2
b. −1
c. 0
d. 2.5
e. −1.6

13. Which has a better relative position: a score of 75 on a statistics test with a mean of 60 and a standard deviation of 10 or a score of 36 on an accounting test with a mean of 30 and a variance of 16?

14. **Test Scores** A student scores 60 on a mathematics test that has a mean of 54 and a standard deviation of 3, and she scores 80 on a history test with a mean of 75 and a standard deviation of 2. On which test did she perform better?

15. Which score indicates the highest relative position?

a. A score of 3.2 on a test with $\overline{X} = 4.6$ and $s = 1.5$
b. A score of 630 on a test with $\overline{X} = 800$ and $s = 200$
c. A score of 43 on a test with $\overline{X} = 50$ and $s = 5$

16. **College Room and Board Costs** Room and board costs for selected schools are summarized in this distribution. Find the approximate cost of room and board corresponding to each of the following percentiles.

Costs (in dollars)	Frequency
3000.5–4000.5	5
4000.5–5000.5	6
5000.5–6000.5	18
6000.5–7000.5	24
7000.5–8000.5	19
8000.5–9000.5	8
9000.5–10,000.5	5

a. 30th percentile
b. 50th percentile
c. 75th percentile
d. 90th percentile

Source: *World Almanac.*

17. Using the data in Exercise 16, find the approximate percentile rank of each of the following costs.

a. 5500
b. 7200
c. 6500
d. 8300

18. **Achievement Test Scores (ans)** The data shown represent the scores on a national achievement test for a group of 10th-grade students. Find the approximate

percentile ranks of these scores by constructing a percentile graph.

a. 220
b. 245
c. 276
d. 280
e. 300

Score	Frequency
196.5–217.5	5
217.5–238.5	17
238.5–259.5	22
259.5–280.5	48
280.5–301.5	22
301.5–322.5	6

19. For the data in Exercise 18, find the approximate scores that correspond to these percentiles.

a. 15th
b. 29th
c. 43rd
d. 65th
e. 80th

20. **Airplane Speeds (ans)** The airborne speeds in miles per hour of 21 planes are shown. Find the approximate values that correspond to the given percentiles by constructing a percentile graph.

Class	Frequency
366–386	4
387–407	2
408–428	3
429–449	2
450–470	1
471–491	2
492–512	3
513–533	4
	21

Source: *The World Almanac and Book of Facts.*

a. 9th
b. 20th
c. 45th
d. 60th
e. 75th

21. Using the data in Exercise 20, find the approximate percentile ranks of the following miles per hour (mph).

a. 380 mph
b. 425 mph
c. 455 mph
d. 505 mph
e. 525 mph

22. **Average Weekly Earnings** The average weekly earnings in dollars for various industries are listed below. Find the percentile rank of each value.

804   736   659   489   777   623   597   524   228

Source: *New York Times Almanac.*

23. For the data from Exercise 22, what value corresponds to the 40th percentile?

24. Test Scores Find the percentile rank for each test score in the data set.

12, 28, 35, 42, 47, 49, 50

25. In Exercise 24, what value corresponds to the 60th percentile?

26. Hurricane Damage Find the percentile rank for each value in the data set. The data represent the values in billions of dollars of the damage of 10 hurricanes.

1.1, 1.7, 1.9, 2.1, 2.2, 2.5, 3.3, 6.2, 6.8, 20.3

Source: Insurance Services Office.

27. What value in Exercise 26 corresponds to the 40th percentile?

28. Test Scores Find the percentile rank for each test score in the data set.

5, 12, 15, 16, 20, 21

29. What test score in Exercise 28 corresponds to the 33rd percentile?

30. Using the procedure shown in Example 3–37, check each data set for outliers.

a. 16, 18, 22, 19, 3, 21, 17, 20
b. 24, 32, 54, 31, 16, 18, 19, 14, 17, 20
c. 321, 343, 350, 327, 200
d. 88, 72, 97, 84, 86, 85, 100
e. 145, 119, 122, 118, 125, 116
f. 14, 16, 27, 18, 13, 19, 36, 15, 20

31. Another measure of average is called the *midquartile;* it is the numerical value halfway between Q_1 and Q_3, and the formula is

$$\text{Midquartile} = \frac{Q_1 + Q_3}{2}$$

Using this formula and other formulas, find Q_1, Q_2, Q_3, the midquartile, and the interquartile range for each data set.

a. 5, 12, 16, 25, 32, 38
b. 53, 62, 78, 94, 96, 99, 103

MINITAB
Step by Step

Calculate Descriptive Statistics from Data

Example MT3–1

1. Enter the data from Example 3–23 into C1 of MINITAB. Name the column **AutoSales.**

2. Select **Stat>Basic Statistics>Display Descriptive Statistics.**

3. The cursor will be blinking in the Variables text box. Double-click C1 AutoSales.

4. Click [Statistics] to view the statistics that can be calculated with this command.

   a) Check the boxes for Mean, Standard deviation, Variance, Coefficient of variation, Median, Minimum, Maximum, and N nonmissing.

   b) Remove the checks from other options.

5. Click [OK] twice. The results will be displayed in the session window as shown.

Descriptive Statistics: AutoSales

Variable	N	Mean	Median	StDev	Variance	CoefVar	Minimum	Maximum
AutoSales	6	12.6	12.4	1.12960	1.276	8.96509	11.2	14.3

Session window results are in text format. A high-resolution graphical window displays the descriptive statistics, a histogram, and a boxplot.

6. Select **Stat>Basic Statistics>Graphical Summary.**

7. Double-click C1 AutoSales.

8. Click [OK].

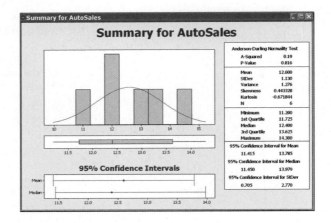

The graphical summary will be displayed in a separate window as shown.

Calculate Descriptive Statistics from a Frequency Distribution

Multiple menu selections must be used to calculate the statistics from a table. We will use data given in Example 3–24.

Enter Midpoints and Frequencies

1. Select **File>New>New Worksheet** to open an empty worksheet.

2. To enter the midpoints into C1, select **Calc>Make Patterned Data>Simple Set of Numbers.**

   a) Type **X** to name the column.

   b) Type in **8** for the First value, **38** for the Last value, and **5** for Steps.

   c) Click [OK].

3. Enter the frequencies in C2. Name the column **f.**

Calculate Columns for f·X and f·X²

4. Select **Calc>Calculator.**

   a) Type in **fX** for the variable and **f*X** in the Expression dialog box. Click [OK].

   b) Select **Edit>Edit Last Dialog** and type in **fX2** for the variable and **f*X**2** for the expression.

   c) Click [OK]. There are now four columns in the worksheet.

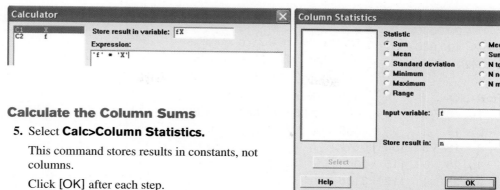

Calculate the Column Sums

5. Select **Calc>Column Statistics.**

   This command stores results in constants, not columns.

   Click [OK] after each step.

   a) Click the option for Sum; then select C2 f for the Input column, and type **n** for Store result in.

   b) Select **Edit>Edit Last Dialog;** then select C3 fX for the column and type **sumX** for storage.

   c) Edit the last dialog box again. This time select C4 fX2 for the column, then type **sumX2** for storage.

To verify the results, navigate to the Project Manager window, then the constants folder of the worksheet. The sums are 20, 490, and 13,310.

Calculate the Mean, Variance, and Standard Deviation

6. Select **Calc>Calculator.**

   a) Type **Mean** for the variable, then click in the box for the Expression and type **sumX/n.** Click [OK]. If you double-click the constants instead of typing them, single quotes will surround the names. The quotes are not required unless the column name has spaces.

   b) Click the **EditLast Dialog** icon and type **Variance** for the variable.

   c) In the expression box type in

   (sumX2-sumX2/n)/(n-1)**

   d) Edit the last dialog box and type **S** for the variable. In the expression box, drag the mouse over the previous expression to highlight it.

   e) Click the button in the keypad for parentheses. Type **SQRT** at the beginning of the line, upper- or lowercase will work. The expression should be SQRT((sumX2-sumX**2/n)/(n-1)).

   f) Click [OK].

Display Results

   g) Select **Data>Display Data,** then highlight all columns and constants in the list.

   h) Click [Select] then [OK].

The session window will display all our work! Create the histogram with instructions from Chapter 2.

Data Display

n   20.0000
sumX   490.000
sumX2 13310.0

Row	X	f	fX	fX2	Mean	Variance	S
1	8	1	8	64	24.5	68.6842	8.28759
2	13	2	26	338			
3	18	3	54	972			
4	23	5	115	2645			
5	28	4	112	3136			
6	33	3	99	3267			
7	38	2	76	2888			

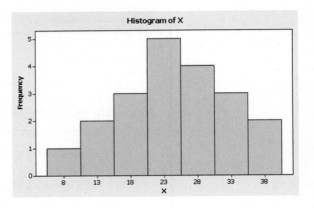

TI-83 Plus or TI-84 Plus

Step by Step

Calculating Descriptive Statistics

To calculate various descriptive statistics:

1. Enter data into L_1.
2. Press **STAT** to get the menu.
3. Press ▶ to move cursor to CALC; then press **1** for 1-Var Stats.
4. Press **2nd [L₁]**, then **ENTER**.

The calculator will display

$\bar{x}$ sample mean

Σx sum of the data values

Σx^2 sum of the squares of the data values

S_x sample standard deviation

σ_x population standard deviation

n number of data values

minX smallest data value

Q_1 lower quartile

Med median

Q_3 upper quartile

maxX largest data value

Example TI3–1

Find the various descriptive statistics for the auto sales data from Example 3–23:

11.2, 11.9, 12.0, 12.8, 13.4, 14.3

Output   Output

Following the steps just shown, we obtain these results, as shown on the screen:

    The mean is 12.6.

    The sum of x is 75.6.

    The sum of x^2 is 958.94.

    The sample standard deviation S_x is 1.1296017.

    The population standard deviation σ_x is 1.031180553.

    The sample size n is 6.

    The smallest data value is 11.2.

    Q_1 is 11.9.

    The median is 12.4.

    Q_3 is 13.4.

    The largest data value is 14.3.

To calculate the mean and standard deviation from grouped data:

  1. Enter the midpoints into L_1.

  2. Enter the frequencies into L_2.

  3. Press **STAT** to get the menu.

  4. Use the arrow keys to move the cursor to CALC; then press **1** for 1-Var Stats.

  5. Press **2nd [L1], 2nd [L2],** then **ENTER.**

Example TI3–2

Calculate the mean and standard deviation for the data given in Examples 3–3 and 3–24.

Class	Frequency	Midpoint
5.5–10.5	1	8
10.5–15.5	2	13
15.5–20.5	3	18
20.5–25.5	5	23
25.5–30.5	4	28
30.5–35.5	3	33
35.5–40.5	2	38

Input	Input	Output

The sample mean is 24.5, and the sample standard deviation is 8.287593772.

To graph a percentile graph, follow the procedure for an ogive but use the cumulative percent in L_2, 100 for Y_{max}, and the data from Example 3–31.

Output

Excel
Step by Step

Measures of Position

Example XL3–3

Find the z scores for each value of the data from Example 3–23. The data represent the amount (in millions of dollars) of European auto sales for a sample of 6 years.

$$11.2 \quad 11.9 \quad 12.0 \quad 12.8 \quad 13.4 \quad 14.3$$

1. On an Excel worksheet enter the data in cells A2–A7. Enter a label for the variable in cell A1.
2. Label cell B1 as z score.
3. Select cell B2.
4. Select the Formulas tab from the toolbar and Insert Function ![fx Insert Function].
5. Select the Statistical category for statistical functions and scroll in the function list to STANDARDIZE and click [OK].

In the STANDARDIZE dialog box:

6. Type A2 for the X value.
7. Type average(A2:A7) for the Mean.
8. Type stdev(A2:A7) for the Standard_dev. Then click [OK].
9. Repeat the procedure above for each data value in column A.

Example XL3–4

Find the percentile rank for each value of the data from Example 3–23. The data represent the amount (in millions of dollars) of European auto sales for a sample of 6 years.

$$11.2 \quad 11.9 \quad 12.0 \quad 12.8 \quad 13.4 \quad 14.3$$

1. On an Excel worksheet enter the data in cells A2–A7. Enter a label for the variable in cell A1.
2. Label cell B1 as z score.
3. Select cell B2.
4. Select the Formulas tab from the toolbar and Insert Function ![fx Insert Function].
5. Select the Statistical category for statistical functions and scroll in the function list to PERCENTRANK and click [OK].

In the PERCENTRANK dialog box:

6. Type A2:A7 for the Array.

7. Type A2 for the X value, then click [OK].

8. Repeat the procedure above for each data value in column A.

The PERCENTRANK function returns the percentile rank as a decimal. To convert this to a percentage, multiply the function output by 100. Make sure to select a new column before multiplying the percentile rank by 100.

Descriptive Statistics in Excel

Example XL3–5

Excel Analysis Tool-Pak Add-in Data Analysis includes an item called Descriptive Statistics that reports many useful measures for a set of data.

1. Enter the data set shown in cells A1 to A9 of a new worksheet.

      12   17   15   16   16   14   18   13   10

See the Excel Step by Step in Chapter 1 for the instructions on loading the Analysis Tool-Pak Add-in.

2. Select the Data tab on the toolbar and select Data Analysis.

3. In the Analysis Tools dialog box, scroll to Descriptive Statistics, then click [OK].

4. Type A1:A9 in the Input Range box and check the Grouped by Columns option.

5. Select the Output Range option and type in cell C1.

6. Check the Summary statistics option and click [OK].

Below is the summary output for this data set.

Column1	
Mean	14.55555556
Standard Error	0.85165054
Median	15
Mode	16
Standard Deviation	2.554951619
Sample Variance	6.527777778
Kurtosis	-0.3943866
Skewness	-0.51631073
Range	8
Minimum	10
Maximum	18
Sum	131
Count	9

3–4   Exploratory Data Analysis

Objective 4

Use the techniques of exploratory data analysis, including boxplots and five-number summaries, to discover various aspects of data.

In traditional statistics, data are organized by using a frequency distribution. From this distribution various graphs such as the histogram, frequency polygon, and ogive can be constructed to determine the shape or nature of the distribution. In addition, various statistics such as the mean and standard deviation can be computed to summarize the data.

The purpose of traditional analysis is to confirm various conjectures about the nature of the data. For example, from a carefully designed study, a researcher might want to know if the proportion of Americans who are exercising today has increased from 10 years ago. This study would contain various assumptions about the population, various definitions such as of exercise, and so on.

In **exploratory data analysis (EDA),** data can be organized using a *stem and leaf plot.* (See Chapter 2.) The measure of central tendency used in EDA is the *median.* The measure of variation used in EDA is the *interquartile range* $Q_3 - Q_1$. In EDA the data are represented graphically using a *boxplot* (sometimes called a box-and-whisker plot). The purpose of exploratory data analysis is to examine data to find out what information can be discovered about the data such as the center and the spread. Exploratory data analysis was developed by John Tukey and presented in his book *Exploratory Data Analysis* (Addison-Wesley, 1977).

The Five-Number Summary and Boxplots

A **boxplot** can be used to graphically represent the data set. These plots involve five specific values:

1. The lowest value of the data set (i.e., minimum)
2. Q_1
3. The median
4. Q_3
5. The highest value of the data set (i.e., maximum)

These values are called a **five-number summary** of the data set.

A **boxplot** is a graph of a data set obtained by drawing a horizontal line from the minimum data value to Q_1, drawing a horizontal line from Q_3 to the maximum data value, and drawing a box whose vertical sides pass through Q_1 and Q_3 with a vertical line inside the box passing through the median or Q_2.

Procedure for constructing a boxplot

1. Find the five-number summary for the data values, that is, the maximum and minimum data values, Q_1 and Q_3, and the median.
2. Draw a horizontal axis with a scale such that it includes the maximum and minimum data values.
3. Draw a box whose vertical sides go through Q_1 and Q_3, and draw a vertical line though the median.
4. Draw a line from the minimum data value to the left side of the box and a line from the maximum data value to the right side of the box.

Example 3–38

Number of Meteorites Found

The number of meteorites found in 10 states of the United States is 89, 47, 164, 296, 30, 215, 138, 78, 48, 39. Construct a boxplot for the data.

Source: Natural History Museum.

Solution

Step 1   Arrange the data in order:

30, 39, 47, 48, 78, 89, 138, 164, 215, 296

Step 2   Find the median.

30, 39, 47, 48, 78, 89, 138, 164, 215, 296
↑
Median

$$\text{Median} = \frac{78 + 89}{2} = 83.5$$

Step 3   Find Q_1.

30, 39, 47, 48, 78
↑
Q_1

Step 4   Find Q_3.

89, 138, 164, 215, 296
↑
Q_3

Step 5   Draw a scale for the data on the x axis.

Step 6   Locate the lowest value, Q_1, median, Q_3, and the highest value on the scale.

Step 7   Draw a box around Q_1 and Q_3, draw a vertical line through the median, and connect the upper value and the lower value to the box. See Figure 3–7.

Figure 3–7

Boxplot for Example 3–38

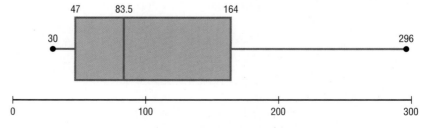

The distribution is somewhat positively skewed.

Information Obtained from a Boxplot

1. *a.* If the median is near the center of the box, the distribution is approximately symmetric.
   b. If the median falls to the left of the center of the box, the distribution is positively skewed.
   c. If the median falls to the right of the center, the distribution is negatively skewed.
2. *a.* If the lines are about the same length, the distribution is approximately symmetric.
   b. If the right line is larger than the left line, the distribution is positively skewed.
   c. If the left line is larger than the right line, the distribution is negatively skewed.

The boxplot in Figure 3–7 indicates that the distribution is slightly positively skewed.

If the boxplots for two or more data sets are graphed on the same axis, the distributions can be compared. To compare the averages, use the location of the medians. To compare the variability, use the interquartile range, i.e., the length of the boxes. Example 3–39 shows this procedure.

Example 3–39

Sodium Content of Cheese

 A dietitian is interested in comparing the sodium content of real cheese with the sodium content of a cheese substitute. The data for two random samples are shown. Compare the distributions, using boxplots.

Real cheese				Cheese substitute			
310	420	45	40	270	180	250	290
220	240	180	90	130	260	340	310

Source: *The Complete Book of Food Counts.*

Solution

Step 1 Find Q_1, MD, and Q_3 for the real cheese data.

40   45   90   180   220   240   310   420
          ↑   ↑   ↑
         Q_1 MD Q_3

$$Q_1 = \frac{45 + 90}{2} = 67.5 \qquad MD = \frac{180 + 220}{2} = 200$$

$$Q_3 = \frac{240 + 310}{2} = 275$$

Step 2 Find Q_1, MD, and Q_3 for the cheese substitute data.

130   180   250   260   270   290   310   340
            ↑   ↑   ↑
           Q_1 MD Q_3

$$Q_1 = \frac{180 + 250}{2} = 215 \qquad MD = \frac{260 + 270}{2} = 265$$

$$Q_3 = \frac{290 + 310}{2} = 300$$

Step 3 Draw the boxplots for each distribution on the same graph. See Figure 3–8.

Step 4   Compare the plots. It is quite apparent that the distribution for the cheese substitute data has a higher median than the median for the distribution for the real cheese data. The variation or spread for the distribution of the real cheese data is larger than the variation for the distribution of the cheese substitute data.

Figure 3–8

Boxplots for
Example 3–39

A *modified boxplot* can be drawn and used to check for outliers. See Exercise 18 in Extending the Concepts in this section.

In exploratory data analysis, *hinges* are used instead of quartiles to construct box-plots. When the data set consists of an even number of values, hinges are the same as quartiles. Hinges for a data set with an odd number of values differ somewhat from quartiles. However, since most calculators and computer programs use quartiles, they will be used in this textbook.

Another important point to remember is that the summary statistics (median and interquartile range) used in exploratory data analysis are said to be *resistant statistics*. A **resistant statistic** is relatively less affected by outliers than a *nonresistant statistic*. The mean and standard deviation are nonresistant statistics. Sometimes when a distribution is skewed or contains outliers, the median and interquartile range may more accurately summarize the data than the mean and standard deviation, since the mean and standard deviation are more affected in this case.

Table 3–5 shows the correspondence between the traditional and the exploratory data analysis approach.

Table 3–5	Traditional versus EDA Techniques	
	Traditional	**Exploratory data analysis**
	Frequency distribution	Stem and leaf plot
	Histogram	Boxplot
	Mean	Median
	Standard deviation	Interquartile range

Applying the Concepts **3–4**

The Noisy Workplace

Assume you work for OSHA (Occupational Safety and Health Administration) and have complaints about noise levels from some of the workers at a state power plant. You charge the power plant with taking decibel readings at six different areas of the plant at different times of the day and week. The results of the data collection are listed. Use boxplots to initially explore the data and make recommendations about which plant areas workers must be provided with protective ear wear. The safe hearing level is at approximately 120 decibels.

Area 1	Area 2	Area 3	Area 4	Area 5	Area 6
30	64	100	25	59	67
12	99	59	15	63	80
35	87	78	30	81	99
65	59	97	20	110	49
24	23	84	61	65	67
59	16	64	56	112	56
68	94	53	34	132	80
57	78	59	22	145	125
100	57	89	24	163	100
61	32	88	21	120	93
32	52	94	32	84	56
45	78	66	52	99	45
92	59	57	14	105	80
56	55	62	10	68	34
44	55	64	33	75	21

See page 188 for the answers.

Exercises 3–4

For Exercises 1–6, identify the five-number summary and find the interquartile range.

1. 8, 12, 32, 6, 27, 19, 54

2. 19, 16, 48, 22, 7

3. 362, 589, 437, 316, 192, 188

4. 147, 243, 156, 632, 543, 303

5. 14.6, 19.8, 16.3, 15.5, 18.2

6. 9.7, 4.6, 2.2, 3.7, 6.2, 9.4, 3.8

For Exercises 7–10, use each boxplot to identify the maximum value, minimum value, median, first quartile, third quartile, and interquartile range.

7.

8.

9.

10.

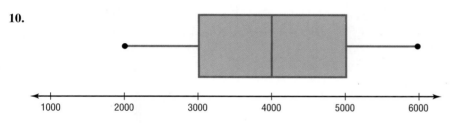

11. Earned Run Average—Number of Games Pitched Construct a boxplot for the following data and comment on the shape of the distribution representing the number of games pitched by major league baseball's earned run average (ERA) leaders for the past few years.

30 34 29 30 34 29 31 33 34 27
30 27 34 32

Source: *World Almanac.*

12. Innings Pitched Construct a boxplot for the following data which represents the number of innings pitched by the ERA leaders for the past few years. Comment on the shape of the distribution.

192 228 186 199 238 217 213 234 264 187
214 115 238 246

Source: *World Almanac.*

13. State Sites for Frogwatch Construct a boxplot for these numbers of state sites for Frogwatch USA. Is the distribution symmetric?

421 395 314 294 289 253 242 238 235 199

Source: www.nwf.org/frogwatch

14. Median Household Incomes Construct a boxplot and comment on the skewness of these data which represent median household income (in dollars) for the

top 10 educated cities (based on the percent of the population with a college degree or higher).

49,297   48,131   43,731   39,752   55,637
57,496   47,221   41,829   42,562   42,442

Source: www.encarta.msn.com

15. Tornadoes in 2005 Construct a boxplot and comment on its skewness for the number of tornadoes recorded each month in 2005.

33   10   62   132   123   316   138   123   133   18
150   26

Source: Storm Prediction Center.

16. Size of Dams These data represent the volumes in cubic yards of the largest dams in the United States and in South America. Construct a boxplot of the data for each region and compare the distributions.

United States	South America
125,628	311,539
92,000	274,026
78,008	105,944
77,700	102,014
66,500	56,242
62,850	46,563
52,435	
50,000	

Source: *New York Times Almanac.*

17. Number of Tornadoes A four-month record for the number of tornadoes in 2003–2005 is given here.

	2005	2004	2003
April	132	125	157
May	123	509	543
June	316	268	292
July	138	124	167

a. Which month had the highest mean number of tornadoes for this 3-year period?

b. Which year has the highest mean number of tornadoes for this 4-month period?

c. Construct three boxplots and compare the distributions.

Source: NWS, Storm Prediction Center.

Extending the Concepts

18. Unhealthful Smog Days A *modified boxplot* can be drawn by placing a box around Q_1 and Q_3 and then extending the whiskers to the largest and/or smallest values within 1.5 times the interquartile range (i.e., $Q_3 - Q_1$). *Mild outliers* are values between 1.5(IQR) and 3(IQR). *Extreme outliers* are data values beyond 3(IQR).

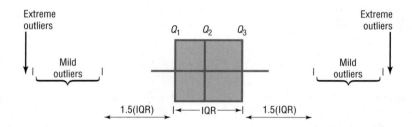

For the data shown here, draw a modified boxplot and identify any mild or extreme outliers. The data represent the number of unhealthful smog days for a specific year for the highest 10 locations.

97	39	43	66	91
43	54	42	53	39

Source: U.S. Public Interest Research Group and Clean Air Network.

Technology *Step by Step*

MINITAB
Step by Step

Construct a Boxplot

1. Type in the data 33, 38, 43, 30, 29, 40, 51, 27, 42, 23, 31. Label the column **Clients.**
2. Select **Stat>EDA>Boxplot.**
3. Double-click Clients to select it for the Y variable.
4. Click on [Labels].
   a) In the Title 1: of the Title/Footnotes folder, type **Number of Clients.**
   b) Press the [Tab] key and type **Your Name** in the text box for Subtitle 1:.

5. Click [OK] twice. The graph will be displayed in a graph window.

Example MT3–2

1. Enter the data for Example 2–13 in Section 2–3. Label the column **CARS-THEFT.**

2. Select **Stat>EDA>Boxplot.**

3. Double-click CARS-THEFT to select it for the Y variable.

4. Click on the drop-down arrow for Annotation.

5. Click on Title, then enter an appropriate title such as **Car Thefts for Large City, U.S.A.**

6. Click [OK] twice.

A high-resolution graph will be displayed in a graph window.

Boxplot Dialog Box and Boxplot

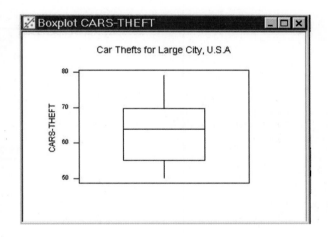

TI-83 Plus or TI-84 Plus
Step by Step

Constructing a Boxplot

To draw a boxplot:

1. Enter data into L_1.

2. Change values in WINDOW menu, if necessary. (*Note:* Make X_{min} somewhat smaller than the smallest data value and X_{max} somewhat larger than the largest data value.) Change Y_{min} to 0 and Y_{max} to 1.

3. Press **[2nd] [STAT PLOT]**, then **1** for Plot 1.

4. Press **ENTER** to turn Plot 1 on.

5. Move cursor to Boxplot symbol (fifth graph) on the Type: line, then press **ENTER.**

6. Make sure Xlist is L$_1$.
7. Make sure Freq is 1.
8. Press **GRAPH** to display the boxplot.
9. Press **TRACE** followed by ◄ or ► to obtain the values from the five-number summary on the boxplot.

To display two boxplots on the same display, follow the above steps and use the 2: Plot 2 and L$_2$ symbols.

Example TI3–3

Construct a boxplot for the data values:

     33, 38, 43, 30, 29, 40, 51, 27, 42, 23, 31

Input

Input

Using the **TRACE** key along with the ◄ and ► keys, we obtain the five-number summary. The minimum value is 23; Q_1 is 29; the median is 33; Q_3 is 42; the maximum value is 51.

Output

Excel
Step by Step

Constructing a Stem and Leaf Plot and a Boxplot
Example XL3–6

Excel does not have procedures to produce stem and leaf plots or boxplots. However, you may construct these plots by using the MegaStat Add-in available on your CD or from the Online Learning Center. If you have not installed this add-in, refer to the instructions in the Excel Step by Step section of Chapter 1.

    To obtain a boxplot and stem and leaf plot:

1. Enter the data values 33, 38, 43, 30, 29, 40, 51, 27, 42, 23, 31 into column A of a new Excel worksheet.

2. Select the Add-Ins tab, then MegaStat from the toolbar.

3. Select Descriptive Statistics from the MegaStat menu.

4. Enter the cell range A1:A11 in the Input range.

5. Check both Boxplot and Stem and Leaf Plot. *Note:* You may leave the other output options unchecked for this example. Click [OK].

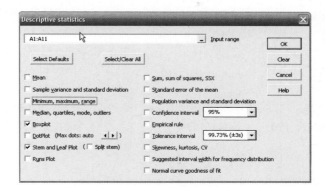

The stem and leaf plot and the boxplot are shown below.

Summary

This chapter explains the basic ways to summarize data. These include measures of central tendency, measures of variation or dispersion, and measures of position. The three most commonly used measures of central tendency are the mean, median, and mode. The midrange is also used occasionally to represent an average. The three most commonly used measurements of variation are the range, variance, and standard deviation.

The most common measures of position are percentiles, quartiles, and deciles. This chapter explains how data values are distributed according to Chebyshev's theorem and the empirical rule. The coefficient of variation is used to describe the standard deviation in relationship to the mean. These methods are commonly called traditional statistical methods and are primarily used to confirm various conjectures about the nature of the data.

Other methods, such as the boxplot and five-number summaries, are part of exploratory data analysis; they are used to examine data to see what they reveal.

After learning the techniques presented in Chapter 2 and this chapter, you will have a substantial knowledge of descriptive statistics. That is, you will be able to collect, organize, summarize, and present data.

Important Terms

bimodal 119

boxplot 170

Chebyshev's theorem 142

coefficient of variation 140

data array 117

decile 159

empirical rule 144

exploratory data analysis (EDA) 170

five-number summary 170

interquartile range (IQR) 159

mean 114

median 117

midrange 122

modal class 120

mode 119

multimodal 119

negatively skewed or left-skewed distribution 125

outlier 159

parameter 114

percentile 151

positively skewed or right-skewed distribution 125

quartile 157

range 132

range rule of thumb 141

resistant statistic 173

standard deviation 135

statistic 114

symmetric distribution 125

unimodal 119

variance 135

weighted mean 123

z score or standard score 150

Important Formulas

Formula for the mean for individual data:

$$\bar{X} = \frac{\Sigma X}{n} \quad \mu = \frac{\Sigma X}{N}$$

Formula for the mean for grouped data:

$$\bar{X} = \frac{\Sigma f \cdot X_m}{n}$$

Formula for the weighted mean:

$$\bar{X} = \frac{\Sigma wX}{\Sigma w}$$

Formula for the midrange:

$$MR = \frac{\text{lowest value} + \text{highest value}}{2}$$

Formula for the range:

$$R = \text{highest value} - \text{lowest value}$$

Formula for the variance for population data:

$$\sigma^2 = \frac{\Sigma(X - \mu)^2}{N}$$

Formula for the variance for sample data (shortcut formula for the unbiased estimator):

$$s^2 = \frac{n(\Sigma X^2) - (\Sigma X)^2}{n(n - 1)}$$

Formula for the variance for grouped data:

$$s^2 = \frac{n(\Sigma f \cdot X_m^2) - (\Sigma f \cdot X_m)^2}{n(n - 1)}$$

Formula for the standard deviation for population data:

$$\sigma = \sqrt{\frac{\Sigma(X - \mu)^2}{N}}$$

Formula for the standard deviation for sample data (shortcut formula):

$$s = \sqrt{\frac{n(\Sigma X^2) - (\Sigma X)^2}{n(n - 1)}}$$

Formula for the standard deviation for grouped data:

$$s = \sqrt{\frac{n(\Sigma f \cdot X_m^2) - (\Sigma f \cdot X_m)^2}{n(n - 1)}}$$

Formula for the coefficient of variation:

$$CVar = \frac{s}{\bar{X}} \cdot 100\% \quad \text{or} \quad CVar = \frac{\sigma}{\mu} \cdot 100\%$$

Range rule of thumb:

$$s \approx \frac{\text{range}}{4}$$

Expression for Chebyshev's theorem: The proportion of values from a data set that will fall within k standard deviations of the mean will be at least

$$1 - \frac{1}{k^2}$$

where k is a number greater than 1.

Formula for the z score (standard score):

$$z = \frac{X - \mu}{\sigma} \quad \text{or} \quad z = \frac{X - \bar{X}}{s}$$

Formula for the cumulative percentage:

$$\text{Cumulative \%} = \frac{\begin{array}{c}\textbf{cumulative}\\\textbf{frequency}\end{array}}{n} \cdot \textbf{100\%}$$

Formula for the percentile rank of a value *X:*

$$\text{Percentile} = \frac{\begin{array}{c}\textbf{number of values}\\\textbf{below } X + \textbf{0.5}\end{array}}{\begin{array}{c}\textbf{total number}\\\textbf{of values}\end{array}} \cdot \textbf{100\%}$$

Formula for finding a value corresponding to a given percentile:

$$c = \frac{n \cdot p}{100}$$

Formula for interquartile range:

$$\text{IQR} = Q_3 - Q_1$$

Review Exercises

 1. Hospitals The following set of data represents the number of hospitals for selected states. Find the mean, median, mode, midrange, range, variance, and standard deviation for the data.

53 84 28 78 35 111 40 166 108 60 123
87 84 74 80 62

Source: *World Almanac.*

2. Elementary and Secondary Schools These data represent the number of both elementary and secondary schools for selected states.

Elementary				Secondary			
938	977	194	518	403	423	85	156
711	599	1196	497	424	327	401	362
824	885	137	575	240	333	44	205
139	913	417	849	43	274	223	285

For each set of data find:

a. Mean   *e.* Range
b. Median   *f.* Variance
c. Mode   *g.* Standard deviation
d. Midrange

Which set of data is more variable?

Source: *World Almanac.*

3. Battery Lives Twelve batteries were tested to see how many hours they would last. The frequency distribution is shown here.

Hours	Frequency
1–3	1
4–6	4
7–9	5
10–12	1
13–15	1

Find each of these.

a. Mean   *c.* Variance
b. Modal class   *d.* Standard deviation

4. SAT Scores The mean SAT math scores for selected states are represented below. Find the mean class, modal class, variance, and standard deviation, and comment on the shape of the data.

Score	Frequency
478–504	4
505–531	6
532–558	2
559–585	2
586–612	2

Source: *World Almanac.*

5. Rise in Tides Shown here is a frequency distribution for the rise in tides at 30 selected locations in the United States.

Rise in tides (inches)	Frequency
12.5–27.5	6
27.5–42.5	3
42.5–57.5	5
57.5–72.5	8
72.5–87.5	6
87.5–102.5	2

Find each of these.

a. Mean   *c.* Variance
b. Modal class   *d.* Standard deviation

6. Fuel Capacity The fuel capacity in gallons of 50 randomly selected 1995 cars is shown here.

Class	Frequency
10–12	6
13–15	4
16–18	14
19–21	15
22–24	8
25–27	2
28–30	1
	50

Find each of these.

a. Mean
b. Modal class
c. Variance
d. Standard deviation

7. **Number of Cavities** In a dental survey of third-grade students, this distribution was obtained for the number of cavities found. Find the average number of cavities for the class. Use the weighted mean.

Number of students	Number of cavities
12	0
8	1
5	2
5	3

8. **Investment Earnings** An investor calculated these percentages of each of three stock investments with payoffs as shown. Find the average payoff. Use the weighted mean.

Stock	Percent	Payoff
A	30	$10,000
B	50	3,000
C	20	1,000

9. **Years of Service of Employees** In an advertisement, a transmission service center stated that the average years of service of its employees were 13. The distribution is shown here. Using the weighted mean, calculate the correct average.

Number of employees	Years of service
8	3
1	6
1	30

10. **Textbooks in Professors' Offices** If the average number of textbooks in professors' offices is 16, the standard deviation is 5, and the average age of the professors is 43, with a standard deviation of 8, which data set is more variable?

11. **Magazines in Bookstores** A survey of bookstores showed that the average number of magazines carried is 56, with a standard deviation of 12. The same survey showed that the average length of time each store had been in business was 6 years, with a standard deviation of 2.5 years. Which is more variable, the number of magazines or the number of years?

12. **Years of Service of Supreme Court Members** The number of years served by selected past members of the U.S. Supreme Court is listed below. Find the percentile rank for each value. Which value corresponds to the 40th percentile? Construct a boxplot for the data and comment on their shape.

19, 15, 16, 24, 17, 4, 3, 31, 23, 5, 33

Source: *World Almanac.*

13. **NFL Salaries** The salaries (in millions of dollars) for 29 NFL teams for the 1999–2000 season are given in this frequency distribution.

Class limits	Frequency
39.9–42.8	2
42.9–45.8	2
45.9–48.8	5
48.9–51.8	5
51.9–54.8	12
54.9–57.8	3

Source: www.NFL.com

a. Construct a percentile graph.
b. Find the values that correspond to the 35th, 65th, and 85th percentiles.
c. Find the percentile of values 44, 48, and 54.

14. Check each data set for outliers.
a. 506, 511, 517, 514, 400, 521
b. 3, 7, 9, 6, 8, 10, 14, 16, 20, 12
c. 14, 18, 27, 26, 19, 13, 5, 25
d. 112, 157, 192, 116, 153, 129, 131

15. **Cost of Car Rentals** A survey of car rental agencies shows that the average cost of a car rental is $0.32 per mile. The standard deviation is $0.03. Using Chebyshev's theorem, find the range in which at least 75% of the data values will fall.

16. **Average Earnings of Workers** The average earnings of year-round full-time workers 25–34 years old with a bachelor's degree or higher were $58,500 in 2003. If the standard deviation is $11,200, what can you say about the percentage of these workers who earn

a. Between $47,300 and $69,700?
b. More than $80,900?
c. How likely is it that someone earns more than $100,000?

Source: *New York Times Almanac.*

17. **Labor Charges** The average labor charge for automobile mechanics is $54 per hour. The standard deviation is $4. Find the minimum percentage of data values that will fall within the range of $48 to $60. Use Chebyshev's theorem.

18. **Costs to Train Employees** For a certain type of job, it costs a company an average of $231 to train an employee to perform the task. The standard deviation is $5. Find the minimum percentage of data values that will fall in the range of $219 to $243. Use Chebyshev's theorem.

19. **Delivery Charges** The average delivery charge for a refrigerator is $32. The standard deviation is $4. Find the minimum percentage of data values that will fall in the range of $20 to $44. Use Chebyshev's theorem.

20. **Exam Grades** Which of these exam grades has a better relative position?

    a. A grade of 82 on a test with $\overline{X} = 85$ and $s = 6$
    b. A grade of 56 on a test with $\overline{X} = 60$ and $s = 5$

21. **Top Movie Sites** The number of sites at which the top nine movies (based on the daily gross earnings) opened in a particular week is indicated below.

3017	3687	2525
2516	2820	2579
3211	3044	2330

    Construct a boxplot for the data.

    The 10th movie on the list opened at only 909 theaters. Add this number to the above set of data and construct a boxplot. Comment on the changes that occur.

    Source: www.showbizdata.com

22. **Hours Worked** The data shown here represent the number of hours that 12 part-time employees at a toy store worked during the weeks before and after Christmas. Construct two boxplots and compare the distributions.

Before	38	16	18	24	12	30	35	32	31	30	24	35
After	26	15	12	18	24	32	14	18	16	18	22	12

23. **Commuter Times** The mean of the times it takes a commuter to get to work in Baltimore is 29.7 minutes. If the standard deviation is 6 minutes, within what limits would you expect approximately 68% of the times to fall? Assume the distribution is approximately bell-shaped.

Statistics Today

How Long Are You Delayed by Road Congestion?—Revisited

The average number of hours per year that a driver is delayed by road congestion is listed here.

Los Angeles	56
Atlanta	53
Seattle	53
Houston	50
Dallas	46
Washington	46
Austin	45
Denver	45
St. Louis	44
Orlando	42
U.S. average	36

Source: Texas Transportation Institute.

By making comparisons using averages, you can see that drivers in these 10 cities are delayed by road congestion more than the national average.

Data Analysis

A Data Bank is found in Appendix D, or on the World Wide Web by following links from
www.mhhe.com/bluman/

1. From the Data Bank, choose one of the following variables: age, weight, cholesterol level, systolic pressure, IQ, or sodium level. Select at least 30 values, and find the mean, median, mode, and midrange. State which measurement of central tendency best describes the average and why.

2. Find the range, variance, and standard deviation for the data selected in Exercise 1.

3. From the Data Bank, choose 10 values from any variable, construct a boxplot, and interpret the results.

4. Randomly select 10 values from the number of suspensions in the local school districts in southwestern Pennsylvania in Data Set V in Appendix D. Find the mean, median, mode, range, variance, and standard deviation of the number of suspensions by using the Pearson coefficient of skewness.

5. Using the data from Data Set VII in Appendix D, find the mean, median, mode, range, variance, and standard deviation of the acreage owned by the municipalities. Comment on the skewness of the data, using the Pearson coefficient of skewness.

Chapter Quiz

Determine whether each statement is true or false. If the statement is false, explain why.

1. When the mean is computed for individual data, all values in the data set are used.

2. The mean cannot be found for grouped data when there is an open class.

3. A single, extremely large value can affect the median more than the mean.

4. One-half of all the data values will fall above the mode, and one-half will fall below the mode.

5. In a data set, the mode will always be unique.

6. The range and midrange are both measures of variation.

7. One disadvantage of the median is that it is not unique.

8. The mode and midrange are both measures of variation.

9. If a person's score on an exam corresponds to the 75th percentile, then that person obtained 75 correct answers out of 100 questions.

Select the best answer.

10. What is the value of the mode when all values in the data set are different?

    a. 0
    b. 1
    c. There is no mode.
    d. It cannot be determined unless the data values are given.

11. When data are categorized as, for example, places of residence (rural, suburban, urban), the most appropriate measure of central tendency is the

    a. Mean   c. Mode
    b. Median   d. Midrange

12. P_{50} corresponds to

    a. Q_2
    b. D_5
    c. IQR
    d. Midrange

13. Which is not part of the five-number summary?

    a. Q_1 and Q_3
    b. The mean
    c. The median
    d. The smallest and the largest data values

14. A statistic that tells the number of standard deviations a data value is above or below the mean is called

    a. A quartile
    b. A percentile
    c. A coefficient of variation
    d. A z score

15. When a distribution is bell-shaped, approximately what percentage of data values will fall within 1 standard deviation of the mean?

    a. 50%
    b. 68%
    c. 95%
    d. 99.7%

Complete these statements with the best answer.

16. A measure obtained from sample data is called a(n) _____.

17. Generally, Greek letters are used to represent _____, and Roman letters are used to represent _____.

18. The positive square root of the variance is called the _____.

19. The symbol for the population standard deviation is _____.

20. When the sum of the lowest data value and the highest data value is divided by 2, the measure is called _____.

21. If the mode is to the left of the median and the mean is to the right of the median, then the distribution is _____ skewed.

22. An extremely high or extremely low data value is called a(n) _____.

23. **Miles per Gallon** The number of highway miles per gallon of the 10 worst vehicles is shown.

    12 15 13 14 15 16 17 16 17 18

    Source: *Pittsburgh Post Gazette.*

    Find each of these.

    a. Mean
    b. Median
    c. Mode
    d. Midrange
    e. Range
    f. Variance
    g. Standard deviation

24. **Errors on a Typing Test** The distribution of the number of errors that 10 students made on a typing test is shown.

Errors	Frequency
0–2	1
3–5	3
6–8	4
9–11	1
12–14	1

Find each of these.

a. Mean   c. Variance
b. Modal class   d. Standard deviation

25. **Inches of Rain** Shown here is a frequency distribution for the number of inches of rain received in 1 year in 25 selected cities in the United States.

Number of inches	Frequency
5.5–20.5	2
20.5–35.5	3
35.5–50.5	8
50.5–65.5	6
65.5–80.5	3
80.5–95.5	3

Find each of these.

a. Mean
b. Modal class
c. Variance
d. Standard deviation

26. **Shipment Times** A survey of 36 selected recording companies showed these numbers of days that it took to receive a shipment from the day it was ordered.

Days	Frequency
1–3	6
4–6	8
7–9	10
10–12	7
13–15	0
16–18	5

Find each of these.

a. Mean
b. Modal class
c. Variance
d. Standard deviation

27. **Best Friends of Students** In a survey of third-grade students, this distribution was obtained for the number of "best friends" each had.

Number of students	Number of best friends
8	1
6	2
5	3
3	0

Find the average number of best friends for the class. Use the weighted mean.

28. **Employee Years of Service** In an advertisement, a retail store stated that its employees averaged 9 years of service. The distribution is shown here.

Number of employees	Years of service
8	2
2	6
3	10

Using the weighted mean, calculate the correct average.

29. **Newspapers for Sale** The average number of newspapers for sale in an airport newsstand is 12, and the standard deviation is 4. The average age of the pilots is 37 years, with a standard deviation of 6 years. Which data set is more variable?

30. **Brands of Toothpaste Carried** A survey of grocery stores showed that the average number of brands of toothpaste carried was 16, with a standard deviation of 5. The same survey showed the average length of time each store was in business was 7 years, with a standard deviation of 1.6 years. Which is more variable, the number of brands or the number of years?

31. **Test Scores** A student scored 76 on a general science test where the class mean and standard deviation were 82 and 8, respectively; he also scored 53 on a psychology test where the class mean and standard deviation were 58 and 3, respectively. In which class was his relative position higher?

32. Which score has the highest relative position?

a. $X = 12$ $\overline{X} = 10$ $s = 4$
b. $X = 170$ $\overline{X} = 120$ $s = 32$
c. $X = 180$ $\overline{X} = 60$ $s = 8$

33. **Sizes of Malls** The number of square feet (in millions) of eight of the largest malls in southwestern Pennsylvania is shown.

1	0.9	1.3	0.8
1.4	0.77	0.7	1.2

Source: International Council of Shopping Centers.

a. Find the percentile for each value.
b. What value corresponds to the 40th percentile?
c. Construct a boxplot and comment on the nature of the distribution.

34. **Exam Scores** On a philosophy comprehensive exam, this distribution was obtained from 25 students.

Score	Frequency
40.5–45.5	3
45.5–50.5	8
50.5–55.5	10
55.5–60.5	3
60.5–65.5	1

a. Construct a percentile graph.
b. Find the values that correspond to the 22nd, 78th, and 99th percentiles.
c. Find the percentiles of the values 52, 43, and 64.

35. **Gas Prices for Rental Cars** The first column of these data represents the prebuy gas price of a rental car, and the second column represents the price charged if the car is returned without refilling the gas tank for a selected car rental company. Draw two boxplots for the data and compare the distributions. (*Note:* The data were collected several years ago.)

Prebuy cost	No prebuy cost
$1.55	$3.80
1.54	3.99
1.62	3.99
1.65	3.85
1.72	3.99
1.63	3.95
1.65	3.94
1.72	4.19
1.45	3.84
1.52	3.94

Source: *USA TODAY.*

36. **SAT Scores** The average national SAT score is 1019. If we assume a bell-shaped distribution and a standard deviation equal to 110, what percentage of scores will you expect to fall above 1129? Above 799?

Source: *New York Times Almanac,* 2002.

Critical Thinking Challenges

1. **Average Cost of Weddings** Averages give us information to help us to see where we stand and enable us to make comparisons. Here is a study on the average cost of a wedding. What type of average—mean, median, mode, or midrange—might have been used for each category?

OTHER PEOPLE'S MONEY

Question: What is the hottest wedding month? **Answer:** It's a tie. September now ranks as high as June in U.S. nuptials. The average attendence is 186 guests. And what kind of tabs are people running up for these affairs? Well, the next time a bride is throwing a bouquet, single women might want to . . . duck!

Reception	**$7246**
Rings	**4042**
Photos/videography.	**1263**
Bridal gown	**790**
Flowers	**775**
Music	**745**
Invitations	**374**
Mother of the bride's dress	**198**
Other (veil, limo, fees, etc.)	**3441**
Average cost of a wedding	**$18,874**

Stats: Bride's 2000 State of the Union Report

Source: Reprinted with permission from the September 2001 Reader's Digest. Copyright © 2001 by The Reader's Digest Assn., Inc.

2. **Average Cost of Smoking** This article states that the average yearly cost of smoking a pack of cigarettes a day is $1190. Find the average cost of a pack of cigarettes in your area, and compute the cost per day for 1 year. Compare your answer with the one in the article.

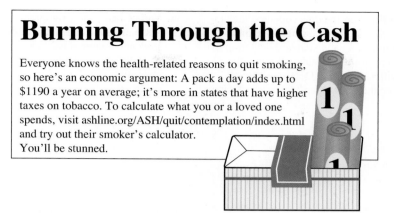

Burning Through the Cash

Everyone knows the health-related reasons to quit smoking, so here's an economic argument: A pack a day adds up to $1190 a year on average; it's more in states that have higher taxes on tobacco. To calculate what you or a loved one spends, visit ashline.org/ASH/quit/contemplation/index.html and try out their smoker's calculator. You'll be stunned.

Source: Reprinted with permission from the April 2002 Reader's Digest. Copyright © 2002 by The Reader's Digest Assn., Inc.

3. **Ages of U.S. Residents** The table shows the median ages of residents for the 10 oldest states and the 10 youngest states of the United States including Washington, D.C. Explain why the median is used instead of the mean.

10 Oldest			10 Youngest		
Rank	**State**	**Median age**	**Rank**	**State**	**Median age**
1	West Virginia	38.9	51	Utah	27.1
2	Florida	38.7	50	Texas	32.3
3	Maine	38.6	49	Alaska	32.4
4	Pennsylvania	38.0	48	Idaho	33.2
5	Vermont	37.7	47	California	33.3
6	Montana	37.5	46	Georgia	33.4
7	Connecticut	37.4	45	Mississippi	33.8
8	New Hampshire	37.1	44	Louisiana	34.0
9	New Jersey	36.7	43	Arizona	34.2
10	Rhode Island	36.7	42	Colorado	34.3

Source: U.S. Census Bureau.

 Data Projects

Where appropriate, use MINITAB, the TI-83 Plus, the TI-84 Plus, or a computer program of your choice to complete the following exercises.

1. **Business and Finance** Use the data collected in data project 1 of Chapter 2 regarding earnings per share. Determine the mean, mode, median, and midrange for the two data sets. Is one measure of center more appropriate than the other for these data? Do the measures of center appear similar? What does this say about the symmetry of the distribution?

2. **Sports and Leisure** Use the data collected in data project 2 of Chapter 2 regarding home runs. Determine the mean, mode, median, and midrange for the two data sets. Is one measure of center more appropriate than the

other for these data? Do the measures of center appear similar? What does this say about the symmetry of the distribution?

3. **Technology** Use the data collected in data project 3 of Chapter 2. Determine the mean for the frequency table created in that project. Find the actual mean length of all 50 songs. How does the grouped mean compare to the actual mean?

4. **Health and Wellness** Use the data collected in data project 6 of Chapter 2 regarding heart rates. Determine the mean and standard deviation for each set of data. Do the means seem very different from one another? Do the standard deviations appear very different from one another?

5. **Politics and Economics** Use the data collected in data project 5 of Chapter 2 regarding delegates. Use the formulas for population mean and standard deviation to compute the parameters for all 50 states. What is the z score associated with California? Delaware? Ohio? Which states are more than 2 standard deviations from the mean?

6. **Your Class** Use your class as a sample. Determine the mean, median, and standard deviation for the age of students in your class. What z score would a 40-year-old have? Would it be unusual to have an age of 40? Determine the skew of the data using the Pearson coefficient of skewness. (See Exercise 48, page 149.)

Answers to Applying the Concepts

Section 3–1   Teacher Salaries

1. The sample mean is $22,921.67, the sample median is $16,500, and the sample mode is $11,000. If you work for the school board and do not want to raise salaries, you could say that the average teacher salary is $22,921.67.

2. If you work for the teachers' union and want a raise for the teachers, either the sample median of $16,500 or the sample mode of $11,000 would be a good measure of center to report.

3. The outlier is $107,000. With the outlier removed, the sample mean is $15,278.18, the sample median is $16,400, and the sample mode is still $11,000. The mean is greatly affected by the outlier and allows the school board to report an average teacher salary that is not representative of a "typical" teacher salary.

4. If the salaries represented every teacher in the school district, the averages would be parameters, since we have data from the entire population.

5. The mean can be misleading in the presence of outliers, since it is greatly affected by these extreme values.

6. Since the mean is greater than both the median and the mode, the distribution is skewed to the right (positively skewed).

Section 3–2   Blood Pressure

1. Chebyshev's theorem does not work for scores within 1 standard deviation of the mean.

2. At least 75% (900) of the normotensive men will fall in the interval 105–141 mm Hg.

3. About 95% (1330) of the normotensive women have diastolic blood pressures between 62 and 90 mm Hg. About 95% (1235) of the hypertensive women have diastolic blood pressures between 68 and 108 mm Hg.

4. About 95% (1140) of the normotensive men have systolic blood pressures between 105 and 141 mm Hg. About 95% (1045) of the hypertensive men have systolic blood pressures between 119 and 187 mm Hg. These two ranges do overlap.

Section 3–3   Determining Dosages

1. The quartiles could be used to describe the data results.

2. Since there are 10 mice in the upper quartile, this would mean that 4 of them survived.

3. The percentiles would give us the position of a single mouse with respect to all other mice.

4. The quartiles divide the data into four groups of equal size.

5. Standard scores would give us the position of a single mouse with respect to the mean time until the onset of sepsis.

Section 3–4   The Noisy Workplace

Boxplot of Noise Level Versus Area

From this boxplot, we see that about 25% of the readings in area 5 are above the safe hearing level of 120 decibels. Those workers in area 5 should definitely have protective ear wear. One of the readings in area 6 is above the safe hearing level. It might be a good idea to provide protective ear wear to those workers in area 6 as well. Areas 1–4 appear to be "safe" with respect to hearing level, with area 4 being the safest.

Probability and Counting Rules

Objectives

After completing this chapter, you should be able to

1 Determine sample spaces and find the probability of an event, using classical probability or empirical probability.

2 Find the probability of compound events, using the addition rules.

3 Find the probability of compound events, using the multiplication rules.

4 Find the conditional probability of an event.

5 Find the total number of outcomes in a sequence of events, using the fundamental counting rule.

6 Find the number of ways that *r* objects can be selected from *n* objects, using the permutation rule.

7 Find the number of ways that *r* objects can be selected from *n* objects without regard to order, using the combination rule.

8 Find the probability of an event, using the counting rules.

Outline

Would You Bet Your Life?

Humans not only bet money when they gamble, but also bet their lives by engaging in unhealthy activities such as smoking, drinking, using drugs, and exceeding the speed limit when driving. Many people don't care about the risks involved in these activities since they do not understand the concepts of probability. On the other hand, people may fear activities that involve little risk to health or life because these activities have been sensationalized by the press and media.

In his book *Probabilities in Everyday Life* (Ivy Books, p. 191), John D. McGervey states

When people have been asked to estimate the frequency of death from various causes, the most overestimated categories are those involving pregnancy, tornadoes, floods, fire, and homicide. The most underestimated categories include deaths from diseases such as diabetes, strokes, tuberculosis, asthma, and stomach cancer (although cancer in general is overestimated).

The question then is, Would you feel safer if you flew across the United States on a commercial airline or if you drove? How much greater is the risk of one way to travel over the other? See Statistics Today—Revisited at the end of the chapter for the answer.

In this chapter, you will learn about probability—its meaning, how it is computed, and how to evaluate it in terms of the likelihood of an event actually happening.

Introduction

A cynical person once said, "The only two sure things are death and taxes." This philosophy no doubt arose because so much in people's lives is affected by chance. From the time you awake until you go to bed, you make decisions regarding the possible events that are governed at least in part by chance. For example, should you carry an umbrella to work today? Will your car battery last until spring? Should you accept that new job?

Probability as a general concept can be defined as the chance of an event occurring. Many people are familiar with probability from observing or playing games of chance, such as card games, slot machines, or lotteries. In addition to being used in games of chance, probability theory is used in the fields of insurance, investments, and weather forecasting and in various other areas. Finally, as stated in Chapter 1, probability is the basis of inferential statistics. For example, predictions are based on probability, and hypotheses are tested by using probability.

The basic concepts of probability are explained in this chapter. These concepts include *probability experiments, sample spaces,* the *addition* and *multiplication rules,* and the *probabilities of complementary events.* Also in this chapter, you will learn the rule for counting, the differences between permutations and combinations, and how to figure out how many different combinations for specific situations exist. Finally, Section 4–5 explains how the counting rules and the probability rules can be used together to solve a wide variety of problems.

4–1 Sample Spaces and Probability

The theory of probability grew out of the study of various games of chance using coins, dice, and cards. Since these devices lend themselves well to the application of concepts of probability, they will be used in this chapter as examples. This section begins by explaining some basic concepts of probability. Then the types of probability and probability rules are discussed.

Basic Concepts

Processes such as flipping a coin, rolling a die, or drawing a card from a deck are called *probability experiments.*

Objective 1
Determine sample spaces and find the probability of an event, using classical probability or empirical probability.

A **probability experiment** is a chance process that leads to well-defined results called outcomes.

An **outcome** is the result of a single trial of a probability experiment.

A trial means flipping a coin once, rolling one die once, or the like. When a coin is tossed, there are two possible outcomes: head or tail. (*Note:* We exclude the possibility of a coin landing on its edge.) In the roll of a single die, there are six possible outcomes: 1, 2, 3, 4, 5, or 6. In any experiment, the set of all possible outcomes is called the *sample space.*

A **sample space** is the set of all possible outcomes of a probability experiment.

Some sample spaces for various probability experiments are shown here.

Experiment	Sample space
Toss one coin	Head, tail
Roll a die	1, 2, 3, 4, 5, 6
Answer a true/false question	True, false
Toss two coins	Head-head, tail-tail, head-tail, tail-head

It is important to realize that when two coins are tossed, there are *four* possible outcomes, as shown in the fourth experiment above. Both coins could fall heads up. Both coins could fall tails up. Coin 1 could fall heads up and coin 2 tails up. Or coin 1 could fall tails up and coin 2 heads up. Heads and tails will be abbreviated as H and T throughout this chapter.

Example 4–1

Rolling Dice

Find the sample space for rolling two dice.

Solution

Since each die can land in six different ways, and two dice are rolled, the sample space can be presented by a rectangular array, as shown in Figure 4–1. The sample space is the list of pairs of numbers in the chart.

Figure 4–1

Sample Space for
Rolling Two Dice
(Example 4–1)

	Die 2					
Die 1	1	2	3	4	5	6
1	(1, 1)	(1, 2)	(1, 3)	(1, 4)	(1, 5)	(1, 6)
2	(2, 1)	(2, 2)	(2, 3)	(2, 4)	(2, 5)	(2, 6)
3	(3, 1)	(3, 2)	(3, 3)	(3, 4)	(3, 5)	(3, 6)
4	(4, 1)	(4, 2)	(4, 3)	(4, 4)	(4, 5)	(4, 6)
5	(5, 1)	(5, 2)	(5, 3)	(5, 4)	(5, 5)	(5, 6)
6	(6, 1)	(6, 2)	(6, 3)	(6, 4)	(6, 5)	(6, 6)

Example 4–2

Drawing Cards

Find the sample space for drawing one card from an ordinary deck of cards.

Solution

Since there are 4 suits (hearts, clubs, diamonds, and spades) and 13 cards for each suit (ace through king), there are 52 outcomes in the sample space. See Figure 4–2.

Figure 4–2

Sample Space for
Drawing a Card
(Example 4–2)

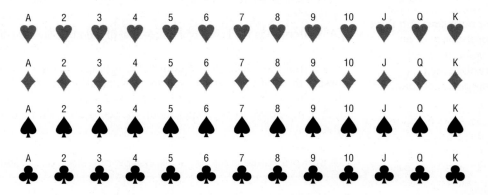

Example 4–3

Gender of Children

Find the sample space for the gender of the children if a family has three children. Use B for boy and G for girl.

Solution

There are two genders, male and female, and each child could be either gender. Hence, there are eight possibilities, as shown here.

BBB   BBG   BGB   GBB   GGG   GGB   GBG   BGG

In Examples 4–1 through 4–3, the sample spaces were found by observation and reasoning; however, another way to find all possible outcomes of a probability experiment is to use a *tree diagram.*

> A **tree diagram** is a device consisting of line segments emanating from a starting point and also from the outcome point. It is used to determine all possible outcomes of a probability experiment.

Example 4–4

Gender of Children

Use a tree diagram to find the sample space for the gender of three children in a family, as in Example 4–3.

Solution

Since there are two possibilities (boy or girl) for the first child, draw two branches from a starting point and label one B and the other G. Then if the first child is a boy, there are two possibilities for the second child (boy or girl), so draw two branches from B and label one B and the other G. Do the same if the first child is a girl. Follow the same procedure for the third child. The completed tree diagram is shown in Figure 4–3. To find the outcomes for the sample space, trace through all the possible branches, beginning at the starting point for each one.

Figure 4–3

Tree Diagram for Example 4–4

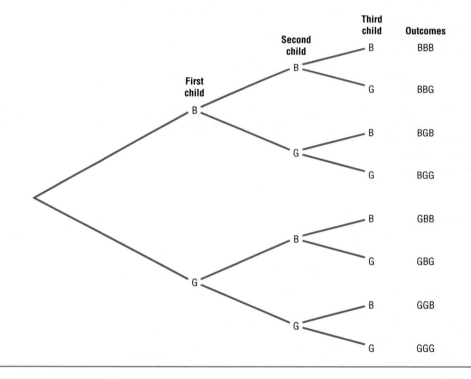

Historical Note

The famous Italian astronomer Galileo (1564–1642) found that a sum of 10 occurs more often than any other sum when three dice are tossed. Previously, it was thought that a sum of 9 occurred more often than any other sum.

Historical Note

A mathematician named Jerome Cardan (1501–1576) used his talents in mathematics and probability theory to make his living as a gambler. He is thought to be the first person to formulate the definition of classical probability.

An outcome was defined previously as the result of a single trial of a probability experiment. In many problems, one must find the probability of two or more outcomes. For this reason, it is necessary to distinguish between an outcome and an event.

An **event** consists of a set of outcomes of a probability experiment.

An event can be one outcome or more than one outcome. For example, if a die is rolled and a 6 shows, this result is called an *outcome,* since it is a result of a single trial. An event with one outcome is called a **simple event.** The event of getting an odd number when a die is rolled is called a **compound event,** since it consists of three outcomes or three simple events. In general, a compound event consists of two or more outcomes or simple events.

There are three basic interpretations of probability:

1. Classical probability
2. Empirical or relative frequency probability
3. Subjective probability

Classical Probability

Classical probability uses sample spaces to determine the numerical probability that an event will happen. You do not actually have to perform the experiment to determine that probability. Classical probability is so named because it was the first type of probability studied formally by mathematicians in the 17th and 18th centuries.

Classical probability assumes that all outcomes in the sample space are equally likely to occur. For example, when a single die is rolled, each outcome has the same probability of occurring. Since there are six outcomes, each outcome has a probability of $\frac{1}{6}$. When a card is selected from an ordinary deck of 52 cards, you assume that the deck has been shuffled, and each card has the same probability of being selected. In this case, it is $\frac{1}{52}$.

Equally likely events are events that have the same probability of occurring.

Formula for Classical Probability

The probability of any event E is

$$\frac{\text{Number of outcomes in } E}{\text{Total number of outcomes in the sample space}}$$

This probability is denoted by

$$P(E) = \frac{n(E)}{n(S)}$$

This probability is called *classical probability,* and it uses the sample space *S*.

Probabilities can be expressed as fractions, decimals, or—where appropriate—percentages. If you ask, "What is the probability of getting a head when a coin is tossed?" typical responses can be any of the following three.

"One-half."

"Point five."

"Fifty percent."[1]

These answers are all equivalent. In most cases, the answers to examples and exercises given in this chapter are expressed as fractions or decimals, but percentages are used where appropriate.

---

[1]Strictly speaking, a percent is not a probability. However, in everyday language, probabilities are often expressed as percents (i.e., there is a 60% chance of rain tomorrow). For this reason, some probabilities will be expressed as percents throughout this book.

Rounding Rule for Probabilities Probabilities should be expressed as reduced fractions or rounded to two or three decimal places. When the probability of an event is an extremely small decimal, it is permissible to round the decimal to the first nonzero digit after the point. For example, 0.0000587 would be 0.00006. When obtaining probabilities from one of the tables in Appendix C, use the number of decimal places given in the table. If decimals are converted to percentages to express probabilities, move the decimal point two places to the right and add a percent sign.

| Example 4–5 | Drawing Cards |

Find the probability of getting a red ace when a card is drawn at random from an ordinary deck of cards.

Solution

Since there are 52 cards and there are 2 red aces, namely, the ace of hearts and the ace of diamonds, $P(\text{red ace}) = \frac{2}{52} = \frac{1}{26}$.

| Example 4–6 | Gender of Children |

If a family has three children, find the probability that two of the three children are girls.

Solution

The sample space for the gender of the children for a family that has three children has eight outcomes, that is, BBB, BBG, BGB, GBB, GGG, GGB, GBG, and BGG. (See Examples 4–3 and 4–4.) Since there are three ways to have two girls, namely, GGB, GBG, and BGG, $P(\text{two girls}) = \frac{3}{8}$.

Historical Note

Ancient Greeks and Romans made crude dice from animal bones, various stones, minerals, and ivory. When the dice were tested mathematically, some were found to be quite accurate.

In probability theory, it is important to understand the meaning of the words *and* and *or*. For example, if you were asked to find the probability of getting a queen *and* a heart when you were drawing a single card from a deck, you would be looking for the queen of hearts. Here the word *and* means "at the same time." The word *or* has two meanings. For example, if you were asked to find the probability of selecting a queen *or* a heart when one card is selected from a deck, you would be looking for one of the 4 queens or one of the 13 hearts. In this case, the queen of hearts would be included in both cases and counted twice. So there would be $4 + 13 - 1 = 16$ possibilities.

On the other hand, if you were asked to find the probability of getting a queen *or* a king, you would be looking for one of the 4 queens or one of the 4 kings. In this case, there would be $4 + 4 = 8$ possibilities. In the first case, both events can occur at the same time; we say that this is an example of the *inclusive or*. In the second case, both events cannot occur at the same time, and we say that this is an example of the *exclusive or*.

| Example 4–7 | Drawing Cards |

A card is drawn from an ordinary deck. Find these probabilities.

a. Of getting a jack

b. Of getting the 6 of clubs (i.e., a 6 and a club)

c. Of getting a 3 or a diamond

d. Of getting a 3 or a 6

Solution

a. Refer to the sample space in Figure 4–2. There are 4 jacks so there are 4 outcomes in event E and 52 possible outcomes in the sample space. Hence,

$$P(\text{jack}) = \tfrac{4}{52} = \tfrac{1}{13}$$

b. Since there is only one 6 of clubs in event E, the probability of getting a 6 of clubs is

$$P(\text{6 of clubs}) = \tfrac{1}{52}$$

c. There are four 3s and 13 diamonds, but the 3 of diamonds is counted twice in this listing. Hence, there are 16 possibilities of drawing a 3 or a diamond, so

$$P(\text{3 or diamond}) = \tfrac{16}{52} = \tfrac{4}{13}$$

This is an example of the inclusive or.

d. Since there are four 3s and four 6s,

$$P(\text{3 or 6}) = \tfrac{8}{52} = \tfrac{2}{13}$$

This is an example of the exclusive or.

There are four basic probability rules. These rules are helpful in solving probability problems, in understanding the nature of probability, and in deciding if your answers to the problems are correct.

Probability Rule 1

The probability of any event E is a number (either a fraction or decimal) between and including 0 and 1. This is denoted by $0 \le P(E) \le 1$.

Rule 1 states that probabilities cannot be negative or greater than 1.

Probability Rule 2

If an event E cannot occur (i.e., the event contains no members in the sample space), its probability is 0.

Example 4–8

Rolling a Die

When a single die is rolled, find the probability of getting a 9.

Solution

Since the sample space is 1, 2, 3, 4, 5, and 6, it is impossible to get a 9. Hence, the probability is $P(9) = \tfrac{0}{6} = 0$.

Probability Rule 3

If an event E is certain, then the probability of E is 1.

In other words, if $P(E) = 1$, then the event E is certain to occur. This rule is illustrated in Example 4–9.

Example 4–9

Rolling a Die

When a single die is rolled, what is the probability of getting a number less than 7?

Solution

Since all outcomes—1, 2, 3, 4, 5, and 6—are less than 7, the probability is

$$P(\text{number less than } 7) = \tfrac{6}{6} = 1$$

The event of getting a number less than 7 is certain.

In other words, probability values range from 0 to 1. When the probability of an event is close to 0, its occurrence is highly unlikely. When the probability of an event is near 0.5, there is about a 50-50 chance that the event will occur; and when the probability of an event is close to 1, the event is highly likely to occur.

Probability Rule 4

The sum of the probabilities of all the outcomes in the sample space is 1.

For example, in the roll of a fair die, each outcome in the sample space has a probability of $\tfrac{1}{6}$. Hence, the sum of the probabilities of the outcomes is as shown.

Outcome	1	2	3	4	5	6
Probability	$\tfrac{1}{6}$	$\tfrac{1}{6}$	$\tfrac{1}{6}$	$\tfrac{1}{6}$	$\tfrac{1}{6}$	$\tfrac{1}{6}$
Sum	$\tfrac{1}{6}$ +	$\tfrac{1}{6}$ +	$\tfrac{1}{6}$ +	$\tfrac{1}{6}$ +	$\tfrac{1}{6}$ +	$\tfrac{1}{6} = \tfrac{6}{6} = 1$

Complementary Events

Another important concept in probability theory is that of *complementary events*. When a die is rolled, for instance, the sample space consists of the outcomes 1, 2, 3, 4, 5, and 6. The event E of getting odd numbers consists of the outcomes 1, 3, and 5. The event of not getting an odd number is called the *complement* of event E, and it consists of the outcomes 2, 4, and 6.

The **complement of an event** E is the set of outcomes in the sample space that are not included in the outcomes of event E. The complement of E is denoted by $\overline{E}$ (read "E bar").

Example 4–10 further illustrates the concept of complementary events.

Example 4–10

Finding Complements

Find the complement of each event.

  a. Rolling a die and getting a 4
  b. Selecting a letter of the alphabet and getting a vowel

      c. Selecting a month and getting a month that begins with a J

      d. Selecting a day of the week and getting a weekday

Solution

      a. Getting a 1, 2, 3, 5, or 6

      b. Getting a consonant (assume *y* is a consonant)

      c. Getting February, March, April, May, August, September, October, November, or December

      d. Getting Saturday or Sunday

The outcomes of an event and the outcomes of the complement make up the entire sample space. For example, if two coins are tossed, the sample space is HH, HT, TH, and TT. The complement of "getting all heads" is not "getting all tails," since the event "all heads" is HH, and the complement of HH is HT, TH, and TT. Hence, the complement of the event "all heads" is the event "getting at least one tail."

Since the event and its complement make up the entire sample space, it follows that the sum of the probability of the event and the probability of its complement will equal 1. That is, $P(E) + P(\overline{E}) = 1$. In Example 4–10, let $E =$ all heads, or HH, and let $\overline{E} =$ at least one tail, or HT, TH, TT. Then $P(E) = \frac{1}{4}$ and $P(\overline{E}) = \frac{3}{4}$; hence, $P(E) + P(\overline{E}) = \frac{1}{4} + \frac{3}{4} = 1$.

The rule for complementary events can be stated algebraically in three ways.

Rule for Complementary Events
$P(\overline{E}) = 1 - P(E)$ or $P(E) = 1 - P(\overline{E})$ or $P(E) + P(\overline{E}) = 1$

Stated in words, the rule is: *If the probability of an event or the probability of its complement is known, then the other can be found by subtracting the probability from 1.* This rule is important in probability theory because at times the best solution to a problem is to find the probability of the complement of an event and then subtract from 1 to get the probability of the event itself.

Example 4–11

Residence of People

If the probability that a person lives in an industrialized country of the world is $\frac{1}{5}$, find the probability that a person does not live in an industrialized country.

Source: *Harper's Index.*

Solution

P(not living in an industrialized country) $= 1 - P$(living in an industrialized country)
$$= 1 - \tfrac{1}{5} = \tfrac{4}{5}$$

Probabilities can be represented pictorially by **Venn diagrams.** Figure 4–4(a) shows the probability of a simple event *E*. The area inside the circle represents the probability of event *E*, that is, $P(E)$. The area inside the rectangle represents the probability of all the events in the sample space $P(S)$.

Figure 4–4

Venn Diagram for the Probability and Complement

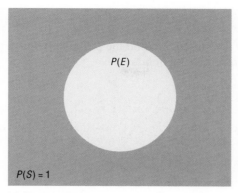

$P(E)$

$P(S) = 1$

$P(E)$

$P(\bar{E})$

(a) Simple probability   **(b)** $P(\bar{E}) = 1 - P(E)$

The Venn diagram that represents the probability of the complement of an event $P(\bar{E})$ is shown in Figure 4–4(b). In this case, $P(\bar{E}) = 1 - P(E)$, which is the area inside the rectangle but outside the circle representing $P(E)$. Recall that $P(S) = 1$ and $P(E) = 1 - P(\bar{E})$. The reasoning is that $P(E)$ is represented by the area of the circle and $P(\bar{E})$ is the probability of the events that are outside the circle.

Empirical Probability

The difference between classical and **empirical probability** is that classical probability assumes that certain outcomes are equally likely (such as the outcomes when a die is rolled), while empirical probability relies on actual experience to determine the likelihood of outcomes. In empirical probability, one might actually roll a given die 6000 times, observe the various frequencies, and use these frequencies to determine the probability of an outcome.

Suppose, for example, that a researcher for the American Automobile Association (AAA) asked 50 people who plan to travel over the Thanksgiving holiday how they will get to their destination. The results can be categorized in a frequency distribution as shown.

Method	Frequency
Drive	41
Fly	6
Train or bus	3
	50

Now probabilities can be computed for various categories. For example, the probability of selecting a person who is driving is $\frac{41}{50}$, since 41 out of the 50 people said that they were driving.

Formula for Empirical Probability

Given a frequency distribution, the probability of an event being in a given class is

$$P(E) = \frac{\text{frequency for the class}}{\text{total frequencies in the distribution}} = \frac{f}{n}$$

This probability is called *empirical probability* and is based on observation.

Example 4–12	**Travel Survey**

In the travel survey just described, find the probability that a person will travel by airplane over the Thanksgiving holiday.

Solution

$$P(E) = \frac{f}{n} = \frac{6}{50} = \frac{3}{25}$$

Note: These figures are based on a AAA survey.

Example 4–13	**Distribution of Blood Types**

In a sample of 50 people, 21 had type O blood, 22 had type A blood, 5 had type B blood, and 2 had type AB blood. Set up a frequency distribution and find the following probabilities.

  a. A person has type O blood.

  b. A person has type A or type B blood.

  c. A person has neither type A nor type O blood.

  d. A person does not have type AB blood.

Source: The American Red Cross.

Solution

Type	Frequency
A	22
B	5
AB	2
O	21
Total	50

  a. $P(\text{O}) = \dfrac{f}{n} = \dfrac{21}{50}$

  b. $P(\text{A or B}) = \dfrac{22}{50} + \dfrac{5}{50} = \dfrac{27}{50}$

   (Add the frequencies of the two classes.)

  c. $P(\text{neither A nor O}) = \dfrac{5}{50} + \dfrac{2}{50} = \dfrac{7}{50}$

   (Neither A nor O means that a person has either type B or type AB blood.)

  d. $P(\text{not AB}) = 1 - P(\text{AB}) = 1 - \dfrac{2}{50} = \dfrac{48}{50} = \dfrac{24}{25}$

   (Find the probability of not AB by subtracting the probability of type AB from 1.)

| Example 4–14 | **Hospital Stays for Maternity Patients** |

Hospital records indicated that maternity patients stayed in the hospital for the number of days shown in the distribution.

Number of days stayed	Frequency
3	15
4	32
5	56
6	19
7	5
	127

Find these probabilities.

a. A patient stayed exactly 5 days.   c. A patient stayed at most 4 days.

b. A patient stayed less than 6 days.   d. A patient stayed at least 5 days.

Solution

a. $P(5) = \dfrac{56}{127}$

b. $P(\text{fewer than 6 days}) = \dfrac{15}{127} + \dfrac{32}{127} + \dfrac{56}{127} = \dfrac{103}{127}$
(Fewer than 6 days means 3, 4, or 5 days.)

c. $P(\text{at most 4 days}) = \dfrac{15}{127} + \dfrac{32}{127} = \dfrac{47}{127}$
(At most 4 days means 3 or 4 days.)

d. $P(\text{at least 5 days}) = \dfrac{56}{127} + \dfrac{19}{127} + \dfrac{5}{127} = \dfrac{80}{127}$
(At least 5 days means 5, 6, or 7 days.)

Empirical probabilities can also be found by using a relative frequency distribution, as shown in Section 2–2. For example, the relative frequency distribution of the travel survey shown previously is

Method	Frequency	Relative frequency
Drive	41	0.82
Fly	6	0.12
Train or bus	3	0.06
	50	1.00

These frequencies are the same as the relative frequencies explained in Chapter 2.

Law of Large Numbers

When a coin is tossed one time, it is common knowledge that the probability of getting a head is $\frac{1}{2}$. But what happens when the coin is tossed 50 times? Will it come up heads

25 times? Not all the time. You should expect about 25 heads if the coin is fair. But due to chance variation, 25 heads will not occur most of the time.

If the empirical probability of getting a head is computed by using a small number of trials, it is usually not exactly $\frac{1}{2}$. However, as the number of trials increases, the empirical probability of getting a head will approach the theoretical probability of $\frac{1}{2}$, if in fact the coin is fair (i.e., balanced). This phenomenon is an example of the **law of large numbers.**

You should be careful to not think that the number of heads and number of tails tend to "even out." As the number of trials increases, the proportion of heads to the total number of trials will approach $\frac{1}{2}$. This law holds for any type of gambling game—tossing dice, playing roulette, and so on.

It should be pointed out that the probabilities that the proportions steadily approach may or may not agree with those theorized in the classical model. If not, it can have important implications, such as "the die is not fair." Pit bosses in Las Vegas watch for empirical trends that do not agree with classical theories, and they will sometimes take a set of dice out of play if observed frequencies are too far out of line with classical expected frequencies.

Subjective Probability

The third type of probability is called *subjective probability.* **Subjective probability** uses a probability value based on an educated guess or estimate, employing opinions and inexact information.

In subjective probability, a person or group makes an educated guess at the chance that an event will occur. This guess is based on the person's experience and evaluation of a solution. For example, a sportswriter may say that there is a 70% probability that the Pirates will win the pennant next year. A physician might say that, on the basis of her diagnosis, there is a 30% chance the patient will need an operation. A seismologist might say there is an 80% probability that an earthquake will occur in a certain area. These are only a few examples of how subjective probability is used in everyday life.

All three types of probability (classical, empirical, and subjective) are used to solve a variety of problems in business, engineering, and other fields.

Probability and Risk Taking

An area in which people fail to understand probability is risk taking. Actually, people fear situations or events that have a relatively small probability of happening rather than those events that have a greater likelihood of occurring. For example, many people think that the crime rate is increasing every year. However, in his book entitled *How Risk Affects Your Everyday Life,* author James Walsh states: "Despite widespread concern about the number of crimes committed in the United States, FBI and Justice Department statistics show that the national crime rate has remained fairly level for 20 years. It even dropped slightly in the early 1990s."

He further states, "Today most media coverage of risk to health and well-being focuses on shock and outrage." Shock and outrage make good stories and can scare us about the wrong dangers. For example, the author states that if a person is 20% overweight, the loss of life expectancy is 900 days (about 3 years), but loss of life expectancy from exposure to radiation emitted by nuclear power plants is 0.02 day. As you can see, being overweight is much more of a threat than being exposed to radioactive emission.

Many people gamble daily with their lives, for example, by using tobacco, drinking and driving, and riding motorcycles. When people are asked to estimate the probabilities or frequencies of death from various causes, they tend to overestimate causes such as accidents, fires, and floods and to underestimate the probabilities of death from diseases (other than cancer), strokes, etc. For example, most people think that their chances of dying of a heart attack are 1 in 20, when in fact they are almost 1 in 3; the chances of dying by pesticide poisoning are 1 in 200,000 (*True Odds* by James Walsh). The reason people think this way is that the news media sensationalize deaths resulting from catastrophic events and rarely mention deaths from disease.

When you are dealing with life-threatening catastrophes such as hurricanes, floods, automobile accidents, or smoking, it is important to get the facts. That is, get the actual numbers from accredited statistical agencies or reliable statistical studies, and then compute the probabilities and make decisions based on your knowledge of probability and statistics.

In summary, then, when you make a decision or plan a course of action based on probability, make sure that you understand the true probability of the event occurring. Also, find out how the information was obtained (i.e., from a reliable source). Weigh the cost of the action and decide if it is worth it. Finally, look for other alternatives or courses of action with less risk involved.

Applying the Concepts 4–1

Tossing a Coin

Assume you are at a carnival and decide to play one of the games. You spot a table where a person is flipping a coin, and since you have an understanding of basic probability, you believe that the odds of winning are in your favor. When you get to the table, you find out that all you have to do is to guess which side of the coin will be facing up after it is tossed. You are assured that the coin is fair, meaning that each of the two sides has an equally likely chance of occurring. You think back about what you learned in your statistics class about probability before you decide what to bet on. Answer the following questions about the coin-tossing game.

1. What is the sample space?
2. What are the possible outcomes?
3. What does the classical approach to probability say about computing probabilities for this type of problem?

You decide to bet on heads, believing that it has a 50% chance of coming up. A friend of yours, who had been playing the game for awhile before you got there, tells you that heads has come up the last 9 times in a row. You remember the law of large numbers.

4. What is the law of large numbers, and does it change your thoughts about what will occur on the next toss?
5. What does the empirical approach to probability say about this problem, and could you use it to solve this problem?
6. Can subjective probabilities be used to help solve this problem? Explain.
7. Assume you could win $1 million if you could guess what the results of the next toss will be. What would you bet on? Why?

See page 257 for the answers.

Exercises 4–1

1. What is a probability experiment?

2. Define *sample space*.

3. What is the difference between an outcome and an event?

4. What are equally likely events?

5. What is the range of the values of the probability of an event?

6. When an event is certain to occur, what is its probability?

7. If an event cannot happen, what value is assigned to its probability?

8. What is the sum of the probabilities of all the outcomes in a sample space?

9. If the probability that it will rain tomorrow is 0.20, what is the probability that it won't rain tomorrow? Would you recommend taking an umbrella?

10. A probability experiment is conducted. Which of these cannot be considered a probability of an outcome?

    a. $\frac{1}{3}$ d. -0.59 g. 1
    b. $-\frac{1}{5}$ e. 0   h. 33%
    c. 0.80   f. 1.45   i. 112%

11. Classify each statement as an example of classical probability, empirical probability, or subjective probability.

    a. The probability that a person will watch the 6 o'clock evening news is 0.15.

    b. The probability of winning at a Chuck-a-Luck game is $\frac{5}{36}$.

    c. The probability that a bus will be in an accident on a specific run is about 6%.

    d. The probability of getting a royal flush when five cards are selected at random is $\frac{1}{649,740}$.

    e. The probability that a student will get a C or better in a statistics course is about 70%.

    f. The probability that a new fast-food restaurant will be a success in Chicago is 35%.

    g. The probability that interest rates will rise in the next 6 months is 0.50.

12. **(ans) Rolling a Die** If a die is rolled one time, find these probabilities.

    a. Of getting a 4
    b. Of getting an even number
    c. Of getting a number greater than 4
    d. Of getting a number less than 7
    e. Of getting a number greater than 0
    f. Of getting a number greater than 3 or an odd number
    g. Of getting a number greater than 3 and an odd number

13. **Rolling Two Dice** If two dice are rolled one time, find the probability of getting these results.

    a. A sum of 6
    b. Doubles
    c. A sum of 7 or 11
    d. A sum greater than 9
    e. A sum less than or equal to 4

14. **(ans) Drawing a Card** If one card is drawn from a deck, find the probability of getting these results.

    a. An ace
    b. A diamond
    c. An ace of diamonds
    d. A 4 or a 6
    e. A 4 or a club
    f. A 6 or a spade
    g. A heart or a club
    h. A red queen
    i. A red card or a 7
    j. A black card and a 10

15. **Shopping Mall Promotion** A shopping mall has set up a promotion as follows. With any mall purchase of $50 or more, the customer gets to spin the wheel shown here. If a number 1 comes up, the customer wins $10. If the number 2 comes up, the customer wins $5; and if the number 3 or 4 comes up, the customer wins a discount coupon. Find the following probabilities.

    a. The customer wins $10.
    b. The customer wins money.
    c. The customer wins a coupon.

16. **Selecting a State** Choose one of the 50 states at random.

    a. What is the probability that it begins with M?
    b. What is the probability that it doesn't begin with a vowel?

17. **Human Blood Types** Human blood is grouped into four types. The percentages of Americans with each type are listed below.

    O 43%   A 40%   B 12%   AB 5%

    Choose one American at random. Find the probability that this person

    a. Has type O blood
    b. Has type A or B
    c. Does not have type O or A

    Source: www.infoplease.com

18. **Gender of College Students** In 2004, 57.2% of all enrolled college students were female. Choose one enrolled student at random. What is the probability that the student was male?

    Source: www.nces.ed.gov

19. Prime Numbers A prime number is a number that is evenly divisible only by 1 and itself. The prime numbers less than 100 are listed below.

2	3	5	7	11	13	17	19	23	29	31
37	41	43	47	53	59	61	67	71	73	79
83	89	97

Choose one of these numbers at random. Find the probability that

a. The number is even

b. The sum of the number's digits is even

c. The number is greater than 50

20. Rural Speed Limits Rural speed limits for all 50 states are indicated below.

60 mph	65 mph	70 mph	75 mph
1 (HI)	18	18	13

Choose one state at random. Find the probability that its speed limit is

a. 60 or 70 miles per hour

b. Greater than 65 miles per hour

c. 70 miles per hour or less

Source: *World Almanac.*

21. Gender of Children A couple has three children. Find each probability.

a. All boys

b. All girls or all boys

c. Exactly two boys or two girls

d. At least one child of each gender

22. Craps Game In the game of craps using two dice, a person wins on the first roll if a 7 or an 11 is rolled. Find the probability of winning on the first roll.

23. Craps Game In a game of craps, a player loses on the roll if a 2, 3, or 12 is tossed on the first roll. Find the probability of losing on the first roll.

24. Computers in Elementary Schools Elementary and secondary schools were classified by the number of computers they had. Choose one of these schools at random.

Computers	1–10	11–20	21–50	51–100	100+
Schools	3170	4590	16,741	23,753	34,803

Choose one school at random. Find the probability that it has

a. 50 or fewer computers

b. More than 100 computers

c. No more than 20 computers

Source: *World Almanac.*

25. Roulette A roulette wheel has 38 spaces numbered 1 through 36, 0, and 00. Find the probability of getting these results.

a. An odd number (Do not count 0 or 00.)

b. A number greater than 27

c. A number that contains the digit 0

d. Based on the answers to parts *a*, *b*, and *c*, which is most likely to occur? Explain why.

26. Gasoline Mileage for Autos and Trucks Of the top 10 cars and trucks based on gas mileage, 4 are Hondas, 3 are Toyotas, and 3 are Volkswagens. Choose one at random. Find the probability that it is

a. Japanese

b. Japanese or German

c. Not foreign

Source: www.autobytel.com

27. Large Monetary Bills in Circulation There are 1,765,000 five thousand dollar bills in circulation and 3,460,000 ten thousand dollar bills in circulation. Choose one bill at random (wouldn't that be nice!). What is the probability that it is a ten thousand dollar bill?

Source: *World Almanac.*

28. Sources of Energy Uses in the United States A breakdown of the sources of energy used in the United States is shown below. Choose one energy source at random. Find the probability that it is

a. Not oil

b. Natural gas or oil

c. Nuclear

Oil 39%	Natural gas 24%	Coal 23%
Nuclear 8%	Hydropower 3%	Other 3%

Source: www.infoplease.com

29. Rolling Dice Roll two dice and multiply the numbers.

a. Write out the sample space.

b. What is the probability that the product is a multiple of 6?

c. What is the probability that the product is less than 10?

30. Federal Government Revenue The source of federal government revenue for a specific year is

50% from individual income taxes

32% from social insurance payroll taxes

10% from corporate income taxes

3% from excise taxes

5% other

If a revenue source is selected at random, what is the probability that it comes from individual or corporate income taxes?

Source: *New York Times Almanac.*

31. **Selecting a Bill** A box contains a $1 bill, a $5 bill, a $10 bill, and a $20 bill. A bill is selected at random, and it is not replaced; then a second bill is selected at random. Draw a tree diagram and determine the sample space.

32. **Tossing Coins** Draw a tree diagram and determine the sample space for tossing four coins.

33. **Selecting Numbered Balls** Four balls numbered 1 through 4 are placed in a box. A ball is selected at random, and its number is noted; then it is replaced. A second ball is selected at random, and its number is noted. Draw a tree diagram and determine the sample space.

34. **Family Dinner Combinations** A family special at a neighborhood restaurant offers dinner for four for $19.99. There are 3 appetizers available, 4 entrees, and 3 desserts from which to choose. The special includes one of each. Represent the possible dinner combinations with a tree diagram.

35. **Required First-Year College Courses** First-year students at a particular college must take one English class, one class in mathematics, a first-year seminar, and an elective. There are 2 English classes to choose from, 3 mathematics classes, 5 electives, and everyone takes the same first-year seminar. Represent the possible schedules using a tree diagram.

36. **Tossing a Coin and Rolling a Die** A coin is tossed; if it falls heads up, it is tossed again. If it falls tails up, a die is rolled. Draw a tree diagram and determine the outcomes.

Extending the Concepts

37. **Distribution of CEO Ages** The distribution of ages of CEOs is as follows:

Age	Frequency
21–30	1
31–40	8
41–50	27
51–60	29
61–70	24
71–up	11

Source: Information based on *USA TODAY* Snapshot.

If a CEO is selected at random, find the probability that his or her age is

a. Between 31 and 40

b. Under 31

c. Over 30 and under 51

d. Under 31 or over 60

38. **Tossing a Coin** A person flipped a coin 100 times and obtained 73 heads. Can the person conclude that the coin was unbalanced?

39. **Medical Treatment** A medical doctor stated that with a certain treatment, a patient has a 50% chance of recovering without surgery. That is, "Either he will get well or he won't get well." Comment on this statement.

40. **Wheel Spinner** The wheel spinner shown here is spun twice. Find the sample space, and then determine the probability of the following events.

a. An odd number on the first spin and an even number on the second spin (*Note:* 0 is considered even.)

b. A sum greater than 4

c. Even numbers on both spins

d. A sum that is odd

e. The same number on both spins

41. **Tossing Coins** Toss three coins 128 times and record the number of heads (0, 1, 2, or 3); then record your results with the theoretical probabilities. Compute the empirical probabilities of each.

42. **Tossing Coins** Toss two coins 100 times and record the number of heads (0, 1, 2). Compute the probabilities of each outcome, and compare these probabilities with the theoretical results.

43. Odds Odds are used in gambling games to make them fair. For example, if you rolled a die and won every time you rolled a 6, then you would win on average once every 6 times. So that the game is fair, the odds of 5 to 1 are given. This means that if you bet $1 and won, you could win $5. On average, you would win $5 once in 6 rolls and lose $1 on the other 5 rolls—hence the term *fair game.*

In most gambling games, the odds given are not fair. For example, if the odds of winning are really 20 to 1, the house might offer 15 to 1 in order to make a profit.

Odds can be expressed as a fraction or as a ratio, such as $\frac{5}{1}$, 5:1, or 5 to 1. Odds are computed in favor of the event or against the event. The formulas for odds are

$$\text{Odds in favor} = \frac{P(E)}{1 - P(E)}$$

$$\text{Odds against} = \frac{P(\overline{E})}{1 - P(\overline{E})}$$

In the die example,

$$\text{Odds in favor of a 6} = \frac{\frac{1}{6}}{\frac{5}{6}} = \frac{1}{5} \text{ or } 1{:}5$$

$$\text{Odds against a 6} = \frac{\frac{5}{6}}{\frac{1}{6}} = \frac{5}{1} \text{ or } 5{:}1$$

Find the odds in favor of and against each event.

a. Rolling a die and getting a 2
b. Rolling a die and getting an even number
c. Drawing a card from a deck and getting a spade
d. Drawing a card and getting a red card
e. Drawing a card and getting a queen
f. Tossing two coins and getting two tails
g. Tossing two coins and getting one tail

4–2

The Addition Rules for Probability

Many problems involve finding the probability of two or more events. For example, at a large political gathering, you might wish to know, for a person selected at random, the probability that the person is a female or is a Republican. In this case, there are three possibilities to consider:

Objective 2

Find the probability of compound events, using the addition rules.

1. The person is a female.
2. The person is a Republican.
3. The person is both a female and a Republican.

Consider another example. At the same gathering there are Republicans, Democrats, and Independents. If a person is selected at random, what is the probability that the person is a Democrat or an Independent? In this case, there are only two possibilities:

1. The person is a Democrat.
2. The person is an Independent.

The difference between the two examples is that in the first case, the person selected can be a female and a Republican at the same time. In the second case, the person selected cannot be both a Democrat and an Independent at the same time. In the second case, the two events are said to be *mutually exclusive;* in the first case, they are not mutually exclusive.

Historical Note

The first book on probability, *The Book of Chance and Games,* was written by Jerome Cardan (1501–1576). Cardan was an astrologer, philosopher, physician, mathematician, and gambler. This book contained techniques on how to cheat and how to catch others at cheating.

Two events are **mutually exclusive events** if they cannot occur at the same time (i.e., they have no outcomes in common).

In another situation, the events of getting a 4 and getting a 6 when a single card is drawn from a deck are mutually exclusive events, since a single card cannot be both a 4 and a 6. On the other hand, the events of getting a 4 and getting a heart on a single draw are not mutually exclusive, since you can select the 4 of hearts when drawing a single card from an ordinary deck.

| Example 4–15 | **Rolling a Die** |

Determine which events are mutually exclusive and which are not, when a single die is rolled.

  a. Getting an odd number and getting an even number
  b. Getting a 3 and getting an odd number
  c. Getting an odd number and getting a number less than 4
  d. Getting a number greater than 4 and getting a number less than 4

Solution

  a. The events are mutually exclusive, since the first event can be 1, 3, or 5 and the second event can be 2, 4, or 6.
  b. The events are not mutually exclusive, since the first event is a 3 and the second can be 1, 3, or 5. Hence, 3 is contained in both events.
  c. The events are not mutually exclusive, since the first event can be 1, 3, or 5 and the second can be 1, 2, or 3. Hence, 1 and 3 are contained in both events.
  d. The events are mutually exclusive, since the first event can be 5 or 6 and the second event can be 1, 2, or 3.

| Example 4–16 | **Drawing a Card** |

Determine which events are mutually exclusive and which are not, when a single card is drawn from a deck.

  a. Getting a 7 and getting a jack
  b. Getting a club and getting a king
  c. Getting a face card and getting an ace
  d. Getting a face card and getting a spade

Solution

Only the events in parts *a* and *c* are mutually exclusive.

The probability of two or more events can be determined by the *addition rules*. The first addition rule is used when the events are mutually exclusive.

Addition Rule 1

When two events A and B are mutually exclusive, the probability that A or B will occur is

$$P(A \text{ or } B) = P(A) + P(B)$$

| Example 4–17 | **Selecting a Doughnut** |

A box contains 3 glazed doughnuts, 4 jelly doughnuts, and 5 chocolate doughnuts. If a person selects a doughnut at random, find the probability that it is either a glazed doughnut or a chocolate doughnut.

Solution

Since the box contains 3 glazed doughnuts, 5 chocolate doughnuts, and a total of 12 doughnuts, $P(\text{glazed or chocolate}) = P(\text{glazed}) + P(\text{chocolate}) = \frac{3}{12} + \frac{5}{12} = \frac{8}{12} = \frac{2}{3}$. The events are mutually exclusive.

Example 4–18	**Political Affiliation at a Rally**

At a political rally, there are 20 Republicans, 13 Democrats, and 6 Independents. If a person is selected at random, find the probability that he or she is either a Democrat or an Independent.

Solution

$$P(\text{Democrat or Independent}) = P(\text{Democrat}) + P(\text{Independent})$$
$$= \frac{13}{39} + \frac{6}{39} = \frac{19}{39}$$

Example 4–19	**Selecting a Day of the Week**

A day of the week is selected at random. Find the probability that it is a weekend day.

Solution

$$P(\text{Saturday or Sunday}) = P(\text{Saturday}) + P(\text{Sunday}) = \frac{1}{7} + \frac{1}{7} = \frac{2}{7}$$

When two events are not mutually exclusive, we must subtract one of the two probabilities of the outcomes that are common to both events, since they have been counted twice. This technique is illustrated in Example 4–20.

Example 4–20	**Drawing a Card**

A single card is drawn at random from an ordinary deck of cards. Find the probability that it is either an ace or a black card.

Solution

Since there are 4 aces and 26 black cards (13 spades and 13 clubs), 2 of the aces are black cards, namely, the ace of spades and the ace of clubs. Hence the probabilities of the two outcomes must be subtracted since they have been counted twice.

$$P(\text{ace or black card}) = P(\text{ace}) + P(\text{black card}) - P(\text{black aces}) = \frac{4}{52} + \frac{26}{52} - \frac{2}{52} = \frac{28}{52} = \frac{7}{13}$$

When events are not mutually exclusive, addition rule 2 can be used to find the probability of the events.

Addition Rule 2

If A and B are *not* mutually exclusive, then

$$P(A \text{ or } B) = P(A) + P(B) - P(A \text{ and } B)$$

Note: This rule can also be used when the events are mutually exclusive, since $P(A$ and $B)$ will always equal 0. However, it is important to make a distinction between the two situations.

| **Example 4–21** | **Selecting a Medical Staff Person** |

In a hospital unit there are 8 nurses and 5 physicians; 7 nurses and 3 physicians are females. If a staff person is selected, find the probability that the subject is a nurse or a male.

Solution

The sample space is shown here.

Staff	**Females**	**Males**	**Total**
Nurses	7	1	8
Physicians	3	2	5
Total	10	3	13

The probability is

$$P(\text{nurse or male}) = P(\text{nurse}) + P(\text{male}) - P(\text{male nurse})$$
$$= \tfrac{8}{13} + \tfrac{3}{13} - \tfrac{1}{13} = \tfrac{10}{13}$$

| **Example 4–22** | **Driving While Intoxicated** |

On New Year's Eve, the probability of a person driving while intoxicated is 0.32, the probability of a person having a driving accident is 0.09, and the probability of a person having a driving accident while intoxicated is 0.06. What is the probability of a person driving while intoxicated or having a driving accident?

Solution

$$P(\text{intoxicated or accident}) = P(\text{intoxicated}) + P(\text{accident})$$
$$- P(\text{intoxicated and accident})$$
$$= 0.32 + 0.09 - 0.06 = 0.35$$

In summary, then, when the two events are mutually exclusive, use addition rule 1. When the events are not mutually exclusive, use addition rule 2.

The probability rules can be extended to three or more events. For three mutually exclusive events A, B, and C,

$$P(A \text{ or } B \text{ or } C) = P(A) + P(B) + P(C)$$

For three events that are *not* mutually exclusive,

$$P(A \text{ or } B \text{ or } C) = P(A) + P(B) + P(C) - P(A \text{ and } B) - P(A \text{ and } C)$$
$$- P(B \text{ and } C) + P(A \text{ and } B \text{ and } C)$$

See Exercises 23 and 24 in this section.

Figure 4–5(a) shows a Venn diagram that represents two mutually exclusive events A and B. In this case, $P(A \text{ or } B) = P(A) + P(B)$, since these events are mutually exclusive

Figure 4–5

Venn Diagrams for the Addition Rules

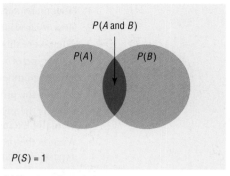

(a) Mutually exclusive events
$P(A \text{ or } B) = P(A) + P(B)$

(b) Nonmutually exclusive events
$P(A \text{ or } B) = P(A) + P(B) - P(A \text{ and } B)$

and do not overlap. In other words, the probability of occurrence of event A or event B is the sum of the areas of the two circles.

Figure 4–5(b) represents the probability of two events that are *not* mutually exclusive. In this case, $P(A \text{ or } B) = P(A) + P(B) - P(A \text{ and } B)$. The area in the intersection or overlapping part of both circles corresponds to $P(A \text{ and } B)$; and when the area of circle A is added to the area of circle B, the overlapping part is counted twice. It must therefore be subtracted once to get the correct area or probability.

Note: Venn diagrams were developed by mathematician John Venn (1834–1923) and are used in set theory and symbolic logic. They have been adapted to probability theory also. In set theory, the symbol $\cup$ represents the *union* of two sets, and $A \cup B$ corresponds to A or B. The symbol $\cap$ represents the *intersection* of two sets, and $A \cap B$ corresponds to A and B. Venn diagrams show only a general picture of the probability rules and do not portray all situations, such as $P(A) = 0$, accurately.

Applying the Concepts **4–2**

Which Pain Reliever Is Best?

Assume that following an injury you received from playing your favorite sport, you obtain and read information on new pain medications. In that information you read of a study that was conducted to test the side effects of two new pain medications. Use the following table to answer the questions and decide which, if any, of the two new pain medications you will use.

Side effect	Number of side effects in 12-week clinical trial		
	Placebo $n = 192$	Drug A $n = 186$	Drug B $n = 188$
Upper respiratory congestion	10	32	19
Sinus headache	11	25	32
Stomach ache	2	46	12
Neurological headache	34	55	72
Cough	22	18	31
Lower respiratory congestion	2	5	1

1. How many subjects were in the study?
2. How long was the study?
3. What were the variables under study?
4. What type of variables are they, and what level of measurement are they on?
5. Are the numbers in the table exact figures?
6. What is the probability that a randomly selected person was receiving a placebo?
7. What is the probability that a person was receiving a placebo or drug A? Are these mutually exclusive events? What is the complement to this event?
8. What is the probability that a randomly selected person was receiving a placebo or experienced a neurological headache?
9. What is the probability that a randomly selected person was not receiving a placebo or experienced a sinus headache?

See page 257 for the answers.

Exercises 4–2

1. Define mutually exclusive events, and give an example of two events that are mutually exclusive and two events that are not mutually exclusive.

2. Determine whether these events are mutually exclusive.

   a. Roll a die: Get an even number, and get a number less than 3.

   b. Roll a die: Get a prime number (2, 3, 5), and get an odd number.

   c. Roll a die: Get a number greater than 3, and get a number less than 3.

   d. Select a student in your class: The student has blonde hair, and the student has blue eyes.

   e. Select a student in your college: The student is a sophomore, and the student is a business major.

   f. Select any course: It is a calculus course, and it is an English course.

   g. Select a registered voter: The voter is a Republican, and the voter is a Democrat.

3. **College Degrees Awarded** The table below represents the college degrees awarded in a recent academic year by gender.

	Bachelor's	Master's	Doctorate
Men	573,079	211,381	24,341
Women	775,424	301,264	21,683

   Choose a degree at random. Find the probability that it is

   a. A bachelor's degree

   b. A doctorate or a degree awarded to a woman

   c. A doctorate awarded to a woman

   d. Not a master's degree

   Source: www.nces.ed.gov

4. **Selecting a Staff Person** At a community swimming pool there are 2 managers, 8 lifeguards, 3 concession stand clerks, and 2 maintenance people. If a person is selected at random, find the probability that the person is either a lifeguard or a manager.

5. **Selecting an Instructor** At a convention there are 7 mathematics instructors, 5 computer science instructors, 3 statistics instructors, and 4 science instructors. If an instructor is selected, find the probability of getting a science instructor or a math instructor.

6. **Selecting a Movie** A media rental store rented the following number of movie titles in each of these categories: 170 horror, 230 drama, 120 mystery, 310 romance, and 150 comedy. If a person selects a movie to rent, find the probability that it is a romance or a comedy. Is this event likely or unlikely to occur? Explain your answer.

7. **Selecting a Nurse** A recent study of 200 nurses found that of 125 female nurses, 56 had bachelor's degrees; and of 75 male nurses, 34 had bachelor's degrees. If a nurse is selected at random, find the probability that the nurse is

   a. A female nurse with a bachelor's degree

   b. A male nurse

   c. A male nurse with a bachelor's degree

   d. Based on your answers to parts a, b, and c, explain which is most likely to occur. Explain why.

8. **Tourist Destinations** The probability that a given tourist goes to the amusement park is 0.47, and the probability that she goes to the water park is 0.58. If the probability that she goes to either the water park or the amusement park is 0.95, what is the probability that she visits both of the parks on vacation?

9. **Sports Participation** At a particular school with 200 male students, 58 play football, 40 play basketball, and 8 play both. What is the probability that a randomly selected male student plays neither sport?

10. **Selecting a Card** A single card is drawn from a deck. Find the probability of selecting the following.

    a. A 4 or a diamond

    b. A club or a diamond

    c. A jack or a black card

11. **Selecting a Student** In a statistics class there are 18 juniors and 10 seniors; 6 of the seniors are females, and 12 of the juniors are males. If a student is selected at random, find the probability of selecting the following.

    a. A junior or a female

    b. A senior or a female

    c. A junior or a senior

12. **Selecting a Book** At a used-book sale, 100 books are adult books and 160 are children's books. Of the adult books, 70 are nonfiction while 60 of the children's books are nonfiction. If a book is selected at random, find the probability that it is

    a. Fiction

    b. Not a children's nonfiction book

    c. An adult book or a children's nonfiction book

13. **Young Adult Residences** According to the Bureau of the Census, the following statistics describe the number (in thousands) of young adults living at home or in a dormitory in the year 2004.

	Ages 18–24	Ages 25–34
Male	7922	2534
Female	5779	995

    Source: *World Almanac.*

    Choose one student at random. Find the probability that the student is

    a. A female student aged 25–34

    b. Male or aged 18–24

    c. Under 25 years of age and not male

14. **Endangered Species** The chart below shows the numbers of endangered and threatened species both here in the United States and abroad.

	Endangered		Threatened	
	United States	**Foreign**	**United States**	**Foreign**
Mammals	68	251	10	20
Birds	77	175	13	6
Reptiles	14	64	22	16
Amphibians	11	8	10	1

    Source: www.infoplease.com

Choose one species at random. Find the probability that it is

    a. Threatened and in the United States

    b. An endangered foreign bird

    c. A mammal or a threatened foreign species

15. **Multiple Births** The number of multiple births in the United States for a recent year indicated that there were 128,665 sets of twins, 7110 sets of triplets, 468 sets of quadruplets, and 85 sets of quintuplets. Choose one set of siblings at random. Find the probability that it

    a. Represented more than two babies

    b. Represented quads or quints

    c. Now choose one baby from these multiple births. What is the probability that the baby was a triplet?

16. **Licensed Drivers in the United States** In a recent year there were the following numbers (in thousands) of licensed drivers in the United States.

	Male	**Female**
Age 19 and under	4746	4517
Age 20	1625	1553
Age 21	1679	1627

    Source: *World Almanac.*

    Choose one driver at random. Find the probability that the driver is

    a. Male and 19 or under

    b. Age 20 or female

    c. At least 20 years old

17. **Cable Channel Programming** Three cable channels (6, 8, and 10) have quiz shows, comedies, and dramas. The number of each is shown here.

Type of show	Channel 6	Channel 8	Channel 10
Quiz show	5	2	1
Comedy	3	2	8
Drama	4	4	2

    If a show is selected at random, find these probabilities.

    a. The show is a quiz show, or it is shown on channel 8.

    b. The show is a drama or a comedy.

    c. The show is shown on channel 10, or it is a drama.

18. **Mail Delivery** A local postal carrier distributes first-class letters, advertisements, and magazines. For a certain day, she distributed the following numbers of each type of item.

Delivered to	First-class letters	Ads	Magazines
Home	325	406	203
Business	732	1021	97

If an item of mail is selected at random, find these probabilities.

a. The item went to a home.

b. The item was an ad, or it went to a business.

c. The item was a first-class letter, or it went to a home.

19. **Medical Tests on Emergency Patients** The frequency distribution shown here illustrates the number of medical tests conducted on 30 randomly selected emergency patients.

Number of tests performed	Number of patients
0	12
1	8
2	2
3	3
4 or more	5

If a patient is selected at random, find these probabilities.

a. The patient has had exactly 2 tests done.

b. The patient has had at least 2 tests done.

c. The patient has had at most 3 tests done.

d. The patient has had 3 or fewer tests done.

e. The patient has had 1 or 2 tests done.

20. A social organization of 32 members sold college sweatshirts as a fundraiser. The results of their sale are shown below.

No. of sweatshirts	No. of students
0	2
1–5	13
6–10	8
11–15	4
16–20	4
20+	1

Choose one student at random. Find the probability that the student sold

a. More than 10 sweatshirts

b. At least one sweatshirt

c. 1–5 or more than 15 sweatshirts

21. **Door-to-Door Sales** A sales representative who visits customers at home finds she sells 0, 1, 2, 3, or 4 items according to the following frequency distribution.

Items sold	Frequency
0	8
1	10
2	3
3	2
4	1

Find the probability that she sells the following.

a. Exactly 1 item

b. More than 2 items

c. At least 1 item

d. At most 3 items

22. **Medical Patients** A recent study of 300 patients found that of 100 alcoholic patients, 87 had elevated cholesterol levels, and of 200 nonalcoholic patients, 43 had elevated cholesterol levels. If a patient is selected at random, find the probability that the patient is the following.

a. An alcoholic with elevated cholesterol level

b. A nonalcoholic

c. A nonalcoholic with nonelevated cholesterol level

23. **Selecting a Card** If one card is drawn from an ordinary deck of cards, find the probability of getting the following.

a. A king or a queen or a jack

b. A club or a heart or a spade

c. A king or a queen or a diamond

d. An ace or a diamond or a heart

e. A 9 or a 10 or a spade or a club

24. **Rolling a Die** Two dice are rolled. Find the probability of getting

a. A sum of 5, 6, or 7

b. Doubles or a sum of 6 or 8

c. A sum greater than 8 or less than 3

d. Based on the answers to parts a, b, and c, which is least likely to occur? Explain why.

25. **Corn Products** U.S. growers harvested 11 billion bushels of corn in 2005. About 1.9 billion bushels were exported, and 1.6 billion bushels were used for ethanol. Choose one bushel of corn at random. What is the probability that it was used either for export or for ethanol?

Source: www.census.gov

26. **Rolling Dice** Three dice are rolled. Find the probability of getting

a. Triples   b. A sum of 5

Extending the Concepts

27. Purchasing a Pizza The probability that a customer selects a pizza with mushrooms or pepperoni is 0.43, and the probability that the customer selects only mushrooms is 0.32. If the probability that he or she selects only pepperoni is 0.17, find the probability of the customer selecting both items.

28. Building a New Home In building new homes, a contractor finds that the probability of a home buyer selecting a two-car garage is 0.70 and of selecting a one-car garage is 0.20. Find the probability that the buyer will select no garage. The builder does not build houses with three-car or more garages.

29. In Exercise 28, find the probability that the buyer will not want a two-car garage.

30. Suppose that $P(A) = 0.42$, $P(B) = 0.38$, and $P(A \cup B) = 0.70$. Are A and B mutually exclusive? Explain.

LAFF-A-DAY

ROSS INSURANCE

SCHOCHET

"I know you haven't had an accident in thirteen years. We're raising your rates because you're about due one."

Source: © King Features Syndicate.

Technology *Step by Step*

MINITAB
Step by Step

Calculate Relative Frequency Probabilities

The random variable X represents the number of days patients stayed in the hospital from Example 4–14.

1. In C1 of a worksheet, type in the values of X. Name the column **X.**
2. In C2 enter the frequencies. Name the column **f.**
3. To calculate the relative frequencies and store them in a new column named Px:

   a) Select **Calc>Calculator.**
   b) Type **Px** in the box for Store result in variable:.
   c) Click in the Expression box, then double-click C2 f.
   d) Type or click the division operator.
   e) Scroll down the function list to Sum, then click [Select].
   f) Double-click C2 f to select it.
   g) Click [OK].

The dialog box and completed worksheet are shown.

↓	C1	C2	C3
	X	f	Px
1	3	15	0.118110
2	4	32	0.251969
3	5	56	0.440945
4	6	19	0.149606
5	7	5	0.039370

If the original data, rather than the table, are in a worksheet, use **Stat>Tables>Tally** to make the tables with percents (Section 2–1).

MINITAB can also make a two-way classification table.

Construct a Contingency Table

1. Select **File>Open Worksheet** to open the Databank.mtw file.

2. Select **Stat>Tables>Crosstabulation . . .**

   a) Double-click C4 SMOKING STATUS to select it For rows:.

   b) Select C11 GENDER for the For Columns: Field.

   c) Click on option for Counts and then [OK].

The session window and completed dialog box are shown.

Tabulated statistics: SMOKING STATUS, GENDER

Rows: SMOKING STATUS   Columns: GENDER

	F	M	All
0	25	22	47
1	18	19	37
2	7	9	16
All	50	50	100

Cell Contents: Count

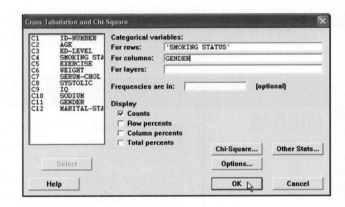

In this sample of 100 there are 25 females who do not smoke compared to 22 men. Sixteen individuals smoke 1 pack or more per day.

TI-83 Plus or TI-84 Plus
Step by Step

To construct a relative frequency table:

1. Enter the data values in L_1 and the frequencies in L_2.

2. Move the cursor to the top of the L_3 column so that L_3 is highlighted.

3. Type L_2 divided by the sample size, then press **ENTER.**

Use the data from Example 4–14.

Excel
Step by Step

Constructing a Relative Frequency Distribution

Use the data from Example 4–14.

1. In a new worksheet, type the label **DAYS** in cell A1. Beginning in cell A2, type in the data for the variable representing the number of days maternity patients stayed in the hospital.

2. In cell B1, type the label for the frequency, **COUNT.** Beginning in cell B2, type in the frequencies.

3. In cell B7, compute the total frequency by selecting the sum icon Σ from the toolbar and press **Enter.**

4. In cell C1, type a label for the relative frequencies, **Rf.** In cell C2, type **=(B2)/(B7)** and **Enter.** In cell C2, type **=(B3)/(B7)** and **Enter.** Repeat this for each of the remaining frequencies.

5. To find the total relative frequency, select the sum icon Σ from the toolbar and **Enter.** This sum should be 1.

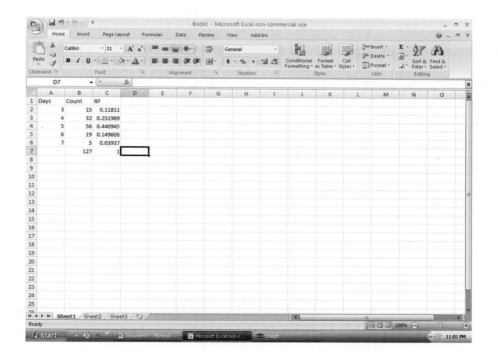

Constructing a Contingency Table
Example XL4–1

For this example, you will need to have the MegaStat Add-In installed on Excel (refer to Chapter 1, Excel Step by Step instructions for instructions on installing MegaStat).

1. Open the Databank.xls file from the CD-ROM that came with your text. To do this:

   Double-click My Computer on the Desktop.

   Double-click the Bluman CD-ROM icon in the CD drive holding the disk.

   Double-click the datasets folder. Then double-click the all_data-sets folder.

   Double-click the bluman_es_data-sets_excel-windows folder. In this folder double-click the Databank.xls file. The Excel program will open automatically once you open this file.

2. Highlight the column labeled SMOKING STATUS to copy these data onto a new Excel worksheet.

3. Click the Microsoft Office Button [icon], select New Blank Workbook, then Create.

4. With cell A1 selected, click the Paste icon on the toolbar to paste the data into the new workbook.

5. Return to the Databank.xls file. Highlight the column labeled Gender. Copy and paste these data into column B of the worksheet containing the SMOKING STATUS data.

6. Type in the categories for SMOKING STATUS, **0, 1,** and **2** into cells C2–C4. In cell D2, type M for male and in cell D3, type F for female.

7. On the toolbar, select Add-Ins. Then select MegaStat. *Note:* You may need to open MegaStat from the file MegaStat.xls saved on your computer's hard drive.

8. Select **Chi-Square/Crosstab>Crosstabulation.**

9. In the Row variable Data range box, type A1:A101. In the Row variable Specification range box, type C2:C4. In the Column variable Data range box, type B1:B101. In the Column variable Specification range box, type D2:D3. Remove any checks from the Output Options. Then click [OK].

Crosstabulation

		GENDER		
		M	F	Total
SMOKING STATUS	0	21	25	46
	1	19	18	37
	2	9	8	17
	Total	49	51	100

<table>
<tr><td>**4–3**</td><td></td></tr>
</table>

The Multiplication Rules and Conditional Probability

Section 4–2 showed that the addition rules are used to compute probabilities for mutually exclusive and non-mutually exclusive events. This section introduces the multiplication rules.

Objective 3

Find the probability of compound events, using the multiplication rules.

The Multiplication Rules

The *multiplication rules* can be used to find the probability of two or more events that occur in sequence. For example, if you toss a coin and then roll a die, you can find the probability of getting a head on the coin *and* a 4 on the die. These two events are said to be *independent* since the outcome of the first event (tossing a coin) does not affect the probability outcome of the second event (rolling a die).

> Two events A and B are **independent events** if the fact that A occurs does not affect the probability of B occurring.

Here are other examples of independent events:

Rolling a die and getting a 6, and then rolling a second die and getting a 3.

Drawing a card from a deck and getting a queen, replacing it, and drawing a second card and getting a queen.

To find the probability of two independent events that occur in sequence, you must find the probability of each event occurring separately and then multiply the answers. For example, if a coin is tossed twice, the probability of getting two heads is $\frac{1}{2} \cdot \frac{1}{2} = \frac{1}{4}$. This result can be verified by looking at the sample space HH, HT, TH, TT. Then $P(\text{HH}) = \frac{1}{4}$.

Multiplication Rule 1

When two events are independent, the probability of both occurring is

$$P(A \text{ and } B) = P(A) \cdot P(B)$$

Example 4–23

Tossing a Coin

A coin is flipped and a die is rolled. Find the probability of getting a head on the coin and a 4 on the die.

Solution

$$P(\text{head and 4}) = P(\text{head}) \cdot P(4) = \frac{1}{2} \cdot \frac{1}{6} = \frac{1}{12}$$

Note that the sample space for the coin is H, T; and for the die it is 1, 2, 3, 4, 5, 6.

The problem in Example 4–23 can also be solved by using the sample space

H1 H2 H3 H4 H5 H6 T1 T2 T3 T4 T5 T6

The solution is $\frac{1}{12}$, since there is only one way to get the head-4 outcome.

| Example 4–24 | **Drawing a Card** |

A card is drawn from a deck and replaced; then a second card is drawn. Find the probability of getting a queen and then an ace.

Solution

The probability of getting a queen is $\frac{4}{52}$, and since the card is replaced, the probability of getting an ace is $\frac{4}{52}$. Hence, the probability of getting a queen and an ace is

$$P(\text{queen and ace}) = P(\text{queen}) \cdot P(\text{ace}) = \frac{4}{52} \cdot \frac{4}{52} = \frac{16}{2704} = \frac{1}{169}$$

| Example 4–25 | **Selecting a Colored Ball** |

An urn contains 3 red balls, 2 blue balls, and 5 white balls. A ball is selected and its color noted. Then it is replaced. A second ball is selected and its color noted. Find the probability of each of these.

 a. Selecting 2 blue balls
 b. Selecting 1 blue ball and then 1 white ball
 c. Selecting 1 red ball and then 1 blue ball

Solution

 a. $P(\text{blue and blue}) = P(\text{blue}) \cdot P(\text{blue}) = \frac{2}{10} \cdot \frac{2}{10} = \frac{4}{100} = \frac{1}{25}$

 b. $P(\text{blue and white}) = P(\text{blue}) \cdot P(\text{white}) = \frac{2}{10} \cdot \frac{5}{10} = \frac{10}{100} = \frac{1}{10}$

 c. $P(\text{red and blue}) = P(\text{red}) \cdot P(\text{blue}) = \frac{3}{10} \cdot \frac{2}{10} = \frac{6}{100} = \frac{3}{50}$

Multiplication rule 1 can be extended to three or more independent events by using the formula

$$P(A \text{ and } B \text{ and } C \text{ and } \ldots \text{ and } K) = P(A) \cdot P(B) \cdot P(C) \cdots P(K)$$

When a small sample is selected from a large population and the subjects are not replaced, the probability of the event occurring changes so slightly that for the most part, it is considered to remain the same. Examples 4–26 and 4–27 illustrate this concept.

| Example 4–26 | **Survey on Stress** |

A Harris poll found that 46% of Americans say they suffer great stress at least once a week. If three people are selected at random, find the probability that all three will say that they suffer great stress at least once a week.

Source: *100% American.*

Solution

Let *S* denote stress. Then

$$P(S \text{ and } S \text{ and } S) = P(S) \cdot P(S) \cdot P(S)$$
$$= (0.46)(0.46)(0.46) \approx 0.097$$

| **Example 4–27** | **Male Color Blindness** |

Approximately 9% of men have a type of color blindness that prevents them from distinguishing between red and green. If 3 men are selected at random, find the probability that all of them will have this type of red-green color blindness.

Source: *USA TODAY.*

Solution

Let C denote red-green color blindness. Then

$$\begin{aligned} P(C \text{ and } C \text{ and } C) &= P(C) \cdot P(C) \cdot P(C) \\ &= (0.09)(0.09)(0.09) \\ &= 0.000729 \end{aligned}$$

Hence, the rounded probability is 0.0007.

In Examples 4–23 through 4–27, the events were independent of one another, since the occurrence of the first event in no way affected the outcome of the second event. On the other hand, when the occurrence of the first event changes the probability of the occurrence of the second event, the two events are said to be *dependent*. For example, suppose a card is drawn from a deck and *not* replaced, and then a second card is drawn. What is the probability of selecting an ace on the first card and a king on the second card?

Before an answer to the question can be given, you must realize that the events are dependent. The probability of selecting an ace on the first draw is $\frac{4}{52}$. If that card is *not* replaced, the probability of selecting a king on the second card is $\frac{4}{51}$, since there are 4 kings and 51 cards remaining. The outcome of the first draw has affected the outcome of the second draw.

Dependent events are formally defined now.

> When the outcome or occurrence of the first event affects the outcome or occurrence of the second event in such a way that the probability is changed, the events are said to be **dependent events.**

Here are some examples of dependent events:

Drawing a card from a deck, not replacing it, and then drawing a second card.

Selecting a ball from an urn, not replacing it, and then selecting a second ball.

Being a lifeguard and getting a suntan.

Having high grades and getting a scholarship.

Parking in a no-parking zone and getting a parking ticket.

To find probabilities when events are dependent, use the multiplication rule with a modification in notation. For the problem just discussed, the probability of getting an ace on the first draw is $\frac{4}{52}$, and the probability of getting a king on the second draw is $\frac{4}{51}$. By the multiplication rule, the probability of both events occurring is

$$\frac{4}{52} \cdot \frac{4}{51} = \frac{16}{2652} = \frac{4}{663}$$

The event of getting a king on the second draw *given* that an ace was drawn the first time is called a *conditional probability.*

The **conditional probability** of an event B in relationship to an event A is the probability that event B occurs after event A has already occurred. The notation for conditional probability is $P(B|A)$. This notation does not mean that B is divided by A; rather, it means the probability that event B occurs given that event A has already occurred. In the card example, $P(B|A)$ is the probability that the second card is a king given that the first card is an ace, and it is equal to $\frac{4}{51}$ since the first card was *not* replaced.

Multiplication Rule 2

When two events are dependent, the probability of both occurring is

$$P(A \text{ and } B) = P(A) \cdot P(B|A)$$

Example 4–28

University Crime

At a university in western Pennsylvania, there were 5 burglaries reported in 2003, 16 in 2004, and 32 in 2005. If a researcher wishes to select at random two burglaries to further investigate, find the probability that both will have occurred in 2004.

Source: IUP Police Department.

Solution

In this case, the events are dependent since the researcher wishes to investigate two distinct cases. Hence the first case is selected and not replaced.

$$P(C_1 \text{ and } C_2) = P(C_1) \cdot P(C_2|C_1) = \tfrac{16}{53} \cdot \tfrac{15}{52} = \tfrac{60}{689}$$

Example 4–29

Homeowner's and Automobile Insurance

World Wide Insurance Company found that 53% of the residents of a city had homeowner's insurance (H) with the company. Of these clients, 27% also had automobile insurance (A) with the company. If a resident is selected at random, find the probability that the resident has both homeowner's and automobile insurance with World Wide Insurance Company.

Solution

$$P(H \text{ and } A) = P(H) \cdot P(A|H) = (0.53)(0.27) = 0.1431$$

This multiplication rule can be extended to three or more events, as shown in Example 4–30.

Example 4–30

Drawing Cards

Three cards are drawn from an ordinary deck and not replaced. Find the probability of these events.

    a. Getting 3 jacks

    b. Getting an ace, a king, and a queen in order

    c. Getting a club, a spade, and a heart in order

    d. Getting 3 clubs

Solution

$$a. \ P(3 \text{ jacks}) = \frac{4}{52} \cdot \frac{3}{51} \cdot \frac{2}{50} = \frac{24}{132,600} = \frac{1}{5525}$$

b. $P(\text{ace and king and queen}) = \dfrac{4}{52} \cdot \dfrac{4}{51} \cdot \dfrac{4}{50} = \dfrac{64}{132{,}600} = \dfrac{8}{16{,}575}$

c. $P(\text{club and spade and heart}) = \dfrac{13}{52} \cdot \dfrac{13}{51} \cdot \dfrac{13}{50} = \dfrac{2197}{132{,}600} = \dfrac{169}{10{,}200}$

d. $P(\text{3 clubs}) = \dfrac{13}{52} \cdot \dfrac{12}{51} \cdot \dfrac{11}{50} = \dfrac{1716}{132{,}600} = \dfrac{11}{850}$

Tree diagrams can be used as an aid to finding the solution to probability problems when the events are sequential. Example 4–31 illustrates the use of tree diagrams.

Example 4–31

Selecting Colored Balls

Box 1 contains 2 red balls and 1 blue ball. Box 2 contains 3 blue balls and 1 red ball. A coin is tossed. If it falls heads up, box 1 is selected and a ball is drawn. If it falls tails up, box 2 is selected and a ball is drawn. Find the probability of selecting a red ball.

Solution

The first two branches designate the selection of either box 1 or box 2. Then from box 1, either a red ball or a blue ball can be selected. Likewise, a red ball or blue ball can be selected from box 2. Hence a tree diagram of the example is shown in Figure 4–6.

Next determine the probabilities for each branch. Since a coin is being tossed for the box selection, each branch has a probability of $\frac{1}{2}$, that is, heads for box 1 or tails for box 2. The probabilities for the second branches are found by using the basic probability rule. For example, if box 1 is selected and there are 2 red balls and 1 blue ball, the probability of selecting a red ball is $\frac{2}{3}$ and the probability of selecting a blue ball is $\frac{1}{3}$. If box 2 is selected and it contains 3 blue balls and 1 red ball, then the probability of selecting a red ball is $\frac{1}{4}$ and the probability of selecting a blue ball is $\frac{3}{4}$.

Next multiply the probability for each outcome, using the rule $P(A \text{ and } B) = P(A) \cdot P(B|A)$. For example, the probability of selecting box 1 and selecting a red ball is $\frac{1}{2} \cdot \frac{2}{3} = \frac{2}{6}$. The probability of selecting box 1 and a blue ball is $\frac{1}{2} \cdot \frac{1}{3} = \frac{1}{6}$. The probability of selecting box 2 and selecting a red ball is $\frac{1}{2} \cdot \frac{1}{4} = \frac{1}{8}$. The probability of selecting box 2 and a blue ball is $\frac{1}{2} \cdot \frac{3}{4} = \frac{3}{8}$. (Note that the sum of these probabilities is 1.)

Finally a red ball can be selected from either box 1 or box 2 so $P(\text{red}) = \frac{2}{6} + \frac{1}{8} = \frac{8}{24} + \frac{3}{24} = \frac{11}{24}$.

Figure 4–6

Tree Diagram for Example 4–31

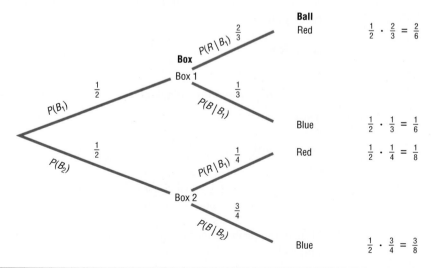

Tree diagrams can be used when the events are independent or dependent, and they can also be used for sequences of three or more events.

Conditional Probability

The conditional probability of an event B in relationship to an event A was defined as the probability that event B occurs after event A has already occurred.

The conditional probability of an event can be found by dividing both sides of the equation for multiplication rule 2 by $P(A)$, as shown:

$$P(A \text{ and } B) = P(A) \cdot P(B|A)$$

$$\frac{P(A \text{ and } B)}{P(A)} = \frac{\cancel{P(A)} \cdot P(B|A)}{\cancel{P(A)}}$$

$$\frac{P(A \text{ and } B)}{P(A)} = P(B|A)$$

Formula for Conditional Probability

The probability that the second event B occurs given that the first event A has occurred can be found by dividing the probability that both events occurred by the probability that the first event has occurred. The formula is

$$P(B|A) = \frac{P(A \text{ and } B)}{P(A)}$$

Examples 4–32, 4–33, and 4–34 illustrate the use of this rule.

Example 4–32

Selecting Colored Chips

A box contains black chips and white chips. A person selects two chips without replacement. If the probability of selecting a black chip *and* a white chip is $\frac{15}{56}$, and the probability of selecting a black chip on the first draw is $\frac{3}{8}$, find the probability of selecting the white chip on the second draw, *given* that the first chip selected was a black chip.

Solution

Let

$$B = \text{selecting a black chip} \qquad W = \text{selecting a white chip}$$

Then

$$P(W|B) = \frac{P(B \text{ and } W)}{P(B)} = \frac{15/56}{3/8}$$

$$= \frac{15}{56} \div \frac{3}{8} = \frac{15}{56} \cdot \frac{8}{3} = \frac{\overset{5}{\cancel{15}}}{\underset{7}{\cancel{56}}} \cdot \frac{\overset{1}{\cancel{8}}}{\underset{1}{\cancel{3}}} = \frac{5}{7}$$

Hence, the probability of selecting a white chip on the second draw given that the first chip selected was black is $\frac{5}{7}$.

| Example 4–33 | Parking Tickets |

The probability that Sam parks in a no-parking zone *and* gets a parking ticket is 0.06, and the probability that Sam cannot find a legal parking space and has to park in the no-parking zone is 0.20. On Tuesday, Sam arrives at school and has to park in a no-parking zone. Find the probability that he will get a parking ticket.

Solution

Let

$$N = \text{parking in a no-parking zone} \qquad T = \text{getting a ticket}$$

Then

$$P(T|N) = \frac{P(N \text{ and } T)}{P(N)} = \frac{0.06}{0.20} = 0.30$$

Hence, Sam has a 0.30 probability of getting a parking ticket, given that he parked in a no-parking zone.

The conditional probability of events occurring can also be computed when the data are given in table form, as shown in Example 4–34.

| Example 4–34 | Survey on Women in the Military |

A recent survey asked 100 people if they thought women in the armed forces should be permitted to participate in combat. The results of the survey are shown.

Gender	Yes	No	Total
Male	32	18	50
Female	8	42	50
Total	40	60	100

Find these probabilities.

a. The respondent answered yes, given that the respondent was a female.

b. The respondent was a male, given that the respondent answered no.

Solution

Let

$$M = \text{respondent was a male} \qquad Y = \text{respondent answered yes}$$
$$F = \text{respondent was a female} \qquad N = \text{respondent answered no}$$

a. The problem is to find $P(Y|F)$. The rule states

$$P(Y|F) = \frac{P(F \text{ and } Y)}{P(F)}$$

The probability $P(F \text{ and } Y)$ is the number of females who responded yes, divided by the total number of respondents:

$$P(F \text{ and } Y) = \frac{8}{100}$$

The probability $P(F)$ is the probability of selecting a female:

$$P(F) = \frac{50}{100}$$

Then

$$P(Y|F) = \frac{P(F \text{ and } Y)}{P(F)} = \frac{8/100}{50/100}$$

$$= \frac{8}{100} \div \frac{50}{100} = \frac{\overset{4}{\cancel{8}}}{\underset{1}{\cancel{100}}} \cdot \frac{\overset{1}{\cancel{100}}}{\underset{25}{\cancel{50}}} = \frac{4}{25}$$

b. The problem is to find $P(M|N)$.

$$P(M|N) = \frac{P(N \text{ and } M)}{P(N)} = \frac{18/100}{60/100}$$

$$= \frac{18}{100} \div \frac{60}{100} = \frac{\overset{3}{\cancel{18}}}{\underset{1}{\cancel{100}}} \cdot \frac{\overset{1}{\cancel{100}}}{\underset{10}{\cancel{60}}} = \frac{3}{10}$$

The Venn diagram for conditional probability is shown in Figure 4–7. In this case,

$$P(B|A) = \frac{P(A \text{ and } B)}{P(A)}$$

which is represented by the area in the intersection or overlapping part of the circles A and B, divided by the area of circle A. The reasoning here is that if you assume A has occurred, then A becomes the sample space for the next calculation and is the denominator of the probability fraction $\dfrac{P(A \text{ and } B)}{P(A)}$. The numerator $P(A \text{ and } B)$ represents the probability of the part of B that is contained in A. Hence, $P(A \text{ and } B)$ becomes the numerator of the probability fraction $\dfrac{P(A \text{ and } B)}{P(A)}$. Imposing a condition reduces the sample space.

Probabilities for "At Least"

The multiplication rules can be used with the complementary event rule (Section 4–1) to simplify solving probability problems involving "at least." Examples 4–35, 4–36, and 4–37 illustrate how this is done.

Figure 4–7

Venn Diagram for Conditional Probability

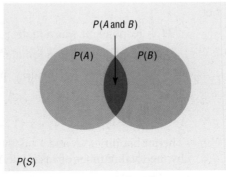

$$P(B|A) = \frac{P(A \text{ and } B)}{P(A)}$$

| Example 4–35 | **Drawing Cards** |

A game is played by drawing 4 cards from an ordinary deck and replacing each card after it is drawn. Find the probability that at least 1 ace is drawn.

Solution

It is much easier to find the probability that no aces are drawn (i.e., losing) and then subtract that value from 1 than to find the solution directly, because that would involve finding the probability of getting 1 ace, 2 aces, 3 aces, and 4 aces and then adding the results.

Let E = at least 1 ace is drawn and $\overline{E}$ = no aces drawn. Then

$$P(\overline{E}) = \frac{48}{52} \cdot \frac{48}{52} \cdot \frac{48}{52} \cdot \frac{48}{52}$$

$$= \frac{12}{13} \cdot \frac{12}{13} \cdot \frac{12}{13} \cdot \frac{12}{13} = \frac{20{,}736}{28{,}561}$$

Hence,

$$P(E) = 1 - P(\overline{E})$$

$$P(\text{winning}) = 1 - P(\text{losing}) = 1 - \frac{20{,}736}{28{,}561} = \frac{7825}{28{,}561} \approx 0.27$$

or a hand with at least 1 ace will win about 27% of the time.

| Example 4–36 | **Tossing Coins** |

A coin is tossed 5 times. Find the probability of getting at least 1 tail.

Solution

It is easier to find the probability of the complement of the event, which is "all heads," and then subtract the probability from 1 to get the probability of at least 1 tail.

$$P(E) = 1 - P(\overline{E})$$

$$P(\text{at least 1 tail}) = 1 - P(\text{all heads})$$

$$P(\text{all heads}) = (\tfrac{1}{2})^5 = \tfrac{1}{32}$$

Hence,

$$P(\text{at least 1 tail}) = 1 - \tfrac{1}{32} = \tfrac{31}{32}$$

| Example 4–37 |

The Neckware Association of America reported that 3% of ties sold in the United States are bow ties. If 4 customers who purchased a tie are randomly selected, find the probability that at least 1 purchased a bow tie.

Solution

Let E = at least 1 bow tie is purchased and $\overline{E}$ = no bow ties are purchased. Then

$$P(E) = 0.03 \qquad \text{and} \qquad P(\overline{E}) = 1 - 0.03 = 0.97$$

$P(\text{no bow ties are purchased}) = (0.97)(0.97)(0.97)(0.97) \approx 0.885$; hence,
$P(\text{at least one bow tie is purchased}) = 1 - 0.885 = 0.115$.

Similar methods can be used for problems involving "at most."

Applying the Concepts **4–3**

Guilty or Innocent?

In July 1964, an elderly woman was mugged in Costa Mesa, California. In the vicinity of the crime a tall, bearded man sat waiting in a yellow car. Shortly after the crime was committed, a young, tall woman, wearing her blond hair in a ponytail, was seen running from the scene of the crime and getting into the car, which sped off. The police broadcast a description of the suspected muggers. Soon afterward, a couple fitting the description was arrested and convicted of the crime. Although the evidence in the case was largely circumstantial, the two people arrested were nonetheless convicted of the crime. The prosecutor based his entire case on basic probability theory, showing the unlikeness of another couple being in that area while having all the same characteristics that the elderly woman described. The following probabilities were used.

Characteristic	Assumed probability
Drives yellow car	1 out of 12
Man over 6 feet tall	1 out of 10
Man wearing tennis shoes	1 out of 4
Man with beard	1 out of 11
Woman with blond hair	1 out of 3
Woman with hair in a ponytail	1 out of 13
Woman over 6 feet tall	1 out of 100

1. Compute the probability of another couple being in that area with the same characteristics.
2. Would you use the addition or multiplication rule? Why?
3. Are the characteristics independent or dependent?
4. How are the computations affected by the assumption of independence or dependence?
5. Should any court case be based solely on probabilities?
6. Would you convict the couple who was arrested even if there were no eyewitnesses?
7. Comment on why in today's justice system no person can be convicted solely on the results of probabilities.
8. In actuality, aren't most court cases based on uncalculated probabilities?

See pages 257 and 258 for the answers.

Exercises 4–3

1. State which events are independent and which are dependent.

   a. Tossing a coin and drawing a card from a deck

   b. Drawing a ball from an urn, not replacing it, and then drawing a second ball

   c. Getting a raise in salary and purchasing a new car

   d. Driving on ice and having an accident

   e. Having a large shoe size and having a high IQ

   f. A father being left-handed and a daughter being left-handed

   g. Smoking excessively and having lung cancer

   h. Eating an excessive amount of ice cream and smoking an excessive amount of cigarettes

2. **Exercise** If 37% of high school students said that they exercise regularly, find the probability that 5 randomly selected high school students will say that they exercise regularly. Would you consider this event likely or unlikely to occur? Explain your answer.

3. **Video and Computer Games** Sixty-nine percent of U.S. heads of households play video or computer games.

Choose 4 heads of households at random. Find the probability that

a. None play video or computer games

b. All four do

Source: www.theesa.com

4. **Seat Belt Use** The Gallup Poll reported that 52% of Americans used a seat belt the last time they got into a car. If 4 people are selected at random, find the probability that they all used a seat belt the last time they got into a car.

Source: *100% American.*

5. **Medical Degrees** If 28% of U.S. medical degrees are conferred to women, find the probability that 3 randomly selected medical school graduates are men. Would you consider this event likely or unlikely to occur? Explain your answer.

6. **Prison Populations** If 25% of U.S. federal prison inmates are not U.S. citizens, find the probability that 2 randomly selected federal prison inmates will not be U.S. citizens.

Source: *Harper's Index.*

7. **Computer Ownership** At a local university 54.3% of incoming first-year students have computers. If 3 students are selected at random, find the following probabilities.

a. None have computers.

b. At least one has a computer.

c. All have computers.

8. **Cards** If 2 cards are selected from a standard deck of 52 cards without replacement, find these probabilities.

a. Both are spades.

b. Both are the same suit.

c. Both are kings.

9. **MLS Players** Of the 216 players on major league soccer rosters, 80.1% are U.S. citizens. If 3 players are selected at random for an exhibition, what is the probability that all are U.S. citizens?

Source: *USA TODAY.*

10. **Cable Television** In 2006, 86% of U.S. households had cable TV. Choose 3 households at random. Find the probability that

a. None of the 3 households had cable TV

b. All 3 households had cable TV

c. At least 1 of the 3 households had cable TV

Source: www.infoplease.com

11. **Working Women and Computer Use** It is reported that 72% of working women use computers at work. Choose 5 working women at random. Find

a. The probability that at least 1 doesn't use a computer at work

b. The probability that all 5 use a computer in their jobs

Source: www.infoplease.com

12. **Flashlight Batteries** A flashlight has 6 batteries, 2 of which are defective. If 2 are selected at random without replacement, find the probability that both are defective.

13. **Leisure Time Exercise** Only 27% of U.S. adults get enough leisure time exercise to achieve cardiovascular fitness. Choose 3 adults at random. Find the probability that

a. All 3 get enough daily exercise

b. At least 1 of the 3 gets enough exercise

Source: www.infoplease.com

14. **Text Messages via Cell Phones** Thirty-five percent of people who own cell phones use their phones to send and receive text messages. Choose 4 cell phone owners at random. What is the probability that none use their phones for texting?

15. **Customer Purchases** In a department store there are 120 customers, 90 of whom will buy at least 1 item. If 5 customers are selected at random, one by one, find the probability that all will buy at least 1 item.

16. **Drawing Cards** Three cards are drawn from a deck *without* replacement. Find these probabilities.

a. All are jacks.

b. All are clubs.

c. All are red cards.

17. **Scientific Study** In a scientific study there are 8 guinea pigs, 5 of which are pregnant. If 3 are selected at random without replacement, find the probability that all are pregnant.

18. In Exercise 17, find the probability that none are pregnant.

19. **Membership in a Civic Organization** In a civic organization, there are 38 members; 15 are men and 23 are women. If 3 members are selected to plan the July 4th parade, find the probability that all 3 are women. Would you consider this event likely or unlikely to occur? Explain your answer.

20. In Exercise 19, find the probability that all 3 members are men.

21. **Sales** A manufacturer makes two models of an item: model I, which accounts for 80% of unit sales, and model II, which accounts for 20% of unit sales. Because

of defects, the manufacturer has to replace (or exchange) 10% of its model I and 18% of its model II. If a model is selected at random, find the probability that it will be defective.

22. **Student Financial Aid** In a recent year 8,073,000 male students and 10,980,000 female students were enrolled as undergraduates. Receiving aid were 60.6% of the male students and 65.2% of the female students. Of those receiving aid, 44.8% of the males got federal aid and 50.4% of the females got federal aid. Choose 1 student at random. (*Hint:* Make a tree diagram.) Find the probability that the student is

   a. A male student without aid

   b. A male student, given that the student has aid

   c. A female student or a student who receives federal aid

   Source: www.nces.gov

23. **Automobile Insurance** An insurance company classifies drivers as low-risk, medium-risk, and high-risk. Of those insured, 60% are low-risk, 30% are medium-risk, and 10% are high-risk. After a study, the company finds that during a 1-year period, 1% of the low-risk drivers had an accident, 5% of the medium-risk drivers had an accident, and 9% of the high-risk drivers had an accident. If a driver is selected at random, find the probability that the driver will have had an accident during the year.

24. **Defective Items** A production process produces an item. On average, 15% of all items produced are defective. Each item is inspected before being shipped, and the inspector misclassifies an item 10% of the time. What proportion of the items will be "classified as good"? What is the probability that an item is defective given that it was classified as good?

25. **Selecting Colored Balls** Urn 1 contains 5 red balls and 3 black balls. Urn 2 contains 3 red balls and 1 black ball. Urn 3 contains 4 red balls and 2 black balls. If an urn is selected at random and a ball is drawn, find the probability it will be red.

26. **Prison Populations** For a recent year, 0.99 of the incarcerated population is adults and 0.07 is female. If an incarcerated person is selected at random, find the probability that the person is a female given that the person is an adult.

   Source: Bureau of Justice.

27. **Rolling Dice** Roll two standard dice and add the numbers. What is the probability of getting a number larger than 9 for the first time on the third roll?

28. **Model Railroad Circuit** A circuit to run a model railroad has 8 switches. Two are defective. If you select 2 switches at random and test them, find the probability

that the second one is defective, given that the first one is defective.

29. **Country Club Activities** At the Avonlea Country Club, 73% of the members play bridge and swim, and 82% play bridge. If a member is selected at random, find the probability that the member swims, given that the member plays bridge.

30. **College Courses** At a large university, the probability that a student takes calculus and is on the dean's list is 0.042. The probability that a student is on the dean's list is 0.21. Find the probability that the student is taking calculus, given that he or she is on the dean's list.

31. **House Types** In Rolling Acres Housing Plan, 42% of the houses have a deck and a garage; 60% have a deck. Find the probability that a home has a garage, given that it has a deck.

32. **Pizza and Salads** In a pizza restaurant, 95% of the customers order pizza. If 65% of the customers order pizza and a salad, find the probability that a customer who orders pizza will also order a salad.

33. **Gift Baskets** The Gift Basket Store had the following premade gift baskets containing the following combinations in stock.

	Cookies	Mugs	Candy
Coffee	20	13	10
Tea	12	10	12

Choose 1 basket at random. Find the probability that it contains

   a. Coffee or candy

   b. Tea given that it contains mugs

   c. Tea and cookies

   Source: www.infoplease.com

34. **Blood Types and Rh Factors** In addition to being grouped into four types, human blood is grouped by its Rhesus (Rh) factor. Consider the figures below which show the distributions of these groups for Americans.

	O	A	B	AB
Rh+	37%	34%	10%	4%
Rh−	6%	6%	2%	1%

Choose 1 American at random. Find the probability that the person

   a. Is a universal donor, i.e., has O negative blood

   b. Has type O blood given that the person is Rh+

   c. Has A+ or AB− blood

   d. Has Rh− given that the person has type B

   Source: www.infoplease.com

35. Doctor Specialties Below are listed the numbers of doctors in various specialties by gender.

	Pathology	Pediatrics	Psychiatry
Male	12,575	33,020	27,803
Female	5,604	33,351	12,292

Choose 1 doctor at random.

a. Find P (Male|pediatrician).

b. Find P (Pathologist|female).

c. Are the characteristics "female" and "pathologist" independent? Explain.

Source: *World Almanac.*

36. Olympic Medals The medal distribution from the 2004 Summer Olympic Games for the top 23 countries is shown below.

	Gold	Silver	Bronze
United States	35	39	29
Russia	27	27	38
China	32	17	14
Australia	17	16	16
Others	133	136	153

Choose 1 medal winner at random.

a. Find the probability that the winner won the gold medal, given that the winner was from the United States.

b. Find the probability that the winner was from the United States, given that she or he won a gold medal.

c. Are the events "medal winner is from United States" and "gold medal won" independent? Explain.

Source: *New York Times Almanac.*

37. Marital Status of Women According to the *Statistical Abstract of the United States,* 70.3% of females ages 20 to 24 have never been married. Choose 5 young women in this age category at random. Find the probability that

a. None have ever been married

b. At least 1 has been married

Source: *New York Times Almanac.*

38. Fatal Accidents The American Automobile Association (AAA) reports that of the fatal car and truck accidents, 54% are caused by car driver error. If 3 accidents are chosen at random, find the probability that

a. All are caused by car driver error

b. None are caused by car driver error

c. At least 1 is caused by car driver error

Source: *AAA quoted on CNN.*

39. On-Time Airplane Arrivals The greater Cincinnati airport led major U.S. airports in on-time arrivals in the last quarter of 2005 with an 84.3% on-time rate. Choose 5 arrivals at random and find the probability that at least 1 was not on time.

Source: www.census.gov

40. Online Electronic Games Fifty-six percent of electronic gamers play games online, and sixty-four percent of those gamers are female. What is the probability that a randomly selected gamer plays games online and is male?

Source: www.tech.msn.com

41. Reading to Children Fifty-eight percent of American children (ages 3 to 5) are read to every day by someone at home. Suppose 5 children are randomly selected. What is the probability that at least 1 is read to every day by someone at home?

Source: Federal Interagency Forum on Child and Family Statistics.

42. Doctoral Assistantships Of Ph.D. students, 60% have paid assistantships. If 3 students are selected at random, find the probabilities

a. All have assistantships

b. None have assistantships

c. At least 1 has an assistantship

Source: U.S. Department of Education/*Chronicle of Higher Education.*

43. Selecting Cards If 4 cards are drawn from a deck of 52 and not replaced, find the probability of getting at least 1 club.

44. Full-Time College Enrollment The majority (69%) of undergraduate students were enrolled in a 4-year college in a recent year. Eighty-one percent of those enrolled attended full-time. Choose 1 enrolled undergraduate student at random. What is the probability that she or he is a part-time student at a 4-year college?

Source: www.census.gov

45. Family and Children's Computer Games It was reported that 19.8% of computer games sold in 2005 were classified as "family and children's." Choose 5 purchased computer games at random. Find the probability that

a. None of the 5 were family and children's

b. At least 1 of the 5 was family and children's

Source: www.theesa.com

46. Medication Effectiveness A medication is 75% effective against a bacterial infection. Find the probability that if 12 people take the medication, at least 1 person's infection will not improve.

47. Tossing a Coin A coin is tossed 5 times; find the probability of getting at least 1 tail. Would you consider this event likely to happen? Explain your answer.

48. Selecting a Letter of the Alphabet If 3 letters of the alphabet are selected at random, find the probability of getting at least 1 letter x. Letters can be used more than once. Would you consider this event likely to happen? Explain your answer.

49. Rolling a Die A die is rolled 7 times. Find the probability of getting at least one 3. Would you consider this event likely to occur? Explain your answer.

50. High School Grades of First-Year College Students Forty-seven percent of first-year college students enrolled in 2005 had an average grade of A in high school compared to 20 percent of first-year college students in 1970. Choose 6 first-year college students at random enrolled in 2005. Find the probability that

a. All had an A average in high school
b. None had an A average in high school
c. At least 1 had an A average in high school

Source: www.census.gov

51. Rolling a Die If a die is rolled 3 times, find the probability of getting at least 1 even number.

52. Selecting a Flower In a large vase, there are 8 roses, 5 daisies, 12 lilies, and 9 orchids. If 4 flowers are selected at random, find the probability that at least 1 of the flowers is a rose. Would you consider this event likely to occur? Explain your answer.

Extending the Concepts

53. Let A and B be two mutually exclusive events. Are A and B independent events? Explain your answer.

54. Types of Vehicles The Bargain Auto Mall has the following cars in stock.

	SUV	Compact	Mid-sized
Foreign	20	50	20
Domestic	65	100	45

Are the events "compact" and "domestic" independent? Explain.

55. College Enrollment An admissions director knows that the probability a student will enroll after a campus visit is 0.55, or $P(E) = 0.55$. While students are on campus visits, interviews with professors are arranged.

The admissions director computes these conditional probabilities for students enrolling after visiting three professors, DW, LP, and MH.

$$P(E|DW) = 0.95 \qquad P(E|LP) = 0.55 \qquad P(E|MH) = 0.15$$

Is there something wrong with the numbers? Explain.

56. Commercials Event A is the event that a person remembers a certain product commercial. Event B is the event that a person buys the product. If $P(B) = 0.35$, comment on each of these conditional probabilities if you were vice president for sales.

a. $P(B|A) = 0.20$
b. $P(B|A) = 0.35$
c. $P(B|A) = 0.55$

4–4 Counting Rules

Many times a person must know the number of all possible outcomes for a sequence of events. To determine this number, three rules can be used: the *fundamental counting rule,* the *permutation rule,* and the *combination rule.* These rules are explained here, and they will be used in Section 4–5 to find probabilities of events.

The first rule is called the **fundamental counting rule.**

The Fundamental Counting Rule

Objective 5

Find the total number of outcomes in a sequence of events, using the fundamental counting rule.

Fundamental Counting Rule

In a sequence of n events in which the first one has k_1 possibilities and the second event has k_2 and the third has k_3, and so forth, the total number of possibilities of the sequence will be

$$k_1 \cdot k_2 \cdot k_3 \cdots k_n$$

Note: In this case *and* means to multiply.

Examples 4–38 through 4–41 illustrate the fundamental counting rule.

| **Example 4–38** | **Tossing a Coin and Rolling a Die** |

A coin is tossed and a die is rolled. Find the number of outcomes for the sequence of events.

Figure 4–8

Complete Tree
Diagram for
Example 4–38

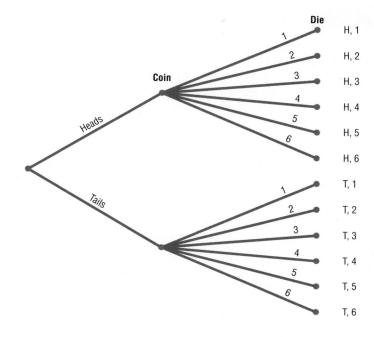

Solution

Since the coin can land either heads up or tails up and since the die can land with any one of six numbers showing face up, there are $2 \cdot 6 = 12$ possibilities. A tree diagram can also be drawn for the sequence of events. See Figure 4–8.

| **Example 4–39** | **Types of Paint** |

A paint manufacturer wishes to manufacture several different paints. The categories include

Color	Red, blue, white, black, green, brown, yellow
Type	Latex, oil
Texture	Flat, semigloss, high gloss
Use	Outdoor, indoor

How many different kinds of paint can be made if you can select one color, one type, one texture, and one use?

Solution

You can choose one color and one type and one texture and one use. Since there are 7 color choices, 2 type choices, 3 texture choices, and 2 use choices, the total number of possible different paints is

Color		**Type**		**Texture**		**Use**	
7	·	2	·	3	·	2	= 84

Example 4–40

Distribution of Blood Types

There are four blood types, A, B, AB, and O. Blood can also be Rh+ and Rh−. Finally, a blood donor can be classified as either male or female. How many different ways can a donor have his or her blood labeled?

Figure 4–9

Complete Tree Diagram for Example 4–40

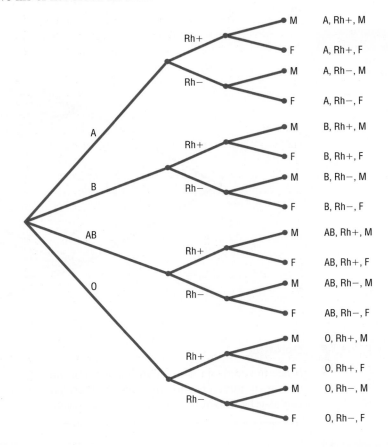

Solution

Since there are 4 possibilities for blood type, 2 possibilities for Rh factor, and 2 possibilities for the gender of the donor, there are $4 \cdot 2 \cdot 2$, or 16, different classification categories, as shown.

Blood type		**Rh**		**Gender**	
4	$\cdot$	2	$\cdot$	2	= 16

A tree diagram for the events is shown in Figure 4–9.

When determining the number of different possibilities of a sequence of events, you must know whether repetitions are permissible.

Example 4–41

Identification Cards

The manager of a department store chain wishes to make four-digit identification cards for her employees. How many different cards can be made if she uses the digits 1, 2, 3, 4, 5, and 6 and repetitions are permitted?

Solution

Since there are 4 spaces to fill on each card and there are 6 choices for each space, the total number of cards that can be made is $6 \cdot 6 \cdot 6 \cdot 6 = 1296$.

___

Now, what if repetitions are not permitted? For Example 4–41, the first digit can be chosen in 6 ways. But the second digit can be chosen in only 5 ways, since there are only five digits left, etc. Thus, the solution is

$$6 \cdot 5 \cdot 4 \cdot 3 = 360$$

The same situation occurs when one is drawing balls from an urn or cards from a deck. If the ball or card is replaced before the next one is selected, then repetitions are permitted, since the same one can be selected again. But if the selected ball or card is not replaced, then repetitions are not permitted, since the same ball or card cannot be selected the second time.

These examples illustrate the fundamental counting rule. In summary: *If repetitions are permitted, then the numbers stay the same going from left to right. If repetitions are not permitted, then the numbers decrease by 1 for each place left to right.*

Two other rules that can be used to determine the total number of possibilities of a sequence of events are the permutation rule and the combination rule.

Factorial Notation

Historical Note

In 1808 Christian Kramp first used the factorial notation.

These rules use *factorial notation*. The factorial notation uses the exclamation point.

$$5! = 5 \cdot 4 \cdot 3 \cdot 2 \cdot 1$$
$$9! = 9 \cdot 8 \cdot 7 \cdot 6 \cdot 5 \cdot 4 \cdot 3 \cdot 2 \cdot 1$$

To use the formulas in the permutation and combination rules, a special definition of $0!$ is needed. $0! = 1$.

Factorial Formulas
For any counting n
$\quad n! = n(n-1)(n-2) \cdots 1$
$\quad 0! = 1$

Permutations

A **permutation** is an arrangement of n objects in a specific order.

___

Examples 4–42 and 4–43 illustrate permutations.

___

Example 4–42   ### Business Location

Suppose a business owner has a choice of 5 locations in which to establish her business. She decides to rank each location according to certain criteria, such as price of the store and parking facilities. How many different ways can she rank the 5 locations?

Solution

There are

$$5! = 5 \cdot 4 \cdot 3 \cdot 2 \cdot 1 = 120$$

different possible rankings. The reason is that she has 5 choices for the first location, 4 choices for the second location, 3 choices for the third location, etc.

In Example 4–42 all objects were used up. But what happens when not all objects are used up? The answer to this question is given in Example 4–43.

Example 4–43

Business Location

Suppose the business owner in Example 4–42 wishes to rank only the top 3 of the 5 locations. How many different ways can she rank them?

Solution

Using the fundamental counting rule, she can select any one of the 5 for first choice, then any one of the remaining 4 locations for her second choice, and finally, any one of the remaining locations for her third choice, as shown.

First choice		**Second choice**		**Third choice**	
5	·	4	·	3	= 60

The solutions in Examples 4–42 and 4–43 are permutations.

Objective 6

Find the number of ways that *r* objects can be selected from *n* objects, using the permutation rule.

Permutation Rule

The arrangement of *n* objects in a specific order using *r* objects at a time is called a *permutation of n objects taking r objects at a time.* It is written as $_nP_r$, and the formula is

$$_nP_r = \frac{n!}{(n-r)!}$$

The notation $_nP_r$ is used for permutations.

$$_6P_4 \text{ means } \frac{6!}{(6-4)!} \quad \text{or} \quad \frac{6!}{2!} = \frac{6 \cdot 5 \cdot 4 \cdot 3 \cdot 2 \cdot 1}{2 \cdot 1} = 360$$

Although Examples 4–42 and 4–43 were solved by the multiplication rule, they can now be solved by the permutation rule.

In Example 4–42, 5 locations were taken and then arranged in order; hence,

$$_5P_5 = \frac{5!}{(5-5)!} = \frac{5!}{0!} = \frac{5 \cdot 4 \cdot 3 \cdot 2 \cdot 1}{1} = 120$$

(Recall that $0! = 1$.)

In Example 4–43, 3 locations were selected from 5 locations, so $n = 5$ and $r = 3$; hence

$$_5P_3 = \frac{5!}{(5-3)!} = \frac{5!}{2!} = \frac{5 \cdot 4 \cdot 3 \cdot \cancel{2} \cdot \cancel{1}}{\cancel{2} \cdot \cancel{1}} = 60$$

Examples 4–44 and 4–45 illustrate the permutation rule.

Example 4–44	**Television News Stories**

A television news director wishes to use 3 news stories on an evening show. One story will be the lead story, one will be the second story, and the last will be a closing story. If the director has a total of 8 stories to choose from, how many possible ways can the program be set up?

Solution

Since order is important, the solution is

$$_8P_3 = \frac{8!}{(8-3)!} = \frac{8!}{5!} = 336$$

Hence, there would be 336 ways to set up the program.

Example 4–45	**School Musical Plays**

A school musical director can select 2 musical plays to present next year. One will be presented in the fall, and one will be presented in the spring. If she has 9 to pick from, how many different possibilities are there?

Solution

Order is important since one play can be presented in the fall and the other play in the spring.

$$_9P_2 = \frac{9!}{(9-2)!} = \frac{9!}{7!} = \frac{9 \cdot 8 \cdot 7!}{7!} = 72$$

There are 72 different possibilities.

Combinations

Suppose a dress designer wishes to select two colors of material to design a new dress, and she has on hand four colors. How many different possibilities can there be in this situation?

Objective 7

Find the number of ways that *r* objects can be selected from *n* objects without regard to order, using the combination rule.

This type of problem differs from previous ones in that the order of selection is not important. That is, if the designer selects yellow and red, this selection is the same as the selection red and yellow. This type of selection is called a *combination*. The difference between a permutation and a combination is that in a combination, the order or arrangement of the objects is not important; by contrast, order *is* important in a permutation. Example 4–46 illustrates this difference.

A selection of distinct objects without regard to order is called a **combination**.

Example 4–46

Letters

Given the letters A, B, C, and D, list the permutations and combinations for selecting two letters.

Solution

The permutations are

AB	BA	CA	DA
AC	BC	CB	DB
AD	BD	CD	DC

In permutations, AB is different from BA. But in combinations, AB is the same as BA since the order of the objects does not matter in combinations. Therefore, if duplicates are removed from a list of permutations, what is left is a list of combinations, as shown.

AB	B̶A̶	C̶A̶	D̶A̶
AC	BC	C̶B̶	D̶B̶
AD	BD	CD	D̶C̶

Hence the combinations of A, B, C, and D are AB, AC, AD, BC, BD, and CD. (Alternatively, BA could be listed and AB crossed out, etc.) The combinations have been listed alphabetically for convenience, but this is not a requirement.

Combinations are used when the order or arrangement is not important, as in the selecting process. Suppose a committee of 5 students is to be selected from 25 students. The five selected students represent a combination, since it does not matter who is selected first, second, etc.

Interesting Fact

The total number of hours spent mowing lawns in the United States each year: 2,220,000,000.

Combination Rule

The number of combinations of *r* objects selected from *n* objects is denoted by $_nC_r$ and is given by the formula

$$_nC_r = \frac{n!}{(n-r)!\,r!}$$

| **Example 4–47** | **Combinations** |

How many combinations of 4 objects are there, taken 2 at a time?

Solution

Since this is a combination problem, the answer is

$$_4C_2 = \frac{4!}{(4-2)!2!} = \frac{4!}{2!2!} = \frac{\overset{2}{\cancel{4}} \cdot 3 \cdot \cancel{2!}}{\cancel{2} \cdot 1 \cdot \cancel{2!}} = 6$$

This is the same result shown in Example 4–46.

Notice that the expression for $_nC_r$ is

$$\frac{n!}{(n-r)!r!}$$

which is the formula for permutations with $r!$ in the denominator. In other words,

$$_nC_r = \frac{_nP_r}{r!}$$

This $r!$ divides out the duplicates from the number of permutations, as shown in Example 4–46. For each two letters, there are two permutations but only one combination. Hence, dividing the number of permutations by $r!$ eliminates the duplicates. This result can be verified for other values of n and r. *Note:* $_nC_n = 1$.

| **Example 4–48** | **Book Reviews** |

A newspaper editor has received 8 books to review. He decides that he can use 3 reviews in his newspaper. How many different ways can these 3 reviews be selected?

Solution

$$_8C_3 = \frac{8!}{(8-3)!3!} = \frac{8!}{5!3!} = \frac{8 \cdot 7 \cdot 6}{3 \cdot 2 \cdot 1} = 56$$

There are 56 possibilities.

| **Example 4–49** | **Committee Selection** |

In a club there are 7 women and 5 men. A committee of 3 women and 2 men is to be chosen. How many different possibilities are there?

Solution

Here, you must select 3 women from 7 women, which can be done in $_7C_3$, or 35, ways. Next, 2 men must be selected from 5 men, which can be done in $_5C_2$, or 10, ways. Finally, by the fundamental counting rule, the total number of different ways is $35 \cdot 10 = 350$, since you are choosing both men and women. Using the formula gives

$$_7C_3 \cdot _5C_2 = \frac{7!}{(7-3)!3!} \cdot \frac{5!}{(5-2)!2!} = 350$$

Table 4–1 summarizes the counting rules.

Table 4–1	Summary of Counting Rules	
Rule	**Definition**	**Formula**
Fundamental counting rule	The number of ways a sequence of n events can occur if the first event can occur in k_1 ways, the second event can occur in k_2 ways, etc.	$k_1 \cdot k_2 \cdot k_3 \cdots k_n$
Permutation rule	The number of permutations of n objects taking r objects at a time (order is important)	$_nP_r = \dfrac{n!}{(n-r)!}$
Combination rule	The number of combinations of r objects taken from n objects (order is not important)	$_nC_r = \dfrac{n!}{(n-r)!r!}$

A list of permutations and combinations is found in Table C of Appendix C.

Applying the Concepts **4–4**

Garage Door Openers

Garage door openers originally had a series of four on/off switches so that homeowners could personalize the frequencies that opened their garage doors. If all garage door openers were set at the same frequency, anyone with a garage door opener could open anyone else's garage door.

1. Use a tree diagram to show how many different positions 4 consecutive on/off switches could be in.

After garage door openers became more popular, another set of 4 on/off switches was added to the systems.

2. Find a pattern of how many different positions are possible with the addition of each on/off switch.
3. How many different positions are possible with 8 consecutive on/off switches?
4. Is it reasonable to assume, if you owned a garage door opener with 8 switches, that someone could use his or her garage door opener to open your garage door by trying all the different possible positions?

In 1989 it was reported that the ignition keys for 1988 Dodge Caravans were made from a single blank that had five cuts on it. Each cut was made at one out of five possible levels. In 1988, assume there were 420,000 Dodge Caravans sold in the United States.

5. How many different possible keys can be made from the same key blank?
6. How many different 1988 Dodge Caravans could any one key start?

Look at the ignition key for your car and count the number of cuts on it. Assume that the cuts are made at one of any of five possible levels. Most car companies use one key blank for all their makes and models of cars.

7. Conjecture how many cars your car company sold over recent years, and then figure out how many other cars your car key could start. What would you do to decrease the odds of someone being able to open another vehicle with his or her key?

See page 258 for the answers.

Exercises 4–4

1. **Zip Codes** How many 5-digit zip codes are possible if digits can be repeated? If there cannot be repetitions?

2. **Batting Order** How many ways can a baseball manager arrange a batting order of 9 players?

3. **Video Games** How many different ways can 7 different video game cartridges be arranged on a shelf?

4. **Seating Arrangements** In how many ways can 5 speakers be seated in a row on a stage?

5. **Shampoo Display** A store manager wishes to display 8 different brands of shampoo in a row. How many ways can this be done?

6. **Show Programs** Three bands and two comics are performing for a student talent show. How many different programs (in terms of order) can be arranged? How many if the comics must perform between bands?

7. **Campus Tours** Student volunteers take visitors on a tour of 7 campus buildings. How many different tours are possible? (Assume order is important.)

8. **Radio Station Call Letters** The call letters of a radio station must have 4 letters. The first letter must be a K or a W. How many different station call letters can be made if repetitions are not allowed? If repetitions are allowed?

9. **Identification Tags** How many different 3-digit identification tags can be made if the digits can be used more than once? If the first digit must be a 5 and repetitions are not permitted?

10. **Book Arrangements** A reference encyclopedia has 12 volumes. Disregarding alphabetical or numerical order, in how many ways can the books be arranged on a shelf?

11. **Selection of Officers** Six students are running for the positions of president and vice-president, and five students are running for secretary and treasurer. If the two highest vote getters in each of the two contests are elected, how many winning combinations can there be?

12. **Automobile Trips** There are 2 major roads from city X to city Y and 4 major roads from city Y to city Z. How many different trips can be made from city X to city Z passing through city Y?

13. Evaluate each of these.

    a. $8!$ e. $_7P_5$ i. $_5P_5$

    b. $10!$ f. $_{12}P_4$ j. $_6P_2$

    c. $0!$ g. $_5P_3$

    d. $1!$ h. $_6P_0$

14. **County Assessments** The County Assessment Bureau decides to reassess homes in 8 different areas. How many different ways can this be accomplished?

15. **Sports Car Stripes** How many different 4-color code stripes can be made on a sports car if each code consists of the colors green, red, blue, and white? All colors are used only once.

16. **Manufacturing Tests** An inspector must select 3 tests to perform in a certain order on a manufactured part. He has a choice of 7 tests. How many ways can he perform 3 different tests?

17. **Threatened Species of Reptiles** There are 22 threatened species of reptiles in the United States. In how many ways can you choose 4 to write about? (Order is not important.)

    Source: www.infoplease.com

18. **Inspecting Restaurants** How many different ways can a city health department inspector visit 5 restaurants in a city with 10 restaurants?

19. How many different 4-letter permutations can be formed from the letters in the word *decagon*?

20. **Cell Phone Models** A particular cell phone company offers 4 models of phones, each in 6 different colors and each available with any one of 5 calling plans. How many combinations are possible?

21. **ID Cards** How many different ID cards can be made if there are 6 digits on a card and no digit can be used more than once?

22. **Free-Sample Requests** An online coupon service has 13 offers for free samples. How may different requests are possible if a customer must request exactly 3 free samples? How many are possible if the customer may request up to 3 free samples?

23. **Ticket Selection** How many different ways can 4 tickets be selected from 50 tickets if each ticket wins a different prize?

24. **Movie Selections** The Foreign Language Club is showing a four-movie marathon of subtitled movies. How many ways can they choose 4 from the 11 available?

25. **Task Assignments** How many ways can an adviser choose 4 students from a class of 12 if they are all assigned the same task? How many ways can the students be chosen if they are each given a different task?

26. **Agency Cases** An investigative agency has 7 cases and 5 agents. How many different ways can the cases be assigned if only 1 case is assigned to each agent?

27. **(ans)** Evaluate each expression.

    a. $_5C_2$ *d.* $_6C_2$ *g.* $_3C_3$ *j.* $_4C_3$

    b. $_8C_3$ *e.* $_6C_4$ *h.* $_9C_7$

    c. $_7C_4$ *f.* $_3C_0$ *i.* $_{12}C_2$

28. **Selecting Cards** How many ways can 3 cards be selected from a standard deck of 52 cards, disregarding the order of selection?

29. **Selecting Bracelets** How many ways are there to select 3 bracelets from a box of 10 bracelets, disregarding the order of selection?

30. **Selecting Players** How many ways can 4 baseball players and 3 basketball players be selected from 12 baseball players and 9 basketball players?

31. **Selecting a Committee** How many ways can a committee of 4 people be selected from a group of 10 people?

32. **Selecting Christmas Presents** If a person can select 3 presents from 10 presents under a Christmas tree, how many different combinations are there?

33. **Questions for a Test** How many different tests can be made from a test bank of 20 questions if the test consists of 5 questions?

34. **Promotional Program** The general manager of a fast-food restaurant chain must select 6 restaurants from 11 for a promotional program. How many different possible ways can this selection be done?

35. **Music Program Selections** A jazz band has prepared 18 selections for a concert tour. At each stop they will perform 10. How many different programs are possible? How many programs are possible if they always begin with the same song and end with the same song?

36. **Freight Train Cars** In a train yard there are 4 tank cars, 12 boxcars, and 7 flatcars. How many ways can a train be made up consisting of 2 tank cars, 5 boxcars, and 3 flatcars? (In this case, order is not important.)

37. **Selecting a Committee** There are 7 women and 5 men in a department. How many ways can a committee of 4 people be selected? How many ways can this committee be selected if there must be 2 men and 2 women on the committee? How many ways can this committee be selected if there must be at least 2 women on the committee?

38. **Selecting Cereal Boxes** Wake Up cereal comes in 2 types, crispy and crunchy. If a researcher has 10 boxes of each, how many ways can she select 3 boxes of each for a quality control test?

39. **Hawaiian Words** The Hawaiian alphabet consists of 7 consonants and 5 vowels. How many three-letter "words" are possible if there are never two consonants together and if a word must always end in a vowel?

40. **Selecting a Jury** How many ways can a jury of 6 women and 6 men be selected from 10 women and 12 men?

41. **Selecting a Golf Foursome** How many ways can a foursome of 2 men and 2 women be selected from 10 men and 12 women in a golf club?

42. **Investigative Team** The state narcotics bureau must form a 5-member investigative team. If it has 25 agents from which to choose, how many different possible teams can be formed?

43. **Dominoes** A domino is a flat rectangular block the face of which is divided into two square parts, each part showing from zero to six pips (or dots). Playing a game consists of playing dominoes with a matching number of pips. Explain why there are 28 dominoes in a complete set.

44. **Charity Event Participants** There are 16 seniors and 15 juniors in a particular social organization. In how many ways can 4 seniors and 2 juniors be chosen to participate in a charity event?

45. **Selecting Commercials** How many ways can a person select 7 television commercials from 11 television commercials?

46. **DVD Selection** How many ways can a person select 8 DVDs from a display of 13 DVDs?

47. **Candy Bar Selection** How many ways can a person select 6 candy bars from a list of 10 and 6 salty snacks from a list of 12 to put in a vending machine?

48. **Selecting a Location** An advertising manager decides to have an ad campaign in which 8 special calculators will be hidden at various locations in a shopping mall. If he has 17 locations from which to pick, how many different possible combinations can he choose?

Permutations and Combinations

49. **Selecting Posters** A buyer decides to stock 8 different posters. How many ways can she select these 8 if there are 20 from which to choose?

50. **Test Marketing Products** Anderson Research Company decides to test-market a product in 6 areas. How many different ways can 3 areas be selected in a certain order for the first test?

51. **Selecting Rats** How many different ways can a researcher select 5 rats from 20 rats and assign each to a different test?

52. **Selecting Musicals** How many different ways can a theatrical group select 2 musicals and 3 dramas from 11 musicals and 8 dramas to be presented during the year?

53. Textbook Selections How many different ways can an instructor select 2 textbooks from a possible 17?

54. Tape Selections How many ways can a person select 8 videotapes from 10 videotapes?

55. Public Service Announcements How many different ways can 5 public service announcements be run during 1 hour?

56. Signal Flags How many different signals can be made by using at least 3 different flags if there are 5 different flags from which to select?

57. Dinner Selections How many ways can a dinner patron select 3 appetizers and 2 vegetables if there are 6 appetizers and 5 vegetables on the menu?

58. Air Pollution The Environmental Protection Agency must investigate 9 mills for complaints of air pollution. How many different ways can a representative select 5 of these to investigate this week?

59. Selecting Officers In a board of directors composed of 8 people, how many ways can one chief executive officer, one director, and one treasurer be selected?

Extending the Concepts

60. Selecting Coins How many different ways can you select one or more coins if you have 2 nickels, 1 dime, and 1 half-dollar?

61. People Seated in a Circle In how many ways can 3 people be seated in a circle? 4? n? (*Hint:* Think of them standing in a line before they sit down and/or draw diagrams.)

62. Seating in a Movie Theater How many different ways can 5 people—A, B, C, D, and E—sit in a row at a movie theater if (*a*) A and B must sit together; (*b*) C must sit to the right of, but not necessarily next to, B; (*c*) D and E will not sit next to each other?

63. Poker Hands Using combinations, calculate the number of each poker hand in a deck of cards. (A poker hand consists of 5 cards dealt in any order.)

a. Royal flush   *c.* Four of a kind
b. Straight flush   *d.* Full house

Technology *Step by Step*

TI-83 Plus or TI-84 Plus
Step by Step

Factorials, Permutations, and Combinations

Factorials *n*!

1. Type the value of n.
2. Press **MATH** and move the cursor to PRB, then press **4** for !.
3. Press **ENTER.**

Permutations $_nP_r$

1. Type the value of n.
2. Press **MATH** and move the cursor to PRB, then press **2** for $_nP_r$.
3. Type the value of r.
4. Press **ENTER.**

Combinations $_nC_r$

1. Type the value of n.
2. Press **MATH** and move the cursor to PRB, then press **3** for $_nC_r$.
3. Type the value of r.
4. Press **ENTER.**

```
5!
              120
8 nPr 3
              336
12 nCr 5
              792
```

Calculate 5!, $_8P_3$, and $_{12}C_5$ (Examples 4–42, 4–44, and 4–48 from the text).

Excel
Step by Step

Permutations, Combinations, and Factorials

To find a value of a permutation, for example, $_5P_3$:

1. In an open cell in an Excel worksheet, select the Formulas tab on the toolbar. Then click the Insert function icon ![fx Insert Function].

2. Select the Statistical function category, then the PERMUT function, and click [OK].

3. Type **5** in the Number box.
4. Type **3** in the Number_chosen box and click [OK].

The selected cell will display the answer: 60.

To find a value of a combination, for example, $_5C_3$:

1. In an open cell, select the Formulas tab on the toolbar. Click the Insert function icon.
2. Select the All function category, then the COMBIN function, and click [OK].

3. Type **5** in the Number box.
4. Type **3** in the Number_chosen box and click [OK].

The selected cell will display the answer: 10.

To find a factorial of a number, for example, 7!:

1. In an open cell, select the Formulas tab on the toolbar. Click the Insert function icon.

2. Select the Math & Trig function category, then the FACT function, and click [OK].

3. Type **7** in the Number box and click [OK].

The selected cell will display the answer: 5040.

4–5

Objective **8**

Find the probability of an event, using the counting rules.

Probability and Counting Rules

The counting rules can be combined with the probability rules in this chapter to solve many types of probability problems. By using the fundamental counting rule, the permutation rules, and the combination rule, you can compute the probability of outcomes of many experiments, such as getting a full house when 5 cards are dealt or selecting a committee of 3 women and 2 men from a club consisting of 10 women and 10 men.

Example 4–50

Four Aces

Find the probability of getting 4 aces when 5 cards are drawn from an ordinary deck of cards.

Solution

There are $_{52}C_5$ ways to draw 5 cards from a deck. There is only 1 way to get 4 aces (i.e., $_4C_4$), but there are 48 possibilities to get the fifth card. Therefore, there are 48 ways to get 4 aces and 1 other card. Hence,

$$P(4 \text{ aces}) = \frac{_4C_4 \cdot 48}{_{52}C_5} = \frac{1 \cdot 48}{2,598,960} = \frac{48}{2,598,960} = \frac{1}{54,145}$$

Example 4-51 | Defective Transistors

A box contains 24 transistors, 4 of which are defective. If 4 are sold at random, find the following probabilities.

    a. Exactly 2 are defective.   *c.* All are defective.

    b. None is defective.   *d.* At least 1 is defective.

Solution

There are $_{24}C_4$ ways to sell 4 transistors, so the denominator in each case will be 10,626.

    a. Two defective transistors can be selected as $_4C_2$ and two nondefective ones as $_{20}C_2$. Hence,

$$P(\text{exactly 2 defectives}) = \frac{_4C_2 \cdot {_{20}C_2}}{_{24}C_4} = \frac{1140}{10,626} = \frac{190}{1771}$$

    b. The number of ways to choose no defectives is $_{20}C_4$. Hence,

$$P(\text{no defectives}) = \frac{_{20}C_4}{_{24}C_4} = \frac{4845}{10,626} = \frac{1615}{3542}$$

    c. The number of ways to choose 4 defectives from 4 is $_4C_4$, or 1. Hence,

$$P(\text{all defective}) = \frac{1}{_{24}C_4} = \frac{1}{10,626}$$

    d. To find the probability of at least 1 defective transistor, find the probability that there are no defective transistors, and then subtract that probability from 1.

$$P(\text{at least 1 defective}) = 1 - P(\text{no defectives})$$

$$= 1 - \frac{_{20}C_4}{_{24}C_4} = 1 - \frac{1615}{3542} = \frac{1927}{3542}$$

Example 4-52 | Magazines

A store has 6 *TV Graphic* magazines and 8 *Newstime* magazines on the counter. If two customers purchased a magazine, find the probability that one of each magazine was purchased.

Solution

$$P(1 \text{ } TV \text{ } Graphic \text{ and } 1 \text{ } Newstime) = \frac{_6C_1 \cdot {_8C_1}}{_{14}C_2} = \frac{6 \cdot 8}{91} = \frac{48}{91}$$

| Example 4–53 | Combination Lock |

A combination lock consists of the 26 letters of the alphabet. If a 3-letter combination is needed, find the probability that the combination will consist of the letters ABC in that order. The same letter can be used more than once. (*Note:* A combination lock is really a permutation lock.)

Solution

Since repetitions are permitted, there are $26 \cdot 26 \cdot 26 = 17{,}576$ different possible combinations. And since there is only one ABC combination, the probability is $P(ABC) = 1/26^3 = 1/17{,}576$.

| Example 4–54 | Tennis Tournament |

There are 8 married couples in a tennis club. If 1 man and 1 woman are selected at random to plan the summer tournament, find the probability that they are married to each other.

Solution

Since there are 8 ways to select the man and 8 ways to select the woman, there are $8 \cdot 8$, or 64, ways to select 1 man and 1 woman. Since there are 8 married couples, the solution is $\frac{8}{64} = \frac{1}{8}$.

As indicated at the beginning of this section, the counting rules and the probability rules can be used to solve a large variety of probability problems found in business, gambling, economics, biology, and other fields.

Applying the Concepts **4–5**

Counting Rules and Probability

One of the biggest problems for students when doing probability problems is to decide which formula or formulas to use. Another problem is to decide whether two events are independent or dependent. Use the following problem to help develop a better understanding of these concepts.

Assume you are given a 5-question multiple-choice quiz. Each question has 5 possible answers: A, B, C, D, and E.

1. How many events are there?
2. Are the events independent or dependent?
3. If you guess at each question, what is the probability that you get all of them correct?
4. What is the probability that a person would guess answer A for each question?

Assume that you are given a test in which you are to match the correct answers in the right column with the questions in the left column. You can use each answer only once.

5. How many events are there?
6. Are the events independent or dependent?
7. What is the probability of getting them all correct if you are guessing?
8. What is the difference between the two problems?

See page 258 for the answers.

Speaking of
Statistics

The Mathematics of Gambling

Gambling is big business. There are state lotteries, casinos, sports betting, and church bingos. It seems that today everybody is either watching or playing Texas Hold 'Em Poker.

Using permutations, combinations, and the probability rules, mathematicians can find the probabilities of various gambling games. Here are the probabilities of the various 5-card poker hands.

Hand	Number of ways	Probability
Straight flush	40	0.000015
Four of a kind	624	0.000240
Full house	3,744	0.001441
Flush	5,108	0.001965
Straight	10,200	0.003925
Three of a kind	54,912	0.021129
Two pairs	123,552	0.047539
One pair	1,098,240	0.422569
Less than one pair	1,302,540	0.501177
Total	2,598,960	1.000000

The chance of winning at gambling games can be compared by using what is called the house advantage, house edge, or house percentage. For example, the house advantage for roulette is about 5.26%, which means in the long run, the house wins 5.26 cents on every $1 bet; or you will lose, on average, 5.26 cents on every $1 you bet. The lower the house advantage, the more favorable the game is to you.

For the game of craps, the house advantage is anywhere between 1.4 and 15%, depending on what you bet on. For the game called keno, the house advantage is 29.5%. The house of advantage for Chuck-a-Luck is 7.87%, and for baccarat, it is either 1.36 or 1.17% depending on your bet.

Slot machines have a house advantage anywhere from about 4 to 10% depending on the geographic location, such as Atlantic City, Las Vegas, and Mississippi, and the amount put in the machine, such as 5¢, 25¢, and $1.

Actually, gamblers found winning strategies for the game blackjack or 21 such as card counting. However, the casinos retaliated by using multiple decks and by banning card counters.

Exercises 4–5

1. **Selecting Cards** Find the probability of getting 2 face cards (king, queen, or jack) when 2 cards are drawn from a deck without replacement.

2. **Selecting a Committee** A parent-teacher committee consisting of 4 people is to be formed from 20 parents and 5 teachers. Find the probability that the committee will consist of these people. (Assume that the selection will be random.)

   a. All teachers

   b. 2 teachers and 2 parents

   c. All parents

   d. 1 teacher and 3 parents

3. **Management Seminar** In a company there are 7 executives: 4 women and 3 men. Three are selected to attend a management seminar. Find these probabilities.

   a. All 3 selected will be women.

   b. All 3 selected will be men.

   c. 2 men and 1 woman will be selected.

   d. 1 man and 2 women will be selected.

4. Senate Partisanship The composition of the Senate of the 107th Congress is

49 Republicans   1 Independent   50 Democrats

A new committee is being formed to study ways to benefit the arts in education. If 3 Senators are selected at random to head the committee, what is the probability that they will all be Republicans? What is the probability that they will all be Democrats? What is the probability that there will be 1 from each party, including the Independent?

Source: *New York Times Almanac.*

5. Congressional Committee Memberships The composition of the 108th Congress is 51 Republicans, 48 Democrats, and 1 Independent. A committee on aid to higher education is to be formed with 3 Senators to be chosen at random to head the committee. Find the probability that the group of 3 consists of

a. All Republicans

b. All Democrats

c. One Democrat, one Republican, and one Independent

6. Defective Resistors A package contains 12 resistors, 3 of which are defective. If 4 are selected, find the probability of getting

a. 0 defective resistors

b. 1 defective resistor

c. 3 defective resistors

7. Winning Tickets If 50 tickets are sold and 2 prizes are to be awarded, find the probability that one person will win 2 prizes if that person buys 2 tickets.

8. Getting a Full House Find the probability of getting a full house (3 cards of one denomination and 2 of another) when 5 cards are dealt from an ordinary deck.

9. Flight School Graduation At a recent graduation at a naval flight school, 18 Marines, 10 members of the Navy, and 3 members of the Coast Guard got their wings. Choose three pilots at random to feature on a training brochure. Find the probability that there will be

a. 1 of each

b. 0 members of the Navy

c. 3 Marines

10. Selecting Cards The red face cards and the black cards numbered 2–9 are put into a bag. Four cards are drawn at random without replacement. Find the following probabilities:

a. All 4 cards are red.

b. 2 cards are red and 2 cards are black.

c. At least 1 of the cards is red.

d. All 4 cards are black.

11. Socks in a Drawer A drawer contains 11 identical red socks and 8 identical black socks. Suppose that you choose 2 socks at random in the dark.

a. What is the probability that you get a pair of red socks?

b. What is the probability that you get a pair of black socks?

c. What is the probability that you get 2 unmatched socks?

d. Where did the other red sock go?

12. Selecting Books Find the probability of selecting 3 science books and 4 math books from 8 science books and 9 math books. The books are selected at random.

13. Rolling Three Dice When 3 dice are rolled, find the probability of getting a sum of 7.

14. Football Team Selection A football team consists of 20 each freshmen and sophomores, 15 juniors, and 10 seniors. Four players are selected at random to serve as captains. Find the probability that

a. All 4 are seniors

b. There is 1 each: freshman, sophomore, junior, and senior

c. There are 2 sophomores and 2 freshmen

d. At least 1 of the students is a senior

15. Arrangement of Washers Find the probability that if 5 different-sized washers are arranged in a row, they will be arranged in order of size.

16. Using the information in Exercise 63 in Section 4–4, find the probability of each poker hand.

a. Royal flush

b. Straight flush

c. Four of a kind

17. Plant Selection All holly plants are dioecious—a male plant must be planted within 30 to 40 feet of the female plants in order to yield berries. A home improvement store has 12 unmarked holly plants for sale, 8 of which are female. If a homeowner buys 3 plants at random, what is the probability that berries will be produced?

Summary

In this chapter, the basic concepts and rules of probability are explained. The three types of probability are classical, empirical, and subjective. Classical probability uses sample spaces. Empirical probability uses frequency distributions and is based on observation. In subjective probability, the researcher makes an educated guess about the chance of an event occurring.

A probability event consists of one or more outcomes of a probability experiment. Two events are said to be mutually exclusive if they cannot occur at the same time. Events can also be classified as independent or dependent. If events are independent, whether or not the first event occurs does not affect the probability of the next event occurring. If the probability of the second event occurring is changed by the occurrence of the first event, then the events are dependent. The complement of an event is the set of outcomes in the sample space that are not included in the outcomes of the event itself. Complementary events are mutually exclusive.

Probability problems can be solved by using the addition rules, the multiplication rules, and the complementary event rules.

Finally, the fundamental counting rule, the permutation rule, and the combination rule can be used to determine the number of outcomes of events; then these numbers can be used to determine the probabilities of events.

Important Terms

classical probability 194

combination 237

complement of an event 197

compound event 194

conditional probability 221

dependent events 221

empirical probability 199

equally likely events 194

event 193

fundamental counting rule 232

independent events 219

law of large numbers 202

mutually exclusive events 207

outcome 191

permutation 235

probability 190

probability experiment 191

sample space 191

simple event 193

subjective probability 202

tree diagram 193

Venn diagrams 198

Important Formulas

Formula for classical probability:

$$P(E) = \frac{\text{number of outcomes in } E}{\text{total number of outcomes in sample space}} = \frac{n(E)}{n(S)}$$

Formula for empirical probability:

$$P(E) = \frac{\text{frequency for class}}{\text{total frequencies in distribution}} = \frac{f}{n}$$

Addition rule 1, for two mutually exclusive events:

$$P(A \text{ or } B) = P(A) + P(B)$$

Addition rule 2, for events that are not mutually exclusive:

$$P(A \text{ or } B) = P(A) + P(B) - P(A \text{ and } B)$$

Multiplication rule 1, for independent events:

$$P(A \text{ and } B) = P(A) \cdot P(B)$$

Multiplication rule 2, for dependent events:

$$P(A \text{ and } B) = P(A) \cdot P(B|A)$$

Formula for conditional probability:

$$P(B|A) = \frac{P(A \text{ and } B)}{P(A)}$$

Formula for complementary events:

$$P(\overline{E}) = 1 - P(E) \quad \text{or} \quad P(E) = 1 - P(\overline{E})$$
$$\text{or} \quad P(E) + P(\overline{E}) = 1$$

Fundamental counting rule: In a sequence of n events in which the first one has k_1 possibilities, the second event has k_2 possibilities, the third has k_3 possibilities, etc., the total number possibilities of the sequence will be

$$k_1 \cdot k_2 \cdot k_3 \cdots k_n$$

Permutation rule: The number of permutations of n objects taking r objects at a time when order is important is

$$_nP_r = \frac{n!}{(n-r)!}$$

Combination rule: The number of combinations of r objects selected from n objects when order is not important is

$$_nC_r = \frac{n!}{(n-r)!r!}$$

Review Exercises

1. When a standard die is rolled, find the probability of getting
   a. A 5
   b. A number larger than 2
   c. An odd number

2. Selecting a Card When a card is selected from a deck, find the probability of getting
   a. A club
   b. A face card or a heart
   c. A 6 and a spade
   d. A king
   e. A red card

3. Software Selection The top-10 selling computer software titles last year consisted of 3 for doing taxes, 5 antivirus or security programs, and 2 "other." Choose one title at random.
   a. What is the probability that it is not used for doing taxes?
   b. What is the probability that it is used for taxes or is one of the "other" programs?

   Source: www.infoplease.com

4. A six-sided die is printed with the numbers 1, 2, 3, 5, 8, and 13. Roll the die once—what is the probability of getting an even number? Roll the die twice and add the numbers. What is the probability of getting an odd sum on the dice?

5. Cordless Phone Survey A recent survey indicated that in a town of 1500 households, 850 had cordless telephones. If a household is randomly selected, find the probability that it has a cordless telephone.

6. Purchasing Sweaters During a sale at a men's store, 16 white sweaters, 3 red sweaters, 9 blue sweaters, and 7 yellow sweaters were purchased. If a customer is selected at random, find the probability that he bought
   a. A blue sweater
   b. A yellow or a white sweater
   c. A red, a blue, or a yellow sweater
   d. A sweater that was not white

7. Budget Rental Cars Cheap Rentals has nothing but budget cars for rental. The probability that a car has air conditioning is 0.5, and the probability that a car has a CD player is 0.37. The probability that a car has both air conditioning and a CD player is 0.06. What is the probability that a randomly selected car has neither air conditioning nor a CD player?

8. Rolling Two Dice When two dice are rolled, find the probability of getting
   a. A sum of 5 or 6
   b. A sum greater than 9
   c. A sum less than 4 or greater than 9
   d. A sum that is divisible by 4
   e. A sum of 14
   f. A sum less than 13

9. Car and Boat Ownership The probability that a person owns a car is 0.80, that a person owns a boat is 0.30, and that a person owns both a car and a boat is 0.12. Find the probability that a person owns either a boat or a car.

10. Car Purchases There is a 0.39 probability that John will purchase a new car, a 0.73 probability that Mary will purchase a new car, and a 0.36 probability that both will purchase a new car. Find the probability that neither will purchase a new car.

11. Online Course Selection Roughly 1 in 6 students enrolled in higher education took at least one online course last fall. Choose 5 enrolled students at random. Find the probability that
   a. All 5 took online courses
   b. None of the 5 took a course online
   c. At least 1 took an online course

   Source: www.encarta.msn.com

12. Borrowing Books Of Americans using library services, 67% borrow books. If 5 patrons are chosen at random, what is the probability that all borrowed books? That none borrowed books?

   Source: American Library Association.

13. **Drawing Cards** Three cards are drawn from an ordinary deck *without* replacement. Find the probability of getting

    a. All black cards
    b. All spades
    c. All queens

14. **Coin Toss and Card Drawn** A coin is tossed and a card is drawn from a deck. Find the probability of getting

    a. A head and a 6
    b. A tail and a red card
    c. A head and a club

15. **Movie Releases** The top five countries for movie releases so far this year are the United States with 471 releases, United Kingdom with 386, Japan with 79, Germany with 316, and France with 132. Choose one new release at random. Find the probability that it is

    a. European
    b. From the United States
    c. German or French
    d. German given that it is European

    Source: www.showbizdata.com

16. **Factory Output** A manufacturing company has three factories: X, Y, and Z. The daily output of each is shown here.

Product	Factory X	Factory Y	Factory Z
TVs	18	32	15
Stereos	6	20	13

    If one item is selected at random, find these probabilities.

    a. It was manufactured at factory X or is a stereo.
    b. It was manufactured at factory Y or factory Z.
    c. It is a TV or was manufactured at factory Z.

17. **Effectiveness of Vaccine** A vaccine has a 90% probability of being effective in preventing a certain disease. The probability of getting the disease if a person is not vaccinated is 50%. In a certain geographic region, 25% of the people get vaccinated. If a person is selected at random, find the probability that he or she will contract the disease.

18. **Television Models** A manufacturer makes three models of a television set, models A, B, and C. A store sells 40% of model A sets, 40% of model B sets, and 20% of model C sets. Of model A sets, 3% have stereo sound; of model B sets, 7% have stereo sound; and of model C sets, 9% have stereo sound. If a set is sold at random, find the probability that it has stereo sound.

19. **Car Purchase** The probability that Sue will live on campus and buy a new car is 0.37. If the probability that she will live on campus is 0.73, find the probability that she will buy a new car, given that she lives on campus.

20. **Applying Shipping Labels** Four unmarked packages have lost their shipping labels, and you must reapply

them. What is the probability that you apply the labels and get all four of them correct? Exactly three correct? Exactly two? At least one correct?

21. **Health Club Membership** Of the members of the Blue River Health Club, 43% have a lifetime membership and exercise regularly (three or more times a week). If 75% of the club members exercise regularly, find the probability that a randomly selected member is a life member, given that he or she exercises regularly.

22. **Bad Weather** The probability that it snows and the bus arrives late is 0.023. José hears the weather forecast, and there is a 40% chance of snow tomorrow. Find the probability that the bus will be late, given that it snows.

23. **Education Level and Smoking** At a large factory, the employees were surveyed and classified according to their level of education and whether they smoked. The data are shown in the table.

	Educational level		
Smoking habit	Not high school graduate	High school graduate	College graduate
Smoke	6	14	19
Do not smoke	18	7	25

    If an employee is selected at random, find these probabilities.

    a. The employee smokes, given that he or she graduated from college.
    b. Given that the employee did not graduate from high school, he or she is a smoker.

24. **War Veterans** Approximately 11% of the civilian population are veterans. Choose 5 civilians at random. What is the probability that none are veterans? What is the probability that at least 1 is a veteran?

    Source: www.factfinder.census.gov

25. **DVD Players** Eighty-one percent of U.S. households have DVD players. Choose 6 households at random. What is the probability that at least one does not have a DVD player?

    Source: www.infoplease.com

26. **Chronic Sinusitis** The U.S. Department of Health and Human Services reports that 15% of Americans have chronic sinusitis. If 5 people are selected at random, find the probability that at least 1 has chronic sinusitis.

    Source: *100% American.*

27. **Automobile License Plate** An automobile license plate consists of 3 letters followed by 4 digits. How many different plates can be made if repetitions are allowed? If repetitions are not allowed? If repetitions are allowed in the letters but not in the digits?

28. Types of Copy Paper White copy paper is offered in 5 different strengths and 11 different degrees of brightness, recycled or not, and acid-free or not. How many different types of paper are available for order?

29. Baseball Players How many ways can 3 outfielders and 4 infielders be chosen from 5 outfielders and 7 infielders?

30. Computer Operators How many different ways can 8 computer operators be seated in a row?

31. Student Representatives How many ways can a student select 2 electives from a possible choice of 10 electives?

32. Committee Representation There are 6 Republican, 5 Democrat, and 4 Independent candidates. How many different ways can a committee of 3 Republicans, 2 Democrats, and 1 Independent be selected?

33. Song Selections A promotional MP3 player is available with the capacity to store 100 songs which can be reordered at the push of a button. How many different arrangements of these songs are possible? (*Note:* Factorials get very big, very fast! How large a factorial will your calculator calculate?)

34. Employee Health Care Plans A new employee has a choice of 5 health care plans, 3 retirement plans, and 2 different expense accounts. If a person selects one of each option, how many different options does he or she have?

35. Course Enrollment There are 12 students who wish to enroll in a particular course. There are only 4 seats left in the classroom. How many different ways can 4 students be selected to attend the class?

36. Candy Selection A candy store allows customers to select 3 different candies to be packaged and mailed. If there are 13 varieties available, how many possible selections can be made?

37. Book Selection If a student can select 5 novels from a reading list of 20 for a course in literature, how many different possible ways can this selection be done?

38. Course Selection If a student can select one of 3 language courses, one of 5 mathematics courses, and one of 4 history courses, how many different schedules can be made?

39. License Plates License plates are to be issued with 3 letters followed by 4 single digits. How many such license plates are possible? If the plates are issued at random, what is the probability that the license plate says USA followed by a number that is divisible by 5?

40. Leisure Activities A newspaper advertises 5 different movies, 3 plays, and 2 baseball games for the weekend. If a couple selects 3 activities, find the probability that they attend 2 plays and 1 movie.

41. Territorial Selection Several territories and colonies today are still under the jurisdiction of another country. France holds the most with 16 territories, the United Kingdom has 15, the United States has 14, and several other countries have territories as well. Choose 3 territories at random from those held by France, the United Kingdom, and the United States. What is the probability that all 3 belong to the same country?

Source: www.infoplease.com

42. Yahtzee Yahtzee is a game played with 5 dice. Players attempt to score points by rolling various combinations. When all 5 dice show the same number, it is called a *Yahtzee* and scores 50 points for the first one and 100 points for each subsequent Yahtzee in the same game. What is the probability that a person throws a Yahtzee on the very first roll? What is the probability that a person throws two Yahtzees on two successive turns?

43. Personnel Classification For a survey, a subject can be classified as follows:

Gender: male or female

Martial status: single, married, widowed, divorced

Occupation: administration, faculty, staff

Draw a tree diagram for the different ways a person can be classified.

Statistics Today

Would You Bet Your Life?—Revisited

In his book *Probabilities in Everyday Life*, John D. McGervey states that the chance of being killed on any given commercial airline flight is almost 1 in 1 million and that the chance of being killed during a transcontinental auto trip is about 1 in 8000. The corresponding probabilities are $1/1,000,000 = 0.000001$ as compared to $1/8000 = 0.000125$. Since the second number is 125 times greater than the first number, you have a much higher risk driving than flying across the United States.

Chapter Quiz

Determine whether each statement is true or false. If the statement is false, explain why.

1. Subjective probability has little use in the real world.

2. Classical probability uses a frequency distribution to compute probabilities.

3. In classical probability, all outcomes in the sample space are equally likely.

4. When two events are not mutually exclusive, $P(A \text{ or } B) = P(A) + P(B)$.

5. If two events are dependent, they must have the same probability of occurring.

6. An event and its complement can occur at the same time.

7. The arrangement ABC is the same as BAC for combinations.

8. When objects are arranged in a specific order, the arrangement is called a combination.

Select the best answer.

9. The probability that an event happens is 0.42. What is the probability that the event won't happen?
   a. −0.42   c. 0
   b. 0.58   d. 1

10. When a meteorologist says that there is a 30% chance of showers, what type of probability is the person using?
    a. Classical   c. Relative
    b. Empirical   d. Subjective

11. The sample space for tossing 3 coins consists of how many outcomes?
    a. 2   c. 6
    b. 4   d. 8

12. The complement of guessing 5 correct answers on a 5-question true/false exam is
    a. Guessing 5 incorrect answers
    b. Guessing at least 1 incorrect answer
    c. Guessing at least 1 correct answer
    d. Guessing no incorrect answers

13. When two dice are rolled, the sample space consists of how many events?
    a. 6   c. 36
    b. 12   d. 54

14. What is $_nP_0$?
    a. 0   c. n
    b. 1   d. It cannot be determined.

15. What is the number of permutations of 6 different objects taken all together?
    a. 0   c. 36
    b. 1   d. 720

16. What is 0!?
    a. 0   c. Undefined
    b. 1   d. 10

17. What is $_nC_n$?
    a. 0   c. n
    b. 1   d. It cannot be determined.

Complete the following statements with the best answer.

18. The set of all possible outcomes of a probability experiment is called the _____.

19. The probability of an event can be any number between and including _____ and _____.

20. If an event cannot occur, its probability is _____.

21. The sum of the probabilities of the events in the sample space is _____.

22. When two events cannot occur at the same time, they are said to be _____.

23. When a card is drawn, find the probability of getting
    a. A jack
    b. A 4
    c. A card less than 6 (an ace is considered above 6)

24. **Selecting a Card** When a card is drawn from a deck, find the probability of getting
    a. A diamond   d. A king
    b. A 5 or a heart   e. A red card
    c. A 5 and a heart

25. **Selecting a Sweater** At a men's clothing store, 12 men purchased blue golf sweaters, 8 purchased green sweaters, 4 purchased gray sweaters, and 7 bought black sweaters. If a customer is selected at random, find the probability that he purchased
    a. A blue sweater
    b. A green or gray sweater
    c. A green or black or blue sweater
    d. A sweater that was not black

26. **Rolling Dice** When 2 dice are rolled, find the probability of getting
    a. A sum of 6 or 7
    b. A sum greater than 8
    c. A sum less than 3 or greater than 8
    d. A sum that is divisible by 3
    e. A sum of 16
    f. A sum less than 11

27. Appliance Ownership The probability that a person owns a microwave oven is 0.75, that a person owns a compact disk player is 0.25, and that a person owns both a microwave and a CD player is 0.16. Find the probability that a person owns either a microwave or a CD player, but not both.

28. Starting Salaries Of the physics graduates of a university, 30% received a starting salary of $30,000 or more. If 5 of the graduates are selected at random, find the probability that all had a starting salary of $30,000 or more.

29. Selecting Cards Five cards are drawn from an ordinary deck *without* replacement. Find the probability of getting

  a. All red cards
  b. All diamonds
  c. All aces

30. Scholarships The probability that Samantha will be accepted by the college of her choice and obtain a scholarship is 0.35. If the probability that she is accepted by the college is 0.65, find the probability that she will obtain a scholarship given that she is accepted by the college.

31. New Car Warranty The probability that a customer will buy a car and an extended warranty is 0.16. If the probability that a customer will purchase a car is 0.30, find the probability that the customer will also purchase the extended warranty.

32. Bowling and Club Membership Of the members of the Spring Lake Bowling Lanes, 57% have a lifetime membership and bowl regularly (three or more times a week). If 70% of the club members bowl regularly, find the probability that a randomly selected member is a lifetime member, given that he or she bowls regularly.

33. Work and Weather The probability that Mike has to work overtime and it rains is 0.028. Mike hears the weather forecast, and there is a 50% chance of rain. Find the probability that he will have to work overtime, given that it rains.

34. Education of Factory Employees At a large factory, the employees were surveyed and classified according to their level of education and whether they attend a sports event at least once a month. The data are shown in the table.

| | **Educational level** | | |
Sports event	**High school graduate**	**Two-year college degree**	**Four-year college degree**
Attend	16	20	24
Do not attend	12	19	25

If an employee is selected at random, find the probability that

  a. The employee attends sports events regularly, given that he or she graduated from college (2- or 4-year degree)
  b. Given that the employee is a high school graduate, he or she does not attend sports events regularly

35. Heart Attacks In a certain high-risk group, the chances of a person having suffered a heart attack are 55%. If 6 people are chosen, find the probability that at least 1 will have had a heart attack.

36. Rolling a Die A single die is rolled 4 times. Find the probability of getting at least one 5.

37. Eye Color If 85% of all people have brown eyes and 6 people are selected at random, find the probability that at least 1 of them has brown eyes.

38. Singer Selection How many ways can 5 sopranos and 4 altos be selected from 7 sopranos and 9 altos?

39. Speaker Selection How many different ways can 8 speakers be seated on a stage?

40. Stocking Machines A soda machine servicer must restock and collect money from 15 machines, each one at a different location. How many ways can she select 4 machines to service in 1 day?

41. ID Cards One company's ID cards consist of 5 letters followed by 2 digits. How many cards can be made if repetitions are allowed? If repetitions are not allowed?

42. How many different arrangements of the letters in the word *number* can be made?

43. Physics Test A physics test consists of 25 true/false questions. How many different possible answer keys can be made?

44. Cellular Telephones How many different ways can 5 cellular telephones be selected from 8 cellular phones?

45. Fruit Selection On a lunch counter, there are 3 oranges, 5 apples, and 2 bananas. If 3 pieces of fruit are selected, find the probability that 1 orange, 1 apple, and 1 banana are selected.

46. Cruise Ship Activities A cruise director schedules 4 different movies, 2 bridge games, and 3 tennis games for a 2-day period. If a couple selects 3 activities, find the probability that they attend 2 movies and 1 tennis game.

47. Committee Selection At a sorority meeting, there are 6 seniors, 4 juniors, and 2 sophomores. If a committee of 3 is to be formed, find the probability that 1 of each will be selected.

48. Banquet Meal Choices For a banquet, a committee can select beef, pork, chicken, or veal; baked potatoes or mashed potatoes; and peas or green beans for a vegetable. Draw a tree diagram for all possible choices of a meat, a potato, and a vegetable.

Critical Thinking Challenges

1. **Con Man Game** Consider this problem: A con man has 3 coins. One coin has been specially made and has a head on each side. A second coin has been specially made, and on each side it has a tail. Finally, a third coin has a head and a tail on it. All coins are of the same denomination. The con man places the 3 coins in his pocket, selects one, and shows you one side. It is heads. He is willing to bet you even money that it is the two-headed coin. His reasoning is that it can't be the two-tailed coin since a head is showing; therefore, there is a 50-50 chance of it being the two-headed coin. Would you take the bet? (*Hint:* See Exercise 1 in Data Projects.)

2. **de Méré Dice Game** Chevalier de Méré won money when he bet unsuspecting patrons that in 4 rolls of 1 die, he could get at least one 6, but he lost money when he bet that in 24 rolls of 2 dice, he could get at least a double 6. Using the probability rules, find the probability of each event and explain why he won the majority of the time on the first game but lost the majority of the time when playing the second game. (*Hint:* Find the probabilities of losing each game and subtract from 1.)

3. **Classical Birthday Problem** How many people do you think need to be in a room so that 2 people will have the same birthday (month and day)? You might think it is 366. This would, of course, guarantee it (excluding leap year), but how many people would need to be in a room so that there would be a 90% probability that 2 people would be born on the same day? What about a 50% probability?

   Actually, the number is much smaller than you may think. For example, if you have 50 people in a room, the probability that 2 people will have the same birthday is 97%. If you have 23 people in a room, there is a 50% probability that 2 people were born on the same day!

   The problem can be solved by using the probability rules. It must be assumed that all birthdays are equally likely, but this assumption will have little effect on the answers. The way to find the answer is by using the complementary event rule as P(2 people having the same birthday) $= 1 - P$(all have different birthdays).

   For example, suppose there were 3 people in the room. The probability that each had a different birthday would be

   $$\frac{365}{365} \cdot \frac{364}{365} \cdot \frac{363}{365} = \frac{_{365}P_3}{365^3} = 0.992$$

   Hence, the probability that at least 2 of the 3 people will have the same birthday will be

   $$1 - 0.992 = 0.008$$

   Hence, for k people, the formula is

   P(at least 2 people have the same birthday)

   $$= 1 - \frac{_{365}P_k}{365^k}$$

   Using your calculator, complete the table and verify that for at least a 50% chance of 2 people having the same birthday, 23 or more people will be needed.

Number of people	Probability that at least 2 have the same birthday
1	0.000
2	0.003
5	0.027
10	
15	
20	
21	
22	
23	

4. We know that if the probability of an event happening is 100%, then the event is a certainty. Can it be concluded that if there is a 50% chance of contracting a communicable disease through contact with an infected person, there would be a 100% chance of contracting the disease if 2 contacts were made with the infected person? Explain your answer.

Data Projects

1. **Business and Finance** Select a pizza restaurant and a sandwich shop. For the pizza restaurant look at the menu to determine how many sizes, crust types, and toppings are available. How many different pizza types are possible? For the sandwich shop determine how many breads, meats, veggies, cheeses, sauces, and condiments are available. How many different sandwich choices are possible?

2. **Sports and Leisure** When poker games are shown on television, there are often percentages displayed that show how likely it is that a certain hand will win. Investigate how these percentages are determined. Show an example with two competing hands in a Texas Hold 'em game. Include the percentages that each hand will win after the deal, the flop, the turn, and the river.

3. **Technology** A music player or music organization program can keep track of how many different artists are in a library. First note how many different artists are in your music library. Then find the probability that if 25 songs are selected at random, none will have the same artist.

4. **Health and Wellness** Assume that the gender distribution of babies is such that one-half the time females are born and one-half the time males are born. In a family of 3 children, what is the probability that all are girls? In a family of 4? Is it unusual that in a family with 4 children all would be girls? In a family of 5?

5. **Politics and Economics** Consider the U.S. Senate. Find out about the composition of any three of the Senate's standing committees. How many different committees of Senators are possible, knowing the party composition of the Senate and the number of committee members from each party for each committee?

6. **Your Class** Research the famous Monty Hall probability problem. Conduct a simulation of the Monty Hall problem online using a simulation program or in class using live "contestants." After 50 simulations compare your results to those stated in the research you did. Did your simulation support the conclusions?

Answers to Applying the Concepts

Section 4–1   Tossing a Coin

1. The sample space is the listing of all possible outcomes of the coin toss.

2. The possible outcomes are heads or tails.

3. Classical probability says that a fair coin has a 50-50 chance of coming up heads or tails.

4. The law of large numbers says that as you increase the number of trials, the overall results will approach the theoretical probability. However, since the coin has no "memory," it still has a 50-50 chance of coming up heads or tails on the next toss. Knowing what has already happened should not change your opinion on what will happen on the next toss.

5. The empirical approach to probability is based on running an experiment and looking at the results. You cannot do that at this time.

6. Subjective probabilities could be used if you believe the coin is biased.

7. Answers will vary; however, they should address that a fair coin has a 50-50 chance of coming up heads or tails on the next flip.

Section 4–2   Which Pain Reliever Is Best?

1. There were $192 + 186 + 188 = 566$ subjects in the study.

2. The study lasted for 12 weeks.

3. The variables are the type of pain reliever and the side effects.

4. Both variables are qualitative and nominal.

5. The numbers in the table are exact figures.

6. The probability that a randomly selected person was receiving a placebo is $192/566 = 0.3392$ (about 34%).

7. The probability that a randomly selected person was receiving a placebo or drug A is $(192 + 186)/566 = 378/566 = 0.6678$ (about 67%). These are mutually

exclusive events. The complement is that a randomly selected person was receiving drug B.

8. The probability that a randomly selected person was receiving a placebo or experienced a neurological headache is $(192 + 55 + 72)/566 = 319/566 = 0.5636$ (about 56%).

9. The probability that a randomly selected person was not receiving a placebo or experienced a sinus headache is $(186 + 188)/566 + 11/566 = 385/566 = 0.6802$ (about 68%).

Section 4–3   Guilty or Innocent?

1. The probability of another couple with the same characteristics being in that area is $\frac{1}{12} \cdot \frac{1}{10} \cdot \frac{1}{4} \cdot \frac{1}{11} \cdot \frac{1}{3} \cdot \frac{1}{13} \cdot \frac{1}{100} = \frac{1}{20,592,000}$, assuming the characteristics are independent of one another.

2. You would use the multiplication rule, since we are looking for the probability of multiple events happening together.

3. We do not know if the characteristics are dependent or independent, but we assumed independence for the calculation in question 1.

4. The probabilities would change if there were dependence among two or more events.

5. Answers will vary. One possible answer is that probabilities can be used to explain how unlikely it is to have a set of events occur at the same time (in this case, how unlikely it is to have another couple with the same characteristics in that area).

6. Answers will vary. One possible answer is that if the only eyewitness was the woman who was mugged and the probabilities are accurate, it seems very unlikely that a couple matching these characteristics would be in that area at that time. This might cause you to convict the couple.

7. Answers will vary. One possible answer is that our probabilities are theoretical and serve a purpose when appropriate, but that court cases are based on much more than impersonal chance.

8. Answers will vary. One possible answer is that juries decide whether to convict a defendant if they find evidence "beyond a reasonable doubt" that the person is guilty. In probability terms, this means that if the defendant was actually innocent, then the chance of seeing the events that occurred is so unlikely as to have occurred by chance. Therefore, the jury concludes that the defendant is guilty.

Section 4–4   Garage Door Openers

1. Four on/off switches lead to 16 different settings.

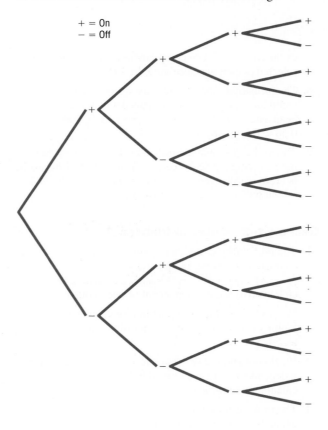

+ = On
− = Off

2. With 5 on/off switches, there are $2^5 = 32$ different settings. With 6 on/off switches, there are $2^6 = 64$ different settings. In general, if there are k on/off switches, there are 2^k different settings.

3. With 8 consecutive on/off switches, there are $2^8 = 256$ different settings.

4. It is less likely for someone to be able to open your garage door if you have 8 on/off settings (probability about 0.4%) than if you have 4 on/off switches (probability about 6.0%). Having 8 on/off switches in the opener seems pretty safe.

5. Each key blank could be made into $5^5 = 3125$ possible keys.

6. If there were 420,000 Dodge Caravans sold in the United States, then any one key could start about $420,000/3125 = 134.4$, or about 134, different Caravans.

7. Answers will vary.

Section 4–5   Counting Rules and Probability

1. There are five different events: each multiple-choice question is an event.

2. These events are independent.

3. If you guess on 1 question, the probability of getting it correct is 0.20. Thus, if you guess on all 5 questions, the probability of getting all of them correct is $(0.20)^5 = 0.00032$.

4. The probability that a person would guess answer A for a question is 0.20, so the probability that a person would guess answer A for each question is $(0.20)^5 = 0.00032$.

5. There are five different events: each matching question is an event.

6. These are dependent events.

7. The probability of getting them all correct if you are guessing is $\frac{1}{5} \cdot \frac{1}{4} \cdot \frac{1}{3} \cdot \frac{1}{2} \cdot \frac{1}{1} = \frac{1}{120} = 0.0083$.

8. The difference between the two problems is that we are sampling without replacement in the second problem, so the denominator changes in the event probabilities.

Discrete Probability Distributions

Objectives

After completing this chapter, you should be able to

1 Construct a probability distribution for a random variable.

2 Find the mean, variance, standard deviation, and expected value for a discrete random variable.

3 Find the exact probability for X successes in n trials of a binomial experiment.

4 Find the mean, variance, and standard deviation for the variable of a binomial distribution.

Outline

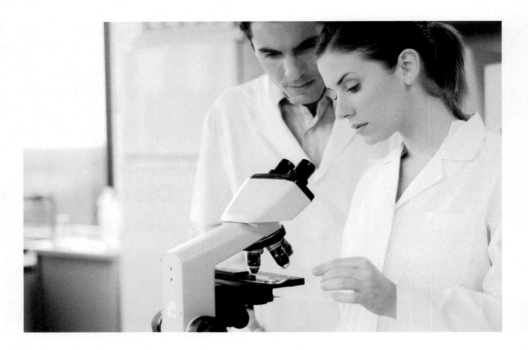

Statistics Today

Is Pooling Worthwhile?

Blood samples are used to screen people for certain diseases. When the disease is rare, health care workers sometimes combine or pool the blood samples of a group of individuals into one batch and then test it. If the test result of the batch is negative, no further testing is needed since none of the individuals in the group has the disease. However, if the test result of the batch is positive, each individual in the group must be tested.

Consider this hypothetical example: Suppose the probability of a person having the disease is 0.05, and a pooled sample of 15 individuals is tested. What is the probability that no further testing will be needed for the individuals in the sample? The answer to this question can be found by using what is called the *binomial distribution*. See Statistics Today—Revisited at the end of the chapter.

This chapter explains probability distributions in general and a specific, often used distribution called the binomial distribution. The Poisson, hypergeometric, and multinomial distributions are also explained.

Introduction

Many decisions in business, insurance, and other real-life situations are made by assigning probabilities to all possible outcomes pertaining to the situation and then evaluating the results. For example, a saleswoman can compute the probability that she will make 0, 1, 2, or 3 or more sales in a single day. An insurance company might be able to assign probabilities to the number of vehicles a family owns. A self-employed speaker might be able to compute the probabilities for giving 0, 1, 2, 3, or 4 or more speeches each week. Once these probabilities are assigned, statistics such as the mean, variance, and standard deviation can be computed for these events. With these statistics, various decisions can be made. The saleswoman will be able to compute the average number of sales she makes per week, and if she is working on commission, she will be able to approximate her weekly income over a period of time, say, monthly. The public speaker will be able to plan ahead and approximate his average income and expenses. The insurance company can use its information to design special computer forms and programs to accommodate its customers' future needs.

This chapter explains the concepts and applications of what is called a *probability distribution.* In addition, a special probability distribution, the *binomial distribution,* is explained.

Probability Distributions

5–1

Objective **1**

Construct a probability distribution for a random variable.

Before probability distribution is defined formally, the definition of a variable is reviewed. In Chapter 1, a *variable* was defined as a characteristic or attribute that can assume different values. Various letters of the alphabet, such as *X, Y,* or *Z,* are used to represent variables. Since the variables in this chapter are associated with probability, they are called *random variables.*

For example, if a die is rolled, a letter such as *X* can be used to represent the outcomes. Then the value that *X* can assume is 1, 2, 3, 4, 5, or 6, corresponding to the outcomes of rolling a single die. If two coins are tossed, a letter, say *Y,* can be used to represent the number of heads, in this case 0, 1, or 2. As another example, if the temperature at 8:00 A.M. is 43° and at noon it is 53°, then the values *T* that the temperature assumes are said to be random, since they are due to various atmospheric conditions at the time the temperature was taken.

A **random variable** is a variable whose values are determined by chance.

Also recall from Chapter 1 that you can classify variables as discrete or continuous by observing the values the variable can assume. If a variable can assume only a specific number of values, such as the outcomes for the roll of a die or the outcomes for the toss of a coin, then the variable is called a *discrete variable.*

Discrete variables have a finite number of possible values or an infinite number of values that can be counted. The word *counted* means that they can be enumerated using the numbers 1, 2, 3, etc. For example, the number of joggers in Riverview Park each day and the number of phone calls received after a TV commercial airs are examples of discrete variables, since they can be counted.

Variables that can assume all values in the interval between any two given values are called *continuous variables.* For example, if the temperature goes from 62 to 78° in a 24-hour period, it has passed through every possible number from 62 to 78. *Continuous random variables are obtained from data that can be measured rather than counted.* Continuous random variables can assume an infinite number of values and can be decimal and fractional values. On a continuous scale, a person's weight might be exactly 183.426 pounds if a scale could measure weight to the thousandths place; however, on a digital scale that measures only to tenths of pounds, the weight would be 183.4 pounds. Examples of continuous variables are heights, weights, temperatures, and time. In this chapter only discrete random variables are used; Chapter 6 explains continuous random variables.

The procedure shown here for constructing a probability distribution for a discrete random variable uses the probability experiment of tossing three coins. Recall that when three coins are tossed, the sample space is represented as TTT, TTH, THT, HTT, HHT, HTH, THH, HHH; and if *X* is the random variable for the number of heads, then *X* assumes the value 0, 1, 2, or 3.

Probabilities for the values of X can be determined as follows:

No heads	**One head**			**Two heads**			**Three heads**
TTT	TTH	THT	HTT	HHT	HTH	THH	HHH
$\frac{1}{8}$	$\frac{1}{8}$	$\frac{1}{8}$	$\frac{1}{8}$	$\frac{1}{8}$	$\frac{1}{8}$	$\frac{1}{8}$	$\frac{1}{8}$
$\frac{1}{8}$		$\frac{3}{8}$			$\frac{3}{8}$		$\frac{1}{8}$

Hence, the probability of getting no heads is $\frac{1}{8}$, one head is $\frac{3}{8}$, two heads is $\frac{3}{8}$, and three heads is $\frac{1}{8}$. From these values, a probability distribution can be constructed by listing the outcomes and assigning the probability of each outcome, as shown here.

Number of heads X	0	1	2	3
Probability $P(X)$	$\frac{1}{8}$	$\frac{3}{8}$	$\frac{3}{8}$	$\frac{1}{8}$

A **discrete probability distribution** consists of the values a random variable can assume and the corresponding probabilities of the values. The probabilities are determined theoretically or by observation.

Discrete probability distributions can be shown by using a graph or a table. Probability distributions can also be represented by a formula. See Exercises 31–36 at the end of this section for examples.

Example 5–1

Rolling a Die

Construct a probability distribution for rolling a single die.

Solution

Since the sample space is 1, 2, 3, 4, 5, 6 and each outcome has a probability of $\frac{1}{6}$, the distribution is as shown.

Outcome X	1	2	3	4	5	6
Probability $P(X)$	$\frac{1}{6}$	$\frac{1}{6}$	$\frac{1}{6}$	$\frac{1}{6}$	$\frac{1}{6}$	$\frac{1}{6}$

Probability distributions can be shown graphically by representing the values of X on the x axis and the probabilities $P(X)$ on the y axis.

Example 5–2

Tossing Coins

Represent graphically the probability distribution for the sample space for tossing three coins.

Number of heads X	0	1	2	3
Probability $P(X)$	$\frac{1}{8}$	$\frac{3}{8}$	$\frac{3}{8}$	$\frac{1}{8}$

Solution

The values that X assumes are located on the x axis, and the values for $P(X)$ are located on the y axis. The graph is shown in Figure 5–1.

Note that for visual appearances, it is not necessary to start with 0 at the origin.

Examples 5–1 and 5–2 are illustrations of *theoretical* probability distributions. You did not need to actually perform the experiments to compute the probabilities. In contrast, to construct actual probability distributions, you must observe the variable over a period of time. They are empirical, as shown in Example 5–3.

Figure 5–1

Probability Distribution for Example 5–2

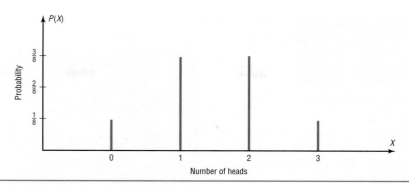

Number of heads

Example 5–3

Baseball World Series

The baseball World Series is played by the winner of the National League and the American League. The first team to win four games wins the World Series. In other words, the series will consist of four to seven games, depending on the individual victories. The data shown consist of the number of games played in the World Series from 1965 through 2005. (There was no World Series in 1994.) The number of games played is represented by the variable X. Find the probability $P(X)$ for each X, construct a probability distribution, and draw a graph for the data.

X	Number of times played
4	8
5	7
6	9
7	$\dfrac{16}{40}$

Solution

The probability $P(X)$ can be computed for each X by dividing the number of games X by the total.

For 4 games, $\frac{8}{40} = 0.200$ For 6 games, $\frac{6}{40} = 0.225$

For 5 games, $\frac{7}{40} = 0.175$ For 7 games, $\frac{16}{40} = 0.400$

The probability distribution is

Number of games X	4	5	6	7
Probability $P(X)$	0.200	0.175	0.225	0.400

The graph is shown in Figure 5–2.

Figure 5–2

Probability Distribution for Example 5–3

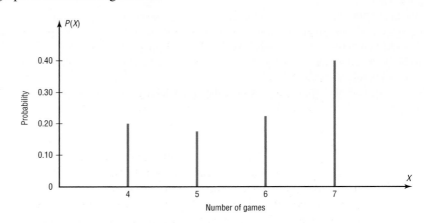

Number of games

Coins, Births, and Other Random (?) Events

Examples of random events such as tossing coins are used in almost all books on probability. But is flipping a coin really a random event?

Tossing coins dates back to ancient Roman times when the coins usually consisted of the Emperor's head on one side (i.e., heads) and another icon such as a ship on the other side (i.e., ships). Tossing coins was used in both fortune telling and ancient Roman games.

A Chinese form of divination called the *I-Ching* (pronounced E-Ching) is thought to be at least 4000 years old. It consists of 64 hexagrams made up of six horizontal lines. Each line is either broken or unbroken, representing the yin and the yang. These 64 hexagrams are supposed to represent all possible situations in life. To consult the I-Ching, a question is asked and then three coins are tossed six times. The way the coins fall, either heads up or heads down, determines whether the line is broken (yin) or unbroken (yang). Once the hexagon is determined, its meaning is consulted and interpreted to get the answer to the question. (*Note:* Another method used to determine the hexagon employs yarrow sticks.)

In the 16th century, a mathematician named Abraham DeMoivre used the outcomes of tossing coins to study what later became known as the normal distribution; however, his work at that time was not widely known.

Mathematicians usually consider the outcomes of a coin toss a random event. That is, each probability of getting a head is $\frac{1}{2}$, and the probability of getting a tail is $\frac{1}{2}$. Also, it is not possible to predict with 100% certainty which outcome will occur. But new studies question this theory. During World War II a South African mathematician named John Kerrich tossed a coin 10,000 times while he was interned in a German prison camp. Unfortunately, the results of his experiment were never recorded, so we don't know the number of heads that occurred.

Several studies have shown that when a coin-tossing device is used, the probability that a coin will land on the same side on which it is placed on the coin-tossing device is about 51%. It would take about 10,000 tosses to become aware of this bias. Furthermore, researchers showed that when a coin is spun on its edge, the coin falls tails up about 80% of the time since there is more metal on the heads side of a coin. This makes the coin slightly heavier on the heads side than on the tails side.

Another assumption commonly made in probability theory is that the number of male births is equal to the number of female births and that the probability of a boy being born is $\frac{1}{2}$ and the probability of a girl being born is $\frac{1}{2}$. We know this is not exactly true.

In the later 1700s, a French mathematician named Pierre Simon Laplace attempted to prove that more males than females are born. He used records from 1745 to 1770 in Paris and showed that the percentage of females born was about 49%. Although these percentages vary somewhat from location to location, further surveys show they are generally true worldwide. Even though there are discrepancies, we generally consider the outcomes to be 50-50 since these discrepancies are relatively small.

Based on this article, would you consider the coin toss at the beginning of a football game fair?

> **Two Requirements for a Probability Distribution**
>
> 1. The sum of the probabilities of all the events in the sample space must equal 1; that is, $\Sigma P(X) = 1$.
> 2. The probability of each event in the sample space must be between or equal to 0 and 1. That is, $0 \le P(X) \le 1$.

The first requirement states that the sum of the probabilities of all the events must be equal to 1. This sum cannot be less than 1 or greater than 1 since the sample space includes *all* possible outcomes of the probability experiment. The second requirement states that the probability of any individual event must be a value from 0 to 1. The reason (as stated in Chapter 4) is that the range of the probability of any individual value can be 0, 1, or any value between 0 and 1. A probability cannot be a negative number or greater than 1.

Example 5–4

Probability Distributions

Determine whether each distribution is a probability distribution.

a.

X	0	5	10	15	20
$P(X)$	$\frac{1}{5}$	$\frac{1}{5}$	$\frac{1}{5}$	$\frac{1}{5}$	$\frac{1}{5}$

c.

X	1	2	3	4
$P(X)$	$\frac{1}{4}$	$\frac{1}{8}$	$\frac{1}{16}$	$\frac{9}{16}$

b.

X	0	2	4	6
$P(X)$	-1.0	1.5	0.3	0.2

d.

X	2	3	7
$P(X)$	0.5	0.3	0.4

Solution

a. Yes, it is a probability distribution.

b. No, it is not a probability distribution, since $P(X)$ cannot be 1.5 or -1.0.

c. Yes, it is a probability distribution.

d. No, it is not, since $\Sigma P(X) = 1.2$.

Many variables in business, education, engineering, and other areas can be analyzed by using probability distributions. Section 5–2 shows methods for finding the mean and standard deviation for a probability distribution.

Applying the Concepts 5–1

Dropping College Courses

Use the following table to answer the questions.

Reason for Dropping a College Course	Frequency	Percentage
Too difficult	45	
Illness	40	
Change in work schedule	20	
Change of major	14	
Family-related problems	9	
Money	7	
Miscellaneous	6	
No meaningful reason	3	

1. What is the variable under study? Is it a random variable?

2. How many people were in the study?

3. Complete the table.

4. From the information given, what is the probability that a student will drop a class because of illness? Money? Change of major?

5. Would you consider the information in the table to be a probability distribution?

6. Are the categories mutually exclusive?

7. Are the categories independent?

8. Are the categories exhaustive?

9. Are the two requirements for a discrete probability distribution met?

See page 295 for the answers.

Exercises 5–1

1. Define and give three examples of a random variable.

2. Explain the difference between a discrete and a continuous random variable.

3. Give three examples of a discrete random variable.

4. Give three examples of a continuous random variable.

5. What is a probability distribution? Give an example.

For Exercises 6 through 11, determine whether the distribution represents a probability distribution. If it does not, state why.

6.
X	2	5	6	8	10
P(X)	$\frac{2}{11}$	$\frac{1}{11}$	$\frac{3}{11}$	$\frac{3}{11}$	$\frac{1}{11}$

7.
X	3	6	8	12
P(X)	0.3	0.5	0.7	−0.8

8.
X	3	6	8
P(X)	−0.3	0.6	0.7

9.
X	1	2	3	4	5
P(X)	$\frac{3}{10}$	$\frac{1}{10}$	$\frac{1}{10}$	$\frac{2}{10}$	$\frac{3}{10}$

10.
X	20	30	40	50
P(X)	0.05	0.35	0.4	0.2

11.
X	5	10	15
P(X)	1.2	0.3	0.5

For Exercises 12 through 18, state whether the variable is discrete or continuous.

12. The speed of a jet airplane

13. The number of cheeseburgers a fast-food restaurant serves each day

14. The number of people who play the state lottery each day

15. The weight of a Siberian tiger

16. The time it takes to complete a marathon

17. The number of mathematics majors in your school

18. The blood pressures of all patients admitted to a hospital on a specific day

For Exercises 19 through 26, construct a probability distribution for the data and draw a graph for the distribution.

19. **Medical Tests** The probabilities that a patient will have 0, 1, 2, or 3 medical tests performed on entering a hospital are $\frac{6}{15}$, $\frac{5}{15}$, $\frac{3}{15}$, and $\frac{1}{15}$, respectively.

20. **Student Volunteers** The probabilities that a student volunteer hosts 1, 2, 3, or 4 prospective first-year students are 0.4, 0.3, 0.2, and 0.1, respectively.

21. **Birthday Cake Sales** The probabilities that a bakery has a demand for 2, 3, 5, or 7 birthday cakes on any given day are 0.35, 0.41, 0.15, and 0.09, respectively.

22. **DVD Rentals** The probabilities that a customer will rent 0, 1, 2, 3, or 4 DVDs on a single visit to the rental store are 0.15, 0.25, 0.3, 0.25, and 0.05, respectively.

23. **Loaded Die** A die is loaded in such a way that the probabilities of getting 1, 2, 3, 4, 5, and 6 are $\frac{1}{2}$, $\frac{1}{6}$, $\frac{1}{12}$, $\frac{1}{12}$, $\frac{1}{12}$, and $\frac{1}{12}$, respectively.

24. **Item Selection** The probabilities that a customer selects 1, 2, 3, 4, and 5 items at a convenience store are 0.32, 0.12, 0.23, 0.18, and 0.15, respectively.

25. **Student Classes** The probabilities that a student is registered for 2, 3, 4, or 5 classes are 0.01, 0.34, 0.62, and 0.03, respectively.

26. **Garage Space** The probabilities that a randomly selected home has garage space for 0, 1, 2, or 3 cars are 0.22, 0.33, 0.37, and 0.08, respectively.

27. **Selecting a Monetary Bill** A box contains three $1 bills, two $5 bills, five $10 bills, and one $20 bill. Construct a probability distribution for the data if x represents the value of a single bill drawn at random and then replaced.

28. **Family with Children** Construct a probability distribution for a family of three children. Let X represent the number of boys.

29. **Drawing a Card** Construct a probability distribution for drawing a card from a deck of 40 cards consisting of 10 cards numbered 1, 10 cards numbered 2, 15 cards numbered 3, and 5 cards numbered 4.

30. **Rolling Two Dice** Using the sample space for tossing two dice, construct a probability distribution for the sums 2 through 12.

Extending the Concepts

A probability distribution can be written in formula notation such as $P(X) = 1/X$, where $X = 2, 3, 6$. The distribution is shown as follows:

X	2	3	6
$P(X)$	$\frac{1}{2}$	$\frac{1}{3}$	$\frac{1}{6}$

For Exercises 31 through 36, write the distribution for the formula and determine whether it is a probability distribution.

31. $P(X) = X/6$ for $X = 1, 2, 3$
32. $P(X) = X$ for $X = 0.2, 0.3, 0.5$
33. $P(X) = X/6$ for $X = 3, 4, 7$
34. $P(X) = X + 0.1$ for $X = 0.1, 0.02, 0.04$
35. $P(X) = X/7$ for $X = 1, 2, 4$
36. $P(X) = X/(X + 2)$ for $X = 0, 1, 2$

5–2   Mean, Variance, Standard Deviation, and Expectation

Objective 2

Find the mean, variance, standard deviation, and expected value for a discrete random variable.

The mean, variance, and standard deviation for a probability distribution are computed differently from the mean, variance, and standard deviation for samples. This section explains how these measures—as well as a new measure called the *expectation*—are calculated for probability distributions.

Mean

In Chapter 3, the mean for a sample or population was computed by adding the values and dividing by the total number of values, as shown in these formulas:

$$\overline{X} = \frac{\Sigma X}{n} \qquad \mu = \frac{\Sigma X}{N}$$

But how would you compute the mean of the number of spots that show on top when a die is rolled? You could try rolling the die, say, 10 times, recording the number of spots, and finding the mean; however, this answer would only approximate the true mean. What about 50 rolls or 100 rolls? Actually, the more times the die is rolled, the better the approximation. You might ask, then, How many times must the die be rolled to get the exact answer? *It must be rolled an infinite number of times.* Since this task is impossible, the previous formulas cannot be used because the denominators would be infinity. Hence, a new method of computing the mean is necessary. This method gives the exact theoretical value of the mean as if it were possible to roll the die an infinite number of times.

Before the formula is stated, an example will be used to explain the concept. Suppose two coins are tossed repeatedly, and the number of heads that occurred is recorded. What will be the mean of the number of heads? The sample space is

HH, HT, TH, TT

Historical Note

A professor, Augustin Louis Cauchy (1789–1857), wrote a book on probability. While he was teaching at the Military School of Paris, one of his students was Napoleon Bonaparte.

and each outcome has a probability of $\frac{1}{4}$. Now, in the long run, you would *expect* two heads (HH) to occur approximately $\frac{1}{4}$ of the time, one head to occur approximately $\frac{1}{2}$ of the time (HT or TH), and no heads (TT) to occur approximately $\frac{1}{4}$ of the time. Hence, on average, you would expect the number of heads to be

$$\tfrac{1}{4} \cdot 2 + \tfrac{1}{2} \cdot 1 + \tfrac{1}{4} \cdot 0 = 1$$

That is, if it were possible to toss the coins many times or an infinite number of times, the *average* of the number of heads would be 1.

Hence, to find the mean for a probability distribution, you must multiply each possible outcome by its corresponding probability and find the sum of the products.

Formula for the Mean of a Probability Distribution

The mean of a random variable with a discrete probability distribution is

$$\mu = X_1 \cdot P(X_1) + X_2 \cdot P(X_2) + X_3 \cdot P(X_3) + \cdots + X_n \cdot P(X_n)$$
$$= \Sigma X \cdot P(X)$$

where $X_1, X_2, X_3, \ldots, X_n$ are the outcomes and $P(X_1), P(X_2), P(X_3), \ldots, P(X_n)$ are the corresponding probabilities.

Note: $\Sigma X \cdot P(X)$ means to sum the products.

Rounding Rule for the Mean, Variance, and Standard Deviation for a Probability Distribution The rounding rule for the mean, variance, and standard deviation for variables of a probability distribution is this: The mean, variance, and standard deviation should be rounded to one more decimal place than the outcome X. When fractions are used, they should be reduced to lowest terms.

Examples 5–5 through 5–8 illustrate the use of the formula.

| Example 5–5 | Rolling a Die |

Find the mean of the number of spots that appear when a die is tossed.

Solution

In the toss of a die, the mean can be computed thus.

Outcome X	1	2	3	4	5	6
Probability $P(X)$	$\frac{1}{6}$	$\frac{1}{6}$	$\frac{1}{6}$	$\frac{1}{6}$	$\frac{1}{6}$	$\frac{1}{6}$

$$\mu = \Sigma X \cdot P(X) = 1 \cdot \tfrac{1}{6} + 2 \cdot \tfrac{1}{6} + 3 \cdot \tfrac{1}{6} + 4 \cdot \tfrac{1}{6} + 5 \cdot \tfrac{1}{6} + 6 \cdot \tfrac{1}{6}$$
$$= \tfrac{21}{6} = 3\tfrac{1}{2} \text{ or } 3.5$$

That is, when a die is tossed many times, the theoretical mean will be 3.5. Note that even though the die cannot show a 3.5, the theoretical average is 3.5.

The reason why this formula gives the theoretical mean is that in the long run, each outcome would occur approximately $\frac{1}{6}$ of the time. Hence, multiplying the outcome by its corresponding probability and finding the sum would yield the theoretical mean. In other words, outcome 1 would occur approximately $\frac{1}{6}$ of the time, outcome 2 would occur approximately $\frac{1}{6}$ of the time, etc.

Example 5–6

Children in a Family

In a family with two children, find the mean of the number of children who will be girls.

Solution

The probability distribution is as follows:

Number of girls X	0	1	2
Probability $P(X)$	$\frac{1}{4}$	$\frac{1}{2}$	$\frac{1}{4}$

Hence, the mean is

$$\mu = \Sigma X \cdot P(X) = 0 \cdot \tfrac{1}{4} + 1 \cdot \tfrac{1}{2} + 2 \cdot \tfrac{1}{4} = 1$$

Example 5–7

Tossing Coins

If three coins are tossed, find the mean of the number of heads that occur. (See the table preceding Example 5–1.)

Solution

The probability distribution is

Number of heads X	0	1	2	3
Probability $P(X)$	$\frac{1}{8}$	$\frac{3}{8}$	$\frac{3}{8}$	$\frac{1}{8}$

The mean is

$$\mu = \Sigma X \cdot P(X) = 0 \cdot \tfrac{1}{8} + 1 \cdot \tfrac{3}{8} + 2 \cdot \tfrac{3}{8} + 3 \cdot \tfrac{1}{8} = \tfrac{12}{8} = 1\tfrac{1}{2} \text{ or } 1.5$$

The value 1.5 cannot occur as an outcome. Nevertheless, it is the long-run or theoretical average.

Example 5–8

Number of Trips of Five Nights or More

The probability distribution shown represents the number of trips of five nights or more that American adults take per year. (That is, 6% do not take any trips lasting five nights or more, 70% take one trip lasting five nights or more per year, etc.) Find the mean.

Number of trips X	0	1	2	3	4
Probability $P(X)$	0.06	0.70	0.20	0.03	0.01

Solution

$$\mu = \Sigma X \cdot P(X)$$
$$= (0)(0.06) + (1)(0.70) + (2)(0.20) + (3)(0.03) + (4)(0.01)$$
$$= 0 + 0.70 + 0.40 + 0.09 + 0.04$$
$$= 1.23 \approx 1.2$$

Hence, the mean of the number of trips lasting five nights or more per year taken by American adults is 1.2.

Fey Manufacturing Co., located in San Francisco, invented the first three-reel, automatic payout slot machine in 1895.

Variance and Standard Deviation

For a probability distribution, the mean of the random variable describes the measure of the so-called long-run or theoretical average, but it does not tell anything about the spread of the distribution. Recall from Chapter 3 that in order to measure this spread or variability, statisticians use the variance and standard deviation. These formulas were used:

$$\sigma^2 = \frac{\Sigma(X-\mu)^2}{N} \qquad \text{or} \qquad \sigma = \sqrt{\frac{\Sigma(X-\mu)^2}{N}}$$

These formulas cannot be used for a random variable of a probability distribution since N is infinite, so the variance and standard deviation must be computed differently.

To find the variance for the random variable of a probability distribution, subtract the theoretical mean of the random variable from each outcome and square the difference. Then multiply each difference by its corresponding probability and add the products. The formula is

$$\sigma^2 = \Sigma[(X-\mu)^2 \cdot P(X)]$$

Finding the variance by using this formula is somewhat tedious. So for simplified computations, a shortcut formula can be used. This formula is algebraically equivalent to the longer one and is used in the examples that follow.

Formula for the Variance of a Probability Distribution

Find the variance of a probability distribution by multiplying the square of each outcome by its corresponding probability, summing those products, and subtracting the square of the mean. The formula for the variance of a probability distribution is

$$\sigma^2 = \Sigma[X^2 \cdot P(X)] - \mu^2$$

The standard deviation of a probability distribution is

$$\sigma = \sqrt{\sigma^2} \qquad \text{or} \qquad \sqrt{\Sigma[X^2 \cdot P(X)] - \mu^2}$$

Remember that the variance and standard deviation cannot be negative.

Example 5–9

Rolling a Die

Compute the variance and standard deviation for the probability distribution in Example 5–5.

Solution

Recall that the mean is $\mu = 3.5$, as computed in Example 5–5. Square each outcome and multiply by the corresponding probability, sum those products, and then subtract the square of the mean.

$$\sigma^2 = (1^2 \cdot \tfrac{1}{6} + 2^2 \cdot \tfrac{1}{6} + 3^2 \cdot \tfrac{1}{6} + 4^2 \cdot \tfrac{1}{6} + 5^2 \cdot \tfrac{1}{6} + 6^2 \cdot \tfrac{1}{6}) - (3.5)^2 = 2.9$$

To get the standard deviation, find the square root of the variance.

$$\sigma = \sqrt{2.9} = 1.7$$

Example 5–10	**Selecting Numbered Balls**

A box contains 5 balls. Two are numbered 3, one is numbered 4, and two are numbered 5. The balls are mixed and one is selected at random. After a ball is selected, its number is recorded. Then it is replaced. If the experiment is repeated many times, find the variance and standard deviation of the numbers on the balls.

Solution

Let X be the number on each ball. The probability distribution is

Number on ball X	3	4	5
Probability $P(X)$	$\frac{2}{5}$	$\frac{1}{5}$	$\frac{2}{5}$

The mean is

$$\mu = \Sigma X \cdot P(X) = 3 \cdot \tfrac{2}{5} + 4 \cdot \tfrac{1}{5} + 5 \cdot \tfrac{2}{5} = 4$$

The variance is

$$\sigma = \Sigma[X^2 \cdot P(X)] - \mu^2$$
$$= 3^2 \cdot \tfrac{2}{5} + 4^2 \cdot \tfrac{1}{5} + 5^2 \cdot \tfrac{2}{5} = 4$$
$$= 16\tfrac{4}{5} - 16$$
$$= \tfrac{4}{5}$$

The standard deviation is

$$\sigma = \sqrt{\frac{4}{5}} = \sqrt{0.8} = 0.894$$

The mean, variance, and standard deviation can also be found by using vertical columns, as shown.

X	$P(X)$	$X \cdot P(X)$	$X^2 \cdot P(X)$
3	0.4	1.2	3.6
4	0.2	0.8	3.2
5	0.4	2.0	10
		$\Sigma X \cdot P(X) = 4.0$	16.8

Find the mean by summing the $\Sigma X \cdot P(X)$ column, and find the variance by summing the $X^2 \cdot P(X)$ column and subtracting the square of the mean.

$$\sigma^2 = 16.8 - 4^2 = 16.8 - 16 = 0.8$$

and

$$\sigma = \sqrt{0.8} = 0.894$$

Example 5–11	**On Hold for Talk Radio**

A talk radio station has four telephone lines. If the host is unable to talk (i.e., during a commercial) or is talking to a person, the other callers are placed on hold. When all lines are in use, others who are trying to call in get a busy signal. The probability that 0, 1, 2, 3, or 4 people will get through is shown in the distribution. Find the variance and standard deviation for the distribution.

X	0	1	2	3	4
$P(X)$	0.18	0.34	0.23	0.21	0.04

Should the station have considered getting more phone lines installed?

Solution

The mean is

$$\mu = \Sigma X \cdot P(X)$$
$$= 0 \cdot (0.18) + 1 \cdot (0.34) + 2 \cdot (0.23) + 3 \cdot (0.21) + 4 \cdot (0.04)$$
$$= 1.6$$

The variance is

$$\sigma^2 = \Sigma[X^2 \cdot P(X)] - \mu^2$$
$$= [0^2 \cdot (0.18) + 1^2 \cdot (0.34) + 2^2 \cdot (0.23) + 3^2 \cdot (0.21) + 4^2 \cdot (0.04)] - 1.6^2$$
$$= [0 + 0.34 + 0.92 + 1.89 + 0.64] - 2.56$$
$$= 3.79 - 2.56 = 1.23$$
$$= 1.2 \text{ (rounded)}$$

The standard deviation is $\sigma = \sqrt{\sigma^2}$, or $\sigma = \sqrt{1.2} = 1.1$.

No. The mean number of people calling at any one time is 1.6. Since the standard deviation is 1.1, most callers would be accommodated by having four phone lines because $\mu + 2\sigma$ would be $1.6 + 2(1.1) = 1.6 + 2.2 = 3.8$. Very few callers would get a busy signal since at least 75% of the callers would either get through or be put on hold. (See Chebyshev's theorem in Section 3–2.)

Expectation

Another concept related to the mean for a probability distribution is that of expected value or expectation. Expected value is used in various types of games of chance, in insurance, and in other areas, such as decision theory.

> The **expected value** of a discrete random variable of a probability distribution is the theoretical average of the variable. The formula is
>
> $$\mu = E(X) = \Sigma X \cdot P(X)$$
>
> The symbol $E(X)$ is used for the expected value.

The formula for the expected value is the same as the formula for the theoretical mean. The expected value, then, is the theoretical mean of the probability distribution. That is, $E(X) = \mu$.

When expected value problems involve money, it is customary to round the answer to the nearest cent.

Example 5–12

Winning Tickets

One thousand tickets are sold at $1 each for a color television valued at $350. What is the expected value of the gain if you purchase one ticket?

Solution

The problem can be set up as follows:

	Win	Lose
Gain X	$349	−$1
Probability $P(X)$	$\dfrac{1}{1000}$	$\dfrac{999}{1000}$

Two things should be noted. First, for a win, the net gain is $349, since you do not get the cost of the ticket ($1) back. Second, for a loss, the gain is represented by a negative number, in this case $-\$1$. The solution, then, is

$$E(X) = \$349 \cdot \frac{1}{1000} + (-\$1) \cdot \frac{999}{1000} = -\$0.65$$

Expected value problems of this type can also be solved by finding the overall gain (i.e., the value of the prize won or the amount of money won, not considering the cost of the ticket for the prize or the cost to play the game) and subtracting the cost of the tickets or the cost to play the game, as shown:

$$E(X) = \$350 \cdot \frac{1}{1000} - \$1 = -\$0.65$$

Here, the overall gain ($350) must be used.

Note that the expectation is $-\$0.65$. This does not mean that you lose $0.65, since you can only win a television set valued at $350 or lose $1 on the ticket. What this expectation means is that the average of the losses is $0.65 for each of the 1000 ticket holders. Here is another way of looking at this situation: If you purchased one ticket each week over a long time, the average loss would be $0.65 per ticket, since theoretically, on average, you would win the set once for each 1000 tickets purchased.

Example 5–13	**Special Die**

A special six-sided die is made in which 3 sides have 6 spots, 2 sides have 4 spots, and 1 side has 1 spot. If the die is rolled, find the expected value of the number of spots that will occur.

Solution

Since there are 3 sides with 6 spots, the probability of getting a 6 is $\frac{3}{6} = \frac{1}{2}$. Since there are 2 sides with 4 spots, the probability of getting 4 spots is $\frac{2}{6} = \frac{1}{3}$. The probability of getting 1 spot is $\frac{1}{6}$ since 1 side has 1 spot.

Gain X	1	4	6
Probability $P(X)$	$\frac{1}{6}$	$\frac{1}{3}$	$\frac{1}{2}$

$$E(X) = 1 \cdot \frac{1}{6} + 4 \cdot \frac{1}{3} + 6\frac{1}{2} = 4\frac{1}{2}$$

Notice you can only get 1, 4, or 6 spots; but if you rolled the die a large number of times and found the average, it would be about $4\frac{1}{2}$.

Example 5–14	**Bond Investment**

A financial adviser suggests that his client select one of two types of bonds in which to invest $5000. Bond X pays a return of 4% and has a default rate of 2%. Bond Y has a $2\frac{1}{2}\%$ return and a default rate of 1%. Find the expected rate of return and decide which bond would be a better investment. When the bond defaults, the investor loses all the investment.

Solution

The return on bond X is $5000 \cdot 4\% = \$200$. The expected return then is

$$E(X) = \$200(0.98) - \$5000(0.02) = \$96$$

The return on bond Y is $5000 \cdot 2\frac{1}{2}\% = \$125$. The expected return then is

$$E(X) = \$125(0.99) - \$5000(0.01) = \$73.75$$

Hence, bond X would be a better investment since the expected return is higher.

In gambling games, if the expected value of the game is zero, the game is said to be fair. If the expected value of a game is positive, then the game is in favor of the player. That is, the player has a better than even chance of winning. If the expected value of the game is negative, then the game is said to be in favor of the house. That is, in the long run, the players will lose money.

In his book *Probabilities in Everyday Life* (Ivy Books, 1986), author John D. McGervy gives the expectations for various casino games. For keno, the house wins $0.27 on every $1.00 bet. For Chuck-a-Luck, the house wins about $0.52 on every $1.00 bet. For roulette, the house wins about $0.90 on every $1.00 bet. For craps, the house wins about $0.88 on every $1.00 bet. The bottom line here is that if you gamble long enough, sooner or later you will end up losing money.

Applying the Concepts **5-2**

Expected Value

On March 28, 1979, the nuclear generating facility at Three Mile Island, Pennsylvania, began discharging radiation into the atmosphere. People exposed to even low levels of radiation can experience health problems ranging from very mild to severe, even causing death. A local newspaper reported that 11 babies were born with kidney problems in the three-county area surrounding the Three Mile Island nuclear power plant. The expected value for that problem in infants in that area was 3. Answer the following questions.

1. What does *expected value* mean?
2. Would you expect the exact value of 3 all the time?
3. If a news reporter stated that the number of cases of kidney problems in newborns was nearly four times as much as was usually expected, do you think pregnant mothers living in that area would be overly concerned?
4. Is it unlikely that 11 occurred by chance?
5. Are there any other statistics that could better inform the public?
6. Assume that 3 out of 2500 babies were born with kidney problems in that three-county area the year before the accident. Also assume that 11 out of 2500 babies were born with kidney problems in that three-county area the year after the accident. What is the real percent of increase in that abnormality?
7. Do you think that pregnant mothers living in that area should be overly concerned after looking at the results in terms of rates?

See page 296 for the answers.

Exercises 5–2

1. **Defective Transistors** From past experience, a company has found that in cartons of transistors, 92% contain no defective transistors, 3% contain one defective transistor, 3% contain two defective transistors, and 2% contain three defective transistors. Find the mean, variance, and standard deviation for the defective transistors.

   About how many extra transistors per day would the company need to replace the defective ones if it used 10 cartons per day?

2. **Suit Sales** The number of suits sold per day at a retail store is shown in the table, with the corresponding probabilities. Find the mean, variance, and standard deviation of the distribution.

Number of suits sold X	19	20	21	22	23
Probability $P(X)$	0.2	0.2	0.3	0.2	0.1

   If the manager of the retail store wants to be sure that he has enough suits for the next 5 days, how many should the manager purchase?

3. **Number of Credit Cards** A bank vice president feels that each savings account customer has, on average, three credit cards. The following distribution represents the number of credit cards people own. Find the mean, variance, and standard deviation. Is the vice president correct?

Number of cards X	0	1	2	3	4
Probability $P(X)$	0.18	0.44	0.27	0.08	0.03

4. **Trivia Quiz** The probabilities that a player will get 5 to 10 questions right on a trivia quiz are shown below. Find the mean, variance, and standard deviation for the distribution.

X	5	6	7	8	9	10
$P(X)$	0.05	0.2	0.4	0.1	0.15	0.1

5. **Cellular Phone Sales** The probability that a cellular phone company kiosk sells X number of new phone contracts per day is shown below. Find the mean, variance, and standard deviation for this probability distribution.

X	4	5	6	8	10
$P(X)$	0.4	0.3	0.1	0.15	0.05

   What is the probability that they will sell 6 or more contracts three days in a row?

6. **Animal Shelter Adoptions** The local animal shelter adopts out cats and dogs each week with the following probabilities.

X	3	4	5	6	7	8
$P(X)$	0.15	0.3	0.25	0.18	0.1	0.02

   Find the mean, variance, and standard deviation for the number of animals adopted each week. What is the probability that they find homes for more than 5 animals in a given week?

7. **Commercials During Children's TV Programs** A concerned parents group determined the number of commercials shown in each of five children's programs over a period of time. Find the mean, variance, and standard deviation for the distribution shown.

Number of commercials X	5	6	7	8	9
Probability $P(X)$	0.2	0.25	0.38	0.10	0.07

8. **Number of Televisions per Household** A study conducted by a TV station showed the number of televisions per household and the corresponding probabilities for each. Find the mean, variance, and standard deviation.

Number of televisions X	1	2	3	4
Probability $P(X)$	0.32	0.51	0.12	0.05

   If you were taking a survey on the programs that were watched on television, how many program diaries would you send to each household in the survey?

9. **Students Using the Math Lab** The number of students using the Math Lab per day is found in the distribution below. Find the mean, variance, and standard deviation for this probability distribution.

X	6	8	10	12	14
$P(X)$	0.15	0.3	0.35	0.1	0.1

   What is the probability that fewer than 8 or more than 12 use the lab in a given day?

10. **Pizza Deliveries** A pizza shop owner determines the number of pizzas that are delivered each day. Find the mean, variance, and standard deviation for the distribution shown. If the manager stated that 45 pizzas were delivered on one day, do you think that this is a believable claim?

Number of deliveries X	35	36	37	38	39
Probability $P(X)$	0.1	0.2	0.3	0.3	0.1

11. **Insurance** An insurance company insures a person's antique coin collection worth $20,000 for an annual premium of $300. If the company figures that the probability of the collection being stolen is 0.002, what will be the company's expected profit?

12. Job Bids A landscape contractor bids on jobs where he can make $3000 profit. The probabilities of getting 1, 2, 3, or 4 jobs per month are shown.

Number of jobs	1	2	3	4
Probability	0.2	0.3	0.4	0.1

Find the contractor's expected profit per month.

13. Rolling Dice If a person rolls doubles when she tosses two dice, she wins $5. For the game to be fair, how much should she pay to play the game?

14. Dice Game A person pays $2 to play a certain game by rolling a single die once. If a 1 or a 2 comes up, the person wins nothing. If, however, the player rolls a 3, 4, 5, or 6, he or she wins the difference between the number rolled and $2. Find the expectation for this game. Is the game fair?

15. Lottery Prizes A lottery offers one $1000 prize, one $500 prize, and five $100 prizes. One thousand tickets are sold at $3 each. Find the expectation if a person buys one ticket.

16. In Exercise 15, find the expectation if a person buys two tickets. Assume that the player's ticket is replaced after each draw and that the same ticket can win more than one prize.

17. Winning the Lottery For a daily lottery, a person selects a three-digit number. If the person plays for $1, she can win $500. Find the expectation. In the same daily lottery, if a person boxes a number, she will win $80. Find the expectation if the number 123 is played for $1 and boxed. (When a number is "boxed," it can win when the digits occur in any order.)

18. Life Insurance A 35-year-old woman purchases a $100,000 term life insurance policy for an annual payment of $360. Based on a period life table for the U.S. government, the probability that she will survive the year is 0.999057. Find the expected value of the policy for the insurance company.

19. Raffle Ticket Sales A civic group sells 1000 raffle tickets to raise $2500 for its namesake charity. First prize is $1000, second prize is $300, and third prize is $200. How much should the group charge for each ticket?

Extending the Concepts

20. Rolling Dice Construct a probability distribution for the sum shown on the faces when two dice are rolled. Find the mean, variance, and standard deviation of the distribution.

21. Rolling a Die When one die is rolled, the expected value of the number of spots is 3.5. In Exercise 20, the mean number of spots was found for rolling two dice. What is the mean number of spots if three dice are rolled?

22. The formula for finding the variance for a probability distribution is

$$\sigma^2 = \Sigma[(X - \mu)^2 \cdot P(X)]$$

Verify algebraically that this formula gives the same result as the shortcut formula shown in this section.

23. Rolling a Die Roll a die 100 times. Compute the mean and standard deviation. How does the result compare with the theoretical results of Example 5–5?

24. Rolling Two Dice Roll two dice 100 times and find the mean, variance, and standard deviation of the sum of the spots. Compare the result with the theoretical results obtained in Exercise 20.

25. Extracurricular Activities Conduct a survey of the number of extracurricular activities your classmates are enrolled in. Construct a probability distribution and find the mean, variance, and standard deviation.

26. Promotional Campaign In a recent promotional campaign, a company offered these prizes and the corresponding probabilities. Find the expected value of winning. The tickets are free.

Number of prizes	Amount	Probability
1	$100,000	$\frac{1}{1,000,000}$
2	10,000	$\frac{1}{50,000}$
5	1,000	$\frac{1}{10,000}$
10	100	$\frac{1}{1000}$

If the winner has to mail in the winning ticket to claim the prize, what will be the expectation if the cost of the stamp is considered? Use the current cost of a stamp for a first-class letter.

This study shows that a part of the brain reacts to the impact of losing, and it might explain why people tend to increase their bets after losing when gambling. Explain how this type of split decision making may influence fighter pilots, firefighters, or police officers, as the article states.

THE GAMBLER'S FALLACY

WHY WE EXPECT TO STRIKE IT RICH AFTER A LOSING STREAK

A GAMBLER USUALLY WAGERS more after taking a loss, in the misguided belief that a run of bad luck increases the probability of a win. We tend to cling to the misconception that past events can skew future odds. "On some level, you're thinking, 'If I just lost, it's going to even out.' The extent to which you're disturbed by a loss seems to go along with risky behavior," says University of Michigan psychologist William Gehring, Ph.D., co-author of a new study linking dicey decision-making to neurological activity originating in the medial frontal cortex, long thought to be an area of the brain used in error detection.

Because people are so driven to up the ante after a loss, Gehring believes that the medial frontal cortex unconsciously influences future decisions based on the impact of the loss, in addition to registering the loss itself.

Gehring drew this conclusion by asking 12 subjects fitted with electrode caps to choose either the number 5 or 25, with the larger number representing the riskier bet.

On any given round, both numbers could amount to a loss, both could amount to a gain or the results could split, one number signifying a loss, the other a gain.

The medial frontal cortex responded to the outcome of a gamble within a quarter of a second, registering sharp electrical impulses only after a loss. Gehring points out that if the medial frontal cortex simply detected errors it would have reacted after participants chose the lesser of two possible gains. In other words, choosing "5" during a round in which both numbers paid off and betting on "25" would have yielded a larger profit.

After the study appeared in *Science*, Gehring received several e-mails from stock traders likening the "gambler's fallacy" to impulsive trading decisions made directly after off-loading a losing security. Researchers speculate that such risky, split-second decision-making could extend to fighter pilots, firemen and policemen—professions in which rapid-fire decisions are crucial and frequent.

—*Dan Schulman*

Source: Psychology Today, August 2002, p. 22. Used with permission.

Technology *Step by Step*

TI-83 Plus or TI-84 Plus
Step by Step

To calculate the mean and variance for a discrete random variable by using the formulas:

1. Enter the x values into L_1 and the probabilities into L_2.
2. Move the cursor to the top of the L_3 column so that L_3 is highlighted.
3. Type L_1 multiplied by L_2, then press **ENTER**.
4. Move the cursor to the top of the L_4 column so that L_4 is highlighted.
5. Type L_1 followed by the x^2 key multiplied by L_2, then press **ENTER**.
6. Type **2nd QUIT** to return to the home screen.
7. Type **2nd LIST,** move the cursor to MATH, type **5** for sum, then type L_3, then press **ENTER**.
8. Type **2nd ENTER,** move the cursor to L_3, type L_4, then press **ENTER**.

Using the data from Example 5–10 gives the following:

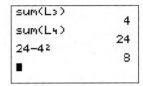

To calculate the mean and standard deviation for a discrete random variable without using the formulas, modify the procedure to calculate the mean and standard deviation from grouped data (Chapter 3) by entering the x values into L_1 and the probabilities into L_2.

5–3   The Binomial Distribution

Many types of probability problems have only two outcomes or can be reduced to two outcomes. For example, when a coin is tossed, it can land heads or tails. When a baby is born, it will be either male or female. In a basketball game, a team either wins or loses. A true/false item can be answered in only two ways, true or false. Other situations can be

Objective 3

Find the exact probability for *X* successes in *n* trials of a binomial experiment.

Historical Note

In 1653, Blaise Pascal created a triangle of numbers called *Pascal's triangle* that can be used in the binomial distribution.

reduced to two outcomes. For example, a medical treatment can be classified as effective or ineffective, depending on the results. A person can be classified as having normal or abnormal blood pressure, depending on the measure of the blood pressure gauge. A multiple-choice question, even though there are four or five answer choices, can be classified as correct or incorrect. Situations like these are called *binomial experiments*.

A **binomial experiment** is a probability experiment that satisfies the following four requirements:

1. There must be a fixed number of trials.
2. Each trial can have only two outcomes or outcomes that can be reduced to two outcomes. These outcomes can be considered as either success or failure.
3. The outcomes of each trial must be independent of one another.
4. The probability of a success must remain the same for each trial.

A binomial experiment and its results give rise to a special probability distribution called the *binomial distribution*.

The outcomes of a binomial experiment and the corresponding probabilities of these outcomes are called a **binomial distribution.**

In binomial experiments, the outcomes are usually classified as successes or failures. For example, the correct answer to a multiple-choice item can be classified as a success, but any of the other choices would be incorrect and hence classified as a failure. The notation that is commonly used for binomial experiments and the binomial distribution is defined now.

Notation for the Binomial Distribution

$P(S)$	The symbol for the probability of success
$P(F)$	The symbol for the probability of failure
p	The numerical probability of a success
q	The numerical probability of a failure

$$P(S) = p \quad \text{and} \quad P(F) = 1 - p = q$$

n	The number of trials
X	The number of successes in n trials

Note that $0 \le X \le n$ and $X = 0, 1, 2, 3, \ldots, n$.

The probability of a success in a binomial experiment can be computed with this formula.

Binomial Probability Formula

In a binomial experiment, the probability of exactly X successes in n trials is

$$P(X) = \frac{n!}{(n - X)!X!} \cdot p^X \cdot q^{n-X}$$

An explanation of why the formula works is given following Example 5–15.

<table>
<tr><td>Example 5–15</td><td>

Tossing Coins

A coin is tossed 3 times. Find the probability of getting exactly two heads.

Solution

This problem can be solved by looking at the sample space. There are three ways to get two heads.

HHH, <u>HHT, HTH, THH,</u> TTH, THT, HTT, TTT

The answer is $\frac{3}{8}$, or 0.375.
</td></tr>
</table>

Looking at the problem in Example 5–15 from the standpoint of a binomial experiment, one can show that it meets the four requirements.

1. There are a fixed number of trials (three).
2. There are only two outcomes for each trial, heads or tails.
3. The outcomes are independent of one another (the outcome of one toss in no way affects the outcome of another toss).
4. The probability of a success (heads) is $\frac{1}{2}$ in each case.

   In this case, $n = 3$, $X = 2$, $p = \frac{1}{2}$, and $q = \frac{1}{2}$. Hence, substituting in the formula gives

$$P(2 \text{ heads}) = \frac{3!}{(3-2)!2!} \cdot \left(\frac{1}{2}\right)^2 \left(\frac{1}{2}\right)^1 = \frac{3}{8} = 0.375$$

which is the same answer obtained by using the sample space.

The same example can be used to explain the formula. First, note that there are three ways to get exactly two heads and one tail from a possible eight ways. They are HHT, HTH, and THH. In this case, then, the number of ways of obtaining two heads from three coin tosses is $_3C_2$, or 3, as shown in Chapter 4. In general, the number of ways to get X successes from n trials without regard to order is

$$_nC_X = \frac{n!}{(n-X)!X!}$$

This is the first part of the binomial formula. (Some calculators can be used for this.)

Next, each success has a probability of $\frac{1}{2}$ and can occur twice. Likewise, each failure has a probability of $\frac{1}{2}$ and can occur once, giving the $(\frac{1}{2})^2(\frac{1}{2})^1$ part of the formula. To generalize, then, each success has a probability of p and can occur X times, and each failure has a probability of q and can occur $n - X$ times. Putting it all together yields the binomial probability formula.

<table>
<tr><td>Example 5–16</td><td>

Survey on Doctor Visits

A survey found that one out of five Americans say he or she has visited a doctor in any given month. If 10 people are selected at random, find the probability that exactly 3 will have visited a doctor last month.

Source: *Reader's Digest.*

Solution

In this case, $n = 10$, $X = 3$, $p = \frac{1}{5}$, and $q = \frac{4}{5}$. Hence,

$$P(3) = \frac{10!}{(10-3)!3!}\left(\frac{1}{5}\right)^3\left(\frac{4}{5}\right)^7 = 0.201$$
</td></tr>
</table>

Example 5–17	Survey on Employment

A survey from Teenage Research Unlimited (Northbrook, Illinois) found that 30% of teenage consumers receive their spending money from part-time jobs. If 5 teenagers are selected at random, find the probability that at least 3 of them will have part-time jobs.

Solution

To find the probability that at least 3 have part-time jobs, it is necessary to find the individual probabilities for 3, or 4, or 5, and then add them to get the total probability.

$$P(3) = \frac{5!}{(5-3)!3!}(0.3)^3(0.7)^2 = 0.132$$

$$P(4) = \frac{5!}{(5-4)!4!}(0.3)^4(0.7)^1 = 0.028$$

$$P(5) = \frac{5!}{(5-5)!5!}(0.3)^5(0.7)^0 = 0.002$$

Hence,

$$P(\text{at least three teenagers have part-time jobs})$$
$$= 0.132 + 0.028 + 0.002 = 0.162$$

Computing probabilities by using the binomial probability formula can be quite tedious at times, so tables have been developed for selected values of n and p. Table B in Appendix C gives the probabilities for individual events. Example 5–18 shows how to use Table B to compute probabilities for binomial experiments.

Example 5–18	Tossing Coins

Solve the problem in Example 5–15 by using Table B.

Solution

Since $n = 3$, $X = 2$, and $p = 0.5$, the value 0.375 is found as shown in Figure 5–3.

Figure 5–3	
Using Table B for Example 5–18	

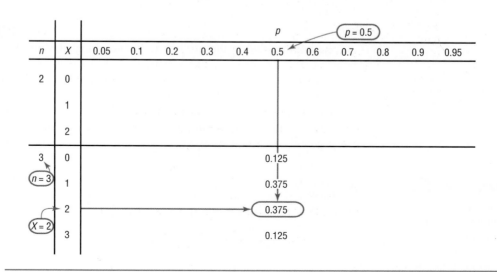

Example 5–19

Survey on Fear of Being Home Alone at Night

Public Opinion reported that 5% of Americans are afraid of being alone in a house at night. If a random sample of 20 Americans is selected, find these probabilities by using the binomial table.

    a. There are exactly 5 people in the sample who are afraid of being alone at night.
    b. There are at most 3 people in the sample who are afraid of being alone at night.
    c. There are at least 3 people in the sample who are afraid of being alone at night.

Source: *100% American* by Daniel Evan Weiss.

Solution

    a. $n = 20$, $p = 0.05$, and $X = 5$. From the table, we get 0.002.
    b. $n = 20$ and $p = 0.05$. "At most 3 people" means 0, or 1, or 2, or 3.
        Hence, the solution is

$$P(0) + P(1) + P(2) + P(3) = 0.358 + 0.377 + 0.189 + 0.060$$
$$= 0.984$$

    c. $n = 20$ and $p = 0.05$. "At least 3 people" means 3, 4, 5, . . . , 20. This problem can best be solved by finding $P(0) + P(1) + P(2)$ and subtracting from 1.

$$P(0) + P(1) + P(2) = 0.358 + 0.377 + 0.189 = 0.924$$
$$1 - 0.924 = 0.076$$

Example 5–20

Driving While Intoxicated

A report from the Secretary of Health and Human Services stated that 70% of single-vehicle traffic fatalities that occur at night on weekends involve an intoxicated driver. If a sample of 15 single-vehicle traffic fatalities that occur at night on a weekend is selected, find the probability that exactly 12 involve a driver who is intoxicated.

Source: *100% American* by Daniel Evan Weiss.

Solution

Now, $n = 15$, $p = 0.70$, and $X = 12$. From Table B, $P(12) = 0.170$. Hence, the probability is 0.17.

    Remember that in the use of the binomial distribution, the outcomes must be independent. For example, in the selection of components from a batch to be tested, each component must be replaced before the next one is selected. Otherwise, the outcomes are not independent. However, a dilemma arises because there is a chance that the same component could be selected again. This situation can be avoided by not replacing the component and using a distribution called the hypergeometric distribution to calculate the probabilities. The hypergeometric distribution is beyond the scope of this book.

Objective 4

Find the mean, variance, and standard deviation for the variable of a binomial distribution.

Mean, Variance, and Standard Deviation for the Binomial Distribution

The mean, variance, and standard deviation of a variable that has the *binomial distribution* can be found by using the following formulas.

    Mean: $\mu = n \cdot p$ Variance: $\sigma^2 = n \cdot p \cdot q$ Standard deviation: $\sigma = \sqrt{n \cdot p \cdot q}$

These formulas are algebraically equivalent to the formulas for the mean, variance, and standard deviation of the variables for probability distributions, but because they are for variables of the binomial distribution, they have been simplified by using algebra. The algebraic derivation is omitted here, but their equivalence is shown in Example 5–21.

| Example 5–21 | Tossing a Coin |

A coin is tossed 4 times. Find the mean, variance, and standard deviation of the number of heads that will be obtained.

Solution

With the formulas for the binomial distribution and $n = 4$, $p = \frac{1}{2}$, and $q = \frac{1}{2}$, the results are

$$\mu = n \cdot p = 4 \cdot \tfrac{1}{2} = 2$$
$$\sigma^2 = n \cdot p \cdot q = 4 \cdot \tfrac{1}{2} \cdot \tfrac{1}{2} = 1$$
$$\sigma = \sqrt{1} = 1$$

From Example 5–21, when four coins are tossed many, many times, the average of the number of heads that appear is 2, and the standard deviation of the number of heads is 1. Note that these are theoretical values.

As stated previously, this problem can be solved by using the formulas for expected value. The distribution is shown.

No. of heads X	0	1	2	3	4
Probability $P(X)$	$\frac{1}{16}$	$\frac{4}{16}$	$\frac{6}{16}$	$\frac{4}{16}$	$\frac{1}{16}$

$$\mu = E(X) = \Sigma X \cdot P(X) = 0 \cdot \tfrac{1}{16} + 1 \cdot \tfrac{4}{16} + 2 \cdot \tfrac{6}{16} + 3 \cdot \tfrac{4}{16} + 4 \cdot \tfrac{1}{16} = \tfrac{32}{16} = 2$$
$$\sigma^2 = \Sigma X^2 \cdot P(X) - \mu^2$$
$$= 0^2 \cdot \tfrac{1}{16} + 1^2 \cdot \tfrac{4}{16} + 2^2 \cdot \tfrac{6}{16} + 3^2 \cdot \tfrac{4}{16} + 4^2 \cdot \tfrac{1}{16} - 2^2 = \tfrac{80}{16} - 4 = 1$$
$$\sigma = \sqrt{1} = 1$$

Hence, the simplified binomial formulas give the same results.

| Example 5–22 | Rolling a Die |

A die is rolled 360 times. Find the mean, variance, and standard deviation of the number of 4s that will be rolled.

Solution

This is a binomial experiment since getting a 4 is a success and not getting a 4 is considered a failure. Hence $n = 360$, $p = \frac{1}{6}$, and $q = \frac{5}{6}$.

$$\mu = n \cdot p = 360 \cdot \tfrac{1}{6} = 60$$
$$\sigma^2 = n \cdot p \cdot q = 360 \cdot \left(\tfrac{1}{6}\right)\left(\tfrac{5}{6}\right) = 50$$
$$\sigma = \sqrt{n \cdot p \cdot q} = \sqrt{50} = 7.07$$

On average, sixty 4s will be rolled. The standard deviation is 7.07.

Example 5–23

Likelihood of Twins

The *Statistical Bulletin* published by Metropolitan Life Insurance Co. reported that 2% of all American births result in twins. If a random sample of 8000 births is taken, find the mean, variance, and standard deviation of the number of births that would result in twins.

Source: *100% American* by Daniel Evan Weiss.

Solution

This is a binomial situation, since a birth can result in either twins or not twins (i.e., two outcomes).

$$\mu = n \cdot p = (8000)(0.02) = 160$$
$$\sigma^2 = n \cdot p \cdot q = (8000)(0.02)(0.98) = 156.8$$
$$\sigma = \sqrt{n \cdot p \cdot q} = \sqrt{156.8} = 12.5$$

For the sample, the average number of births that would result in twins is 160, the variance is 156.8, or 157, and the standard deviation is 12.5, or 13 if rounded.

Applying the Concepts **5–3**

Unsanitary Restaurants

Health officials routinely check sanitary conditions of restaurants. Assume you visit a popular tourist spot and read in the newspaper that in 3 out of every 7 restaurants checked, there were unsatisfactory health conditions found. Assuming you are planning to eat out 10 times while you are there on vacation, answer the following questions.

1. How likely is it that you will eat at three restaurants with unsanitary conditions?
2. How likely is it that you will eat at four or five restaurants with unsanitary conditions?
3. Explain how you would compute the probability of eating in at least one restaurant with unsanitary conditions. Could you use the complement to solve this problem?
4. What is the most likely number to occur in this experiment?
5. How variable will the data be around the most likely number?
6. Is this a binomial distribution?
7. If it is a binomial distribution, does that mean that the likelihood of a success is always 50% since there are only two possible outcomes?

Check your answers by using the following computer-generated table.

Mean = 4.3	Std. dev. = 1.56557	
X	**P(X)**	**Cum. Prob.**
0	0.00362	0.00362
1	0.02731	0.03093
2	0.09272	0.12365
3	0.18651	0.31016
4	0.24623	0.55639
5	0.22291	0.77930
6	0.14013	0.91943
7	0.06041	0.97983
8	0.01709	0.99692
9	0.00286	0.99979
10	0.00022	1.00000

See page 296 for the answers.

Exercises 5–3

1. Which of the following are binomial experiments or can be reduced to binomial experiments?

   a. Surveying 100 people to determine if they like Sudsy Soap

   b. Tossing a coin 100 times to see how many heads occur

   c. Drawing a card with replacement from a deck and getting a heart

   d. Asking 1000 people which brand of cigarettes they smoke

   e. Testing four different brands of aspirin to see which brands are effective

   f. Testing one brand of aspirin by using 10 people to determine whether it is effective

   g. Asking 100 people if they smoke

   h. Checking 1000 applicants to see whether they were admitted to White Oak College

   i. Surveying 300 prisoners to see how many different crimes they were convicted of

   j. Surveying 300 prisoners to see whether this is their first offense

2. **(ans)** Compute the probability of X successes, using Table B in Appendix C.

   a. $n = 2, p = 0.30, X = 1$

   b. $n = 4, p = 0.60, X = 3$

   c. $n = 5, p = 0.10, X = 0$

   d. $n = 10, p = 0.40, X = 4$

   e. $n = 12, p = 0.90, X = 2$

   f. $n = 15, p = 0.80, X = 12$

   g. $n = 17, p = 0.05, X = 0$

   h. $n = 20, p = 0.50, X = 10$

   i. $n = 16, p = 0.20, X = 3$

3. Compute the probability of X successes, using the binomial formula.

   a. $n = 6, X = 3, p = 0.03$

   b. $n = 4, X = 2, p = 0.18$

   c. $n = 5, X = 3, p = 0.63$

   d. $n = 9, X = 0, p = 0.42$

   e. $n = 10, X = 5, p = 0.37$

For Exercises 4 through 13, assume all variables are binomial. (*Note:* If values are not found in Table B of Appendix C, use the binomial formula.)

4. **Burglar Alarms** A burglar alarm system has six fail-safe components. The probability of each failing is 0.05. Find these probabilities.

   a. Exactly three will fail.

   b. Fewer than two will fail.

   c. None will fail.

   d. Compare the answers for parts *a*, *b*, and *c*, and explain why the results are reasonable.

5. **True/False Exam** A student takes a 20-question, true/false exam and guesses on each question. Find the probability of passing if the lowest passing grade is 15 correct out of 20. Would you consider this event likely to occur? Explain your answer.

6. **Multiple-Choice Exam** A student takes a 20-question, multiple-choice exam with five choices for each question and guesses on each question. Find the probability of guessing at least 15 out of 20 correctly. Would you consider this event likely or unlikely to occur? Explain your answer.

7. **Driving to Work Alone** It is reported that 77% of workers aged 16 and over drive to work alone. Choose 8 workers at random. Find the probability that

   a. All drive to work alone

   b. More than one-half drive to work alone

   c. Exactly 3 drive to work alone

   Source: www.factfinder.census.gov

8. **High School Dropouts** Approximately 10.3% of American high school students drop out of school before graduation. Choose 10 students entering high school at random. Find the probability that

   a. No more than two drop out

   b. At least 6 graduate

   c. All 10 stay in school and graduate

   Source: www.infoplease.com

9. **Survey on Concern for Criminals** In a survey, 3 of 4 students said the courts show "too much concern" for criminals. Find the probability that at most 3 out of 7 randomly selected students will agree with this statement.

   Source: *Harper's Index.*

10. **Labor Force Couples** The percentage of couples where both parties are in the labor force is 52.1. Choose 5 couples at random. Find the probability that

    a. None of the couples have both persons working

    b. More than 3 of the couples have both persons in the labor force

    c. Fewer than 2 of the couples have both parties working

    Source: www.bls.gov

11. **College Education and Business World Success** R. H. Bruskin Associates Market Research found that 40% of Americans do not think that having a college education is important to succeed in the business world. If a random sample of five Americans is selected, find these probabilities.

    a. Exactly 2 people will agree with that statement.

    b. At most 3 people will agree with that statement.

    c. At least 2 people will agree with that statement.

    d. Fewer than 3 people will agree with that statement.

    Source: *100% American* by Daniel Evans Weiss.

12. **Destination Weddings** Twenty-six percent of couples who plan to marry this year are planning destination weddings. In a random sample of 12 couples who plan to marry, find the probability that

    a. Exactly 6 couples will have a destination wedding
    b. At least 6 couples will have a destination wedding
    c. Fewer than 5 couples will have a destination wedding

    Source: *Time* magazine.

13. **People Who Have Some College Education** Fifty-three percent of all persons in the U.S. population have at least some college education. Choose 10 persons at random. Find the probability that

    a. Exactly one-half have some college education
    b. At least 5 do not have any college education
    c. Fewer than 5 have some college education

    Source: *New York Times Almanac.*

14. **(ans)** Find the mean, variance, and standard deviation for each of the values of n and p when the conditions for the binomial distribution are met.

    a. $n = 100, p = 0.75$
    b. $n = 300, p = 0.3$
    c. $n = 20, p = 0.5$
    d. $n = 10, p = 0.8$
    e. $n = 1000, p = 0.1$
    f. $n = 500, p = 0.25$
    g. $n = 50, p = \frac{2}{5}$
    h. $n = 36, p = \frac{1}{6}$

15. **Social Security Recipients** A study found that 1% of Social Security recipients are too young to vote. If 800 Social Security recipients are randomly selected, find the mean, variance, and standard deviation of the number of recipients who are too young to vote.

    Source: *Harper's Index.*

16. Find the mean, variance, and standard deviation for the number of heads when 20 coins are tossed.

17. **Defective Calculators** If 3% of calculators are defective, find the mean, variance, and standard deviation of a lot of 300 calculators.

18. **Federal Government Employee E-mail Use** It has been reported that 83% of federal government employees use e-mail. If a sample of 200 federal government employees is selected, find the mean, variance, and standard deviation of the number who use e-mail.

    Source: *USA TODAY.*

19. **Watching Fireworks** A survey found that 21% of Americans watch fireworks on television on July 4. Find the mean, variance, and standard deviation of the number of individuals who watch fireworks on television on July 4 if a random sample of 1000 Americans is selected.

    Source: USA Snapshot, *USA TODAY.*

20. **Alternate Sources of Fuel** Eighty-five percent of Americans favor spending government money to develop alternative sources of fuel for automobiles. For a random sample of 120 Americans, find the mean, variance, and standard deviation for the number who favor government spending for alternative fuels.

    Source: www.pollingreport.com

21. **Survey on Bathing Pets** A survey found that 25% of pet owners had their pets bathed professionally rather than do it themselves. If 18 pet owners are randomly selected, find the probability that exactly 5 people have their pets bathed professionally.

    Source: USA Snapshot, *USA TODAY.*

22. **Survey on Answering Machine Ownership** In a survey, 63% of Americans said they own an answering machine. If 14 Americans are selected at random, find the probability that exactly 9 own an answering machine.

    Source: USA Snapshot, *USA TODAY.*

23. **Poverty and the Federal Government** One out of every three Americans believes that the U.S. government should take "primary responsibility" for eliminating poverty in the United States. If 10 Americans are selected, find the probability that at most 3 will believe that the U.S. government should take primary responsibility for eliminating poverty.

    Source: *Harper's Index.*

24. **Internet Purchases** Thirty-two percent of adult Internet users have purchased products or services online. For a random sample of 200 adult Internet users, find the mean, variance, and standard deviation for the number who have purchased goods or services online.

    Source: www.infoplease.com

25. **Survey on Internet Awareness** In a survey, 58% of American adults said they had never heard of the Internet. If 20 American adults are selected at random, find the probability that exactly 12 will say they have never heard of the Internet.

    Source: *Harper's Index.*

26. **Job Elimination** In the past year, 13% of businesses have eliminated jobs. If 5 businesses are selected at random, find the probability that at least 3 have eliminated jobs during the last year.

    Source: *USA TODAY.*

27. **Survey of High School Seniors** Of graduating high school seniors, 14% said that their generation will be remembered for their social concerns. If 7 graduating seniors are selected at random, find the probability that either 2 or 3 will agree with that statement.

    Source: *USA TODAY.*

28. Is this a binomial distribution? Explain.

X	0	1	2	3
$P(X)$	0.064	0.288	0.432	0.216

Extending the Concepts

29. Children in a Family The graph shown here represents the probability distribution for the number of girls in a family of three children. From this graph, construct a probability distribution.

P(X)

Probability

0.375

0.250

0.125

0   1   2   3

Number of girls

X

30. Construct a binomial distribution graph for the number of defective computer chips in a lot of 4 if $p = 0.3$.

Technology *Step by Step*

MINITAB

Step by Step

The Binomial Distribution

Calculate a Binomial Probability

From Example 5–19, it is known that 5% of the population is afraid of being alone at night. If a random sample of 20 Americans is selected, what is the probability that exactly 5 of them are afraid?

$$n = 20 \qquad p = 0.05 \ (5\%) \qquad \text{and} \qquad X = 5 \ (5 \text{ out of } 20)$$

No data need to be entered in the worksheet.

1. Select **Calc>Probability Distributions>Binomial.**

2. Click the option for Probability.

3. Click in the text box for Number of trials:.

4. Type in **20,** then Tab to Probability of success, then type **.05.**

5. Click the option for Input constant, then type in **5.** Leave the text box for Optional storage empty. If the name of a constant such as K1 is entered here, the results are stored but not displayed in the session window.

6. Click [OK]. The results are visible in the session window.

Probability Density Function

Binomial with n = 20 and p = 0.05

x   f(x)

5 0.0022446

Construct a Binomial Distribution

These instructions will use $n = 20$ and $p = 0.05$.

1. Select **Calc>Make Patterned Data>Simple Set of Numbers.**

2. You must enter three items:

   a) Enter **X** in the box for Store patterned data in:. MINITAB will use the first empty column of the active worksheet and name it X.

   b) Press Tab. Enter the value of **0** for the first value. Press Tab.

   c) Enter **20** for the last value. This value should be n. In steps of:, the value should be 1.

3. Click [OK].

4. Select **Calc>Probability Distributions>Binomial.**

5. In the dialog box you must enter five items.

   a) Click the button for Probability.

   b) In the box for Number of trials enter **20.**

   c) Enter **.05** in the Probability of success.

   d) Check the button for Input columns, then type the column name, **X,** in the text box.

   e) Click in the box for Optional storage, then type **Px.**

6. Click [OK]. The first available column will be named Px, and the calculated probabilities will be stored in it.

7. To view the completed table, click the worksheet icon on the toolbar.

Graph a Binomial Distribution

The table must be available in the worksheet.

1. Select **Graph>Scatterplot,** then Simple.

   a) Double-click on C2 Px for the Y variable and C1 X for the X variable.

   b) Click [Data view], then Project lines, then [OK]. Deselect any other type of display that may be selected in this list.

   c) Click on [Labels], then Title/Footnotes.

   d) Type an appropriate title, such as **Binomial Distribution n = 20, p = .05.**

   e) Press Tab to the Subtitle 1, then type in Your Name.

   f) Optional: Click [Scales] then [Gridlines] then check the box for Y major ticks.

   g) Click [OK] twice.

The graph will be displayed in a window. Right-click the control box to save, print, or close the graph.

TI-83 Plus or TI-84 Plus
Step by Step

Binomial Random Variables

To find the probability for a binomial variable:
Press **2nd [DISTR]** then **0** for binomial pdf((Note: On the TI-84 Plus Use A)
The form is binompdf(n,p,X).

Example: $n = 20$, $X = 5$, $p = .05$. (Example 5–19a from the text) binompdf(20,.05,5)

Example: $n = 20$, $X = 0, 1, 2, 3$, $p = .05$. (Example 5–19b from the text)
binompdf(20,.05,{0,1,2,3})
The calculator will display the probabilities in a list. Use the arrow keys to view entire display.

To find the cumulative probability for a binomial random variable:
Press **2nd [DISTR]** then **A (ALPHA MATH)** for binomcdf((Note: On the TI-84 Plus Use B)
The form is binomcdf(n,p,X). This will calculate the cumulative probability for values from 0 to X.

Example: $n = 20$, $X = 0, 1, 2, 3$, $p = .05$ (Example 5–19b from the text)
binomcdf(20,.05,3)

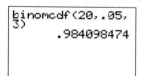

To construct a binomial probability table:

1. Enter the X values 0 through n into L_1.

2. Move the cursor to the top of the L_2 column so that L_2 is highlighted.

3. Type the command binompdf(n,p,L_1), then press **ENTER.**

Example: $n = 20$, $p = .05$ (Example 5–19 from the text)

Excel
Step by Step

Creating a Binomial Distribution and Graph

These instructions will demonstrate how Excel can be used to construct a binomial distribution table for $n = 20$ and $p = 0.35$.

1. Type **X** for the binomial variable label in cell A1 of an Excel worksheet.
2. Type **P(X)** for the corresponding probabilities in cell B1.
3. Enter the integers from 0 to 20 in column A starting at cell A2. Select the Data tab from the toolbar. Then select Data Analysis. Under Analysis Tools, select Random Number Generation and click [OK].
4. In the Random Number Generation dialog box, enter the following:
   a) Number of Variables: **1**
   b) Distribution: Patterned
   c) Parameters: From **0** to **20** in steps of **1**, repeating each number: **1** times and repeating each sequence **1** times
   d) Output range: **A2:A21**
5. Then click [OK].

Random Number
Generation Dialog Box

6. To determine the probability corresponding to the first value of the binomial random variable, select cell B2 and type: **=BINOMDIST(0,20,.35,FALSE).** This will give the probability of obtaining 0 successes in 20 trials of a binomial experiment for which the probability of success is 0.35.
7. Repeat step **6,** changing the first parameter, for each of the values of the random variable from column A.

Note: If you wish to obtain the cumulative probabilities for each of the values in column A, you can type: **=BINOMDIST(0,20,.35,TRUE)** and repeat for each of the values in column A.

To create the graph:

1. Select the Insert tab from the toolbar and the Column Chart.
2. Select the Clustered Column (the first column chart under the 2-D Column selections).
3. You will need to edit the data for the chart.
   a) Right-click the mouse on any location of the chart. Click the Select Data option. The Select Data Source dialog box will appear.
   b) Click **X** in the Legend Entries box and click Remove.
   c) Click the Edit button under Horizontal Axis Labels to insert a range for the variable X.
   d) When the Axis Labels box appears, highlight cells A2 to A21 on the worksheet, then click [OK].
4. To change the title of the chart:
   a) Left-click once on the current title.
   b) Type a new title for the chart, for example, Binomial Distribution (20, .35, .65).

Summary

Many variables have special probability distributions. This chapter presented several of the most common probability distributions, including the binomial distribution, the multinomial distribution, the Poisson distribution, and the hypergeometric distribution.

The binomial distribution is used when there are only two outcomes for an experiment, there are a fixed number of trials, the probability is the same for each trial, and the outcomes are independent of one another.

A probability distribution can be graphed, and the mean, variance, and standard deviation can be found. The mathematical expectation can also be calculated for a probability distribution. Expectation is used in insurance and games of chance.

Important Terms

binomial distribution 279

binomial experiment 279

discrete probability distribution 262

expected value 272

random variable 261

Important Formulas

Formula for the mean of a probability distribution:

$$\mu = \Sigma X \cdot P(X)$$

Formulas for the variance and standard deviation of a probability distribution:

$$\sigma^2 = \Sigma[X^2 \cdot P(X)] - \mu^2$$
$$\sigma = \sqrt{\Sigma[X^2 \cdot P(X)] - \mu^2}$$

Formula for expected value:

$$E(X) = \Sigma X \cdot P(X)$$

Binomial probability formula:

$$P(X) = \frac{n!}{(n - X)!X!} \cdot p^X \cdot q^{n-X}$$

Formula for the mean of the binomial distribution:

$$\mu = n \cdot p$$

Formulas for the variance and standard deviation of the binomial distribution:

$$\sigma^2 = n \cdot p \cdot q \qquad \sigma = \sqrt{n \cdot p \cdot q}$$

Review Exercises

For Exercises 1 through 3, determine whether the distribution represents a probability distribution. If it does not, state why.

1.

X	1	2	3	4	5
P(X)	$\frac{1}{10}$	$\frac{3}{10}$	$\frac{1}{10}$	$\frac{2}{10}$	$\frac{3}{10}$

2.

X	10	20	30
P(X)	0.1	0.4	0.3

3.

X	8	12	16	20
P(X)	$\frac{5}{6}$	$\frac{1}{12}$	$\frac{1}{12}$	$\frac{1}{12}$

4. **Emergency Calls** The number of emergency calls a local police department receives per 24-hour period is distributed as shown here. Construct a graph for the data.

Number of calls X	10	11	12	13	14
Probability P(X)	0.02	0.12	0.40	0.31	0.15

5. **Credit Cards** A large retail company encourages its employees to get customers to apply for the store credit card. Below is the distribution for the number of credit card applications received per employee for an 8-hour shift.

X	0	1	2	3	4	5
P(X)	0.27	0.28	0.20	0.15	0.08	0.02

   a. What is the probability that an employee will get 2 or 3 applications during any given shift?
   b. Find the mean, variance, and standard deviation for this probability distribution.

6. **Coins in a Box** A box contains 5 pennies, 3 dimes, 1 quarter, and 1 half-dollar. Construct a probability distribution and draw a graph for the data.

7. **Tie Purchases** At Tyler's Tie Shop, Tyler found the probabilities that a customer will buy 0, 1, 2, 3, or 4 ties, as shown. Construct a graph for the distribution.

Number of ties X	0	1	2	3	4
Probability P(X)	0.30	0.50	0.10	0.08	0.02

8. **Customers in a Bank** A bank has a drive-through service. The number of customers arriving during a 15-minute period is distributed as shown. Find the mean, variance, and standard deviation for the distribution.

Number of customers X	0	1	2	3	4
Probability P(X)	0.12	0.20	0.31	0.25	0.12

9. **Museum Visitors** At a small community museum, the number of visitors per hour during the day has the distribution shown here. Find the mean, variance, and standard deviation for the data.

Number of visitors X	13	14	15	16	17
Probability P(X)	0.12	0.15	0.29	0.25	0.19

10. **Cans of Paint Purchased** During a recent paint sale at Corner Hardware, the number of cans of paint purchased was distributed as shown. Find the mean, variance, and standard deviation of the distribution.

Number of cans X	1	2	3	4	5
Probability P(X)	0.42	0.27	0.15	0.10	0.06

11. **Inquiries Received** The number of inquiries received per day for a college catalog is distributed as shown. Find the mean, variance, and standard deviation for the data.

Number of inquiries X	22	23	24	25	26	27
Probability P(X)	0.08	0.19	0.36	0.25	0.07	0.05

12. **Outdoor Regatta** A producer plans an outdoor regatta for May 3. The cost of the regatta is $8000. This includes advertising, security, printing tickets, entertainment, etc. The producer plans to make $15,000 profit if all goes well. However, if it rains, the regatta will have to be canceled. According to the weather report, the probability of rain is 0.3. Find the producer's expected profit.

13. **Card Game** A game is set up as follows: All the diamonds are removed from a deck of cards, and these 13 cards are placed in a bag. The cards are mixed up, and then one card is chosen at random (and then replaced). The player wins according to the following rules.

   If the ace is drawn, the player loses $20.
   If a face card is drawn, the player wins $10.
   If any other card (2–10) is drawn, the player wins $2.

   How much should be charged to play this game in order for it to be fair?

14. Using Exercise 13, how much should be charged if instead of winning $2 for drawing a 2–10, the player wins the amount shown on the card in dollars?

15. Let x be a binomial random variable with $n = 12$ and $p = 0.3$. Find the following:
   a. $P(X = 8)$
   b. $P(X < 5)$
   c. $P(X \geq 10)$
   d. $P(4 < X \leq 9)$

16. **Internet Access via Cell Phone** Fourteen percent of cell phone users use their cell phones to access the Internet. In

a random sample of 10 cell phone users, what is the probability that exactly 2 have used their phones to access the Internet? More than 2?

Source: www.infoplease.com

17. Drug Calculation Test If 75% of nursing students are able to pass a drug calculation test, find the mean, variance, and standard deviation of the number of students who pass the test in a sample of 180 nursing students.

18. Flu Shots It has been reported that 63% of adults aged 65 and over got their flu shots last year. In a random sample of 300 adults aged 65 and over, find the mean, variance, and standard deviation for the number who got their flu shots.

Source: U.S. Center for Disease Control and Prevention.

19. U.S. Police Chiefs and the Death Penalty The chance that a U.S. police chief believes the death penalty "significantly reduces the number of homicides" is 1 in 4. If a random sample of 8 police chiefs is selected, find the probability that at most 3 believe that the death penalty significantly reduces the number of homicides.

Source: *Harper's Index.*

20. Household Wood Burning *American Energy Review* reported that 27% of American households burn wood. If a random sample of 500 American households is selected, find the mean, variance, and standard deviation of the number of households that burn wood.

Source: *100% American* by Daniel Evan Weiss.

21. Pizza for Breakfast Three out of four American adults under age 35 have eaten pizza for breakfast. If a random sample of 20 adults under age 35 is selected, find the probability that exactly 16 have eaten pizza for breakfast.

Source: *Harper's Index.*

22. Unmarried Women According to survey records, 75.4% of women aged 20–24 have never been married. In a random sample of 250 young women aged 20–24, find the mean, variance, and standard deviation for the number who are or who have been married.

Source: www.infoplease.com

Statistics Today

Is Pooling Worthwhile?—Revisited

In the case of the pooled sample, the probability that only one test will be needed can be determined by using the binomial distribution. The question being asked is, In a sample of 15 individuals, what is the probability that no individual will have the disease? Hence, $n = 15$, $p = 0.05$, and $X = 0$. From Table B in Appendix C, the probability is 0.463, or 46% of the time, only one test will be needed. For screening purposes, then, pooling samples in this case would save considerable time, money, and effort as opposed to testing every individual in the population.

Chapter Quiz

Determine whether each statement is true or false. If the statement is false, explain why.

1. The expected value of a random variable can be thought of as a long-run average.

2. The number of courses a student is taking this semester is an example of a continuous random variable.

3. When the binomial distribution is used, the outcomes must be dependent.

4. A binomial experiment has a fixed number of trials.

Complete these statements with the best answer.

5. Random variable values are determined by _____.

6. The mean for a binomial variable can be found by using the formula _____.

7. One requirement for a probability distribution is that the sum of all the events in the sample space must equal _____.

Select the best answer.

8. What is the sum of the probabilities of all outcomes in a probability distribution?
   - *a.* 0
   - *b.* $\frac{1}{2}$
   - *c.* 1
   - *d.* It cannot be determined.

9. How many outcomes are there in a binomial experiment?
   - *a.* 0
   - *b.* 1
   - *c.* 2
   - *d.* It varies.

10. The number of trials for a binomial experiment
   - *a.* Can be infinite
   - *b.* Is unchanged
   - *c.* Is unlimited
   - *d.* Must be fixed

For questions 11 through 14, determine if the distribution represents a probability distribution. If not, state why.

11.

X	1	2	3	4	5
P(X)	$\frac{1}{7}$	$\frac{2}{7}$	$\frac{2}{7}$	$\frac{3}{7}$	$\frac{2}{7}$

12.

X	3	6	9	12	15
P(X)	0.3	0.5	0.1	0.08	0.02

13.

X	50	75	100
P(X)	0.5	0.2	0.3

14.

X	4	8	12	16
P(X)	$\frac{1}{6}$	$\frac{3}{12}$	$\frac{1}{2}$	$\frac{1}{12}$

15. **Calls for a Fire Company** The number of fire calls the Conestoga Valley Fire Company receives per day is distributed as follows:

Number X	5	6	7	8	9
Probability P(X)	0.28	0.32	0.09	0.21	0.10

Construct a graph for the data.

16. **Telephones per Household** A study was conducted to determine the number of telephones each household has. The data are shown here.

Number of telephones	0	1	2	3	4
Frequency	2	30	48	13	7

Construct a probability distribution and draw a graph for the data.

17. **CD Purchases** During a recent CD sale at Matt's Music Store, the number of CDs customers purchased was distributed as follows:

Number X	0	1	2	3	4
Probability P(X)	0.10	0.23	0.31	0.27	0.09

Find the mean, variance, and standard deviation of the distribution.

18. **Calls for a Crisis Hot Line** The number of calls received per day at a crisis hot line is distributed as follows:

Number X	30	31	32	33	34
Probability P(X)	0.05	0.21	0.38	0.25	0.11

Find the mean, variance, and standard deviation of the distribution.

19. **Selecting a Card** There are 6 playing cards placed face down in a box. They are the 4 of diamonds, the 5 of hearts, the 2 of clubs, the 10 of spades, the 3 of diamonds, and the 7 of hearts. A person selects a card. Find the expected value of the draw.

20. **Selecting a Card** A person selects a card from an ordinary deck of cards. If it is a black card, she wins $2. If it is a red card between or including 3 and 7, she wins $10. If it is a red face card, she wins $25; and if it is a black jack, she wins an extra $100. Find the expectation of the game.

21. **Carpooling** If 40% of all commuters ride to work in carpools, find the probability that if 8 workers are selected, 5 will ride in carpools.

22. **Employed Women** If 60% of all women are employed outside the home, find the probability that in a sample of 20 women,
   a. Exactly 15 are employed
   b. At least 10 are employed
   c. At most 5 are not employed outside the home

23. **Driver's Exam** If 80% of the applicants are able to pass a driver's proficiency road test, find the mean, variance, and standard deviation of the number of people who pass the test in a sample of 300 applicants.

24. **Meeting Attendance** A history class has 75 members. If there is a 12% absentee rate per class meeting, find the mean, variance, and standard deviation of the number of students who will be absent from each class.

Critical Thinking Challenges

1. **Lottery Numbers** Pennsylvania has a lottery entitled "Big 4." To win, a player must correctly match four digits from a daily lottery in which four digits are selected. Find the probability of winning.

2. **Lottery Numbers** In the Big 4 lottery, for a bet of $100, the payoff is $5000. What is the expected value of winning? Is it worth it?

3. **Lottery Numbers** If you played the same four-digit number every day (or any four-digit number for that matter) in the Big 4, how often (in years) would you win, assuming you have average luck?

4. **Chuck-a-Luck** In the game Chuck-a-Luck, three dice are rolled. A player bets a certain amount (say $1.00) on a number from 1 to 6. If the number appears on 1 die, the person wins $1.00. If it appears on 2 dice, the person wins $2.00, and if it appears on all 3 dice, the person wins $3.00. What are the chances of winning $1.00? $2.00? $3.00?

5. **Chuck-a-Luck** What is the expected value of the game of Chuck-a-Luck if a player bets $1.00 on one number?

Data Projects

1. **Business and Finance** Assume that a life insurance company would like to make a profit of $250 on a $100,000 policy sold to a person whose probability of surviving the year is 0.9985. What premium should the company charge the customer? If the company would like to make a $250 profit on a $100,000 policy at a premium of $500, what is the lowest life expectancy it should accept for a customer?

2. **Sports and Leisure** Baseball, hockey, and basketball all use a seven-game series to determine their championship. Find the probability that with two evenly matched teams a champion will be found in 4 games. Repeat for 5, 6, and 7 games. Look at the historical results for the three sports. How do the actual results compare to the theoretical?

3. **Technology** Use your most recent itemized phone bill for the data in this problem. Assume that incoming and outgoing calls are equal in the population (why is this a reasonable assumption?). This means assume $p = 0.5$. For the number of calls you made last month, what would be the mean number of outgoing calls in a random selection of calls? Also, compute the standard deviation. Was the number of outgoing calls you made an unusual amount given the above? In a selection of 12 calls, what is the probability that less than 3 were outgoing?

4. **Health and Wellness** Use Red Cross data to determine the percentage of the population with an Rh factor that is positive (A+, B+, AB+, or O+ blood types). Use that value for p. How many students in your class have a positive Rh factor? Is this an unusual amount?

5. **Politics and Economics** Find out what percentage of citizens in your state is registered to vote. Assuming that this is a binomial variable, what would be the mean number of registered voters in a random group of citizens with a sample size equal to the number of students in your class? Also determine the standard deviation. How many students in your class are registered to vote? Is this an unusual number, given the above?

6. **Your Class** Have each student in class toss 4 coins on her or his desk, and note how many heads are showing. Create a frequency table displaying the results. Compare the frequency table to the theoretical probability distribution for the outcome when 4 coins are tossed. Find the mean for the frequency table. How does it compare with the mean for the probability distribution?

Answers to Applying the Concepts

Section 5–1   Dropping College Courses

1. The random variable under study is the reason for dropping a college course.

2. There were a total of 144 people in the study.

3. The complete table is as follows:

Reason for dropping a college course	Frequency	Percentage
Too difficult	45	31.25
Illness	40	27.78
Change in work schedule	20	13.89
Change of major	14	9.72
Family-related problems	9	6.25
Money	7	4.86
Miscellaneous	6	4.17
No meaningful reason	3	2.08

4. The probability that a student will drop a class because of illness is about 28%. The probability that a student will drop a class because of money is about 5%. The probability that a student will drop a class because of a change of major is about 10%.

5. The information is not itself a probability distribution, but it can be used as one.

6. The categories are not necessarily mutually exclusive, but we treated them as such in computing the probabilities.

7. The categories are not independent.

8. The categories are exhaustive.

9. Since all the probabilities are between 0 and 1, inclusive, and the probabilities sum to 1, the requirements for a discrete probability distribution are met.

Section 5–2   Expected Value

1. The expected value is the mean in a discrete probability distribution.

2. We would expect variation from the expected value of 3.

3. Answers will vary. One possible answer is that pregnant mothers in that area might be overly concerned upon hearing that the number of cases of kidney problems in newborns was nearly 4 times what was usually expected. Other mothers (particularly those who had taken a statistics course!) might ask for more information about the claim.

4. Answers will vary. One possible answer is that it does seem unlikely to have 11 newborns with kidney problems when we expect only 3 newborns to have kidney problems.

5. The public might better be informed by percentages or rates (e.g., rate per 1000 newborns).

6. The increase of 8 babies born with kidney problems represents a 0.32% increase (less than $\frac{1}{2}$%).

7. Answers will vary. One possible answer is that the percentage increase does not seem to be something to be overly concerned about.

Section 5–3   Unsanitary Restaurants

1. The probability of eating at 3 restaurants with unsanitary conditions out of the 10 restaurants is 0.18651.

2. The probability of eating at 4 or 5 restaurants with unsanitary conditions out of the 10 restaurants is $0.24623 + 0.22291 = 0.46914$.

3. To find this probability, you could add the probabilities for eating at 1, 2, . . . , 10 unsanitary restaurants. An easier way to compute the probability is to subtract the probability of eating at no unsanitary restaurants from 1 (using the complement rule).

4. The highest probability for this distribution is 4, but the expected number of unsanitary restaurants that you would eat at is $10 \cdot \frac{3}{7} = 4.3$.

5. The standard deviation for this distribution is $\sqrt{(10)(\frac{3}{7})(\frac{4}{7})} = 1.56$.

6. This is a binomial distribution. We have two possible outcomes: "success" is eating in an unsanitary restaurant; "failure" is eating in a sanitary restaurant. The probability that one restaurant is unsanitary is independent of the probability that any other restaurant is unsanitary. The probability that a restaurant is unsanitary remains constant at $\frac{3}{7}$. And we are looking at the number of unsanitary restaurants that we eat at out of 10 "trials."

7. The likelihood of success will vary from situation to situation. Just because we have two possible outcomes, this does not mean that each outcome occurs with probability 0.50.

6

The Normal Distribution

Objectives

After completing this chapter, you should be able to

1 Identify distributions as symmetric or skewed.

2 Identify the properties of a normal distribution.

3 Find the area under the standard normal distribution, given various *z* values.

4 Find probabilities for a normally distributed variable by transforming it into a standard normal variable.

5 Find specific data values for given percentages, using the standard normal distribution.

6 Use the central limit theorem to solve problems involving sample means for large samples.

7 Use the normal approximation to compute probabilities for a binomial variable.

Outline

What Is Normal?

Medical researchers have determined so-called normal intervals for a person's blood pressure, cholesterol, triglycerides, and the like. For example, the normal range of systolic blood pressure is 110 to 140. The normal interval for a person's triglycerides is from 30 to 200 milligrams per deciliter (mg/dl). By measuring these variables, a physician can determine if a patient's vital statistics are within the normal interval or if some type of treatment is needed to correct a condition and avoid future illnesses. The question then is, How does one determine the so-called normal intervals? See Statistics Today—Revisited at the end of the chapter.

In this chapter, you will learn how researchers determine normal intervals for specific medical tests by using a normal distribution. You will see how the same methods are used to determine the lifetimes of batteries, the strength of ropes, and many other traits.

Introduction

Random variables can be either discrete or continuous. Discrete variables and their distributions were explained in Chapter 5. Recall that a discrete variable cannot assume all values between any two given values of the variables. On the other hand, a continuous variable can assume all values between any two given values of the variables. Examples of continuous variables are the heights of adult men, body temperatures of rats, and cholesterol levels of adults. Many continuous variables, such as the examples just mentioned, have distributions that are bell-shaped, and these are called *approximately normally distributed variables*. For example, if a researcher selects a random sample of 100 adult women, measures their heights, and constructs a histogram, the researcher gets a graph similar to the one shown in Figure 6–1(a). Now, if the researcher increases the sample size and decreases the width of the classes, the histograms will look like the ones shown in Figure 6–1(b) and (c). Finally, if it were possible to measure exactly the heights of all adult females in the United States and plot them, the histogram would approach what is called a *normal distribution,* shown in Figure 6–1(d). This distribution is also known as

Figure 6–1

Histograms for the Distribution of Heights of Adult Women

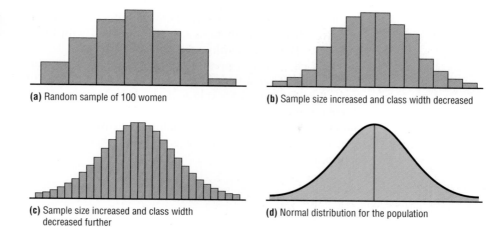

(a) Random sample of 100 women

(b) Sample size increased and class width decreased

(c) Sample size increased and class width decreased further

(d) Normal distribution for the population

Figure 6–2

Normal and Skewed Distributions

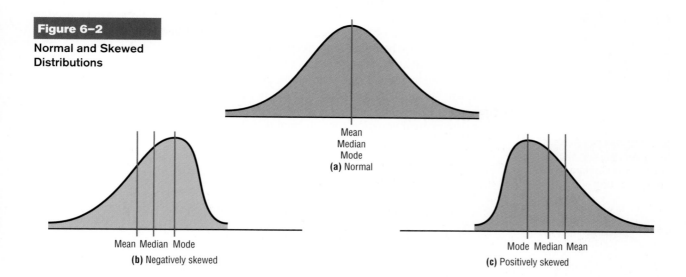

Mean
Median
Mode
(a) Normal

Mean Median Mode
(b) Negatively skewed

Mode Median Mean
(c) Positively skewed

a *bell curve* or a *Gaussian distribution,* named for the German mathematician Carl Friedrich Gauss (1777–1855), who derived its equation.

No variable fits a normal distribution perfectly, since a normal distribution is a theoretical distribution. However, a normal distribution can be used to describe many variables, because the deviations from a normal distribution are very small. This concept will be explained further in Section 6–1.

Objective 1

Identify distributions as symmetric or skewed.

When the data values are evenly distributed about the mean, a distribution is said to be a **symmetric distribution.** (A normal distribution is symmetric.) Figure 6–2(a) shows a symmetric distribution. When the majority of the data values fall to the left or right of the mean, the distribution is said to be *skewed.* When the majority of the data values fall to the right of the mean, the distribution is said to be a **negatively or left-skewed distribution.** The mean is to the left of the median, and the mean and the median are to the left of the mode. See Figure 6–2(b). When the majority of the data values fall to the left of the mean, a distribution is said to be a **positively or right-skewed distribution.** The mean falls to the right of the median, and both the mean and the median fall to the right of the mode. See Figure 6–2(c).

The "tail" of the curve indicates the direction of skewness (right is positive, left is negative). These distributions can be compared with the ones shown in Figure 3–1 in Chapter 3. Both types follow the same principles.

This chapter will present the properties of a normal distribution and discuss its applications. Then a very important fact about a normal distribution called the *central limit theorem* will be explained. Finally, the chapter will explain how a normal distribution curve can be used as an approximation to other distributions, such as the binomial distribution. Since a binomial distribution is a discrete distribution, a correction for continuity may be employed when a normal distribution is used for its approximation.

6–1   Normal Distributions

Objective **2**

Identify the properties of a normal distribution.

In mathematics, curves can be represented by equations. For example, the equation of the circle shown in Figure 6–3 is $x^2 + y^2 = r^2$, where r is the radius. A circle can be used to represent many physical objects, such as a wheel or a gear. Even though it is not possible to manufacture a wheel that is perfectly round, the equation and the properties of a circle can be used to study many aspects of the wheel, such as area, velocity, and acceleration. In a similar manner, the theoretical curve, called a *normal distribution curve,* can be used to study many variables that are not perfectly normally distributed but are nevertheless approximately normal.

The mathematical equation for a normal distribution is

$$y = \frac{e^{-(X-\mu)^2/(2\sigma^2)}}{\sigma\sqrt{2\pi}}$$

Figure 6–3

Graph of a Circle and an Application

Circle

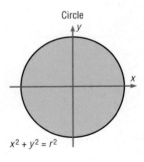

$x^2 + y^2 = r^2$

Wheel

where

$e \approx 2.718$ ($\approx$ means "is approximately equal to")

$\pi \approx 3.14$

μ = population mean

σ = population standard deviation

This equation may look formidable, but in applied statistics, tables or technology is used for specific problems instead of the equation.

Another important consideration in applied statistics is that the area under a normal distribution curve is used more often than the values on the y axis. Therefore, when a normal distribution is pictured, the y axis is sometimes omitted.

Circles can be different sizes, depending on their diameters (or radii), and can be used to represent wheels of different sizes. Likewise, normal curves have different shapes and can be used to represent different variables.

The shape and position of a normal distribution curve depend on two parameters, the *mean* and the *standard deviation.* Each normally distributed variable has its own normal distribution curve, which depends on the values of the variable's mean and standard deviation. Figure 6–4(a) shows two normal distributions with the same mean values but different standard deviations. The larger the standard deviation, the more dispersed, or spread out, the distribution is. Figure 6–4(b) shows two normal distributions with the same standard deviation but with different means. These curves have the same shapes but are located at different positions on the x axis. Figure 6–4(c) shows two normal distributions with different means and different standard deviations.

Figure 6–4

Shapes of Normal Distributions

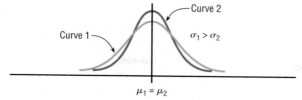

(a) Same means but different standard deviations

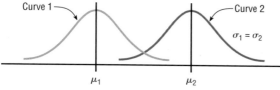

(b) Different means but same standard deviations

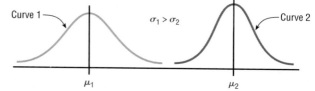

(c) Different means and different standard deviations

Historical Notes

The discovery of the equation for a normal distribution can be traced to three mathematicians. In 1733, the French mathematician Abraham DeMoivre derived an equation for a normal distribution based on the random variation of the number of heads appearing when a large number of coins were tossed. Not realizing any connection with the naturally occurring variables, he showed this formula to only a few friends. About 100 years later, two mathematicians, Pierre Laplace in France and Carl Gauss in Germany, derived the equation of the normal curve independently and without any knowledge of DeMoivre's work. In 1924, Karl Pearson found that DeMoivre had discovered the formula before Laplace or Gauss.

A **normal distribution** is a continuous, symmetric, bell-shaped distribution of a variable.

The properties of a normal distribution, including those mentioned in the definition, are explained next.

Summary of the Properties of the Theoretical Normal Distribution

1. A normal distribution curve is bell-shaped.
2. The mean, median, and mode are equal and are located at the center of the distribution.
3. A normal distribution curve is unimodal (i.e., it has only one mode).
4. The curve is symmetric about the mean, which is equivalent to saying that its shape is the same on both sides of a vertical line passing through the center.
5. The curve is continuous; that is, there are no gaps or holes. For each value of X, there is a corresponding value of Y.
6. The curve never touches the x axis. Theoretically, no matter how far in either direction the curve extends, it never meets the x axis—but it gets increasingly closer.
7. The total area under a normal distribution curve is equal to 1.00, or 100%. This fact may seem unusual, since the curve never touches the x axis, but one can prove it mathematically by using calculus. (The proof is beyond the scope of this textbook.)
8. The area under the part of a normal curve that lies within 1 standard deviation of the mean is approximately 0.68, or 68%; within 2 standard deviations, about 0.95, or 95%; and within 3 standard deviations, about 0.997, or 99.7%. See Figure 6–5, which also shows the area in each region.

The values given in item 8 of the summary follow the *empirical rule* for data given in Section 3–2.

You must know these properties in order to solve problems involving distributions that are approximately normal.

Figure 6–5

Areas Under a Normal Distribution Curve

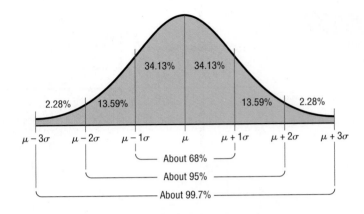

The Standard Normal Distribution

Since each normally distributed variable has its own mean and standard deviation, as stated earlier, the shape and location of these curves will vary. In practical applications, then, you would have to have a table of areas under the curve for each variable. To simplify this situation, statisticians use what is called the *standard normal distribution*.

Objective 3

Find the area under the standard normal distribution, given various z values.

> The **standard normal distribution** is a normal distribution with a mean of 0 and a standard deviation of 1.

The standard normal distribution is shown in Figure 6–6.

The values under the curve indicate the proportion of area in each section. For example, the area between the mean and 1 standard deviation above or below the mean is about 0.3413, or 34.13%.

The formula for the standard normal distribution is

$$y = \frac{e^{-z^2/2}}{\sqrt{2\pi}}$$

All normally distributed variables can be transformed into the standard normally distributed variable by using the formula for the standard score:

$$z = \frac{\text{value} - \text{mean}}{\text{standard deviation}} \qquad \text{or} \qquad z = \frac{X - \mu}{\sigma}$$

This is the same formula used in Section 3–3. The use of this formula will be explained in Section 6–3.

As stated earlier, the area under a normal distribution curve is used to solve practical application problems, such as finding the percentage of adult women whose height is between 5 feet 4 inches and 5 feet 7 inches, or finding the probability that a new battery will last longer than 4 years. Hence, the major emphasis of this section will be to show the procedure for finding the area under the standard normal distribution curve for any z value. The applications will be shown in Section 6–2. Once the X values are transformed by using the preceding formula, they are called z values. The **z value** is actually the number of standard deviations that a particular X value is away from the mean. Table E in Appendix C gives the area (to four decimal places) under the standard normal curve for any z value from −3.49 to 3.49.

Figure 6–6

Standard Normal
Distribution

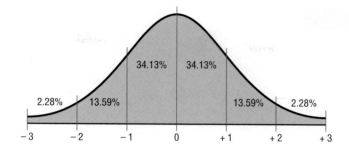

34.13%   34.13%

2.28%   13.59%   13.59%   2.28%

−3   −2   −1   0   +1   +2   +3

Finding Areas Under the Standard Normal Distribution Curve

For the solution of problems using the standard normal distribution, a four-step procedure is recommended with the use of the Procedure Table shown.

Step 1   Draw the normal distribution curve and shade the area.

Step 2   Find the appropriate figure in the Procedure Table and follow the directions
given.

There are three basic types of problems, and all three are summarized in the
Procedure Table. Note that this table is presented as an aid in understanding how to use
the standard normal distribution table and in visualizing the problems. After learning
the procedures, you should *not* find it necessary to refer to the Procedure Table for every
problem.

Procedure Table

Finding the Area Under the Standard Normal Distribution Curve

1. To the left of any z value:
   Look up the z value in the table and use the area given.

2. To the right of any z value:
   Look up the z value and subtract the area from 1.

3. Between any two z values:
   Look up both z values and subtract the
   corresponding areas.

Figure 6–7

Table E Area Value for
z = 1.39

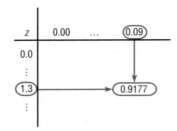

Table E in Appendix C gives the area under the normal distribution curve to the left of any *z* value given in two decimal places. For example, the area to the left of a *z* value of 1.39 is found by looking up 1.3 in the left column and 0.09 in the top row. Where the two lines meet gives an area of 0.9177. See Figure 6–7.

Example 6–1

Find the area to the left of *z* = 1.99.

Solution

Step 1   Draw the figure. The desired area is shown in Figure 6–8.

Figure 6–8

Area Under the
Standard Normal
Distribution Curve for
Example 6–1

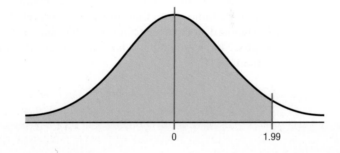

Step 2   We are looking for the area under the standard normal distribution curve to the left of *z* = 1.99. Since this is an example of the first case, look up the area in the table. It is 0.9767. Hence 97.67% of the area is less than *z* = 1.99.

Example 6–2

Find the area to the right of *z* = −1.16.

Solution

Step 1   Draw the figure. The desired area is shown in Figure 6–9.

Figure 6–9

Area Under the
Standard Normal
Distribution Curve for
Example 6–2

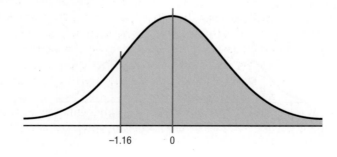

Step 2   We are looking for the area to the right of $z = -1.16$. This is an example of the second case. Look up the area for $z = -1.16$. It is 0.3770. Subtract it from 1.000. $1.000 - 0.1230 = 0.8770$. Hence 87.70% of the area under the standard normal distribution curve is to the left of $z = -1.16$.

Example 6–3   Find the area between $z = +1.68$ and $z = -1.37$.

Solution

Step 1   Draw the figure as shown. The desired area is shown in Figure 6–10.

Figure 6–10

Area Under the
Standard Normal
Distribution Curve
for Example 6–3

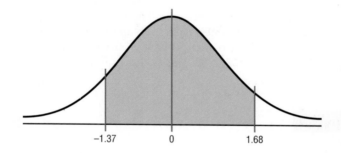

Step 2   Since the area desired is between two given z values, look up the areas corresponding to the two z values and subtract the smaller area from the larger area. (Do not subtract the z values.) The area for $z = +1.68$ is 0.9535, and the area for $z = -1.37$ is 0.0853. The area between the two z values is $0.9535 - 0.0853 = 0.8682$ or 86.82%.

A Normal Distribution Curve as a Probability Distribution Curve

A normal distribution curve can be used as a probability distribution curve for normally distributed variables. Recall that a normal distribution is a *continuous distribution,* as opposed to a discrete probability distribution, as explained in Chapter 5. The fact that it is continuous means that there are no gaps in the curve. In other words, for every z value on the x axis, there is a corresponding height, or frequency, value.

The area under the standard normal distribution curve can also be thought of as a probability. That is, if it were possible to select any z value at random, the probability of choosing one, say, between 0 and 2.00 would be the same as the area under the curve between 0 and 2.00. In this case, the area is 0.4772. Therefore, the probability of randomly selecting any z value between 0 and 2.00 is 0.4772. The problems involving probability are solved in the same manner as the previous examples involving areas in this section. For example, if the problem is to find the probability of selecting a z value between 2.25 and 2.94, solve it by using the method shown in case 3 of the Procedure Table.

For probabilities, a special notation is used. For example, if the problem is to find the probability of any z value between 0 and 2.32, this probability is written as $P(0 < z < 2.32)$.

Note: In a continuous distribution, the probability of any exact z value is 0 since the area would be represented by a vertical line above the value. But vertical lines in theory have no area. So $P(a \leq z \leq b) = P(a < z < b)$.

Example 6–4

Find the probability for each.

    a. $P(0 < z < 2.32)$
    b. $P(z < 1.65)$
    c. $P(z > 1.91)$

Solution

    a. $P(0 < z < 2.32)$ means to find the area under the standard normal distribution curve between 0 and 2.32. First look up the area corresponding to 2.32. It is 0.9898. Then look up the area corresponding to $z = 0$. It is 0.500. Subtract the two areas: $0.9898 - 0.5000 = 0.4898$. Hence the probability is 0.4898, or 48.98%. This is shown in Figure 6–11.

Figure 6–11

Area Under the
Standard Normal
Distribution Curve for
Part *a* of Example 6–4

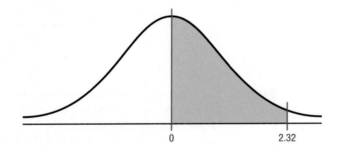

                             0   2.32

    b. $P(z < 1.65)$ is represented in Figure 6–12. Look up the area corresponding to $z = 1.65$ in Table E. It is 0.9505. Hence, $P(z < 1.65) = 0.9505$, or 95.05%.

Figure 6–12

Area Under the
Standard Normal
Distribution Curve
for Part *b* of
Example 6–4

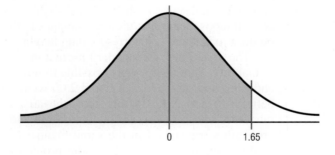

                             0   1.65

    c. $P(z > 1.91)$ is shown in Figure 6–13. Look up the area that corresponds to $z = 1.91$. It is 0.9719. Then subtract this area from 1.0000. $P(z < 1.91) = 1.0000 - 0.9719 = 0.0281$, or 2.81%.

Figure 6–13

Area Under the
Standard Normal
Distribution Curve
for Part c of
Example 6–4

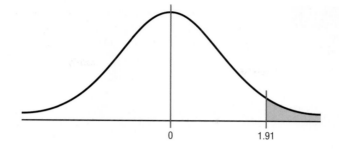

Sometimes, one must find a specific z value for a given area under the standard normal distribution curve. The procedure is to work backward, using Table E.

Since Table E is cumulative, it is necessary to locate the cumulative area up to a given z value. Example 6–5 shows this.

Example 6–5

Find the z value such that the area under the standard normal distribution curve between 0 and the z value is 0.2123.

Solution

Draw the figure. The area is shown in Figure 6–14.

Figure 6–14

Area Under the
Standard Normal
Distribution Curve for
Example 6–5

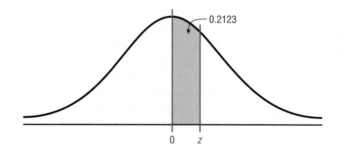

In this case it is necessary to add 0.5000 to the given area of 0.2123 to get the cumulative area of 0.7123. Look up the area in Table E. The value in the left column is 0.5, and the top value is 0.06, so the positive z value for the area $z = 0.56$.

Next, find the area in Table E, as shown in Figure 6–15. Then read the correct z value in the left column as 0.5 and in the top row as 0.06, and add these two values to get 0.56.

Figure 6–15

Finding the z Value
from Table E for
Example 6–5

Figure 6–16

The Relationship
Between Area and
Probability

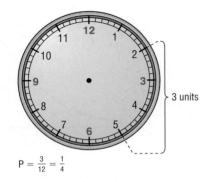

$P = \frac{3}{12} = \frac{1}{4}$

(a) Clock

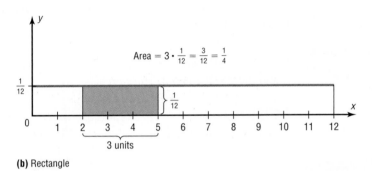

(b) Rectangle

If the exact area cannot be found, use the closest value. For example, if you wanted to find the z value for an area 0.9241, the closest area is 0.9236, which gives a z value of 1.43. See Table E in Appendix C.

The rationale for using an area under a continuous curve to determine a probability can be understood by considering the example of a watch that is powered by a battery. When the battery goes dead, what is the probability that the minute hand will stop somewhere between the numbers 2 and 5 on the face of the watch? In this case, the values of the variable constitute a continuous variable since the hour hand can stop anywhere on the dial's face between 0 and 12 (one revolution of the minute hand). Hence, the sample space can be considered to be 12 units long, and the distance between the numbers 2 and 5 is $5 - 2$, or 3 units. Hence, the probability that the minute hand stops on a number between 2 and 5 is $\frac{3}{12} = \frac{1}{4}$. See Figure 6–16(a).

The problem could also be solved by using a graph of a continuous variable. Let us assume that since the watch can stop anytime at random, the values where the minute hand would land are spread evenly over the range of 0 through 12. The graph would then consist of a *continuous uniform distribution* with a range of 12 units. Now if we require the area under the curve to be 1 (like the area under the standard normal distribution), the height of the rectangle formed by the curve and the x axis would need to be $\frac{1}{12}$. The reason is that the area of a rectangle is equal to the base times the height. If the base is 12 units long, then the height has to be $\frac{1}{12}$ since $12 \cdot \frac{1}{12} = 1$.

The area of the rectangle with a base from 2 through 5 would be $3 \cdot \frac{1}{12}$, or $\frac{1}{4}$. See Figure 6–16(b). Notice that the area of the small rectangle is the same as the probability found previously. Hence the area of this rectangle corresponds to the probability of this event. The same reasoning can be applied to the standard normal distribution curve shown in Example 6–5.

Finding the area under the standard normal distribution curve is the first step in solving a wide variety of practical applications in which the variables are normally distributed. Some of these applications will be presented in Section 6–2.

Applying the Concepts 6–1

Assessing Normality

Many times in statistics it is necessary to see if a set of data values is approximately normally distributed. There are special techniques that can be used. One technique is to draw a histogram for the data and see if it is approximately bell-shaped. (*Note:* It does not have to be exactly symmetric to be bell-shaped.)

The numbers of branches of the 50 top libraries are shown.

67	84	80	77	97	59	62	37	33	42
36	54	18	12	19	33	49	24	25	22
24	29	9	21	21	24	31	17	15	21
13	19	19	22	22	30	41	22	18	20
26	33	14	14	16	22	26	10	16	24

Source: *The World Almanac and Book of Facts.*

1. Construct a frequency distribution for the data.

2. Construct a histogram for the data.

3. Describe the shape of the histogram.

4. Based on your answer to question 3, do you feel that the distribution is approximately normal?

In addition to the histogram, distributions that are approximately normal have about 68% of the values fall within 1 standard deviation of the mean, about 95% of the data values fall within 2 standard deviations of the mean, and almost 100% of the data values fall within 3 standard deviations of the mean. (See Figure 6–5.)

5. Find the mean and standard deviation for the data.

6. What percent of the data values fall within 1 standard deviation of the mean?

7. What percent of the data values fall within 2 standard deviations of the mean?

8. What percent of the data values fall within 3 standard deviations of the mean?

9. How do your answers to questions 6, 7, and 8 compare to 68, 95, and 100%, respectively?

10. Does your answer help support the conclusion you reached in question 4? Explain.

(More techniques for assessing normality are explained in Section 6–2.)
See pages 351 and 352 for the answers.

Exercises 6–1

1. What are the characteristics of a normal distribution?

2. Why is the standard normal distribution important in statistical analysis?

3. What is the total area under the standard normal distribution curve?

4. What percentage of the area falls below the mean? Above the mean?

5. About what percentage of the area under the normal distribution curve falls within 1 standard deviation above and below the mean? 2 standard deviations? 3 standard deviations?

For Exercises 6 through 25, find the area under the standard normal distribution curve.

6. Between $z = 0$ and $z = 1.89$

7. Between $z = 0$ and $z = 0.75$

8. Between $z = 0$ and $z = -0.46$

9. Between $z = 0$ and $z = -2.07$

10. To the right of $z = 2.11$

11. To the right of $z = 0.23$

12. To the left of $z = -0.75$

13. To the left of $z = -1.43$

14. Between $z = 1.23$ and $z = 1.90$

15. Between $z = 1.05$ and $z = 1.78$

16. Between $z = -0.96$ and $z = -0.36$

17. Between $z = -1.56$ and $z = -1.83$

18. Between $z = 0.24$ and $z = -1.12$

19. Between $z = -1.53$ and $z = -2.08$

20. To the left of $z = 1.31$

21. To the left of $z = 2.11$

22. To the right of $z = -1.92$

23. To the right of $z = -0.25$

24. To the left of $z = -2.15$ and to the right of $z = 1.62$

25. To the right of $z = 1.92$ and to the left of $z = -0.44$

In Exercises 26 through 39, find the probabilities for each, using the standard normal distribution.

26. $P(0 < z < 1.96)$

27. $P(0 < z < 0.67)$

28. $P(-1.23 < z < 0)$

29. $P(-1.57 < z < 0)$

30. $P(z > 0.82)$

31. $P(z > 2.83)$

32. $P(z < -1.77)$

33. $P(z < -1.21)$

34. $P(-0.20 < z < 1.56)$

35. $P(-2.46 < z < 1.74)$

36. $P(1.12 < z < 1.43)$

37. $P(1.46 < z < 2.97)$

38. $P(z > -1.43)$

39. $P(z < 1.42)$

For Exercises 40 through 45, find the z value that corresponds to the given area.

40.

41.

42.

43.

44.

45.

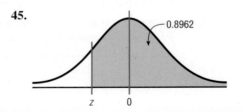

46. Find the z value to the right of the mean so that

  a. 54.78% of the area under the distribution curve lies to the left of it.

  b. 69.85% of the area under the distribution curve lies to the left of it.

  c. 88.10% of the area under the distribution curve lies to the left of it.

47. Find the z value to the left of the mean so that

  a. 98.87% of the area under the distribution curve lies to the right of it.

  b. 82.12% of the area under the distribution curve lies to the right of it.

  c. 60.64% of the area under the distribution curve lies to the right of it.

48. Find two z values so that 48% of the middle area is bounded by them.

49. Find two z values, one positive and one negative, that are equidistant from the mean so that the areas in the two tails total the following values.

    a. 5%

    b. 10%

    c. 1%

Extending the Concepts

50. In the standard normal distribution, find the values of z for the 75th, 80th, and 92nd percentiles.

51. Find $P(-1 < z < 1)$, $P(-2 < z < 2)$, and $P(-3 < z < 3)$. How do these values compare with the empirical rule?

52. Find z_0 such that $P(z > z_0) = 0.1234$.

53. Find z_0 such that $P(-1.2 < z < z_0) = 0.8671$.

54. Find z_0 such that $P(z_0 < z < 2.5) = 0.7672$.

55. Find z_0 such that the area between z_0 and $z = -0.5$ is 0.2345 (two answers).

56. Find z_0 such that $P(-z_0 < z < z_0) = 0.76$.

57. Find the equation for the standard normal distribution by substituting 0 for μ and 1 for σ in the equation

$$y = \frac{e^{-(X-\mu)^2/(2\sigma^2)}}{\sigma\sqrt{2\pi}}$$

58. Graph by hand the standard normal distribution by using the formula derived in Exercise 57. Let $\pi \approx 3.14$ and $e \approx 2.718$. Use X values of $-2, -1.5, -1, -0.5, 0, 0.5, 1, 1.5,$ and 2. (Use a calculator to compute the y values.)

Technology *Step by Step*

MINITAB
Step by Step

The Standard Normal Distribution

It is possible to determine the height of the density curve given a value of z, the cumulative area given a value of z, or a z value given a cumulative area. Examples are from Table E in Appendix C.

Find the Area to the Left of $z = 1.39$

1. Select **Calc>Probability Distributions>Normal.** There are three options.

2. Click the button for Cumulative probability. In the center section, the mean and standard deviation for the standard normal distribution are the defaults. The mean should be **0,** and the standard deviation should be **1.**

3. Click the button for Input Constant, then click inside the text box and type in **1.39.** Leave the storage box empty.

4. Click [OK].

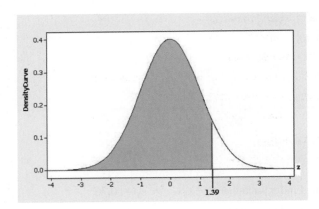

Cumulative Distribution Function

Normal with mean = 0 and standard deviation = 1

$x\ P(\ X <= x\ )$

1.39   0.917736

The graph is not shown in the output.

The session window displays the result, 0.917736. If you choose the optional storage, type in a variable name such as **K1.** The result will be stored in the constant and will not be in the session window.

Find the Area to the Right of −2.06

1. Select **Calc>Probability Distributions>Normal.**

2. Click the button for Cumulative probability.

3. Click the button for Input Constant, then enter **−2.06** in the text box. Do not forget the minus sign.

4. Click in the text box for Optional storage and type **K1.**

5. Click [OK]. The area to the left of −2.06 is stored in K1 but not displayed in the session window.

   To determine the area to the right of the z value, subtract this constant from 1, then display the result.

6. Select **Calc>Calculator.**

   a) Type **K2** in the text box for Store result in:.

   b) Type in the expression **1 − K1,** then click [OK].

7. Select **Data>Display Data.** Drag the mouse over K1 and K2, then click [Select] and [OK].

   The results will be in the session window and stored in the constants.

Data Display

K1   0.0196993

K2   0.980301

8. To see the constants and other information about the worksheet, click the Project Manager icon. In the left pane click on the green worksheet icon, and then click the constants folder. You should see all constants and their values in the right pane of the Project Manager.

9. For the third example calculate the two probabilities and store them in K1 and K2.

10. Use the calculator to subtract K1 from K2 and store in K3.

    The calculator and project manager windows are shown.

Calculate a z Value Given the Cumulative Probability

Find the z value for a cumulative probability of 0.025.

1. Select **Calc>Probability Distributions>Normal.**

2. Click the option for Inverse cumulative probability, then the option for Input constant.

3. In the text box type **.025,** the cumulative area, then click [OK].

4. In the dialog box, the z value will be returned, -1.960.

Inverse Cumulative Distribution Function
Normal with mean $= 0$ and standard deviation $= 1$

P (X <= x)	x
0.025	-1.95996

In the session window z is -1.95996.

TI-83 Plus or TI-84 Plus
Step by Step

```
normalcdf(1.11,E
99)
     .1334995565
normalcdf(-E99,-
1.93)
     .0268033499
■
```

```
normalcdf(2,2.47
)
     .0159944012
invNorm(.7123)
     .560116461
■
```

Standard Normal Random Variables

To find the probability for a standard normal random variable:
Press **2nd [DISTR],** then **2** for normalcdf(
The form is normalcdf(lower z score, upper z score).
Use E99 for ∞ (infinity) and $-$E99 for $-\infty$ (negative infinity). Press **2nd [EE]** to get E.

Example: Area to the right of $z = 1.11$
normalcdf(1.11,E99)

Example: Area to the left of $z = -1.93$
normalcdf($-$E99,$-$1.93)

Example: Area between $z = 2.00$ and $z = 2.47$
normalcdf(2.00,2.47)

To find the percentile for a standard normal random variable:
Press **2nd [DISTR],** then **3** for the invNorm(
The form is invNorm(area to the left of z score)

Example: Find the z score such that the area under the standard normal curve to the left of it is 0.7123
invNorm(.7123)

Excel
Step by Step

The Standard Normal Distribution

Finding areas under the standard normal distribution curve

Example XL6–1

Find the area to the left of $z = 1.99$.
In a blank cell type: =NORMSDIST(1.99)
Answer: 0.976705

Example XL6–2

Find the area to the right of $z = -2.04$.
In a blank cell type: = 1-NORMSDIST($-$2.04)
Answer: 0.979325

Example XL6–3

Find the area between $z = -2.04$ and $z = 1.99$.
In a blank cell type: =NORMSDIST(1.99) − NORMSDIST(−2.04)
Answer: 0.956029

Finding a z value given an area under the standard normal distribution curve

Example XL6–4

Find a z score given the cumulative area (area to the left of z) is 0.0250.
In a blank cell type: =NORMSINV(.025)
Answer: −1.95996

6–2   Applications of the Normal Distribution

Objective 4

Find probabilities for a normally distributed variable by transforming it into a standard normal variable.

The standard normal distribution curve can be used to solve a wide variety of practical problems. The only requirement is that the variable be normally or approximately normally distributed. There are several mathematical tests to determine whether a variable is normally distributed. See the Critical Thinking Challenges on page 350. For all the problems presented in this chapter, you can assume that the variable is normally or approximately normally distributed.

To solve problems by using the standard normal distribution, transform the original variable to a standard normal distribution variable by using the formula

$$z = \frac{\text{value} - \text{mean}}{\text{standard deviation}} \quad \text{or} \quad z = \frac{X - \mu}{\sigma}$$

This is the same formula presented in Section 3–3. This formula transforms the values of the variable into standard units or z values. Once the variable is transformed, then the Procedure Table and Table E in Appendix C can be used to solve problems.

For example, suppose that the scores for a standardized test are normally distributed, have a mean of 100, and have a standard deviation of 15. When the scores are transformed to z values, the two distributions coincide, as shown in Figure 6–17. (Recall that the z distribution has a mean of 0 and a standard deviation of 1.)

Figure 6–17

Test Scores and Their Corresponding z Values

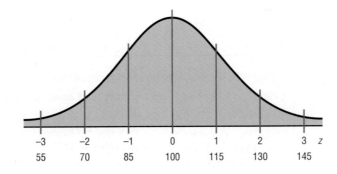

To solve the application problems in this section, transform the values of the variable to z values and then find the areas under the standard normal distribution, as shown in Section 6–1.

Example 6–6	**Holiday Spending**

A survey by the National Retail Federation found that women spend on average $146.21 for the Christmas holidays. Assume the standard deviation is $29.44. Find the percentage of women who spend less than $160.00. Assume the variable is normally distributed.

Solution

Step 1   Draw the figure and represent the area as shown in Figure 6–18.

Figure 6–18	
Area Under a Normal Curve for Example 6–6	$146.21 $160

Step 2   Find the z value corresponding to $160.00.

$$z = \frac{X - \mu}{\sigma} = \frac{\$160.00 - \$146.21}{\$29.44} = 0.47$$

Hence $160.00 is 0.47 of a standard deviation above the mean of $146.21, as shown in the z distribution in Figure 6–19.

Figure 6–19	
Area and z Values for Example 6–6	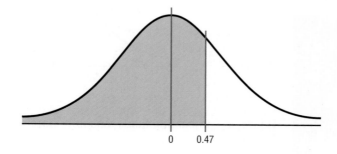 0 0.47

Step 3   Find the area, using Table E. The area under the curve to the left of $z = 0.47$ is 0.6808.

Therefore 0.6808, or 68.08%, of the women spend less than $160.00 at Christmas time.

Example 6–7	**Monthly Newspaper Recycling**

Each month, an American household generates an average of 28 pounds of newspaper for garbage or recycling. Assume the standard deviation is 2 pounds. If a household is selected at random, find the probability of its generating

 a. Between 27 and 31 pounds per month

 b. More than 30.2 pounds per month

Assume the variable is approximately normally distributed.

Source: Michael D. Shook and Robert L. Shook, *The Book of Odds.*

Solution a

Step 1 Draw the figure and represent the area. See Figure 6–20.

Figure 6–20

Figure 6–20

Area Under a Normal
Curve for Part *a* of
Example 6–7

Step 2 Find the two z values.

$$z_1 = \frac{X - \mu}{\sigma} = \frac{27 - 28}{2} = -\frac{1}{2} = -0.5$$

$$z_2 = \frac{X - \mu}{\sigma} = \frac{31 - 28}{2} = \frac{3}{2} = 1.5$$

Step 3 Find the appropriate area, using Table E. The area to the left of z_2 is 0.9332, and the area to the left of z_1 is 0.3085. Hence the area between z_1 and z_2 is $0.9332 - 0.3085 = 0.6247$. See Figure 6–21.

Figure 6–21

Area and *z* Values for
Part *a* of Example 6–7

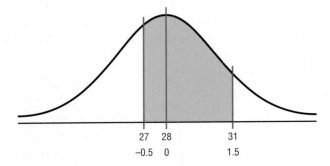

Hence, the probability that a randomly selected household generates between 27 and 31 pounds of newspapers per month is 62.47%.

Solution b

Step 1 Draw the figure and represent the area, as shown in Figure 6–22.

Figure 6–22

Area Under a Normal
Curve for Part *b* of
Example 6–7

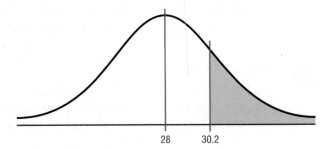

Step 2 Find the z value for 30.2.

$$z = \frac{X - \mu}{\sigma} = \frac{30.2 - 28}{2} = \frac{2.2}{2} = 1.1$$

Step 3 Find the appropriate area. The area to the left of $z = 1.1$ is 0.8643. Hence the area to the right of $z = 1.1$ is $1.0000 - 0.8643 = 0.1357$.

Hence, the probability that a randomly selected household will accumulate more than 30.2 pounds of newspapers is 0.1357, or 13.57%.

A normal distribution can also be used to answer questions of "How many?" This application is shown in Example 6–8.

Example 6–8

Emergency Call Response Time

The American Automobile Association reports that the average time it takes to respond to an emergency call is 25 minutes. Assume the variable is approximately normally distributed and the standard deviation is 4.5 minutes. If 80 calls are randomly selected, approximately how many will be responded to in less than 15 minutes?

Source: Michael D. Shook and Robert L. Shook, *The Book of Odds.*

Solution

To solve the problem, find the area under a normal distribution curve to the left of 15.

Step 1 Draw a figure and represent the area as shown in Figure 6–23.

Figure 6–23

Area Under a
Normal Curve for
Example 6–8

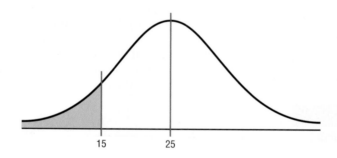

Step 2 Find the z value for 15.

$$z = \frac{X - \mu}{\sigma} = \frac{15 - 25}{4.5} = -2.22$$

Step 3 Find the area to the left of $z = -2.22$. It is 0.0132.

Step 4 To find how many calls will be made in less than 15 minutes, multiply the sample size 80 by 0.0132 to get 1.056. Hence, 1.056, or approximately 1, call will be responded to in under 15 minutes.

Note: For problems using percentages, be sure to change the percentage to a decimal before multiplying. Also, round the answer to the nearest whole number, since it is not possible to have 1.056 calls.

Finding Data Values Given Specific Probabilities

A normal distribution can also be used to find specific data values for given percentages. This application is shown in Example 6–9.

Example 6–9	

Police Academy Qualifications

To qualify for a police academy, candidates must score in the top 10% on a general abilities test. The test has a mean of 200 and a standard deviation of 20. Find the lowest possible score to qualify. Assume the test scores are normally distributed.

Objective **5**

Find specific data values for given percentages, using the standard normal distribution.

Solution

Since the test scores are normally distributed, the test value X that cuts off the upper 10% of the area under a normal distribution curve is desired. This area is shown in Figure 6–24.

Figure 6–24

Area Under a Normal Curve for Example 6–9

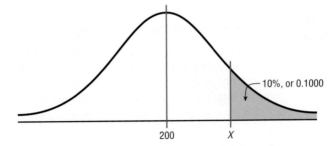

Work backward to solve this problem.

Step 1   Subtract 0.1000 from 1.000 to get the area under the normal distribution to the left of x: $1.0000 - 0.10000 = 0.9000$.

Step 2   Find the z value that corresponds to an area of 0.9000 by looking up 0.9000 in the area portion of Table E. If the specific value cannot be found, use the closest value—in this case 0.8997, as shown in Figure 6–25. The corresponding z value is 1.28. (If the area falls exactly halfway between two z values, use the larger of the two z values. For example, the area 0.9500 falls halfway between 0.9495 and 0.9505. In this case use 1.65 rather than 1.64 for the z value.)

Figure 6–25

Finding the z Value from Table E (Example 6–9)

z	.00	.01	.02	.03	.04	.05	.06	.07	.08	.09
0.0										
0.1										
0.2										
⋮										
1.1										
1.2									0.8997	0.9015
1.3										
1.4										
⋮										

Specific value
0.9000

Closest value

Step 3   Substitute in the formula $z = (X - \mu)/\sigma$ and solve for X.

$$1.28 = \frac{X - 200}{20}$$

$$(1.28)(20) + 200 = X$$

$$25.60 + 200 = X$$

$$225.60 = X$$

$$226 = X$$

A score of 226 should be used as a cutoff. Anybody scoring 226 or higher qualifies.

Interesting Fact

Americans are the largest consumers of chocolate. We spend $16.6 billion annually.

Instead of using the formula shown in step 3, you can use the formula $X = z \cdot \sigma + \mu$. This is obtained by solving

$$z = \frac{X - \mu}{\sigma}$$

for X as shown.

$z \cdot \sigma = X - \mu$ Multiply both sides by σ.

$z \cdot \sigma + \mu = X$ Add μ to both sides.

$X = z \cdot \sigma + \mu$ Exchange both sides of the equation.

Formula for Finding X

When you must find the value of X, you can use the following formula:

$$X = z \cdot \sigma + \mu$$

Example 6–10

Systolic Blood Pressure

For a medical study, a researcher wishes to select people in the middle 60% of the population based on blood pressure. If the mean systolic blood pressure is 120 and the standard deviation is 8, find the upper and lower readings that would qualify people to participate in the study.

Solution

Assume that blood pressure readings are normally distributed; then cutoff points are as shown in Figure 6–26.

Figure 6–26

Area Under a
Normal Curve for
Example 6–10

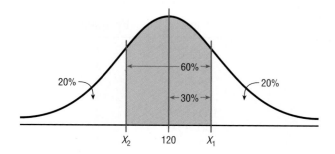

Figure 6–26 shows that two values are needed, one above the mean and one below the mean. To get the area to the left of the positive z value, add $0.5000 + 0.3000 = 0.8000$ (30% = 0.3000). The z value closest to 0.8000 is 0.84. Substituting in the formula $X = z\sigma + \mu$ gives

$$X_1 = z\sigma + \mu = (0.84)(8) + 120 = 126.72$$

The area to the left of the negative z value is 20%, or 2.000. The area closest to 0.2000 is -0.84.

$$X_2 = (-0.84)(8) + 120 = 113.28$$

Therefore, the middle 60% will have blood pressure readings of $113.28 < X < 126.72$.

As shown in this section, a normal distribution is a useful tool in answering many questions about variables that are normally or approximately normally distributed.

Determining Normality

A normally shaped or bell-shaped distribution is only one of many shapes that a distribution can assume; however, it is very important since many statistical methods require that the distribution of values (shown in subsequent chapters) be normally or approximately normally shaped.

There are several ways statisticians check for normality. The easiest way is to draw a histogram for the data and check its shape. If the histogram is not approximately bell-shaped, then the data are not normally distributed.

Skewness can be checked by using Pearson's index PI of skewness. The formula is

$$PI = \frac{3(\bar{X} - \text{median})}{s}$$

If the index is greater than or equal to $+1$ or less than or equal to -1, it can be concluded that the data are significantly skewed.

In addition, the data should be checked for outliers by using the method shown in Chapter 3. Even one or two outliers can have a big effect on normality.

Examples 6–11 and 6–12 show how to check for normality.

Example 6–11

Technology Inventories

 A survey of 18 high-technology firms showed the number of days' inventory they had on hand. Determine if the data are approximately normally distributed.

5	29	34	44	45	63	68	74	74
81	88	91	97	98	113	118	151	158

Source: *USA TODAY.*

Solution

Step 1 Construct a frequency distribution and draw a histogram for the data, as shown in Figure 6–27.

Class	Frequency
5–29	2
30–54	3
55–79	4
80–104	5
105–129	2
130–154	1
155–179	1

Figure 6–27

Histogram for Example 6–11

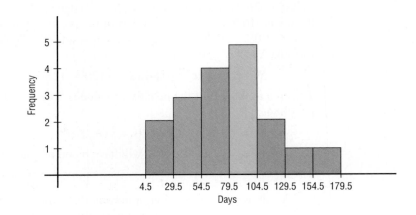

Since the histogram is approximately bell-shaped, we can say that the distribution is approximately normal.

Step 2   Check for skewness. For these data, $\overline{X} = 79.5$, median $= 77.5$, and $s = 40.5$. Using Pearson's index of skewness gives

$$PI = \frac{3(79.5 - 77.5)}{40.5}$$

$$= 0.148$$

In this case, the PI is not greater than $+1$ or less than -1, so it can be concluded that the distribution is not significantly skewed.

Step 3   Check for outliers. Recall that an outlier is a data value that lies more than 1.5 (IQR) units below Q_1 or 1.5 (IQR) units above Q_3. In this case, $Q_1 = 45$ and $Q_3 = 98$; hence, IQR $= Q_3 - Q_1 = 98 - 45 = 53$. An outlier would be a data value less than $45 - 1.5(53) = -34.5$ or a data value larger than $98 + 1.5(53) = 177.5$. In this case, there are no outliers.

Since the histogram is approximately bell-shaped, the data are not significantly skewed, and there are no outliers, it can be concluded that the distribution is approximately normally distributed.

Example 6–12   **Number of Baseball Games Played**

 The data shown consist of the number of games played each year in the career of Baseball Hall of Famer Bill Mazeroski. Determine if the data are approximately normally distributed.

81	148	152	135	151	152
159	142	34	162	130	162
163	143	67	112	70	

Source: *Greensburg Tribune Review.*

Solution

Step 1   Construct a frequency distribution and draw a histogram for the data. See Figure 6–28.

Figure 6–28

Histogram for
Example 6–12

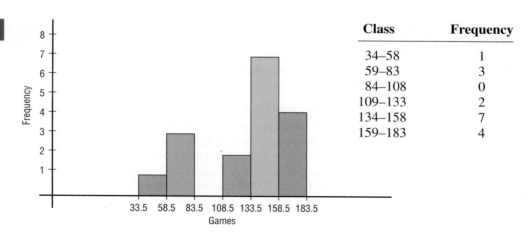

Class	Frequency
34–58	1
59–83	3
84–108	0
109–133	2
134–158	7
159–183	4

The histogram shows that the frequency distribution is somewhat negatively skewed.

Step 2   Check for skewness; $\bar{X} = 127.24$, median $= 143$, and $s = 39.87$.

$$PI = \frac{3(\bar{X} - \text{median})}{s}$$

$$= \frac{3(127.24 - 143)}{39.87}$$

$$= -1.19$$

Since the PI is less than -1, it can be concluded that the distribution is significantly skewed to the left.

Step 3   Check for outliers. In this case, $Q_1 = 96.5$ and $Q_3 = 155.5$. IQR $= Q_3 - Q_1 = 155.5 - 96.5 = 59$. Any value less than $96.5 - 1.5(59) = 8$ or above $155.5 + 1.5(59) = 244$ is considered an outlier. There are no outliers.

In summary, the distribution is somewhat negatively skewed.

Another method that is used to check normality is to draw a *normal quantile plot. Quantiles,* sometimes called *fractiles,* are values that separate the data set into approximately equal groups. Recall that quartiles separate the data set into four approximately equal groups, and deciles separate the data set into 10 approximately equal groups. A normal quantile plot consists of a graph of points using the data values for the *x* coordinates and the *z* values of the quantiles corresponding to the *x* values for the *y* coordinates. (*Note:* The calculations of the *z* values are somewhat complicated, and technology is usually used to draw the graph. The Technology Step by Step section shows how to draw a normal quantile plot.) If the points of the quantile plot do not lie in an approximately straight line, then normality can be rejected.

There are several other methods used to check for normality. A method using normal probability graph paper is shown in the Critical Thinking Challenge section at the end of this chapter, and the chi-square goodness-of-fit test is shown in Chapter 11. Two other tests sometimes used to check normality are the Kolmogorov-Smikirov test and the Lilliefors test. An explanation of these tests can be found in advanced textbooks.

Applying the Concepts 6–2

Smart People

Assume you are thinking about starting a Mensa chapter in your hometown of Visiala, California, which has a population of about 10,000 people. You need to know how many people would qualify for Mensa, which requires an IQ of at least 130. You realize that IQ is normally distributed with a mean of 100 and a standard deviation of 15. Complete the following.

1. Find the approximate number of people in Visiala who are eligible for Mensa.
2. Is it reasonable to continue your quest for a Mensa chapter in Visiala?
3. How could you proceed to find out how many of the eligible people would actually join the new chapter? Be specific about your methods of gathering data.
4. What would be the minimum IQ score needed if you wanted to start an Ultra-Mensa club that included only the top 1% of IQ scores?

See page 352 for the answers.

Exercises 6–2

1. **Admission Charge for Movies** The average admission charge for a movie is $5.81. If the distribution of movie admission charges is approximately normal with a standard deviation of $0.81, what is the probability that a randomly selected admission charge is less than $3.50?

   Source: *New York Times Almanac.*

2. **Teachers' Salaries** The average annual salary for all U.S. teachers is $47,750. Assume that the distribution is normal and the standard deviation is $5680. Find the probability that a randomly selected teacher earns

   a. Between $35,000 and $45,000 a year
   b. More than $40,000 a year
   c. If you were applying for a teaching position and were offered $31,000 a year, how would you feel (based on this information)?

   Source: *New York Times Almanac.*

3. **Population in U.S. Jails** The average daily jail population in the United States is 706,242. If the distribution is normal and the standard deviation is 52,145, find the probability that on a randomly selected day, the jail population is

   a. Greater than 750,000
   b. Between 600,000 and 700,000

   Source: *New York Times Almanac.*

4. **SAT Scores** The national average SAT score (for Verbal and Math) is 1028. If we assume a normal distribution with $\sigma = 92$, what is the 90th percentile score? What is the probability that a randomly selected score exceeds 1200?

   Source: *New York Times Almanac.*

5. **Chocolate Bar Calories** The average number of calories in a 1.5-ounce chocolate bar is 225. Suppose that the distribution of calories is approximately normal with $\sigma = 10$. Find the probability that a randomly selected chocolate bar will have

   a. Between 200 and 220 calories
   b. Less than 200 calories

   Source: *The Doctor's Pocket Calorie, Fat, and Carbohydrate Counter.*

6. **Monthly Mortgage Payments** The average monthly mortgage payment including principal and interest is $982 in the United States. If the standard deviation is approximately $180 and the mortgage payments are approximately normally distributed, find the probability that a randomly selected monthly payment is

   a. More than $1000
   b. More than $1475
   c. Between $800 and $1150

   Source: *World Almanac.*

7. **Professors' Salaries** The average salary for a Queens College full professor is $85,900. If the average salaries are normally distributed with a standard deviation of $11,000, find these probabilities.

   a. The professor makes more than $90,000.
   b. The professor makes more than $75,000.

   Source: AAUP, *Chronicle of Higher Education.*

8. **Doctoral Student Salaries** Full-time Ph.D. students receive an average of $12,837 per year. If the average salaries are normally distributed with a standard deviation of $1500, find these probabilities.

   a. The student makes more than $15,000.
   b. The student makes between $13,000 and $14,000.

   Source: U.S. Education Dept., *Chronicle of Higher Education.*

9. **Miles Driven Annually** The mean number of miles driven per vehicle annually in the United States is 12,494 miles. Choose a randomly selected vehicle, and assume the annual mileage is normally distributed with a standard deviation of 1290 miles. What is the probability that the vehicle was driven more than 15,000 miles? Less than 8000 miles? Would you buy a vehicle if you had been told that it had been driven less than 6000 miles in the past year?

   Source: *World Almanac.*

10. **Commute Time to Work** The average commute to work (one way) is 25 minutes according to the 2005 American Community Survey. If we assume that commuting times are normally distributed and that the standard deviation is 6.1 minutes, what is the probability that a randomly selected commuter spends more than 30 minutes commuting one way? Less than 18 minutes?

   Source: www.census.gov

11. **Credit Card Debt** The average credit card debt for college seniors is $3262. If the debt is normally distributed with a standard deviation of $1100, find these probabilities.

   a. That the senior owes at least $1000
   b. That the senior owes more than $4000
   c. That the senior owes between $3000 and $4000

   Source: *USA TODAY.*

12. **Price of Gasoline** The average retail price of gasoline (all types) for the first half of 2005 was 212.2 cents. What would the standard deviation have to be in order for a 15% probability that a gallon of gas costs less than $1.80?

   Source: *World Almanac.*

13. **Time for Mail Carriers** The average time for a mail carrier to cover a route is 380 minutes, and the standard deviation is 16 minutes. If one of these trips is selected at random, find the probability that the carrier will have the following route time. Assume the variable is normally distributed.

a. At least 350 minutes

b. At most 395 minutes

c. How might a mail carrier estimate a range for the time he or she will spend en route?

14. Newborn Elephant Weights Newborn elephant calves usually weigh between 200 and 250 pounds—until October 2006, that is. An Asian elephant at the Houston (Texas) Zoo gave birth to a male calf weighing in at a whopping 384 pounds! Mack (like the truck) is believed to be the heaviest elephant calf ever born at a facility accredited by the Association of Zoos and Aquariums. If, indeed, the mean weight for newborn elephant calves is 225 pounds with a standard deviation of 45 pounds, what is the probability of a newborn weighing at least 384 pounds? Assume that the weights of newborn elephants are normally distributed.

Source: www.houstonzoo.org

15. Waiting to Be Seated The average waiting time to be seated for dinner at a popular restaurant is 23.5 minutes, with a standard deviation of 3.6 minutes. Assume the variable is normally distributed. When a patron arrives at the restaurant for dinner, find the probability that the patron will have to wait the following time.

a. Between 15 and 22 minutes

b. Less than 18 minutes or more than 25 minutes

c. Is it likely that a person will be seated in less than 15 minutes?

16. Salary of Full-Time Male Professors The average salary of a male full professor at a public four-year institution offering classes at the doctoral level is $99,685. For a female full professor at the same kind of institution, the salary is $90,330. If the standard deviation for the salaries of both genders is approximately $5200 and the salaries are normally distributed, find the 80th percentile salary for male professors and for female professors.

Source: *World Almanac.*

17. Used Boat Prices A marine sales dealer finds that the average price of a previously owned boat is $6492. He decides to sell boats that will appeal to the middle 66% of the market in terms of price. Find the maximum and minimum prices of the boats the dealer will sell. The standard deviation is $1025, and the variable is normally distributed. Would a boat priced at $5550 be sold in this store?

18. Itemized Charitable Contributions The average charitable contribution itemized per income tax return in Pennsylvania is $792. Suppose that the distribution of contributions is normal with a standard deviation of $103. Find the limits for the middle 50% of contributions.

Source: IRS, *Statistics of Income Bulletin.*

19. New Home Sizes A contractor decided to build homes that will include the middle 80% of the market. If the average size of homes built is 1810 square feet,

find the maximum and minimum sizes of the homes the contractor should build. Assume that the standard deviation is 92 square feet and the variable is normally distributed.

Source: Michael D. Shook and Robert L. Shook, *The Book of Odds.*

20. New Home Prices If the average price of a new one-family home is $246,300 with a standard deviation of $15,000, find the minimum and maximum prices of the houses that a contractor will build to satisfy the middle 80% of the market. Assume that the variable is normally distributed.

Source: *New York Times Almanac.*

21. Cost of Personal Computers The average price of a personal computer (PC) is $949. If the computer prices are approximately normally distributed and $\sigma = \$100$, what is the probability that a randomly selected PC costs more than $1200? The least expensive 10% of personal computers cost less than what amount?

Source: *New York Times Almanac.*

22. Reading Improvement Program To help students improve their reading, a school district decides to implement a reading program. It is to be administered to the bottom 5% of the students in the district, based on the scores on a reading achievement exam. If the average score for the students in the district is 122.6, find the cutoff score that will make a student eligible for the program. The standard deviation is 18. Assume the variable is normally distributed.

23. Used Car Prices An automobile dealer finds that the average price of a previously owned vehicle is $8256. He decides to sell cars that will appeal to the middle 60% of the market in terms of price. Find the maximum and minimum prices of the cars the dealer will sell. The standard deviation is $1150, and the variable is normally distributed.

24. Ages of Amtrak Passenger Cars The average age of Amtrak passenger train cars is 19.4 years. If the distribution of ages is normal and 20% of the cars are older than 22.8 years, find the standard deviation.

Source: *New York Times Almanac.*

25. Lengths of Hospital Stays The average length of a hospital stay for all diagnoses is 4.8 days. If we assume that the lengths of hospital stays are normally distributed with a variance of 2.1, then 10% of hospital stays are longer than how many days? Thirty percent of stays are less than how many days?

Source: www.cdc.gov

26. High School Competency Test A mandatory competency test for high school sophomores has a normal distribution with a mean of 400 and a standard deviation of 100.

a. The top 3% of students receive $500. What is the minimum score you would need to receive this award?

b. The bottom 1.5% of students must go to summer school. What is the minimum score you would need to stay out of this group?

27. Product Marketing An advertising company plans to market a product to low-income families. A study states that for a particular area, the average income per family is $24,596 and the standard deviation is $6256. If the company plans to target the bottom 18% of the families based on income, find the cutoff income. Assume the variable is normally distributed.

28. Bottled Drinking Water Americans drank an average of 23.2 gallons of bottled water per capita in 2004. If the standard deviation is 2.7 gallons and the variable is normally distributed, find the probability that a randomly selected American drank more than 25 gallons of bottled water. What is the probability that the selected person drank between 18 and 26 gallons?

Source: www.census.gov

29. Wristwatch Lifetimes The mean lifetime of a wristwatch is 25 months, with a standard deviation of 5 months. If the distribution is normal, for how many months should a guarantee be made if the manufacturer does not want to exchange more than 10% of the watches? Assume the variable is normally distributed.

30. Security Officer Stress Tolerance To qualify for security officers' training, recruits are tested for stress tolerance. The scores are normally distributed, with a mean of 62 and a standard deviation of 8. If only the top 15% of recruits are selected, find the cutoff score.

31. In the distributions shown, state the mean and standard deviation for each. *Hint:* See Figures 6-5 and 6-6. Also the vertical lines are 1 standard deviation apart.

a.

b.

c.

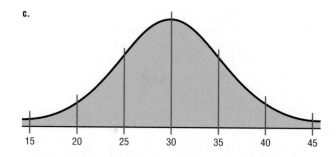

32. SAT Scores Suppose that the mathematics SAT scores for high school seniors for a specific year have a mean of 456 and a standard deviation of 100 and are approximately normally distributed. If a subgroup of these high school seniors, those who are in the National Honor Society, is selected, would you expect the distribution of scores to have the same mean and standard deviation? Explain your answer.

33. Given a data set, how could you decide if the distribution of the data was approximately normal?

34. If a distribution of raw scores were plotted and then the scores were transformed to z scores, would the shape of the distribution change? Explain your answer.

35. In a normal distribution, find σ when $\mu = 110$ and 2.87% of the area lies to the right of 112.

36. In a normal distribution, find μ when σ is 6 and 3.75% of the area lies to the left of 85.

37. In a certain normal distribution, 1.25% of the area lies to the left of 42, and 1.25% of the area lies to the right of 48. Find μ and σ.

38. Exam Scores An instructor gives a 100-point examination in which the grades are normally distributed. The mean is 60 and the standard deviation is 10. If there are 5% A's and 5% F's, 15% B's and 15% D's, and 60% C's, find the scores that divide the distribution into those categories.

39. Drive-in Movies The data shown represent the number of outdoor drive-in movies in the United States for a 14-year period. Check for normality.

2084	1497	1014	910	899	870	837	859
848	826	815	750	637	737		

Source: National Association of Theater Owners.

40. Cigarette Taxes The data shown represent the cigarette tax (in cents) for 30 randomly selected states. Check for normality.

3	58	5	65	17	48	52	75	21	76	58	36
100	111	34	41	23	44	33	50	13	18	7	12
20	24	66	28	28	31						

Source: Commerce Clearing House.

41. Box Office Revenues The data shown represent the box office total revenue (in millions of dollars) for a randomly selected sample of the top-grossing films in 2001. Check for normality.

294	241	130	144	113	70	97	94	91	202	74	79
71	67	67	56	180	199	165	114	60	56	53	51

Source: *USA TODAY.*

 42. Number of Runs Made The data shown represent the number of runs made each year during Bill Mazeroski's career. Check for normality.

30	59	69	50	58	71	55	43	66	52	56	62
36	13	29	17	3							

Source: *Greensburg Tribune Review.*

Technology *Step by Step*

MINITAB
Step by Step

Determining Normality

There are several ways in which statisticians test a data set for normality. Four are shown here.

Construct a Histogram

Inspect the histogram for shape.

Data

5	29	34	44	45
63	68	74	74	81
88	91	97	98	113
118	151	158		

1. Enter the data in the first column of a new worksheet. Name the column Inventory.

2. Use **Stat>Basic Statistics>Graphical Summary** presented in Section 3–3 to create the histogram. Is it symmetric? Is there a single peak?

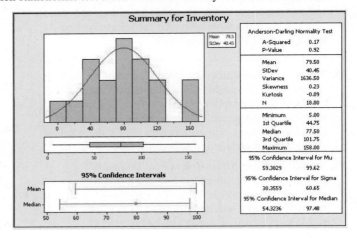

Check for Outliers

Inspect the boxplot for outliers. There are no outliers in this graph. Furthermore, the box is in the middle of the range, and the median is in the middle of the box. Most likely this is not a skewed distribution either.

Calculate Pearson's Index of Skewness

The measure of skewness in the graphical summary is not the same as Pearson's index. Use the calculator and the formula.

$$PI = \frac{3(\overline{X} - \text{median})}{s}$$

3. Select **Calc>Calculator,** then type **PI** in the text box for Store result in:.

4. Enter the expression: **3*(MEAN(C1)−MEDI(C1))/(STDEV(C1)).** Make sure you get all the parentheses in the right place!

5. Click [OK]. The result, 0.148318, will be stored in the first row of C2 named PI. Since it is smaller than +1, the distribution is not skewed.

Construct a Normal Probability Plot

6. Select **Graph>Probability Plot,** then Single and click [OK].

7. Double-click C1 Inventory to select the data to be graphed.

8. Click [Distribution] and make sure that Normal is selected. Click [OK].

9. Click [Labels] and enter the title for the graph: **Quantile Plot for Inventory.** You may also put **Your Name** in the subtitle.

10. Click [OK] twice. Inspect the graph to see if the graph of the points is linear.

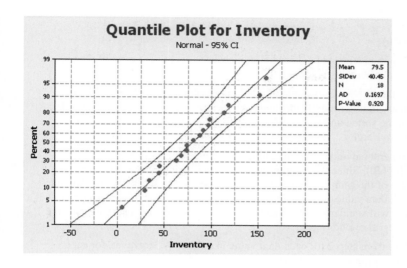

Quantile Plot for Inventory
Normal – 95% CI

Mean	79.5
StDev	40.45
N	18
AD	0.1697
P-Value	0.920

These data are nearly normal.

What do you look for in the plot?

a) An "S curve" indicates a distribution that is too thick in the tails, a uniform distribution, for example.

b) Concave plots indicate a skewed distribution.

c) If one end has a point that is extremely high or low, there may be outliers.

This data set appears to be nearly normal by every one of the four criteria!

TI-83 Plus or TI-84 Plus
Step by Step

Normal Random Variables

To find the probability for a normal random variable:
Press **2nd [DISTR],** then **2** for normalcdf(
The form is normalcdf(lower x value, upper x value, μ, σ)
Use E99 for ∞ (infinity) and $-$E99 for $-\infty$ (negative infinity). Press **2nd [EE]** to get E.

Example: Find the probability that x is between 27 and 31 when $\mu = 28$ and $\sigma = 2$ (Example 6–7a from the text).
normalcdf(27,31,28,2)

To find the percentile for a normal random variable:
Press **2nd [DISTR],** then **3** for invNorm(
The form is invNorm(area to the left of x value, μ, σ)

Example: Find the 90th percentile when $\mu = 200$ and $\sigma = 20$ (Example 6–9 from text).
invNorm(.9,200,20)

```
normalcdf(27,31,
28,2)
         .6246552391
invNorm(.9,200,2
0)
         225.6310313
```

To construct a normal quantile plot:

1. Enter the data values into L_1.

2. Press **2nd [STAT PLOT]** to get the STAT PLOT menu.

3. Press **1** for Plot 1.

4. Turn on the plot by pressing **ENTER** while the cursor is flashing over ON.

5. Move the cursor to the normal quantile plot (6th graph).

6. Make sure L_1 is entered for the Data List and X is highlighted for the Data Axis.

7. Press **WINDOW** for the Window menu. Adjust Xmin and Xmax according to the data values. Adjust Ymin and Ymax as well, Ymin $= -3$ and Ymax $= 3$ usually work fine.

8. Press **GRAPH.**

Using the data from the previous example gives

Since the points in the normal quantile plot lie close to a straight line, the distribution is approximately normal.

Excel
Step by Step

Normal Quantile Plot

Excel can be used to construct a normal quantile plot in order to examine if a set of data is approximately normally distributed.

1. Enter the data from the MINITAB example into column A of a new worksheet. The data should be sorted in ascending order. If the data are not already sorted in ascending order, highlight the data to be sorted and select the Sort & Filter icon from the toolbar. Then select Sort Smallest to Largest.

2. After all the data are entered and sorted in column A, select cell B1. Type: =NORMSINV(1/(2*18)). Since the sample size is 18, each score represents $\frac{1}{18}$, or approximately 5.6%, of the sample. Each data value is assumed to subdivide the data into equal intervals. Each data value corresponds to the midpoint of a particular subinterval. Thus, this procedure will standardize the data by assuming each data value represents the midpoint of a subinterval of width $\frac{1}{18}$.

3. Repeat the procedure from step 2 for each data value in column A. However, for each subsequent value in column A, enter the next odd multiple of $\frac{1}{36}$ in the argument for the NORMSINV function. For example, in cell B2, type: =NORMSINV(3/(2*18)). In cell B3, type: =NORMSINV(5/(2*18)), and so on until all the data values have corresponding z scores.

4. Highlight the data from columns A and B, and select Insert, then Scatter chart. Select the Scatter with only markers (the first Scatter chart).

5. To insert a title to the chart: Left-click on any region of the chart. Select Chart Tools and Layout from the toolbar. Then select Chart Title.

6. To insert a label for the variable on the horizontal axis: Left-click on any region of the chart. Select Chart Tools and Layout form the toolbar. Then select Axis Titles>Primary Horizontal Axis Title.

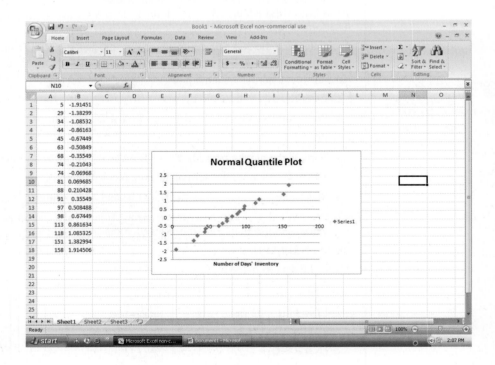

The points on the chart appear to lie close to a straight line. Thus, we deduce that the data are approximately normally distributed.

Objective 6

Use the central limit theorem to solve problems involving sample means for large samples.

The Central Limit Theorem

In addition to knowing how individual data values vary about the mean for a population, statisticians are interested in knowing how the means of samples of the same size taken from the same population vary about the population mean.

Distribution of Sample Means

Suppose a researcher selects a sample of 30 adult males and finds the mean of the measure of the triglyceride levels for the sample subjects to be 187 milligrams/deciliter. Then suppose a second sample is selected, and the mean of that sample is found to be 192 milligrams/deciliter. Continue the process for 100 samples. What happens then is that the mean becomes a random variable, and the sample means 187, 192, 184, . . . , 196 constitute a *sampling distribution of sample means.*

> A **sampling distribution of sample means** is a distribution using the means computed from all possible random samples of a specific size taken from a population.

If the samples are randomly selected with replacement, the sample means, for the most part, will be somewhat different from the population mean μ. These differences are caused by sampling error.

> **Sampling error** is the difference between the sample measure and the corresponding population measure due to the fact that the sample is not a perfect representation of the population.

When all possible samples of a specific size are selected with replacement from a population, the distribution of the sample means for a variable has two important properties, which are explained next.

> **Properties of the Distribution of Sample Means**
>
> 1. The mean of the sample means will be the same as the population mean.
> 2. The standard deviation of the sample means will be smaller than the standard deviation of the population, and it will be equal to the population standard deviation divided by the square root of the sample size.

The following example illustrates these two properties. Suppose a professor gave an 8-point quiz to a small class of four students. The results of the quiz were 2, 6, 4, and 8. For the sake of discussion, assume that the four students constitute the population. The mean of the population is

$$\mu = \frac{2 + 6 + 4 + 8}{4} = 5$$

The standard deviation of the population is

$$\sigma = \sqrt{\frac{(2-5)^2 + (6-5)^2 + (4-5)^2 + (8-5)^2}{4}} = 2.236$$

The graph of the original distribution is shown in Figure 6–29. This is called a *uniform distribution.*

Now, if all samples of size 2 are taken with replacement and the mean of each sample is found, the distribution is as shown.

Sample	Mean		Sample	Mean
2, 2	2		6, 2	4
2, 4	3		6, 4	5
2, 6	4		6, 6	6
2, 8	5		6, 8	7
4, 2	3		8, 2	5
4, 4	4		8, 4	6
4, 6	5		8, 6	7
4, 8	6		8, 8	8

A frequency distribution of sample means is as follows.

$\overline{X}$	f
2	1
3	2
4	3
5	4
6	3
7	2
8	1

For the data from the example just discussed, Figure 6–30 shows the graph of the sample means. The histogram appears to be approximately normal.

The mean of the sample means, denoted by $\mu_{\overline{X}}$, is

$$\mu_{\overline{X}} = \frac{2 + 3 + \cdots + 8}{16} = \frac{80}{16} = 5$$

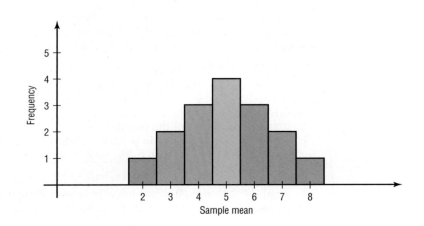

which is the same as the population mean. Hence,

$$\mu_{\bar{X}} = \mu$$

The standard deviation of sample means, denoted by $\sigma_{\bar{X}}$, is

$$\sigma_{\bar{X}} = \sqrt{\frac{(2-5)^2 + (3-5)^2 + \cdots + (8-5)^2}{16}} = 1.581$$

which is the same as the population standard deviation, divided by $\sqrt{2}$:

$$\sigma_{\bar{X}} = \frac{2.236}{\sqrt{2}} = 1.581$$

(*Note:* Rounding rules were not used here in order to show that the answers coincide.)

In summary, if all possible samples of size n are taken with replacement from the same population, the mean of the sample means, denoted by $\mu_{\bar{X}}$, equals the population mean μ; and the standard deviation of the sample means, denoted by $\sigma_{\bar{X}}$, equals $\sigma/\sqrt{n}$. The standard deviation of the sample means is called the **standard error of the mean.** Hence,

$$\sigma_{\bar{X}} = \frac{\sigma}{\sqrt{n}}$$

A third property of the sampling distribution of sample means pertains to the shape of the distribution and is explained by the **central limit theorem.**

The Central Limit Theorem

As the sample size n increases without limit, the shape of the distribution of the sample means taken with replacement from a population with mean μ and standard deviation σ will approach a normal distribution. As previously shown, this distribution will have a mean μ and a standard deviation $\sigma/\sqrt{n}$.

If the sample size is sufficiently large, the central limit theorem can be used to answer questions about sample means in the same manner that a normal distribution can be used to answer questions about individual values. The only difference is that a new formula must be used for the z values. It is

$$z = \frac{\bar{X} - \mu}{\sigma/\sqrt{n}}$$

Notice that $\bar{X}$ is the sample mean, and the denominator must be adjusted since means are being used instead of individual data values. The denominator is the standard deviation of the sample means.

If a large number of samples of a given size are selected from a normally distributed population, or if a large number of samples of a given size that is greater than or equal to 30 are selected from a population that is not normally distributed, and the sample means are computed, then the distribution of sample means will look like the one shown in Figure 6–31. Their percentages indicate the areas of the regions.

It's important to remember two things when you use the central limit theorem:

1. When the original variable is normally distributed, the distribution of the sample means will be normally distributed, for any sample size n.

2. When the distribution of the original variable might not be normal, a sample size of 30 or more is needed to use a normal distribution to approximate the distribution of the sample means. The larger the sample, the better the approximation will be.

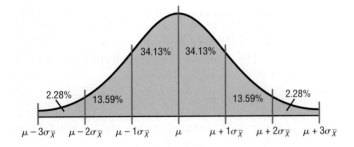

Examples 6–13 through 6–15 show how the standard normal distribution can be used to answer questions about sample means.

Example 6–13

Hours That Children Watch Television

A. C. Neilsen reported that children between the ages of 2 and 5 watch an average of 25 hours of television per week. Assume the variable is normally distributed and the standard deviation is 3 hours. If 20 children between the ages of 2 and 5 are randomly selected, find the probability that the mean of the number of hours they watch television will be greater than 26.3 hours.

Source: Michael D. Shook and Robert L. Shook, *The Book of Odds.*

Solution

Since the variable is approximately normally distributed, the distribution of sample means will be approximately normal, with a mean of 25. The standard deviation of the sample means is

$$\sigma_{\overline{X}} = \frac{\sigma}{\sqrt{n}} = \frac{3}{\sqrt{20}} = 0.671$$

The distribution of the means is shown in Figure 6–32, with the appropriate area shaded.

Figure 6–32

**Distribution of
the Means for
Example 6–13**

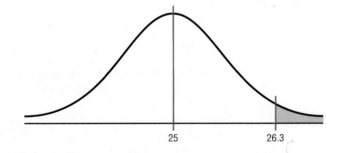

The *z* value is

$$z = \frac{\overline{X} - \mu}{\sigma/\sqrt{n}} = \frac{26.3 - 25}{3/\sqrt{20}} = \frac{1.3}{0.671} = 1.94$$

The area to the right of 1.94 is $1.000 - 0.9738 = 0.0262$, or 2.62%.

One can conclude that the probability of obtaining a sample mean larger than 26.3 hours is 2.62% [i.e., $P(\overline{X} > 26.3) = 2.62\%$].

Example 6–14	The average age of a vehicle registered in the United States is 8 years, or 96 months. Assume the standard deviation is 16 months. If a random sample of 36 vehicles is selected, find the probability that the mean of their age is between 90 and 100 months.

Source: *Harper's Index.*

Solution

Since the sample is 30 or larger, the normality assumption is not necessary. The desired area is shown in Figure 6–33.

Figure 6–33

Area Under a Normal Curve for Example 6–14

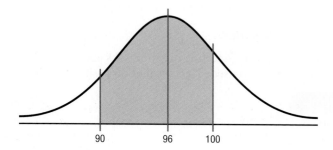

The two z values are

$$z_1 = \frac{90 - 96}{16/\sqrt{36}} = -2.25$$

$$z_2 = \frac{100 - 96}{16/\sqrt{36}} = 1.50$$

To find the area between the two z values of -2.25 and 1.50, look up the corresponding area in Table E and subtract one from the other. The area for $z = -2.25$ is 0.0122, and the area for $z = 1.50$ is 0.9332. Hence the area between the two values is $0.9332 - 0.0122 = 0.9210$, or 92.1%.

Hence, the probability of obtaining a sample mean between 90 and 100 months is 92.1%; that is, $P(90 < \overline{X} < 100) = 92.1\%$.

Students sometimes have difficulty deciding whether to use

$$z = \frac{\overline{X} - \mu}{\sigma/\sqrt{n}} \qquad \text{or} \qquad z = \frac{X - \mu}{\sigma}$$

The formula

$$z = \frac{\overline{X} - \mu}{\sigma/\sqrt{n}}$$

should be used to gain information about a sample mean, as shown in this section. The formula

$$z = \frac{X - \mu}{\sigma}$$

is used to gain information about an individual data value obtained from the population. Notice that the first formula contains $\overline{X}$, the symbol for the sample mean, while the second formula contains X, the symbol for an individual data value. Example 6–15 illustrates the uses of the two formulas.

| Example 6-15 | Meat Consumption |

The average number of pounds of meat that a person consumes per year is 218.4 pounds. Assume that the standard deviation is 25 pounds and the distribution is approximately normal.

Source: Michael D. Shook and Robert L. Shook, *The Book of Odds.*

a. Find the probability that a person selected at random consumes less than 224 pounds per year.
b. If a sample of 40 individuals is selected, find the probability that the mean of the sample will be less than 224 pounds per year.

Solution

a. Since the question asks about an individual person, the formula $z = (X - \mu)/\sigma$ is used. The distribution is shown in Figure 6–34.

| Figure 6-34 |

Area Under a Normal Curve for Part *a* of Example 6-15

218.4 224
Distribution of individual data values for the population

The z value is

$$z = \frac{X - \mu}{\sigma} = \frac{224 - 218.4}{25} = 0.22$$

The area to the left of $z = 0.22$ is 0.5871. Hence, the probability of selecting an individual who consumes less than 224 pounds of meat per year is 0.5871, or 58.71% [i.e., $P(X < 224) = 0.5871$].

b. Since the question concerns the mean of a sample with a size of 40, the formula $z = (\overline{X} - \mu)/(\sigma/\sqrt{n})$ is used. The area is shown in Figure 6–35.

| Figure 6-35 |

Area Under a Normal Curve for Part *b* of Example 6-15

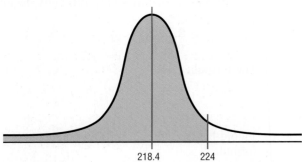

218.4   224
Distribution of means for all samples of size 40 taken from the population

The z value is

$$z = \frac{\overline{X} - \mu}{\sigma/\sqrt{n}} = \frac{224 - 218.4}{25/\sqrt{40}} = 1.42$$

The area to the left of $z = 1.42$ is 0.9222.

Hence, the probability that the mean of a sample of 40 individuals is less than 224 pounds per year is 0.9222, or 92.22%. That is, $P(\overline{X} < 224) = 0.9222$.

Comparing the two probabilities, you can see that the probability of selecting an individual who consumes less than 224 pounds of meat per year is 58.71%, but the probability of selecting a sample of 40 people with a mean consumption of meat that is less than 224 pounds per year is 92.22%. This rather large difference is due to the fact that the distribution of sample means is much less variable than the distribution of individual data values. (*Note:* An individual person is the equivalent of saying $n = 1$.)

Finite Population Correction Factor (Optional)

The formula for the standard error of the mean $\sigma/\sqrt{n}$ is accurate when the samples are drawn with replacement or are drawn without replacement from a very large or infinite population. Since sampling with replacement is for the most part unrealistic, a *correction factor* is necessary for computing the standard error of the mean for samples drawn without replacement from a finite population. Compute the correction factor by using the expression

$$\sqrt{\frac{N - n}{N - 1}}$$

where N is the population size and n is the sample size.

This correction factor is necessary if relatively large samples are taken from a small population, because the sample mean will then more accurately estimate the population mean and there will be less error in the estimation. Therefore, the standard error of the mean must be multiplied by the correction factor to adjust for large samples taken from a small population. That is,

$$\sigma_{\overline{X}} = \frac{\sigma}{\sqrt{n}} \cdot \sqrt{\frac{N - n}{N - 1}}$$

Finally, the formula for the z value becomes

$$z = \frac{\overline{X} - \mu}{\dfrac{\sigma}{\sqrt{n}} \cdot \sqrt{\dfrac{N - n}{N - 1}}}$$

When the population is large and the sample is small, the correction factor is generally not used, since it will be very close to 1.00.

The formulas and their uses are summarized in Table 6–1.

Interesting Fact

The bubonic plague killed more than 25 million people in Europe between 1347 and 1351.

Table 6–1	Summary of Formulas and Their Uses
Formula	**Use**
1. $z = \dfrac{X - \mu}{\sigma}$	Used to gain information about an individual data value when the variable is normally distributed.
2. $z = \dfrac{\overline{X} - \mu}{\sigma/\sqrt{n}}$	Used to gain information when applying the central limit theorem about a sample mean when the variable is normally distributed or when the sample size is 30 or more.

Applying the Concepts **6–3**

Central Limit Theorem

Twenty students from a statistics class each collected a random sample of times on how long it took students to get to class from their homes. All the sample sizes were 30. The resulting means are listed.

Student	Mean	Std. Dev.	Student	Mean	Std. Dev.
1	22	3.7	11	27	1.4
2	31	4.6	12	24	2.2
3	18	2.4	13	14	3.1
4	27	1.9	14	29	2.4
5	20	3.0	15	37	2.8
6	17	2.8	16	23	2.7
7	26	1.9	17	26	1.8
8	34	4.2	18	21	2.0
9	23	2.6	19	30	2.2
10	29	2.1	20	29	2.8

1. The students noticed that everyone had different answers. If you randomly sample over and over from any population, with the same sample size, will the results ever be the same?

2. The students wondered whose results were right. How can they find out what the population mean and standard deviation are?

3. Input the means into the computer and check to see if the distribution is normal.

4. Check the mean and standard deviation of the means. How do these values compare to the students' individual scores?

5. Is the distribution of the means a sampling distribution?

6. Check the sampling error for students 3, 7, and 14.

7. Compare the standard deviation of the sample of the 20 means. Is that equal to the standard deviation from student 3 divided by the square of the sample size? How about for student 7, or 14?

See page 352 for the answers.

Exercises 6–3

1. If samples of a specific size are selected from a population and the means are computed, what is this distribution of means called?

2. Why do most of the sample means differ somewhat from the population mean? What is this difference called?

3. What is the mean of the sample means?

4. What is the standard deviation of the sample means called? What is the formula for this standard deviation?

5. What does the central limit theorem say about the shape of the distribution of sample means?

6. What formula is used to gain information about an individual data value when the variable is normally distributed?

7. What formula is used to gain information about a sample mean when the variable is normally distributed or when the sample size is 30 or more?

For Exercises 8 through 25, assume that the sample is taken from a large population and the correction factor can be ignored.

8. **Glass Garbage Generation** A survey found that the American family generates an average of 17.2 pounds of glass garbage each year. Assume the standard deviation of the distribution is 2.5 pounds. Find the probability that the mean of a sample of 55 families will be between 17 and 18 pounds.

Source: Michael D. Shook and Robert L. Shook, *The Book of Odds.*

9. **College Costs** The mean undergraduate cost for tuition, fees, room, and board for four-year institutions was $26,489 for the 2004–2005 academic year. Suppose

that σ = \$3204 and that 36 four-year institutions are randomly selected. Find the probability that the sample mean cost for these 36 schools is

a. Less than \$25,000

b. Greater than \$26,000

c. Between \$24,000 and \$26,000

Source: www.nces.ed.gov

10. **Teachers' Salaries in Connecticut** The average teacher's salary in Connecticut (ranked first among states) is \$57,337. Suppose that the distribution of salaries is normal with a standard deviation of \$7500.

a. What is the probability that a randomly selected teacher makes less than \$52,000 per year?

b. If we sample 100 teachers' salaries, what is the probability that the sample mean is less than \$56,000?

Source: *New York Times Almanac.*

11. **Weights of 15-Year-Old Males** The mean weight of 15-year-old males is 142 pounds, and the standard deviation is 12.3 pounds. If a sample of thirty-six 15-year-old males is selected, find the probability that the mean of the sample will be greater than 144.5 pounds. Assume the variable is normally distributed. Based on your answer, would you consider the group overweight?

12. **Teachers' Salaries in North Dakota** The average teacher's salary in North Dakota is \$35,441. Assume a normal distribution with σ = \$5100.

a. What is the probability that a randomly selected teacher's salary is greater than \$45,000?

b. For a sample of 75 teachers, what is the probability that the sample mean is greater than \$38,000?

Source: *New York Times Almanac.*

13. **Fuel Efficiency for U.S. Light Vehicles** The average fuel efficiency of U.S. light vehicles (cars, SUVs, minivans, vans, and light trucks) for 2005 was 21 mpg. If the standard deviation of the population was 2.9 and the gas ratings were normally distributed, what is the probability that the mean mpg for a random sample of 25 light vehicles is under 20? Between 20 and 25?

Source: *World Almanac.*

14. **SAT Scores** The national average SAT score (for Verbal and Math) is 1028. Suppose that nothing is known about the shape of the distribution and that the standard deviation is 100. If a random sample of 200 scores were selected and the sample mean were calculated to be 1050, would you be surprised? Explain.

Source: *New York Times Almanac.*

15. **Sodium in Frozen Food** The average number of milligrams (mg) of sodium in a certain brand of low-salt microwave frozen dinners is 660 mg, and the standard deviation is 35 mg. Assume the variable is normally distributed.

a. If a single dinner is selected, find the probability that the sodium content will be more than 670 mg.

b. If a sample of 10 dinners is selected, find the probability that the mean of the sample will be larger than 670 mg.

c. Why is the probability for part *a* greater than that for part *b*?

16. **Worker Ages** The average age of chemical engineers is 37 years with a standard deviation of 4 years. If an engineering firm employs 25 chemical engineers, find the probability that the average age of the group is greater than 38.2 years old. If this is the case, would it be safe to assume that the engineers in this group are generally much older than average?

17. **Water Use** The *Old Farmer's Almanac* reports that the average person uses 123 gallons of water daily. If the standard deviation is 21 gallons, find the probability that the mean of a randomly selected sample of 15 people will be between 120 and 126 gallons. Assume the variable is normally distributed.

18. **Medicare Hospital Insurance** The average yearly Medicare Hospital Insurance benefit per person was \$4064 in a recent year. If the benefits are normally distributed with a standard deviation of \$460, find the probability that the mean benefit for a random sample of 20 patients is

a. Less than \$3800

b. More than \$4100

Source: *New York Times Almanac.*

19. **Amount of Laundry Washed Each Year** Procter & Gamble reported that an American family of four washes an average of 1 ton (2000 pounds) of clothes each year. If the standard deviation of the distribution is 187.5 pounds, find the probability that the mean of a randomly selected sample of 50 families of four will be between 1980 and 1990 pounds.

Source: *The Harper's Index Book.*

20. **Per Capita Income of Delaware Residents** In a recent year, Delaware had the highest per capita annual income with \$51,803. If σ = \$4850, what is the probability that a random sample of 34 state residents had a mean income greater than \$50,000? Less than \$48,000?

Source: *New York Times Almanac.*

21. **Time to Complete an Exam** The average time it takes a group of adults to complete a certain achievement test is 46.2 minutes. The standard deviation is 8 minutes. Assume the variable is normally distributed.

a. Find the probability that a randomly selected adult will complete the test in less than 43 minutes.

b. Find the probability that if 50 randomly selected adults take the test, the mean time it takes the group to complete the test will be less than 43 minutes.

   c. Does it seem reasonable that an adult would finish the test in less than 43 minutes? Explain.

   d. Does it seem reasonable that the mean of the 50 adults could be less than 43 minutes?

22. Systolic Blood Pressure Assume that the mean systolic blood pressure of normal adults is 120 millimeters of mercury (mm Hg) and the standard deviation is 5.6. Assume the variable is normally distributed.

   a. If an individual is selected, find the probability that the individual's pressure will be between 120 and 121.8 mm Hg.

   b. If a sample of 30 adults is randomly selected, find the probability that the sample mean will be between 120 and 121.8 mm Hg.

   c. Why is the answer to part *a* so much smaller than the answer to part *b*?

23. Cholesterol Content The average cholesterol content of a certain brand of eggs is 215 milligrams, and the standard deviation is 15 milligrams. Assume the variable is normally distributed.

   a. If a single egg is selected, find the probability that the cholesterol content will be greater than 220 milligrams.

   b. If a sample of 25 eggs is selected, find the probability that the mean of the sample will be larger than 220 milligrams.

Source: *Living Fit.*

24. Ages of Proofreaders At a large publishing company, the mean age of proofreaders is 36.2 years, and the standard deviation is 3.7 years. Assume the variable is normally distributed.

   a. If a proofreader from the company is randomly selected, find the probability that his or her age will be between 36 and 37.5 years.

   b. If a random sample of 15 proofreaders is selected, find the probability that the mean age of the proofreaders in the sample will be between 36 and 37.5 years.

25. Weekly Income of Private Industry Information Workers The average weekly income of information workers in private industry is $777. If the standard deviation is $77, what is the probability that a random sample of 50 information workers will earn, on average, more than $800 per week? Do we need to assume a normal distribution? Explain.

Source: *World Almanac.*

Extending the Concepts

For Exercises 26 and 27, check to see whether the correction factor should be used. If so, be sure to include it in the calculations.

26. Life Expectancies In a study of the life expectancy of 500 people in a certain geographic region, the mean age at death was 72.0 years, and the standard deviation was 5.3 years. If a sample of 50 people from this region is selected, find the probability that the mean life expectancy will be less than 70 years.

27. Home Values A study of 800 homeowners in a certain area showed that the average value of the homes was $82,000, and the standard deviation was $5000. If 50 homes are for sale, find the probability that the mean of the values of these homes is greater than $83,500.

28. Breaking Strength of Steel Cable The average breaking strength of a certain brand of steel cable is 2000 pounds, with a standard deviation of 100 pounds. A sample of 20 cables is selected and tested. Find the sample mean that will cut off the upper 95% of all samples of size 20 taken from the population. Assume the variable is normally distributed.

29. The standard deviation of a variable is 15. If a sample of 100 individuals is selected, compute the standard error of the mean. What size sample is necessary to double the standard error of the mean?

30. In Exercise 29, what size sample is needed to cut the standard error of the mean in half?

6–4	**The Normal Approximation to the Binomial Distribution**

A normal distribution is often used to solve problems that involve the binomial distribution since when *n* is large (say, 100), the calculations are too difficult to do by hand using the binomial distribution. Recall from Chapter 5 that a binomial distribution has the following characteristics:

  1. There must be a fixed number of trials.

  2. The outcome of each trial must be independent.

3. Each experiment can have only two outcomes or outcomes that can be reduced to two outcomes.

4. The probability of a success must remain the same for each trial.

Also, recall that a binomial distribution is determined by n (the number of trials) and p (the probability of a success). When p is approximately 0.5, and as n increases, the shape of the binomial distribution becomes similar to that of a normal distribution. The larger n is and the closer p is to 0.5, the more similar the shape of the binomial distribution is to that of a normal distribution.

Objective 7

Use the normal approximation to compute probabilities for a binomial variable.

But when p is close to 0 or 1 and n is relatively small, a normal approximation is inaccurate. As a rule of thumb, statisticians generally agree that a normal approximation should be used only when $n \cdot p$ and $n \cdot q$ are both greater than or equal to 5. (*Note:* $q = 1 - p$.) For example, if p is 0.3 and n is 10, then $np = (10)(0.3) = 3$, and a normal distribution should not be used as an approximation. On the other hand, if $p = 0.5$ and $n = 10$, then $np = (10)(0.5) = 5$ and $nq = (10)(0.5) = 5$, and a normal distribution can be used as an approximation. See Figure 6–36.

Figure 6–36

Comparison of the Binomial Distribution and a Normal Distribution

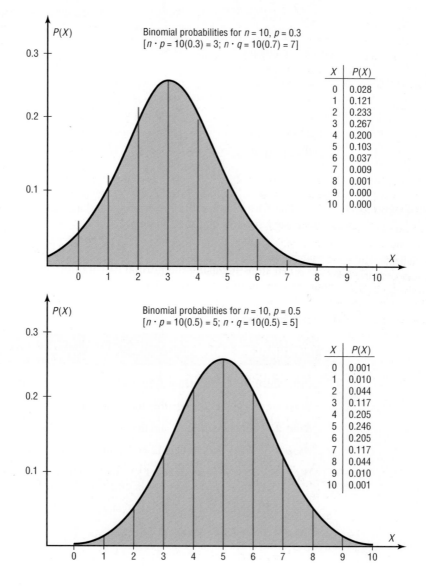

In addition to the previous condition of $np \geq 5$ and $nq \geq 5$, a correction for continuity may be used in the normal approximation.

A **correction for continuity** is a correction employed when a continuous distribution is used to approximate a discrete distribution.

The continuity correction means that for any specific value of X, say 8, the boundaries of X in the binomial distribution (in this case, 7.5 to 8.5) must be used. (See Section 1–2.) Hence, when you employ a normal distribution to approximate the binomial, you must use the boundaries of any specific value X as they are shown in the binomial distribution. For example, for $P(X = 8)$, the correction is $P(7.5 < X < 8.5)$. For $P(X \leq 7)$, the correction is $P(X < 7.5)$. For $P(X \geq 3)$, the correction is $P(X > 2.5)$.

Students sometimes have difficulty deciding whether to add 0.5 or subtract 0.5 from the data value for the correction factor. Table 6–2 summarizes the different situations.

Table 6–2	Summary of the Normal Approximation to the Binomial Distribution
Binomial	**Normal**
When finding:	Use:
1. $P(X = a)$	$P(a - 0.5 < X < a + 0.5)$
2. $P(X \geq a)$	$P(X > a - 0.5)$
3. $P(X > a)$	$P(X > a + 0.5)$
4. $P(X \leq a)$	$P(X < a + 0.5)$
5. $P(X < a)$	$P(X < a - 0.5)$

For all cases, $\mu = n \cdot p$, $\sigma = \sqrt{n \cdot p \cdot q}$, $n \cdot p \geq 5$, and $n \cdot q \geq 5$.

The formulas for the mean and standard deviation for the binomial distribution are necessary for calculations. They are

$$\mu = n \cdot p \qquad \text{and} \qquad \sigma = \sqrt{n \cdot p \cdot q}$$

The steps for using the normal distribution to approximate the binomial distribution are shown in this Procedure Table.

Procedure Table

Procedure for the Normal Approximation to the Binomial Distribution

Step 1   Check to see whether the normal approximation can be used.

Step 2   Find the mean μ and the standard deviation σ.

Step 3   Write the problem in probability notation, using X.

Step 4   Rewrite the problem by using the continuity correction factor, and show the corresponding area under the normal distribution.

Step 5   Find the corresponding z values.

Step 6   Find the solution.

| **Example 6–16** | **Reading While Driving** |

A magazine reported that 6% of American drivers read the newspaper while driving. If 300 drivers are selected at random, find the probability that exactly 25 say they read the newspaper while driving.

Source: USA Snapshot, *USA TODAY.*

Solution

Here, $p = 0.06$, $q = 0.94$, and $n = 300$.

Step 1   Check to see whether a normal approximation can be used.

$np = (300)(0.06) = 18$ $nq = (300)(0.94) = 282$

Since $np \geq 5$ and $nq \geq 5$, the normal distribution can be used.

Step 2   Find the mean and standard deviation.

$\mu = np = (300)(0.06) = 18$

$\sigma = \sqrt{npq} = \sqrt{(300)(0.06)(0.94)} = \sqrt{16.92} = 4.11$

Step 3   Write the problem in probability notation: $P(X = 25)$.

Step 4   Rewrite the problem by using the continuity correction factor. See approximation number 1 in Table 6–2: $P(25 - 0.5 < X < 25 + 0.5) = P(24.5 < X < 25.5)$. Show the corresponding area under the normal distribution curve. See Figure 6–37.

| **Figure 6–37** |

Area Under a Normal Curve and *X* Values for Example 6–16

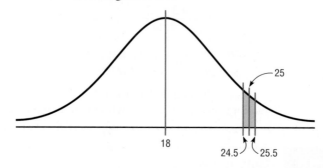

Step 5   Find the corresponding z values. Since 25 represents any value between 24.5 and 25.5, find both z values.

$z_1 = \dfrac{25.5 - 18}{4.11} = 1.82$ $z_2 = \dfrac{24.5 - 18}{4.11} = 1.58$

Step 6   The area to the left of $z = 1.82$ is 0.9656, and the area to the left of $z = 1.58$ is 0.9429. The area between the two z values is $0.9656 - 0.9429 = 0.0227$, or 2.27%. Hence, the probability that exactly 25 people read the newspaper while driving is 2.27%.

| **Example 6–17** | **Widowed Bowlers** |

Of the members of a bowling league, 10% are widowed. If 200 bowling league members are selected at random, find the probability that 10 or more will be widowed.

Solution

Here, $p = 0.10$, $q = 0.90$, and $n = 200$.

Step 1   Since $np = (200)(0.10) = 20$ and $nq = (200)(0.90) = 180$, the normal approximation can be used.

Step 2 $\mu = np = (200)(0.10) = 20$

           $\sigma = \sqrt{npq} = \sqrt{(200)(0.10)(0.90)} = \sqrt{18} = 4.24$

Step 3 $P(X \geq 10)$

Step 4   See approximation number 2 in Table 6–2: $P(X > 10 - 0.5) = P(X > 9.5)$. The desired area is shown in Figure 6–38.

Figure 6–38

Area Under a Normal Curve and X Value for Example 6–17

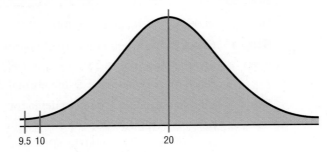

9.5 10   20

Step 5   Since the problem is to find the probability of 10 or more positive responses, a normal distribution graph is as shown in Figure 6–38. Hence, the area between 9.5 and 20 must be added to 0.5000 to get the correct approximation. The z value is

$$z = \frac{9.5 - 20}{4.24} = -2.48$$

Step 6   The area to the left of $z = -2.48$ is 0.0066. Hence the area to the right of $z = -2.48$ is $1.0000 - 0.0066 = 0.9934$, or 99.34%.

     It can be concluded, then, that the probability of 10 or more widowed people in a random sample of 200 bowling league members is 99.34%.

Example 6–18

Batting Averages

If a baseball player's batting average is 0.320 (32%), find the probability that the player will get at most 26 hits in 100 times at bat.

Solution

Here, $p = 0.32$, $q = 0.68$, and $n = 100$.

Step 1   Since $np = (100)(0.320) = 32$ and $nq = (100)(0.680) = 68$, the normal distribution can be used to approximate the binomial distribution.

Step 2 $\mu = np = (100)(0.320) = 32$

           $\sigma = \sqrt{npq} = \sqrt{(100)(0.32)(0.68)} = \sqrt{21.76} = 4.66$

Step 3 $P(X \leq 26)$

Step 4   See approximation number 4 in Table 6–2: $P(X < 26 + 0.5) = P(X < 26.5)$. The desired area is shown in Figure 6–39.

Step 5   The z value is

$$z = \frac{26.5 - 32}{4.66} = -1.18$$

Figure 6–39

Area Under a
Normal Curve for
Example 6–18

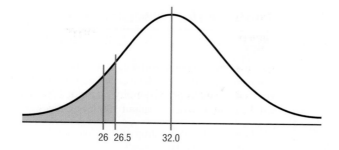

Step 6 The area to the left of $z = -1.18$ is 0.1190. Hence the probability is 0.1190, or 11.9%.

The closeness of the normal approximation is shown in Example 6–19.

Example 6–19

When $n = 10$ and $p = 0.5$, use the binomial distribution table (Table B in Appendix C) to find the probability that $X = 6$. Then use the normal approximation to find the probability that $X = 6$.

Solution

From Table B, for $n = 10$, $p = 0.5$, and $X = 6$, the probability is 0.205.
    For a normal approximation,

$$\mu = np = (10)(0.5) = 5$$

$$\sigma = \sqrt{npq} = \sqrt{(10)(0.5)(0.5)} = 1.58$$

Now, $X = 6$ is represented by the boundaries 5.5 and 6.5. So the z values are

$$z_1 = \frac{6.5 - 5}{1.58} = 0.95 \qquad z_2 = \frac{5.5 - 5}{1.58} = 0.32$$

The corresponding area for 0.95 is 0.8289, and the corresponding area for 0.32 is 0.6255. The area between the two z values of 0.95 and 0.32 is $0.8289 - 0.6255 = 0.2034$, which is very close to the binomial table value of 0.205. See Figure 6–40.

Figure 6–40

Area Under a
Normal Curve for
Example 6–19

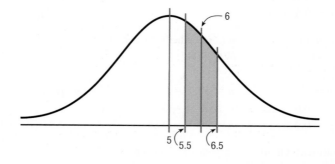

The normal approximation also can be used to approximate other distributions, such as the Poisson distribution (see Table C in Appendix C).

Applying the Concepts 6–4

How Safe Are You?

Assume one of your favorite activities is mountain climbing. When you go mountain climbing, you have several safety devices to keep you from falling. You notice that attached to one of your safety hooks is a reliability rating of 97%. You estimate that throughout the next year you will be using this device about 100 times. Answer the following questions.

1. Does a reliability rating of 97% mean that there is a 97% chance that the device will not fail any of the 100 times?
2. What is the probability of at least one failure?
3. What is the complement of this event?
4. Can this be considered a binomial experiment?
5. Can you use the binomial probability formula? Why or why not?
6. Find the probability of at least two failures.
7. Can you use a normal distribution to accurately approximate the binomial distribution? Explain why or why not.
8. Is correction for continuity needed?
9. How much safer would it be to use a second safety hook independently of the first?

See page 352 for the answers.

Exercises 6–4

1. Explain why a normal distribution can be used as an approximation to a binomial distribution. What conditions must be met to use the normal distribution to approximate the binomial distribution? Why is a correction for continuity necessary?

2. (ans) Use the normal approximation to the binomial to find the probabilities for the specific value(s) of X.

   a. $n = 30, p = 0.5, X = 18$
   b. $n = 50, p = 0.8, X = 44$
   c. $n = 100, p = 0.1, X = 12$
   d. $n = 10, p = 0.5, X \geq 7$
   e. $n = 20, p = 0.7, X \leq 12$
   f. $n = 50, p = 0.6, X \leq 40$

3. Check each binomial distribution to see whether it can be approximated by a normal distribution (i.e., are $np \geq 5$ and $nq \geq 5$?).

   a. $n = 20, p = 0.5$ d. $n = 50, p = 0.2$
   b. $n = 10, p = 0.6$ e. $n = 30, p = 0.8$
   c. $n = 40, p = 0.9$ f. $n = 20, p = 0.85$

4. **School Enrollment** Of all 3- to 5-year-old children, 56% are enrolled in school. If a sample of 500 such children is randomly selected, find the probability that at least 250 will be enrolled in school.

   Source: *Statistical Abstract of the United States.*

5. **Youth Smoking** Two out of five adult smokers acquired the habit by age 14. If 400 smokers are randomly selected, find the probability that 170 or more acquired the habit by age 14.

   Source: *Harper's Index.*

6. **Theater No-shows** A theater owner has found that 5% of patrons do not show up for the performance that they purchased tickets for. If the theater has 100 seats, find the probability that 6 or more patrons will not show up for the sold-out performance.

7. **Percentage of Americans Who Have Some College Education** The percentage of Americans 25 years or older who have at least some college education is 53.1%. In a random sample of 300 Americans 25 years old or older, what is the probability that more than 175 have at least some college education?

   Source: *New York Times Almanac.*

8. **Household Computers** According to recent surveys, 60% of households have personal computers. If a random sample of 180 households is selected, what is the probability that more than 60 but fewer than 100 have a personal computer?

   Source: *New York Times Almanac.*

9. **Female Americans Who Have Completed 4 Years of College** The percentage of female Americans 25 years

old and older who have completed 4 years of college or more is 26.1. In a random sample of 200 American women who are at least 25, what is the probability that at least 50 have completed 4 years of college or more?

Source: *New York Times Almanac.*

10. **Population of College Cities** College students often make up a substantial portion of the population of college cities and towns. State College, Pennsylvania, ranks first with 71.1% of its population made up of college students. What is the probability that in a random sample of 150 people from State College, more than 50 are not college students?

Source: www.infoplease.com

11. **Elementary School Teachers** Women comprise 80.3% of all elementary school teachers. In a random sample of 300 elementary teachers, what is the probability that more than three-fourths are women?

Source: *New York Times Almanac.*

12. **Telephone Answering Devices** Seventy-eight percent of U.S. homes have a telephone answering device. In a random sample of 250 homes, what is the probability that fewer than 50 do not have a telephone answering device?

Source: *New York Times Almanac.*

13. **Parking Lot Construction** The mayor of a small town estimates that 35% of the residents in the town favor the construction of a municipal parking lot. If there are 350 people at a town meeting, find the probability that at least 100 favor construction of the parking lot. Based on your answer, is it likely that 100 or more people would favor the parking lot?

14. **Residences of U.S. Citizens** According to the U.S. Census, 67.5% of the U.S. population were born in their state of residence. In a random sample of 200 Americans, what is the probability that fewer than 125 were born in their state of residence?

Source: www.census.gov

Extending the Concepts

15. Recall that for use of a normal distribution as an approximation to the binomial distribution, the conditions $np \geq 5$ and $nq \geq 5$ must be met. For each given probability, compute the minimum sample size needed for use of the normal approximation.

   a. $p = 0.1$ *d.* $p = 0.8$
   b. $p = 0.3$ *e.* $p = 0.9$
   c. $p = 0.5$

Summary

A normal distribution can be used to describe a variety of variables, such as heights, weights, and temperatures. A normal distribution is bell-shaped, unimodal, symmetric, and continuous; its mean, median, and mode are equal. Since each variable has its own distribution with mean μ and standard deviation σ, mathematicians use the standard normal distribution, which has a mean of 0 and a standard deviation of 1. Other approximately normally distributed variables can be transformed to the standard normal distribution with the formula $z = (X - \mu)/\sigma$.

A normal distribution can also be used to describe a sampling distribution of sample means. These samples must be of the same size and randomly selected with replacement from the population. The means of the samples will differ somewhat from the population mean, since samples are generally not perfect representations of the population from which they came. The mean of the sample means will be equal to the population mean; and the standard deviation of the sample means will be equal to the population standard deviation, divided by the square root of the sample size. The central limit theorem states that as the size of the samples increases, the distribution of sample means will be approximately normal.

A normal distribution can be used to approximate other distributions, such as a binomial distribution. For a normal distribution to be used as an approximation, the conditions $np \geq 5$ and $nq \geq 5$ must be met. Also, a correction for continuity may be used for more accurate results.

Important Terms

central limit theorem 331

correction for
continuity 340

negatively or left-skewed
distribution 299

normal distribution 301

positively or right-skewed
distribution 299

sampling distribution of
sample means 329

sampling error 329

standard error of the
mean 331

standard normal
distribution 302

symmetric
distribution 299

z value 302

Important Formulas

Formula for the z value (or standard score):

$$z = \frac{X - \mu}{\sigma}$$

Formula for finding a specific data value:

$$X = z \cdot \sigma + \mu$$

Formula for the mean of the sample means:

$$\mu_{\bar{X}} = \mu$$

Formula for the standard error of the mean:

$$\sigma_{\bar{X}} = \frac{\sigma}{\sqrt{n}}$$

Formula for the z value for the central limit theorem:

$$z = \frac{\bar{X} - \mu}{\sigma/\sqrt{n}}$$

Formulas for the mean and standard deviation for the
binomial distribution:

$$\mu = n \cdot p \qquad \sigma = \sqrt{n \cdot p \cdot q}$$

Review Exercises

1. Find the area under the standard normal distribution
   curve for each.

   a. Between $z = 0$ and $z = 1.95$
   b. Between $z = 0$ and $z = 0.37$
   c. Between $z = 1.32$ and $z = 1.82$
   d. Between $z = -1.05$ and $z = 2.05$
   e. Between $z = -0.03$ and $z = 0.53$
   f. Between $z = +1.10$ and $z = -1.80$
   g. To the right of $z = 1.99$
   h. To the right of $z = -1.36$
   i. To the left of $z = -2.09$
   j. To the left of $z = 1.68$

2. Using the standard normal distribution, find each
   probability.

   a. $P(0 < z < 2.07)$
   b. $P(-1.83 < z < 0)$
   c. $P(-1.59 < z < +2.01)$
   d. $P(1.33 < z < 1.88)$
   e. $P(-2.56 < z < 0.37)$
   f. $P(z > 1.66)$
   g. $P(z < -2.03)$
   h. $P(z > -1.19)$
   i. $P(z < 1.93)$
   j. $P(z > -1.77)$

3. **Per Capita Spending on Health Care** The average per
   capita spending on health care in the United States is
   $5274. If the standard deviation is $600 and the
   distribution of health care spending is approximately
   normal, what is the probability that a randomly selected
   person spends more than $6000? Find the limits of the
   middle 50% of individual health care expenditures.

   Source: *World Almanac.*

4. **Salaries for Actuaries** The average salary for
   graduates entering the actuarial field is $40,000. If the
   salaries are normally distributed with a standard
   deviation of $5000, find the probability that

   a. An individual graduate will have a salary over
      $45,000.
   b. A group of nine graduates will have a group average
      over $45,000.

   Source: www.BeAnActuary.org

5. **Speed Limits** The speed limit on Interstate 75 around
   Findlay, Ohio, is 65 mph. On a clear day with no
   construction, the mean speed of automobiles was
   measured at 63 mph with a standard deviation of 8 mph.
   If the speeds are normally distributed, what percentage
   of the automobiles are exceeding the speed limit? If the

Highway Patrol decides to ticket only motorists exceeding 72 mph, what percentage of the motorists might they arrest?

6. **Monthly Spending for Paging and Messaging Services** The average individual monthly spending in the United States for paging and messaging services is $10.15. If the standard deviation is $2.45 and the amounts are normally distributed, what is the probability that a randomly selected user of these services pays more than $15.00 per month? Between $12.00 and $14.00 per month?

Source: *New York Times Almanac.*

7. **Average Precipitation** For the first 7 months of the year, the average precipitation in Toledo, Ohio, is 19.32 inches. If the average precipitation is normally distributed with a standard deviation of 2.44 inches, find these probabilities.

   a. A randomly selected year will have precipitation greater than 18 inches for the first 7 months.
   b. Five randomly selected years will have an average precipitation greater than 18 inches for the first 7 months.

Source: *Toledo Blade.*

8. **Suitcase Weights** The average weight of an airline passenger's suitcase is 45 pounds. The standard deviation is 2 pounds. If 15% of the suitcases are overweight, find the maximum weight allowed by the airline. Assume the variable is normally distributed.

9. **Confectionary Products** Americans ate an average of 25.7 pounds of confectionary products each last year and spent an average of $61.50 per person doing so. If the standard deviation for consumption is 3.75 pounds and the standard deviation for the amount spent is $5.89, find the following:

   a. The probability that the sample mean confectionary consumption for a random sample of 40 American consumers was greater than 27 pounds.
   b. The probability that for a random sample of 50, the sample mean for confectionary spending exceeded $60.00.

Source: www.census.gov

10. **Retirement Income** Of the total population of American households, including older Americans and perhaps some not so old, 17.3% receive retirement income. In a random sample of 120 households, what is the probability that greater than 20 households but less than 35 households receive a retirement income?

Source: www.bls.gov

11. **Portable CD Player Lifetimes** A recent study of the life span of portable compact disc players found the average to be 3.7 years with a standard deviation of 0.6 year. If a random sample of 32 people who own CD players is selected, find the probability that the mean

lifetime of the sample will be less than 3.4 years. If the mean is less than 3.4 years, would you consider that 3.7 years might be incorrect?

12. **Slot Machines** The probability of winning on a slot machine is 5%. If a person plays the machine 500 times, find the probability of winning 30 times. Use the normal approximation to the binomial distribution.

13. **Multiple-Job Holders** According to the government 5.3% of those employed are multiple-job holders. In a random sample of 150 people who are employed, what is the probability that fewer than 10 hold multiple jobs? What is the probability that more than 50 are not multiple-job holders?

Source: www.bls.gov

14. **Enrollment in Personal Finance Course** In a large university, 30% of the incoming first-year students elect to enroll in a personal finance course offered by the university. Find the probability that of 800 randomly selected incoming first-year students, at least 260 have elected to enroll in the course.

15. **U.S. Population** Of the total population of the United States, 20% live in the northeast. If 200 residents of the United States are selected at random, find the probability that at least 50 live in the northeast.

Source: *Statistical Abstract of the United States.*

16. **Heights of Active Volcanoes** The heights (in feet above sea level) of a random sample of the world's active volcanoes are shown here. Check for normality.

13,435	5,135	11,339	12,224	7,470
9,482	12,381	7,674	5,223	5,631
3,566	7,113	5,850	5,679	15,584
5,587	8,077	9,550	8,064	2,686
5,250	6,351	4,594	2,621	9,348
6,013	2,398	5,658	2,145	3,038

Source: *New York Times Almanac.*

17. **Private Four-Year College Enrollment** A random sample of enrollments in Pennsylvania's private four-year colleges is listed here. Check for normality.

1350	1886	1743	1290	1767
2067	1118	3980	1773	4605
1445	3883	1486	980	1217
3587				

Source: *New York Times Almanac.*

18. Construct a set of at least 15 data values which appear to be normally distributed. Verify the normality by using one of the methods introduced in this text.

Chapter Quiz

Determine whether each statement is true or false. If the statement is false, explain why.

1. The total area under a normal distribution is infinite.

2. The standard normal distribution is a continuous distribution.

3. All variables that are approximately normally distributed can be transformed to standard normal variables.

4. The z value corresponding to a number below the mean is always negative.

5. The area under the standard normal distribution to the left of $z = 0$ is negative.

6. The central limit theorem applies to means of samples selected from different populations.

Select the best answer.

7. The mean of the standard normal distribution is
   a. 0   c. 100
   b. 1   d. Variable

8. Approximately what percentage of normally distributed data values will fall within 1 standard deviation above or below the mean?
   a. 68%   c. 99.7%
   b. 95%   d. Variable

9. Which is not a property of the standard normal distribution?
   a. It's symmetric about the mean.
   b. It's uniform.
   c. It's bell-shaped.
   d. It's unimodal.

10. When a distribution is positively skewed, the relationship of the mean, median, and mode from left to right will be
    a. Mean, median, mode   c. Median, mode, mean
    b. Mode, median, mean   d. Mean, mode, median

11. The standard deviation of all possible sample means equals
    a. The population standard deviation
    b. The population standard deviation divided by the population mean

c. The population standard deviation divided by the square root of the sample size
d. The square root of the population standard deviation

Complete the following statements with the best answer.

12. When one is using the standard normal distribution, $P(z < 0) =$ _____.

13. The difference between a sample mean and a population mean is due to _____.

14. The mean of the sample means equals _____.

15. The standard deviation of all possible sample means is called _____.

16. The normal distribution can be used to approximate the binomial distribution when $n \cdot p$ and $n \cdot q$ are both greater than or equal to _____.

17. The correction factor for the central limit theorem should be used when the sample size is greater than _____ the size of the population.

18. Find the area under the standard normal distribution for each.
    a. Between 0 and 1.50
    b. Between 0 and -1.25
    c. Between 1.56 and 1.96
    d. Between -1.20 and -2.25
    e. Between -0.06 and 0.73
    f. Between 1.10 and -1.80
    g. To the right of $z = 1.75$
    h. To the right of $z = -1.28$
    i. To the left of $z = -2.12$
    j. To the left of $z = 1.36$

19. Using the standard normal distribution, find each probability.
    a. $P(0 < z < 2.16)$
    b. $P(-1.87 < z < 0)$
    c. $P(-1.63 < z < 2.17)$
    d. $P(1.72 < z < 1.98)$
    e. $P(-2.17 < z < 0.71)$
    f. $P(z > 1.77)$
    g. $P(z < -2.37)$
    h. $P(z > -1.73)$

   i. $P(z < 2.03)$
   j. $P(z > -1.02)$

20. Amount of Rain in a City The average amount of rain per year in Greenville is 49 inches. The standard deviation is 8 inches. Find the probability that next year Greenville will receive the following amount of rainfall. Assume the variable is normally distributed.

   a.   At most 55 inches of rain
   b.   At least 62 inches of rain
   c.   Between 46 and 54 inches of rain
   d.   How many inches of rain would you consider to be an extremely wet year?

21. Heights of People The average height of a certain age group of people is 53 inches. The standard deviation is 4 inches. If the variable is normally distributed, find the probability that a selected individual's height will be

   a.   Greater than 59 inches
   b.   Less than 45 inches
   c.   Between 50 and 55 inches
   d.   Between 58 and 62 inches

22. Lemonade Consumption The average number of gallons of lemonade consumed by the football team during a game is 20, with a standard deviation of 3 gallons. Assume the variable is normally distributed. When a game is played, find the probability of using

   a.   Between 20 and 25 gallons
   b.   Less than 19 gallons
   c.   More than 21 gallons
   d.   Between 26 and 28 gallons

23. Years to Complete a Graduate Program The average number of years a person takes to complete a graduate degree program is 3. The standard deviation is 4 months. Assume the variable is normally distributed. If an individual enrolls in the program, find the probability that it will take

   a.   More than 4 years to complete the program
   b.   Less than 3 years to complete the program
   c.   Between 3.8 and 4.5 years to complete the program
   d.   Between 2.5 and 3.1 years to complete the program

24. Passengers on a Bus On the daily run of an express bus, the average number of passengers is 48. The standard deviation is 3. Assume the variable is normally distributed. Find the probability that the bus will have

   a.   Between 36 and 40 passengers
   b.   Fewer than 42 passengers
   c.   More than 48 passengers
   d.   Between 43 and 47 passengers

25. Thickness of Library Books The average thickness of books on a library shelf is 8.3 centimeters. The standard deviation is 0.6 centimeter. If 20% of the books are oversized, find the minimum thickness of the oversized books on the library shelf. Assume the variable is normally distributed.

26. Membership in an Organization Membership in an elite organization requires a test score in the upper 30% range. If $\mu = 115$ and $\sigma = 12$, find the lowest acceptable score that would enable a candidate to apply for membership. Assume the variable is normally distributed.

27. Repair Cost for Microwave Ovens The average repair cost of a microwave oven is $55, with a standard deviation of $8. The costs are normally distributed. If 12 ovens are repaired, find the probability that the mean of the repair bills will be greater than $60.

28. Electric Bills The average electric bill in a residential area is $72 for the month of April. The standard deviation is $6. If the amounts of the electric bills are normally distributed, find the probability that the mean of the bill for 15 residents will be less than $75.

29. Sleep Survey According to a recent survey, 38% of Americans get 6 hours or less of sleep each night. If 25 people are selected, find the probability that 14 or more people will get 6 hours or less of sleep each night. Does this number seem likely?

Source: *Amazing Almanac.*

30. Factory Union Membership If 10% of the people in a certain factory are members of a union, find the probability that, in a sample of 2000, fewer than 180 people are union members.

31. Household Online Connection The percentage of U.S. households that have online connections is 44.9%. In a random sample of 420 households, what is the probability that fewer than 200 have online connections?

Source: *New York Times Almanac.*

32. Computer Ownership Fifty-three percent of U.S. households have a personal computer. In a random sample of 250 households, what is the probability that fewer than 120 have a PC?

Source: *New York Times Almanac.*

33. Calories in Fast-Food Sandwiches The number of calories contained in a selection of fast-food sandwiches is shown here. Check for normality.

390	405	580	300	320
540	225	720	470	560
535	660	530	290	440
390	675	530	1010	450
320	460	290	340	610
430	530			

Source: *The Doctor's Pocket Calorie, Fat, and Carbohydrate Counter.*

34. GMAT Scores The average GMAT scores for the top-30 ranked graduate schools of business are listed here. Check for normality.

718	703	703	703	700	690	695	705	690	688
676	681	689	686	691	669	674	652	680	670
651	651	637	662	641	645	645	642	660	636

Source: *U.S. News & World Report Best Graduate Schools.*

Critical Thinking Challenges

Sometimes a researcher must decide whether a variable is normally distributed. There are several ways to do this. One simple but very subjective method uses special graph paper, which is called *normal probability paper*. For the distribution of systolic blood pressure readings given in Chapter 3 of the textbook, the following method can be used:

1. Make a table, as shown.

Boundaries	Frequency	Cumulative frequency	Cumulative percent frequency
89.5–104.5	24		
104.5–119.5	62		
119.5–134.5	72		
134.5–149.5	26		
149.5–164.5	12		
164.5–179.5	4		
	200		

2. Find the cumulative frequencies for each class, and place the results in the third column.

3. Find the cumulative percents for each class by dividing each cumulative frequency by 200 (the total frequencies) and multiplying by 100%. (For the first class, it would be 24/200 × 100% = 12%.) Place these values in the last column.

4. Using the normal probability paper shown in Table 6–3, label the *x* axis with the class boundaries as shown and plot the percents.

5. If the points fall approximately in a straight line, it can be concluded that the distribution is normal. Do you feel that this distribution is approximately normal? Explain your answer.

6. To find an approximation of the mean or median, draw a horizontal line from the 50% point on the *y* axis over to the curve and then a vertical line down to the *x* axis. Compare this approximation of the mean with the computed mean.

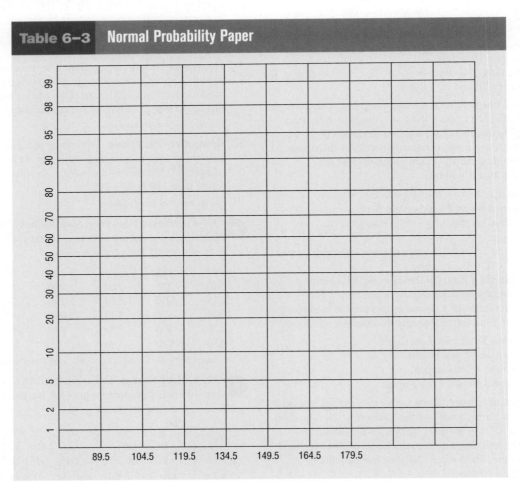

Table 6–3   Normal Probability Paper

7. To find an approximation of the standard deviation, locate the values on the *x* axis that correspond to the 16 and 84% values on the *y* axis. Subtract these two values and divide the result by 2. Compare this approximate standard deviation to the computed standard deviation.

8. Explain why the method used in step 7 works.

Data Projects

1. Business and Finance Use the data collected in data project 1 of Chapter 2 regarding earnings per share to complete this problem. Use the mean and standard deviation computed in data project 1 of Chapter 3 as estimates for the population parameters. What value separates the top 5% of stocks from the others?

2. Sports and Leisure Find the mean and standard deviation for the batting average for a player in the most recently completed MBL season. What batting average would separate the top 5% of all hitters from the rest? What is the probability that a randomly selected player bats over 0.300? What is the probability that a team of 25 players has a mean that is above 0.275?

3. Technology Use the data collected in data project 3 of Chapter 2 regarding song lengths. If the sample estimates for mean and standard deviation are used as replacements for the population parameters for this data set, what song length separates the bottom 5% and top 5% from the other values?

4. Health and Wellness Use the data regarding heart rates collected in data project 4 of Chapter 2 for this problem. Use the sample mean and standard deviation as estimates of the population parameters. For the before-exercise data, what heart rate separates the top 10% from the other values? For the after-exercise data, what heart rate separates the bottom 10% from the other values? If a student was selected at random, what is the probability that her or his mean heart rate before exercise was less than 72? If 25 students were selected at random, what is the probability that their mean heart rate before exercise was less than 72?

5. Politics and Economics Use the data collected in data project 6 of Chapter 2 regarding Math SAT scores to complete this problem. What are the mean and standard deviation for statewide Math SAT scores? What SAT score separates the bottom 10% of states from the others? What is the probability that a randomly selected state has a statewide SAT score above 500?

6. Your Class Confirm the two formulas hold true for the central limit theorem for the population containing the elements {1, 5, 10}. First, compute the population mean and standard deviation for the data set. Next, create a list of all 9 of the possible two-element samples that can be created with replacement: {1, 1}, {1, 5}, etc. For each of the 9 compute the sample mean. Now find the mean of the sample means. Does it equal the population mean? Compute the standard deviation of the sample means. Does it equal the population standard deviation, divided by the square root of *n*?

Answers to Applying the Concepts

Section 6–1   Assessing Normality

1. Answers will vary. One possible frequency distribution is the following:

Branches	Frequency
0–9	1
10–19	14
20–29	17
30–39	7
40–49	3
50–59	2
60–69	2
70–79	1
80–89	2
90–99	1

2. Answers will vary according to the frequency distribution in question 1. This histogram matches the frequency distribution in question 1.

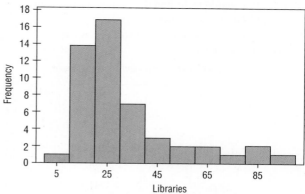

Histogram of Libraries

3. The histogram is unimodal and skewed to the right (positively skewed).

4. The distribution does not appear to be normal.

5. The mean number of branches is $\bar{x} = 31.4$, and the standard deviation is $s = 20.6$.

6. Of the data values, 80% fall within 1 standard deviation of the mean (between 10.8 and 52).

7. Of the data values, 92% fall within 2 standard deviations of the mean (between 0 and 72.6).

8. Of the data values, 98% fall within 3 standard deviations of the mean (between 0 and 93.2).

9. My values in questions 6–8 differ from the 68, 95, and 100% that we would see in a normal distribution.

10. These values support the conclusion that the distribution of the variable is not normal.

Section 6–2   Smart People

1. $z = \frac{130 - 100}{15} = 2$. The area to the right of 2 in the standard normal table is about 0.0228, so I would expect about $10,000(0.0228) = 228$ people in Visiala to qualify for Mensa.

2. It does seem reasonable to continue my quest to start a Mensa chapter in Visiala.

3. Answers will vary. One possible answer would be to randomly call telephone numbers (both home and cell phones) in Visiala, ask to speak to an adult, and ask whether the person would be interested in joining Mensa.

4. To have an Ultra-Mensa club, I would need to find the people in Visiala who have IQs that are at least 2.326 standard deviations above average. This means that I would need to recruit those with IQs that are at least 135:

$$2.326 = \frac{x - 100}{15} \Rightarrow x = 100 + 2.326(15) = 134.89$$

Section 6–3   Central Limit Theorem

1. It is very unlikely that we would ever get the same results for any of our random samples. While it is a remote possibility, it is highly unlikely.

2. A good estimate for the population mean would be to find the average of the students' sample means. Similarly, a good estimate for the population standard deviation would be to find the average of the students' sample standard deviations.

3. The distribution appears to be somewhat left (negatively) skewed.

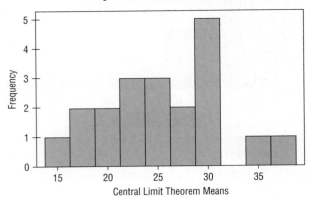

Histogram of Central Limit Theorem Means

4. The mean of the students' means is 25.4, and the standard deviation is 5.8.

5. The distribution of the means is not a sampling distribution, since it represents just 20 of all possible samples of size 30 from the population.

6. The sampling error for student 3 is $18 - 25.4 = -7.4$; the sampling error for student 7 is $26 - 25.4 = +0.6$; the sampling error for student 14 is $29 - 25.4 = +3.6$.

7. The standard deviation for the sample of the 20 means is greater than the standard deviations for each of the individual students. So it is not equal to the standard deviation divided by the square root of the sample size.

Section 6–4   How Safe Are You?

1. A reliability rating of 97% means that, on average, the device will not fail 97% of the time. We do not know how many times it will fail for any particular set of 100 climbs.

2. The probability of at least 1 failure in 100 climbs is $1 - (0.97)^{100} = 1 - 0.0476 = 0.9524$ (about 95%).

3. The complement of the event in question 2 is the event of "no failures in 100 climbs."

4. This can be considered a binomial experiment. We have two outcomes: success and failure. The probability of the equipment working (success) remains constant at 97%. We have 100 independent climbs. And we are counting the number of times the equipment works in these 100 climbs.

5. We could use the binomial probability formula, but it would be very messy computationally.

6. The probability of at least two failures *cannot* be estimated with the normal distribution (see below). So the probability is $1 - [(0.97)^{100} + 100(0.97)^{99}(0.03)] = 1 - 0.1946 = 0.8054$ (about 80.5%).

7. We *should not* use the normal approximation to the binomial since $nq < 10$.

8. If we had used the normal approximation, we would have needed a correction for continuity, since we would have been approximating a discrete distribution with a continuous distribution.

9. Since a second safety hook will be successful or fail independently of the first safety hook, the probability of failure drops from 3% to $(0.03)(0.03) = 0.0009$, or 0.09%.

Confidence Intervals and Sample Size

Objectives

After completing this chapter, you should be able to

1 Find the confidence interval for the mean when σ is known.

2 Determine the minimum sample size for finding a confidence interval for the mean.

3 Find the confidence interval for the mean when σ is unknown.

4 Find the confidence interval for a proportion.

5 Determine the minimum sample size for finding a confidence interval for a proportion.

6 Find a confidence interval for a variance and a standard deviation.

Statistics Today

Would You Change the Channel?

A survey by the Roper Organization found that 45% of the people who were offended by a television program would change the channel, while 15% would turn off their television sets. The survey further stated that the margin of error is 3 percentage points, and 4000 adults were interviewed.

Several questions arise:

1. How do these estimates compare with the true population percentages?
2. What is meant by a margin of error of 3 percentage points?
3. Is the sample of 4000 large enough to represent the population of all adults who watch television in the United States?

See Statistics Today—Revisited at the end of the chapter for the answers.

After reading this chapter, you will be able to answer these questions, since this chapter explains how statisticians can use statistics to make estimates of parameters.

Source: The Associated Press.

Introduction

One aspect of inferential statistics is **estimation,** which is the process of estimating the value of a parameter from information obtained from a sample. For example, *The Book of Odds,* by Michael D. Shook and Robert L. Shook (New York: Penguin Putnam, Inc.), contains the following statements:

> *"One out of 4 Americans is currently dieting." (Calorie Control Council)*
> *"Seventy-two percent of Americans have flown on commercial airlines." ("The Bristol Meyers Report: Medicine in the Next Century")*
> *"The average kindergarten student has seen more than 5000 hours of television." (U.S. Department of Education)*

"The average school nurse makes $32,786 a year." (National Association of School Nurses)
"The average amount of life insurance is $108,000 per household with life insurance."
(American Council of Life Insurance)

Since the populations from which these values were obtained are large, these values are only *estimates* of the true parameters and are derived from data collected from samples.

The statistical procedures for estimating the population mean, proportion, variance, and standard deviation will be explained in this chapter.

An important question in estimation is that of sample size. How large should the sample be in order to make an accurate estimate? This question is not easy to answer since the size of the sample depends on several factors, such as the accuracy desired and the probability of making a correct estimate. The question of sample size will be explained in this chapter also.

7–1 · Confidence Intervals for the Mean When σ Is Known and Sample Size

Objective 1

Find the confidence interval for the mean when σ is known.

Suppose a college president wishes to estimate the average age of students attending classes this semester. The president could select a random sample of 100 students and find the average age of these students, say, 22.3 years. From the sample mean, the president could infer that the average age of all the students is 22.3 years. This type of estimate is called a *point estimate*.

> A **point estimate** is a specific numerical value estimate of a parameter. The best point estimate of the population mean μ is the sample mean $\overline{X}$.

You might ask why other measures of central tendency, such as the median and mode, are not used to estimate the population mean. The reason is that the means of samples vary less than other statistics (such as medians and modes) when many samples are selected from the same population. Therefore, the sample mean is the best estimate of the population mean.

Sample measures (i.e., statistics) are used to estimate population measures (i.e., parameters). These statistics are called **estimators.** As previously stated, the sample mean is a better estimator of the population mean than the sample median or sample mode.

A good estimator should satisfy the three properties described now.

Three Properties of a Good Estimator

1. The estimator should be an **unbiased estimator.** That is, the expected value or the mean of the estimates obtained from samples of a given size is equal to the parameter being estimated.

2. The estimator should be consistent. For a **consistent estimator,** as sample size increases, the value of the estimator approaches the value of the parameter estimated.

3. The estimator should be a **relatively efficient estimator.** That is, of all the statistics that can be used to estimate a parameter, the relatively efficient estimator has the smallest variance.

Confidence Intervals

As stated in Chapter 6, the sample mean will be, for the most part, somewhat different from the population mean due to sampling error. Therefore, you might ask a second question: How good is a point estimate? The answer is that there is no way of knowing how close a particular point estimate is to the population mean.

This answer places some doubt on the accuracy of point estimates. For this reason, statisticians prefer another type of estimate, called an *interval estimate*.

An **interval estimate** of a parameter is an interval or a range of values used to estimate the parameter. This estimate may or may not contain the value of the parameter being estimated.

In an interval estimate, the parameter is specified as being between two values. For example, an interval estimate for the average age of all students might be $26.9 < \mu < 27.7$, or 27.3 ± 0.4 years.

Either the interval contains the parameter or it does not. A degree of confidence (usually a percent) can be assigned before an interval estimate is made. For instance, you may wish to be 95% confident that the interval contains the true population mean. Another question then arises. Why 95%? Why not 99 or 99.5%?

If you desire to be more confident, such as 99 or 99.5% confident, then you must make the interval larger. For example, a 99% confidence interval for the mean age of college students might be $26.7 < \mu < 27.9$, or 27.3 ± 0.6. Hence, a tradeoff occurs. To be more confident that the interval contains the true population mean, you must make the interval wider.

The **confidence level** of an interval estimate of a parameter is the probability that the interval estimate will contain the parameter, assuming that a large number of samples are selected and that the estimation process on the same parameter is repeated.

A **confidence interval** is a specific interval estimate of a parameter determined by using data obtained from a sample and by using the specific confidence level of the estimate.

Intervals constructed in this way are called *confidence intervals*. Three common confidence intervals are used: the 90, the 95, and the 99% confidence intervals.

The algebraic derivation of the formula for determining a confidence interval for a mean will be shown later. A brief intuitive explanation will be given first.

The central limit theorem states that when the sample size is large, approximately 95% of the sample means taken from a population and same sample size will fall within ± 1.96 standard errors of the population mean, that is,

$$\mu \pm 1.96\left(\frac{\sigma}{\sqrt{n}}\right)$$

Now, if a specific sample mean is selected, say, $\overline{X}$, there is a 95% probability that the interval $\mu \pm 1.96(\sigma/\sqrt{n})$ contains $\overline{X}$. Likewise, there is a 95% probability that the interval specified by

$$\overline{X} \pm 1.96\left(\frac{\sigma}{\sqrt{n}}\right)$$

will contain μ, as will be shown later. Stated another way,

$$\overline{X} - 1.96\left(\frac{\sigma}{\sqrt{n}}\right) < \mu < \overline{X} + 1.96\left(\frac{\sigma}{\sqrt{n}}\right)$$

Historical Notes

Point and interval estimates were known as long ago as the late 1700s. However, it wasn't until 1937 that a mathematician, J. Neyman, formulated practical applications for them.

Hence, you can be 95% confident that the population mean is contained within that interval when the values of the variable are normally distributed in the population.

The value used for the 95% confidence interval, 1.96, is obtained from Table E in Appendix C. For a 99% confidence interval, the value 2.58 is used instead of 1.96 in the formula. This value is also obtained from Table E and is based on the standard normal distribution. Since other confidence intervals are used in statistics, the symbol $z_{\alpha/2}$ (read "zee sub alpha over two") is used in the general formula for confidence intervals. The Greek letter α (alpha) represents the total area in both tails of the standard normal distribution curve, and $\alpha/2$ represents the area in each one of the tails. More will be said after Examples 7–1 and 7–2 about finding other values for $z_{\alpha/2}$.

The relationship between α and the confidence level is that the stated confidence level is the percentage equivalent to the decimal value of $1 - \alpha$, and vice versa. When the 95% confidence interval is to be found, $\alpha = 0.05$, since $1 - 0.05 = 0.95$, or 95%. When $\alpha = 0.01$, then $1 - \alpha = 1 - 0.01 = 0.99$, and the 99% confidence interval is being calculated.

Formula for the Confidence Interval of the Mean for a Specific α

$$\bar{X} - z_{\alpha/2}\left(\frac{\sigma}{\sqrt{n}}\right) < \mu < \bar{X} + z_{\alpha/2}\left(\frac{\sigma}{\sqrt{n}}\right)$$

For a 90% confidence interval, $z_{\alpha/2} = 1.65$; for a 95% confidence interval, $z_{\alpha/2} = 1.96$; and for a 99% confidence interval, $z_{\alpha/2} = 2.58$.

The term $z_{\alpha/2}(\sigma/\sqrt{n})$ is called the *maximum error of the estimate* (also called the *margin of error*). For a specific value, say, $\alpha = 0.05$, 95% of the sample means will fall within this error value on either side of the population mean, as previously explained. See Figure 7–1.

Figure 7–1

95% Confidence Interval

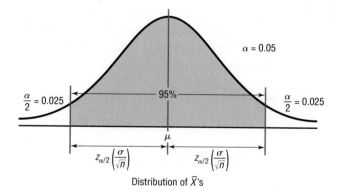

Distribution of $\bar{X}$'s

When $n \geq 30$, s can be substituted for σ, but a different distribution is used.

The **maximum error of the estimate** is the maximum likely difference between the point estimate of a parameter and the actual value of the parameter.

A more detailed explanation of the maximum error of the estimate follows Examples 7–1 and 7–2, which illustrate the computation of confidence intervals.

Rounding Rule for a Confidence Interval for a Mean When you are computing a confidence interval for a population mean by using *raw data,* round off to one more decimal place than the number of decimal places in the original data. When you are computing a confidence interval for a population mean by using a sample mean and a standard deviation, round off to the same number of decimal places as given for the mean.

| Example 7–1 | Days It Takes to Sell an Aveo |

A researcher wishes to estimate the number of days it takes an automobile dealer to sell a Chevrolet Aveo. A sample of 50 cars had a mean time on the dealer's lot of 54 days. Assume the population standard deviation to be 6.0 days. Find the best point estimate of the population mean and the 95% confidence interval of the population mean.

Source: Based on information obtained from Power Information Network.

Solution

The best point estimate of the mean is 54 days. For the 95% confidence interval use $z = 1.96$.

$$54 - 1.96\left(\frac{6.0}{\sqrt{50}}\right) < \mu < 54 + 1.96\left(\frac{6.0}{\sqrt{50}}\right)$$

$$54 - 1.7 < \mu < 54 + 1.7$$

$$52.3 < \mu < 55.7 \text{ or } 54 \pm 1.7$$

Hence one can say with 95% confidence that the interval between 52.3 and 55.7 days does contain the population mean, based on a sample of 50 automobiles.

| Example 7–2 | Ages of Automobiles |

A survey of 30 adults found that the mean age of a person's primary vehicle is 5.6 years. Assuming the standard deviation of the population is 0.8 year, find the best point estimate of the population mean and the 99% confidence interval of the population mean.

Source: Based on information in *USA TODAY*.

Solution

The best point estimate of the population mean is 5.6 years.

$$5.6 - 2.58\left(\frac{0.8}{\sqrt{30}}\right) < \mu < 5.6 + 2.58\left(\frac{0.8}{\sqrt{30}}\right)$$

$$5.6 - 0.38 < \mu < 5.6 + 0.38$$

$$5.22 < \mu < 5.98$$

or $$5.2 < \mu < 6.0 \text{ (rounded)}$$

Hence, one can be 99% confident that the mean age of all primary vehicles is between 5.2 and 6.0 years, based on 30 vehicles.

Another way of looking at a confidence interval is shown in Figure 7–2. According to the central limit theorem, approximately 95% of the sample means fall within 1.96 standard deviations of the population mean if the sample size is 30 or more or if σ is known when n is less than 30 and the population is normally distributed. If it were possible to build a confidence interval about each sample mean, as was done in Examples 7–1

Figure 7–2

95% Confidence Interval for Sample Means

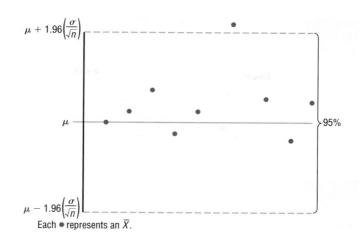

Each ● represents an $\bar{X}$.

Figure 7–3

95% Confidence Intervals for Each Sample Mean

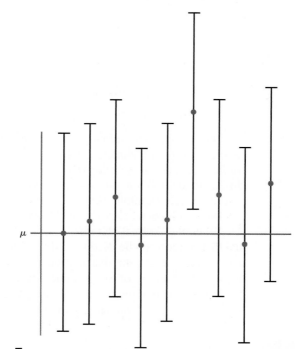

Each I represents an interval about a sample mean.

and 7–2 for μ, 95% of these intervals would contain the population mean, as shown in Figure 7–3. Hence, you can be 95% confident that an interval built around a specific sample mean would contain the population mean. If you desire to be 99% confident, you must enlarge the confidence intervals so that 99 out of every 100 intervals contain the population mean.

Since other confidence intervals (besides 90, 95, and 99%) are sometimes used in statistics, an explanation of how to find the values for $z_{\alpha/2}$ is necessary. As stated previously, the Greek letter α represents the total of the areas in both tails of the normal distribution. The value for α is found by subtracting the decimal equivalent for the desired confidence level from 1. For example, if you wanted to find the 98% confidence interval, you would change 98% to 0.98 and find $\alpha = 1 - 0.98$, or 0.02. Then $\alpha/2$ is obtained by dividing α by 2. So $\alpha/2$ is 0.02/2, or 0.01. Finally, $z_{0.01}$ is the z value that will give an area of 0.01 in the right tail of the standard normal distribution curve. See Figure 7–4.

Figure 7–4

Finding $\alpha/2$ for a 98% Confidence Interval

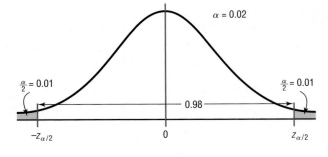

Figure 7–5

Finding $z_{\alpha/2}$ for a 98% Confidence Interval

	Table E
	The Standard Normal Distribution

z	.00	.01	.02	.03	...	.09
0.0						
0.1						
⋮						
2.3				0.9901		

Once $\alpha/2$ is determined, the corresponding $z_{\alpha/2}$ value can be found by using the procedure shown in Chapter 6, which is reviewed here. To get the $z_{\alpha/2}$ value for a 98% confidence interval, subtract 0.01 from 1.0000 to get 0.9900. Next, locate the area that is closest to 0.9900 (in this case, 0.9901) in Table E, and then find the corresponding z value. In this example, it is 2.33. See Figure 7–5.

For confidence intervals, only the positive z value is used in the formula.

When the original variable is normally distributed and σ is known, the standard normal distribution can be used to find confidence intervals regardless of the size of the sample. When $n \geq 30$, the distribution of means will be approximately normal even if the original distribution of the variable departs from normality.

When σ is unknown, s can be used as an estimate of σ, but a different distribution is used for the critical values. This method is explained in Section 7–2.

Example 7–3

Credit Union Assets

 The following data represent a sample of the assets (in millions of dollars) of 30 credit unions in southwestern Pennsylvania. Find the 90% confidence interval of the mean.

12.23	16.56	4.39
2.89	1.24	2.17
13.19	9.16	1.42
73.25	1.91	14.64
11.59	6.69	1.06
8.74	3.17	18.13
7.92	4.78	16.85
40.22	2.42	21.58
5.01	1.47	12.24
2.27	12.77	2.76

Source: *Pittsburgh Post Gazette.*

Solution

Step 1 Find the mean and standard deviation for the data. Use the formulas shown in Chapter 3 or your calculator. The mean $\bar{X} = 11.091$. Assume the standard deviation of the population is 14.405.

Step 2 Find $\alpha/2$. Since the 90% confidence interval is to be used, $\alpha = 1 - 0.90 = 0.10$, and

$$\frac{\alpha}{2} = \frac{0.10}{2} = 0.05$$

Step 3 Find $z_{\alpha/2}$. Subtract 0.05 from 1.000 to get 0.9500. The corresponding z value obtained from Table E is 1.65. (*Note:* This value is found by using the z value for an area between 0.9495 and 0.9505. A more precise z value obtained mathematically is 1.645 and is sometimes used; however, 1.65 will be used in this textbook.)

Step 4 Substitute in the formula

$$\bar{X} - z_{\alpha/2}\left(\frac{\sigma}{\sqrt{n}}\right) < \mu < \bar{X} + z_{\alpha/2}\left(\frac{\sigma}{\sqrt{n}}\right)$$

$$11.091 - 1.65\left(\frac{14.405}{\sqrt{30}}\right) < \mu < 11.091 + 1.65\left(\frac{14.405}{\sqrt{30}}\right)$$

$$11.091 - 4.339 < \mu < 11.091 + 4.339$$

$$6.752 < \mu < 15.430$$

Hence, one can be 90% confident that the population mean of the assets of all credit unions is between \$6.752 million and \$15.430 million, based on a sample of 30 credit unions.

Comment to Computer and Statistical Calculator Users

This chapter and subsequent chapters include examples using raw data. If you are using computer or calculator programs to find the solutions, the answers you get may vary somewhat from the ones given in the textbook. This is so because computers and calculators do not round the answers in the intermediate steps and can use 12 or more decimal places for computation. Also, they use more exact values than those given in the tables in the back of this book. These discrepancies are part and parcel of statistics.

Sample Size

Objective 2

Determine the minimum sample size for finding a confidence interval for the mean.

Sample size determination is closely related to statistical estimation. Quite often, you ask, How large a sample is necessary to make an accurate estimate? The answer is not simple, since it depends on three things: the maximum error of the estimate, the population standard deviation, and the degree of confidence. For example, how close to the true mean do you want to be (2 units, 5 units, etc.), and how confident do you wish to be (90, 95, 99%, etc.)? For the purpose of this chapter, it will be assumed that the population standard deviation of the variable is known or has been estimated from a previous study.

The formula for sample size is derived from the maximum error of the estimate formula

$$E = z_{\alpha/2}\left(\frac{\sigma}{\sqrt{n}}\right)$$

and this formula is solved for n as follows:

$$E\sqrt{n} = z_{\alpha/2}(\sigma)$$

$$\sqrt{n} = \frac{z_{\alpha/2} \cdot \sigma}{E}$$

Hence, $n = \left(\frac{z_{\alpha/2} \cdot \sigma}{E}\right)^2$

Formula for the Minimum Sample Size Needed for an Interval Estimate of the Population Mean

$$n = \left(\frac{z_{\alpha/2} \cdot \sigma}{E}\right)^2$$

where E is the maximum error of estimate. If necessary, round the answer up to obtain a whole number. That is, if there is any fraction or decimal portion in the answer, use the next whole number for sample size n.

Example 7–4

Depth of a River

A scientist wishes to estimate the average depth of a river. He wants to be 99% confident that the estimate is accurate within 2 feet. From a previous study, the standard deviation of the depths measured was 4.38 feet.

Solution

Since $\alpha = 0.01$ (or $1 - 0.99$), $z_{\alpha/2} = 2.58$ and $E = 2$. Substituting in the formula,

$$n = \left(\frac{z_{\alpha/2} \cdot \sigma}{E}\right)^2 = \left[\frac{(2.58)(4.38)}{2}\right]^2 = 31.92$$

Round the value 31.92 up to 32. Therefore, to be 99% confident that the estimate is within 2 feet of the true mean depth, the scientist needs at least a sample of 32 measurements. (Always round n up to the next whole number. For example, if $n = 31.2$, round it up to 32.)

Notice that when you are finding the sample size, the size of the population is irrelevant when the population is large or infinite or when sampling is done with replacement. In other cases, an adjustment is made in the formula for computing sample size. This adjustment is beyond the scope of this book.

The formula for determining sample size requires the use of the population standard deviation. What happens when σ is unknown? In this case, an attempt is made to estimate σ. One such way is to use the standard deviation s obtained from a sample taken previously as an estimate for σ. The standard deviation can also be estimated by dividing the range by 4.

Sometimes, interval estimates rather than point estimates are reported. For instance, you may read a statement: "On the basis of a sample of 200 families, the survey estimates that an American family of two spends an average of $84 per week for groceries. One

Interesting Fact

It has been estimated that the amount of pizza consumed every day in the United States would cover a farm consisting of 75 acres.

can be 95% confident that this estimate is accurate within $3 of the true mean." This statement means that the 95% confidence interval of the true mean is

$$\$84 - \$3 < \mu < \$84 + \$3$$
$$\$81 < \mu < \$87$$

The algebraic derivation of the formula for a confidence interval is shown next. As explained in Chapter 6, the sampling distribution of the mean is approximately normal when large samples ($n \geq 30$) are taken from a population. Also,

$$z = \frac{\bar{X} - \mu}{\sigma/\sqrt{n}}$$

Furthermore, there is a probability of $1 - \alpha$ that a z will have a value between $-z_{\alpha/2}$ and $+z_{\alpha/2}$. Hence,

$$-z_{\alpha/2} < \frac{\bar{X} - \mu}{\sigma/\sqrt{n}} < z_{\alpha/2}$$

By using algebra, the formula can be rewritten as

$$-z_{\alpha/2} \cdot \frac{\sigma}{\sqrt{n}} < \bar{X} - \mu < z_{\alpha/2} \cdot \frac{\sigma}{\sqrt{n}}$$

Subtracting $\bar{X}$ from both sides and from the middle gives

$$-\bar{X} - z_{\alpha/2} \cdot \frac{\sigma}{\sqrt{n}} < -\mu < -\bar{X} + z_{\alpha/2} \cdot \frac{\sigma}{\sqrt{n}}$$

Multiplying by -1 gives

$$\bar{X} + z_{\alpha/2} \cdot \frac{\sigma}{\sqrt{n}} > \mu > \bar{X} - z_{\alpha/2} \cdot \frac{\sigma}{\sqrt{n}}$$

Reversing the inequality yields the formula for the confidence interval:

$$\bar{X} - z_{\alpha/2} \cdot \frac{\sigma}{\sqrt{n}} < \mu < \bar{X} + z_{\alpha/2} \cdot \frac{\sigma}{\sqrt{n}}$$

Applying the Concepts **7–1**

Making Decisions with Confidence Intervals

Assume you work for Kimberly Clark Corporation, the makers of Kleenex. The job you are presently working on requires you to decide how many Kleenexes are to be put in the new automobile glove compartment boxes. Complete the following.

1. How will you decide on a reasonable number of Kleenexes to put in the boxes?

2. When do people usually need Kleenexes?

3. What type of data collection technique would you use?

4. Assume you found out that from your sample of 85 people, on average about 57 Kleenexes are used throughout the duration of a cold, with a population standard deviation of 15. Use a confidence interval to help you decide how many Kleenexes will go in the boxes.

5. Explain how you decided how many Kleenexes will go in the boxes.

See page 396 for the answers.

Exercises 7–1

1. What is the difference between a point estimate and an interval estimate of a parameter? Which is better? Why?

2. What information is necessary to calculate a confidence interval?

3. What is the maximum error of the estimate?

4. What is meant by the 95% confidence interval of the mean?

5. What are three properties of a good estimator?

6. What statistic best estimates μ?

7. What is necessary to determine the sample size?

8. In determining the sample size for a confidence interval, is the size of the population relevant?

9. Find each.

   a. $z_{\alpha/2}$ for the 99% confidence interval
   b. $z_{\alpha/2}$ for the 98% confidence interval
   c. $z_{\alpha/2}$ for the 95% confidence interval
   d. $z_{\alpha/2}$ for the 90% confidence interval
   e. $z_{\alpha/2}$ for the 94% confidence interval

10. **Number of Faculty** The numbers of faculty at 32 randomly selected state-controlled colleges and universities with enrollment under 12,000 students are shown below. Use these data to estimate the mean number of faculty at all state-controlled colleges and universities with enrollment under 12,000 with 92% confidence. Assume $\sigma = 165.1$.

211	384	396	211	224	337	395	121	356
621	367	408	515	280	289	180	431	176
318	836	203	374	224	121	412	134	539
471	638	425	159	324				

    Source: *World Almanac.*

11. **Reading Scores** A sample of the reading scores of 35 fifth-graders has a mean of 82. The standard deviation of the population is 15.

    a. Find the best point estimate of the mean.
    b. Find the 95% confidence interval of the mean reading scores of all fifth-graders.
    c. Find the 99% confidence interval of the mean reading scores of all fifth-graders.
    d. Which interval is larger? Explain why.

12. **Freshmen's GPA** First-semester GPAs for a random selection of freshmen at a large university are shown below. Estimate the true mean GPA of the freshman class with 99% confidence. Assume $\sigma = 0.62$.

1.9	3.2	2.0	2.9	2.7	3.3
2.8	3.0	3.8	2.7	2.0	1.9
2.5	2.7	2.8	3.2	3.0	3.8
3.1	2.7	3.5	3.8	3.9	2.7
2.0	2.8	1.9	4.0	2.2	2.8
2.1	2.4	3.0	3.4	2.9	2.1

13. **Workers' Distractions** A recent study showed that the modern working person experiences an average of 2.1 hours per day of distractions (phone calls, e-mails, impromptu visits, etc.). A random sample of 50 workers for a large corporation found that these workers were distracted an average of 1.8 hours per day and the population standard deviation was 20 minutes. Estimate the true mean population distraction time with 90% confidence, and compare your answer to the results of the study.

Source: *Time Almanac.*

14. **Golf Averages** A study of 35 golfers showed that their average score on a particular course was 92. The standard deviation of the population is 5.

    a. Find the best point estimate of the mean.
    b. Find the 95% confidence interval of the mean score for all golfers.
    c. Find the 95% confidence interval of the mean score if a sample of 60 golfers is used instead of a sample of 35.
    d. Which interval is smaller? Explain why.

15. **Actuary Exams** A survey of 35 individuals who passed the seven exams and obtained the rank of Fellow in the actuarial field finds the average salary to be $150,000. If the standard deviation for the population is $15,000, construct a 95% confidence interval for all Fellows.

Source: www.BeAnActuary.org

16. **Number of Farms** A random sample of the number of farms (in thousands) in various states follows. Estimate the mean number of farms per state with 90% confidence. Assume $\sigma = 31$.

47	95	54	33	64	4	8	57	9	80
8	90	3	49	4	44	79	80	48	16
68	7	15	21	52	6	78	109	40	50
29									

    Source: *New York Times Almanac.*

17. **Television Viewing** A study of 415 kindergarten students showed that they have seen on average 5000 hours of television. If the sample standard deviation of the population is 900, find the 95% confidence level of the mean for all students. If a parent claimed that his children watched 4000 hours, would the claim be believable?

Source: U.S. Department of Education.

18. Day Care Tuition A random sample of 50 four-year-olds attending day care centers provided a yearly tuition average of $3987 and the population standard deviation of $630. Find the 90% confidence interval of the true mean. If a day care center were starting up and wanted to keep tuition low, what would be a reasonable amount to charge?

19. Hospital Noise Levels Noise levels at various area urban hospitals were measured in decibels. The mean of the noise levels in 84 corridors was 61.2 decibels, and the standard deviation of the population was 7.9. Find the 95% confidence interval of the true mean.

Source: M. Bayo, A. Garcia, and A. Garcia, "Noise Levels in an Urban Hospital and Workers' Subjective Responses," *Archives of Environmental Health* 50, no. 3, p. 249 (May–June 1995). Reprinted with permission of the Helen Dwight Reid Educational Foundation. Published by Heldref Publications, 1319 Eighteenth St. N.W., Washington, D.C. 20036-1802. Copyright © 1995.

20. Length of Growing Seasons The growing seasons for a random sample of 35 U.S. cities were recorded, yielding a sample mean of 190.7 days and the population standard deviation of 54.2 days. Estimate the true mean population of the growing season with 95% confidence.

Source: *The Old Farmer's Almanac.*

21. Time on Homework A university dean of students wishes to estimate the average number of hours students spend doing homework per week. The standard deviation from a previous study is 6.2 hours. How large a sample must be selected if he wants to be 99% confident of finding whether the true mean differs from the sample mean by 1.5 hours?

22. In the hospital study cited in Exercise 19, the mean noise level in the 171 ward areas was 58.0 decibels, and the population standard deviation is 4.8. Find the 90% confidence interval of the true mean.

Source: M. Bayo, A. Garcia, and A. Garcia, "Noise Levels in an Urban Hospital and Workers' Subjective Responses," *Archives of Environmental Health* 50, no. 3, p. 249 (May–June 1995). Reprinted with permission of the Helen Dwight Reid Educational Foundation. Published by Heldref Publications, 1319 Eighteenth St. N.W., Washington, D.C. 20036-1802. Copyright © 1995.

23. Chocolate Chips per Cookie It is desired to estimate the mean number of chocolate chips per cookie for a large national brand. How many cookies would have to be sampled to estimate the true mean number of chips per cookie within 2 chips with 98% confidence? Assume that $\sigma = 10.1$ chips.

24. Cost of Pizzas A pizza shop owner wishes to find the 95% confidence interval of the true mean cost of a large plain pizza. How large should the sample be if she wishes to be accurate to within $0.15? A previous study showed that the standard deviation of the price was $0.26.

25. National Accounting Examination If the variance of a national accounting examination is 900, how large a sample is needed to estimate the true mean score within 5 points with 99% confidence?

26. Commuting Times in New York The 90% confidence interval for the mean one-way commuting time in New York City is $37.8 < \mu < 38.8$ minutes. Construct a 95% confidence interval based on the same data. Which interval provides more information?

Source: www.census.gov

MINITAB
Step by Step

Finding a *z* Confidence Interval for the Mean

For Example 7–3, find the 90% confidence interval estimate for the mean amount of assets for credit unions in southwestern Pennsylvania.

1. Maximize the worksheet, then enter the data into **C1** of a MINITAB worksheet. If sigma is known, skip to step 3.

2. Calculate the standard deviation for the sample. It will be used as an estimate for sigma.

   a) Select **Calc>Column statistics.**

   b) Click the option for Standard deviation.

   c) Enter **C1** Assets for the Input variable and **s** for Store in:.

3. Select **Stat>Basic Statistics>1-Sample Z.**

4. Select C1 Assets for the Samples in Columns.
5. Click in the box for Standard Deviation and enter **s.** Leave the box for Test mean empty.
6. Click the [Options] button. In the dialog box make sure the Confidence Level is 90 and the Alternative is not equal.
7. Optional: Click [Graphs], then select Boxplot of data. The boxplot of these data would clearly show the outliers!
8. Click [OK] twice. The results will be displayed in the session window.

One-Sample Z: Assets

```
The assumed sigma = 14.4054
Variable      N        Mean       StDev     SE Mean          90% CI
Assets       30      11.0907     14.4054     2.6301      (6.7646, 15.4167)
```

TI-83 Plus or TI-84 Plus
Step by Step

Finding a z Confidence Interval for the Mean (Data)

1. Enter the data into L_1.
2. Press **STAT** and move the cursor to TESTS.
3. Press **7** for ZInterval.
4. Move the cursor to Data and press **ENTER.**
5. Type in the appropriate values.
6. Move the cursor to Calculate and press **ENTER.**

Example TI7–1

This is Example 7–3 from the text. Find the 90% confidence interval for the population mean, given the data values.

12.23	2.89	13.19	73.25	11.59	8.74	7.92	40.22	5.01	2.27
16.56	1.24	9.16	1.91	6.69	3.17	4.78	2.42	1.47	12.77
4.39	2.17	1.42	14.64	1.06	18.13	16.85	21.58	12.24	2.76

The population standard deviation σ is unknown. Since the sample size is $n = 30$, you can use the sample standard deviation s as an approximation for σ. After the data values are entered in L_1 (step 1 above), press **STAT,** move the cursor to CALC, press **1** for 1-Var Stats, then press **ENTER.** The sample standard deviation of 14.40544747 will be one of the statistics listed. Then continue with step 2. At step 5 on the line for σ, press **VARS** for variables, press **5** for Statistics, press **3** for S_x.

The 90% confidence interval is $6.765 < \mu < 15.417$. The difference between these limits and the ones in Example 7–3 is due to rounding.

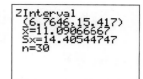

Finding a *z* Confidence Interval for the Mean (Statistics)

1. Press **STAT** and move the cursor to TESTS.
2. Press **7** for ZInterval.
3. Move the cursor to Stats and press **ENTER**.
4. Type in the appropriate values.
5. Move the cursor to Calculate and press **ENTER**.

Example TI7–2

Find the 95% confidence interval for the population mean, given $\sigma = 2$, $\overline{X} = 23.2$, and $n = 50$.

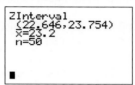

The 95% confidence interval is $22.6 < \mu < 23.8$.

Excel
Step by Step

Finding a *z* Confidence Interval for the Mean

Excel has a procedure to compute the maximum error of the estimate. But it does not compute confidence intervals. However, you may determine confidence intervals for the mean by using the MegaStat Add-in available on your CD. If you have not installed this add-in, do so following the instructions from the Chapter 1 Excel Step by Step.

Example XL7–1

Find the 95% confidence interval for the mean if $\sigma = 11$, using this sample:

43	52	18	20	25	45	43	21	42	32	24	32	19	25	26
44	42	41	41	53	22	25	23	21	27	33	36	47	19	20

1. Enter the data into an Excel worksheet.
2. From the toolbar, select Add-Ins, **MegaStat>Confidence Intervals/Sample Size.**
   Note: You may need to open **MegaStat** from the **MegaStat.xls** file on your computer's hard drive.
3. Enter the mean of the data, **32.03.**
4. Select *z* for the standard normal distribution.
5. Enter **11** for the standard deviation and **30** for *n*, the sample size.
6. Either type in or scroll to 95% for the Confidence Level, then click [OK].

The result of the procedure is shown next.

Confidence interval—mean

```
    95% Confidence level
 32.03 Mean
    11 Standard deviation
    30 n
 1.960 z
 3.936 Half-width
35.966 Upper confidence limit
28.094 Lower confidence limit
```

7-2

Objective **3**

Find the confidence interval for the mean when σ is unknown.

Confidence Intervals for the Mean When σ Is Unknown

When σ is known and the sample size is 30 or more, or the population is normally distributed if sample size is less than 30, the confidence interval for the mean can be found by using the z distribution as shown in Section 7–1. However, most of the time, the value of σ is not known, so it must be estimated by using s, namely, the standard deviation of the sample. When s is used, especially when the sample size is small, critical values greater than the values for $z_{\alpha/2}$ are used in confidence intervals in order to keep the interval at a given level, such as the 95%. These values are taken from the *Student t distribution,* most often called the **t distribution.**

To use this method, the samples must be simple random samples, and the population from which the samples were taken must be normally or approximately normally distributed, or the sample size must be 30 or more.

Some important characteristics of the t distribution are described now.

Historical Notes

The t distribution was formulated in 1908 by an Irish brewing employee named W. S. Gosset. Gosset was involved in researching new methods of manufacturing ale. Because brewing employees were not allowed to publish results, Gosset published his finding using the pseudonym *Student;* hence, the t distribution is sometimes called *Student's t distribution.*

Characteristics of the *t* Distribution

The t distribution shares some characteristics of the normal distribution and differs from it in others. The t distribution is similar to the standard normal distribution in these ways:

1. It is bell-shaped.
2. It is symmetric about the mean.
3. The mean, median, and mode are equal to 0 and are located at the center of the distribution.
4. The curve never touches the x axis.

The t distribution differs from the standard normal distribution in the following ways:

1. The variance is greater than 1.
2. The t distribution is actually a family of curves based on the concept of *degrees of freedom,* which is related to sample size.
3. As the sample size increases, the t distribution approaches the standard normal distribution. See Figure 7–6.

Many statistical distributions use the concept of degrees of freedom, and the formulas for finding the degrees of freedom vary for different statistical tests. The **degrees of freedom** are the number of values that are free to vary after a sample statistic has been computed, and they tell the researcher which specific curve to use when a distribution consists of a family of curves.

For example, if the mean of 5 values is 10, then 4 of the 5 values are free to vary. But once 4 values are selected, the fifth value must be a specific number to get a sum of 50, since $50 \div 5 = 10$. Hence, the degrees of freedom are $5 - 1 = 4$, and this value tells the researcher which t curve to use.

Figure 7–6

The *t* Family of Curves

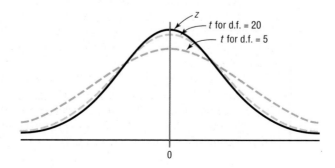

The symbol d.f. will be used for degrees of freedom. The degrees of freedom for a confidence interval for the mean are found by subtracting 1 from the sample size. That is, d.f. $= n - 1$. *Note:* For some statistical tests used later in this book, the degrees of freedom are not equal to $n - 1$.

The formula for finding a confidence interval about the mean by using the t distribution is given now.

> **Formula for a Specific Confidence Interval for the Mean When σ Is Unknown and $n < 30$**
>
> $$\bar{X} - t_{\alpha/2}\left(\frac{s}{\sqrt{n}}\right) < \mu < \bar{X} + t_{\alpha/2}\left(\frac{s}{\sqrt{n}}\right)$$
>
> The degrees of freedom are $n - 1$.

The values for $t_{\alpha/2}$ are found in Table F in Appendix C. The top row of Table F, labeled Confidence Intervals, is used to get these values. The other two rows, labeled One tail and Two tails, will be explained in Chapter 8 and should not be used here.

Example 7–5 shows how to find the value in Table F for $t_{\alpha/2}$.

Example 7–5

Find the $t_{\alpha/2}$ value for a 95% confidence interval when the sample size is 22.

Solution

The d.f. $= 22 - 1$, or 21. Find 21 in the left column and 95% in the row labeled Confidence Intervals. The intersection where the two meet gives the value for $t_{\alpha/2}$, which is 2.080. See Figure 7–7.

Figure 7–7

Finding $t_{\alpha/2}$ for Example 7–5

	Table F						
	The t Distribution						
	Confidence Intervals	50%	80%	90%	95%	98%	99%
d.f.	One tail α	0.25	0.10	0.05	0.025	0.01	0.005
	Two tails α	0.50	0.20	0.10	0.05	0.02	0.01
1							
2							
3							
⋮							
21						2.080	2.518	2.831
⋮							
$(z)\infty$			0.674	1.282[a]	1.645[b]	1.960	2.326[c]	2.576[d]

When d.f. is greater than 30, it may fall between two table values. For example, if d.f. $= 68$, it falls between 65 and 70. Many textbooks say to use the closest value; for example, 68 is closer to 70 than 65; however, in this textbook a conservative approach is used. In this case, always round down to the nearest table value. In this case, 68 rounds down to 65.

Note: At the bottom of Table F where d.f. is large or ∞, the $z_{\alpha/2}$ values can be found for specific confidence intervals. The reason is that as the degrees of freedom increase, the t distribution approaches the standard normal distribution.

Examples 7–6 and 7–7 show how to find the confidence interval when you are using the t distribution.

Example 7–6

Sleeping Time

Ten randomly selected people were asked how long they slept at night. The mean time was 7.1 hours, and the standard deviation was 0.78 hour. Find the 95% confidence interval of the mean time. Assume the variable is normally distributed.

Source: Based on information in *Number Freaking*.

Solution

Since σ is unknown and s must replace it, the t distribution (Table F) must be used for the confidence interval. Hence, with 9 degrees of freedom $t_{\alpha/2} = 2.262$. The 95% confidence interval can be found by substituting in the formula.

$$\bar{X} - t_{\alpha/2}\left(\frac{s}{\sqrt{n}}\right) < \mu < \bar{X} + t_{\alpha/2}\left(\frac{s}{\sqrt{n}}\right)$$

$$7.1 - 2.262\left(\frac{0.78}{\sqrt{10}}\right) < \mu < 7.1 + 2.262\left(\frac{0.78}{\sqrt{10}}\right)$$

$$7.1 - 0.56 < \mu < 7.1 + 0.56$$

$$6.54 < \mu < 7.66$$

Therefore, one can be 95% confident that the population mean is between 6.54 and 7.66 inches.

Example 7–7

Home Fires Started by Candles

The data represent a sample of the number of home fires started by candles for the past several years. (Data are from the National Fire Protection Association.) Find the 99% confidence interval for the mean number of home fires started by candles each year.

| 5460 | 5900 | 6090 | 6310 | 7160 | 8440 | 9930 |

Solution

Step 1   Find the mean and standard deviation for the data. Use the formulas in Chapter 3 or your calculator. The mean $\bar{X} = 7041.4$. The standard deviation $s = 1610.3$.

Step 2   Find $t_{\alpha/2}$ in Table F. Use the 99% confidence interval with d.f. = 6. It is 3.707.

Step 3   Substitute in the formula and solve.

$$\bar{X} - t_{\alpha/2}\left(\frac{s}{\sqrt{n}}\right) < \mu < \bar{X} + t_{\alpha/2}\left(\frac{s}{\sqrt{n}}\right)$$

$$7041.4 - 3.707\left(\frac{1610.3}{\sqrt{7}}\right) < \mu < 7041.4 + 3.707\left(\frac{1610.3}{\sqrt{7}}\right)$$

$$7041.4 - 2256.2 < \mu < 7041.4 + 2256.2$$

$$4785.2 < \mu < 9297.6$$

One can be 99% confident that the population mean number of home fires started by candles each year is between 4785.2 and 9297.6, based on a sample of home fires occurring over a period of 7 years.

Figure 7–8

When to Use the *z* or *t* Distribution

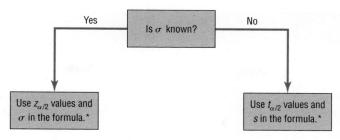

*If $n < 30$, the variable must be normally distributed.

Students sometimes have difficulty deciding whether to use $z_{\alpha/2}$ or $t_{\alpha/2}$ values when finding confidence intervals for the mean. As stated previously, when σ is known, $z_{\alpha/2}$ values can be used *no matter what the sample size is,* as long as the variable is normally distributed or $n \geq 30$. When σ is unknown and $n \geq 30$, then *s* can be used in the formula and $t_{\alpha/2}$ values can be used. Finally, when σ is unknown and $n < 30$, *s* is used in the formula and $t_{\alpha/2}$ values are used, as long as the variable is approximately normally distributed. These rules are summarized in Figure 7–8.

Applying the Concepts **7–2**

Sport Drink Decision

Assume you get a new job as a coach for a sports team, and one of your first decisions is to choose the sports drink that the team will use during practices and games. You obtain a *Sports Report* magazine so you can use your statistical background to help you make the best decision. The following table lists the most popular sports drinks and some important information about each of them. Answer the following questions about the table.

Drink	Calories	Sodium	Potassium	Cost
Gatorade	60	110	25	$1.29
Powerade	68	77	32	1.19
All Sport	75	55	55	0.89
10-K	63	55	35	0.79
Exceed	69	50	44	1.59
1st Ade	58	58	25	1.09
Hydra Fuel	85	23	50	1.89

1. Would this be considered a small sample?

2. Compute the mean cost per container, and create a 90% confidence interval about that mean. Do all the costs per container fall inside the confidence interval? If not, which ones do not?

3. Are there any you would consider outliers?

4. How many degrees of freedom are there?

5. If cost is a major factor influencing your decision, would you consider cost per container or cost per serving?

6. List which drink you would recommend and why.

See page 396 for the answers.

Exercises 7–2

1. What are the properties of the *t* distribution?

2. What is meant by *degrees of freedom?*

3. When should the *t* distribution be used to find a confidence interval for the mean?

4. (**ans**) Find the values for each.

   a. $t_{\alpha/2}$ and $n = 18$ for the 99% confidence interval for the mean

   b. $t_{\alpha/2}$ and $n = 23$ for the 95% confidence interval for the mean

   c. $t_{\alpha/2}$ and $n = 15$ for the 98% confidence interval for the mean

   d. $t_{\alpha/2}$ and $n = 10$ for the 90% confidence interval for the mean

   e. $t_{\alpha/2}$ and $n = 20$ for the 95% confidence interval for the mean

For Exercises 5 through 20, assume that all variables are approximately normally distributed.

5. **Hemoglobin** The average hemoglobin reading for a sample of 20 teachers was 16 grams per 100 milliliters, with a sample standard deviation of 2 grams. Find the 99% confidence interval of the true mean.

6. **Digital Camera Prices** The prices (in dollars) for a particular model of digital camera with 6.0 megapixels and an optical 3X zoom lens are shown below for 10 online retailers. Estimate the true mean price for this particular model with 95% confidence.

   225 240 215 206 211 210 193 250 225 202

7. **Women Representatives in State Legislature** A state representative wishes to estimate the mean number of women representatives per state legislature. A random sample of 17 states is selected, and the number of women representatives is shown. Based on the sample, what is the point estimate of the mean? Find the 90% confidence interval of the mean population. (*Note:* The population mean is actually 31.72, or about 32.) Compare this value to the point estimate and the confidence interval. There is something unusual about the data. Describe it and state how it would affect the confidence interval.

5	33	35	37	24
31	16	45	19	13
18	29	15	39	18
58	132			

8. **State Gasoline Taxes** A random sample of state gasoline taxes (in cents) is shown here for 12 states. Use the data to estimate the true population mean gasoline tax with 90% confidence. Does your interval contain the national average of 21 cents?

21.5	23	16	20.7	25.9
20	25.3	17	28	30
20	31			

   Source: *World Almanac.*

9. **College Wrestler Weights** A sample of six college wrestlers had an average weight of 276 pounds with a sample standard deviation of 12 pounds. Find the 90% confidence interval of the true mean weight of all college wrestlers. If a coach claimed that the average weight of the wrestlers on the team was 310, would the claim be believable?

10. **Dance Company Students** The number of students who belong to the dance company at each of several randomly selected small universities is shown below. Estimate the true population mean size of a university dance company with 99% confidence.

21	25	32	22	28	30	29	30
47	26	35	26	35	26	28	28
32	27	40					

11. **Distance Traveled to Work** A recent study of 28 employees of XYZ company showed that the mean of the distance they traveled to work was 14.3 miles. The standard deviation of the sample mean was 2 miles. Find the 95% confidence interval of the true mean. If a manager wanted to be sure that most of his employees would not be late, how much time would he suggest they allow for the commute if the average speed were 30 miles per hour?

12. **Thunderstorm Speeds** A meteorologist who sampled 13 thunderstorms found that the average speed at which they traveled across a certain state was 15 miles per hour. The standard deviation of the sample was 1.7 miles per hour. Find the 99% confidence interval of the mean. If a meteorologist wanted to use the highest speed to predict the times it would take storms to travel across the state in order to issue warnings, what figure would she likely use?

13. **Students per Teacher in U.S. Public Schools** The national average for the number of students per teacher for all U.S. public schools is 15.9. A random sample of 12 school districts from a moderately populated area showed that the mean number of students per teacher was 19.2 with a variance of 4.41. Estimate the true mean number of students per teacher with 95% confidence. How does your estimate compare with the national average?

    Source: *World Almanac.*

14. **Stress Test** For a group of 10 men subjected to a stress situation, the mean number of heartbeats per minute was 126, and the standard deviation was 4. Find the 95% confidence interval of the true mean.

15. For the stress test described in Exercise 14, six women had an average heart rate of 115 beats per minute. The standard deviation of the sample was 6 beats. Find the 95% confidence interval of the true mean for the women.

16. Hospital Noise Levels For a sample of 24 operating rooms taken in the hospital study mentioned in Exercise 19 in Section 7–1, the mean noise level was 41.6 decibels, and the standard deviation was 7.5. Find the 95% confidence interval of the true mean of the noise levels in the operating rooms.

Source: M. Bayo, A. Garcia, and A. Garcia, "Noise Levels in an Urban Hospital and Workers' Subjective Responses," *Archives of Environmental Health* 50, no. 3, p. 249 (May–June 1995). Reprinted with permission of the Helen Dwight Reid Educational Foundation. Published by Heldref Publications, 1319 Eighteenth St. N.W., Washington, D.C. 20036-1802. Copyright © 1995.

 17. Costs for a 30-Second Spot on Cable Television The approximate costs for a 30-second spot for various cable networks in a random selection of cities are shown below. Estimate the true population mean cost for a 30-second advertisement on cable network with 90% confidence.

14	55	165	9	15	66	23	30	150
22	12	13	54	73	55	41	78	

Source: www.spotrunner.com

18. Football Player Heart Rates For a group of 22 college football players, the mean heart rate after a morning workout session was 86 beats per minute, and the standard deviation was 5. Find the 90% confidence interval of the true mean for all college football players after a workout session. If a coach did not want to work his team beyond its capacity, what maximum value should he use for the mean number of heartbeats per minute?

19. Grooming Times for Men and Women It has been reported that 20- to 24-year-old men spend an average of 37 minutes per day grooming and 20- to 24-year-old women spend an average of 49 minutes per day grooming. Ask your classmates for their individual grooming time per day (unless you're an 8:00 A.M. class), and use the data to estimate the true mean grooming time for your school with 95% confidence.

Source: *Time* magazine, Oct. 2006.

20. Unhealthy Days in Cities The number of unhealthy days based on the AQI (Air Quality Index) for a random sample of metropolitan areas is shown. Construct a 98% confidence interval based on the data.

61	12	6	40	27	38	93	5	13	40

Source: *New York Times Almanac.*

Extending the Concepts

21. A *one-sided confidence* interval can be found for a mean by using

$$\mu > \overline{X} - t_\alpha \frac{s}{\sqrt{n}} \quad \text{or} \quad \mu < \overline{X} + t_\alpha \frac{s}{\sqrt{n}}$$

where t_α is the value found under the row labeled One tail. Find two one-sided 95% confidence intervals of the population mean for the data shown, and interpret the answers. The data represent the daily revenues in dollars from 20 parking meters in a small municipality.

2.60	1.05	2.45	2.90
1.30	3.10	2.35	2.00
2.40	2.35	2.40	1.95
2.80	2.50	2.10	1.75
1.00	2.75	1.80	1.95

Technology *Step by Step*

MINITAB
Step by Step

Find a *t* Interval for the Mean

For Example 7–7, find the 99% confidence interval for the mean number of home fires started by candles each year.

1. Type the data into C1 of a MINITAB worksheet. Name the column **HomeFires.**

2. Select **Stat>Basic Statistics>1-Sample t.**

3. Double-click C1 HomeFires for the Samples in Columns.

4. Click on [Options] and be sure the Confidence Level is 99 and the Alternative is not equal.

5. Click [OK] twice.

6. Check for normality:

a) Select **Graph>Probability Plot,** then Single.

b) Select C1 HomeFires for the variable. The normal plot is concave, a skewed distribution.

Probability Plot of HomeFires
Normal - 99% CI

In the session window you will see the results. The 99% confidence interval estimate for μ is between 4784.99 and 9784.99. The sample size, mean, standard deviation, and standard error of the mean are also shown.

However, this small sample appears to have a nonnormal population. The interval is less likely to contain the true mean.

One-Sample T: HomeFires

```
Variable    N      Mean     StDev    SE Mean        99% CI
HomeFires   7    7041.43   1610.27    608.63    (4784.99, 9297.87)
```

TI-83 Plus or TI-84 Plus
Step by Step

Finding a *t* Confidence Interval for the Mean (Data)

1. Enter the data into L_1.
2. Press **STAT** and move the cursor to TESTS.
3. Press **8** for TInterval.
4. Move the cursor to Data and press **ENTER**.
5. Type in the appropriate values.
6. Move the cursor to Calculate and press **ENTER**.

Finding a *t* Confidence Interval for the Mean (Statistics)

1. Press **STAT** and move the cursor to TESTS.
2. Press **8** for TInterval.
3. Move the cursor to Stats and press **ENTER**.
4. Type in the appropriate values.
5. Move the cursor to Calculate and press **ENTER**.

Excel
Step by Step

Finding a *t* Confidence Interval for the Mean

Excel has a procedure to compute the maximum error of the estimate. But it does not compute confidence intervals. However, you may determine confidence intervals for the mean by using the MegaStat Add-in available on your CD. If you have not installed this add-in, do so following the instructions from the Chapter 1 Excel Step by Step.

Example XL7–2

Find the 95% confidence interval, using these sample data:

625   675   535   406   512   680   483   522   619   575

1. Enter the data into an Excel worksheet.

2. From the toolbar, select Add-Ins, **MegaStat>Confidence Intervals/Sample Size.** *Note:* You may need to open **MegaStat** from the **MegaStat.xls** file on your computer's hard drive.

3. Enter the mean of the data, **563.2.**

4. Select *t* for the *t* distribution.

5. Enter **87.9** for the standard deviation and **10** for *n*, the sample size.

6. Either type in or scroll to 95% for the Confidence Level, then click [OK].

The result of the procedure is shown next.

Confidence interval—mean

```
  95% Confidence level
563.2 Mean
 87.9 Standard deviation
   10 n
2.262 t (d.f. = 9)
62.880 Half-width
626.080 Upper confidence limit
500.320 Lower confidence limit
```

7–3 Confidence Intervals and Sample Size for Proportions

Objective 4

Find the confidence interval for a proportion.

A *USA TODAY* Snapshots feature stated that 12% of the pleasure boats in the United States were named *Serenity*. The parameter 12% is called a **proportion.** It means that of all the pleasure boats in the United States, 12 out of every 100 are named *Serenity*. A proportion represents a part of a whole. It can be expressed as a fraction, decimal, or percentage. In this case, $12\% = 0.12 = \frac{12}{100}$ or $\frac{3}{25}$. Proportions can also represent probabilities. In this case, if a pleasure boat is selected at random, the probability that it is called *Serenity* is 0.12.

Proportions can be obtained from samples or populations. The following symbols will be used.

Symbols Used in Proportion Notation

p = population proportion

$\hat{p}$ (read "*p* hat") = sample proportion

For a sample proportion,

$$\hat{p} = \frac{X}{n} \quad \text{and} \quad \hat{q} = \frac{n - X}{n} \quad \text{or} \quad \hat{q} = 1 - \hat{p}$$

where X = number of sample units that possess the characteristics of interest and n = sample size.

For example, in a study, 200 people were asked if they were satisfied with their job or profession; 162 said that they were. In this case, $n = 200$, $X = 162$, and $\hat{p} = X/n = 162/200 = 0.81$. It can be said that for this sample, 0.81, or 81%, of those surveyed were satisfied with their job or profession. The sample proportion is $\hat{p} = 0.81$.

The proportion of people who did not respond favorably when asked if they were satisfied with their job or profession constituted $\hat{q}$, where $\hat{q} = (n - X)/n$. For this survey, $\hat{q} = (200 - 162)/200 = 38/200$, or 0.19, or 19%.

When $\hat{p}$ and $\hat{q}$ are given in decimals or fractions, $\hat{p} + \hat{q} = 1$. When $\hat{p}$ and $\hat{q}$ are given in percentages, $\hat{p} + \hat{q} = 100\%$. It follows, then, that $\hat{q} = 1 - \hat{p}$, or $\hat{p} = 1 - \hat{q}$, when $\hat{p}$ and $\hat{q}$ are in decimal or fraction form. For the sample survey on job satisfaction, $\hat{q}$ can also be found by using $\hat{q} = 1 - \hat{p}$, or $1 - 0.81 = 0.19$.

Similar reasoning applies to population proportions; that is, $p = 1 - q$, $q = 1 - p$, and $p + q = 1$, when p and q are expressed in decimal or fraction form. When p and q are expressed as percentages, $p + q = 100\%$, $p = 100\% - q$, and $q = 100\% - p$.

Example 7–8	**Air Conditioned Households**

In a recent survey of 150 households, 54 had central air conditioning. Find $\hat{p}$ and $\hat{q}$, where $\hat{p}$ is the proportion of households that have central air conditioning.

Solution

Since $X = 54$ and $n = 150$,

$$\hat{p} = \frac{X}{n} = \frac{54}{150} = 0.36 = 36\%$$

$$\hat{q} = \frac{n - X}{n} = \frac{150 - 54}{150} = \frac{96}{150} = 0.64 = 64\%$$

You can also find $\hat{q}$ by using the formula $\hat{q} = 1 - \hat{p}$. In this case, $\hat{q} = 1 - 0.36 = 0.64$.

As with means, the statistician, given the sample proportion, tries to estimate the population proportion. Point and interval estimates for a population proportion can be made by using the sample proportion. For a point estimate of p (the population proportion), $\hat{p}$ (the sample proportion) is used. On the basis of the three properties of a good estimator, $\hat{p}$ is unbiased, consistent, and relatively efficient. But as with means, one is not able to decide how good the point estimate of p is. Therefore, statisticians also use an interval estimate for a proportion, and they can assign a probability that the interval will contain the population proportion.

The confidence interval for a particular p is based on the sampling distribution of $\hat{p}$. When the sample size n is no more than 5% of the population size, the sampling distribution of $\hat{p}$ is approximately normal with a mean of p and a standard deviation of $\sqrt{\frac{pq}{n}}$, where $q = 1 - p$.

Confidence Intervals

To construct a confidence interval about a proportion, you must use the maximum error of the estimate, which is

$$E = z_{\alpha/2} \sqrt{\frac{\hat{p}\hat{q}}{n}}$$

Confidence intervals about proportions must meet the criteria that $n\hat{p} \geq 5$ and $n\hat{q} \geq 5$.

Formula for a Specific Confidence Interval for a Proportion
$$\hat{p} - z_{\alpha/2} \sqrt{\frac{\hat{p}\hat{q}}{n}} < p < \hat{p} + z_{\alpha/2} \sqrt{\frac{\hat{p}\hat{q}}{n}}$$ when $n\hat{p}$ and $n\hat{q}$ are each greater than or equal to 5.

Rounding Rule for a Confidence Interval for a Proportion Round off to three decimal places.

Example 7–9	**Male Nurses**

A sample of 500 nursing applications included 60 from men. Find the 90% confidence interval of the true proportion of men who applied to the nursing program.

Solution

Since $\alpha = 1 - 0.90 = 0.10$ and $z_{\alpha/2} = 1.65$, substituting in the formula

$$\hat{p} - z_{\alpha/2}\sqrt{\frac{\hat{p}\hat{q}}{n}} < p < \hat{p} + z_{\alpha/2}\sqrt{\frac{\hat{p}\hat{q}}{n}}$$

when $\hat{p} = 60/500 = 0.12$ and $\hat{q} = 1 - 0.12 = 0.88$, you get

$$0.12 - 1.65\sqrt{\frac{(0.12)(0.88)}{500}} < p < 0.12 + 1.65\sqrt{\frac{(0.12)(0.88)}{500}}$$

$$0.12 - 0.024 < p < 0.12 + 0.024$$

$$0.096 < p < 0.144$$

or

$$9.6\% < p < 14.4\%$$

Hence, you can be 90% confident that the percentage of applicants who are men is between 9.6 and 14.4%.

When a specific percentage is given, the percentage becomes $\hat{p}$ when it is changed to a decimal. For example, if the problem states that 12% of the applicants were men, then $\hat{p} = 0.12$.

Example 7–10

Religious Books

A survey of 1721 people found that 15.9% of individuals purchase religious books at a Christian bookstore. Find the 95% confidence interval of the true proportion of people who purchase their religious books at a Christian bookstore.

Source: Baylor University.

Solution

Here $\hat{p} = 0.159$ (i.e., 15.9%), and $\hat{q} = 1 - 0.159 = 0.841$. For the 95% confidence interval $z_{\alpha/2} = 1.96$.

$$\hat{p} - z_{\alpha/2}\sqrt{\frac{\hat{p}\hat{q}}{n}} < p < \hat{p} + z_{\alpha/2}\sqrt{\frac{\hat{p}\hat{q}}{n}}$$

$$0.159 - 1.96\sqrt{\frac{(0.159)(0.841)}{1721}} < p < 0.159 + 1.96\sqrt{\frac{(0.159)(0.841)}{1721}}$$

$$0.142 < p < 0.176$$

Hence, you can say with 95% confidence that the true percentage is between 14.2 and 17.6%.

Sample Size for Proportions

To find the sample size needed to determine a confidence interval about a proportion, use this formula:

Objective 5

Determine the minimum sample size for finding a confidence interval for a proportion.

Formula for Minimum Sample Size Needed for Interval Estimate of a Population Proportion

$$n = \hat{p}\hat{q}\left(\frac{z_{\alpha/2}}{E}\right)^2$$

If necessary, round up to obtain a whole number.

This formula can be found by solving the maximum error of the estimate value for n in the formula

$$E = z_{\alpha/2}\sqrt{\frac{\hat{p}\hat{q}}{n}}$$

There are two situations to consider. First, if some approximation of $\hat{p}$ is known (e.g., from a previous study), that value can be used in the formula.

Second, if no approximation of $\hat{p}$ is known, you should use $\hat{p} = 0.5$. This value will give a sample size sufficiently large to guarantee an accurate prediction, given the confidence interval and the error of estimate. The reason is that when $\hat{p}$ and $\hat{q}$ are each 0.5, the product $\hat{p}\hat{q}$ is at maximum, as shown here.

$\hat{p}$	$\hat{q}$	$\hat{p}\hat{q}$
0.1	0.9	0.09
0.2	0.8	0.16
0.3	0.7	0.21
0.4	0.6	0.24
0.5	**0.5**	**0.25**
0.6	0.4	0.24
0.7	0.3	0.21
0.8	0.2	0.16
0.9	0.1	0.09

Example 7–11

Home Computers

A researcher wishes to estimate, with 95% confidence, the proportion of people who own a home computer. A previous study shows that 40% of those interviewed had a computer at home. The researcher wishes to be accurate within 2% of the true proportion. Find the minimum sample size necessary.

Solution

Since $z_{\alpha/2} = 1.96$, $E = 0.02$, $\hat{p} = 0.40$, and $\hat{q} = 0.60$, then

$$n = \hat{p}\hat{q}\left(\frac{z_{\alpha/2}}{E}\right)^2 = (0.40)(0.60)\left(\frac{1.96}{0.02}\right)^2 = 2304.96$$

which, when rounded up, is 2305 people to interview.

Example 7–12

Car Phone Ownership

The same researcher wishes to estimate the proportion of executives who own a car phone. She wants to be 90% confident and be accurate within 5% of the true proportion. Find the minimum sample size necessary.

Solution

Since there is no prior knowledge of $\hat{p}$, statisticians assign the values $\hat{p} = 0.5$ and $\hat{q} = 0.5$. The sample size obtained by using these values will be large enough to ensure the specified degree of confidence. Hence,

$$n = \hat{p}\hat{q}\left(\frac{z_{\alpha/2}}{E}\right)^2 = (0.5)(0.5)\left(\frac{1.65}{0.05}\right)^2 = 272.25$$

which, when rounded up, is 273 executives to ask.

In determining the sample size, the size of the population is irrelevant. Only the degree of confidence and the maximum error are necessary to make the determination.

Does Success Bring Happiness?

W. C. Fields said, "Start every day off with a smile and get it over with."

Do you think people are happy because they are successful, or are they successful because they are just happy people? A recent survey conducted by *Money* magazine showed that 34% of the people surveyed said that they were happy because they were successful; however, 63% said that they were successful because they were happy individuals. The people surveyed had an average household income of $75,000 or more. The margin of error was ±2.5%. Based on the information in this article, what would be the confidence interval for each percent?

Applying the Concepts 7–3

Contracting Influenza

To answer the questions, use the following table describing the percentage of people who reported contracting influenza by gender and race/ethnicity.

	Influenza	
Characteristic	**Percent**	**(95% CI)**
Gender		
Men	48.8	(47.1–50.5%)
Women	51.5	(50.2–52.8%)
Race/ethnicity		
Caucasian	52.2	(51.1–53.3%)
African American	33.1	(29.5–36.7%)
Hispanic	47.6	(40.9–54.3%)
Other	39.7	(30.8–48.5%)
Total	50.4	(49.3–51.5%)

Forty-nine states and the District of Columbia participated in the study. Weighted means were used. The sample size was 19,774. There were 12,774 women and 7000 men.

1. Explain what (95% CI) means.
2. How large is the error for men reporting influenza?
3. What is the sample size?
4. How does sample size affect the size of the confidence interval?
5. Would the confidence intervals be larger or smaller for a 90% CI, using the same data?
6. Where does the 51.5% under influenza for women fit into its associated 95% CI?

See page 396 for the answers.

Exercises 7–3

1. In each case, find $\hat{p}$ and $\hat{q}$.

   a. $n = 80$ and $X = 40$
   b. $n = 200$ and $X = 90$
   c. $n = 130$ and $X = 60$
   d. $n = 60$ and $X = 35$
   e. $n = 95$ and $X = 43$

2. (**ans**) Find $\hat{p}$ and $\hat{q}$ for each percentage. (Use each percentage for $\hat{p}$.)

   a. 15%
   b. 37%
   c. 71%
   d. 51%
   e. 79%

3. Vacations A U.S. Travel Data Center survey conducted for *Better Homes and Gardens* of 1500 adults found that 39% said that they would take more vacations this year than last year. Find the 95% confidence interval for the true proportion of adults who said that they will travel more this year.

Source: *USA TODAY.*

4. Regular Voters in America Thirty-five percent of adult Americans are regular voters. A random sample of 250 adults in a medium-size college town were surveyed, and it was found that 110 were regular voters. Estimate the true proportion of regular voters with 90% confidence and comment on your results.

Source: *Time* magazine, Oct. 2006.

5. Private Schools The proportion of students in private schools is around 11%. A random sample of 450 students from a wide geographic area indicated that 55 attended private schools. Estimate the true proportion of students attending private schools with 95% confidence. How does your estimate compare to 11%?

Source: National Center for Education Statistics (www.nces.ed.gov).

6. Belief in Haunted Places A random sample of 205 college students was asked if they believed that places could be haunted, and 65 of them responded yes. Estimate the true proportion of college students who believe in the possibility of haunted places with 99% confidence. According to *Time* magazine, 37% of Americans believe that places can be haunted.

Source: *Time* magazine, Oct. 2006.

7. Work Interruptions A survey found that out of 200 workers, 168 said they were interrupted three or more times an hour by phone messages, faxes, etc. Find the 90% confidence interval of the population proportion of workers who are interrupted three or more times an hour.

Source: Based on information from *USA TODAY* Snapshot.

8. Travel to Outer Space A CBS News/*New York Times* poll found that 329 out of 763 adults said they would travel to outer space in their lifetime, given the chance. Estimate the true proportion of adults who would like to travel to outer space with 92% confidence.

Source: www.pollingreport.com

9. High School Graduates Who Take the SAT The national average for the percentage of high school graduates taking the SAT is 49%, but the state averages vary from a low of 4% to a high of 92%. A random sample of 300 graduating high school seniors was polled across a particular tristate area, and it was found that 195 of them had taken the SAT. Estimate the true proportion of high school graduates in this region who take the SAT with 95% confidence.

Source: *World Almanac.*

10. Canoe Survey A survey of 50 first-time white-water canoers showed that 23 did not want to repeat the experience. Find the 90% confidence interval of the true proportion of canoers who did not wish to canoe the rapids a second time. If a rafting company wants to distribute brochures for repeat trips, what is the minimum number it should print?

11. DVD Players A survey of 85 families showed that 36 owned at least one DVD player. Find the 99% confidence interval of the true proportion of families who own at least one DVD player. If another survey in a different location found that the proportion of families who owned at least one DVD player was 0.52, would you consider that the proportion of families in this area was larger than in the area where the original survey was done?

12. Students Who Major in Business It has been reported that 20.4% of incoming freshmen indicate that they will major in business or a related field. A random sample of 400 incoming college freshmen was asked their preference, and 95 replied that they were considering business as a major. Estimate the true proportion of freshman business majors with 98% confidence. Does your interval contain 20.4?

Source: *New York Times Almanac.*

13. Financial Well-being In a Gallup Poll of 1005 individuals, 452 thought they were worse off financially than a year ago. Find the 95% confidence interval for the true proportion of individuals who feel they are worse off financially.

Source: Gallup Poll.

14. **Fighting U.S. Hunger** In a poll of 1000 likely voters, 560 say that the United States spends too little on fighting hunger at home. Find a 95% confidence interval for the true proportion of voters who feel this way.

    Source: Alliance to End Hunger.

15. **Vitamins for Women** A medical researcher wishes to determine the percentage of females who take vitamins. He wishes to be 99% confident that the estimate is within 2 percentage points of the true proportion. A recent study of 180 females showed that 25% took vitamins.

    a. How large should the sample size be?

    b. If no estimate of the sample proportion is available, how large should the sample be?

16. **Widows** A recent study indicated that 29% of the 100 women over age 55 in the study were widows.

    a. How large a sample must you take to be 90% confident that the estimate is within 0.05 of the true proportion of women over age 55 who are widows?

    b. If no estimate of the sample proportion is available, how large should the sample be?

17. **Direct Satellite Television** It is believed that 25% of U.S. homes have a direct satellite television receiver.

How large a sample is necessary to estimate the true population of homes which do with 95% confidence and within 3 percentage points? How large a sample is necessary if nothing is known about the proportion?

Source: *New York Times Almanac.*

18. **Obesity** Obesity is defined as a *body mass index* (BMI) of 3 kg/m^2 or more. A 95% confidence interval for the percentage of U.S. adults aged 20 years and over who were obese was found to be 22.4 to 23.5%. What was the sample size?

    Source: National Center for Health Statistics (www.cdc.gov/nchs).

19. **Unmarried Americans** Nearly one-half of Americans aged 25 to 29 are unmarried. How large a sample is necessary to estimate the true proportion of unmarried Americans in this age group within 2½ percentage points with 90% confidence?

    Source: *Time* magazine, Oct. 2006.

20. **Diet Habits** A federal report indicated that 27% of children ages 2 to 5 years had a good diet—an increase over previous years. How large a sample is needed to estimate the true proportion of children with good diets within 2% with 95% confidence?

    Source: Federal Interagency Forum on Child and Family Statistics, *Washington Observer-Reporter.*

Extending the Concepts

21. **Gun Control** If a sample of 600 people is selected and the researcher decides to have a maximum error of the estimate of 4% on the specific proportion who favor gun control, find the degree of confidence. A recent study showed that 50% were in favor of some form of gun control.

22. **Survey on Politics** In a study, 68% of 1015 adults said that they believe the Republicans favor the rich. If the margin of error was 3 percentage points, what was the confidence interval used for the proportion?

    Source: *USA TODAY.*

Technology *Step by Step*

MINITAB
Step by Step

Find a Confidence Interval for a Proportion

MINITAB will calculate a confidence interval, given the statistics from a sample *or* given the raw data. In Example 7–9, in a sample of 500 nursing applications 60 were from men. Find the 90% confidence interval estimate for the true proportion of male applicants.

1. Select **Stat>Basic Statistics>1 Proportion.**

2. Click on the button for Summarized data. No data will be entered in the worksheet.

3. Click in the box for Number of trials and enter **500.**

4. In the Number of events box, enter **60.**

5. Click on [Options].

6. Type **90** for the confidence level.

7. Check the box for Use test and interval based on normal distribution.

8. Click [OK] twice.

The results for the confidence interval will be displayed in the session window.

Test and CI for One Proportion

```
Test of p = 0.5 vs p not = 0.
Sample   X     N    Sample p         90% CI            Z-Value   P-Value
1        60    500  0.120000  (0.096096, 0.143904)     -16.99    0.000
```

TI-83 Plus or TI-84 Plus
Step by Step

Finding a Confidence Interval for a Proportion

1. Press **STAT** and move the cursor to TESTS.

2. Press **A (ALPHA, MATH)** for 1-PropZInt.

3. Type in the appropriate values.

4. Move the cursor to Calculate and press **ENTER.**

Example TI7–3

Find the 95% confidence interval of p when $X = 60$ and $n = 500$, as in Example 7–9.

The 95% confidence level for p is $0.09152 < p < 0.14848$. Also $\hat{p}$ is given.

Excel
Step by Step

Finding a Confidence Interval for a Proportion

Excel has a procedure to compute the maximum error of the estimate. But it does not compute confidence intervals. However, you may determine confidence intervals for a proportion by using the MegaStat Add-in available on your CD. If you have not installed this add-in, do so following the instructions from the Chapter 1 Excel Step by Step.

Example XL7–3

There were 500 nursing applications in a sample, including 60 from men. Find the 90% confidence interval for the true proportion of male applicants.

1. From the toolbar, select Add-Ins, **MegaStat>Confidence Intervals/Sample Size.** *Note:* You may need to open **MegaStat** from the **MegaStat.xls** file on your computer's hard drive.

2. In the dialog box, select Confidence interval–*p.*

3. Enter **60** in the box labeled *p*; *p* will automatically change to *x.*

Speaking of
Statistics

Here is a survey about college students' credit card usage. Suggest several ways that the study could have been more meaningful if confidence intervals had been used.

OTHER PEOPLE'S MONEY

Undergrads love their plastic. That means—you guessed it—students are learning to become debtors. According to the Public Interest Research Groups, only half of all students pay off card balances in full each month, 36% sometimes do and 14% never do. Meanwhile, 48% have paid a late fee. Here's how undergrads stack up, according to Nellie Mae, a provider of college loans:

Undergrads with a credit card **78%**

Average number of cards owned . . **3**

Average student card debt **$1236**

Students with 4 or more cards. . . . **32%**

Balances of $3000 to $7000 . . . . . **13%**

Balances over $7000. . . . . **9%**

Reprinted with permission from the January 2002 Reader's Digest.
Copyright © 2002 by The Reader's Digest Assn. Inc.

4. Enter **500** in the box labeled *n*.

5. Either type in or scroll to 90% for the Confidence Level, then click [OK].

The result of the procedure is shown next.

Confidence interval—proportion

```
  90% Confidence level
0.12 Proportion
 500 n
1.645 z
0.024 Half-width
0.144 Upper confidence limit
0.096 Lower confidence limit
```

7–4

Confidence Intervals for Variances and Standard Deviations

Objective 6

Find a confidence interval for a variance and a standard deviation.

In Sections 7–1 through 7–3 confidence intervals were calculated for means and proportions. This section will explain how to find confidence intervals for variances and standard deviations. In statistics, the variance and standard deviation of a variable are as important as the mean. For example, when products that fit together (such as pipes) are manufactured, it is important to keep the variations of the diameters of the products as small as possible; otherwise, they will not fit together properly and will have to be scrapped. In the manufacture of medicines, the variance and standard deviation of the medication in the pills play an important role in making sure patients receive the proper dosage. For these reasons, confidence intervals for variances and standard deviations are necessary.

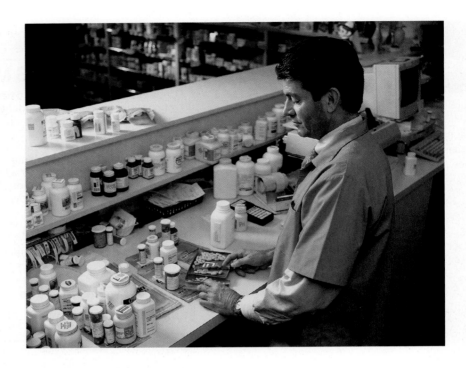

Historical Note

The χ^2 distribution with
2 degrees of freedom
was formulated by a
mathematician named
Hershel in 1869
while he was studying
the accuracy of
shooting arrows at a
target. Many other
mathematicians have
since contributed to its
development.

To calculate these confidence intervals, a new statistical distribution is needed. It is called the **chi-square distribution.**

The chi-square variable is similar to the t variable in that its distribution is a family of curves based on the number of degrees of freedom. The symbol for chi-square is χ^2 (Greek letter chi, pronounced "ki"). Several of the distributions are shown in Figure 7–9, along with the corresponding degrees of freedom. The chi-square distribution is obtained from the values of $(n - 1)s^2/\sigma^2$ when random samples are selected from a normally distributed population whose variance is σ^2.

A chi-square variable cannot be negative, and the distributions are skewed to the right. At about 100 degrees of freedom, the chi-square distribution becomes somewhat symmetric. The area under each chi-square distribution is equal to 1.00, or 100%.

Table G in Appendix C gives the values for the chi-square distribution. These values are used in the denominators of the formulas for confidence intervals. Two different values

Figure 7–9

The Chi-Square Family of Curves

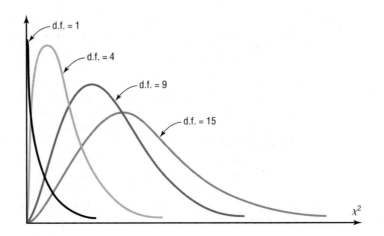

are used in the formula because the distribution is not symmetric. One value is found on the left side of the table, and the other is on the right. See Figure 7–10. For example, to find the table values corresponding to the 95% confidence interval, you must first change 95% to a decimal and subtract it from 1 ($1 - 0.95 = 0.05$). Then divide the answer by 2 ($\alpha/2 = 0.05/2 = 0.025$). This is the column on the right side of the table, used to get the values for χ^2_{right}. To get the value for χ^2_{left}, subtract the value of $\alpha/2$ from 1 ($1 - 0.05/2 = 0.975$). Finally, find the appropriate row corresponding to the degrees of freedom $n - 1$. A similar procedure is used to find the values for a 90 or 99% confidence interval.

Figure 7–10

Chi-Square Distribution for d.f. = $n - 1$

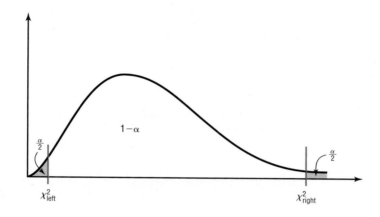

Example 7–13

Find the values for χ^2_{right} and χ^2_{left} for a 90% confidence interval when $n = 25$.

Solution

To find χ^2_{right}, subtract $1 - 0.90 = 0.10$ and divide by 2 to get 0.05.
    To find χ^2_{left}, subtract $1 - 0.05$ to get 0.95. Hence, use the 0.95 and 0.05 columns and the row corresponding to 24 d.f. See Figure 7–11.

Figure 7–11

χ^2 Table for Example 7–13

					Table G					
					The Chi-square Distribution					
Degrees of					α					
freedom	0.995	0.99	0.975	0.95	0.90	0.10	0.05	0.025	0.01	0.005
1										
2										
⋮										
24				13.848			36.415			

χ^2_{left} χ^2_{right}

The answers are

$$\chi^2_{\text{right}} = 36.415$$
$$\chi^2_{\text{left}} = 13.848$$

See Figure 7–12.

Figure 7–12

χ^2 Distribution for Example 7–13

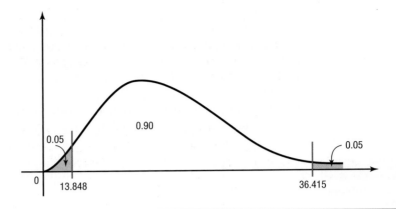

Useful estimates for σ^2 and σ are s^2 and s, respectively.

To find confidence intervals for variances and standard deviations, you must assume that the variable is normally distributed.

The formulas for the confidence intervals are shown here.

Formula for the Confidence Interval for a Variance

$$\frac{(n-1)s^2}{\chi^2_{\text{right}}} < \sigma^2 < \frac{(n-1)s^2}{\chi^2_{\text{left}}}$$

d.f. $= n - 1$

Formula for the Confidence Interval for a Standard Deviation

$$\sqrt{\frac{(n-1)s^2}{\chi^2_{\text{right}}}} < \sigma < \sqrt{\frac{(n-1)s^2}{\chi^2_{\text{left}}}}$$

d.f. $= n - 1$

Recall that s^2 is the symbol for the sample variance and s is the symbol for the sample standard deviation. If the problem gives the sample standard deviation s, be sure to *square* it when you are using the formula. But if the problem gives the sample variance s^2, *do not square it* when you are using the formula, since the variance is already in square units.

Rounding Rule for a Confidence Interval for a Variance or Standard Deviation When you are computing a confidence interval for a population variance or standard deviation by using raw data, round off to one more decimal place than the number of decimal places in the original data.

When you are computing a confidence interval for a population variance or standard deviation by using a sample variance or standard deviation, round off to the same number of decimal places as given for the sample variance or standard deviation.

Example 7–14 shows how to find a confidence interval for a variance and standard deviation.

Example 7–14

Nicotine Content

Find the 95% confidence interval for the variance and standard deviation of the nicotine content of cigarettes manufactured if a sample of 20 cigarettes has a standard deviation of 1.6 milligrams.

Solution

Since $\alpha = 0.05$, the two critical values, respectively, for the 0.025 and 0.975 levels for 19 degrees of freedom are 32.852 and 8.907. The 95% confidence interval for the variance is found by substituting in the formula.

$$\frac{(n-1)s^2}{\chi^2_{\text{right}}} < \sigma^2 < \frac{(n-1)s^2}{\chi^2_{\text{left}}}$$

$$\frac{(20-1)(1.6)^2}{32.852} < \sigma^2 < \frac{(20-1)(1.6)^2}{8.907}$$

$$1.5 < \sigma^2 < 5.5$$

Hence, you can be 95% confident that the true variance for the nicotine content is between 1.5 and 5.5.

For the standard deviation, the confidence interval is

$$\sqrt{1.5} < \sigma < \sqrt{5.5}$$

$$1.2 < \sigma < 2.3$$

Hence, you can be 95% confident that the true standard deviation for the nicotine content of all cigarettes manufactured is between 1.2 and 2.3 milligrams based on a sample of 20 cigarettes.

Example 7–15

Cost of Ski Lift Tickets

Find the 90% confidence interval for the variance and standard deviation for the price in dollars of an adult single-day ski lift ticket. The data represent a selected sample of nationwide ski resorts. Assume the variable is normally distributed.

59	54	53	52	51
39	49	46	49	48

Source: *USA TODAY.*

Solution

Step 1   Find the variance for the data. Use the formulas in Chapter 3 or your calculator. The variance $s^2 = 28.2$.

Step 2   Find χ^2_{right} and χ^2_{left} from Table G in Appendix C. Since $\alpha = 0.10$, the two critical values are 3.325 and 16.919, using d.f. = 9 and 0.95 and 0.05.

Step 3   Substitute in the formula and solve.

$$\frac{(n-1)s^2}{\chi^2_{\text{right}}} < \sigma^2 < \frac{(n-1)s^2}{\chi^2_{\text{left}}}$$

$$\frac{(10-1)(28.2)}{16.919} < \sigma^2 < \frac{(10-1)(28.2)}{3.325}$$

$$15.0 < \sigma^2 < 76.3$$

For the standard deviation

$$\sqrt{15} < \sigma < \sqrt{76.3}$$

$$3.87 < \sigma < 8.73$$

Hence you can be 90% confident that the standard deviation for the price of all single-day ski lift tickets of the population is between $3.87 and $8.73 based on a sample of 10 nationwide ski resorts. (Two decimal places are used since the data are in dollars and cents.)

Note: If you are using the standard deviation instead (as in Example 7–14) of the variance, be sure to square the standard deviation when substituting in the formula.

Applying the Concepts **7–4**

Confidence Interval for Standard Deviation

Shown are the ages (in years) of the Presidents at the time of their deaths.

67	90	83	85	73	80	78	79
68	71	53	65	74	64	77	56
66	63	70	49	57	71	67	71
58	60	72	67	57	60	90	63
88	78	46	64	81	93		

1. Do the data represent a population or a sample?

2. Select a random sample of 12 ages and find the variance and standard deviation.

3. Find the 95% confidence interval of the standard deviation.

4. Find the standard deviation of all the data values.

5. Does the confidence interval calculated in question 3 contain the mean?

6. If it does not, give a reason why.

7. What assumption(s) must be considered for constructing the confidence interval in step 3?

See page 396 for the answers.

Exercises 7–4

1. What distribution must be used when computing confidence intervals for variances and standard deviations?

2. What assumption must be made when computing confidence intervals for variances and standard deviations?

3. Using Table G, find the values for χ^2_{left} and χ^2_{right}.

　　a. $\alpha = 0.05, n = 12$
　　b. $\alpha = 0.10, n = 20$
　　c. $\alpha = 0.05, n = 27$
　　d. $\alpha = 0.01, n = 6$
　　e. $\alpha = 0.10, n = 41$

4. Lifetimes of Disposable Cameras Find the 90% confidence interval for the variance and standard deviation for the lifetime of disposable camera batteries if a sample of 16 disposable camera batteries has a standard deviation of 2.1 months. Assume the variable is normally distributed. Do you feel that the lifetimes of the batteries are relatively consistent?

5. Carbohydrates in Yogurt The number of carbohydrates (in grams) per 8-ounce serving of yogurt for each of a random selection of brands is listed below. Estimate the true population variance and standard deviation for the number of carbohydrates per 8-ounce serving of yogurt with 95% confidence.

17	42	41	20	39	41	35	15	43
25	38	33	42	23	17	25	34	

6. Weights of Containers Find the 99% confidence interval for the variance and standard deviation of the weights of 25 one-gallon containers of motor oil if a sample of 14 containers has a variance of 3.2. The weights are given in ounces. Assume the variable is normally distributed.

7. Cost of Knee Replacement Surgery U.S. insurers' costs for knee replacement surgery range from $17,627 to $25,462. Estimate the population variance (standard deviation) in cost with 98% confidence based on a random sample of 10 persons who have had this surgery. The retail costs (for uninsured persons) for the same procedure range from $40,640 to $58,702. Estimate the population variance and standard deviation in cost with 98% confidence based on a sample of 10 persons, and compare your two intervals.

Source: *Time Almanac.*

8. Age of College Students Find the 90% confidence interval for the variance and standard deviation of the ages of seniors at Oak Park College if a sample of 24 students has a standard deviation of 2.3 years. Assume the variable is normally distributed.

9. New-Car Lease Fees A new-car dealer is leasing various brand-new models for the monthly rates (in dollars) listed below. Estimate the true population variance (and standard deviation) in leasing rates with 90% confidence.

169   169   199   239   239   249

10. Stock Prices A random sample of stock prices per share (in dollars) is shown. Find the 90%

confidence interval for the variance and standard deviation for the prices. Assume the variable is normally distributed.

26.69	13.88	28.37	12.00
75.37	7.50	47.50	43.00
3.81	53.81	13.62	45.12
6.94	28.25	28.00	60.50
40.25	10.87	46.12	14.75

Source: *Pittsburgh Tribune Review.*

11. Oil Changes A service station advertises that customers will have to wait no more than 30 minutes for an oil change. A sample of 28 oil changes has a standard deviation of 5.2 minutes. Find the 95% confidence interval of the population standard deviation of the time spent waiting for an oil change.

12. Home Ownership Rates The percentage rates of home ownership for 8 randomly selected states are listed below. Estimate the population variance and standard deviation for the percentage rate of home ownership with 99% confidence.

66.0   75.8   70.9   73.9   63.4   68.5   73.3   65.9

Source: *World Almanac.*

Extending the Concepts

13. Calculator Battery Lifetimes A confidence interval for a standard deviation for large samples taken from a normally distributed population can be approximated by

$$s - z_{\alpha/2} \frac{s}{\sqrt{2n}} < \sigma < s + z_{\alpha/2} \frac{s}{\sqrt{2n}}$$

Find the 95% confidence interval for the population standard deviation of calculator batteries. A sample of 200 calculator batteries has a standard deviation of 18 months.

Technology *Step by Step*

TI-83 Plus or TI-84 Plus

Step by Step

The TI-83 Plus and TI-84 Plus do not have a built-in confidence interval for the variance or standard deviation. However, the downloadable program named SDINT is available on your CD and Online Learning Center. Follow the instructions with your CD for downloading the program.

Finding a Confidence Interval for the Variance and Standard Deviation (Data)

1. Enter the data values into L_1.

2. Press **PRGM,** move the cursor to the program named SDINT, and press **ENTER** twice.

3. Press **1** for Data.

4. Type L_1 for the list and press **ENTER.**

5. Type the confidence level and press **ENTER.**

6. Press **ENTER** to clear the screen.

Example TI7–4

 This refers to Example 7–15 in the text. Find the 90% confidence interval for the variance and standard deviation for the data:

59   54   53   52   51   39   49   46   49   48

```
LIST ?L₁




```

```
ENTER CONF LEVEL
(0 < CL <1)

CONF LEVEL=.9

```

```
CONF LEVEL .9
S= 5.31   n=10

CONF INT FOR σx²
{15.01,76.39}
CONF INT FOR σx
{3.87,8.74}
ENTER TO CLEAR
```

Finding a Confidence Interval for the Variance and Standard Deviation (Statistics)

1. Press **PRGM,** move the cursor to the program named SDINT, and press **ENTER** twice.

2. Press **2** for Stats.

3. Type the sample standard deviation and press **ENTER.**

4. Type the sample size and press **ENTER.**

5. Type the confidence level and press **ENTER.**

6. Press **ENTER** to clear the screen.

Example TI7–5

This refers to Example 7–14 in the text. Find the 95% confidence interval for the variance and standard deviation, given $n = 20$ and $s = 1.6$.

```
S= 1.6
N= 20




```

```
ENTER CONF LEVEL
(0 < CL <1)

CONF LEVEL=.95■

```

```
CONF LEVEL .95
S= 1.6   n=20

CONF INT FOR σx²
{1.48,5.46}
CONF INT FOR σx
{1.22,2.34}
ENTER TO CLEAR
```

Summary

An important aspect of inferential statistics is estimation. Estimations of parameters of populations are accomplished by selecting a random sample from that population and choosing and computing a statistic that is the best estimator of the parameter. A good estimator must be unbiased, consistent, and relatively efficient. The best estimators of μ and p are $\overline{X}$ and $\hat{p}$, respectively. The best estimators of σ^2 and σ are s^2 and s, respectively.

There are two types of estimates of a parameter: point estimates and interval estimates. A point estimate is a specific value. For example, if a researcher wishes to estimate the average length of a certain adult fish, a sample of the fish is selected and measured. The mean of this sample is computed, for example, 3.2 centimeters. From this sample mean, the researcher estimates the population mean to be 3.2 centimeters.

The problem with point estimates is that the accuracy of the estimate cannot be determined. For this reason, statisticians prefer to use the interval estimate. By computing an interval about the sample value, statisticians can be 95 or 99% (or some other percentage) confident that their estimate contains the true parameter. The confidence level is determined by the researcher. The higher the confidence level, the wider the interval of the estimate must be. For example, a 95% confidence interval of the true mean length of a certain species of fish might be

$$3.17 < \mu < 3.23$$

whereas the 99% confidence interval might be

$$3.15 < \mu < 3.25$$

When the confidence interval of the mean is computed, the z or t values are used, depending on whether the population standard deviation is known. If σ is known, the z values can be used. If σ is not known, the t values are used. When the sample size is less than 30, the population should be normally distributed.

Closely related to computing confidence intervals is the determination of the sample size to make an estimate of the mean. This information is needed to determine the minimum sample size necessary.

1. The degree of confidence must be stated.
2. The population standard deviation must be known or be able to be estimated.
3. The maximum error of the estimate must be stated.

Confidence intervals and sample sizes can also be computed for proportions, using the normal distribution; and confidence intervals for variances and standard deviations can be computed, using the chi-square distribution. A confidence interval is given as point estimate $\pm$ the maximum error of the estimate.

Important Terms

chi-square distribution 384	degrees of freedom 368	maximum error of the estimate 357	relatively efficient estimator 355
confidence interval 356	estimation 354	point estimate 355	t distribution 368
confidence level 356	estimator 355	proportion 375	unbiased estimator 355
consistent estimator 355	interval estimate 356		

Important Formulas

Formula for the confidence interval of the mean when σ is known (when $n \geq 30$, s can be used if σ is unknown):

$$\overline{X} - z_{\alpha/2}\left(\frac{\sigma}{\sqrt{n}}\right) < \mu < \overline{X} + z_{\alpha/2}\left(\frac{\sigma}{\sqrt{n}}\right)$$

Formula for the sample size for means:

$$n = \left(\frac{z_{\alpha/2} \cdot \sigma}{E}\right)^2$$

where E is the maximum error.

Formula for the confidence interval of the mean when σ is unknown:

$$\overline{X} - t_{\alpha/2}\left(\frac{s}{\sqrt{n}}\right) < \mu < \overline{X} + t_{\alpha/2}\left(\frac{s}{\sqrt{n}}\right)$$

Formula for the confidence interval for a proportion:

$$\hat{p} - z_{\alpha/2}\sqrt{\frac{\hat{p}\hat{q}}{n}} < p < \hat{p} + z_{\alpha/2}\sqrt{\frac{\hat{p}\hat{q}}{n}}$$

where $\hat{p} = X/n$ and $\hat{q} = 1 - \hat{p}$.

Formula for the sample size for proportions:

$$n = \hat{p}\hat{q}\left(\frac{z_{\alpha/2}}{E}\right)^2$$

Formula for the confidence interval for a variance:

$$\frac{(n-1)s^2}{\chi^2_{\text{right}}} < \sigma^2 < \frac{(n-1)s^2}{\chi^2_{\text{left}}}$$

Formula for confidence interval for a standard deviation:

$$\sqrt{\frac{(n-1)s^2}{\chi^2_{\text{right}}}} < \sigma < \sqrt{\frac{(n-1)s^2}{\chi^2_{\text{left}}}}$$

Review Exercises

1. Eight chemical elements do not have isotopes (different forms of the same element having the same atomic number but different atomic weights). A random sample of 30 of the elements which do have isotopes showed a mean number of 19.63 isotopes per element and the population a standard deviation of 18.73. Estimate the true mean number of isotopes for all elements with isotopes with 90% confidence.

   Source: *Time Almanac.*

2. **Presidential Travel** In a survey of 1004 individuals, 442 felt that President George W. Bush spent too much time away from Washington. Find a 95% confidence interval for the true population proportion.

   Source: *USA TODAY/CNN/Gallup Poll.*

3. **Vacation Days** A U.S. Travel Data Center survey reported that Americans stayed an average of 7.5 nights when they went on vacation. The sample size was 1500. Find a point estimate of the population mean. Find the 95% confidence interval of the true mean. Assume the population standard deviation was 0.8.

   Source: *USA TODAY.*

4. **Lengths of Children's Animated Films** The lengths (in minutes) of a random selection of popular children's animated films are listed below. Estimate the true mean length of all children's animated films with 95% confidence.

   93   83   76   92   77   81   78   100   78   76   75

5. **Dog Bites to Postal Workers** For a certain urban area, in a sample of 5 months, on average 28 mail carriers were bitten by dogs each month. The standard deviation of the sample was 3. Find the 90% confidence interval of the true mean number of mail carriers who are bitten by dogs each month. Assume the variable is normally distributed.

6. **Teachers' Salaries** A researcher is interested in estimating the average salary of teachers in a large urban school district. She wants to be 95% confident that her estimate is correct. If the standard deviation is $1050, how large a sample is needed to be accurate within $200?

7. **Postage Costs** A researcher wishes to estimate, within $25, the true average amount of postage a community college spends each year. If she wishes to be 90% confident, how large a sample is necessary? The standard deviation is known to be $80.

8. **Vacation Sites** A U.S. Travel Data Center's survey of 1500 adults found that 42% of respondents stated that they favor historical sites as vacations. Find the 95% confidence interval of the true proportion of all adults who favor visiting historical sites as vacations.

   Source: *USA TODAY.*

9. **Snow Removal Survey** In a recent study of 75 people, 41 said they were dissatisfied with their community's snow removal service. Find the 95% confidence interval of the true proportion of individuals who are dissatisfied with their community's snow removal service. Based on the results, should the supervisor consider making improvements in the snow removal service?

10. A local county has a very active adult education venue. A random sample of the population showed that 189 out of 400 persons 16 years old or older participated in some type of formal adult education activities, such as basic skills training, apprenticeships, personal interest courses, and part-time college or university degree programs. Estimate the true proportion of adults participating in some kind of formal education program with 98% confidence.

11. **Health Insurance Coverage for Children** A federal report stated that 88% of children under age 18 were covered by health insurance in 2000. How large a sample is needed to estimate the true proportion of covered children with 90% confidence with a confidence interval 0.05 wide?

    Source: *Washington Observer-Reporter.*

12. **Child Care Programs** A study found that 73% of prekindergarten children ages 3 to 5 whose mothers had a bachelor's degree or higher were enrolled in center-based early childhood care and education programs. How large a sample is needed to estimate the true proportion within 3 percentage points with 95% confidence? How large a sample is needed if you had no prior knowledge of the proportion?

13. **Baseball Diameters** The standard deviation of the diameter of 18 baseballs was 0.29 cm. Find the 95% confidence interval of the true standard deviation of the diameters of the baseballs. Do you think the manufacturing process should be checked for inconsistency?

14. **MPG for Lawn Mowers** A random sample of 22 lawn mowers was selected, and the motors were tested to see how many miles per gallon of gasoline each one obtained. The variance of the measurements was 2.6. Find the 95% confidence interval of the true variance.

15. **Lifetimes of Snowmobiles** A random sample of 15 snowmobiles was selected, and the lifetime (in months) of the batteries was measured. The variance of the sample was 8.6. Find the 90% confidence interval of the true variance.

16. **Length of Children's Animated Films** Use the data from Exercise 4 to estimate the population variance (standard deviation) in length of children's animated films with 99% confidence.

Data Projects

The Data Bank is found in Appendix D, or on the World Wide Web by following links from www.mhhe.com/bluman/.

1. From the Data Bank choose a variable, find the mean, and construct the 95 and 99% confidence intervals of the population mean. Use a sample of at least 30 subjects. Find the mean of the population, and determine whether it falls within the confidence interval.

2. Repeat Exercise 1, using a different variable and a sample of 15.

3. Repeat Exercise 1, using a proportion. For example, construct a confidence interval for the proportion of individuals who did not complete high school.

4. From Data Set III in Appendix D, select a sample of 30 values and construct the 95 and 99% confidence intervals of the mean length in miles of major North American rivers. Find the mean of all the values, and determine if the confidence intervals contain the mean.

5. From Data Set VI in Appendix D, select a sample of 20 values and find the 90% confidence interval of the mean of the number of acres. Find the mean of all the values, and determine if the confidence interval contains the mean.

6. Select a random sample of 20 of the record high temperatures in the United States, found in Data Set I in Appendix D. Find the proportion of temperatures below 110°. Construct a 95% confidence interval for this proportion. Then find the true proportion of temperatures below 110°, using all the data. Is the true proportion contained in the confidence interval? Explain.

Chapter Quiz

Determine whether each statement is true or false. If the statement is false, explain why.

1. Interval estimates are preferred over point estimates since a confidence level can be specified.

2. For a specific confidence interval, the larger the sample size, the smaller the maximum error of the estimate will be.

3. An estimator is consistent if, as the sample size decreases, the value of the estimator approaches the value of the parameter estimated.

4. To determine the sample size needed to estimate a parameter, you must know the maximum error of the estimate.

Select the best answer.

5. When a 99% confidence interval is calculated instead of a 95% confidence interval with n being the same, the maximum error of estimate will be
   a. Smaller
   b. Larger
   c. The same
   d. It cannot be determined.

6. The best point estimate of the population mean is
   a. The sample mean
   b. The sample median
   c. The sample mode
   d. The sample midrange

7. When the population standard deviation is unknown and the sample size is less than 30, what table value should be used in computing a confidence interval for a mean?
   a. z
   b. t
   c. Chi-square
   d. None of the above

Complete the following statements with the best answer.

8. A good estimator should be _____, _____, and _____.

9. The maximum difference between the point estimate of a parameter and the actual value of the parameter is called _____.

10. The statement "The average height of an adult male is 5 feet 10 inches" is an example of a(n) _____ estimate.

11. The three confidence intervals used most often are the _____%, _____%, and _____%.

12. **Shopping Survey** A random sample of 49 shoppers showed that they spend an average of $23.45 per visit at the Saturday Mornings Bookstore. The standard deviation of the population is $2.80. Find a point estimate of the population mean. Find the 90% confidence interval of the true mean.

13. **Doctor Visit Costs** An irate patient complained that the cost of a doctor's visit was too high. She randomly surveyed 20 other patients and found that the mean amount of money they spent on each doctor's visit was $44.80. The standard deviation of the sample was $3.53. Find a point estimate of the population mean. Find the 95% confidence interval of the population mean. Assume the variable is normally distributed.

14. **Weights of Minivans** The average weight of 40 randomly selected minivans was 4150 pounds. The standard deviation was 480 pounds. Find a point estimate of the population mean. Find the 99% confidence interval of the true mean weight of the minivans.

15. **Ages of Insurance Representatives** In a study of 10 insurance sales representatives from a certain large city, the average age of the group was 48.6 years and the standard deviation was 4.1 years. Assume the variable is normally distributed. Find the 95% confidence interval of the population mean age of all insurance sales representatives in that city.

16. **Patients Treated in Hospital Emergency Rooms** In a hospital, a sample of 8 weeks was selected, and it was found that an average of 438 patients was treated in the emergency room each week. The standard deviation was 16. Find the 99% confidence interval of the true mean. Assume the variable is normally distributed.

17. **Burglaries** For a certain urban area, it was found that in a sample of 4 months, an average of 31 burglaries occurred each month. The standard deviation was 4. Assume the variable is normally distributed. Find the 90% confidence interval of the true mean number of burglaries each month.

18. **Hours Spent Studying** A university dean wishes to estimate the average number of hours that freshmen study each week. The standard deviation from a previous study is 2.6 hours. How large a sample must be selected if he wants to be 99% confident of finding whether the true mean differs from the sample mean by 0.5 hour?

19. **Money Spent on Road Repairs** A researcher wishes to estimate within $300 the true average amount of money a county spends on road repairs each year. If she wants to be 90% confident, how large a sample is necessary? The standard deviation is known to be $900.

20. **Bus Ridership** A recent study of 75 workers found that 53 people rode the bus to work each day. Find the 95% confidence interval of the proportion of all workers who rode the bus to work.

21. **Emergency Room Accidents** In a study of 150 accidents that required treatment in an emergency room, 36% involved children under 6 years of age. Find the 90% confidence interval of the true proportion of accidents that involve children under the age of 6.

22. **Television Set Ownership** A survey of 90 families showed that 40 owned at least one television set. Find the 95% confidence interval of the true proportion of families who own at least one television set.

23. **Skipping Lunch** A nutritionist wishes to determine, within 3%, the true proportion of adults who do not eat any lunch. If he wishes to be 95% confident that his estimate contains the population proportion, how large a sample will be necessary? A previous study found that 15% of the 125 people surveyed said they did not eat lunch.

24. **Novel Pages** A sample of 25 novels has a standard deviation of 9 pages. Find the 95% confidence interval of the population standard deviation.

25. **Truck Safety Check** Find the 90% confidence interval for the variance and standard deviation for the time it takes a state police inspector to check a truck for safety if a sample of 27 trucks has a standard deviation of 6.8 minutes. Assume the variable is normally distributed.

26. **Automobile Pollution** A sample of 20 automobiles has a pollution by-product release standard deviation of 2.3 ounces when 1 gallon of gasoline is used. Find the 90% confidence interval of the population standard deviation.

Critical Thinking Challenges

A confidence interval for a median can be found by using these formulas

$$U = \frac{n+1}{2} + \frac{z_{\alpha/2}\sqrt{n}}{2} \qquad \text{(round up)}$$

$$L = n - U + 1$$

to define positions in the set of ordered data values.

Suppose a data set has 30 values, and you want to find the 95% confidence interval for the median. Substituting in the formulas, you get

$$U = \frac{30+1}{2} + \frac{1.96\sqrt{30}}{2} = 21 \qquad \text{(rounded up)}$$

$$L = 30 - 21 + 1 = 10$$

when $n = 30$ and $z_{\alpha/2} = 1.96$.

Arrange the data in order from smallest to largest, and then select the 10th and 21st values of the data array; hence, $X_{10} <$ median $< X_{21}$.

Find the 90% confidence interval for the median for the given data.

84	49	3	133	85	4340	461	60	28	97
14	252	18	16	24	346	254	29	254	6
31	104	72	29	391	19	125	10	6	17
72	31	23	225	72	5	61	366	77	8
26	8	55	138	158	846	123	47	21	82

 # Data Projects

1. **Business and Finance** Use 30 stocks classified as the Dow Jones industrials as the sample. Note the amount each stock has gained or lost in the last quarter. Compute the mean and standard deviation for the data set. Compute the 95% confidence interval for the mean and the 95% confidence interval for the standard deviation. Compute the percentage of stocks that had a gain in the last quarter. Find a 95% confidence interval for the percentage of stocks with a gain.

2. **Sports and Leisure** Use the top home run hitter from each major league baseball team as the data set. Find the mean and the standard deviation for the number of home runs hit by the top hitter on each team. Find a 95% confidence interval for the mean number of home runs hit.

3. **Technology** Use the data collected in data project 3 of Chapter 2 regarding song lengths. Select a specific genre and compute the percentage of songs in the sample that are of that genre. Create a 95% confidence interval for the true percentage. Use the entire music library and find the population percentage of the library with that genre. Does the population percentage fall within the confidence interval?

4. **Health and Wellness** Use your class as the sample. Have each student take her or his temperature on a healthy day. Compute the mean and standard deviation for the sample. Create a 95% confidence interval for the mean temperature. Does the confidence interval obtained support the long-held belief that the average body temperature is 98.6°F?

5. **Politics and Economics** Select five political polls and note the margin of error, sample size, and percent favoring the candidate for each. For each poll, determine the level of confidence that must have been used to obtain the margin of error given, knowing the percent favoring the candidate and number of participants. Is there a pattern that emerges?

6. **Your Class** Have each student compute his or her body mass index (BMI) (703 times weight in pounds, divided by the quantity height in inches squared). Find the mean and standard deviation for the data set. Compute a 95% confidence interval for the mean BMI of a student. A BMI score over 30 is considered obese. Does the confidence interval indicate that the mean for BMI could be in the obese range?

Answers to Applying the Concepts

Section 7–1 Making Decisions with Confidence Intervals

1. Answers will vary. One possible answer is to find out the average number of Kleenexes that a group of randomly selected individuals use in a 2-week period.

2. People usually need Kleenexes when they have a cold or when their allergies are acting up.

3. If we want to concentrate on the number of Kleenexes used when people have colds, we select a random sample of people with colds and have them keep a record of how many Kleenexes they use during their colds.

4. Answers may vary. I will use a 95% confidence interval:

$$\bar{x} \pm 1.96\frac{\sigma}{\sqrt{n}} = 57 \pm 1.96\frac{15}{\sqrt{85}} = 57 \pm 3.2$$

I am 95% confident that the interval 53.8–60.2 contains the true mean number of Kleenexes used by people when they have colds. It seems reasonable to put 60 Kleenexes in the new automobile glove compartment boxes.

5. Answers will vary. Since I am 95% confident that the interval contains the true average, any number of Kleenexes between 54 and 60 would be reasonable. Sixty seemed to be the most reasonable answer, since it is close to 2 standard deviations above the sample mean.

Section 7–2 Sport Drink Decision

1. Answers will vary. One possible answer is that this is a small sample since we are only looking at seven popular sport drinks.

2. The mean cost per container is $1.25, with standard deviation of $0.39. The 90% confidence interval is

$$\bar{X} \pm t_{\alpha/2}\frac{s}{\sqrt{n}} = 1.25 \pm 1.943\frac{0.39}{\sqrt{7}} = 1.25 \pm 0.29$$

or $0.96 < \mu < 1.54$

The 10-K, All Sport, Exceed, and Hydra Fuel all fall outside of the confidence interval.

3. None of the values appear to be outliers.

4. There are $7 - 1 = 6$ degrees of freedom.

5. Cost per serving would impact my decision on purchasing a sport drink, since this would allow me to compare the costs on an equal scale.

6. Answers will vary.

Section 7–3 Contracting Influenza

1. (95% CI) means that these are the 95% confidence intervals constructed from the data.

2. The margin of error for men reporting influenza is $\frac{50.5 - 47.1}{2} = 1.7\%$.

3. The total sample size was 19,774.

4. The larger the sample size, the smaller the margin of error (all other things being held constant).

5. A 90% confidence interval would be narrower (smaller) than a 95% confidence interval, since we need to include fewer values in the interval.

6. The 51.5% is the middle of the confidence interval, since it is the point estimate for the confidence interval.

Section 7–4 Confidence Interval for Standard Deviation

1. The data represent a population, since we have the age at death for all deceased Presidents (at the time of the writing of this book).

2. Answers will vary. One possible sample is 56, 67, 53, 46, 63, 77, 63, 57, 71, 57, 80, 65, which results in a standard deviation of 9.9 years and a variance of 98.0.

3. Answers will vary. The 95% confidence interval for the standard deviation is $\sqrt{\frac{(n-1)s^2}{\chi^2_{right}}}$ to $\sqrt{\frac{(n-1)s^2}{\chi^2_{left}}}$. In this case we have $\sqrt{\frac{(12-1)9.9^2}{21.920}} = \sqrt{49.1839} = 7.0$ to $\sqrt{\frac{(12-1)9.9^2}{3.8158}} = \sqrt{282.538} = 16.8$, or 7.0 to 16.8 years.

4. The standard deviation for all the data values is 11.6 years.

5. Answers will vary. Yes, the confidence interval does contain the population standard deviation.

6. Answers will vary.

7. We need to assume that the distribution of ages at death is normal.

Hypothesis Testing

Objectives

After completing this chapter, you should be able to

1. Understand the definitions used in hypothesis testing.

2. State the null and alternative hypotheses.

3. Find critical values for the z test.

4. State the five steps used in hypothesis testing.

5. Test means when σ is known, using the z test.

6. Test means when σ is unknown, using the t test.

7. Test proportions, using the z test.

8. Test variances or standard deviations, using the chi-square test.

9. Test hypotheses, using confidence intervals.

Outline

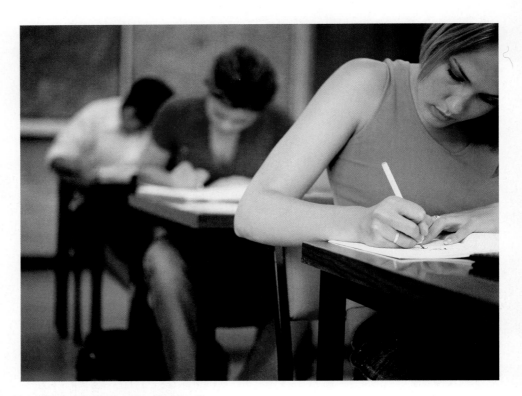

How Much Better Is Better?

Suppose a school superintendent reads an article which states that the overall mean score for the SAT is 910. Furthermore, suppose that, for a sample of students, the average of the SAT scores in the superintendent's school district is 960. Can the superintendent conclude that the students in his school district scored higher than average? At first glance, you might be inclined to say yes, since 960 is higher than 910. But recall that the means of samples vary about the population mean when samples are selected from a specific population. So the question arises, Is there a real difference in the means, or is the difference simply due to chance (i.e., sampling error)? In this chapter, you will learn how to answer that question by using statistics that explain hypothesis testing. See Statistics Today—Revisited for the answer. In this chapter, you will learn how to answer many questions of this type by using statistics that are explained in the theory of hypothesis testing.

Introduction

Researchers are interested in answering many types of questions. For example, a scientist might want to know whether the earth is warming up. A physician might want to know whether a new medication will lower a person's blood pressure. An educator might wish to see whether a new teaching technique is better than a traditional one. A retail merchant might want to know whether the public prefers a certain color in a new line of fashion. Automobile manufacturers are interested in determining whether seat belts will reduce the severity of injuries caused by accidents. These types of questions can be addressed through statistical **hypothesis testing,** which is a decision-making process for evaluating claims about a population. In hypothesis testing, the researcher must define the population under study, state the particular hypotheses that will be investigated, give the significance level, select a sample from the population, collect the data, perform the calculations required for the statistical test, and reach a conclusion.

Hypotheses concerning parameters such as means and proportions can be investigated. There are two specific statistical tests used for hypotheses concerning means: the *z test* and the *t test*. This chapter will explain in detail the hypothesis-testing procedure along with the *z* test and the *t* test. In addition, a hypothesis-testing procedure for testing a single variance or standard deviation using the chi-square distribution is explained in Section 8–5.

The three methods used to test hypotheses are

1. The traditional method
2. The *P*-value method
3. The confidence interval method

The *traditional method* will be explained first. It has been used since the hypothesis-testing method was formulated. A newer method, called the *P-value method,* has become popular with the advent of modern computers and high-powered statistical calculators. It will be explained at the end of Section 8–2. The third method, the *confidence interval method,* is explained in Section 8–6 and illustrates the relationship between hypothesis testing and confidence intervals.

8–1   Steps in Hypothesis Testing–Traditional Method

Every hypothesis-testing situation begins with the statement of a hypothesis.

> A **statistical hypothesis** is a conjecture about a population parameter. This conjecture may or may not be true.

Objective 1

Understand the definitions used in hypothesis testing.

There are two types of statistical hypotheses for each situation: the null hypothesis and the alternative hypothesis.

> The **null hypothesis,** symbolized by H_0, is a statistical hypothesis that states that there is no difference between a parameter and a specific value, or that there is no difference between two parameters.
>
> The **alternative hypothesis,** symbolized by H_1, is a statistical hypothesis that states the existence of a difference between a parameter and a specific value, or states that there is a difference between two parameters.

(*Note:* Although the definitions of null and alternative hypotheses given here use the word *parameter,* these definitions can be extended to include other terms such as *distributions* and *randomness.* This is explained in later chapters.)

As an illustration of how hypotheses should be stated, three different statistical studies will be used as examples.

Situation A   A medical researcher is interested in finding out whether a new medication will have any undesirable side effects. The researcher is particularly concerned with the pulse rate of the patients who take the medication. Will the pulse rate increase, decrease, or remain unchanged after a patient takes the medication?

Objective 2

State the null and alternative hypotheses.

Since the researcher knows that the mean pulse rate for the population under study is 82 beats per minute, the hypotheses for this situation are

$$H_0: \mu = 82 \qquad \text{and} \qquad H_1: \mu \neq 82$$

The null hypothesis specifies that the mean will remain unchanged, and the alternative hypothesis states that it will be different. This test is called a *two-tailed test* (a term that will be formally defined later in this section), since the possible side effects of the medicine could be to raise or lower the pulse rate.

Situation B   A chemist invents an additive to increase the life of an automobile battery. If the mean lifetime of the automobile battery without the additive is 36 months, then her hypotheses are

$$H_0: \mu = 36 \qquad \text{and} \qquad H_1: \mu > 36$$

In this situation, the chemist is interested only in increasing the lifetime of the batteries, so her alternative hypothesis is that the mean is greater than 36 months. The null hypothesis is that the mean is equal to 36 months. This test is called *right-tailed,* since the interest is in an increase only.

Situation C   A contractor wishes to lower heating bills by using a special type of insulation in houses. If the average of the monthly heating bills is $78, her hypotheses about heating costs with the use of insulation are

$$H_0: \mu = \$78 \qquad \text{and} \qquad H_1: \mu < \$78$$

This test is a *left-tailed test,* since the contractor is interested only in lowering heating costs.

To state hypotheses correctly, researchers must translate the *conjecture* or *claim* from words into mathematical symbols. The basic symbols used are as follows:

Equal to	$=$	Greater than	$>$
Not equal to	$\neq$	Less than	$<$

The null and alternative hypotheses are stated together, and the null hypothesis contains the equals sign, as shown (where k represents a specified number).

Two-tailed test	Right-tailed test	Left-tailed test
$H_0: \mu = k$	$H_0: \mu = k$	$H_0: \mu = k$
$H_1: \mu \neq k$	$H_1: \mu > k$	$H_1: \mu < k$

The formal definitions of the different types of tests are given later in this section.

In this book, the null hypothesis is always stated using the equals sign. This is done because in most professional journals, and when we test the null hypothesis, the assumption is that the mean, proportion, or standard deviation is equal to a given specific value. Also, when a researcher conducts a study, he or she is generally looking for evidence to support a claim. Therefore, the claim should be stated as the alternative hypothesis, i.e., using $<$ or $>$ or $\neq$. Because of this, the alternative hypothesis is sometimes called the **research hypothesis.**

Table 8–1 Hypothesis-Testing Common Phrases	
$>$	**$<$**
Is greater than	Is less than
Is above	Is below
Is higher than	Is lower than
Is longer than	Is shorter than
Is bigger than	Is smaller than
Is increased	Is decreased or reduced from
$=$	**$\neq$**
Is equal to	Is not equal to
Is the same as	Is different from
Has not changed from	Has changed from
Is the same as	Is not the same as

A claim, though, can be stated as either the null hypothesis or the alternative hypothesis; however, the statistical evidence can only *support* the claim if it is the alternative hypothesis. Statistical evidence can be used to *reject* the claim if the claim is the null hypothesis. These facts are important when you are stating the conclusion of a statistical study.

Table 8–1 shows some common phrases that are used in hypotheses and conjectures, and the corresponding symbols. This table should be helpful in translating verbal conjectures into mathematical symbols.

Example 8–1

State the null and alternative hypotheses for each conjecture.

   a. A researcher thinks that if expectant mothers use vitamin pills, the birth weight of the babies will increase. The average birth weight of the population is 8.6 pounds.

   b. An engineer hypothesizes that the mean number of defects can be decreased in a manufacturing process of compact disks by using robots instead of humans for certain tasks. The mean number of defective disks per 1000 is 18.

   c. A psychologist feels that playing soft music during a test will change the results of the test. The psychologist is not sure whether the grades will be higher or lower. In the past, the mean of the scores was 73.

Solution

   a. H_0: $\mu = 8.6$ and H_1: $\mu > 8.6$

   b. H_0: $\mu = 18$ and H_1: $\mu < 18$

   c. H_0: $\mu = 73$ and H_1: $\mu \neq 73$

After stating the hypothesis, the researcher designs the study. The researcher selects the correct *statistical test,* chooses an appropriate *level of significance,* and formulates a plan for conducting the study. In situation A, for instance, the researcher will select a sample of patients who will be given the drug. After allowing a suitable time for the drug to be absorbed, the researcher will measure each person's pulse rate.

Recall that when samples of a specific size are selected from a population, the means of these samples will vary about the population mean, and the distribution of the sample means will be approximately normal when the sample size is 30 or more. (See Section 6–3.) So even if the null hypothesis is true, the mean of the pulse rates of the sample of patients will not, in most cases, be exactly equal to the population mean of 82 beats per minute. There are two possibilities. Either the null hypothesis is true, and the difference between the sample mean and the population mean is due to chance; *or* the null hypothesis is false, and the sample came from a population whose mean is not 82 beats per minute but is some other value that is not known. These situations are shown in Figure 8–1.

The farther away the sample mean is from the population mean, the more evidence there would be for rejecting the null hypothesis. The probability that the sample came from a population whose mean is 82 decreases as the distance or absolute value of the difference between the means increases.

If the mean pulse rate of the sample were, say, 83, the researcher would probably conclude that this difference was due to chance and would not reject the null hypothesis. But if the sample mean were, say, 90, then in all likelihood the researcher would conclude that the medication increased the pulse rate of the users and would reject the null hypothesis. The question is, Where does the researcher draw the line? This decision is not made on feelings or intuition; it is made statistically. That is, the difference must be significant and in all likelihood not due to chance. Here is where the concepts of statistical test and level of significance are used.

Figure 8–1

Situations in Hypothesis Testing

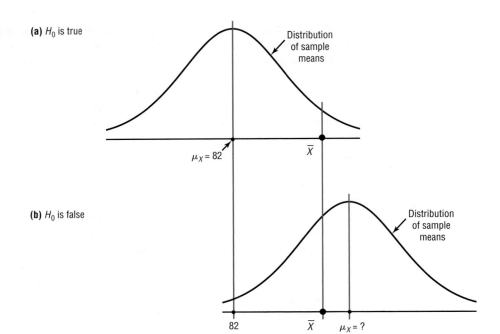

A **statistical test** uses the data obtained from a sample to make a decision about whether the null hypothesis should be rejected.

The numerical value obtained from a statistical test is called the **test value.**

In this type of statistical test, the mean is computed for the data obtained from the sample and is compared with the population mean. Then a decision is made to reject or not reject the null hypothesis on the basis of the value obtained from the statistical test. If the difference is significant, the null hypothesis is rejected. If it is not, then the null hypothesis is not rejected.

In the hypothesis-testing situation, there are four possible outcomes. In reality, the null hypothesis may or may not be true, and a decision is made to reject or not reject it on the basis of the data obtained from a sample. The four possible outcomes are shown in Figure 8–2. Notice that there are two possibilities for a correct decision and two possibilities for an incorrect decision.

Figure 8–2

Possible Outcomes of a Hypothesis Test

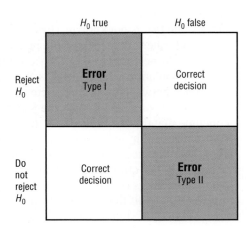

If a null hypothesis is true and it is rejected, then a *type I error* is made. In situation A, for instance, the medication might not significantly change the pulse rate of all the users in the population; but it might change the rate, by chance, of the subjects in the sample. In this case, the researcher will reject the null hypothesis when it is really true, thus committing a type I error.

On the other hand, the medication might not change the pulse rate of the subjects in the sample, but when it is given to the general population, it might cause a significant increase or decrease in the pulse rate of users. The researcher, on the basis of the data obtained from the sample, will not reject the null hypothesis, thus committing a *type II error*.

In situation B, the additive might not significantly increase the lifetimes of automobile batteries in the population, but it might increase the lifetimes of the batteries in the sample. In this case, the null hypothesis would be rejected when it was really true. This would be a type I error. On the other hand, the additive might not work on the batteries selected for the sample, but if it were to be used in the general population of batteries, it might significantly increase their lifetimes. The researcher, on the basis of information obtained from the sample, would not reject the null hypothesis, thus committing a type II error.

A **type I error** occurs if you reject the null hypothesis when it is true.

A **type II error** occurs if you do not reject the null hypothesis when it is false.

The hypothesis-testing situation can be likened to a jury trial. In a jury trial, there are four possible outcomes. The defendant is either guilty or innocent, and he or she will be convicted or acquitted. See Figure 8–3.

Now the hypotheses are

H_0: The defendant is innocent

H_1: The defendant is not innocent (i.e., guilty)

Next, the evidence is presented in court by the prosecutor, and based on this evidence, the jury decides the verdict, innocent or guilty.

If the defendant is convicted but he or she did not commit the crime, then a type I error has been committed. See block 1 of Figure 8–3. On the other hand, if the defendant is convicted and he or she has committed the crime, then a correct decision has been made. See block 2.

If the defendant is acquitted and he or she did not commit the crime, a correct decision has been made by the jury. See block 3. However, if the defendant is acquitted and he or she did commit the crime, then a type II error has been made. See block 4.

Figure 8–3

Hypothesis Testing and a Jury Trial

H_0: The defendant is innocent.
H_1: The defendant is not innocent.

The results of a trial can be shown as follows:

	H_0 true (innocent)	H_0 false (not innocent)
Reject H_0 (convict)	Type I error 1.	Correct decision 2.
Do not reject H_0 (acquit)	Correct decision 3.	Type II error 4.

The decision of the jury does not prove that the defendant did or did not commit the crime. The decision is based on the evidence presented. If the evidence is strong enough, the defendant will be convicted in most cases. If the evidence is weak, the defendant will be acquitted in most cases. Nothing is proved absolutely. Likewise, the decision to reject or not reject the null hypothesis does not prove anything. *The only way to prove anything statistically is to use the entire population,* which, in most cases, is not possible. The decision, then, is made on the basis of probabilities. That is, when there is a large difference between the mean obtained from the sample and the hypothesized mean, the null hypothesis is probably not true. The question is, How large a difference is necessary to reject the null hypothesis? Here is where the level of significance is used.

> The **level of significance** is the maximum probability of committing a type I error. This probability is symbolized by α (Greek letter **alpha**). That is, $P(\text{type I error}) = \alpha$.

The probability of a type II error is symbolized by β, the Greek letter **beta**. That is, $P(\text{type II error}) = \beta$. In most hypothesis-testing situations, β cannot be easily computed; however, α and β are related in that decreasing one increases the other.

Statisticians generally agree on using three arbitrary significance levels: the 0.10, 0.05, and 0.01 levels. That is, if the null hypothesis is rejected, the probability of a type I error will be 10%, 5%, or 1%, depending on which level of significance is used. Here is another way of putting it: When $\alpha = 0.10$, there is a 10% chance of rejecting a true null hypothesis; when $\alpha = 0.05$, there is a 5% chance of rejecting a true null hypothesis; and when $\alpha = 0.01$, there is a 1% chance of rejecting a true null hypothesis.

In a hypothesis-testing situation, the researcher decides what level of significance to use. It does not have to be the 0.10, 0.05, or 0.01 level. It can be any level, depending on the seriousness of the type I error. After a significance level is chosen, a *critical value* is selected from a table for the appropriate test. If a z test is used, for example, the z table (Table E in Appendix C) is consulted to find the critical value. The critical value determines the critical and noncritical regions.

> The **critical value** separates the critical region from the noncritical region. The symbol for critical value is C.V.
>
> The **critical** or **rejection region** is the range of values of the test value that indicates that there is a significant difference and that the null hypothesis should be rejected.
>
> The **noncritical** or **nonrejection region** is the range of values of the test value that indicates that the difference was probably due to chance and that the null hypothesis should not be rejected.

The critical value can be on the right side of the mean or on the left side of the mean for a one-tailed test. Its location depends on the inequality sign of the alternative hypothesis. For example, in situation B, where the chemist is interested in increasing the average lifetime of automobile batteries, the alternative hypothesis is $H_1: \mu > 36$. Since the inequality sign is $>$, the null hypothesis will be rejected only when the sample mean is significantly greater than 36. Hence, the critical value must be on the right side of the mean. Therefore, this test is called a right-tailed test.

> A **one-tailed test** indicates that the null hypothesis should be rejected when the test value is in the critical region on one side of the mean. A one-tailed test is either a **right-tailed test** or **left-tailed test,** depending on the direction of the inequality of the alternative hypothesis.

Figure 8–4

Finding the Critical Value for $\alpha = 0.01$ (Right-Tailed Test)

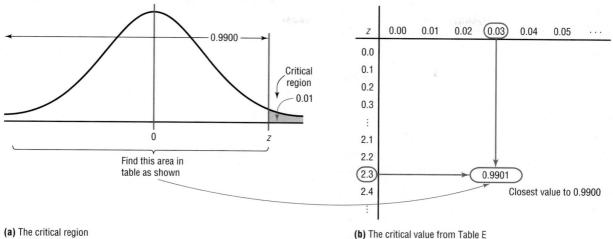

(a) The critical region

(b) The critical value from Table E

To obtain the critical value, the researcher must choose an alpha level. In situation B, suppose the researcher chose $\alpha = 0.01$. Then the researcher must find a z value such that 1% of the area falls to the right of the z value and 99% falls to the left of the z value, as shown in Figure 8–4(a).

Objective **3**

Find critical values for the z test.

Next, the researcher must find the area value in Table E closest to 0.9900. The critical z value is 2.33, since that value gives the area closest to 0.9900 (that is, 0.9901), as shown in Figure 8–4(b).

The critical and noncritical regions and the critical value are shown in Figure 8–5.

Figure 8–5

Critical and Noncritical Regions for $\alpha = 0.01$ (Right-Tailed Test)

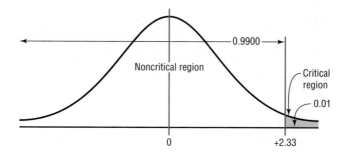

Now, move on to situation C, where the contractor is interested in lowering the heating bills. The alternative hypothesis is H_1: $\mu < \$78$. Hence, the critical value falls to the left of the mean. This test is thus a left-tailed test. At $\alpha = 0.01$, the critical value is -2.33, since 0.0099 is the closest value to 0.01. This is shown in Figure 8–6.

When a researcher conducts a two-tailed test, as in situation A, the null hypothesis can be rejected when there is a significant difference in either direction, above or below the mean.

Figure 8–6

Critical and Noncritical Regions for $\alpha = 0.01$ (Left-Tailed Test)

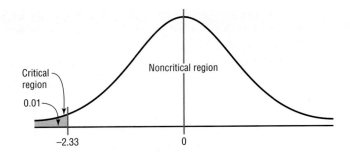

> In a **two-tailed test,** the null hypothesis should be rejected when the test value is in either of the two critical regions.

For a two-tailed test, then, the critical region must be split into two equal parts. If $\alpha = 0.01$, then one-half of the area, or 0.005, must be to the right of the mean and one-half must be to the left of the mean, as shown in Figure 8–7.

In this case, the z value on the left side is found by looking up the z value corresponding to an area of 0.0050. The z value falls about halfway between -2.57 and -2.58 corresponding to the areas 0.0049 and 0.0051. The average of -2.57 and -2.58 is $[(-2.57) + (-2.58)] \div 2 = -2.575$ so if the z value is needed to 3 decimal places, -2.575 is used; however, if the z value is rounded to 2 decimal places, -2.58 is used.

On the right side, it is necessary to find the z value corresponding to $0.99 + 0.005$, or 0.9950. Again, the value falls between 0.9949 and 0.9951, so $+2.575$ or 2.58 can be used. See Figure 8–7.

Figure 8–7

Finding the Critical Values for $\alpha = 0.01$ (Two-Tailed Test)

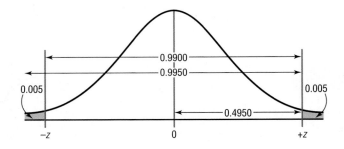

The critical values are $+2.58$ and -2.58, as shown in Figure 8–8.

Figure 8–8

Critical and Noncritical Regions for $\alpha = 0.01$ (Two-Tailed Test)

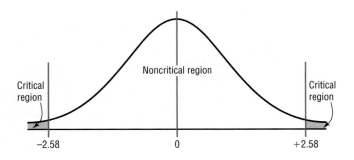

Similar procedures are used to find other values of α.

Figure 8–9 with rejection regions shaded shows the critical value (C.V.) for the three situations discussed in this section for values of $\alpha = 0.10$, $\alpha = 0.05$, and $\alpha = 0.01$. The procedure for finding critical values is outlined next (where k is a specified number).

Figure 8–9

Summary of
Hypothesis Testing
and Critical Values

$H_0: \mu = k$
$H_1: \mu < k$
$\begin{cases} \alpha = 0.10, \text{ C.V.} = -1.28 \\ \alpha = 0.05, \text{ C.V.} = -1.65 \\ \alpha = 0.01, \text{ C.V.} = -2.33 \end{cases}$

(a) Left-tailed

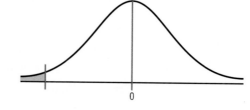

$H_0: \mu = k$
$H_1: \mu > k$
$\begin{cases} \alpha = 0.10, \text{ C.V.} = +1.28 \\ \alpha = 0.05, \text{ C.V.} = +1.65 \\ \alpha = 0.01, \text{ C.V.} = +2.33 \end{cases}$

(b) Right-tailed

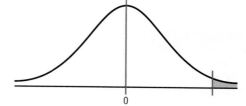

$H_0: \mu = k$
$H_1: \mu \neq k$
$\begin{cases} \alpha = 0.10, \text{ C.V.} = \pm 1.65 \\ \alpha = 0.05, \text{ C.V.} = \pm 1.96 \\ \alpha = 0.01, \text{ C.V.} = \pm 2.58 \end{cases}$

(c) Two-tailed

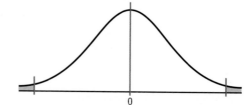

Procedure Table

Finding the Critical Values for Specific α Values, Using Table E

Step 1   Draw the figure and indicate the appropriate area.

   a. If the test is left-tailed, the critical region, with an area equal to α, will be on the left side of the mean.

   b. If the test is right-tailed, the critical region, with an area equal to α, will be on the right side of the mean.

   c. If the test is two-tailed, α must be divided by 2; one-half of the area will be to the right of the mean, and one-half will be to the left of the mean.

Step 2   a. For a left-tailed test, use the z value that corresponds to the area equivalent to α in Table E.

   b. For a right-tailed test, use the z value that corresponds to the area equivalent to $1 - \alpha$.

   c. For a two-tailed test, use the z value that corresponds to $\alpha/2$ for the left value. It will be negative. For the right value, use the z value that corresponds to the area equivalent to $1 - \alpha/2$. It will be positive.

| **Example 8–2** | Using Table E in Appendix C, find the critical value(s) for each situation and draw the appropriate figure, showing the critical region. |

       a. A left-tailed test with $\alpha = 0.10$.

       b. A two-tailed test with $\alpha = 0.02$.

       c. A right-tailed test with $\alpha = 0.005$.

Solution *a*

Step 1   Draw the figure and indicate the appropriate area. Since this is a left-tailed test, the area of 0.10 is located in the left tail, as shown in Figure 8–10.

Step 2   Find the area closest to 0.1000 in Table E. In this case, it is 0.1003. Find the z value which corresponds to the area 0.1003. It is -1.28. See Figure 8–10.

Figure 8–10

Critical Value and
Critical Region for
part *a* of Example 8–2

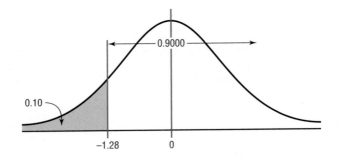

Solution *b*

Step 1   Draw the figure and indicate the appropriate area. In this case, there are two areas equivalent to $\alpha/2$, or $0.02/2 = 0.01$.

Step 2   For the left z critical value, find the area closest to $\alpha/2$, or $0.02/2 = 0.01$. In this case, it is 0.0099.

          For the right z critical value, find the area closest to $1 - \alpha/2$, or $1 - 0.02/2 = 0.9900$. In this case, it is 0.9901.

          Find the z values for each of the areas. For 0.0099, $z = -2.33$. For the area of 0.9901, $z = 0.9901$, $z = +2.33$. See Figure 8–11.

Figure 8–11

Critical Values and
Critical Regions for
part *b* of Example 8–2

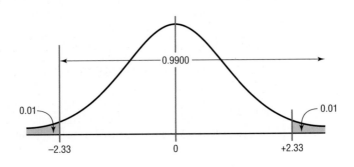

Solution c

Step 1   Draw the figure and indicate the appropriate area. Since this is a right-tailed test, the area 0.005 is located in the right tail, as shown in Figure 8–12.

Figure 8–12

Critical Value and
Critical Region for
part *c* of Example 8–2

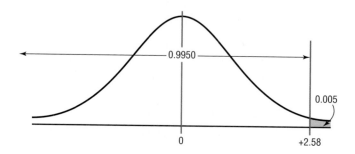

Step 2   Find the area closest to $1 - \alpha$, or $1 - 0.005 = 0.9950$. In this case, it is 0.9949 or 0.9951.

The two *z* values corresponding to 0.9949 and 0.9951 are +2.57 and +2.58. Since 0.9500 is halfway between these two values, find the average of the two values $(+2.57 + 2.58) \div 2 = +2.575$. However, 2.58 is most often used. See Figure 8–12.

Objective **4**

State the five steps
used in hypothesis
testing.

In hypothesis testing, the following steps are recommended.

1. State the hypotheses. Be sure to state both the null and the alternative hypotheses.

2. Design the study. This step includes selecting the correct statistical test, choosing a level of significance, and formulating a plan to carry out the study. The plan should include information such as the definition of the population, the way the sample will be selected, and the methods that will be used to collect the data.

3. Conduct the study and collect the data.

4. Evaluate the data. The data should be tabulated in this step, and the statistical test should be conducted. Finally, decide whether to reject or not reject the null hypothesis.

5. Summarize the results.

For the purposes of this chapter, a simplified version of the hypothesis-testing procedure will be used, since designing the study and collecting the data will be omitted. The steps are summarized in the Procedure Table.

Procedure Table

Solving Hypothesis-Testing Problems (Traditional Method)

Step 1   State the hypotheses and identify the claim.

Step 2   Find the critical value(s) from the appropriate table in Appendix C.

Step 3   Compute the test value.

Step 4   Make the decision to reject or not reject the null hypothesis.

Step 5   Summarize the results.

Applying the Concepts **8–1**

Eggs and Your Health

The Incredible Edible Egg company recently found that eating eggs does not increase a person's blood serum cholesterol. Five hundred subjects participated in a study that lasted for 2 years. The participants were randomly assigned to either a no-egg group or a moderate-egg group. The blood serum cholesterol levels were checked at the beginning and at the end of the study. Overall, the groups' levels were not significantly different. The company reminds us that eating eggs is healthy if done in moderation. Many of the previous studies relating eggs and high blood serum cholesterol jumped to improper conclusions.

Using this information, answer these questions.

1. What prompted the study?
2. What is the population under study?
3. Was a sample collected?
4. What was the hypothesis?
5. Were data collected?
6. Were any statistical tests run?
7. What was the conclusion?

See page 465 for the answers.

Exercises 8–1

1. Define *null* and *alternative hypotheses,* and give an example of each.

2. What is meant by a type I error? A type II error? How are they related?

3. What is meant by a statistical test?

4. Explain the difference between a one-tailed and a two-tailed test.

5. What is meant by the critical region? The noncritical region?

6. What symbols are used to represent the null hypothesis and the alternative hypothesis?

7. What symbols are used to represent the probabilities of type I and type II errors?

8. Explain what is meant by a significant difference.

9. When should a one-tailed test be used? A two-tailed test?

10. List the steps in hypothesis testing.

11. In hypothesis testing, why can't the hypothesis be proved true?

12. **(ans)** Using the z table (Table E), find the critical value (or values) for each.

    a. $\alpha = 0.05$, two-tailed test
    b. $\alpha = 0.01$, left-tailed test
    c. $\alpha = 0.005$, right-tailed test
    d. $\alpha = 0.01$, right-tailed test
    e. $\alpha = 0.05$, left-tailed test
    f. $\alpha = 0.02$, left-tailed test
    g. $\alpha = 0.05$, right-tailed test
    h. $\alpha = 0.01$, two-tailed test
    i. $\alpha = 0.04$, left-tailed test
    j. $\alpha = 0.02$, right-tailed test

13. For each conjecture, state the null and alternative hypotheses.

    a. The average age of community college students is 24.6 years.
    b. The average income of accountants is $51,497.
    c. The average age of attorneys is greater than 25.4 years.
    d. The average score of 50 high school basketball games is less than 88.
    e. The average pulse rate of male marathon runners is less than 70 beats per minute.
    f. The average cost of a DVD player is $79.95.
    g. The average weight loss for a sample of people who exercise 30 minutes per day for 6 weeks is 8.2 pounds.

8–2

z Test for a Mean

Objective 5

Test means when σ is known, using the *z* test.

In this chapter, two statistical tests will be explained: the *z* test is used when σ is known, and the *t* test is used when σ is unknown. This section explains the *z* test, and Section 8–3 explains the *t* test.

Many hypotheses are tested using a statistical test based on the following general formula:

$$\text{Test value} = \frac{(\text{observed value}) - (\text{expected value})}{\text{standard error}}$$

The observed value is the statistic (such as the mean) that is computed from the sample data. The expected value is the parameter (such as the mean) that you would expect to obtain if the null hypothesis were true—in other words, the hypothesized value. The denominator is the standard error of the statistic being tested (in this case, the standard error of the mean).

The *z* test is defined formally as follows.

The **z test** is a statistical test for the mean of a population. It can be used when $n \geq 30$, or when the population is normally distributed and σ is known.

The formula for the *z* test is

$$z = \frac{\overline{X} - \mu}{\sigma/\sqrt{n}}$$

where

$\overline{X}$ = sample mean
μ = hypothesized population mean
σ = population standard deviation
n = sample size

For the *z* test, the observed value is the value of the sample mean. The expected value is the value of the population mean, assuming that the null hypothesis is true. The denominator $\sigma/\sqrt{n}$ is the standard error of the mean.

The formula for the *z* test is the same formula shown in Chapter 6 for the situation where you are using a distribution of sample means. Recall that the central limit theorem allows you to use the standard normal distribution to approximate the distribution of sample means when $n \geq 30$.

Note: Your first encounter with hypothesis testing can be somewhat challenging and confusing, since there are many new concepts being introduced at the same time. *To understand all the concepts, you must carefully follow each step in the examples and try each exercise that is assigned.* Only after careful study and patience will these concepts become clear.

As stated in Section 8–1, there are five steps for solving *hypothesis-testing* problems:

Step 1   State the hypotheses and identify the claim.

Step 2   Find the critical value(s).

Step 3   Compute the test value.

Step 4   Make the decision to reject or not reject the null hypothesis.

Step 5   Summarize the results.

Example 8–3 illustrates these five steps.

Speaking of
Statistics

This study found that people who used pedometers reported having increased energy, mood improvement, and weight loss. State possible null and alternative hypotheses for the study. What would be a likely population? What is the sample size? Comment on the sample size.

RD HEALTH

Step to It

IT FITS in your hand, costs less than $30, and will make you feel great. Give up? A pedometer. Brenda Rooney, an epidemiologist at Gundersen Lutheran Medical Center in LaCrosse, Wis., gave 500 people pedometers and asked them to take 10,000 steps—about five miles—a day. (Office workers typically average about 4000 steps a day.) By the end of eight weeks, 56 percent reported having more energy, 47 percent improved their mood and 50 percent lost weight. The subjects reported that seeing their total step-count motivated them to take more.

— JENNIFER BRAUNSCHWEIGER

Source: Reprinted with permission from the April 2002 Reader's Digest. Copyright © 2002 by The Reader's Digest Assn. Inc.

Example 8–3	**Professors' Salaries**

A researcher reports that the average salary of assistant professors is more than $42,000. A sample of 30 assistant professors has a mean salary of $43,260. At $\alpha = 0.05$, test the claim that assistant professors earn more than $42,000 per year. The standard deviation of the population is $5230.

Solution

Step 1 State the hypotheses and identify the claim.

H_0: $\mu = \$42,000$ and H_1: $\mu > \$42,000$ (claim)

Step 2 Find the critical value. Since $\alpha = 0.05$ and the test is a right-tailed test, the critical value is $z = +1.65$.

Step 3 Compute the test value.

$$z = \frac{\overline{X} - \mu}{\sigma/\sqrt{n}} = \frac{\$43,260 - \$42,000}{\$5230/\sqrt{30}} = 1.32$$

Step 4 Make the decision. Since the test value, $+1.32$, is less than the critical value, $+1.65$, and is not in the critical region, the decision is to not reject the null hypothesis. This test is summarized in Figure 8–13.

Figure 8–13

Summary of the z Test of Example 8–3

Step 5 Summarize the results. There is not enough evidence to support the claim that assistant professors earn more on average than $42,000 per year.

Comment: Even though in Example 8–3 the sample mean of $43,260 is higher than the hypothesized population mean of $42,000, it is not *significantly* higher. Hence, the difference may be due to chance. When the null hypothesis is not rejected, there is still a probability of a type II error, i.e., of not rejecting the null hypothesis when it is false.

The probability of a type II error is not easily ascertained. For now, it is only necessary to realize that the probability of type II error exists when the decision is not to reject the null hypothesis.

Also note that when the null hypothesis is not rejected, it cannot be accepted as true. There is merely not enough evidence to say that it is false. This guideline may sound a little confusing, but the situation is analogous to a jury trial. The verdict is either guilty or not guilty and is based on the evidence presented. If a person is judged not guilty, it does not mean that the person is proved innocent; it only means that there was not enough evidence to reach the guilty verdict.

Example 8–4

Costs of Men's Athletic Shoes

A researcher claims that the average cost of men's athletic shoes is less than $80. He selects a random sample of 36 pairs of shoes from a catalog and finds the following costs (in dollars). (The costs have been rounded to the nearest dollar.) Is there enough evidence to support the researcher's claim at $\alpha = 0.10$? Assume $\sigma = 19.2$.

60	70	75	55	80	55
50	40	80	70	50	95
120	90	75	85	80	60
110	65	80	85	85	45
75	60	90	90	60	95
110	85	45	90	70	70

Solution

Step 1 State the hypotheses and identify the claim

$$H_0: \mu = \$80 \quad \text{and} \quad H_1: \mu < \$80 \text{ (claim)}$$

Step 2 Find the critical value. Since $\alpha = 0.10$ and the test is a left-tailed test, the critical value is -1.28.

Step 3 Compute the test value. Since the exercise gives raw data, it is necessary to find the mean of the data. Using the formulas in Chapter 3 or your calculator gives $\overline{X} = 75.0$ and $\sigma = 19.2$. Substitute in the formula

$$z = \frac{\overline{X} - \mu}{\sigma/\sqrt{n}} = \frac{75 - 80}{19.2/\sqrt{36}} = -1.56$$

Step 4 Make the decision. Since the test value, -1.56, falls in the critical region, the decision is to reject the null hypothesis. See Figure 8–14.

Figure 8–14

Critical and Test Values for Example 8–4

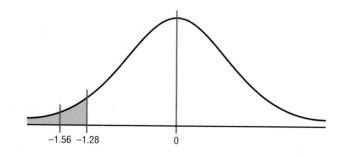

$-1.56 \quad -1.28 \qquad\qquad 0$

Step 5 Summarize the results. There is enough evidence to support the claim that the average cost of men's athletic shoes is less than $80.

Comment: In Example 8–4, the difference is said to be significant. However, when the null hypothesis is rejected, there is always a chance of a type I error. In this case, the probability of a type I error is at most 0.10, or 10%.

Example 8–5

Cost of Rehabilitation

The Medical Rehabilitation Education Foundation reports that the average cost of rehabilitation for stroke victims is $24,672. To see if the average cost of rehabilitation is different at a particular hospital, a researcher selects a random sample of 35 stroke victims at the hospital and finds that the average cost of their rehabilitation is $25,226. The standard deviation of the population is $3251. At $\alpha = 0.01$, can it be concluded that the average cost of stroke rehabilitation at a particular hospital is different from $24,672?

Source: Snapshot, *USA TODAY.*

Solution

Step 1 State the hypotheses and identify the claim.

$$H_0: \mu = \$24{,}672 \qquad \text{and} \qquad H_1: \mu \neq \$24{,}672 \text{ (claim)}$$

Step 2 Find the critical values. Since $\alpha = 0.01$ and the test is a two-tailed test, the critical values are $+2.58$ and -2.58.

Step 3 Compute the test value.

$$z = \frac{\bar{X} - \mu}{\sigma/\sqrt{n}} = \frac{25{,}226 - 24{,}672}{3251/\sqrt{35}} = 1.01$$

Step 4 Make the decision. Do not reject the null hypothesis, since the test value falls in the noncritical region, as shown in Figure 8–15.

Figure 8–15

**Critical and Test Values
for Example 8–5**

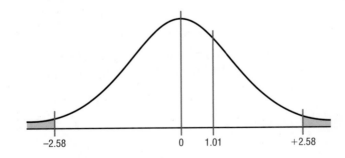

Step 5 Summarize the results. There is not enough evidence to support the claim that the average cost of rehabilitation at the particular hospital is different from $24,672.

Figure 8–16

Outcomes of a
Hypothesis-Testing
Situation

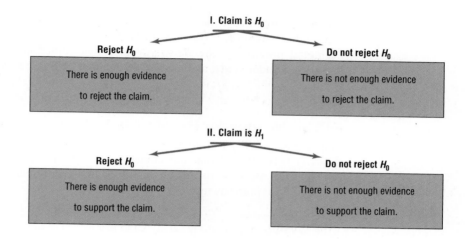

When σ is unknown, the *t* test must be used. The *t* test will be explained in Section 8–3.

Students sometimes have difficulty summarizing the results of a hypothesis test. Figure 8–16 shows the four possible outcomes and the summary statement for each situation.

First, the claim can be either the null or alternative hypothesis, and one should identify which it is. Second, after the study is completed, the null hypothesis is either rejected or not rejected. From these two facts, the decision can be identified in the appropriate block of Figure 8–16.

For example, suppose a researcher claims that the mean weight of an adult animal of a particular species is 42 pounds. In this case, the claim would be the null hypothesis, H_0: $\mu = 42$, since the researcher is asserting that the parameter is a specific value. If the null hypothesis is rejected, the conclusion would be that there is enough evidence to reject the claim that the mean weight of the adult animal is 42 pounds. See Figure 8–17(a).

On the other hand, suppose the researcher claims that the mean weight of the adult animals is not 42 pounds. The claim would be the alternative hypothesis H_1: $\mu \neq 42$. Furthermore, suppose that the null hypothesis is not rejected. The conclusion, then, would be that there is not enough evidence to support the claim that the mean weight of the adult animals is not 42 pounds. See Figure 8–17(b).

Figure 8–17

Outcomes of a
Hypothesis-Testing
Situation for Two
Specific Cases

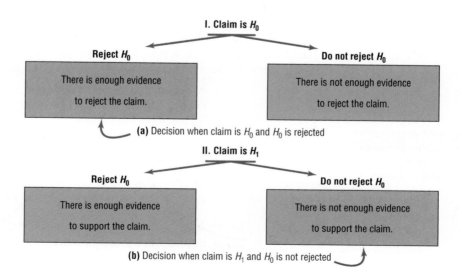

Again, remember that nothing is being proved true or false. The statistician is only stating that there is or is not enough evidence to say that a claim is *probably* true or false. As noted previously, the only way to prove something would be to use the entire population under study, and usually this cannot be done, especially when the population is large.

P-Value Method for Hypothesis Testing

Statisticians usually test hypotheses at the common α levels of 0.05 or 0.01 and sometimes at 0.10. Recall that the choice of the level depends on the seriousness of the type I error. Besides listing an α value, many computer statistical packages give a *P*-value for hypothesis tests.

The ***P*-value** (or probability value) is the probability of getting a sample statistic (such as the mean) or a more extreme sample statistic in the direction of the alternative hypothesis when the null hypothesis is true.

In other words, the *P*-value is the actual area under the standard normal distribution curve (or other curve, depending on what statistical test is being used) representing the probability of a particular sample statistic or a more extreme sample statistic occurring if the null hypothesis is true.

For example, suppose that an alternative hypothesis is H_1: $\mu > 50$ and the mean of a sample is $\overline{X} = 52$. If the computer printed a *P*-value of 0.0356 for a statistical test, then the probability of getting a sample mean of 52 or greater is 0.0356 if the true population mean is 50 (for the given sample size and standard deviation). The relationship between the *P*-value and the α value can be explained in this manner. For $P = 0.0356$, the null hypothesis would be rejected at $\alpha = 0.05$ but not at $\alpha = 0.01$. See Figure 8–18.

When the hypothesis test is two-tailed, the area in one tail must be doubled. For a two-tailed test, if α is 0.05 and the area in one tail is 0.0356, the *P*-value will be $2(0.0356) = 0.0712$. That is, the null hypothesis should not be rejected at $\alpha = 0.05$, since 0.0712 is greater than 0.05. In summary, then, if the *P*-value is less than α, reject the null hypothesis. If the *P*-value is greater than α, do not reject the null hypothesis.

The *P*-values for the z test can be found by using Table E in Appendix C. First find the area under the standard normal distribution curve corresponding to the z test value. For a left-tailed test, use the area given in the table; for a right-tailed test, use 1.0000 minus the area given in the table. To get the *P*-value for a two-tailed test, double the area you found in the tail. This procedure is shown in step 3 of Examples 8–6 and 8–7.

The *P*-value method for testing hypotheses differs from the traditional method somewhat. The steps for the *P*-value method are summarized next.

Figure 8–18

Comparison of α
Values and *P*-Values

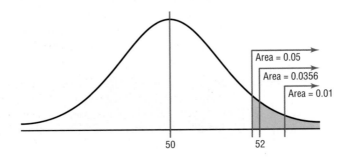

Procedure Table

Solving Hypothesis-Testing Problems (*P*-Value Method)

Step 1   State the hypotheses and identify the claim.

Step 2   Compute the test value.

Step 3   Find the *P*-value.

Step 4   Make the decision.

Step 5   Summarize the results.

Examples 8–6 and 8–7 show how to use the *P*-value method to test hypotheses.

Example 8–6

Cost of College Tuition

A researcher wishes to test the claim that the average cost of tuition and fees at a four-year public college is greater than $5700. She selects a random sample of 36 four-year public colleges and finds the mean to be $5950. The population standard deviation is $659. Is there evidence to support the claim at $\alpha = 0.05$? Use the *P*-value method.

Source: Based on information from the College Board.

Solution

Step 1   State the hypotheses and identify the claim. H_0: $= \$5700$ and H_1: $\mu > \$5700$ (claim).

Step 2   Compute the test value.

$$z = \frac{\overline{X} - \mu}{\sigma/\sqrt{n}} = \frac{5950 - 5700}{659/\sqrt{36}} = 2.28$$

Step 3   Find the *P*-value. Using Table E in Appendix C, find the corresponding area under the normal distribution for $z = 2.28$. It is 0.9887. Subtract this value for the area from 1.0000 to find the area in the right tail.

$1.0000 - 0.9887 = 0.0113$

Hence the *P*-value is 0.0113.

Step 4   Make the decision. Since the *P*-value is less than 0.05, the decision is to reject the null hypothesis. See Figure 8–19.

Figure 8–19

P-Value and α Value for Example 8–6

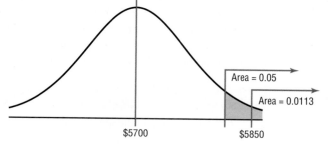

Step 5   Summarize the results. There is enough evidence to support the claim that the tuition and fees at four-year public colleges are greater than $5700.

Note: Had the researcher chosen $\alpha = 0.01$, the null hypothesis would not have been rejected since the *P*-value (0.0113) is greater than 0.01.

| Example 8–7 | Wind Speed |

A researcher claims that the average wind speed in a certain city is 8 miles per hour. A sample of 32 days has an average wind speed of 8.2 miles per hour. The standard deviation of the population is 0.6 mile per hour. At $\alpha = 0.05$, is there enough evidence to reject the claim? Use the P-value method.

Solution

Step 1 State the hypotheses and identify the claim.

$$H_0\colon \mu = 8 \text{ (claim)} \qquad \text{and} \qquad H_1\colon \mu \neq 8$$

Step 2 Compute the test value.

$$z = \frac{8.2 - 8}{0.6/\sqrt{32}} = 1.89$$

Step 3 Find the P-value. Using Table E, find the corresponding area for $z = 1.89$. It is 0.9706. Subtract the value from 1.0000.

$$1.0000 - 0.9706 = 0.0294$$

Since this is a two-tailed test, the area of 0.0294 must be doubled to get the P-value.

$$2(0.0294) = 0.0588$$

Step 4 Make the decision. The decision is to not reject the null hypothesis, since the P-value is greater than 0.05. See Figure 8–20.

| Figure 8–20 |

P-Values and α Values for Example 8–7

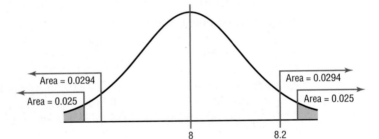

Step 5 Summarize the results. There is not enough evidence to reject the claim that the average wind speed is 8 miles per hour.

In Examples 8–6 and 8–7, the P-value and the α value were shown on a normal distribution curve to illustrate the relationship between the two values; however, it is not necessary to draw the normal distribution curve to make the decision whether to reject the null hypothesis. You can use the following rule:

Decision Rule When Using a P-Value

If P-value $\leq \alpha$, reject the null hypothesis.

If P-value $> \alpha$, do not reject the null hypothesis.

In Example 8–6, P-value = 0.0113 and $\alpha = 0.05$. Since P-value $\leq \alpha$, the null hypothesis was rejected. In Example 8–7, P-value = 0.0588 and $\alpha = 0.05$. Since P-value $> \alpha$, the null hypothesis was not rejected.

The *P*-values given on calculators and computers are slightly different from those found with Table E. This is so because *z* values and the values in Table E have been rounded. *Also, most calculators and computers give the exact P-value for two-tailed tests, so it should not be doubled (as it should when the area found in Table E is used).*

A clear distinction between the α value and the *P*-value should be made. The α value is chosen by the researcher *before* the statistical test is conducted. The *P*-value is computed after the sample mean has been found.

There are two schools of thought on *P*-values. Some researchers do not choose an α value but report the *P*-value and allow the reader to decide whether the null hypothesis should be rejected.

In this case, the following guidelines can be used, but be advised that these guidelines are not written in stone, and some statisticians may have other opinions.

Guidelines for *P*-Values

If *P*-value ≤ 0.01, reject the null hypothesis. The difference is highly significant.

If *P*-value > 0.01 but *P*-value ≤ 0.05, reject the null hypothesis. The difference is significant.

If *P*-value > 0.05 but *P*-value ≤ 0.10, consider the consequences of type I error before rejecting the null hypothesis.

If *P*-value > 0.10, do not reject the null hypothesis. The difference is not significant.

Others decide on the α value in advance and use the *P*-value to make the decision, as shown in Examples 8–6 and 8–7. A note of caution is needed here: If a researcher selects $\alpha = 0.01$ and the *P*-value is 0.03, the researcher may decide to change the α value from 0.01 to 0.05 so that the null hypothesis will be rejected. This, of course, should not be done. If the α level is selected in advance, it should be used in making the decision.

One additional note on hypothesis testing is that the researcher should distinguish between *statistical significance* and *practical significance*. When the null hypothesis is rejected at a specific significance level, it can be concluded that the difference is probably not due to chance and thus is statistically significant. However, the results may not have any practical significance. For example, suppose that a new fuel additive increases the miles per gallon that a car can get by $\frac{1}{4}$ mile for a sample of 1000 automobiles. The results may be statistically significant at the 0.05 level, but it would hardly be worthwhile to market the product for such a small increase. Hence, there is no practical significance to the results. It is up to the researcher to use common sense when interpreting the results of a statistical test.

Applying the Concepts **8–2**

Car Thefts

You recently received a job with a company that manufactures an automobile antitheft device. To conduct an advertising campaign for the product, you need to make a claim about the number of automobile thefts per year. Since the population of various cities in the United States varies, you decide to use rates per 10,000 people. (The rates are based on the number of people living in the cities.) Your boss said that last year the theft rate per 10,000 people was 44 vehicles. You want to see if it has changed. The following are rates per 10,000 people for 36 randomly selected locations in the United States.

55	42	125	62	134	73
39	69	23	94	73	24
51	55	26	66	41	67
15	53	56	91	20	78
70	25	62	115	17	36
58	56	33	75	20	16

Source: Based on information from the National Insurance Crime Bureau.

Using this information, answer these questions.

1. What hypotheses would you use?
2. Is the sample considered small or large?
3. What assumption must be met before the hypothesis test can be conducted?
4. Which probability distribution would you use?
5. Would you select a one- or two-tailed test? Why?
6. What critical value(s) would you use?
7. Conduct a hypothesis test. Use $\sigma = 30.3$.
8. What is your decision?
9. What is your conclusion?
10. Write a brief statement summarizing your conclusion.
11. If you lived in a city whose population was about 50,000, how many automobile thefts per year would you expect to occur?

See page 465 for the answers.

Exercises 8–2

For Exercises 1 through 13, perform each of the following steps.

a. State the hypotheses and identify the claim.
b. Find the critical value(s).
c. Compute the test value.
d. Make the decision.
e. Summarize the results.

Use diagrams to show the critical region (or regions), and use the traditional method of hypothesis testing unless otherwise specified.

1. **Walking with a Pedometer** An increase in walking has been shown to contribute to a healthier life-style. A sedentary American takes an average of 5000 steps per day (and 65% of Americans are overweight). A group of health-conscious employees of a large health care system volunteered to wear pedometers for a month to record their steps. It was found that a random sample of 40 walkers took an average of 5430 steps per day, and the population standard deviation is 600 steps. At $\alpha = 0.05$ can it be concluded that they walked more than the mean number of 5000 steps per day?

   Source: www.msn.com/health

2. **Credit Card Debt** It has been reported that the average credit card debt for college seniors is $3262. The student senate at a large university feels that their seniors have a debt much less than this, so it conducts a study of 50 randomly selected seniors and finds that the average debt is $2995, and the population standard deviation is $1100. With $\alpha = 0.05$, is the student senate correct?

   Source: *USA TODAY.*

3. **Revenue of Large Businesses** A researcher estimates that the average revenue of the largest

businesses in the United States is greater than $24 billion. A sample of 50 companies is selected, and the revenues (in billions of dollars) are shown. At $\alpha = 0.05$, is there enough evidence to support the researcher's claim? $\sigma = 28.7$.

178	122	91	44	35
61	56	46	20	32
30	28	28	20	27
29	16	16	19	15
41	38	36	15	25
31	30	19	19	19
24	16	15	15	19
25	25	18	14	15
24	23	17	17	22
22	21	20	17	20

Source: *New York Times Almanac.*

4. **Salaries of Ph.D. Students** Full-time Ph.D. students receive an average salary of $12,837 according to the U.S. Department of Education. The dean of graduate studies at a large state university feels that Ph.D. students in his state earn more than this. He surveys 44 randomly selected students and finds their average salary is $14,445, and the population standard deviation is $1500. With $\alpha = 0.05$, is the dean correct?

   Source: U.S. Department of Education/*Chronicle of Higher Education.*

5. **Health Care Expenses** The mean annual expenditure per 25- to 34-year-old consumer for health care is $1468. This includes health insurance, medical services, and drugs and medical supplies. Students at a large university took a survey, and it was found that for a sample of 60 students, the mean health care expense was $1520, and the population standard deviation is $198. Is there sufficient evidence at $\alpha = 0.01$ to conclude that their health care expenditure differs from the national average of $1468? Is the conclusion different at $\alpha = 0.05$?

   Source: *Time Almanac.*

6. **Peanut Production in Virginia** The average production of peanuts in Virginia is 3000 pounds per acre. A new plant food has been developed and is tested on 60 individual plots of land. The mean yield with the new plant food is 3120 pounds of peanuts per acre, and the population standard deviation is 578 pounds. At $\alpha = 0.05$, can you conclude that the average production has increased?

Source: *The Old Farmer's Almanac.*

7. **Heights of 1-Year-Olds** The average 1-year-old (both genders) is 29 inches tall. A random sample of 30 one-year-olds in a large day care franchise resulted in the following heights. At $\alpha = 0.05$, can it be concluded that the average height differs from 29 inches? Assume $\sigma = 2.61$.

25	32	35	25	30	26.5	26	25.5	29.5	32
30	28.5	30	32	28	31.5	29	29.5	30	34
29	32	27	28	33	28	27	32	29	29.5

Source: www.healthepic.com

8. **Salaries of Government Employees** The mean salary of federal government employees on the General Schedule is $59,593. The average salary of 30 state employees who do similar work is $58,800 with $\sigma = \$1500$. At the 0.01 level of significance, can it be concluded that state employees earn on average less than federal employees?

Source: *New York Times Almanac.*

9. **Undergraduate School Expenses** The average undergraduate cost for tuition, fees, room, and board for all institutions last year was $26,025. A random sample of 40 institutions of higher learning this year indicated that the mean tuition, fees, room, and board for the sample was $27,690, and the population standard deviation is $5492. At the 0.05 level of significance, is there sufficient evidence that the cost has increased?

Source: *Time Almanac.*

10. **Home Prices in Pennsylvania** A real estate agent claims that the average price of a home sold in Beaver County, Pennsylvania, is $60,000. A random sample of 36 homes sold in the county is selected, and the prices in dollars are shown. Is there enough evidence to reject the agent's claim at $\alpha = 0.05$? Assume $\sigma = \$76,025$.

9,500	54,000	99,000	94,000	80,000
29,000	121,500	184,750	15,000	164,450
6,000	13,000	188,400	121,000	308,000
42,000	7,500	32,900	126,900	25,225
95,000	92,000	38,000	60,000	211,000
15,000	28,000	53,500	27,000	21,000
76,000	85,000	25,225	40,000	97,000
284,000				

Source: *Pittsburgh Tribune-Review.*

11. **Use of Disposable Cups** The average college student goes through 500 disposable cups in a year. To raise environmental awareness, a student group at a large university volunteered to help count how many cups were used by students on their campus. A random sample of 50 students' results found that they used a mean of 476 cups with $\sigma = 42$ cups. At $\alpha = 0.01$, is there sufficient evidence to conclude that the mean differs from 500?

Source: www.esc.mtu.edu

12. **Public School Teachers' Salaries** The average salary for public school teachers for a specific year was reported to be $39,385. A random sample of 50 public school teachers in a particular state had a mean of $41,680, and the population standard deviation is $5975. Is there sufficient evidence at the $\alpha = 0.05$ level to conclude that the mean salary differs from $39,385?

Source: *New York Times Almanac.*

13. **Ages of U.S. Senators** The mean age of Senators in the 109th Congress was 60.35 years. A random sample of 40 senators from various state senates had an average age of 55.4 years, and the population standard deviation is 6.5 years. At $\alpha = 0.05$, is there sufficient evidence that state senators are on average younger than the Senators in Washington?

Source: *CG Today.*

14. What is meant by a *P*-value?

15. State whether the null hypothesis should be rejected on the basis of the given *P*-value.

   a. *P*-value = 0.258, $\alpha = 0.05$, one-tailed test
   b. *P*-value = 0.0684, $\alpha = 0.10$, two-tailed test
   c. *P*-value = 0.0153, $\alpha = 0.01$, one-tailed test
   d. *P*-value = 0.0232, $\alpha = 0.05$, two-tailed test
   e. *P*-value = 0.002, $\alpha = 0.01$, one-tailed test

16. **Soft Drink Consumption** A researcher claims that the yearly consumption of soft drinks per person is 52 gallons. In a sample of 50 randomly selected people, the mean of the yearly consumption was 56.3 gallons. The standard deviation of the population is 3.5 gallons. Find the *P*-value for the test. On the basis of the *P*-value, is the researcher's claim valid?

Source: U.S. Department of Agriculture.

17. **Stopping Distances** A study found that the average stopping distance of a school bus traveling 50 miles per hour was 264 feet. A group of automotive engineers decided to conduct a study of its school buses and found that for 20 buses, the average stopping distance of buses traveling 50 miles per hour was 262.3 feet. The standard deviation of the population was 3 feet. Test the claim that the average stopping distance of the company's buses is actually less than 264 feet. Find the *P*-value. On the basis of the *P*-value, should the null hypothesis be rejected at $\alpha = 0.01$? Assume that the variable is normally distributed.

Source: Snapshot, *USA TODAY*, March 12, 1992.

18. **Copy Machine Use** A store manager hypothesizes that the average number of pages a person copies on the store's copy machine is less than 40. A sample of 50 customers' orders is selected. At $\alpha = 0.01$, is there enough evidence to support the claim? Use the *P*-value hypothesis-testing method. Assume $\sigma = 30.9$.

2	2	2	5	32
5	29	8	2	49
21	1	24	72	70
21	85	61	8	42
3	15	27	113	36
37	5	3	58	82
9	2	1	6	9
80	9	51	2	122
21	49	36	43	61
3	17	17	4	1

19. Burning Calories by Playing Tennis A health researcher read that a 200-pound male can burn an average of 546 calories per hour playing tennis. Thirty-six males were randomly selected and tested. The mean of the number of calories burned per hour was 544.8. Test the claim that the average number of calories burned is actually less than 546, and find the P-value. On the basis of the P-value, should the null hypothesis be rejected at $\alpha = 0.01$? The standard deviation of the population is 3. Can it be concluded that the average number of calories burned is less than originally thought?

20. Breaking Strength of Cable A special cable has a breaking strength of 800 pounds. The standard deviation of the population is 12 pounds. A researcher selects a sample of 20 cables and finds that the average breaking strength is 793 pounds. Can he reject the claim that the breaking strength is 800 pounds? Find the P-value. Should the null hypothesis be rejected at $\alpha = 0.01$? Assume that the variable is normally distributed.

21. Farm Sizes The average farm size in the United States is 444 acres. A random sample of 40 farms in Oregon indicated a mean size of 430 acres, and the population standard deviation is 52 acres. At $\alpha = 0.05$, can it be concluded that the average farm in Oregon differs from the national mean? Use the P-value method.

Source: New York Times Almanac.

22. Farm Sizes Ten years ago, the average acreage of farms in a certain geographic region was 65 acres. The standard deviation of the population was 7 acres. A recent study consisting of 22 farms showed that the average was 63.2 acres per farm. Test the claim, at $\alpha = 0.10$, that the average has not changed by finding the P-value for the test. Assume that σ has not changed and the variable is normally distributed.

23. Transmission Service A car dealer recommends that transmissions be serviced at 30,000 miles. To see whether her customers are adhering to this recommendation, the dealer selects a sample of 40 customers and finds that the average mileage of the automobiles serviced is 30,456. The standard deviation of the population is 1684 miles. By finding the P-value, determine whether the owners are having their transmissions serviced at 30,000 miles. Use $\alpha = 0.10$. Do you think the α value of 0.10 is an appropriate significance level?

24. Speeding Tickets A motorist claims that the South Boro Police issue an average of 60 speeding tickets per day. These data show the number of speeding tickets issued each day for a period of one month. Assume σ is 13.42. Is there enough evidence to reject the motorist's claim at $\alpha = 0.05$? Use the P-value method.

72	45	36	68	69	71	57	60
83	26	60	72	58	87	48	59
60	56	64	68	42	57	57	
58	63	49	73	75	42	63	

25. Sick Days A manager states that in his factory, the average number of days per year missed by the employees due to illness is less than the national average of 10. The following data show the number of days missed by 40 employees last year. Is there sufficient evidence to believe the manager's statement at $\alpha = 0.05$? $\sigma = 3.63$. Use the P-value method.

0	6	12	3	3	5	4	1
3	9	6	0	7	6	3	4
7	4	7	1	0	8	12	3
2	5	10	5	15	3	2	5
3	11	8	2	2	4	1	9

Extending the Concepts

26. Suppose a statistician chose to test a hypothesis at $\alpha = 0.01$. The critical value for a right-tailed test is $+2.33$. If the test value was 1.97, what would the decision be? What would happen if, after seeing the test value, she decided to choose $\alpha = 0.05$? What would the decision be? Explain the contradiction, if there is one.

27. Hourly Wage The president of a company states that the average hourly wage of her employees is $8.65. A sample of 50 employees has the distribution shown.

At $\alpha = 0.05$, is the president's statement believable? Assume $\sigma = 0.105$.

Class	Frequency
8.35–8.43	2
8.44–8.52	6
8.53–8.61	12
8.62–8.70	18
8.71–8.79	10
8.80–8.88	2

Technology *Step by Step*

MINITAB
Step by Step

Hypothesis Test for the Mean and the *z* Distribution

MINITAB can be used to calculate the test statistic and its *P*-value. The *P*-value approach does not require a critical value from the table. If the *P*-value is smaller than α, the null hypothesis is rejected. For Example 8–4, test the claim that the mean shoe cost is less than $80.

1. Enter the data into a column of MINITAB. Do not try to type in the dollar signs! Name the column **ShoeCost.**

2. If sigma is known, skip to step 3; otherwise estimate sigma from the sample standard deviation *s*.

Calculate the Standard Deviation in the Sample

    a) Select **Calc>Column Statistics.**

    b) Check the button for Standard deviation.

    c) Select ShoeCost for the Input variable.

    d) Type **s** in the text box for Store the result in:.

    e) Click [OK].

Calculate the Test Statistic and *P*-Value

3. Select **Stat>Basic Statistics>1 Sample Z,** then select ShoeCost in the Variable text box.

4. Click in the text box and enter the value of sigma or type *s*, the sample standard deviation.

5. Click in the text box for Test mean, and enter the hypothesized value of **80.**

6. Click on [Options].

    a) Change the Confidence level to **90.**

    b) Change the Alternative to less than. This setting is crucial for calculating the *P*-value.

7. Click [OK] twice.

One-Sample Z: ShoeCost
```
Test of mu = 80 vs < 80
The assumed sigma 19.161
                                            90%
                                           Upper
Variable    N     Mean     StDev   SE Mean  Bound      Z      P
ShoeCost    36   75.0000   19.1610  3.1935  79.0926  -1.57  0.059
```

Since the *P*-value of 0.059 is less than α, reject the null hypothesis. There is enough evidence in the sample to conclude the mean cost is less than $80.

TI-83 Plus or TI-84 Plus
Step by Step

Hypothesis Test for the Mean and the *z* Distribution (Data)

1. Enter the data values into L_1.
2. Press **STAT** and move the cursor to TESTS.
3. Press **l** for ZTest.
4. Move the cursor to Data and press **ENTER**.
5. Type in the appropriate values.
6. Move the cursor to the appropriate alternative hypothesis and press **ENTER**.
7. Move the cursor to Calculate and press **ENTER**.

Example TI8–1

This relates to Example 8–4 from the text. At the 10% significance level, test the claim that $\mu < 80$ given the data values.

60	70	75	55	80	55	50	40	80	70	50	95
120	90	75	85	80	60	110	65	80	85	85	45
75	60	90	90	60	95	110	85	45	90	70	70

The population standard deviation σ is unknown. Since the sample size $n = 36 \geq 30$, you can use the sample standard deviation s as an approximation for σ. After the data values are entered in L_1 (step 1), press **STAT**, move the cursor to CALC, press **1** for 1-Var Stats, then press **ENTER**. The sample standard deviation of 19.16097224 will be one of the statistics listed. Then continue with step 2. At step 5 on the line for σ press **VARS** for variables, press **5** for Statistics, press **3** for S_x.

The test statistic is $z = -1.565682556$, and the *P*-value is 0.0587114841.

Hypothesis Test for the Mean and the *z* Distribution (Statistics)

1. Press **STAT** and move the cursor to TESTS.
2. Press **1** for ZTest.
3. Move the cursor to Stats and press **ENTER**.
4. Type in the appropriate values.
5. Move the cursor to the appropriate alternative hypothesis and press **ENTER**.
6. Move the cursor to Calculate and press **ENTER**.

Example TI8–2

This relates to Example 8–3 from the text. At the 5% significance level, test the claim that $\mu > 42{,}000$ given $\sigma = 5230$, $\overline{X} = 43{,}260$, and $n = 30$.

The test statistic is $z = 1.319561037$, and the *P*-value is 0.0934908728.

Excel
Step by Step

Hypothesis Test for the Mean: *z* Test

Excel does not have a procedure to conduct a hypothesis test for the mean. However, you may conduct the test of the mean by using the MegaStat Add-in available on your CD. If you have not installed this add-in, do so, following the instructions from the Chapter 1 Excel Step by Step.

Example XL8–1

This example relates to Example 8–4 from the text. At the 10% significance level, test the claim that $\mu < 80$. The MegaStat *z* test uses the *P*-value method. Therefore, it is not necessary to enter a significance level.

1. Enter the data into column A of a new worksheet.
2. From the toolbar, select Add-Ins, **MegaStat>Hypothesis Tests>Mean vs. Hypothesized Value.** *Note:* You may need to open MegaStat from the MegaStat.xls file on your computer's hard drive.

3. Select data input and type **A1:A36** as the Input Range.

4. Type **80** for the Hypothesized mean and select the "less than" Alternative.

5. Select *z* test and click [OK].

The result of the procedure is shown next.

Hypothesis Test: Mean vs. Hypothesized Value

```
80.000  Hypothesized value
75.000  Mean data
19.161  Standard deviation
 3.193  Standard error
    36  n

-1.57  z
0.0587  P-value (one-tailed, lower)
```

8–3 *t* Test for a Mean

Objective 6

Test means when σ is unknown, using the *t* test.

When the population standard deviation is unknown, the *z* test is not normally used for testing hypotheses involving means. A different test, called the *t test*, is used. The distribution of the variable should be approximately normal.

As stated in Chapter 7, the *t* distribution is similar to the standard normal distribution in the following ways.

1. It is bell-shaped.

2. It is symmetric about the mean.

3. The mean, median, and mode are equal to 0 and are located at the center of the distribution.

4. The curve never touches the *x* axis.

The *t* distribution differs from the standard normal distribution in the following ways.

1. The variance is greater than 1.

2. The *t* distribution is a family of curves based on the *degrees of freedom*, which is a number related to sample size. (Recall that the symbol for degrees of freedom is d.f. See Section 7–2 for an explanation of degrees of freedom.)

3. As the sample size increases, the *t* distribution approaches the normal distribution.

The *t* test is defined next.

The **_t_ test** is a statistical test for the mean of a population and is used when the population is normally or approximately normally distributed, σ is unknown.

The formula for the *t* test is

$$t = \frac{\overline{X} - \mu}{s/\sqrt{n}}$$

The degrees of freedom are d.f. $= n - 1$.

The formula for the *t* test is similar to the formula for the *z* test. But since the population standard deviation σ is unknown, the sample standard deviation *s* is used instead.

The critical values for the *t* test are given in Table F in Appendix C. For a one-tailed test, find the α level by looking at the top row of the table and finding the appropriate column. Find the degrees of freedom by looking down the left-hand column.

Notice that the degrees of freedom are given for values from 1 through 30, then at intervals above 30. When the degrees of freedom are above 30, some textbooks will tell you to use the nearest table value; however, in this textbook, you should always round down to the nearest table value. For example, if d.f. = 59, use d.f. = 55 to find the critical value or values. This is a conservative approach.

As the degrees of freedom get larger, the critical values approach the z values. Hence the bottom values (large sample size) are the same as the z values that were used in the last section.

Example 8–8

Find the critical t value for $\alpha = 0.05$ with d.f. = 16 for a right-tailed t test.

Solution

Find the 0.05 column in the top row and 16 in the left-hand column. Where the row and column meet, the appropriate critical value is found; it is $+1.746$. See Figure 8–21.

Figure 8–21

Finding the Critical Value for the t Test in Table F (Example 8–8)

d.f.	One tail, α 0.25	0.10	(0.05)	0.025	0.01	0.005
	Two tails, α 0.50	0.20	0.10	0.05	0.02	0.01
1						
2						
3						
4						
5						
⋮						
14						
15						
16			1.746			
17						
18						
⋮						

Example 8–9

Find the critical t value for $\alpha = 0.01$ with d.f. = 22 for a left-tailed test.

Solution

Find the 0.01 column in the row labeled One tail, and find 22 in the left column. The critical value is -2.508 since the test is a one-tailed left test.

Example 8–10

Find the critical values for $\alpha = 0.10$ with d.f. = 18 for a two-tailed t test.

Solution

Find the 0.10 column in the row labeled Two tails, and find 18 in the column labeled d.f. The critical values are $+1.734$ and -1.734.

Example 8–11

Find the critical value for $\alpha = 0.05$ with d.f. = 28 for a right-tailed *t* test.

Solution

Find the 0.05 column in the One-tail row and 28 in the left column. The critical value is $+1.701$.

When you test hypotheses by using the *t* test (traditional method), follow the same procedure as for the *z* test, except use Table F.

Step 1   State the hypotheses and identify the claim.

Step 2   Find the critical value(s) from Table F.

Step 3   Compute the test value.

Step 4   Make the decision to reject or not reject the null hypothesis.

Step 5   Summarize the results.

Remember that the t test should be used when the population is approximately normally distributed and the population standard deviation is unknown.
Examples 8–12 through 8–14 illustrate the application of the *t* test.

Example 8–12

Hospital Infections

A medical investigation claims that the average number of infections per week at a hospital in southwestern Pennsylvania is 16.3. A random sample of 10 weeks had a mean number of 17.7 infections. The sample standard deviation is 1.8. Is there enough evidence to reject the investigator's claim at $\alpha = 0.05$?

Source: Based on information obtained from Pennsylvania Health Care Cost Containment Council.

Solution

Step 1 H_0: $\mu = 16.3$ (claim) and H_1: $\mu \neq 16.3$.

Step 2   The critical values are $+2.262$ and -2.262 for $\alpha = 0.05$ and d.f. = 9.

Step 3   The test value is

$$t = \frac{\overline{X} - \mu}{s/\sqrt{n}} = \frac{17.7 - 16.3}{1.8/\sqrt{10}} = 2.46$$

Step 4   Reject the null hypothesis since $2.46 > 2.262$. See Figure 8–22.

Figure 8–22

Summary of the *t* Test of Example 8–12

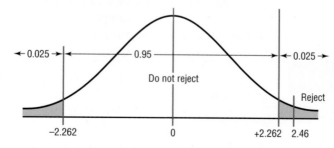

Step 5   There is enough evidence to reject the claim that the average number of infections is 16.3.

Example 8–13

Substitute Teachers' Salaries

An educator claims that the average salary of substitute teachers in school districts in Allegheny County, Pennsylvania, is less than $60 per day. A random sample of eight school districts is selected, and the daily salaries (in dollars) are shown. Is there enough evidence to support the educator's claim at $\alpha = 0.10$?

$$60 \quad 56 \quad 60 \quad 55 \quad 70 \quad 55 \quad 60 \quad 55$$

Source: *Pittsburgh Tribune-Review.*

Solution

Step 1 H_0: $\mu = \$60$ and H_1: $\mu < \$60$ (claim).

Step 2 At $\alpha = 0.10$ and d.f. $= 7$, the critical value is -1.415.

Step 3 To compute the test value, the mean and standard deviation must be found. Using either the formulas in Chapter 3 or your calculator, $\overline{X} = \$58.88$, and $s = 5.08$, you find

$$t = \frac{\overline{X} - \mu}{s/\sqrt{n}} = \frac{58.88 - 60}{5.08/\sqrt{8}} = -0.624$$

Step 4 Do not reject the null hypothesis since -0.624 falls in the noncritical region. See Figure 8–23.

Figure 8–23

Critical Value and Test Value for Example 8–13

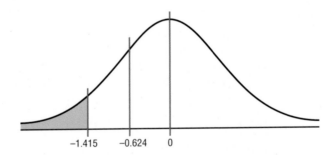

$$-1.415 \quad -0.624 \quad 0$$

Step 5 There is not enough evidence to support the educator's claim that the average salary of substitute teachers in Allegheny County is less than $60 per day.

The *P*-values for the *t* test can be found by using Table F; however, specific *P*-values for *t* tests cannot be obtained from the table since only selected values of α (for example, 0.01, 0.05) are given. To find specific *P*-values for *t* tests, you would need a table similar to Table E for each degree of freedom. Since this is not practical, only *intervals* can be found for *P*-values. Examples 8–14 to 8–16 show how to use Table F to determine intervals for *P*-values for the *t* test.

Example 8–14

Find the *P*-value when the *t* test value is 2.056, the sample size is 11, and the test is right-tailed.

Solution

To get the *P*-value, look across the row with 10 degrees of freedom (d.f. $= n - 1$) in Table F and find the two values that 2.056 falls between. They are 1.812 and 2.228. Since this is a right-tailed test, look up to the row labeled One tail, α and find the two α values corresponding to 1.812 and 2.228. They are 0.05 and 0.025, respectively. See Figure 8–24.

Figure 8–24

Finding the *P*-Value for Example 8–14

Confidence intervals	50%	80%	90%	95%	98%	99%
One tail, α	0.25	0.10	(0.05)	(0.025)	0.01	0.005
d.f. Two tails, α	0.50	0.20	0.10	0.05	0.02	0.01
1	1.000	3.078	6.314	12.706	31.821	63.657
2	0.816	1.886	2.920	4.303	6.965	9.925
3	0.765	1.638	2.353	3.182	4.541	5.841
4	0.741	1.533	2.132	2.776	3.747	4.604
5	0.727	1.476	2.015	2.571	3.365	4.032
6	0.718	1.440	1.943	2.447	3.143	3.707
7	0.711	1.415	1.895	2.365	2.998	3.499
8	0.706	1.397	1.860	2.306	2.896	3.355
9	0.703	1.383	1.833	2.262	2.821	3.250
10	0.700	1.372	(1.812) *	(2.228)	2.764	3.169
11	0.697	1.363	1.796	2.201	2.718	3.106
12	0.695	1.356	1.782	2.179	2.681	3.055
13	0.694	1.350	1.771	2.160	2.650	3.012
14	0.692	1.345	1.761	2.145	2.624	2.977
15	0.691	1.341	1.753	2.131	2.602	2.947
⋮	⋮	⋮	⋮	⋮	⋮	⋮
(z) ∞	0.674	1.282	1.645	1.960	2.326	2.576

*2.056 falls between 1.812 and 2.228.

Hence, the *P*-value would be contained in the interval $0.025 < P\text{-value} < 0.05$. This means that the *P*-value is between 0.025 and 0.05. If α were 0.05, you would reject the null hypothesis since the *P*-value is less than 0.05. But if α were 0.01, you would not reject the null hypothesis since the *P*-value is greater than 0.01. (Actually, it is greater than 0.025.)

Example 8–15

Find the *P*-value when the *t* test value is 2.983, the sample size is 6, and the test is two-tailed.

Solution

To get the *P*-value, look across the row with d.f. = 5 and find the two values that 2.983 falls between. They are 2.571 and 3.365. Then look up to the row labeled Two tails, α to find the corresponding α values.

In this case, they are 0.05 and 0.02. Hence the *P*-value is contained in the interval $0.02 < P\text{-value} < 0.05$. This means that the *P*-value is between 0.02 and 0.05. In this case, if $\alpha = 0.05$, the null hypothesis can be rejected since *P*-value < 0.05; but if $\alpha = 0.01$, the null hypothesis cannot be rejected since *P*-value > 0.01 (actually *P*-value > 0.02).

Note: **Since many of you will be using calculators or computer programs that give the specific *P*-value for the *t* test and other tests presented later in this textbook, these specific values, in addition to the intervals, will be given for the answers to the examples and exercises.**

The *P*-value obtained from a calculator for Example 8–14 is 0.033. The *P*-value obtained from a calculator for Example 8–15 is 0.031.

To test hypotheses using the *P*-value method, follow the same steps as explained in Section 8–2. These steps are repeated here.

Step 1   State the hypotheses and identify the claim.

Step 2   Compute the test value.

Step 3   Find the *P*-value.

Step 4   Make the decision.

Step 5   Summarize the results.

This method is shown in Example 8–16.

Example 8–16   **Jogger's Oxygen Uptake**

A physician claims that joggers' maximal volume oxygen uptake is greater than the average of all adults. A sample of 15 joggers has a mean of 40.6 milliliters per kilogram (ml/kg) and a standard deviation of 6 ml/kg. If the average of all adults is 36.7 ml/kg, is there enough evidence to support the physician's claim at $\alpha = 0.05$?

Solution

Step 1   State the hypotheses and identify the claim.

$$H_0: \mu = 36.7 \qquad \text{and} \qquad H_1: \mu > 36.7 \text{ (claim)}$$

Step 2   Compute the test value. The test value is

$$t = \frac{\bar{X} - \mu}{s/\sqrt{n}} = \frac{40.6 - 36.7}{6/\sqrt{15}} = 2.517$$

Step 3   Find the *P*-value. Looking across the row with d.f. = 14 in Table F, you sees that 2.517 falls between 2.145 and 2.624, corresponding to $\alpha = 0.025$ and $\alpha = 0.01$ since this is a right-tailed test. Hence, *P*-value > 0.01 and *P*-value < 0.025 or 0.01 < *P*-value < 0.025. That is, the *P*-value is somewhere between 0.01 and 0.025. (The *P*-value obtained from a calculator is 0.012.)

Step 4   Reject the null hypothesis since *P*-value < 0.05 (that is, *P*-value < α).

Step 5   There is enough evidence to support the claim that the joggers' maximal volume oxygen uptake is greater than 36.7 ml/kg.

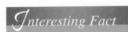

Interesting Fact

The area of Alaska contains $\frac{1}{6}$ of the total area of the United States.

Students sometimes have difficulty deciding whether to use the *z* test or *t* test. The rules are the same as those pertaining to confidence intervals.

1. If σ is known, use the *z* test. The variable must be normally distributed if $n < 30$.

2. If σ is unknown but $n \geq 30$, use the *t* test.

3. If σ is unknown and $n < 30$, use the *t* test. (The population must be approximately normally distributed.)

These rules are summarized in Figure 8–25.

Can Sunshine Relieve Pain?

A study conducted at the University of Pittsburgh showed that hospital patients in rooms with lots of sunlight required less pain medication the day after surgery and during their total stay in the hospital than patients who were in darker rooms.

Patients in the sunny rooms averaged 3.2 milligrams of pain reliever per hour for their total stay as opposed to 4.1 milligrams per hour for those in darker rooms. This study compared two groups of patients. Although no statistical tests were mentioned in the article, what statistical test do you think the researchers used to compare the groups?

Figure 8–25

Using the *z* or *t* Test

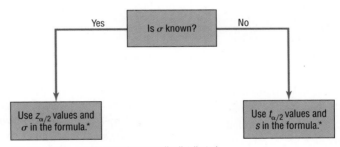

*If *n* < 30, the variable must be normally distributed.

Applying the Concepts 8–3

How Much Nicotine Is in Those Cigarettes?

A tobacco company claims that its best-selling cigarettes contain at most 40 mg of nicotine. This claim is tested at the 1% significance level by using the results of 15 randomly selected cigarettes. The mean was 42.6 mg and the standard deviation is 3.7 mg. Evidence suggests that nicotine is normally distributed. Information from a computer output of the hypothesis test is listed.

Sample mean = 42.6
Sample standard deviation = 3.7
Sample size = 15
Degrees of freedom = 14

P-value = 0.008
Significance level = 0.01
Test statistic *t* = 2.72155
Critical value *t* = 2.62610

1. What are the degrees of freedom?

2. Is this a *z* or *t* test?

3. Is this a comparison of one or two samples?

4. Is this a right-tailed, left-tailed, or two-tailed test?

5. From observing the *P*-value, what would you conclude?

6. By comparing the test statistic to the critical value, what would you conclude?

7. Is there a conflict in this output? Explain.

8. What has been proved in this study?

See page 465 for the answers.

Exercises 8–3

1. In what ways is the *t* distribution similar to the standard normal distribution? In what ways is the *t* distribution different from the standard normal distribution?

2. What are the degrees of freedom for the *t* test?

3. Find the critical value (or values) for the *t* test for each.

   a. $n = 10$, $\alpha = 0.05$, right-tailed
   b. $n = 18$, $\alpha = 0.10$, two-tailed
   c. $n = 6$, $\alpha = 0.01$, left-tailed
   d. $n = 9$, $\alpha = 0.025$, right-tailed
   e. $n = 15$, $\alpha = 0.05$, two-tailed
   f. $n = 23$, $\alpha = 0.005$, left-tailed
   g. $n = 28$, $\alpha = 0.01$, two-tailed
   h. $n = 17$, $\alpha = 0.02$, two-tailed

4. **(ans)** Using Table F, find the *P*-value interval for each test value.

   a. $t = 2.321$, $n = 15$, right-tailed
   b. $t = 1.945$, $n = 28$, two-tailed
   c. $t = -1.267$, $n = 8$, left-tailed
   d. $t = 1.562$, $n = 17$, two-tailed
   e. $t = 3.025$, $n = 24$, right-tailed
   f. $t = -1.145$, $n = 5$, left-tailed
   g. $t = 2.179$, $n = 13$, two-tailed
   h. $t = 0.665$, $n = 10$, right-tailed

For Exercises 5 through 18, perform each of the following steps.

   a. State the hypotheses and identify the claim.
   b. Find the critical value(s).
   c. Find the test value.
   d. Make the decision.
   e. Summarize the results.

Use the traditional method of hypothesis testing unless otherwise specified.

Assume that the population is approximately normally distributed.

5. **Veterinary Expenses of Cat Owners** According to the American Pet Products Manufacturers Association, cat owners spend an average of $179 annually in routine veterinary visits. A random sample of local cat owners revealed that 10 randomly selected owners spent an average of $205 with $s = \$26$. Is there a significant statistical difference at $\alpha = 0.01$?

Source: www.hsus.org/pets

6. **Park Acreage** A state executive claims that the average number of acres in western Pennsylvania state parks is less than 2000 acres. A random sample of five parks is selected, and the number of acres is shown. At $\alpha = 0.01$, is there enough evidence to support the claim?

| 959 | 1187 | 493 | 6249 | 541 |

Source: *Pittsburgh Tribune-Review.*

7. **State and Local Taxes** The U.S. average for state and local taxes for a family of four is $4172. A random sample of 20 families in a northeastern state indicates that they paid an annual amount of $4560 with a standard deviation of $1590. At $\alpha = 0.05$, is there sufficient evidence to conclude that they pay more than the national average of $4172?

Source: *New York Times Almanac.*

8. **Commute Time to Work** A survey of 15 large U.S. cities finds that the average commute time one way is 25.4 minutes. A chamber of commerce executive feels that the commute in his city is less and wants to publicize this. He randomly selects 25 commuters and finds the average is 22.1 minutes with a standard deviation of 5.3 minutes. At $\alpha = 0.10$, is he correct?

Source: *New York Times Almanac.*

9. **Heights of Tall Buildings** A researcher estimates that the average height of the buildings of 30 or more stories in a large city is at least 700 feet. A random sample of 10 buildings is selected, and the heights in feet are shown. At $\alpha = 0.025$, is there enough evidence to reject the claim?

| 485 | 511 | 841 | 725 | 615 |
| 520 | 535 | 635 | 616 | 582 |

Source: *Pittsburgh Tribune-Review.*

10. **Exercise and Reading Time Spent by Men** Men spend an average of 29 minutes per day on weekends and holidays exercising and playing sports. They spend an average of 23 minutes per day reading. A random sample of 25 men resulted in a mean of 35 minutes exercising with a standard deviation of 6.9 minutes and an average of 20.5 minutes reading with $s = 7.2$ minutes. At $\alpha = 0.05$ for both, is there sufficient evidence that these two results differ from the national means?

Source: *Time* magazine.

11. **Cost of College** The average undergraduate cost for tuition, fees, and room and board for two-year institutions last year was $13,252. The following year, a random sample of 20 two-year institutions had a mean of $15,560 and a standard deviation of $3500. Is there sufficient evidence at the $\alpha = 0.01$ level to conclude that the mean cost has increased?

Source: *New York Times Almanac.*

12. **Income of College Students' Parents** A large university reports that the mean salary of parents of an entering class is $91,600. To see how this compares to his university, a president surveys 28 randomly selected families and finds that their average income is $88,500. If the standard deviation is $10,000, can the president conclude that there is a difference? At $\alpha = 0.10$, is he correct?

Source: *Chronicle of Higher Education.*

13. **Cost of Making a Movie** During a recent year the average cost of making a movie was $54.8 million. This year, a random sample of 15 recent action movies had an average production cost of $62.3 million with a variance of $90.25 million. At the 0.05 level of significance, can it be concluded that it costs more than average to produce an action movie?

Source: *New York Times Almanac.*

14. **Chocolate Chip Cookie Calories** The average 1-ounce chocolate chip cookie contains 110 calories. A random sample of 15 different brands of 1-ounce chocolate chip cookies resulted in the following calorie amounts. At the $\alpha = 0.01$ level, is there sufficient evidence that the average calorie content is greater than 110 calories?

100	125	150	160	185	125	155	145	160
100	150	140	135	120	110			

Source: *The Doctor's Pocket Calorie, Fat, and Carbohydrate Counter.*

15. **Earnings of Financial Specialists** Average weekly earnings for those working in financial activities is $623. A group of employees working for a large national accounting firm felt that they earned more. The mean weekly earnings for a random sample of 21 employees showed an average weekly earning of $650 with a standard deviation of $72. At $\alpha = 0.01$, can it be concluded that the employees are correct?

Source: *New York Times Almanac.*

16. **Water Consumption** The *Old Farmer's Almanac* stated that the average consumption of water per person per day was 123 gallons. To test the hypothesis that this figure may no longer be true, a researcher randomly selected 16 people and found that they used on average 119 gallons per day and $s = 5.3$. At $\alpha = 0.05$, is there enough evidence to say that the *Old Farmer's Almanac* figure might no longer be correct? Use the *P*-value method.

17. **Doctor Visits** A report by the Gallup Poll stated that on average a woman visits her physician 5.8 times a year. A researcher randomly selects 20 women and obtained these data.

3	2	1	3	7	2	9	4	6	6
8	0	5	6	4	2	1	3	4	1

At $\alpha = 0.05$ can it be concluded that the average is still 5.8 visits per year? Use the *P*-value method.

18. **Number of Jobs** The U.S. Bureau of Labor and Statistics reported that a person between the ages of 18 and 34 has had an average of 9.2 jobs. To see if this average is correct, a researcher selected a sample of 8 workers between the ages of 18 and 34 and asked how many different places they had worked. The results were as follows:

8	12	15	6	1	9	13	2

At $\alpha = 0.05$ can it be concluded that the mean is 9.2? Use the *P*-value method. Give one reason why the respondents might not have given the exact number of jobs that they have worked.

19. **Teaching Assistants' Stipends** A random sample of stipends of teaching assistants in economics is listed. Is there sufficient evidence at the $\alpha = 0.05$ level to conclude that the average stipend differs from $15,000? The stipends listed (in dollars) are for the academic year.

14,000	18,000	12,000	14,356	13,185
13,419	14,000	11,981	17,604	12,283
16,338	15,000			

Source: *Chronicle of Higher Education.*

20. **Average Family Size** The average family size was reported as 3.18. A random sample of families in a particular school district resulted in the following family sizes:

5	4	5	4	4	3	6	4	3	3	5
6	3	3	2	7	4	5	2	2	2	3
5	2									

At $\alpha = 0.05$, does the average family size differ from the national average?

Source: *New York Times Almanac.*

Technology *Step by Step*

MINITAB
Step by Step

Hypothesis Test for the Mean and the *t* Distribution

This relates to Example 8–13. Test the claim that the average salary for substitute teachers is less than $60 per day.

1. Enter the data into **C1** of a MINITAB worksheet. Do not use the dollar sign. Name the column **Salary.**
2. Select **Stat>Basic Statistics>1-Sample t.**
3. Choose C1 Salary as the variable.
4. Click inside the text box for Test mean, and enter the hypothesized value of **60.**
5. Click [Options].
6. The Alternative should be less than.
7. Click [OK] twice.

In the session window, the *P*-value for the test is 0.276.

One-Sample T: Salary
```
Test of mu = 60 vs < 60
                                        90% Upper
Variable   N     Mean    StDev   SE Mean   Bound      T       P
Salary     8   58.8750   5.0832   1.7972   61.4179   -0.63   0.276
```
We cannot reject H_0. There is not enough evidence in the sample to conclude the mean salary is less than $60.

TI-83 Plus or TI-84 Plus
Step by Step

Hypothesis Test for the Mean and the *t* Distribution (Data)

1. Enter the data values into L_1.
2. Press **STAT** and move the cursor to TESTS.
3. Press **2** for T-Test.
4. Move the cursor to Data and press **ENTER.**
5. Type in the appropriate values.
6. Move the cursor to the appropriate alternative hypothesis and press **ENTER.**
7. Move the cursor to Calculate and press **ENTER.**

Hypothesis Test for the Mean and the *t* Distribution (Statistics)

1. Press **STAT** and move the cursor to TESTS.
2. Press **2** for T-Test.

3. Move the cursor to Stats and press **ENTER**.
4. Type in the appropriate values.
5. Move the cursor to the appropriate alternative hypothesis and press **ENTER**.
6. Move the cursor to Calculate and press **ENTER**.

Excel
Step by Step

Hypothesis Test for the Mean: *t* Test

Excel does not have a procedure to conduct a hypothesis test for the mean. However, you may conduct the test of the mean using the MegaStat Add-in available on your CD. If you have not installed this add-in, do so, following the instructions from the Chapter 1 Excel Step by Step.

Example XL8–2

This example relates to Example 8–13 from the text. At the 10% significance level, test the claim that $\mu < 60$. The MegaStat *t* test uses the *P*-value method. Therefore, it is not necessary to enter a significance level.

1. Enter the data into column A of a new worksheet.
2. From the toolbar, select Add-Ins, **MegaStat>Hypothesis Tests>Mean vs. Hypothesized Value.** *Note:* You may need to open MegaStat from the MegaStat.xls file on your computer's hard drive.
3. Select data input and type **A1:A8** as the Input Range.
4. Type **60** for the Hypothesized mean and select the "less than" Alternative.
5. Select *t* test and click [OK].

The result of the procedure is shown next.

Hypothesis Test: Mean vs. Hypothesized Value

```
60.000  Hypothesized value
58.875  Mean data
 5.083  Standard deviation
 1.797  Standard error
     8  n
     7  d.f.

-0.63   t
0.2756  P-value (one-tailed, lower)
```

8–4   *z* Test for a Proportion

Objective 7

Test proportions, using the *z* test.

Many hypothesis-testing situations involve proportions. Recall from Chapter 7 that a *proportion* is the same as a percentage of the population.

These data were obtained from *The Book of Odds* by Michael D. Shook and Robert L. Shook (New York: Penguin Putnam, Inc.):

- 59% of consumers purchase gifts for their fathers.
- 85% of people over 21 said they have entered a sweepstakes.
- 51% of Americans buy generic products.
- 35% of Americans go out for dinner once a week.

A hypothesis test involving a population proportion can be considered as a binomial experiment when there are only two outcomes and the probability of a success does not change from trial to trial. Recall from Section 5–3 that the mean is $\mu = np$ and the standard deviation is $\sigma = \sqrt{npq}$ for the binomial distribution.

Since a normal distribution can be used to approximate the binomial distribution when $np \geq 5$ and $nq \geq 5$, the standard normal distribution can be used to test hypotheses for proportions.

Formula for the z Test for Proportions

$$z = \frac{\hat{p} - p}{\sqrt{pq/n}}$$

where

$$\hat{p} = \frac{X}{n} \quad \text{(sample proportion)}$$

p = population proportion
n = sample size

The formula is derived from the normal approximation to the binomial and follows the general formula

$$\text{Test value} = \frac{(\text{observed value}) - (\text{expected value})}{\text{standard error}}$$

We obtain $\hat{p}$ from the sample (i.e., observed value), p is the expected value (i.e., hypothesized population proportion), and $\sqrt{pq/n}$ is the standard error.

The formula $z = \frac{\hat{p} - p}{\sqrt{pq/n}}$ can be derived from the formula $z = \frac{X - \mu}{\sigma}$ by substituting $\mu = np$ and $\sigma = \sqrt{npq}$ and then dividing both numerator and denominator by n. Some algebra is used. See Exercise 23 in this section.

The steps for hypothesis testing are the same as those shown in Section 8–3. Table E is used to find critical values and *P*-values.

Examples 8–17 to 8–19 show the traditional method of hypothesis testing. Example 8–20 shows the *P*-value method.

Sometimes it is necessary to find $\hat{p}$, as shown in Examples 8–17, 8–19, and 8–20, and sometimes $\hat{p}$ is given in the exercise. See Example 8–18.

Example 8–17 | **People Who Are Trying to Avoid Trans Fats**

A dietitian claims that 60% of people are trying to avoid trans fats in their diets. She randomly selected 200 people and found that 128 people stated that they were trying to avoid trans fats in their diets. At $\alpha = 0.05$, is there enough evidence to reject the dietitian's claim?

Source: Based on a survey by the Gallup Poll.

Solution

Step 1 State the hypothesis and identify the claim.

H_0: $p = 0.60$ (claim)   and H_1: $p \neq 0.60$

Step 2 Find the critical values. Since $\alpha = 0.05$ and the test value is two-tailed, the critical values are ± 1.96.

Step 3 Compute the test value. First, it is necessary to find $\hat{p}$.

$$\hat{p} = \frac{X}{n} = \frac{128}{200} = 64 \qquad p = 0.60 \qquad 1 - 0.60 = 0.40$$

Substitute in the formula.

$$Z = \frac{\hat{p} - p}{\sqrt{pq/n}} = \frac{0.64 - 0.60}{\sqrt{(0.60)(0.40)/200}} = 1.15$$

Step 4 Make the decision. Do not reject the null hypothesis since the test value falls outside the critical region, as shown in Figure 8–26.

Figure 8–26

Critical and Test Values for Example 8–17

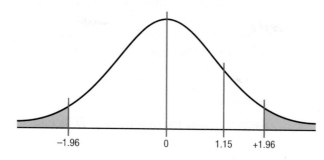

Step 5 Summarize the results. There is not enough evidence to reject the claim that 60% of people are trying to avoid trans fats in their diets.

Example 8–18

Survey on Call-Waiting Service

A telephone company representative estimates that 40% of its customers have call-waiting service. To test this hypothesis, she selected a sample of 100 customers and found that 37% had call waiting. At $\alpha = 0.01$, is there enough evidence to reject the claim?

Solution

Step 1 State the hypotheses and identify the claim.

$$H_0: p = 0.40 \text{ (claim)} \qquad \text{and} \qquad H_1: p \neq 0.40$$

Step 2 Find the critical value(s). Since $\alpha = 0.01$ and this test is two-tailed, the critical values are ± 2.58.

Step 3 Compute the test value. It is not necessary to find $\hat{p}$ since it is given in the exercise; $\hat{p} = 0.37$. Substitute in the formula and solve.

$$p = 0.40 \qquad \text{and} \qquad q = 1 - 0.40 = 0.60$$

$$z = \frac{\hat{p} - p}{\sqrt{pq/n}} = \frac{0.37 - 0.40}{\sqrt{(0.40)(0.60)/100}} = -0.612$$

Step 4 Make the decision. Do not reject the null hypothesis, since the test value falls in the noncritical region, as shown in Figure 8–27.

Figure 8–27

Critical and Test Values for Example 8–18

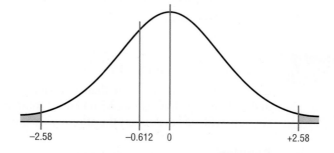

Step 5 Summarize the results. There is not enough evidence to reject the claim that 40% of the telephone company's customers have call waiting.

Example 8–19

Replacing $1 Bills with $1 Coins

A statistician read that at least 77% of the population oppose replacing $1 bills with $1 coins. To see if this claim is valid, the statistician selected a sample of 80 people and found that 55 were opposed to replacing the $1 bills. At $\alpha = 0.01$, test the claim that at least 77% of the population are opposed to the change.

Source: *USA TODAY.*

Solution

Step 1 State the hypotheses and identify the claim.

$$H_0: p = 0.77 \text{ (claim)} \qquad \text{and} \qquad H_1: p < 0.77$$

Step 2 Find the critical value(s). Since $\alpha = 0.01$ and the test is left-tailed, the critical value is -2.33.

Step 3 Compute the test value.

$$\hat{p} = \frac{X}{n} = \frac{55}{80} = 0.6875$$

$$p = 0.77 \qquad \text{and} \qquad q = 1 - 0.77 = 0.23$$

$$z = \frac{\hat{p} - p}{\sqrt{pq/n}} = \frac{0.6875 - 0.77}{\sqrt{(0.77)(0.23)/80}} = -1.75$$

Step 4 Do not reject the null hypothesis, since the test value does not fall in the critical region, as shown in Figure 8–28.

Figure 8–28

Critical and Test Values for Example 8–19

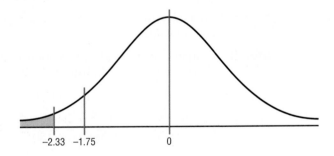

Step 5 There is not enough evidence to reject the claim that at least 77% of the population oppose replacing $1 bills with $1 coins.

Example 8–20

Attorney Advertisements

An attorney claims that more than 25% of all lawyers advertise. A sample of 200 lawyers in a certain city showed that 63 had used some form of advertising. At $\alpha = 0.05$, is there enough evidence to support the attorney's claim? Use the *P*-value method.

Solution

Step 1 State the hypotheses and identify the claim.

$$H_0: p = 0.25 \qquad \text{and} \qquad H_1: p > 0.25 \text{ (claim)}$$

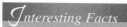

Step 2 Compute the test value.

$$\hat{p} = \frac{X}{n} = \frac{63}{200} = 0.315$$

$$p = 0.25 \qquad \text{and} \qquad q = 1 - 0.25 = 0.75$$

$$z = \frac{\hat{p} - p}{\sqrt{pq/n}} = \frac{0.315 - 0.25}{\sqrt{(0.25)(0.75)/200}} = 2.12$$

Step 3 Find the *P*-value. The area under the curve for $z = 2.12$ is 0.9830. Subtracting the area from 1.0000, you get $1.0000 - 0.9830 = 0.0170$. The *P*-value is 0.0170.

Step 4 Reject the null hypothesis, since $0.0170 < 0.05$ (that is, *P*-value < 0.05). See Figure 8–29.

Figure 8–29

P-Value and α Value for Example 8–20

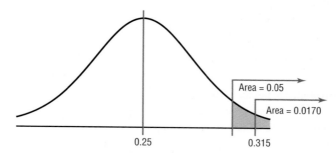

Area = 0.05

Area = 0.0170

0.25   0.315

Step 5 There is enough evidence to support the attorney's claim that more than 25% of the lawyers use some form of advertising.

Applying the Concepts 8–4

Quitting Smoking

Assume you are part of a research team that compares products designed to help people quit smoking. Condor Consumer Products Company would like more specific details about the study to be made available to the scientific community. Review the following and then answer the questions about how you would have conducted the study.

New StopSmoke

No method has been proved more effective. StopSmoke provides significant advantages over all other methods. StopSmoke is simpler to use, and it requires no weaning. StopSmoke is also significantly less expensive than the leading brands. StopSmoke's superiority has been proved in two independent studies.

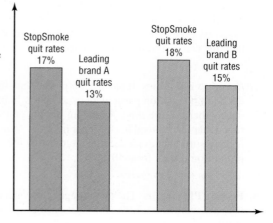

1. What were the statistical hypotheses?
2. What were the null hypotheses?
3. What were the alternative hypotheses?
4. Were any statistical tests run?
5. Were one- or two-tailed tests run?
6. What were the levels of significance?

7. If a type I error was committed, explain what it would have been.

8. If a type II error was committed, explain what it would have been.

9. What did the studies prove?

10. Two statements are made about significance. One states that StopSmoke provides significant advantages, and the other states that StopSmoke is significantly less expensive than other leading brands. Are they referring to statistical significance? What other type of significance is there?

See page 465 for the answers.

Exercises 8–4

1. Give three examples of proportions.

2. Why is a proportion considered a binomial variable?

3. When you are testing hypotheses by using proportions, what are the necessary requirements?

4. What are the mean and the standard deviation of a proportion?

For Exercises 5 through 15, perform each of the following steps.

a. State the hypotheses and identify the claim.

b. Find the critical value(s).

c. Compute the test value.

d. Make the decision.

e. Summarize the results.

Use the traditional method of hypothesis testing unless otherwise specified.

5. **Home Ownership** A recent survey found that 68.6% of the population own their homes. In a random sample of 150 heads of households, 92 responded that they owned their homes. At the $\alpha = 0.01$ level of significance, does that suggest a difference from the national proportion?

Source: *World Almanac.*

6. **Stocks and Mutual Fund Ownership** It has been found that 50.3% of U.S. households own stocks and mutual funds. A random sample of 300 heads of households indicated that 171 owned some type of stock. At what level of significance would you conclude that this was a significant difference?

Source: www.census.gov

7. **Computer Hobbies** It has been reported that 40% of the adult population participate in computer hobbies during their leisure time. A random sample of 180 adults found that 65 engaged in computer hobbies. At $\alpha = 0.01$, is there sufficient evidence to conclude that the proportion differs from 40%?

Source: *New York Times Almanac.*

8. **Female Physicians** The percentage of physicians who are women is 27.9%. In a survey of physicians employed by a large university health system, 45 of

120 randomly selected physicians were women. Is there sufficient evidence at the 0.05 level of significance to conclude that the proportion of women physicians at the university health system exceeds 27.9%?

Source: *New York Times Almanac.*

9. **Answering Machine Ownership** It has been reported in an almanac that 78% of Americans own an answering machine. A random sample of 143 college professors at small liberal arts schools revealed that 100 owned an answering machine. At $\alpha = 0.05$, test the claim that the percentage is the same as stated in the almanac.

Source: *World Almanac.*

10. **Undergraduate Enrollment** It has been found that 85.6% of all enrolled college and university students in the United States are undergraduates. A random sample of 500 enrolled college students in a particular state revealed that 420 of them were undergraduates. Is there sufficient evidence to conclude that the proportion differs from the national percentage? Use $\alpha = 0.05$.

Source: *Time Almanac.*

11. **Fatal Accidents** The American Automobile Association (AAA) claims that 54% of fatal car/truck accidents are caused by driver error. A researcher studies 30 randomly selected accidents and finds that 14 were caused by driver error. Using $\alpha = 0.05$, can the AAA claim be refuted?

Source: AAA/CNN.

12. **Exercise to Reduce Stress** A survey by *Men's Health* magazine stated that 14% of men said they used exercise to reduce stress. Use $\alpha = 0.10$. A random sample of 100 men was selected, and 10 said that they used exercise to relieve stress. Use the *P*-value method to test the claim. Could the results be generalized to all adult Americans?

13. **After-School Snacks** In the *Journal of the American Dietetic Association,* it was reported that 54% of kids said that they had a snack after school. A random sample of 60 kids was selected, and 36 said that they had a snack after school. Use $\alpha = 0.01$ and the *P*-value method to test the claim. On the basis of the results, should parents be concerned about their children eating a healthy snack?

14. Natural Gas Heat The Energy Information Administration reported that 51.7% of homes in the United States were heated by natural gas. A random sample of 200 homes found that 115 were heated by natural gas. Does the evidence support the claim, or has the percentage changed? Use $\alpha = 0.05$ and the *P*-value method. What could be different if the sample were taken in a different geographic area?

15. Youth Smoking Researchers suspect that 18% of all high school students smoke at least one pack of cigarettes a day. At Wilson High School, with an enrollment of 300 students, a study found that 50 students smoked at least one pack of cigarettes a day. At $\alpha = 0.05$, test the claim that 18% of all high school students smoke at least one pack of cigarettes a day. Use the *P*-value method.

16. Credit Card Usage For a certain year a study reports that the percentage of college students using credit cards was 83%. A college dean of student services feels that this is too high for her university, so she randomly selects 50 students and finds that 40 of them use credit cards. At $\alpha = 0.04$, is she correct about her university?

Source: *USA TODAY.*

17. Borrowing Library Books For Americans using library services, the American Library Association (ALA) claims that 67% borrow books. A library director feels that this is not true so he randomly selects 100 borrowers and finds that 82 borrowed books. Can he show that the ALA claim is incorrect? Use $\alpha = 0.05$.

Source: American Library Association; *USA TODAY.*

18. Doctoral Students' Salaries Nationally, at least 60% of Ph.D. students have paid assistantships. A college dean feels that this is not true in his state, so he randomly selects 50 Ph.D. students and finds that 26 have assistantships. At $\alpha = 0.05$, is the dean correct?

Source: U.S. Department of Education, *Chronicle of Higher Education.*

19. Football Injuries A report by the NCAA states that 57.6% of football injuries occur during practices. A head trainer claims that this is too high for his conference, so he randomly selects 36 injuries and finds that 17 occurred during practices. Is his claim correct, at $\alpha = 0.05$?

Source: *NCAA Sports Medicine Handbook.*

20. Foreign Languages Spoken in Homes Approximately 19.4% of the U.S. population 5 years old and older speaks a language other than English at home. In a large metropolitan area it was found that out of 400 randomly selected residents over 5 years of age, 94 spoke a language other than English at home. Is there sufficient evidence to conclude that the proportion is higher than the national proportion? You choose the level of significance.

Source: www.census.gov

Extending the Concepts

When *np* or *nq* is not 5 or more, the binomial table (Table B in Appendix C) must be used to find critical values in hypothesis tests involving proportions.

21. Coin Tossing A coin is tossed 9 times and 3 heads appear. Can you conclude that the coin is not balanced? Use $\alpha = 0.10$. [*Hint:* Use the binomial table and find $2P(X \le 3)$ with $p = 0.5$ and $n = 9$.]

22. First-Class Airline Passengers In the past, 20% of all airline passengers flew first class. In a sample of 15 passengers, 5 flew first class. At $\alpha = 0.10$, can you conclude that the proportions have changed?

23. Show that $z = \dfrac{\hat{p} - p}{\sqrt{pq/n}}$ can be derived from $z = \dfrac{X - \mu}{\sigma}$ by substituting $\mu = np$ and $\sigma = \sqrt{npq}$ and dividing both numerator and denominator by *n*.

Technology *Step by Step*

MINITAB
Step by Step

Hypothesis Test for One Proportion and the *z* Distribution

MINITAB will calculate the test statistic and *P*-value for a test of a proportion, given the statistics from a sample or given the raw data. For Example 8–18, test the claim that 40% of all telephone customers have call-waiting service.

1. Select **Stat>Basic Statistics>1 Proportion.**
2. Click on the button for Summarized data. There are no data to enter in the worksheet.
3. Click in the box for Number of trials and enter **100.**
4. In the Number of events box enter **37.**
5. Click on [Options].
6. Type the complement of α, **99** for the confidence level.

7. Very important! Check the box for Use test and interval based on normal distribution.

8. Click [OK] twice.

The results for the confidence interval will be displayed in the session window. Since the *P*-value of 0.540 is greater than $\alpha = 0.01$, the null hypothesis cannot be rejected.

Test and CI for One Proportion

```
Test of p = 0.4 vs p not = 0.4
Sample   X    N   Sample p          99% CI          Z-Value  P-Value
1       37  100   0.370000  (0.245638, 0.494362)    -0.61    0.540
```

There is not enough evidence to conclude that the proportion is different from 40%.

TI-83 Plus or TI-84 Plus
Step by Step

Hypothesis Test for the Proportion

1. Press **STAT** and move the cursor to TESTS.
2. Press **5** for 1-PropZTest.
3. Type in the appropriate values.
4. Move the cursor to the appropriate alternative hypothesis and press **ENTER.**
5. Move the cursor to Calculate and press **ENTER.**

Example TI8–3

This pertains to Example 8–18 in the text. Test the claim that $p = 40\%$, given $n = 100$ and $\hat{p} = 0.37$.

   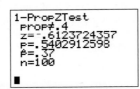

The test statistic is $z = -0.6123724357$, and the *P*-value is 0.5402912598.

Excel
Step by Step

Hypothesis Test for the Proportion: *z* Test

Excel does not have a procedure to conduct a hypothesis test for the population proportion. However, you may conduct the test of the proportion, using the MegaStat Add-in available on your CD. If you have not installed this add-in, do so, following the instructions from the Chapter 1 Excel Step by Step.

Example XL8–4

This example relates to Example 8–18 from the text. At the 1% significance level, test the claim that $p = 0.40$. The MegaStat test of the population proportion uses the *P*-value method. Therefore, it is not necessary to enter a significance level.

1. From the toolbar, select Add-Ins, **MegaStat>Hypothesis Tests>Proportion vs. Hypothesized Value.** *Note:* You may need to open MegaStat from the MegaStat.xls file on your computer's hard drive.

2. Type **0.37** for the Observed proportion, *p*.

3. Type **0.40** for the Hypothesized proportion, *p*.

4. Type **100** for the sample size, *n*.

5. Select the "not equal" Alternative.

6. Click [OK].

The result of the procedure is shown next.

Hypothesis Test for Proportion vs. Hypothesized Value

```
   Observed      Hypothesized
      0.37           0.4     p (as decimal)
    37/100        40/100     p (as fraction)
        37.          40.     X
       100           100     n

             0.049           standard error
            −0.61            z
             0.5403          p-value (two-tailed)
```

8–5 χ^2 **Test for a Variance or Standard Deviation**

Objective 8

Test variances or standard deviations, using the chi-square test.

In Chapter 7, the chi-square distribution was used to construct a confidence interval for a single variance or standard deviation. This distribution is also used to test a claim about a single variance or standard deviation.

To find the area under the chi-square distribution, use Table G in Appendix C. There are three cases to consider:

1. Finding the chi-square critical value for a specific α when the hypothesis test is right-tailed.

2. Finding the chi-square critical value for a specific α when the hypothesis test is left-tailed.

3. Finding the chi-square critical values for a specific α when the hypothesis test is two-tailed.

Example 8–21

Find the critical chi-square value for 15 degrees of freedom when $\alpha = 0.05$ and the test is right-tailed.

Solution

The distribution is shown in Figure 8–30.

Figure 8–30

Chi-Square Distribution for Example 8–21

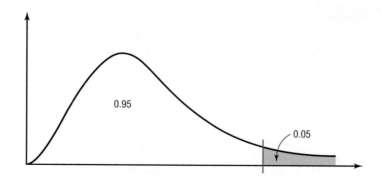

Find the α value at the top of Table G, and find the corresponding degrees of freedom in the left column. The critical value is located where the two columns meet—in this case, 24.996. See Figure 8–31.

Figure 8–31

Locating the Critical Value in Table G for Example 8–21

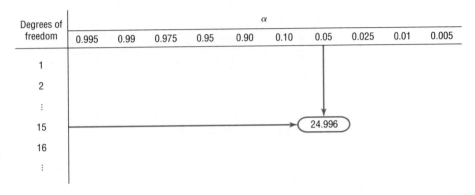

Example 8–22

Find the critical chi-square value for 10 degrees of freedom when $\alpha = 0.05$ and the test is left-tailed.

Solution

This distribution is shown in Figure 8–32.

Figure 8–32

Chi-Square Distribution for Example 8–22

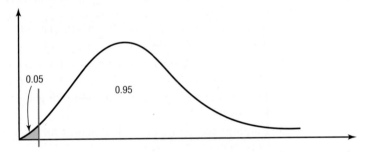

When the test is left-tailed, the α value must be subtracted from 1, that is, $1 - 0.05 = 0.95$. The left side of the table is used, because the chi-square table gives the area to the right of the critical value, and the chi-square statistic cannot be negative. The table is set up so that it gives the values for the area to the right of the critical value. In this case, 95% of the area will be to the right of the value.

For 0.95 and 10 degrees of freedom, the critical value is 3.940. See Figure 8–33.

Figure 8–33

Locating the Critical Value in Table G for Example 8–22

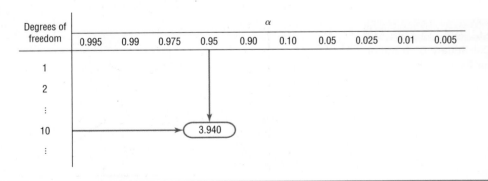

Example 8–23

Find the critical chi-square values for 22 degrees of freedom when $\alpha = 0.05$ and a two-tailed test is conducted.

Solution

When a two-tailed test is conducted, the area must be split, as shown in Figure 8–34. Note that the area to the right of the larger value is 0.025 (0.05/2 or $\alpha/2$), and the area to the right of the smaller value is 0.975 (1.00 − 0.05/2 or 1 − $\alpha/2$).

Figure 8–34

Chi-Square Distribution for Example 8–23

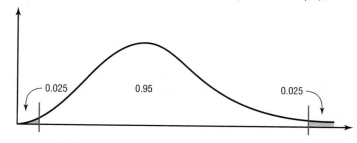

Remember that chi-square values cannot be negative. Hence, you must use α values in the table of 0.025 and 0.975. With 22 degrees of freedom, the critical values are 36.781 and 10.982, respectively.

After the degrees of freedom reach 30, Table G gives values only for multiples of 10 (40, 50, 60, etc.). When the exact degrees of freedom sought are not specified in the table, the closest smaller value should be used. For example, if the given degrees of freedom are 36, use the table value for 30 degrees of freedom. This guideline keeps the type I error equal to or below the α value.

When you are testing a claim about a single variance using the **chi-square test,** there are three possible test situations: right-tailed test, left-tailed test, and two-tailed test.

If a researcher believes the variance of a population to be greater than some specific value, say, 225, then the researcher states the hypotheses as

$$H_0: \sigma^2 = 225 \qquad \text{and} \qquad H_1: \sigma^2 > 225$$

and conducts a right-tailed test.

If the researcher believes the variance of a population to be less than 225, then the researcher states the hypotheses as

$$H_0: \sigma^2 = 225 \qquad \text{and} \qquad H_1: \sigma^2 < 225$$

and conducts a left-tailed test.

Finally, if a researcher does not wish to specify a direction, she or he states the hypotheses as

$$H_0: \sigma^2 = 225 \qquad \text{and} \qquad H_1: \sigma^2 \neq 225$$

and conducts a two-tailed test.

Formula for the Chi-Square Test for a Single Variance

$$\chi^2 = \frac{(n-1)s^2}{\sigma^2}$$

with degrees of freedom equal to $n - 1$ and where

n = sample size
s^2 = sample variance
σ^2 = population variance

You might ask, Why is it important to test variances? There are several reasons. First, in any situation where consistency is required, such as in manufacturing, you would like to have the smallest variation possible in the products. For example, when bolts are manufactured, the variation in diameters due to the process must be kept to a minimum, or the nuts will not fit them properly. In education, consistency is required on a test. That is, if the same students take the same test several times, they should get approximately the same grades, and the variance of each of the student's grades should be small. On the other hand, if the test is to be used to judge learning, the overall standard deviation of all the grades should be large so that you can differentiate those who have learned the subject from those who have not learned it.

Three assumptions are made for the chi-square test, as outlined here.

Unusual Stat

About 20% of cats owned in the United States are overweight.

Assumptions for the Chi-Square Test for a Single Variance

1. The sample must be randomly selected from the population.
2. The population must be normally distributed for the variable under study.
3. The observations must be independent of one another.

The traditional method for hypothesis testing follows the same five steps listed earlier. They are repeated here.

Step 1 State the hypotheses and identify the claim.

Step 2 Find the critical value(s).

Step 3 Compute the test value.

Step 4 Make the decision.

Step 5 Summarize the results.

Examples 8–24 through 8–26 illustrate the traditional hypothesis-testing procedure for variances.

Example 8–24

Variation of Test Scores

An instructor wishes to see whether the variation in scores of the 23 students in her class is less than the variance of the population. The variance of the class is 198. Is there enough evidence to support the claim that the variation of the students is less than the population variance ($\sigma^2 = 225$) at $\alpha = 0.05$? Assume that the scores are normally distributed.

Solution

Step 1 State the hypotheses and identify the claim.

$$H_0: \sigma^2 = 225 \qquad \text{and} \qquad H_1: \sigma^2 < 225 \text{ (claim)}$$

Step 2 Find the critical value. Since this test is left-tailed and $\alpha = 0.05$, use the value $1 - 0.05 = 0.95$. The degrees of freedom are $n - 1 = 23 - 1 = 22$. Hence, the critical value is 12.338. Note that the critical region is on the left, as shown in Figure 8–35.

Figure 8–35

Critical Value for
Example 8–24

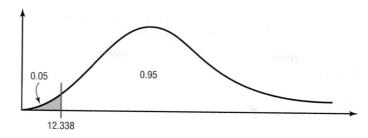

Step 3   Compute the test value.

$$\chi^2 = \frac{(n-1)s^2}{\sigma^2} = \frac{(23-1)(198)}{225} = 19.36$$

Step 4   Make the decision. Since the test value 19.36 falls in the noncritical region, as shown in Figure 8–36, the decision is to not reject the null hypothesis.

Figure 8–36

Critical and Test Values
for Example 8–24

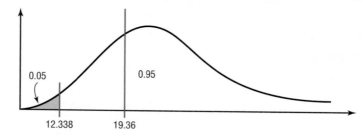

Step 5   Summarize the results. There is not enough evidence to support the claim that the variation in test scores of the instructor's students is less than the variation in scores of the population.

Example 8–25

Outpatient Surgery

   A hospital administrator believes that the standard deviation of the number of people using outpatient surgery per day is greater than 8. A random sample of 15 days is selected. The data are shown. At $\alpha = 0.10$, is there enough evidence to support the administrator's claim? Assume the variable is normally distributed.

25	30	5	15	18
42	16	9	10	12
12	38	8	14	27

Solution

Step 1   State the hypotheses and identify the claim.

$H_0: \sigma^2 = 64$ and $H_1: \sigma^2 > 64$ (claim)

Since the standard deviation is given, it should be squared to get the variance.

Step 2   Find the critical value. Since this test is right-tailed with d.f. of $15 - 1 = 14$ and $\alpha = 0.10$, the critical value is 21.064.

Step 3   Compute the test value. Since raw data are given, the standard deviation of the sample must be found by using the formula in Chapter 3 or your calculator. It is $s = 11.2$.

$$\chi^2 = \frac{(n-1)s^2}{\sigma^2} = \frac{(15-1)(11.2)^2}{64} = 27.44$$

Step 4   Make the decision. The decision is to reject the null hypothesis since the test value, 27.44, is greater than the critical value, 21.064, and falls in the critical region. See Figure 8–37.

Figure 8–37

Critical and Test Value for Example 8–25

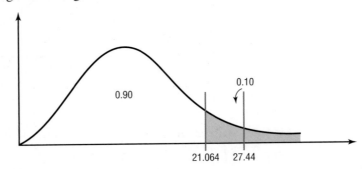

Step 5   Summarize the results. There is enough evidence to support the claim that the standard deviation is greater than 8.

Example 8–26

Nicotine Content of Cigarettes

A cigarette manufacturer wishes to test the claim that the variance of the nicotine content of its cigarettes is 0.644. Nicotine content is measured in milligrams, and assume that it is normally distributed. A sample of 20 cigarettes has a standard deviation of 1.00 milligram. At $\alpha = 0.05$, is there enough evidence to reject the manufacturer's claim?

Solution

Step 1   State the hypotheses and identify the claim.

$$H_0: \sigma^2 = 0.644 \text{ (claim)} \qquad \text{and} \qquad H_1: \sigma^2 \neq 0.644$$

Step 2   Find the critical values. Since this test is a two-tailed test at $\alpha = 0.05$, the critical values for 0.025 and 0.975 must be found. The degrees of freedom are 19; hence, the critical values are 32.852 and 8.907, respectively. The critical or rejection regions are shown in Figure 8–38.

Figure 8–38

Critical Values for Example 8–26

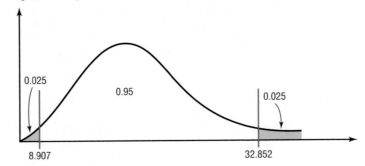

Step 3   Compute the test value.

$$\chi^2 = \frac{(n-1)s^2}{\sigma^2} = \frac{(20-1)(1.0)^2}{0.644} = 29.5$$

Since the standard deviation s is given in the problem, it must be squared for the formula.

Step 4   Make the decision. Do not reject the null hypothesis, since the test value falls between the critical values ($8.907 < 29.5 < 32.852$) and in the noncritical region, as shown in Figure 8–39.

Figure 8–39

Critical and Test Values
for Example 8–26

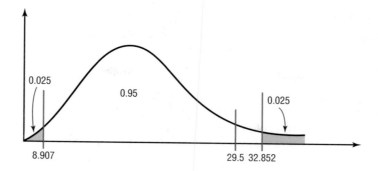

Step 5 Summarize the results. There is not enough evidence to reject the manufacturer's claim that the variance of the nicotine content of the cigarettes is equal to 0.644.

Approximate *P*-values for the chi-square test can be found by using Table G in Appendix C. The procedure is somewhat more complicated than the previous procedures for finding *P*-values for the *z* and *t* tests since the chi-square distribution is not exactly symmetric and χ^2 values cannot be negative. As we did for the *t* test, we will determine an *interval* for the *P*-value based on the table. Examples 8–27 through 8–29 show the procedure.

Example 8–27

Find the *P*-value when $\chi^2 = 19.274$, $n = 8$, and the test is right-tailed.

Solution

To get the *P*-value, look across the row with d.f. $= 7$ in Table G and find the two values that 19.274 falls between. They are 18.475 and 20.278. Look up to the top row and find the α values corresponding to 18.475 and 20.278. They are 0.01 and 0.005, respectively. See Figure 8–40. Hence the *P*-value is contained in the interval $0.005 < P\text{-value} < 0.01$. (The *P*-value obtained from a calculator is 0.007.)

Figure 8–40

P-Value Interval for
Example 8–27

Degrees of freedom	α									
	0.995	0.99	0.975	0.95	0.90	0.10	0.05	0.025	0.01	0.005
1	—	—	0.001	0.004	0.016	2.706	3.841	5.024	6.635	7.879
2	0.010	0.020	0.051	0.103	0.211	4.605	5.991	7.378	9.210	10.597
3	0.072	0.115	0.216	0.352	0.584	6.251	7.815	9.348	11.345	12.838
4	0.207	0.297	0.484	0.711	1.064	7.779	9.488	11.143	13.277	14.860
5	0.412	0.554	0.831	1.145	1.610	9.236	11.071	12.833	15.086	16.750
6	0.676	0.872	1.237	1.635	2.204	10.645	12.592	14.449	16.812	18.548
7	0.989	1.239	1.690	2.167	2.833	12.017	11.067	16.013	18.475	20.278
8	1.344	1.646	2.180	2.733	3.490	13.362	15.507	17.535	20.090	21.955
9	1.735	2.088	2.700	3.325	4.168	14.684	16.919	19.023	21.666	23.589
10	2.156	2.558	3.247	3.940	4.865	15.987	18.307	20.483	23.209	25.188
⋮	⋮	⋮	⋮	⋮	⋮	⋮	⋮	⋮	⋮	⋮
100	67.328	70.065	74.222	77.929	82.358	118.498	124.342	129.561	135.807	140.169

*19.274 falls between 18.475 and 20.278

Example 8–28

Find the P-value when $\chi^2 = 3.823$, $n = 13$, and the test is left-tailed.

Solution

To get the P-value, look across the row with d.f. $= 12$ and find the two values that 3.823 falls between. They are 3.571 and 4.404. Look up to the top row and find the values corresponding to 3.571 and 4.404. They are 0.99 and 0.975, respectively. When the χ^2 test value falls on the left side, each of the values must be subtracted from 1 to get the interval that P-value falls between.

$$1 - 0.99 = 0.01 \qquad \text{and} \qquad 1 - 0.975 = 0.025$$

Hence the P-value falls in the interval

$$0.01 < P\text{-value} < 0.025$$

(The P-value obtained from a calculator is 0.014.)

When the χ^2 test is two-tailed, both interval values must be doubled. If a two-tailed test were being used in Example 8–28, then the interval would be $2(0.01) < P\text{-value} < 2(0.025)$, or $0.02 < P\text{-value} < 0.05$.

The P-value method for hypothesis testing for a variance or standard deviation follows the same steps shown in the preceding sections.

Step 1 State the hypotheses and identify the claim.

Step 2 Compute the test value.

Step 3 Find the P-value.

Step 4 Make the decision.

Step 5 Summarize the results.

Example 8–29 shows the P-value method for variances or standard deviations.

Example 8–29

Car Inspection Times

A researcher knows from past studies that the standard deviation of the time it takes to inspect a car is 16.8 minutes. A sample of 24 cars is selected and inspected. The standard deviation is 12.5 minutes. At $\alpha = 0.05$, can it be concluded that the standard deviation has changed? Use the P-value method.

Solution

Step 1 State the hypotheses and identify the claim.

$$H_0\colon \sigma = 16.8 \qquad \text{and} \qquad H_1\colon \sigma \neq 16.8 \text{ (claim)}$$

Step 2 Compute the test value.

$$\chi^2 = \frac{(n-1)s^2}{\sigma^2} = \frac{(24-1)(12.5)^2}{(16.8)^2} = 12.733$$

Step 3 Find the P-value. Using Table G with d.f. $= 23$, the value 12.733 falls between 11.689 and 13.091, corresponding to 0.975 and 0.95, respectively. Since these values are found on the left side of the distribution, each value must be subtracted from 1. Hence $1 - 0.975 = 0.025$ and $1 - 0.95 = 0.05$. Since this is a two-tailed test, the area must be doubled to obtain the P-value interval. Hence $0.05 < P\text{-value} < 0.10$, or somewhere between 0.05 and 0.10. (The P-value obtained from a calculator is 0.085.)

Step 4 Make the decision. Since $\alpha = 0.05$ and the P-value is between 0.05 and 0.10, the decision is to not reject the null hypothesis since P-value $> \alpha$.

Step 5 Summarize the results. There is not enough evidence to support the claim that the standard deviation has changed.

Applying the Concepts 8–5

Testing Gas Mileage Claims

Assume that you are working for the Consumer Protection Agency and have recently been getting complaints about the highway gas mileage of the new Dodge Caravans. Chrysler Corporation agrees to allow you to randomly select 40 of its new Dodge Caravans to test the highway mileage. Chrysler claims that the Caravans get 28 mpg on the highway. Your results show a mean of 26.7 and a standard deviation of 4.2. You support Chrysler's claim.

1. Show why you support Chrysler's claim by listing the P-value from your output. After more complaints, you decide to test the variability of the miles per gallon on the highway. From further questioning of Chrysler's quality control engineers, you find they are claiming a standard deviation of 2.1.

2. Test the claim about the standard deviation.

3. Write a short summary of your results and any necessary action that Chrysler must take to remedy customer complaints.

4. State your position about the necessity to perform tests of variability along with tests of the means.

See pages 465 and 466 for the answers.

Exercises 8–5

1. Using Table G, find the critical value(s) for each, show the critical and noncritical regions, and state the appropriate null and alternative hypotheses. Use $\sigma^2 = 225$.

   a. $\alpha = 0.05$, $n = 18$, right-tailed
   b. $\alpha = 0.10$, $n = 23$, left-tailed
   c. $\alpha = 0.05$, $n = 15$, two-tailed
   d. $\alpha = 0.10$, $n = 8$, two-tailed
   e. $\alpha = 0.01$, $n = 17$, right-tailed
   f. $\alpha = 0.025$, $n = 20$, left-tailed
   g. $\alpha = 0.01$, $n = 13$, two-tailed
   h. $\alpha = 0.025$, $n = 29$, left-tailed

2. (ans) Using Table G, find the P-value interval for each χ^2 test value.

   a. $\chi^2 = 29.321$, $n = 16$, right-tailed
   b. $\chi^2 = 10.215$, $n = 25$, left-tailed
   c. $\chi^2 = 24.672$, $n = 11$, two-tailed
   d. $\chi^2 = 23.722$, $n = 9$, right-tailed
   e. $\chi^2 = 13.974$, $n = 28$, two-tailed
   f. $\chi^2 = 10.571$, $n = 19$, left-tailed
   g. $\chi^2 = 12.144$, $n = 6$, two-tailed
   h. $\chi^2 = 8.201$, $n = 23$, two-tailed

For Exercises 3 through 9, assume that the variables are normally or approximately normally distributed. Use the traditional method of hypothesis testing unless otherwise specified.

3. **Calories in Pancake Syrup** A nutritionist claims that the standard deviation of the number of calories in 1 tablespoon of the major brands of pancake syrup is 60. A sample of major brands of syrup is selected, and the number of calories is shown. At $\alpha = 0.10$, can the claim be rejected?

53	210	100	200	100	220
210	100	240	200	100	210
100	210	100	210	100	60

Source: Based on information from *The Complete Book of Food Counts* by Corrine T. Netzer, Dell Publishers, New York.

4. **High Temperatures in January** Daily weather observations for southwestern Pennsylvania for the first three weeks of January show daily high temperatures as follows: 55, 44, 51, 59, 62, 60, 46, 51, 37, 30, 46, 51, 53, 57, 57, 39, 28, 37, 35, and 28 degrees Fahrenheit. The normal standard deviation in high temperatures for this time period is usually no more than 8 degrees. A meteorologist believes that with the unusual trend in

temperatures the standard deviation is greater. At $\alpha = 0.05$, can we conclude that the standard deviation is greater than 8 degrees?

Source: www.wunderground.com

5. **Stolen Aircraft** Test the claim that the standard deviation of the number of aircraft stolen each year in the United States is less than 15 if a sample of 12 years had a standard deviation of 13.6. Use $\alpha = 0.05$.

Source: Aviation Crime Prevention Institute.

6. **Weights of Football Players** A random sample of weights (in pounds) of football players at a local college is listed. At $\alpha = 0.05$, is there sufficient evidence that the standard deviation of all football players at the college is less than 10 pounds?

| 195 | 185 | 200 | 190 | 210 | 180 | 190 | 185 | 195 | 185 |
| 175 | 180 | 195 | 185 | 195 | 190 | 180 | 185 |

Source: Football Preview, *Washington Observer-Reporter.*

7. **Transferring Phone Calls** The manager of a large company claims that the standard deviation of the time (in minutes) that it takes a telephone call to be transferred to the correct office in her company is 1.2 minutes or less. A sample of 15 calls is selected, and the calls are timed. The standard deviation of the sample is 1.8 minutes. At $\alpha = 0.01$, test the claim that the standard deviation is less than or equal to 1.2 minutes. Use the P-value method.

8. **Soda Bottle Content** A machine fills 12-ounce bottles with soda. For the machine to function properly, the standard deviation of the sample must be less than or equal to 0.03 ounce. A sample of eight bottles is selected, and the number of ounces of soda in each bottle is given. At $\alpha = 0.05$, can we reject the claim that the machine is functioning properly? Use the P-value method.

| 12.03 | 12.10 | 12.02 | 11.98 |
| 12.00 | 12.05 | 11.97 | 11.99 |

9. **Calories in Doughnuts** A random sample of 20 different kinds of doughnuts had the following calorie counts. At $\alpha = 0.01$, is there sufficient evidence to conclude that the standard deviation is greater than 20 calories?

| 290 | 320 | 260 | 220 | 300 | 310 | 310 | 270 | 250 | 230 |
| 270 | 260 | 310 | 200 | 250 | 250 | 270 | 210 | 260 | 300 |

Source: *The Doctor's Pocket Calorie, Fat, and Carbohydrate Counter.*

10. **Exam Grades** A statistics professor is used to having a variance in his class grades of no more

than 100. He feels that his current group of students is different, and so he examines a random sample of midterm grades (listed below.) At $\alpha = 0.05$, can it be concluded that the variance in grades exceeds 100?

92.3	89.4	76.9	65.2	49.1
96.7	69.5	72.8	67.5	52.8
88.5	79.2	72.9	68.7	75.8

11. **Tornado Deaths** A researcher claims that the standard deviation of the number of deaths annually from tornadoes in the United States is less than 35. If a sample of 11 randomly selected years had a standard deviation of 32, is the claim believable? Use $\alpha = 0.05$.

Source: National Oceanic and Atmospheric Administration.

12. **Interstate Speeds** It has been reported that the standard deviation of the speeds of drivers on Interstate 75 near Findlay, Ohio, is 8 miles per hour for all vehicles. A driver feels from experience that this is very low. A survey is conducted, and for 50 drivers the standard deviation is 10.5 miles per hour. At $\alpha = 0.05$, is the driver correct?

13. **Home Run Totals** A random sample of home run totals for National League Home Run Champions from 1938 to 2001 is shown. At the 0.05 level of significance, is there sufficient evidence to conclude that the variance is greater than 25?

| 34 | 47 | 43 | 23 | 36 | 50 | 42 |
| 44 | 43 | 40 | 39 | 41 | 47 | 45 |

Source: *New York Times Almanac.*

14. **Heights of Volcanoes** A sample of heights (in feet) of active volcanoes in North America, outside of Alaska, is listed below. Is there sufficient evidence that the standard deviation in heights of volcanoes outside Alaska is less than the standard deviation in heights of Alaskan volcanoes, which is 2385.9 feet? Use $\alpha = 0.05$.

| 10,777 | 8159 | 11,240 | 10,456 |
| 14,163 | 8363 |

Source: *Time Almanac.*

15. **Manufactured Machine Parts** A manufacturing process produces machine parts with measurements the standard deviation of which must be no more than 0.52 mm. A random sample of 20 parts in a given lot revealed a standard deviation in measurement of 0.568 mm. Is there sufficient evidence at $\alpha = 0.05$ to conclude that the standard deviation of the parts is outside the required guidelines?

Technology *Step by Step*

MINITAB
Step by Step

Hypothesis Test for Variance

For Example 8–25, test the administrator's claim that the standard deviation is greater than 8. There is no menu item to calculate the test statistic and *P*-value directly.

Calculate the Standard Deviation and Sample Size

1. Enter the data into a column of MINITAB. Name the column **OutPatients.**
2. The standard deviation and sample size will be calculated and stored.
   a) Select **Calc>Column Statistics.**
   b) Check the button for Standard deviation. You can only do one of these statistics at a time.
   c) Use OutPatients for the Input variable.
   d) Store the result in s, then click [OK].
3. Select **Edit>Edit Last Dialog Box,** then do three things:
   a) Change the Statistic option from Standard Deviation to N nonmissing.
   b) Type **n** in the text box for Store the result.
   c) Click [OK].

Calculate the Chi-Square Test Statistic

4. Select **Calc>Calculator.**

   a) In the text box for Store result in variable: type in **K3.** The chi-square value will be stored in a constant so it can be used later.
   b) In the expression, type in the formula as shown. The double asterisk is the symbol used for a power.
   c) Click [OK]. The chi-square value of 27.44 will be stored in K3.

Calculate the *P*-Value

   d) Select **Calc>Probability Distributions>Chi-Square.**
   e) Click the button for Cumulative probability.
   f) Type in **14** for Degrees of freedom.
   g) Click in the text box for Input constant and type **K3.**
   h) Type in **K4** for Optional storage.
   i) Click [OK]. Now K4 contains the area to the left of the chi-square test statistic.

   Subtract the cumulative area from 1 to find the area on the right side of the chi-square test statistic. This is the *P*-value for a right-tailed test.

   j) Select **Calc>Calculator.**
   k) In the text box for Store result in variable, type in P-Value.
   l) The expression $1 - K4$ calculates the complement of the cumulative area.
   m) Click [OK].

The result will be shown in the first row of C2, 0.0168057. Since the *P*-value is less than α, reject the null hypothesis. The standard deviation in the sample is 11.2, the point estimate for the true standard deviation σ.

TI-83 Plus or TI-84 Plus
Step by Step

The TI-83 Plus and TI-84 Plus do not have a built-in hypothesis test for the variance or standard deviation. However, the downloadable program named SDHYP is available on your CD and Online Learning Center. Follow the instructions with your CD for downloading the program.

Performing a Hypothesis Test for the Variance and Standard Deviation (Data)

1. Enter the values into L_1.
2. Press **PRGM,** move the cursor to the program named SDHYP, and press **ENTER** twice.
3. Press **1** for Data.
4. Type L_1 for the list and press **ENTER**.
5. Type the number corresponding to the type of alternative hypothesis.
6. Type the value of the hypothesized variance and press **ENTER**.
7. Press **ENTER** to clear the screen.

Example TI8–4

This pertains to Example 8–25 in the text. Test the claim that $\sigma > 8$ for these data.

$$25 \quad 30 \quad 5 \quad 15 \quad 18 \quad 42 \quad 16 \quad 9 \quad 10 \quad 12 \quad 12 \quad 38 \quad 8 \quad 14 \quad 27$$

  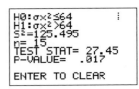

Since *P*-value = 0.017 < 0.1, we reject H_0 and conclude H_1. Therefore, there is enough evidence to support the claim that the standard deviation of the number of people using outpatient surgery is greater than 8.

Performing a Hypothesis Test for the Variance and Standard Deviation (Statistics)

1. Press **PRGM,** move the cursor to the program named SDHYP, and press **ENTER** twice.
2. Press **2** for Stats.
3. Type the sample standard deviation and press **ENTER**.
4. Type the sample size and press **ENTER**.
5. Type the number corresponding to the type of alternative hypothesis.
6. Type the value of the hypothesized variance and press **ENTER**.
7. Press **ENTER** to clear the screen.

Example TI8–5

This pertains to Example 8–26 in the text. Test the claim that $\sigma^2 = 0.644$, given $n = 20$ and $s = 1$.

Since *P*-value = 0.117 > 0.05, we do not reject H_0 and do not conclude H_1. Therefore, there is not enough evidence to reject the manufacturer's claim that the variance of the nicotine content of the cigarettes is equal to 0.644.

Excel
Step by Step

Hypothesis Test for the Variance: Chi-Square Test

Excel does not have a procedure to conduct a hypothesis test for the variance. However, you may conduct the test of the variance using the MegaStat Add-in available on your CD. If you have not installed this add-in, do so, following the instructions from the Chapter 1 Excel Step by Step.

Example XL8–4

This example relates to Example 8–26 from the text. At the 5% significance level, test the claim that $\sigma^2 = 0.644$. The MegaStat chi-square test of the population variance uses the P-value method. Therefore, it is not necessary to enter a significance level.

1. Type a label for the variable: Nicotine in cell A1.
2. Type the observed variance: **1** in cell A2.
3. Type the sample size: **20** in cell A3.
4. From the toolbar, select Add-Ins, **MegaStat>Hypothesis Tests>Chi-Square Variance Test.** *Note:* You may need to open MegaStat from the MegaStat.xls file on your computer's hard drive.
5. Select summary input.
6. Type **A1:A3** for the Input Range.
7. Type **0.644** for the Hypothesized variance and select the "not equal" Alternative.
8. Click [OK].

The result of the procedure is shown next.

Chi-Square Variance Test

```
 0.64   Hypothesized variance
 1.00   Observed variance of nicotine
   20   n
   19   d.f.
29.50   Chi-square

0.1169  P-value (two-tailed)
```

8–6 Confidence Intervals and Hypothesis Testing

Objective 9

Test hypotheses, using confidence intervals.

In hypothesis testing, another concept that might be of interest to students in elementary statistics is the relationship between hypothesis testing and confidence intervals.

There is a relationship between confidence intervals and hypothesis testing. When the null hypothesis is rejected in a hypothesis-testing situation, the confidence interval for the mean using the same level of significance *will not* contain the hypothesized mean. Likewise, when the null hypothesis is not rejected, the confidence interval computed using the same level of significance *will* contain the hypothesized mean. Examples 8–30 and 8–31 show this concept for two-tailed tests.

Example 8–30 Sugar Production

Sugar is packed in 5-pound bags. An inspector suspects the bags may not contain 5 pounds. A sample of 50 bags produces a mean of 4.6 pounds and a standard deviation of 0.7 pound. Is there enough evidence to conclude that the bags do not contain 5 pounds as stated at $\alpha = 0.05$? Also, find the 95% confidence interval of the true mean.

Solution

Now H_0: $\mu = 5$ and H_1: $\mu \neq 5$ (claim). The critical values are $+1.96$ and -1.96. The test value is

$$z = \frac{\overline{X} - \mu}{s/\sqrt{n}} = \frac{4.6 - 5.0}{0.7/\sqrt{50}} = \frac{-0.4}{0.099} = -4.04$$

Since $-4.04 < -1.96$, the null hypothesis is rejected. There is enough evidence to support the claim that the bags do not weigh 5 pounds.

The 95% confidence for the mean is given by

$$\overline{X} - z_{\alpha/2}\frac{s}{\sqrt{n}} < \mu < \overline{X} + z_{\alpha/2}\frac{s}{\sqrt{n}}$$

$$4.6 - (1.96)\left(\frac{0.7}{\sqrt{50}}\right) < \mu < 4.6 + (1.96)\left(\frac{0.7}{\sqrt{50}}\right)$$

$$4.4 < \mu < 4.8$$

Notice that the 95% confidence interval of μ does *not* contain the hypothesized value $\mu = 5$. Hence, there is agreement between the hypothesis test and the confidence interval.

Example 8–31   **Hog Weights**

A researcher claims that adult hogs fed a special diet will have an average weight of 200 pounds. A sample of 10 hogs has an average weight of 198.2 pounds and a standard deviation of 3.3 pounds. At $\alpha = 0.05$, can the claim be rejected? Also, find the 95% confidence interval of the true mean.

Solution

Now H_0: $\mu = 200$ pounds (claim) and H_1: $\mu \neq 200$ pounds. The t test must be used since σ is unknown. It is assumed that hog weights are normally distributed. The critical values at $\alpha = 0.05$ with 9 degrees of freedom are $+2.262$ and -2.262. The test value is

$$t = \frac{\overline{X} - \mu}{s/\sqrt{n}} = \frac{198.2 - 200}{3.3/\sqrt{10}} = \frac{-1.8}{1.0436} = -1.72$$

Thus, the null hypothesis is not rejected. There is not enough evidence to reject the claim that the weight of the adult hogs is 200 pounds.

The 95% confidence interval of the mean is

$$\overline{X} - t_{\alpha/2}\frac{s}{\sqrt{n}} < \mu < \overline{X} + t_{\alpha/2}\frac{s}{\sqrt{n}}$$

$$198.2 - (2.262)\left(\frac{3.3}{\sqrt{10}}\right) < \mu < 198.2 + (2.262)\left(\frac{3.3}{\sqrt{10}}\right)$$

$$198.2 - 2.361 < \mu < 198.2 + 2.361$$

$$195.8 < \mu < 200.6$$

The 95% confidence interval does contain the hypothesized mean $\mu = 200$. Again there is agreement between the hypothesis test and the confidence interval.

In summary, then, when the null hypothesis is rejected at a significance level of α, the confidence interval computed at the $1 - \alpha$ level will not contain the value of the mean that is stated in the null hypothesis. On the other hand, when the null hypothesis is not rejected, the confidence interval computed at the same significance level will contain the value of the mean stated in the null hypothesis. These results are true for other hypothesis-testing situations and are not limited to means tests.

The relationship between confidence intervals and hypothesis testing presented here is valid for two-tailed tests. The relationship between one-tailed hypothesis tests and one-sided or one-tailed confidence intervals is also valid; however, this technique is beyond the scope of this textbook.

Applying the Concepts **8–6**

Consumer Protection Agency Complaints

Hypothesis testing and testing claims with confidence intervals are two different approaches that lead to the same conclusion. In the following activities, you will compare and contrast those two approaches.

Assume you are working for the Consumer Protection Agency and have recently been getting complaints about the highway gas mileage of the new Dodge Caravans. Chrysler Corporation agrees to allow you to randomly select 40 of its new Dodge Caravans to test the highway mileage. Chrysler claims that the vans get 28 mpg on the highway. Your results show a mean of 26.7 and a standard deviation of 4.2. You are not certain if you should create a confidence interval or run a hypothesis test. You decide to do both at the same time.

1. Draw a normal curve, labeling the critical values, critical regions, test statistic, and population mean. List the significance level and the null and alternative hypotheses.
2. Draw a confidence interval directly below the normal distribution, labeling the sample mean, error, and boundary values.
3. Explain which parts from each approach are the same and which parts are different.
4. Draw a picture of a normal curve and confidence interval where the sample and hypothesized means are equal.
5. Draw a picture of a normal curve and confidence interval where the lower boundary of the confidence interval is equal to the hypothesized mean.
6. Draw a picture of a normal curve and confidence interval where the sample mean falls in the left critical region of the normal curve.

See page 466 for the answers.

Exercises 8–6

1. **Ski Shop Sales** A ski shop manager claims that the average of the sales for her shop is $1800 a day during the winter months. Ten winter days are selected at random, and the mean of the sales is $1830. The standard deviation of the population is $200. Can you reject the claim at $\alpha = 0.05$? Find the 95% confidence interval of the mean. Does the confidence interval interpretation agree with the hypothesis test results? Explain. Assume that the variable is normally distributed.

2. **One-Way Airfares** The average one-way airfare from Pittsburgh to Washington, D.C., is $236. A random

sample of 20 one-way fares during a particular month had a mean of $210 with a standard deviation of $43. At $\alpha = 0.02$, is there sufficient evidence to conclude a difference from the stated mean? Use the sample statistics to construct a 98% confidence interval for the true mean one-way airfare from Pittsburgh to Washington, D.C., and compare your interval to the results of the test. Do they support or contradict one another?

Source: www.fedstats.gov

3. **Condominium Monthly Maintenance Fees** The sales manager of a rental agency claims that the monthly

maintenance fee for a condominium in the Lakewood region is $86. Past surveys showed that the standard deviation of the population is $6. A sample of 15 owners shows that they pay an average of $84. Test the manager's claim at $\alpha = 0.01$. Find the 99% confidence interval of the mean. Does the confidence interval interpretation agree with the results of the hypothesis test? Explain. Assume that the variable is normally distributed.

4. **Canoe Trip Times** The average time it takes a person in a one-person canoe to complete a certain river course is 47 minutes. Because of rapid currents in the spring, a group of 10 people traverse the course in 42 minutes. The standard deviation, known from previous trips, is 7 minutes. Test the claim that this group's time was different because of the strong currents. Use $\alpha = 0.10$. Find the 90% confidence level of the true mean. Does the confidence interval interpretation agree with the results of the hypothesis test? Explain. Assume that the variable is normally distributed.

5. **Working at Home** Workers with a formal arrangement with their employer to be paid for time worked at home worked an average of 19 hours per week. A random sample of 15 mortgage brokers indicated that they worked a mean of 21.3 hours per week with a standard deviation of 6.5 hours. At $\alpha = 0.05$, is there sufficient evidence to conclude a difference? Construct a 95% confidence interval for the true mean number of paid working hours at home. Compare the results of your confidence interval to the conclusion of your hypothesis test and discuss the implications.

Source: www.bls.gov

6. **Newspaper Reading Times** A survey taken several years ago found that the average time a person spent reading the local daily newspaper was 10.8 minutes. The standard deviation of the population was 3 minutes. To see whether the average time had changed since the newspaper's format was revised, the newspaper editor surveyed 36 individuals. The average time that the 36 people spent reading the paper was 12.2 minutes. At $\alpha = 0.02$, is there a change in the average time an individual spends reading the newspaper? Find the 98% confidence interval of the mean. Do the results agree? Explain.

Summary

This chapter introduces the basic concepts of hypothesis testing. A statistical hypothesis is a conjecture about a population. There are two types of statistical hypotheses: the null and the alternative hypotheses. The null hypothesis states that there is no difference, and the alternative hypothesis specifies a difference. To test the null hypothesis, researchers use a statistical test. Many test values are computed by using

$$\text{Test value} = \frac{(\text{observed value}) - (\text{expected value})}{\text{standard error}}$$

Two common statistical tests for hypotheses about a mean are the z test and the t test. The z test is used either when the population standard deviation is known and the variable is normally distributed or when σ is known and the sample size is greater than or equal to 30. When the population standard deviation is not known and the variable is normally distributed, the sample standard deviation is used, but a t test should be conducted instead. The z test is also used to test proportions when $np \geq 5$ and $nq \geq 5$.

Researchers compute a test value from the sample data in order to decide whether the null hypothesis should be rejected. Statistical tests can be one-tailed or two-tailed, depending on the hypotheses.

The null hypothesis is rejected when the difference between the population parameter and the sample statistic is said to be significant. The difference is significant when the test value falls in the critical region of the distribution. The critical region is determined by α, the level of significance of the test. The level is the probability of committing a type I error. This error occurs when the null hypothesis is rejected when it is true. Three generally agreed upon significance levels are 0.10, 0.05, and 0.01. A second kind of error, the type II error, can occur when the null hypothesis is not rejected when it is false.

Finally, you can test a single variance by using a chi-square test.

All hypothesis-testing situations using the traditional method should include the following steps:

1. State the null and alternative hypotheses and identify the claim.
2. State an alpha level and find the critical value(s).
3. Compute the test value.
4. Make the decision to reject or not reject the null hypothesis.
5. Summarize the results.

All hypothesis-testing situations using the *P*-value method should include the following steps:

1. State the hypotheses and identify the claim.
2. Compute the test value.
3. Find the *P*-value.
4. Make the decision.
5. Summarize the results.

Important Terms

α (alpha) 404

alternative hypothesis 399

β (beta) 404

chi-square test 445

critical or rejection region 404

critical value 404

hypothesis testing 398

left-tailed test 404

level of significance 404

noncritical or nonrejection region 404

null hypothesis 399

one-tailed test 404

P-value 416

research hypothesis 400

right-tailed test 404

statistical hypothesis 399

statistical test 402

test value 402

t test 425

two-tailed test 406

type I error 403

type II error 403

z test 411

Important Formulas

Formula for the *z* test for means:

$$z = \frac{\bar{X} - \mu}{\sigma/\sqrt{n}}$$ **if $n < 30$, variable must be normally distributed**

Formula for the *t* test for means:

$$t = \frac{\bar{X} - \mu}{s/\sqrt{n}}$$ **if $n < 30$, variable must be normally distributed**

Formula for the *z* test for proportions:

$$z = \frac{X - \mu}{\sigma}$$ or $$z = \frac{\hat{p} - p}{\sqrt{pq/n}}$$

Formula for the chi-square test for variance or standard deviation:

$$\chi^2 = \frac{(n-1)s^2}{\sigma^2}$$

Review Exercises

For Exercises 1 through 19, perform each of the following steps.

a. State the hypotheses and identify the claim.
b. Find the critical value(s).
c. Compute the test value.
d. Make the decision.
e. Summarize the results.

Use the traditional method of hypothesis testing unless otherwise specified.

 1. High Temperatures in the United States A meteorologist claims that the average of the highest temperatures in the United States is 98°. A random sample of 50 cities is selected, and the highest temperatures are recorded. The data are shown. At $\alpha = 0.05$, can the claim be rejected? $\sigma = 7.71$.

97	94	96	105	99
96	80	95	101	97
101	87	88	97	94
98	95	88	94	94
99	99	98	96	96
97	98	99	92	97
99	108	97	98	114
91	96	102	99	102
100	93	88	102	99
98	80	95	101	61

Source: *The World Almanac & Book of Facts.*

2. **Salaries for Actuaries** Nationwide graduates entering the actuarial field earn $40,000. A college placement officer feels that this number is too low. She surveys 36 graduates entering the actuarial field and finds the average salary to be $41,000. The population standard deviation is $3000. Can her claim be supported at $\alpha = 0.05$?

Source: BeAnActuary.org

3. **Monthly Home Rent** The average monthly rent for a one-bedroom home in San Francisco is $1229. A random sample of 15 one-bedroom homes about 15 miles outside of San Francisco had a mean rent of $1350. The population standard deviation is $250. At $\alpha = 0.05$, can we conclude that the monthly rent outside San Francisco differs from that in the city?

Source: *New York Times Almanac.*

4. **Salaries for Actuaries** Nationwide, the average salary of actuaries who achieve the rank of Fellow is $150,000. An insurance executive wants to see how this compares with Fellows within his company. He checks the salaries of eight Fellows and finds the average salary to be $155,500 with a standard deviation of $15,000. Can he conclude that Fellows in his company make more than the national average, using $\alpha = 0.05$?

Source: BeAnActuary.org

5. **Debt of College Graduates** A random sample of the average debt (in dollars) at graduation from 30 of the top 100 public colleges and universities is listed below. Is there sufficient evidence at $\alpha = 0.01$ to conclude that the population mean debt at graduation is less than $18,000?

16,012	15,784	16,597	18,105	12,665	14,734
17,225	16,953	15,309	15,297	14,437	14,835
13,607	13,374	19,410	18,385	22,312	16,656
20,142	17,821	12,701	22,400	15,730	17,673
18,978	13,661	12,580	14,392	16,000	15,176

Source: www.Kiplinger.com

6. **Tennis Fans** The Tennis Industry Association stated that the average age of a tennis fan is 32 years. To test the claim, a researcher selected a random sample of 18 tennis fans and found that the mean of their ages was 31.3 years and the standard deviation was 2.8 years. At $\alpha = 0.05$ does it appear that the average age is lower than what was stated by the Tennis Industry Association? Use the *P*-value method, and assume the variable is approximately normally distributed.

7. **Whooping Crane Eggs** Once down to about 15, the world's only wild flock of whooping cranes now numbers a record 237 birds in its Texas Coastal Bend wintering ground (www.SunHerald.com). The average whooping crane egg weighs 208 grams. A new batch of eggs was recently weighed, and their weights are listed below. At $\alpha = 0.01$, is there sufficient evidence to conclude that the weight is greater than 208 grams?

210	208.5	211.6	212	210.3
210.2	209	206.4	209.7	

Source: http:whoopers.usgs.gov

8. **Union Membership** Nationwide 13.7% of employed wage and salary workers are union members (down from 20.1% in 1983). A random sample of 300 local wage and salary workers showed that 50 belonged to a union. At $\alpha = 0.05$, is there sufficient evidence to conclude that the proportion of union membership differs from 13.7%?

Source: *Time Almanac.*

9. **Federal Prison Populations** Nationally 60.2% of federal prisoners are serving time for drug offenses. A warden feels that in his prison the percentage is even higher. He surveys 400 inmates' records and finds that 260 of the inmates are drug offenders. At $\alpha = 0.05$, is he correct?

Source: *New York Times Almanac.*

10. **Free School Lunches** It has been reported that 59.3% of U.S. school lunches served are free or at a reduced price. A random sample of 300 children in a large metropolitan area indicated that 156 of them received lunch free or at a reduced price. At the 0.01 level of significance, is there sufficient evidence to conclude that the proportion is less than 59.3%?

Source: www.fns.usda.gov

11. **Portable Radio Ownership** A radio manufacturer claims that 65% of teenagers 13 to 16 years old have their own portable radios. A researcher wishes to test the claim and selects a random sample of 80 teenagers. She finds that 57 have their own portable radios. At $\alpha = 0.05$, should the claim be rejected? Use the *P*-value method.

12. **Weights of Football Players** A football coach claims that the average weight of all the opposing teams' members is 225 pounds. For a test of the claim, a sample of 50 players is taken from all the opposing teams. The mean is found to be 230 pounds. The population standard deviation is 15 pounds. At $\alpha = 0.01$, test the coach's claim. Find the *P*-value and make the decision.

13. **Time Until Indigestion Relief** An advertisement claims that Fasto Stomach Calm will provide relief from indigestion in less than 10 minutes. For a test of the claim, 35 individuals were given the product; the average time until relief was 9.25 minutes. From past studies, the standard deviation of the population is known to be 2 minutes. Can you conclude that the claim is justified? Find the P-value and let $\alpha = 0.05$.

14. **Times of Videos** A film editor feels that the standard deviation for the number of minutes in a video is 3.4 minutes. A sample of 24 videos has a standard deviation of 4.2 minutes. At $\alpha = 0.05$, is the sample standard deviation different from what the editor hypothesized?

15. **Fuel Consumption** The standard deviation of the fuel consumption of a certain automobile is hypothesized to be greater than or equal to 4.3 miles per gallon. A sample of 20 automobiles produced a standard deviation of 2.6 miles per gallon. Is the standard deviation really less than previously thought? Use $\alpha = 0.05$ and the P-value method.

16. **Apartment Rental Rates** A real estate agent claims that the standard deviation of the rental rates of apartments in a certain county is $95. A random sample of rates in dollars is shown. At $\alpha = 0.02$, can the claim be refuted?

400	345	325	395	400	300
375	435	495	525	290	460
425	250	200	525	375	390

Source: *Pittsburgh Tribune-Review.*

17. **Games Played by NBA Scoring Leaders** A random sample of the number of games played by individual NBA scoring leaders is found below. Is there sufficient evidence to conclude that the variance in games played differs from 40? Use $\alpha = 0.05$.

| 72 | 79 | 80 | 74 | 82 |
| 79 | 82 | 78 | 60 | 75 |

Source: *Time Almanac.*

18. **Tire Inflation** To see whether people are keeping their car tires inflated to the correct level of 35 pounds per square inch (psi), a tire company manager selects a sample of 36 tires and checks the pressure. The mean of the sample is 33.5 psi, and the population standard deviation is 3 psi. Are the tires properly inflated? Use $\alpha = 0.10$. Find the 90% confidence interval of the mean. Do the results agree? Explain.

19. **Plant Leaf Lengths** A biologist knows that the average length of a leaf of a certain full-grown plant is 4 inches. The standard deviation of the population is 0.6 inch. A sample of 20 leaves of that type of plant given a new type of plant food had an average length of 4.2 inches. Is there reason to believe that the new food is responsible for a change in the growth of the leaves? Use $\alpha = 0.01$. Find the 99% confidence interval of the mean. Do the results concur? Explain. Assume that the variable is approximately normally distributed.

Statistics Today

How Much Better Is Better?—Revisited

Now that you have learned the techniques of hypothesis testing presented in this chapter, you realize that the difference between the sample mean and the population mean must be *significant* before you can conclude that the students really scored above average. The superintendent should follow the steps in the hypothesis-testing procedure and be able to reject the null hypothesis before announcing that his students scored higher than average.

Data Analysis

The Data Bank is found in Appendix D, or on the World Wide Web by following links from
www.mhhe.com/bluman/

1. From the Data Bank, select a random sample of at least 30 individuals, and test one or more of the following hypotheses by using the z test. Use $\alpha = 0.05$.

   a. For serum cholesterol, $H_0: \mu = 220$ milligram percent (mg%).

   b. For systolic pressure, $H_0: \mu = 120$ millimeters of mercury (mm Hg).

   c. For IQ, $H_0: \mu = 100$.

   d. For sodium level, $H_0: \mu = 140$ milliequivalents per liter (mEq/l).

2. Select a random sample of 15 individuals and test one or more of the hypotheses in Exercise 1 by using the t test. Use $\alpha = 0.05$.

3. Select a random sample of at least 30 individuals, and using the z test for proportions, test one or more of the following hypotheses. Use $\alpha = 0.05$.

   a. For educational level, H_0: $p = 0.50$ for level 2.
   b. For smoking status, H_0: $p = 0.20$ for level 1.
   c. For exercise level, H_0: $p = 0.10$ for level 1.
   d. For gender, H_0: $p = 0.50$ for males.

4. Select a sample of 20 individuals and test the hypothesis H_0: $\sigma^2 = 225$ for IQ level. Use $\alpha = 0.05$.

5. Using the data from Data Set XIII, select a sample of 10 hospitals and test H_0: $\mu = 250$ and H_1: $\mu < 250$ for the number of beds. Use $\alpha = 0.05$.

6. Using the data obtained in Exercise 5, test the hypothesis H_0: $\sigma \geq 150$. Use $\alpha = 0.05$.

Chapter Quiz

Determine whether each statement is true or false. If the statement is false, explain why.

1. No error is committed when the null hypothesis is rejected when it is false.

2. When you are conducting the t test, the population must be approximately normally distributed.

3. The test value separates the critical region from the noncritical region.

4. The values of a chi-square test cannot be negative.

5. The chi-square test for variances is always one-tailed.

Select the best answer.

6. When the value of α is increased, the probability of committing a type I error is

   a. Decreased
   b. Increased
   c. The same
   d. None of the above

7. If you wish to test the claim that the mean of the population is 100, the appropriate null hypothesis is

   a. $\bar{X} = 100$
   b. $\mu \geq 100$
   c. $\mu \leq 100$
   d. $\mu = 100$

8. The degrees of freedom for the chi-square test for variances or standard deviations are

   a. 1
   b. n
   c. $n - 1$
   d. None of the above

9. For the z test, if σ is unknown and $n \geq 30$, one can substitute _____ for σ.

   a. n
   b. s
   c. χ^2
   d. t

Complete the following statements with the best answer.

10. Rejecting the null hypothesis when it is true is called a(n) _____ error.

11. The probability of a type II error is referred to as _____.

12. A conjecture about a population parameter is called a(n) _____.

13. To test the claim that the mean is greater than 87, you would use a(n) _____-tailed test.

14. The degrees of freedom for the t test are _____.

For the following exercises where applicable:

   a. State the hypotheses and identify the claim.
   b. Find the critical value(s).
   c. Compute the test value.
   d. Make the decision.
   e. Summarize the results.

Use the traditional method of hypothesis testing unless otherwise specified.

 15. Ages of Professional Women A sociologist wishes to see if it is true that for a certain group of professional women, the average age at which they have their first child is 28.6 years. A random sample of 36 women is selected, and their ages at the birth of their first child are recorded. At $\alpha = 0.05$, does the evidence refute the sociologist's assertion? $\sigma = 4.18$.

32	28	26	33	35	34
29	24	22	25	26	28
28	34	33	32	30	29
30	27	33	34	28	25
24	33	25	37	35	33
34	36	38	27	29	26

16. **Home Closing Costs** A real estate agent believes that the average closing cost of purchasing a new home is $6500 over the purchase price. She selects 40 new home sales at random and finds that the average closing costs are $6600. The standard deviation of the population is $120. Test her belief at $\alpha = 0.05$.

17. **Chewing Gum Use** A recent study stated that if a person chewed gum, the average number of sticks of gum he or she chewed daily was 8. To test the claim, a researcher selected a random sample of 36 gum chewers and found the mean number of sticks of gum chewed per day was 9. The standard deviation of the population is 1. At $\alpha = 0.05$, is the number of sticks of gum a person chews per day actually greater than 8?

18. **Hotel Rooms** A travel agent claims that the average of the number of rooms in hotels in a large city is 500. At $\alpha = 0.01$ is the claim realistic? The data for a sample of six hotels are shown.

    713   300   292   311   598   401   618

    Give a reason why the claim might be deceptive.

19. **Heights of Models** In a New York modeling agency, a researcher wishes to see if the average height of female models is really less than 67 inches, as the chief claims. A sample of 20 models has an average height of 65.8 inches. The standard deviation of the sample is 1.7 inches. At $\alpha = 0.05$, is the average height of the models really less than 67 inches? Use the *P*-value method.

20. **Experience of Taxi Drivers** A taxi company claims that its drivers have an average of at least 12.4 years' experience. In a study of 15 taxi drivers, the average experience was 11.2 years. The standard deviation was 2. At $\alpha = 0.10$, is the number of years' experience of the taxi drivers really less than the taxi company claimed?

21. **Ages of Robbery Victims** A recent study in a small city stated that the average age of robbery victims was 63.5 years. A sample of 20 recent victims had a mean of 63.7 years and a standard deviation of 1.9 years. At $\alpha = 0.05$, is the average age higher than originally believed? Use the *P*-value method.

22. **First-Time Marriages** A magazine article stated that the average age of women who are getting married for the first time is 26 years. A researcher decided to test this hypothesis at $\alpha = 0.02$. She selected a sample of 25 women who were recently married for the first time and found the average was 25.1 years. The standard deviation was 3 years. Should the null hypothesis be rejected on the basis of the sample?

23. **Survey on Vitamin Usage** A survey in *Men's Health* magazine reported that 39% of cardiologists said that they took vitamin E supplements. To see if this is still true, a researcher randomly selected 100 cardiologists and found that 36 said that they took vitamin E supplements. At $\alpha = 0.05$ test the claim that 39% of the cardiologists took vitamin E supplements. A recent study said that taking too much vitamin E might be

harmful. How might this study make the results of the previous study invalid?

24. **Breakfast Survey** A dietitian read in a survey that at least 55% of adults do not eat breakfast at least 3 days a week. To verify this, she selected a random sample of 80 adults and asked them how many days a week they skipped breakfast. A total of 50% responded that they skipped breakfast at least 3 days a week. At $\alpha = 0.10$, test the claim.

25. **Caffeinated Beverage Survey** A Harris Poll found that 35% of people said that they drink a caffeinated beverage to combat midday drowsiness. A recent survey found that 19 out of 48 people stated that they drank a caffeinated beverage to combat midday drowsiness. At $\alpha = 0.02$ is the claim of the percentage found in the Harris Poll believable?

26. **Radio Ownership** A magazine claims that 75% of all teenage boys have their own radios. A researcher wished to test the claim and selected a random sample of 60 teenage boys. She found that 54 had their own radios. At $\alpha = 0.01$, should the claim be rejected?

27. Find the *P*-value for the *z* test in Exercise 15.

28. Find the *P*-value for the *z* test in Exercise 16.

29. **Pages in Romance Novels** A copyeditor thinks the standard deviation for the number of pages in a romance novel is greater than 6. A sample of 25 novels has a standard deviation of 9 pages. At $\alpha = 0.05$, is it higher, as the editor hypothesized?

30. **Seed Germination Times** It has been hypothesized that the standard deviation of the germination time of radish seeds is 8 days. The standard deviation of a sample of 60 radish plants' germination times was 6 days. At $\alpha = 0.01$, test the claim.

31. **Pollution By-products** The standard deviation of the pollution by-products released in the burning of 1 gallon of gas is 2.3 ounces. A sample of 20 automobiles tested produced a standard deviation of 1.9 ounces. Is the standard deviation really less than previously thought? Use $\alpha = 0.05$.

32. **Strength of Wrapping Cord** A manufacturer claims that the standard deviation of the strength of wrapping cord is 9 pounds. A sample of 10 wrapping cords produced a standard deviation of 11 pounds. At $\alpha = 0.05$, test the claim. Use the *P*-value method.

33. Find the 90% confidence interval of the mean in Exercise 15. Is μ contained in the interval?

34. Find the 95% confidence interval for the mean in Exercise 16. Is μ contained in the interval?

Critical Thinking Challenges

The power of a test $(1 - \beta)$ can be calculated when a specific value of the mean is hypothesized in the alternative hypothesis; for example, let H_0: $\mu = 50$ and let H_1: $\mu = 52$. To find the power of a test, it is necessary to find the value of β. This can be done by the following steps:

Step 1   For a specific value of α find the corresponding value of $\overline{X}$, using $z = \dfrac{\overline{X} - \mu}{\sigma/\sqrt{n}}$, where μ is the hypothesized value given in H_0. Use a right-tailed test.

Step 2   Using the value of $\overline{X}$ found in step 1 and the value of μ in the alternative hypothesis,

find the area corresponding to z in the formula $z = \dfrac{\overline{X} - \mu}{\sigma/\sqrt{n}}$.

Step 3   Subtract this area from 0.5000. This is the value of β.

Step 4   Subtract the value of β from 1. This will give you the power of a test. See Figure 8–41.

1. Find the power of a test, using the hypotheses given previously and $\alpha = 0.05$, $\sigma = 3$, and $n = 30$.

2. Select several other values for μ in H_1 and compute the power of the test. Generalize the results.

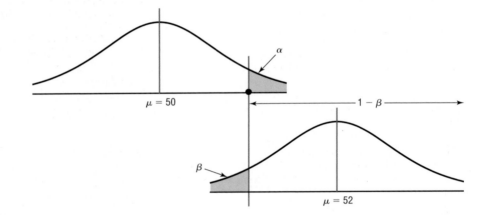

Figure 8–41

Relationship Among α, β, and the Power of a Test

Data Projects

Use a significance level of 0.05 for all tests below.

1. **Business and Finance** Use the Dow Jones Industrial stocks in data project 1 of Chapter 7 as your data set. Find the gain or loss for each stock over the last quarter. Test the claim that the mean is that the stocks broke even (no gain or loss indicates a mean of 0).

2. **Sports and Leisure** Use the most recent NFL season for your data. For each team, find the quarterback rating for the number one quarterback. Test the claim that the mean quarterback rating for a number one quarterback is more than 80.

3. **Technology** Use your last month's itemized cell phone bill for your data. Determine the percentage of your text messages that were outgoing. Test the claim that a majority of your text messages were outgoing. Determine the mean, median, and standard deviation for the length of a call. Test the claim that the mean length

of a call is longer than the value for you found for the median length.

4. **Health and Wellness** Use the data collected in data project 4 of Chapter 7 for this exercise. Test the claim that the mean body temperature is less than 98.6 degrees Fahrenheit.

5. **Politics and Economics** Use the most recent results of the Presidential primary elections for both parties. Determine what percentage of voters in your state voted for the eventual Democratic nominee for President and what percentage voted for the eventual Republican nominee. Test the claim that a majority of your state favored the candidate who won the nomination for each party.

6. **Your Class** Use the data collected in data project 6 of Chapter 7 for this exercise. Test the claim that the mean BMI for a student is more than 25.

Answers to Applying the Concepts

Section 8–1   Eggs and Your Health

1. The study was prompted by claims that linked foods high in cholesterol to high blood serum cholesterol.

2. The population under study is people in general.

3. A sample of 500 subjects was collected.

4. The hypothesis was that eating eggs did not increase blood serum cholesterol.

5. Blood serum cholesterol levels were collected.

6. Most likely but we are not told which test.

7. The conclusion was that eating a moderate amount of eggs will not significantly increase blood serum cholesterol level.

Section 8–2   Car Thefts

1. The hypotheses are H_0: $\mu = 44$ and H_1: $\mu \neq 44$.

2. This sample can be considered large for our purposes.

3. The variable needs to be normally distributed.

4. We will use a z distribution.

5. Since we are interested in whether the car theft rate has changed, we use a two-tailed test.

6. Answers may vary. At the $\alpha = 0.05$ significance level, the critical values are $z = \pm 1.96$.

7. The sample mean is $\overline{X} = 55.97$, and the population standard deviation is 30.30. Our test statistic is $z = \frac{55.97 - 44}{30.30/\sqrt{36}} = 2.37$.

8. Since $2.37 > 1.96$, we reject the null hypothesis.

9. There is enough evidence to conclude that the car theft rate has changed.

10. Answers will vary. Based on our sample data, it appears that the car theft rate has changed from 44 vehicles per 10,000 people. In fact, the data indicate that the car theft rate has increased.

11. Based on our sample, we would expect 55.97 car thefts per 10,000 people, so we would expect $(55.97)(5) = 279.85$, or about 280, car thefts in the city.

Section 8–3   How Much Nicotine Is in Those Cigarettes?

1. We have $15 - 1 = 14$ degrees of freedom.

2. This is a t test.

3. We are only testing one sample.

4. This is a right-tailed test, since the hypotheses of the tobacco company are H_0: $\mu = 40$ and H_1: $\mu > 40$.

5. The P-value is 0.008, which is less than the significance level of 0.01. We reject the tobacco company's claim.

6. Since the test statistic (2.72) is greater than the critical value (2.62), we reject the tobacco company's claim.

7. There is no conflict in this output, since the results based on the P-value and on the critical value agree.

8. Answers will vary. It appears that the company's claim is false and that there is more than 40 mg of nicotine in its cigarettes.

Section 8–4   Quitting Smoking

1. The statistical hypotheses were that StopSmoke helps more people quit smoking than the other leading brands.

2. The null hypotheses were that StopSmoke has the same effectiveness as or is not as effective as the other leading brands.

3. The alternative hypotheses were that StopSmoke helps more people quit smoking than the other leading brands. (The alternative hypotheses are the statistical hypotheses.)

4. No statistical tests were run that we know of.

5. Had tests been run, they would have been one-tailed tests.

6. Some possible significance levels are 0.01, 0.05, and 0.10.

7. A type I error would be to conclude that StopSmoke is better when it really is not.

8. A type II error would be to conclude that StopSmoke is not better when it really is.

9. These studies proved nothing. Had statistical tests been used, we could have tested the effectiveness of StopSmoke.

10. Answers will vary. One possible answer is that more than likely the statements are talking about practical significance and not statistical significance, since we have no indication that any statistical tests were conducted.

Section 8–5   Testing Gas Mileage Claims

1. The hypotheses are H_0: $\mu = 28$ and H_1: $\mu < 28$. The value of our test statistic is $z = -1.96$, and the associated P-value is 0.02514. We would reject Chrysler's claim that the Dodge Caravans are getting 28 mpg.

2. The hypotheses are H_0: $\sigma = 2.1$ and H_1: $\sigma > 2.1$. The value of our test statistic is $\chi^2 = \frac{(n-1)s^2}{\sigma^2} = \frac{(39)4.2^2}{2.1^2} = 156$, and the associated P-value is approximately zero. We would reject Chrysler's claim that the standard deviation is 2.1 mpg.

3. Answers will vary. It is recommended that Chrysler lower its claim about the highway miles per gallon of the Dodge Caravans. Chrysler should also try to reduce variability in miles per gallon and provide confidence intervals for the highway miles per gallon.

4. Answers will vary. There are cases when a mean may be fine, but if there is a lot of variability about the mean, there will be complaints (due to the lack of consistency).

Section 8–6   Consumer Protection Agency Complaints

1. Answers will vary.
2. Answers will vary.
3. Answers will vary.
4. Answers will vary.
5. Answers will vary.
6. Answers will vary.

CHAPTER 9

Testing the Difference Between Two Means, Two Proportions, and Two Variances

Objectives

After completing this chapter, you should be able to

1 Test the difference between sample means, using the *z* test.

2 Test the difference between two means for independent samples, using the *t* test.

3 Test the difference between two means for dependent samples.

4 Test the difference between two proportions.

5 Test the difference between two variances or standard deviations.

Outline

Introduction

9–1 Testing the Difference Between Two Means: Using the *z* Test

9–2 Testing the Difference Between Two Means of Independent Samples: Using the *t* Test

9–3 Testing the Difference Between Two Means: Dependent Samples

9–4 Testing the Difference Between Proportions

9–5 Testing the Difference Between Two Variances

Summary

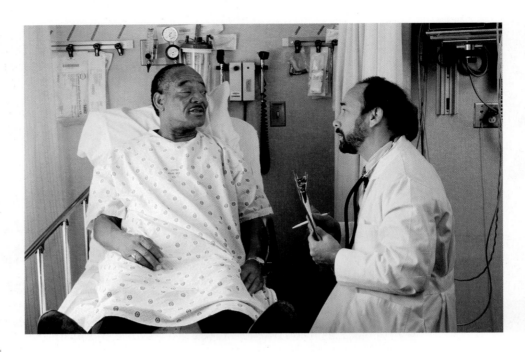

Statistics Today

To Vaccinate or Not to Vaccinate? Small or Large?

Influenza is a serious disease among the elderly, especially those living in nursing homes. Those residents are more susceptible to influenza than elderly persons living in the community because the former are usually older and more debilitated, and they live in a closed environment where they are exposed more so than community residents to the virus if it is introduced into the home. Three researchers decided to investigate the use of vaccine and its value in determining outbreaks of influenza in small nursing homes.

These researchers surveyed 83 licensed homes in seven counties in Michigan. Part of the study consisted of comparing the number of people being vaccinated in small nursing homes (100 or fewer beds) with the number in larger nursing homes (more than 100 beds). Unlike the statistical methods presented in Chapter 8, these researchers used the techniques explained in this chapter to compare two sample proportions to see if there was a significant difference in the vaccination rates of patients in small nursing homes compared to those in large nursing homes. See Statistics Today—Revisited at the end of the chapter.

Source: Nancy Arden, Arnold S. Monto, and Suzanne E. Ohmit, "Vaccine Use and the Risk of Outbreaks in a Sample of Nursing Homes During an Influenza Epidemic," *American Journal of Public Health* 85, no. 3 (March 1995), pp. 399–401. Copyright 1995 by the American Public Health Association.

Introduction

The basic concepts of hypothesis testing were explained in Chapter 8. With the z, t, and χ^2 tests, a sample mean, variance, or proportion can be compared to a specific population mean, variance, or proportion to determine whether the null hypothesis should be rejected.

There are, however, many instances when researchers wish to compare two sample means, using experimental and control groups. For example, the average lifetimes of two different brands of bus tires might be compared to see whether there is any difference in tread wear. Two different brands of fertilizer might be tested to see whether one is better than the other for growing plants. Or two brands of cough syrup might be tested to see whether one brand is more effective than the other.

In the comparison of two means, the same basic steps for hypothesis testing shown in Chapter 8 are used, and the z and t tests are also used. When comparing two means by using the t test, the researcher must decide if the two samples are *independent* or *dependent*. The concepts of independent and dependent samples will be explained in Sections 9–2 and 9–3.

The z test can be used to compare two proportions, as shown in Section 9–4. Finally, two variances can be compared by using an F test as shown in Section 9–5.

9–1	# Testing the Difference Between Two Means: Using the z Test

Objective 1

Test the difference between sample means, using the z test.

Suppose a researcher wishes to determine whether there is a difference in the average age of nursing students who enroll in a nursing program at a community college and those who enroll in a nursing program at a university. In this case, the researcher is not interested in the average age of all beginning nursing students; instead, he is interested in *comparing* the means of the two groups. His research question is, Does the mean age of nursing students who enroll at a community college differ from the mean age of nursing students who enroll at a university? Here, the hypotheses are

$$H_0: \mu_1 = \mu_2$$
$$H_1: \mu_1 \neq \mu_2$$

where

$\mu_1 =$ mean age of all beginning nursing students at the community college
$\mu_2 =$ mean age of all beginning nursing students at the university

Another way of stating the hypotheses for this situation is

$$H_0: \mu_1 - \mu_2 = 0$$
$$H_1: \mu_1 - \mu_2 \neq 0$$

If there is no difference in population means, subtracting them will give a difference of zero. If they are different, subtracting will give a number other than zero. Both methods of stating hypotheses are correct; however, the first method will be used in this book.

Assumptions for the Test to Determine the Difference Between Two Means

1. The samples must be independent of each other. That is, there can be no relationship between the subjects in each sample.
2. The standard deviations of both populations must be known, and if the sample sizes are less than 30, the populations must be normally or approximately normally distributed.

The theory behind testing the difference between two means is based on selecting pairs of samples and comparing the means of the pairs. The population means need not be known.

All possible pairs of samples are taken from populations. The means for each pair of samples are computed and then subtracted, and the differences are plotted. If both populations have the same mean, then most of the differences will be zero or close to zero.

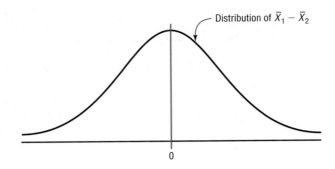

Figure 9–1

Differences of Means of Pairs of Samples

$\mathcal{U}$*nusual Stats*

Adult children who live with their parents spend more than 2 hours a day doing household chores. According to a study, daughters contribute about 17 hours a week and sons about 14.4 hours.

Occasionally, there will be a few large differences due to chance alone, some positive and others negative. If the differences are plotted, the curve will be shaped like a normal distribution and have a mean of zero, as shown in Figure 9–1.

The variance of the difference $\overline{X}_1 - \overline{X}_2$ is equal to the sum of the individual variances of $\overline{X}_1$ and $\overline{X}_2$. That is,

$$\sigma^2_{\overline{X}_1 - \overline{X}_2} = \sigma^2_{\overline{X}_1} + \sigma^2_{\overline{X}_2}$$

where $\qquad \sigma^2_{\overline{X}_1} = \dfrac{\sigma^2_1}{n_1} \qquad$ and $\qquad \sigma^2_{\overline{X}_2} = \dfrac{\sigma^2_2}{n_2}$

So the standard deviation of $\overline{X}_1 - \overline{X}_2$ is

$$\sqrt{\dfrac{\sigma^2_1}{n_1} + \dfrac{\sigma^2_2}{n_2}}$$

Formula for the *z* Test for Comparing Two Means from Independent Populations

$$z = \dfrac{(\overline{X}_1 - \overline{X}_2) - (\mu_1 - \mu_2)}{\sqrt{\dfrac{\sigma^2_1}{n_1} + \dfrac{\sigma^2_2}{n_2}}}$$

This formula is based on the general format of

$$\text{Test value} = \dfrac{(\text{observed value}) - (\text{expected value})}{\text{standard error}}$$

where $\overline{X}_1 - \overline{X}_2$ is the observed difference, and the expected difference $\mu_1 - \mu_2$ is zero when the null hypothesis is $\mu_1 = \mu_2$, since that is equivalent to $\mu_1 - \mu_2 = 0$. Finally, the standard error of the difference is

$$\sqrt{\dfrac{\sigma^2_1}{n_1} + \dfrac{\sigma^2_2}{n_2}}$$

In the comparison of two sample means, the difference may be due to chance, in which case the null hypothesis will not be rejected, and the researcher can assume that the means of the populations are basically the same. The difference in this case is not significant. See Figure 9–2(a). On the other hand, if the difference is significant, the null hypothesis is rejected and the researcher can conclude that the population means are different. See Figure 9–2(b).

Figure 9–2

Hypothesis-Testing Situations in the Comparison of Means

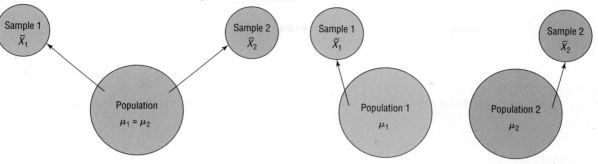

(a) Difference is not significant

Do not reject H_0: $\mu_1 = \mu_2$ since $\bar{X}_1 - \bar{X}_2$ is not significant.

(b) Difference is significant

Reject H_0: $\mu_1 = \mu_2$ since $\bar{X}_1 - \bar{X}_2$ is significant.

These tests can also be one-tailed, using the following hypotheses:

Right-tailed			Left-tailed		
H_0: $\mu_1 = \mu_2$	or	H_0: $\mu_1 - \mu_2 = 0$	H_0: $\mu_1 = \mu_2$	or	H_0: $\mu_1 - \mu_2 = 0$
H_1: $\mu_1 > \mu_2$		H_1: $\mu_1 - \mu_2 > 0$	H_1: $\mu_1 < \mu_2$		H_1: $\mu_1 - \mu_2 < 0$

The same critical values used in Section 8–2 are used here. They can be obtained from Table E in Appendix C.

If σ_1^2 and σ_2^2 are not known, the researcher can use the variances from each sample s_1^2 and s_2^2, but a t test must be used. This will be explained in Section 9–2.

The basic format for hypothesis testing using the traditional method is reviewed here.

Step 1 State the hypotheses and identify the claim.

Step 2 Find the critical value(s).

Step 3 Compute the test value.

Step 4 Make the decision.

Step 5 Summarize the results.

Example 9–1

Hotel Room Cost

A survey found that the average hotel room rate in New Orleans is $88.42 and the average room rate in Phoenix is $80.61. Assume that the data were obtained from two samples of 50 hotels each and that the standard deviations of the populations are $5.62 and $4.83, respectively. At $\alpha = 0.05$, can it be concluded that there is a significant difference in the rates?

Source: *USA TODAY.*

Solution

Step 1 State the hypotheses and identify the claim.

$$H_0: \mu_1 = \mu_2 \qquad \text{and} \qquad H_1: \mu_1 \neq \mu_2 \text{ (claim)}$$

Step 2 Find the critical values. Since $\alpha = 0.05$, the critical values are $+1.96$ and -1.96.

Step 3 Compute the test value.

$$z = \frac{(\overline{X}_1 - \overline{X}_2) - (\mu_1 - \mu_2)}{\sqrt{\dfrac{\sigma_1^2}{n_1} + \dfrac{\sigma_2^2}{n_2}}} = \frac{(88.42 - 80.61) - 0}{\sqrt{\dfrac{5.62^2}{50} + \dfrac{4.83^2}{50}}} = 7.45$$

Step 4 Make the decision. Reject the null hypothesis at $\alpha = 0.05$, since $7.45 > 1.96$. See Figure 9–3.

Figure 9–3

Critical and Test Values for Example 9–1

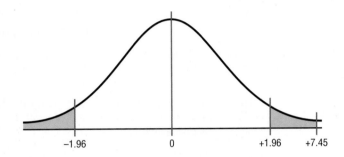

Step 5 Summarize the results. There is enough evidence to support the claim that the means are not equal. Hence, there is a significant difference in the rates.

The *P*-values for this test can be determined by using the same procedure shown in Section 8–2. For example, if the test value for a two-tailed test is 1.40, then the *P*-value obtained from Table E is 0.1616. This value is obtained by looking up the area for $z = 1.40$, which is 0.9192. Then 0.9192 is subtracted from 1.0000 to get 0.0808. Finally, this value is doubled to get 0.1616 since the test is two-tailed. If $\alpha = 0.05$, the decision would be to not reject the null hypothesis, since *P*-value $> \alpha$.

The *P*-value method for hypothesis testing for this chapter also follows the same format as stated in Chapter 8. The steps are reviewed here.

Step 1 State the hypotheses and identify the claim.

Step 2 Compute the test value.

Step 3 Find the *P*-value.

Step 4 Make the decision.

Step 5 Summarize the results.

Example 9–2 illustrates these steps.

Example 9–2

College Sports Offerings

A researcher hypothesizes that the average number of sports that colleges offer for males is greater than the average number of sports that colleges offer for females. A sample of the number of sports offered by colleges is shown. At $\alpha = 0.10$, is there enough evidence to support the claim? Assume σ_1 and $\sigma_2 = 3.3$.

	Males					Females			
6	11	11	8	15	6	8	11	13	8
6	14	8	12	18	7	5	13	14	6
6	9	5	6	9	6	5	5	7	6
6	9	18	7	6	10	7	6	5	5
15	6	11	5	5	16	10	7	8	5
9	9	5	5	8	7	5	5	6	5
8	9	6	11	6	9	18	13	7	10
9	5	11	5	8	7	8	5	7	6
7	7	5	10	7	11	4	6	8	7
10	7	10	8	11	14	12	5	8	5

Source: *USA TODAY.*

Solution

Step 1 State the hypotheses and identify the claim.

$$H_0: \mu_1 = \mu_2 \qquad \text{and} \qquad H_1: \mu_1 > \mu_2 \text{ (claim)}$$

Step 2 Compute the test value. Using a calculator or the formula in Chapter 3, find the mean for each data set.

For the males $\overline{X}_1 = 8.6$ and $\sigma_1 = 3.3$

For the females $\overline{X}_2 = 7.9$ and $\sigma_2 = 3.3$

Substitute in the formula.

$$z = \frac{(\overline{X}_1 - \overline{X}_2) - (\mu_1 - \mu_2)}{\sqrt{\dfrac{\sigma_1^2}{n_1} + \dfrac{\sigma_2^2}{n_2}}} = \frac{(8.6 - 7.9) - 0}{\sqrt{\dfrac{3.3^2}{50} + \dfrac{3.3^2}{50}}} = 1.06*$$

Step 3 Find the *P*-value. For $z = 1.06$, the area is 0.8554, and $1.0000 - 0.8554 = 0.1446$, or a *P*-value of 0.1446.

Step 4 Make the decision. Since the *P*-value is larger than α (that is, $0.1446 > 0.10$), the decision is to not reject the null hypothesis. See Figure 9–4.

Step 5 Summarize the results. There is not enough evidence to support the claim that colleges offer more sports for males than they do for females.

Figure 9–4

P-Value and α Value for Example 9–2

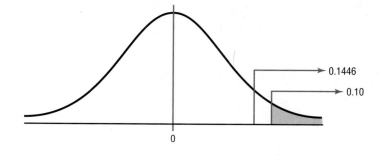

Note: Calculator results may differ due to rounding.

Sometimes, the researcher is interested in testing a specific difference in means other than zero. For example, he or she might hypothesize that the nursing students at a community college are, on average, 3.2 years older than those at a university. In this case, the hypotheses are

$$H_0: \mu_1 - \mu_2 = 3.2 \quad \text{and} \quad H_1: \mu_1 - \mu_2 > 3.2$$

The formula for the z test is still

$$z = \frac{(\bar{X}_1 - \bar{X}_2) - (\mu_1 - \mu_2)}{\sqrt{\dfrac{\sigma_1^2}{n_1} + \dfrac{\sigma_2^2}{n_2}}}$$

where $\mu_1 - \mu_2$ is the hypothesized difference or expected value. In this case, $\mu_1 - \mu_2 = 3.2$.

Confidence intervals for the difference between two means can also be found. When you are hypothesizing a difference of zero, if the confidence interval contains zero, the null hypothesis is not rejected. If the confidence interval does not contain zero, the null hypothesis is rejected.

Confidence intervals for the difference between two means can be found by using this formula:

Formula for the z Confidence Interval for Difference Between Two Means

$$(\bar{X}_1 - \bar{X}_2) - z_{\alpha/2}\sqrt{\frac{\sigma_1^2}{n_1} + \frac{\sigma_2^2}{n_2}} < \mu_1 - \mu_2 < (\bar{X}_1 - \bar{X}_2) + z_{\alpha/2}\sqrt{\frac{\sigma_1^2}{n_1} + \frac{\sigma_2^2}{n_2}}$$

Example 9–3

Find the 95% confidence interval for the difference between the means for the data in Example 9–1.

Solution

Substitute in the formula, using $z_{\alpha/2} = 1.96$.

$$(\bar{X}_1 - \bar{X}_2) - z_{\alpha/2}\sqrt{\frac{\sigma_1^2}{n_1} + \frac{\sigma_2^2}{n_2}} < \mu_1 - \mu_2$$

$$< (\bar{X}_1 - \bar{X}_2) + z_{\alpha/2}\sqrt{\frac{\sigma_1^2}{n_1} + \frac{\sigma_2^2}{n_2}}$$

$$(88.42 - 80.61) - 1.96\sqrt{\frac{5.62^2}{50} + \frac{4.83^2}{50}} < \mu_1 - \mu_2$$

$$< (88.42 - 80.61) + 1.96\sqrt{\frac{5.62^2}{50} + \frac{4.83^2}{50}}$$

$$7.81 - 2.05 < \mu_1 - \mu_2 < 7.81 + 2.05$$

$$5.76 < \mu_1 - \mu_2 < 9.86$$

Since the confidence interval does not contain zero, the decision is to reject the null hypothesis, which agrees with the previous result.

Applying the Concepts **9–1**

Home Runs

For a sports radio talk show, you are asked to research the question whether more home runs are hit by players in the National League or by players in the American League. You decide to use the home run leaders from each league for a 40-year period as your data. The numbers are shown.

National League

47	49	73	50	65	70	49	47	40	43
46	35	38	40	47	39	49	37	37	36
40	37	31	48	48	45	52	38	38	36
44	40	48	45	45	36	39	44	52	47

American League

47	57	52	47	48	56	56	52	50	40
46	43	44	51	36	42	49	49	40	43
39	39	22	41	45	46	39	32	36	32
32	32	37	33	44	49	44	44	49	32

Using the data given, answer the following questions.

1. Define a population.
2. What kind of sample was used?
3. Do you feel that it is representative?
4. What are your hypotheses?
5. What significance level will you use?
6. What statistical test will you use?
7. What are the test results? (Assume $\sigma_1 = 8.8$ and $\sigma_2 = 7.8$.)
8. What is your decision?
9. What can you conclude?
10. Do you feel that using the data given really answers the original question asked?
11. What other data might be used to answer the question?

See pages 525 and 526 for the answers.

Exercises 9–1

1. Explain the difference between testing a single mean and testing the difference between two means.

2. When a researcher selects all possible pairs of samples from a population in order to find the difference between the means of each pair, what will be the shape of the distribution of the differences when the original distributions are normally distributed? What will be the mean of the distribution? What will be the standard deviation of the distribution?

3. What two assumptions must be met when you are using the z test to test differences between two means? Can the sample standard deviations s_1 and s_2 be used in place of the population standard deviations σ_1 and σ_2?

4. Show two different ways to state that the means of two populations are equal.

For Exercises 5 through 17, perform each of the following steps.

a. State the hypotheses and identify the claim.
b. Find the critical value(s).
c. Compute the test value.
d. Make the decision.
e. Summarize the results.

Use the traditional method of hypothesis testing unless otherwise specified.

5. **Lengths of Major U.S. Rivers** A researcher wishes to see if the average length of the major rivers in the United States is the same as the average length of the major rivers in Europe. The data (in miles) of a sample of rivers are shown. At $\alpha = 0.01$, is there enough evidence to reject the claim? Assume $\sigma_1 = 450$ and $\sigma_2 = 474$.

United States			Europe		
729	560	434	481	724	820
329	332	360	532	357	505
450	2315	865	1776	1122	496
330	410	1036	1224	634	230
329	800	447	1420	326	626
600	1310	652	877	580	210
1243	605	360	447	567	252
525	926	722	824	932	600
850	310	430	634	1124	1575
532	375	1979	565	405	2290
710	545	259	675	454	
300	470	425			

Source: *The World Almanac and Book of Facts.*

6. Wind Speeds The average wind speed in Casper, Wyoming, has been found to be 12.7 miles per hour, and in Phoenix, Arizona, it is 6.2 miles per hour. To test the relationship between the averages, the average wind speed was calculated for a sample of 31 days for each city. The results are reported below. Is there sufficient evidence at $\alpha = 0.05$ to conclude that the average wind speed is greater in Casper than in Phoenix?

	Casper	Phoenix
Sample size	31	31
Sample mean	12.85 mph	7.9 mph
Population standard deviation	3.3 mph	2.8 mph

Source: *World Almanac.*

7. Commuting Times The Bureau of the Census reports that the average commuting time for citizens of both Baltimore, Maryland, and Miami, Florida, is approximately 29 minutes. To see if their commuting times appear to be any different in the winter, random samples of 40 drivers were surveyed in each city and the average commuting time for the month of January was calculated for both cities. The results are provided below. At the 0.05 level of significance, can it be concluded that the commuting times are different in the winter?

	Miami	Baltimore
Sample size	40	40
Sample mean	28.5 min	35.2 min
Population standard deviation	7.2 min	9.1 min

Source: www.census.gov

8. Heights of 9-Year-Olds At age 9 the average weight (21.3 kg) and the average height (124.5 cm) for both boys and girls are exactly the same. A random sample of 9-year-olds yielded these results. Estimate the mean difference in height between boys and girls with 95% confidence. Does your interval support the given claim?

	Boys	Girls
Sample size	60	50
Mean height, cm	123.5	126.2
Population variance	98	120

Source: www.healthepic.com

9. Length of Hospital Stays The average length of "short hospital stays" for men is slightly longer than that for women, 5.2 days versus 4.5 days. A random sample of recent hospital stays for both men and women revealed the following. At $\alpha = 0.01$, is there sufficient evidence to conclude that the average hospital stay for men is longer than the average hospital stay for women?

	Men	Women
Sample size	32	30
Sample mean	5.5 days	4.2 days
Population standard deviation	1.2 days	1.5 days

Source: www.cdc.gov/nchs

10. Home Prices A real estate agent compares the selling prices of homes in two municipalities in southwestern Pennsylvania to see if there is a difference. The results of the study are shown. Is there enough evidence to reject the claim that the average cost of a home in both locations is the same? Use $\alpha = 0.01$.

Scott	Ligonier
$\bar{X}_1 = \$93{,}430^*$	$\bar{X}_2 = \$98{,}043^*$
$\sigma_1 = \$5602$	$\sigma_2 = \$4731$
$n_1 = 35$	$n_2 = 40$

*Based on information from RealSTATs.

11. Women Science Majors In a study of women science majors, the following data were obtained on two groups, those who left their profession within a few months after graduation (leavers) and those who remained in their profession after they graduated (stayers). Test the claim that those who stayed had a higher science grade point average than those who left. Use $\alpha = 0.05$.

Leavers	Stayers
$\bar{X}_1 = 3.16$	$\bar{X}_2 = 3.28$
$\sigma_1 = 0.52$	$\sigma_2 = 0.46$
$n_1 = 103$	$n_2 = 225$

Source: Paula Rayman and Belle Brett, "Women Science Majors: What Makes a Difference in Persistence after Graduation?" *The Journal of Higher Education.*

12. ACT Scores A survey of 1000 students nationwide showed a mean ACT score of 21.4. A survey of 500 Ohio scores showed a mean of 20.8. If the population standard deviation in each case is 3, can we conclude that Ohio is below the national average? Use $\alpha = 0.05$.

Source: Report of WFIN radio.

13. Money Spent on College Sports A school administrator hypothesizes that colleges spend more for male sports than they do for female sports. A sample of two different colleges is selected, and the annual expenses (in dollars) per student at each school are shown. At $\alpha = 0.01$, is there enough evidence to support the claim? Assume $\sigma_1 = 3830$ and $\sigma_2 = 2745$.

Males

7,040	6,576	1,664	12,919	8,605
22,220	3,377	10,128	7,723	2,063
8,033	9,463	7,656	11,456	12,244
6,670	12,371	9,626	5,472	16,175
8,383	623	6,797	10,160	8,725
14,029	13,763	8,811	11,480	9,544
15,048	5,544	10,652	11,267	10,126
8,796	13,351	7,120	9,505	9,571
7,551	5,811	9,119	9,732	5,286
5,254	7,550	11,015	12,403	12,703

Females

10,333	6,407	10,082	5,933	3,991
7,435	8,324	6,989	16,249	5,922
7,654	8,411	11,324	10,248	6,030
9,331	6,869	6,502	11,041	11,597
5,468	7,874	9,277	10,127	13,371
7,055	6,909	8,903	6,925	7,058
12,745	12,016	9,883	14,698	9,907
8,917	9,110	5,232	6,959	5,832
7,054	7,235	11,248	8,478	6,502
7,300	993	6,815	9,959	10,353

Source: *USA TODAY.*

14. Monthly Social Security Benefits The average monthly Social Security benefit in 2004 for retired workers was $954.90 and for disabled workers was $894.10. Researchers used data from the Social Security records to test the claim that the difference in monthly benefits between the two groups was greater than $30. Based on the following information, can the researchers' claim be supported at the 0.05 level of significance?

	Retired	Disabled
Sample size	60	60
Mean benefit	$960.50	$902.89
Population standard deviation	$98	$101

Source: *New York Times Almanac.*

15. Self-Esteem Scores In the study cited in Exercise 11, the researchers collected the data shown here on a self-esteem questionnaire. At $\alpha = 0.05$, can it be concluded that there is a difference in the self-esteem scores of the two groups? Use the *P*-value method.

Leavers	Stayers
$\bar{X}_1 = 3.05$	$\bar{X}_2 = 2.96$
$\sigma_1 = 0.75$	$\sigma_2 = 0.75$
$n_1 = 103$	$n_2 = 225$

Source: Paula Rayman and Belle Brett, "Women Science Majors: What Makes a Difference in Persistence after Graduation?" *The Journal of Higher Education.*

16. Ages of College Students The dean of students wants to see whether there is a significant difference in ages of resident students and commuting students. She selects a sample of 50 students from each group. The ages are shown here. At $\alpha = 0.05$, decide if there is enough

evidence to reject the claim of no difference in the ages of the two groups. Use the standard deviations from the samples and the *P*-value method. Assume $\sigma_1 = 3.68$ and $\sigma_2 = 4.7$.

Resident students

22	25	27	23	26	28	26	24
25	20	26	24	27	26	18	19
18	30	26	18	18	19	32	23
19	19	18	29	19	22	18	22
26	19	19	21	23	18	20	18
22	21	19	21	21	22	18	20
19	23						

Commuter students

18	20	19	18	22	25	24	35
23	18	23	22	28	25	20	24
26	30	22	22	22	21	18	20
19	26	35	19	19	18	19	32
29	23	21	19	36	27	27	20
20	21	18	19	23	20	19	19
20	25						

17. Problem-Solving Ability Two groups of students are given a problem-solving test, and the results are compared. Find the 90% confidence interval of the true difference in means.

Mathematics majors	Computer science majors
$\bar{X}_1 = 83.6$	$\bar{X}_2 = 79.2$
$\sigma_1 = 4.3$	$\sigma_2 = 3.8$
$n_1 = 36$	$n_2 = 36$

18. Credit Card Debt The average credit card debt for a recent year was $9205. Five years earlier the average credit card debt was $6618. Assume sample sizes of 35 were used and the population standard deviations of both samples were $1928. Is there enough evidence to believe that the average credit card debt has increased? Use $\alpha = 0.05$. Give a possible reason as to why or why not the debt was increased.

Source: CardWeb.com

19. Literacy Scores Adults aged 16 or older were assessed in three types of literacy in 2003: prose, document, and quantitative. The scores in document literacy were the same for 19- to 24-year-olds and for 40- to 49-year-olds. A random sample of scores from a later year showed the following statistics.

Age group	Mean score	Population standard deviation	Sample size
19–24	280	56.2	40
40–49	315	52.1	35

Construct a 95% confidence interval for the true difference in mean scores for these two groups. What does your interval say about the claim that there is no difference in mean scores?

Source: www.nces.ed.gov

20. **Battery Voltage** Two brands of batteries are tested, and their voltage is compared. The data follow. Find the 95% confidence interval of the true difference in the means. Assume that both variables are normally distributed.

Brand X	Brand Y
$\bar{X}_1 = 9.2$ volts	$\bar{X}_2 = 8.8$ volts
$\sigma_1 = 0.3$ volt	$\sigma_2 = 0.1$ volt
$n_1 = 27$	$n_2 = 30$

Extending the Concepts

21. **Exam Scores at Private and Public Schools** A researcher claims that students in a private school have exam scores that are at most 8 points higher than those of students in public schools. Random samples of 60 students from each type of school are selected and given an exam. The results are shown. At $\alpha = 0.05$, test the claim.

Private school	Public school
$\bar{X}_1 = 110$	$\bar{X}_2 = 104$
$\sigma_1 = 15$	$\sigma_2 = 15$
$n_1 = 60$	$n_2 = 60$

Technology *Step by Step*

TI-83 Plus or TI-84 Plus

Step by Step

Hypothesis Test for the Difference Between Two Means and *z* Distribution (Data)

1. Enter the data values into L_1 and L_2.
2. Press **STAT** and move the cursor to TESTS.
3. Press **3** for 2-SampZTest.
4. Move the cursor to Data and press **ENTER**.
5. Type in the appropriate values.
6. Move the cursor to the appropriate alternative hypothesis and press **ENTER**.
7. Move the cursor to Calculate and press **ENTER**.

Hypothesis Test for the Difference Between Two Means and *z* Distribution (Statistics)

1. Press **STAT** and move the cursor to TESTS.
2. Press **3** for 2-SampZTest.
3. Move the cursor to Stats and press **ENTER**.
4. Type in the appropriate values.
5. Move the cursor to the appropriate alternative hypothesis and press **ENTER**.
6. Move the cursor to Calculate and press **ENTER**.

Confidence Interval for the Difference Between Two Means and *z* Distribution (Data)

1. Enter the data values into L_1 and L_2.
2. Press **STAT** and move the cursor to TESTS.
3. Press **9** for 2-SampZInt.
4. Move the cursor to Data and press **ENTER**.
5. Type in the appropriate values.
6. Move the cursor to Calculate and press **ENTER**.

Confidence Interval for the Difference Between Two Means and *z* Distribution (Statistics)

1. Press **STAT** and move the cursor to TESTS.
2. Press **9** for 2-SampZInt.
3. Move the cursor to Stats and press **ENTER**.
4. Type in the appropriate values.
5. Move the cursor to Calculate and press **ENTER**.

Excel
Step by Step

z Test for the Difference Between Two Means

Excel has a two-sample *z* test included in the Data Analysis Add-in. To perform a *z* test for the difference between the means of two populations, given two independent samples, do this:

1. Enter the first sample data set into column A.
2. Enter the second sample data set into column B.
3. If the population variances are not known but $n \geq 30$ for both samples, use the formulas =VAR(A1:A*n*) and =VAR(B1:B*n*), where A*n* and B*n* are the last cells with data in each column, to find the variances of the sample data sets.
4. Select the Data tab from the toolbar. Then select **Data Analysis**.
5. In the Analysis Tools box, select *z* test: Two sample for Means.
6. Type the ranges for the data in columns A and B and type a value (usually 0) for the Hypothesized Mean Difference.
7. If the population variances are known, type them for Variable 1 and Variable 2. Otherwise, use the sample variances obtained in step 3.
8. Specify the confidence level Alpha.
9. Specify a location for the output, and click [OK].

Example XL9–1

 Test the claim that the two population means are equal, using the sample data provided here, at $\alpha = 0.05$. Assume the population variances are $\sigma_A^2 = 10.067$ and $\sigma_B^2 = 7.067$.

Set A	10	2	15	18	13	15	16	14	18	12	15	15	14	18	16
Set B	5	8	10	9	9	11	12	16	8	8	9	10	11	7	6

The two-sample *z* test dialog box is shown (before the variances are entered); the results appear in the table that Excel generates. Note that the *P*-value and critical *z* value are provided for both the one-tailed test and the two-tailed test. The *P*-values here are expressed in scientific notation: 7.09045E-06 = 7.09045×10^{-6} = 0.00000709045. Because this value is less than 0.05, we reject the null hypothesis and conclude that the population means are not equal.

Two-Sample *z* Test
Dialog Box

```
z-Test: Two Sample for Means                    [?] [X]

 ┌─Input────────────────────────────────┐    ┌──────────┐
 │ Variable 1 Range:    $A$1:$A$15    🔲 │    │    OK    │
 │                                       │    └──────────┘
 │ Variable 2 Range:    $B$1:$B$15    🔲 │    ┌──────────┐
 │                                       │    │  Cancel  │
 │ Hypothesized Mean Difference:  0      │    └──────────┘
 │                                       │    ┌──────────┐
 │ Variable 1 Variance (known):          │    │   Help   │
 │                                       │    └──────────┘
 │ Variable 2 Variance (known):          │
 │                                       │
 │ ☐ Labels                              │
 │                                       │
 │ Alpha:  0.05                          │
 └───────────────────────────────────────┘
 ┌─Output options────────────────────────┐
 │ ⦿ Output Range:      e3            🔲  │
 │ ○ New Worksheet Ply:                  │
 │ ○ New Workbook                        │
 └───────────────────────────────────────┘
```

z-Test: Two Sample for Means		
	Variable 1	Variable 2
Mean	14.06666667	9.266666667
Known Variance	10.067	7.067
Observations	15	15
Hypothesized Mean Difference	0	
z	4.491149228	
P(Z<=z) one-tail	3.54522E-06	
z Critical one-tail	1.644853	
P(Z<=z) two-tail	7.09045E-06	
z Critical two-tail	1.959961082	

9–2   Testing the Difference Between Two Means of Independent Samples: Using the *t* Test

In Section 9–1, the *z* test was used to test the difference between two means when the population standard deviations were known and the variables were normally or approximately normally distributed, or when both sample sizes were greater than or equal to 30. In many situations, however, these conditions cannot be met—that is, the population standard deviations are not known. In these cases, a *t* test is used to test the difference between means when the two samples are independent and when the samples are taken from two normally or approximately normally distributed populations. Samples are **independent samples** when they are not related.

Objective 2

Test the difference between two means for independent samples, using the *t* test.

Formula for the *t* Test–For Testing the Difference Between Two Means–Independent Samples

Variances are assumed to be unequal:

$$t = \frac{(\bar{X}_1 - \bar{X}_2) - (\mu_1 - \mu_2)}{\sqrt{\dfrac{s_1^2}{n_1} + \dfrac{s_2^2}{n_2}}}$$

where the degrees of freedom are equal to the smaller of $n_1 - 1$ or $n_2 - 1$.

The formula

$$t = \frac{(\bar{X}_1 - \bar{X}_2) - (\mu_1 - \mu_2)}{\sqrt{\dfrac{s_1^2}{n_1} + \dfrac{s_2^2}{n_2}}}$$

follows the format of

$$\text{Test value} = \frac{(\text{observed value}) - (\text{expected value})}{\text{standard error}}$$

where $\bar{X}_1 - \bar{X}_2$ is the observed difference between sample means and where the expected value $\mu_1 - \mu_2$ is equal to zero when no difference between population means is hypothesized. The denominator $\sqrt{s_1^2/n_1 + s_2^2/n_2}$ is the standard error of the difference between two means. Since mathematical derivation of the standard error is somewhat complicated, it will be omitted here.

Example 9–4	**Farm Sizes**

The average size of a farm in Indiana County, Pennsylvania, is 191 acres. The average size of a farm in Greene County, Pennsylvania, is 199 acres. Assume the data were obtained from two samples with standard deviations of 38 and 12 acres, respectively, and sample sizes of 8 and 10, respectively. Can it be concluded at $\alpha = 0.05$ that the average size of the farms in the two counties is different? Assume the populations are normally distributed.

Source: *Pittsburgh Tribune-Review.*

Solution

Step 1 State the hypotheses and identify the claim for the means.

$$H_0: \mu_1 = \mu_2 \quad \text{and} \quad H_1: \mu_1 \neq \mu_2 \text{ (claim)}$$

Step 2 Find the critical values. Since the test is two-tailed, since $\alpha = 0.05$, and since the variances are unequal, the degrees of freedom are the smaller of $n_1 - 1$ or $n_2 - 1$. In this case, the degrees of freedom are $8 - 1 = 7$. Hence, from Table F, the critical values are $+2.365$ and -2.365.

Step 3 Compute the test value. Since the variances are unequal, use the first formula.

$$t = \frac{(\bar{X}_1 - \bar{X}_2) - (\mu_1 - \mu_2)}{\sqrt{\dfrac{s_1^2}{n_1} + \dfrac{s_2^2}{n_2}}} = \frac{(191 - 199) - 0}{\sqrt{\dfrac{38^2}{8} + \dfrac{12^2}{10}}} = -0.57$$

Step 4 Make the decision. Do not reject the null hypothesis, since $-0.57 > -2.365$. See Figure 9–5.

Figure 9–5	
Critical and Test Values for Example 9–4	

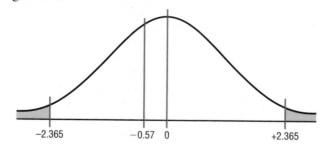

Step 5 Summarize the results. There is not enough evidence to support the claim that the average size of the farms is different.

When raw data are given in the exercises, use your calculator or the formulas in Chapter 3 to find the means and variances for the data sets. Then follow the procedures shown in this section to test the hypotheses.

Confidence intervals can also be found for the difference between two means with this formula:

Confidence Intervals for the Difference of Two Means: Independent Samples

Variances assumed to be unequal:

$$(\bar{X}_1 - \bar{X}_2) - t_{\alpha/2}\sqrt{\frac{s_1^2}{n_1} + \frac{s_2^2}{n_2}} < \mu_1 - \mu_2 < (\bar{X}_1 - \bar{X}_2) + t_{\alpha/2}\sqrt{\frac{s_1^2}{n_1} + \frac{s_2^2}{n_2}}$$

d.f. = smaller value of $n_1 - 1$ or $n_2 - 1$

| Example 9–5 | Find the 95% confidence interval for the data in Example 9–4. |

Solution

Substitute in the formula.

$$(\bar{X}_1 - \bar{X}_2) - t_{\alpha/2}\sqrt{\frac{s_1^2}{n_1} + \frac{s_2^2}{n_2}} < \mu_1 - \mu_2$$

$$< (\bar{X}_1 - \bar{X}_2) + t_{\alpha/2}\sqrt{\frac{s_1^2}{n_1} + \frac{s_2^2}{n_2}}$$

$$(191 - 199) - 2.365\sqrt{\frac{38^2}{8} + \frac{12^2}{10}} < \mu_1 - \mu_2$$

$$< (191 - 199) + 2.365\sqrt{\frac{38^2}{8} + \frac{12^2}{10}}$$

$$-41.02 < \mu_1 - \mu_2 < 25.02$$

Since 0 is contained in the interval, the decision is to not reject the null hypothesis H_0: $\mu_1 = \mu_2$.

In many statistical software packages, a different method is used to compute the degrees of freedom for this t test. They are determined by the formula

$$\text{d.f.} = \frac{(s_1^2/n_1 + s_2^2/n_2)^2}{(s_1^2/n_1)^2/(n_1 - 1) + (s_2^2/n_2)^2/(n_2 - 1)}$$

This formula will not be used in this textbook.

There are actually two different options for the use of t tests. *One option is used when the variances of the populations are not equal, and the other option is used when the variances are equal.* To determine whether two sample variances are equal, the researcher can use an F test, as shown in Section 9–5.

When the variances are assumed to be equal, this formula is used and

$$t = \frac{(\bar{X}_1 - \bar{X}_2) - (\mu_1 - \mu_2)}{\sqrt{\dfrac{(n_1 - 1)s_1^2 + (n_2 - 1)s_2^2}{n_1 + n_2 - 2}}\sqrt{\dfrac{1}{n_1} + \dfrac{1}{n_2}}}$$

follows the format of

$$\text{Test value} = \frac{(\text{observed value}) - (\text{expected value})}{\text{standard error}}$$

For the numerator, the terms are the same as in the previously given formula. However, a note of explanation is needed for the denominator of the second test statistic. Since both populations are assumed to have the same variance, the standard error is computed with what is called a pooled estimate of the variance. A **pooled estimate of the variance** is a weighted average of the variance using the two sample variances and the *degrees of freedom* of each variance as the weights. Again, since the algebraic derivation of the standard error is somewhat complicated, it is omitted.

Note, however, that not all statisticians are in agreement about using the F test before using the t test. Some believe that conducting the F and t tests at the same level of significance will change the overall level of significance of the t test. Their reasons are beyond the scope of this textbook. Because of this, we will assume that $\sigma_1 \neq \sigma_2$ in this textbook.

Applying the Concepts 9–2

Too Long on the Telephone

A company collects data on the lengths of telephone calls made by employees in two different divisions. The mean and standard deviation for the sales division are 10.26 and 8.56, respectively. The mean and standard deviation for the shipping and receiving division are 6.93 and 4.93, respectively. A hypothesis test was run, and the computer output follows.

> Significance level = 0.01
> Degrees of freedom = 56
> Confidence interval limits = −0.18979, 6.84979
> Test statistic $t = 1.89566$
> Critical value $t = −2.0037, 2.0037$
> *P*-value = 0.06317
> Significance level = 0.05

1. Are the samples independent or dependent?
2. How many were in the study?
3. Which number from the output is compared to the significance level to check if the null hypothesis should be rejected?
4. Which number from the output gives the probability of a type I error that is calculated from the sample data?
5. Which number from the output is the result of dividing the two sample variances?
6. Was a right-, left-, or two-tailed test done? Why?
7. What are your conclusions?
8. What would your conclusions be if the level of significance were initially set at 0.10?

See page 526 for the answers.

Exercises 9–2

For Exercises 1 through 11, perform each of these steps. Assume that all variables are normally or approximately normally distributed.

    a. State the hypotheses and identify the claim.
    b. Find the critical value(s).
    c. Compute the test value.
    d. Make the decision.
    e. Summarize the results.

Use the traditional method of hypothesis testing unless otherwise specified.

1. **Assessed Home Values** A real estate agent wishes to determine whether tax assessors and real estate appraisers agree on the values of homes. A random sample of the two groups appraised 10 homes. The data are shown here. Is there a significant difference in the values of the homes for each group? Let $\alpha = 0.05$. Find the 95% confidence interval for the difference of the means.

Real estate appraisers	Tax assessors
$\overline{X}_1 = \$83{,}256$	$\overline{X}_2 = \$88{,}354$
$s_1 = \$3256$	$s_2 = \$2341$
$n_1 = 10$	$n_2 = 10$

2. **Hours Spent Watching Television** According to the Nielsen Media Research, children (ages 2–11) spend an average of 21 hours 30 minutes watching television per week while teens (ages 12–17) spend an average of 20 hours 40 minutes. Based on the sample statistics obtained below, is there sufficient evidence to conclude a difference in average television watching times between the two groups? Use $\alpha = 0.01$.

	Children	Teens
Sample mean	22.45	18.50
Sample variance	16.4	18.2
Sample size	15	15

Source: *Time Almanac.*

3. **NFL Salaries** An agent claims that there is no difference between the pay of safeties and linebackers in the NFL. A survey of 15 safeties found an average salary of $501,580, and a survey of 15 linebackers found an average salary of $513,360. If the standard deviation in the first sample was $20,000 and the standard deviation in the second sample is $18,000, is the agent correct? Use $\alpha = 0.05$.

Source: *NFL Players Assn./USA TODAY.*

4. **Cyber School Enrollment** The data show the number of students attending cyber charter schools in Allegheny County and the number of students attending

cyber schools in counties surrounding Allegheny County. At $\alpha = 0.01$ is there enough evidence to support the claim that the average number of students in school districts in Allegheny County who attend cyber schools is greater than those who attend cyber schools in school districts outside Allegheny County? Give a factor that should be considered in interpreting this answer.

Allegheny County	Outside Allegheny County
25 75 38 41 27 32	57 25 38 14 10 29

Source: *Pittsburgh Tribune-Review.*

5. **Ages of Homes** Whiting, Indiana, leads the "Top 100 Cities with the Oldest Houses" list with the average age of houses being 66.4 years. Farther down the list resides Franklin, Pennsylvania, with an average house age of 59.4 years. Researchers selected a random sample of 20 houses in each city and obtained the following statistics. At $\alpha = 0.05$, can it be concluded that the houses in Whiting are older? Use the *P*-value method.

	Whiting	Franklin
Mean age	62.1 years	55.6 years
Standard deviation	5.4 years	3.9 years

Source: www.city-data.com

6. **Missing Persons** A researcher wishes to test the claim that, on average, more juveniles than adults are classified as missing persons. Records for the last 5 years are shown. At $\alpha = 0.10$, is there enough evidence to support the claim?

Juveniles	65,513	65,934	64,213	61,954	59,167
Adults	31,364	34,478	36,937	35,946	38,209

Source: *USA TODAY.*

7. **IRS Tax Return Help** The local branch of the Internal Revenue Service spent an average of 21 minutes helping each of 10 people prepare their tax returns. The standard deviation was 5.6 minutes. A volunteer tax preparer spent an average of 27 minutes helping 14 people prepare their taxes. The standard deviation was 4.3 minutes. At $\alpha = 0.02$, is there a difference in the average time spent by the two services? Find the 98% confidence interval for the two means.

8. **Volunteer Work of College Students** Females and males alike from the general adult population volunteer an average of 4.2 hours per week. A random sample of 20 female college students and 18 male college students indicated these results concerning the amount of time spent in volunteer service per week. At the 0.01 level of significance, is there sufficient evidence to conclude that a difference exists between the mean number of volunteer hours per week for male and female college students?

	Male	Female
Sample mean	2.5	3.8
Sample variance	2.2	3.5
Sample size	18	20

Source: *New York Times Almanac.*

9. **Moisture Content of Fruits and Vegetables** Listed below is the moisture content (by percent) for random samples of different fruits and vegetables. At the 0.05 level of significance, can it be concluded that fruits differ from vegetables in average moisture content?

Fruits		Vegetables	
Apricot	86	Artichoke	85
Banana	75	Bamboo shoots	91
Avocado	72	Beets	88
Blackberry	88	Broccoli	89
Clementine	87	Cucumber	95
Fig	79	Iceberg lettuce	96
Pink grapefruit	92	Mushroom	92
Mango	84	Radish	95
		Tomato	94

Source: www.nutritiondata.com

10. **Hospital Stays for Maternity Patients** Health Care Knowledge Systems reported that an insured woman spends on average 2.3 days in the hospital for a routine childbirth, while an uninsured woman spends on average 1.9 days. Assume two samples of 16 women each were used in both samples. The standard deviation of the first sample is equal to 0.6 day, and the standard deviation of the second sample is 0.3 day. At $\alpha = 0.01$, test the claim that the means are equal. Find the 99% confidence interval for the differences of the means. Use the *P*-value method.

Source: Michael D. Shook and Robert L. Shook, *The Book of Odds.*

11. **Hockey's Highest Scorers** The number of points held by a sample of the NHL's highest scorers for both the Eastern Conference and the Western Conference is shown below. At $\alpha = 0.05$, can it be concluded that there is a difference in means based on these data?

Eastern Conference				Western Conference			
83	60	75	58	77	59	72	58
78	59	70	58	37	57	66	55
62	61	59		61			

Source: www.foxsports.com

12. **Medical School Enrollments** A random sample of enrollments from medical schools that specialize in research and from those that are noted for primary care is listed. Find the 90% confidence interval for the difference in the means.

Research				Primary care			
474	577	605	663	783	605	427	728
783	467	670	414	546	474	371	107
813	443	565	696	442	587	293	277
692	694	277	419	662	555	527	320
884							

Source: *U.S. News & World Report Best Graduate Schools.*

13. Out-of-State Tuitions The out-of-state tuitions (in dollars) for random samples of both public and private four-year colleges in a New England state are listed. Find the 95% confidence interval for the difference in the means.

Private		Public	
13,600	13,495	7,050	9,000
16,590	17,300	6,450	9,758
23,400	12,500	7,050	7,871
		16,100	

Source: *New York Times Almanac.*

Technology *Step by Step*

MINITAB
Step by Step

Test the Difference Between Two Means: Independent Samples*

MINITAB will calculate the test statistic and *P*-value for differences between the means for two populations when the population standard deviations are unknown.

For Example 9–2, is the average number of sports for men higher than the average number for women?

1. Enter the data for Example 9–2 into C1 and C2. Name the columns **MaleS** and **FemaleS.**

2. Select **Stat>Basic Statistics>2-Sample t.**

3. Click the button for Samples in different columns.

There is one sample in each column.

4. Click in the box for First:. Double-click C1 MaleS in the list.

5. Click in the box for Second:, then double-click C2 FemaleS in the list. Do not check the box for Assume equal variances. MINITAB will use the large sample formula. The completed dialog box is shown.

6. Click [Options].

   a) Type in **90** for the Confidence level and **0** for the Test mean.

   b) Select greater than for the Alternative. This option affects the *P*-value. It must be correct.

7. Click [OK] twice. Since the *P*-value is greater than the significance level, $0.172 > 0.1$, do not reject the null hypothesis.

Two-Sample t-Test and CI: MaleS, FemaleS
```
Two-sample  t  for  MaleS  vs FemaleS
            N    Mean   StDev  SE Mean
MaleS      50    8.56   3.26    0.46
FemaleS    50    7.94   3.27    0.46
Difference = mu (MaleS) - mu (FemaleS)
Estimate for difference: 0.620000
90% lower bound for difference: -0.221962
t-Test of difference = 0 (vs >): t-Value = 0.95 P-Value = 0.172 DF = 97
```

*MINITAB does not calculate a *z* test statistic. This statistic can be used instead.

TI-83 Plus or TI-84 Plus
Step by Step

Hypothesis Test for the Difference Between Two Means and t Distribution (Statistics)

1. Press **STAT** and move the cursor to TESTS.
2. Press **4** for 2-SampTTest.
3. Move the cursor to Stats and press **ENTER**.
4. Type in the appropriate values.
5. Move the cursor to the appropriate alternative hypothesis and press **ENTER**.
6. On the line for Pooled, move the cursor to No (standard deviations are assumed not equal) and press **ENTER**.
7. Move the cursor to Calculate and press **ENTER**.

Confidence Interval for the Difference Between Two Means and t Distribution (Data)

1. Enter the data values into L_1 and L_2.
2. Press **STAT** and move the cursor to TESTS.
3. Press **0** for 2-SampTInt.
4. Move the cursor to Data and press **ENTER**.
5. Type in the appropriate values.
6. On the line for Pooled, move the cursor to No (standard deviations are assumed not equal) and press **ENTER**.
7. Move the cursor to Calculate and press **ENTER**.

Confidence Interval for the Difference Between Two Means and t Distribution (Statistics)

1. Press **STAT** and move the cursor to TESTS.
2. Press **0** for 2-SampTInt.
3. Move the cursor to Stats and press **ENTER**.
4. Type in the appropriate values.
5. On the line for Pooled, move the cursor to No (standard deviations are assumed not equal) and press **ENTER**.
6. Move the cursor to Calculate and press **ENTER**.

Excel
Step by Step

Testing the Difference Between Two Means: Independent Samples

Excel has a two-sample t test included in the Data Analysis Add-in. The following example shows how to perform a t test for the difference between two means.

Example XL9–2

Test the claim that there is no difference between population means based on these sample data. Assume the population variances are not equal. Use $\alpha = 0.05$.

Set A	32	38	37	36	36	34	39	36	37	42
Set B	30	36	35	36	31	34	37	33	32	

1. Enter the 10-number data set A into column A.
2. Enter the 9-number data set B into column B.
3. Select the Data tab from the toolbar. Then select Data Analysis.
4. In the Data Analysis box, under Analysis Tools select t-test: Two-Sample Assuming Unequal Variances, and click [OK].

5. In Input, type in the Variable 1 Range: **A1:A10** and the Variable 2 Range: **B1:B9.**
6. Type **0** for the Hypothesized Mean Difference.
7. Type **0.05** for Alpha.
8. In Output options, type D9 for the Output Range, then click [OK].

Two-Sample *t* Test in Excel

t-Test: Two-Sample Assuming Unequal Variances

	Variable 1	Variable 2
Mean	36.7	33.77777778
Variance	7.344444444	5.944444444
Observations	10	9
Hypothesized Mean Difference	0	
df	17	
t Stat	2.474205364	
P(T<=t) one-tail	0.012095	
t Critical one-tail	1.739606716	
P(T<=t) two-tail	0.024189999	
t Critical two-tail	2.109815559	

Note: You may need to increase the column width to see all the results. To do this:
1. Highlight the columns D, E, and F.
2. Select **Format>AutoFit** Column Width.

The output reports both one- and two-tailed *P*-values.

9–3

Testing the Difference Between Two Means: Dependent Samples

Objective 3

Test the difference between two means for dependent samples.

In Section 9–2, the *t* test was used to compare two sample means when the samples were independent. In this section, a different version of the *t* test is explained. This version is used when the samples are dependent. Samples are considered to be **dependent samples** when the subjects are paired or matched in some way.

    For example, suppose a medical researcher wants to see whether a drug will affect the reaction time of its users. To test this hypothesis, the researcher must pretest the subjects in the sample first. That is, they are given a test to ascertain their normal reaction times. Then after taking the drug, the subjects are tested again, using a posttest. Finally, the means of the two tests are compared to see whether there is a difference. Since the same subjects are used in both cases, the samples are *related;* subjects scoring high on the pretest will generally score high on the posttest, even after consuming the drug. Likewise, those scoring lower on the pretest will tend to score lower on the posttest. To take this effect into account, the researcher employs a *t* test, using the differences between the pretest values and the posttest values. Thus only the gain or loss in values is compared.

Here are some other examples of dependent samples. A researcher may want to design an SAT preparation course to help students raise their test scores the second time they take the SAT. Hence, the differences between the two exams are compared. A medical specialist may want to see whether a new counseling program will help subjects lose weight. Therefore, the preweights of the subjects will be compared with the postweights.

Besides samples in which the same subjects are used in a pre-post situation, there are other cases where the samples are considered dependent. For example, students might be matched or paired according to some variable that is pertinent to the study; then one student is assigned to one group, and the other student is assigned to a second group. For instance, in a study involving learning, students can be selected and paired according to their IQs. That is, two students with the same IQ will be paired. Then one will be assigned to one sample group (which might receive instruction by computers), and the other student will be assigned to another sample group (which might receive instruction by the lecture discussion method). These assignments will be done randomly. Since a student's IQ is important to learning, it is a variable that should be controlled. By matching subjects on IQ, the researcher can eliminate the variable's influence, for the most part. Matching, then, helps to reduce type II error by eliminating extraneous variables.

Two notes of caution should be mentioned. First, when subjects are matched according to one variable, the matching process does not eliminate the influence of other variables. Matching students according to IQ does not account for their mathematical ability or their familiarity with computers. Since not all variables influencing a study can be controlled, it is up to the researcher to determine which variables should be used in matching. Second, when the same subjects are used for a pre-post study, sometimes the knowledge that they are participating in a study can influence the results. For example, if people are placed in a special program, they may be more highly motivated to succeed simply because they have been selected to participate; the program itself may have little effect on their success.

When the samples are dependent, a special *t* test for dependent means is used. This test employs the difference in values of the matched pairs. The hypotheses are as follows:

Two-tailed	Left-tailed	Right-tailed
H_0: $\mu_D = 0$	H_0: $\mu_D = 0$	H_0: $\mu_D = 0$
H_1: $\mu_D \neq 0$	H_1: $\mu_D < 0$	H_1: $\mu_D > 0$

where μ_D is the symbol for the expected mean of the difference of the matched pairs. The general procedure for finding the test value involves several steps.

First, find the differences of the values of the pairs of data.

$$D = X_1 - X_2$$

Second, find the mean $\overline{D}$ of the differences, using the formula

$$\overline{D} = \frac{\Sigma D}{n}$$

where *n* is the number of data pairs. Third, find the standard deviation s_D of the differences, using the formula

$$s_D = \sqrt{\frac{n\Sigma D^2 - (\Sigma D)^2}{n(n-1)}}$$

Fourth, find the estimated standard error $s_{\bar{D}}$ of the differences, which is

$$s_{\bar{D}} = \frac{s_D}{\sqrt{n}}$$

Finally, find the test value, using the formula

$$t = \frac{\bar{D} - \mu_D}{s_D/\sqrt{n}} \qquad \text{with d.f.} = n - 1$$

The formula in the final step follows the basic format of

$$\text{Test value} = \frac{(\text{observed value}) - (\text{expected value})}{\text{standard error}}$$

where the observed value is the mean of the differences. The expected value μ_D is zero if the hypothesis is $\mu_D = 0$. The standard error of the difference is the standard deviation of the difference, divided by the square root of the sample size. Both populations must be normally or approximately normally distributed. Example 9–6 illustrates the hypothesis-testing procedure in detail.

Example 9–6

Vitamin for Increased Strength

A physical education director claims by taking a special vitamin, a weight lifter can increase his strength. Eight athletes are selected and given a test of strength, using the standard bench press. After 2 weeks of regular training, supplemented with the vitamin, they are tested again. Test the effectiveness of the vitamin regimen at $\alpha = 0.05$. Each value in these data represents the maximum number of pounds the athlete can bench-press. Assume that the variable is approximately normally distributed.

Athlete	1	2	3	4	5	6	7	8
Before (X_1)	210	230	182	205	262	253	219	216
After (X_2)	219	236	179	204	270	250	222	216

Solution

Step 1 State the hypotheses and identify the claim. For the vitamin to be effective, the before weights must be significantly less than the after weights; hence, the mean of the differences must be less than zero.

$$H_0: \mu_D = 0 \qquad \text{and} \qquad H_1: \mu_D < 0 \ (\text{claim})$$

Step 2 Find the critical value. The degrees of freedom are $n - 1$. In this case, d.f. = $8 - 1 = 7$. The critical value for a left-tailed test with $\alpha = 0.05$ is -1.895.

Step 3 Compute the test value.

a. Make a table.

Before (X_1)	After (X_2)	A $D = X_1 - X_2$	B $D^2 = (X_1 - X_2)^2$
210	219		
230	236		
182	179		
205	204		
262	270		
253	250		
219	222		
216	216		

b. Find the differences and place the results in column A.

$$210 - 219 = -9$$
$$230 - 236 = -6$$
$$182 - 179 = +3$$
$$205 - 204 = +1$$
$$262 - 270 = -8$$
$$253 - 250 = +3$$
$$219 - 222 = -3$$
$$216 - 216 = \underline{\quad 0 \quad}$$
$$\Sigma D = -19$$

c. Find the mean of the differences.

$$\overline{D} = \frac{\Sigma D}{n} = \frac{-19}{8} = -2.375$$

d. Square the differences and place the results in column B.

$$(-9)^2 = 81$$
$$(-6)^2 = 36$$
$$(+3)^2 = 9$$
$$(+1)^2 = 1$$
$$(-8)^2 = 64$$
$$(+3)^2 = 9$$
$$(-3)^2 = 9$$
$$0^2 = \underline{\quad 0 \quad}$$
$$\Sigma D^2 = 209$$

The completed table is shown next.

Before (X_1)	After (X_2)	A $D = X_1 - X_2$	B $D^2 = (X_1 - X_2)^2$
210	219	−9	81
230	236	−6	36
182	179	+3	9
205	204	+1	1
262	270	−8	64
253	250	+3	9
219	222	−3	9
216	216	0	0
		$\Sigma D = -19$	$\Sigma D^2 = 209$

e. Find the standard deviation of the differences.

$$s_D = \sqrt{\frac{n\Sigma D^2 - (\Sigma D)^2}{n(n-1)}}$$

$$= \sqrt{\frac{8 \cdot 209 - (-19)^2}{8(8-1)}}$$

$$= \sqrt{\frac{1672 - 361}{56}}$$

$$= 4.84$$

f. Find the test value.

$$t = \frac{\overline{D} - \mu_D}{s_D/\sqrt{n}} = \frac{-2.375 - 0}{4.84/\sqrt{8}} = -1.388$$

Step 4   Make the decision. The decision is not to reject the null hypothesis at $\alpha = 0.05$, since $-1.388 > -1.895$, as shown in Figure 9–6.

Figure 9–6

Critical and Test Values
for Example 9–6

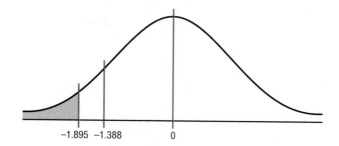

-1.895 -1.388 0

Step 5   Summarize the results. There is not enough evidence to support the claim that the vitamin increases the strength of weight lifters.

The formulas for this t test are summarized next.

Formulas for the t Test for Dependent Samples

$$t = \frac{\overline{D} - \mu_D}{s_D/\sqrt{n}}$$

with d.f. $= n - 1$ and where

$$\overline{D} = \frac{\Sigma D}{n} \quad \text{and} \quad s_D = \sqrt{\frac{n\Sigma D^2 - (\Sigma D)^2}{n(n-1)}}$$

Example 9–7

Cholesterol Levels

A dietitian wishes to see if a person's cholesterol level will change if the diet is supplemented by a certain mineral. Six subjects were pretested, and then they took the mineral supplement for a 6-week period. The results are shown in the table. (Cholesterol level is measured in milligrams per deciliter.) Can it be concluded that the cholesterol level has been changed at $\alpha = 0.10$? Assume the variable is approximately normally distributed.

Subject	1	2	3	4	5	6
Before (X_1)	210	235	208	190	172	244
After (X_2)	190	170	210	188	173	228

Solution

Step 1   State the hypotheses and identify the claim. If the diet is effective, the before cholesterol levels should be different from the after levels.

$H_0: \mu_D = 0$ and $H_1: \mu_D \neq 0$ (claim)

Step 2   Find the critical value. The degrees of freedom are 5. At $\alpha = 0.10$, the critical values are ± 2.015.

Step 3   Compute the test value.

a. Make a table.

Before (X_1)	After (X_2)	**A** $D = X_1 - X_2$	**B** $D^2 = (X_1 - X_2)^2$
210	190		
235	170		
208	210		
190	188		
172	173		
244	228		

b. Find the differences and place the results in column A.

$$210 - 190 = 20$$
$$235 - 170 = 65$$
$$208 - 210 = -2$$
$$190 - 188 = 2$$
$$172 - 173 = -1$$
$$244 - 228 = \underline{16}$$
$$\Sigma D = 100$$

c. Find the mean of the differences.

$$\overline{D} = \frac{\Sigma D}{n} = \frac{100}{6} = 16.7$$

d. Square the differences and place the results in column B.

$$(20)^2 = 400$$
$$(65)^2 = 4225$$
$$(-2)^2 = 4$$
$$(2)^2 = 4$$
$$(-1)^2 = 1$$
$$(16)^2 = \underline{256}$$
$$\Sigma D^2 = 4890$$

Then complete the table as shown.

Before (X_1)	After (X_2)	**A** $D = X_1 - X_2$	**B** $D^2 = (X_1 - X_2)^2$
210	190	20	400
235	170	65	4225
208	210	-2	4
190	188	2	4
172	173	-1	1
244	228	$\underline{16}$	$\underline{256}$
		$\Sigma D = 100$	$\Sigma D^2 = 4890$

e. Find the standard deviation of the differences.

$$s_D = \sqrt{\frac{n\Sigma D^2 - (\Sigma D)^2}{n(n-1)}}$$

$$= \sqrt{\frac{6 \cdot 4890 - 100^2}{6(6-1)}}$$

$$= \sqrt{\frac{29{,}340 - 10{,}000}{30}}$$

$$= 25.4$$

f. Find the test value.

$$t = \frac{\overline{D} - \mu_D}{s_D/\sqrt{n}} = \frac{16.7 - 0}{25.4/\sqrt{6}} = 1.610$$

Step 4   Make the decision. The decision is to not reject the null hypothesis, since the test value 1.610 is in the noncritical region, as shown in Figure 9–7.

Figure 9–7

Critical and Test Values for Example 9–7

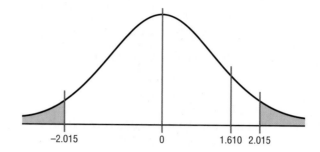

| −2.015 | 0 | 1.610 2.015 |

Step 5   Summarize the results. There is not enough evidence to support the claim that the mineral changes a person's cholesterol level.

The steps for this *t* test are summarized in the Procedure Table.

Procedure Table

Testing the Difference Between Means for Dependent Samples

Step 1   State the hypotheses and identify the claim.

Step 2   Find the critical value(s).

Step 3   Compute the test value.

   a. Make a table, as shown.

		A	**B**
X_1	X_2	$D = X_1 - X_2$	$D^2 = (X_1 - X_2)^2$
⋮	⋮		
		$\Sigma D = $ _____	$\Sigma D^2 = $ _____

   b. Find the differences and place the results in column A.

   $$D = X_1 - X_2$$

   c. Find the mean of the differences.

   $$\overline{D} = \frac{\Sigma D}{n}$$

   d. Square the differences and place the results in column B. Complete the table.

   $$D^2 = (X_1 - X_2)^2$$

Procedure Table (*continued*)

  e. Find the standard deviation of the differences.

  $$s_D = \sqrt{\frac{n\sum D^2 - (\sum D)^2}{n(n-1)}}$$

  f. Find the test value.

  $$t = \frac{\overline{D} - \mu_D}{s_D/\sqrt{n}} \qquad \text{with d.f.} = n - 1$$

Step 4   Make the decision.

Step 5   Summarize the results.

The *P*-values for the *t* test are found in Table F. For a two-tailed test with d.f. = 5 and $t = 1.610$, the *P*-value is found between 1.476 and 2.015; hence, $0.10 < P\text{-value} < 0.20$. Thus, the null hypothesis cannot be rejected at $\alpha = 0.10$.

If a specific difference is hypothesized, this formula should be used

$$t = \frac{\overline{D} - \mu_D}{s_D/\sqrt{n}}$$

where μ_D is the hypothesized difference.

For example, if a dietitian claims that people on a specific diet will lose an average of 3 pounds in a week, the hypotheses are

$$H_0\!: \mu_D = 3 \qquad \text{and} \qquad H_1\!: \mu_D \neq 3$$

The value 3 will be substituted in the test statistic formula for μ_D.

Confidence intervals can be found for the mean differences with this formula.

Confidence Interval for the Mean Difference

$$\overline{D} - t_{\alpha/2}\frac{s_D}{\sqrt{n}} < \mu_D < \overline{D} + t_{\alpha/2}\frac{s_D}{\sqrt{n}}$$

d.f. = $n - 1$

Example 9–8

Find the 90% confidence interval for the data in Example 9–7.

Solution

Substitute in the formula.

$$\overline{D} - t_{\alpha/2}\frac{s_D}{\sqrt{n}} < \mu_D < \overline{D} + t_{\alpha/2}\frac{s_D}{\sqrt{n}}$$

$$16.7 - 2.015 \cdot \frac{25.4}{\sqrt{6}} < \mu_D < 16.7 + 2.015 \cdot \frac{25.4}{\sqrt{6}}$$

$$16.7 - 20.89 < \mu_D < 16.7 + 20.89$$

$$-4.19 < \mu_D < 37.59$$

Since 0 is contained in the interval, the decision is to not reject the null hypothesis $H_0\!: \mu_D = 0$.

Can Video Games Save Lives?

Can playing video games help doctors perform surgery? The answer is yes. A study showed that surgeons who played video games for at least 3 hours each week made about 37% fewer mistakes and finished operations 27% faster than those who did not play video games.

The type of surgery that they performed is called *laparoscopic* surgery, where the surgeon inserts a tiny video camera into the body and uses a joystick to maneuver the surgical instruments while watching the results on a television monitor. This study compares two groups and uses proportions. What statistical test do you think was used to compare the percentages? (See Section 9–4.)

Applying the Concepts 9–3

Air Quality

As a researcher for the EPA, you have been asked to determine if the air quality in the United States has changed over the past 2 years. You select a random sample of 10 metropolitan areas and find the number of days each year that the areas failed to meet acceptable air quality standards. The data are shown.

Year 1	18	125	9	22	138	29	1	19	17	31
Year 2	24	152	13	21	152	23	6	31	34	20

Source: *The World Almanac and Book of Facts.*

Based on the data, answer the following questions.

1. What is the purpose of the study?
2. Are the samples independent or dependent?
3. What hypotheses would you use?
4. What is(are) the critical value(s) that you would use?
5. What statistical test would you use?
6. How many degrees of freedom are there?
7. What is your conclusion?
8. Could an independent means test have been used?
9. Do you think this was a good way to answer the original question?

See page 526 for the answers.

Exercises 9–3

1. Classify each as independent or dependent samples.

   a. Heights of identical twins

   b. Test scores of the same students in English and psychology

   c. The effectiveness of two different brands of aspirin

   d. Effects of a drug on reaction time, measured by a before-and-after test

   e. The effectiveness of two different diets on two different groups of individuals

For Exercises 2 through 10, perform each of these steps. Assume that all variables are normally or approximately normally distributed.

   a. State the hypotheses and identify the claim.

   b. Find the critical value(s).

   c. Compute the test value.

   d. Make the decision.

   e. Summarize the results.

Use the traditional method of hypothesis testing unless otherwise specified.

2. **Retention Test Scores** A sample of non-English majors at a selected college was used in a study to see if the student retained more from reading a 19th-century novel or by watching it in DVD form. Each student was assigned one novel to read and a different one to watch, and then they were given a 20-point written quiz on each novel. The test results are shown below. At $\alpha = 0.05$, can it be concluded that the book scores are higher than the DVD scores?

Book	90	80	90	75	80	90	84
DVD	85	72	80	80	70	75	80

3. **Improving Study Habits** As an aid for improving students' study habits, nine students were randomly selected to attend a seminar on the importance of education in life. The table shows the number of hours each student studied per week before and after the seminar. At $\alpha = 0.10$, did attending the seminar increase the number of hours the students studied per week?

Before	9	12	6	15	3	18	10	13	7
After	9	17	9	20	2	21	15	22	6

4. **Obstacle Course Times** An obstacle course was set up on a campus, and 10 volunteers were given a chance to complete it while they were being timed. They then sampled a new energy drink and were given the opportunity to run the course again. The "before" and "after" times in seconds are shown below. Is there sufficient evidence at $\alpha = 0.05$ to conclude that the students did better the second time? Discuss possible reasons for your results.

Student	1	2	3	4	5	6	7	8
Before	67	72	80	70	78	82	69	75
After	68	70	76	65	75	78	65	68

5. **Sleep Report** Students in a statistics class were asked to report the number of hours they slept on weeknights and on weekends. At $\alpha = 0.05$, is there sufficient evidence that there is a difference in the mean number of hours slept?

Student	1	2	3	4	5	6	7	8
Hours, Sun.–Thurs.	8	5.5	7.5	8	7	6	6	8
Hours, Fri.–Sat.	4	7	10.5	12	11	9	6	9

6. **PGA Golf Scores** At a recent PGA tournament (the Honda Classic at Palm Beach Gardens, Florida) the following scores were posted for eight randomly selected golfers for two consecutive days. At $\alpha = 0.05$, is there evidence of a difference in mean scores for the two days?

Golfer	1	2	3	4	5	6	7	8
Thursday	67	65	68	68	68	70	69	70
Friday	68	70	69	71	72	69	70	70

Source: *Washington Observer-Reporter.*

7. **Reducing Errors in Grammar** A composition teacher wishes to see whether a new grammar program will reduce the number of grammatical errors her students make when writing a two-page essay. The data are shown here. At $\alpha = 0.025$, can it be concluded that the number of errors has been reduced?

Student	1	2	3	4	5	6
Errors before	12	9	0	5	4	3
Errors after	9	6	1	3	2	3

8. **Amounts of Shrimp Caught** According to the National Marine Fisheries Service, the amounts of shrimp landed during the month of January (in thousands of pounds) are shown below for several Gulf Coast states for three selected years. At the 0.05 level of significance, is there sufficient evidence to conclude a difference in the mean production between 2007 and 2006? Between 2006 and 2005?

	Florida	Alabama	Mississippi	Louisiana	Texas
2007	344.4	207.0	169.0	1711.5	861.8
2006	1262.0	960.0	529.0	1969.0	1405.0
2005	944.0	541.0	330.0	2300.0	613.0

Source: www.st.nmfs.gov

 9. Pulse Rates of Identical Twins A researcher wanted to compare the pulse rates of identical twins to see whether there was any difference. Eight sets of twins were selected. The rates are given in the table as number of beats per minute. At $\alpha = 0.01$, is there a significant difference in the average pulse rates of twins? Find the

99% confidence interval for the difference of the two. Use the *P*-value method.

Twin A	87	92	78	83	88	90	84	93
Twin B	83	95	79	83	86	93	80	86

 10. Assessed Land Values A reporter hypothesizes that the average assessed values of land in a large city have changed during a 5-year period. A random sample of wards is selected, and the data (in millions of dollars) are shown. At $\alpha = 0.05$, can it be concluded that the average taxable assessed values have changed? Use the *P*-value method.

Ward	A	B	C	D	E	F	G	H	I	J	K	L	M	N	O	P
1994	184	414	22	99	116	49	24	50	282	25	141	45	12	37	9	17
1999	161	382	22	109	120	52	28	50	297	40	148	56	20	38	9	19

Source: *Pittsburgh Tribune-Review.*

Extending the Concepts

11. Instead of finding the mean of the differences between X_1 and X_2 by subtracting $X_1 - X_2$, you can find it by finding the means of X_1 and X_2 and then subtracting the means. Show that these two procedures will yield the same results.

Technology *Step by Step*

MINITAB
Step by Step

Test the Difference Between Two Means: Dependent Samples

For Example 9–6, test the effectiveness of the vitamin regimen. Is there a difference in the strength of the athletes after the treatment?

1. Enter the data into C1 and C2. Name the columns **Before** and **After.**

2. Select **Stat>Basic Statistics>Paired t.**

3. Double-click C1 Before for First sample.

4. Double-click C2 After for Second sample. The second sample will be subtracted from the first. The differences are not stored or displayed.

5. Click [Options].

6. Change the Alternative to less than.

7. Click [OK] twice.

Paired t-Test and CI: BEFORE, AFTER
```
Paired t for BEFORE - AFTER
              N     Mean     StDev    SE Mean
BEFORE        8  222.125    25.920      9.164
AFTER         8  224.500    27.908      9.867
Difference    8  -2.37500   4.83846    1.71065

95% upper bound for mean difference: 0.86597
t-Test of mean difference = 0 (vs < 0) : t-Value = -1.39  P-Value = 0.104.
```

Since the *P*-value is 0.104, do not reject the null hypothesis. The sample difference of -2.38 in the strength measurement is not statistically significant.

TI-83 Plus or TI-84 Plus
Step by Step

Hypothesis Test for the Difference Between Two Means: Dependent Samples

1. Enter the data values into L_1 and L_2.
2. Move the cursor to the top of the L_3 column so that L_3 is highlighted.
3. Type $L_1 - L_2$, then press **ENTER**.
4. Press **STAT** and move the cursor to TESTS.
5. Press **2** for TTest.
6. Move the cursor to Data and press **ENTER**.
7. Type in the appropriate values, using **0** for μ_0 and L_3 for the list.
8. Move the cursor to the appropriate alternative hypothesis and press **ENTER**.
9. Move the cursor to Calculate and press **ENTER**.

Confidence Interval for the Difference Between Two Means: Dependent Samples

1. Enter the data values into L_1 and L_2.
2. Move the cursor to the top of the L_3 column so that L_3 is highlighted.
3. Type $L_1 - L_2$, then press **ENTER**.
4. Press **STAT** and move the cursor to TESTS.
5. Press **8** for TInterval.
6. Move the cursor to Stats and press **ENTER**.
7. Type in the appropriate values, using L_3 for the list.
8. Move the cursor to Calculate and press **ENTER**.

Excel
Step by Step

Testing the Difference Between Two Means: Dependent Samples
Example XL9–3

Test the claim that there is no difference between population means based on these sample paired data. Use $\alpha = 0.05$.

Set A	33	35	28	29	32	34	30	34
Set B	27	29	36	34	30	29	28	24

1. Enter the 8-number data set A into column A.
2. Enter the 8-number data set B into column B.
3. Select the Data tab from the toolbar. Then select Data Analysis.
4. In the Data Analysis box, under Analysis Tools select *t*-test: Paired Two Sample for Means, and click [OK].
5. In Input, type in the Variable 1 Range: **A1:A8** and the Variable 2 Range: **B1:B8**.
6. Type **0** for the Hypothesized Mean Difference.

7. Type **0.05** for Alpha.

8. In Output options, type **D5** for the Output Range, then click [OK].

t-Test: Paired Two Sample for Means		
	Variable 1	Variable 2
Mean	31.875	29.625
Variance	6.696428571	14.55357143
Observations	8	8
Pearson Correlation	-0.757913399	
Hypothesized Mean Difference	0	
df	7	
t Stat	1.057517468	
P(T<=t) one-tail	0.1626994	
t Critical one-tail	1.894578604	
P(T<=t) two-tail	0.3253988	
t Critical two-tail	2.364624251	

Note: You may need to increase the column width to see all the results. To do this:

1. Highlight the columns D, E, and F.

2. Select **Format>AutoFit** Column Width.

The output shows a *P*-value of 0.3253988 for the two-tailed case. This value is greater than the alpha level of 0.05, so we fail to reject the null hypothesis.

9–4   Testing the Difference Between Proportions

Objective **4**

Test the difference between two proportions.

The *z* test with some modifications can be used to test the equality of two proportions. For example, a researcher might ask, Is the proportion of men who exercise regularly less than the proportion of women who exercise regularly? Is there a difference in the percentage of students who own a personal computer and the percentage of nonstudents who own one? Is there a difference in the proportion of college graduates who pay cash for purchases and the proportion of non-college graduates who pay cash?

Recall from Chapter 7 that the symbol $\hat{p}$ ("p hat") is the sample proportion used to estimate the population proportion, denoted by p. For example, if in a sample of 30 college students, 9 are on probation, then the sample proportion is $\hat{p} = \frac{9}{30}$, or 0.3. The population proportion p is the number of all students who are on probation, divided by the number of students who attend the college. The formula for $\hat{p}$ is

$$\hat{p} = \frac{X}{n}$$

where

X = number of units that possess the characteristic of interest
n = sample size

When you are testing the difference between two population proportions p_1 and p_2, the hypotheses can be stated thus, if no difference between the proportions is hypothesized.

$$H_0: p_1 = p_2 \qquad \text{or} \qquad H_0: p_1 - p_2 = 0$$
$$H_1: p_1 \neq p_2 \qquad \qquad H_1: p_1 - p_2 \neq 0$$

Similar statements using $<$ or $>$ in the alternate hypothesis can be formed for one-tailed tests.

For two proportions, $\hat{p}_1 = X_1/n_1$ is used to estimate p_1 and $\hat{p}_2 = X_2/n_2$ is used to estimate p_2. The standard error of the difference is

$$\sigma_{\hat{p}_1 - \hat{p}_2} = \sqrt{\sigma_{p_1}^2 + \sigma_{p_2}^2} = \sqrt{\frac{p_1 q_1}{n_1} + \frac{p_2 q_2}{n_2}}$$

where $\sigma_{p_1}^2$ and $\sigma_{p_2}^2$ are the variances of the proportions, $q_1 = 1 - p_1$, $q_2 = 1 - p_2$, and n_1 and n_2 are the respective sample sizes.

Since p_1 and p_2 are unknown, a weighted estimate of p can be computed by using the formula

$$\bar{p} = \frac{n_1 \hat{p}_1 + n_2 \hat{p}_2}{n_1 + n_2}$$

and $\bar{q} = 1 - \bar{p}$. This weighted estimate is based on the hypothesis that $p_1 = p_2$. Hence, $\bar{p}$ is a better estimate than either $\hat{p}_1$ or $\hat{p}_2$, since it is a combined average using both $\hat{p}_1$ and $\hat{p}_2$.

Since $\hat{p}_1 = X_1/n_1$ and $\hat{p}_2 = X_2/n_2$, $\bar{p}$ can be simplified to

$$\bar{p} = \frac{X_1 + X_2}{n_1 + n_2}$$

Finally, the standard error of the difference in terms of the weighted estimate is

$$\sigma_{\hat{p}_1 - \hat{p}_2} = \sqrt{\bar{p}\bar{q}\left(\frac{1}{n_1} + \frac{1}{n_2}\right)}$$

The formula for the test value is shown next.

Formula for the z Test for Comparing Two Proportions

$$z = \frac{(\hat{p}_1 - \hat{p}_2) - (p_1 - p_2)}{\sqrt{\bar{p}\bar{q}\left(\frac{1}{n_1} + \frac{1}{n_2}\right)}}$$

where

$$\bar{p} = \frac{X_1 + X_2}{n_1 + n_2} \qquad \hat{p}_1 = \frac{X_1}{n_1}$$

$$\bar{q} = 1 - \bar{p} \qquad \hat{p}_2 = \frac{X_2}{n_2}$$

This formula follows the format

$$\text{Test value} = \frac{(\text{observed value}) - (\text{expected value})}{\text{standard error}}$$

There are two requirements for use of the z test: (1) The samples must be independent of each other, and (2) $n_1 p_1$ and $n_1 q_1$ must be 5 or more, and $n_2 p_2$ and $n_2 q_2$ must be 5 or more.

Example 9–9	### Vaccination Rates in Nursing Homes

In the nursing home study mentioned in the chapter-opening Statistics Today, the researchers found that 12 out of 34 small nursing homes had a resident vaccination rate of less than 80%, while 17 out of 24 large nursing homes had a vaccination rate of less than 80%. At $\alpha = 0.05$, test the claim that there is no difference in the proportions of the small and large nursing homes with a resident vaccination rate of less than 80%.

Source: Nancy Arden, Arnold S. Monto, and Suzanne E. Ohmit, "Vaccine Use and the Risk of Outbreaks in a Sample of Nursing Homes During an Influenza Epidemic," *American Journal of Public Health.*

Solution

Let $\hat{p}_1$ be the proportion of the small nursing homes with a vaccination rate of less than 80% and $\hat{p}_2$ be the proportion of the large nursing homes with a vaccination rate of less than 80%. Then

$$\hat{p}_1 = \frac{X_1}{n_1} = \frac{12}{34} = 0.35 \qquad \text{and} \qquad \hat{p}_2 = \frac{X_2}{n_2} = \frac{17}{24} = 0.71$$

$$\bar{p} = \frac{X_1 + X_2}{n_1 + n_2} = \frac{12 + 17}{34 + 24} = \frac{29}{58} = 0.5$$

$$\bar{q} = 1 - \bar{p} = 1 - 0.5 = 0.5$$

Now, follow the steps in hypothesis testing.

Step 1   State the hypotheses and identify the claim.

$$H_0: p_1 = p_2 \text{ (claim)} \qquad \text{and} \qquad H_1: p_1 \neq p_2$$

Step 2   Find the critical values. Since $\alpha = 0.05$, the critical values are $+1.96$ and -1.96.

Step 3   Compute the test value.

$$z = \frac{(\hat{p}_1 - \hat{p}_2) - (p_1 - p_2)}{\sqrt{\bar{p}\,\bar{q}\left(\dfrac{1}{n_1} + \dfrac{1}{n_2}\right)}}$$

$$= \frac{(0.35 - 0.71) - 0}{\sqrt{(0.5)(0.5)\left(\dfrac{1}{34} + \dfrac{1}{24}\right)}} = \frac{-0.36}{0.1333} = -2.7$$

Step 4   Make the decision. Reject the null hypothesis, since $-2.7 < -1.96$. See Figure 9–8.

Step 5   Summarize the results. There is enough evidence to reject the claim that there is no difference in the proportions of small and large nursing homes with a resident vaccination rate of less than 80%.

Figure 9–8

**Critical and Test Values
for Example 9–9**

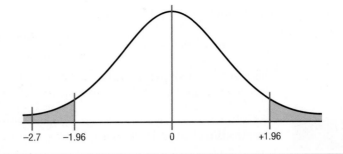

Example 9–10   ### Missing Work

In a sample of 200 workers, 45% said that they missed work because of personal illness. Ten years ago in a sample of 200 workers, 35% said that they missed work because of personal illness. At $\alpha = 0.01$, is there a difference in the proportion?

Solution

Since the statistics are given in percentages, $\hat{p}_1 = 45\%$, or 0.45, and $\hat{p}_2 = 35\%$, or 0.35. To compute $\bar{p}$, you must find X_1 and X_2.

$$X_1 = \hat{p}_1 n_1 = 0.45(200) = 90$$

$$X_2 = \hat{p}_2 n_2 = 0.35(200) = 70$$

$$\bar{p} = \frac{X_1 + X_2}{n_1 + n_2} = \frac{90 + 70}{200 + 200} = \frac{160}{400} = 0.4$$

$$\bar{q} = 1 - \bar{p} = 1 - 0.4 = 0.6$$

Step 1   State the hypotheses and identify the claim.

$$H_0: p_1 = p_2 \quad \text{and} \quad H_1: p_1 \neq p_2 \text{ (claim)}$$

Step 2   Find the critical values. Since $\alpha = 0.01$, the critical values are $+2.58$ and -2.58.

Step 3   Compute the test value.

$$z = \frac{(\hat{p}_1 - \hat{p}_2) - (p_1 - p_2)}{\sqrt{\bar{p}\,\bar{q}\left(\dfrac{1}{n_1} + \dfrac{1}{n_2}\right)}} = \frac{(0.45 - 0.35) - 0}{\sqrt{(0.6)(0.4)\left(\dfrac{1}{200} + \dfrac{1}{200}\right)}} = 2.04$$

Step 4   Make the decision. Do not reject the null hypothesis since $2.04 < 2.58$. See Figure 9–9.

Figure 9–9

**Critical and Test Values
for Example 9–10**

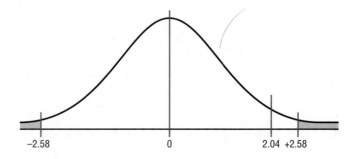

Step 5   Summarize the results. There is not enough evidence to support the claim that there is a difference in proportions.

Statistics

Is More Expensive Better?

An article in the *Journal of the American Medical Association* explained a study done on placebo pain pills. Researchers randomly assigned 82 healthy people to two groups. The individuals in the first group were given sugar pills, but they were told that the pills were a new, fast-acting opioid pain reliever similar to codeine and that they were listed at $2.50 each. The individuals in the other group received the same sugar pills but were told that the pills had been marked down to 10¢ each.

Each group received electrical shocks before and after taking the pills. They were then asked if the pills reduced the pain. Eighty-five percent of the group who were told that the pain pills cost $2.50 said that they were effective, while 61% of the group who received the supposedly discounted pills said that they were effective.

State possible null and alternative hypotheses for this study. What statistical test could be used in this study? What might be the conclusion of the study?

The *P*-value for the difference of proportions can be found from Table E, as shown in Section 9–1. For Example 9–10, 3.99 is beyond 3.09; hence, the null hypothesis can be rejected since the *P*-value is less than 0.001.

The formula for the confidence interval for the difference between two proportions is shown next.

Confidence Interval for the Difference Between Two Proportions

$$(\hat{p}_1 - \hat{p}_2) - z_{\alpha/2}\sqrt{\frac{\hat{p}_1\hat{q}_1}{n_1} + \frac{\hat{p}_2\hat{q}_2}{n_2}} < p_1 - p_2 < (\hat{p}_1 - \hat{p}_2) + z_{\alpha/2}\sqrt{\frac{\hat{p}_1\hat{q}_1}{n_1} + \frac{\hat{p}_2\hat{q}_2}{n_2}}$$

Example 9–11   Find the 95% confidence interval for the difference of proportions for the data in Example 9–9.

Solution

$$\hat{p}_1 = \frac{12}{34} = 0.35 \qquad \hat{q}_1 = 0.65$$

$$\hat{p}_2 = \frac{17}{24} = 0.71 \qquad \hat{q}_2 = 0.29$$

Substitute in the formula.

$$(\hat{p}_1 - \hat{p}_2) - z_{\alpha/2}\sqrt{\frac{\hat{p}_1\hat{q}_1}{n_1} + \frac{\hat{p}_2\hat{q}_2}{n_2}} < p_1 - p_2$$

$$< (\hat{p}_1 - \hat{p}_2) + z_{\alpha/2}\sqrt{\frac{\hat{p}_1\hat{q}_1}{n_1} + \frac{\hat{p}_2\hat{q}_2}{n_2}}$$

$$(0.35 - 0.71) - 1.96\sqrt{\frac{(0.35)(0.65)}{34} + \frac{(0.71)(0.29)}{24}}$$

$$< p_1 - p_2 < (0.35 - 0.71) + 1.96\sqrt{\frac{(0.35)(0.65)}{34} + \frac{(0.71)(0.29)}{24}}$$

$$-0.36 - 0.242 < p_1 - p_2 < -0.36 + 0.242$$

$$-0.602 < p_1 - p_2 < -0.118$$

Since 0 is not contained in the interval, the decision is to reject the null hypothesis $H_0: p_1 = p_2$.

Applying the Concepts **9–4**

Smoking and Education

You are researching the hypothesis that there is no difference in the percent of public school students who smoke and the percent of private school students who smoke. You find these results from a recent survey.

School	Percent who smoke
Public	32.3
Private	14.5

Based on these figures, answer the following questions.

1. What hypotheses would you use if you wanted to compare percentages of the public school students who smoke with the private school students who smoke?
2. What critical value(s) would you use?
3. What statistical test would you use to compare the two percentages?
4. What information would you need to complete the statistical test?
5. Suppose you found that 1000 individuals in each group were surveyed. Could you perform the statistical test?
6. If so, complete the test and summarize the results.

See page 526 for the answers.

Exercises 9–4

1a. Find the proportions $\hat{p}$ and $\hat{q}$ for each.

   a. $n = 48, X = 34$

   b. $n = 75, X = 28$

   c. $n = 100, X = 50$

   d. $n = 24, X = 6$

   e. $n = 144, X = 12$

1b. Find each X, given $\hat{p}$.

   a. $\hat{p} = 0.16, n = 100$

   b. $\hat{p} = 0.08, n = 50$

   c. $\hat{p} = 6\%, n = 800$

   d. $\hat{p} = 52\%, n = 200$

   e. $\hat{p} = 20\%, n = 150$

2. Find $\bar{p}$ and $\bar{q}$ for each.

   a. $X_1 = 60, n_1 = 100, X_2 = 40, n_2 = 100$

   b. $X_1 = 22, n_1 = 50, X_2 = 18, n_2 = 30$

   c. $X_1 = 18, n_1 = 60, X_2 = 20, n_2 = 80$

   d. $X_1 = 5, n_1 = 32, X_2 = 12, n_2 = 48$

   e. $X_1 = 12, n_1 = 75, X_2 = 15, n_2 = 50$

For Exercises 3 through 14, perform these steps.

   a. State the hypotheses and identify the claim.

   b. Find the critical value(s).

   c. Compute the test value.

   d. Make the decision.

   e. Summarize the results.

Use the traditional method of hypothesis testing unless otherwise specified.

3. Racial Makeup of Two Cities Dallas, Texas, and Stafford, Texas, are numbers 57 and 58, respectively, on the top 100 most racially diverse cities in the United States with 35.6% of the population being white. A random sample of 300 residents from each city was surveyed, and the results are listed below. At the 0.01 level of significance, is there sufficient evidence to conclude a difference in the proportions of nonwhite residents in these two cities?

   Dallas: 98 of 300 surveyed were white

   Stafford: 120 of 300 surveyed were white

Source: www.city-data.com

4. Undergraduate Financial Aid A study is conducted to determine if the percent of women who receive financial aid in undergraduate school is different from the percent of men who receive financial aid in undergraduate school. A random sample of undergraduates revealed these results. At $\alpha = 0.01$, is there significant evidence to reject the null hypothesis?

	Women	Men
Sample size	250	300
Number receiving aid	200	180

Source: U.S. Department of Education, National Center for Education Statistics.

5. Female Cashiers and Servers Labor statistics indicate that 77% of cashiers and servers are women. A random sample of cashiers and servers in a large metropolitan area found that 112 of 150 cashiers and 150 of 200 servers were women. At the 0.05 level of significance, is there sufficient evidence to conclude that a difference exists between the proportion of servers and the proportion of cashiers who are women?

Source: *New York Times Almanac.*

6. Animal Bites of Postal Workers In Cleveland, a sample of 73 mail carriers showed that 10 had been bitten by an animal during one week. In Philadelphia, in a sample of 80 mail carriers, 16 had received animal bites. Is there a significant difference in the proportions? Use $\alpha = 0.05$. Find the 95% confidence interval for the difference of the two proportions.

7. Lecture versus Computer-Assisted Instruction A survey found that 83% of the men questioned preferred computer-assisted instruction to lecture and 75% of the women preferred computer-assisted instruction to lecture. There were 100 individuals in each sample. At $\alpha = 0.05$, test the claim that there is no difference in the proportion of men and the proportion of women who favor computer-assisted instruction over lecture. Find the 95% confidence interval for the difference of the two proportions.

8. Leisure Time In a sample of 50 men, 44 said that they had less leisure time today than they had 10 years ago. In a sample of 50 women, 48 women said that they had less leisure time than they had 10 years ago. At $\alpha = 0.10$ is there a difference in the proportion? Find the 90% confidence interval for the difference of the two proportions. Does the confidence interval contain 0? Give a reason why this information would be of interest to a researcher.

Source: Based on statistics from Market Directory.

9. Desire to Be Rich In a sample of 80 Americans, 55% wished that they were rich. In a sample of 90 Europeans, 45% wished that they were rich. At $\alpha = 0.01$, is there a difference in the proportions? Find the 99% confidence interval for the difference of the two proportions.

10. Seat Belt Use In a sample of 200 men, 130 said they used seat belts. In a sample of 300 women, 63 said they used seat belts. Test the claim that men are more safety-conscious than women, at $\alpha = 0.01$. Use the P-value method.

11. Dog Ownership A survey found that in a sample of 75 families, 26 owned dogs. A survey done 15 years ago found that in a sample of 60 families, 26 owned dogs. At $\alpha = 0.05$ has the proportion of dog owners changed over the 15-year period? Find the 95% confidence interval of the true difference in the proportions. Does the confidence interval contain 0? Why would this fact be important to a researcher?

Source: Based on statistics from the American Veterinary Medical Association.

12. **Bullying** Bullying is a problem at any age but especially for students aged 12 to 18. A study showed that 7.2% of all students in this age bracket reported being bullied at school during the past six months with 6th grade having the highest incidence at 13.9% and 12th grade the lowest at 2.2%. To see if there is a difference between public and private schools, 200 students were randomly selected from each. At the 0.05 level of significance, can a difference be concluded?

	Private	Public
Sample size	200	200
No. bullied	13	16

Source: www.nces.ed.gov

13. **Survey on Inevitability of War** A sample of 200 teenagers shows that 50 believe that war is inevitable, and a sample of 300 people over age 60 shows that 93 believe war is inevitable. Is the proportion of teenagers who believe war is inevitable different from the proportion of people over age 60 who do? Use $\alpha = 0.01$. Find the 99% confidence interval for the difference of the two proportions.

14. **Hypertension** It has been found that 26% of men 20 years and older suffer from hypertension (high blood pressure) and 31.5% of women are hypertensive. A random sample of 150 of each gender was selected from recent hospital records, and the following results were obtained. Can you conclude that a higher percentage of women have high blood pressure? Use $\alpha = 0.05$.

Men   43 patients had high blood pressure
Women   52 patients had high blood pressure

Source: www.nchs.gov

15. **Partisan Support of Salary Increase Bill** Find the 99% confidence interval for the difference in the population proportions for the data of a study in which 80% of the 150 Republicans surveyed favored the bill for a salary increase and 60% of the 200 Democrats surveyed favored the bill for a salary increase.

16. **Percentage of Female Workers** The Miami County commissioners feel that a higher percentage of women work there than in neighboring Greene County. To test this, they randomly select 1000 women in each county and find that in Miami, 622 women work and in Greene, 594 work. Using $\alpha = 0.05$, do you think the Miami County commissioners are correct?

Source: 2000 U.S. Census/*Dayton Daily News.*

17. **Never Married Individuals** In a recent year the U.S. Census reported that 32.6% of men aged 15 and older had never married. The percentage of women never married for the same age group was 25.6%. Based on the data below, can it be concluded that the percentage of never married men is greater than the proportion of never married women? Use $\alpha = 0.05$.

	Men	Women
Never married	99	81
Sample size	300	300

Source: *World Almanac.*

18. **Smoking Survey** National statistics show that 23% of men smoke and 18.5% of women do. A random sample of 180 men indicated that 50 were smokers, and of 150 women surveyed, 39 indicated that they smoked. Construct a 98% confidence interval for the true difference in proportions of male and female smokers. Comment on your interval—does it support the claim that there is a difference?

Source: www.nchs.gov

19. **College Education** The percentages of adults 25 years of age and older who have completed 4 or more years of college are 23.6% for females and 27.8% for males. A random sample of women and men who were 25 years old or older was surveyed with these results. Estimate the true difference in proportions with 95% confidence, and compare your interval with the *Almanac* statistics.

	Women	Men
Sample size	350	400
No. who completed 4 or more years	100	115

Source: *New York Times Almanac.*

Extending the Concepts

20. If there is a significant difference between p_1 and p_2 and between p_2 and p_3, can you conclude that there is a significant difference between p_1 and p_3?

MINITAB
Step by Step

Test the Difference Between Two Proportions

For Example 9–9, test for a difference in the resident vaccination rates between small and large nursing homes.

1. This test does not require data. It doesn't matter what is in the worksheet.

2. Select **Stat>Basic Statistics>2 Proportions.**

3. Click the button for Summarized data.

4. Press **TAB** to move cursor to the first sample box for Trials.

   a) Enter **34, TAB,** then enter **12.**

   b) Press **TAB** or click in the second sample text box for Trials.

   c) Enter **24, TAB,** then enter **17.**

5. Click on [Options]. Check the box for Use pooled estimate of p for test. The Confidence level should be 95%, and the Test difference should be 0.

6. Click [OK] twice. The results are shown in the session window.

Test and CI for Two Proportions

```
Sample   X    N    Sample p
1        12   34   0.352941
2        17   24   0.708333


Difference = p (1) - p (2)
Estimate for difference:  -0.355392
95% CI for difference:  (-0.598025, -0.112759)
Test for difference = 0 (vs not = 0):  Z = -2.67 P-Value = 0.008
```

The *P*-value of the test is 0.008. Reject the null hypothesis. The difference is statistically significant. Of all small nursing homes 35%, compared to 71% of all large nursing homes, have an immunization rate of 80%. We can't tell why, only that there is a difference.

TI-83 Plus or TI-84 Plus
Step by Step

Hypothesis Test for the Difference Between Two Proportions

1. Press **STAT** and move the cursor to TESTS.
2. Press **6** for 2-PropZTEST.
3. Type in the appropriate values.
4. Move the cursor to the appropriate alternative hypothesis and press **ENTER**.
5. Move the cursor to Calculate and press **ENTER**.

Confidence Interval for the Difference Between Two Proportions

1. Press **STAT** and move the cursor to TESTS.
2. Press **B (ALPHA APPS)** for 2-PropZInt.
3. Type in the appropriate values.
4. Move the cursor to Calculate and press **ENTER**.

Excel
Step by Step

Testing the Difference Between Two Proportions

Excel does not have a procedure to test the difference between two population proportions. However, you may conduct this test using the MegaStat Add-in available on your CD. If you have not installed this add-in, do so, following the instructions from the Chapter 1 Excel Step by Step.

We will use the summary information from Example 9–9.

1. From the toolbar, select Add-Ins, **MegaStat>Hypothesis Tests>Compare Two Independent Proportions**. *Note:* You may need to open MegaStat from the MegaStat.xls file on your computer's hard drive.
2. Under Group 1, type **12** for p and **34** for n. Under Group 2, type **17** for p and **24** for n. MegaStat automatically changes p to X unless a decimal value less than 1 is typed in for these.
3. Type **0** for the Hypothesized difference and select the "not equal" Alternative, and click [OK].

Hypothesis Test for Two Independent Proportions

p_1	p_2		p_c	
0.3529	0.7083		0.5	p (as decimal)
12/34	17/24		29/58	p (as fraction)
12.	17.		29.	X
34	24		58	n

	−0.3554	Difference
	0.	Hypothesized difference
	0.1333	Standard error
	−2.67	z
	0.0077	P-value (two-tailed)

9–5

Testing the Difference Between Two Variances

In addition to comparing two means, statisticians are interested in comparing two variances or standard deviations. For example, is the variation in the temperatures for a certain month for two cities different?

In another situation, a researcher may be interested in comparing the variance of the cholesterol of men with the variance of the cholesterol of women. For the comparison of two variances or standard deviations, an **F test** is used. The F test should not be confused with the chi-square test, which compares a single sample variance to a specific population variance, as shown in Chapter 8.

Objective 5

Test the difference between two variances or standard deviations.

If two independent samples are selected from two normally distributed populations in which the variances are equal ($\sigma_1^2 = \sigma_2^2$) and if the variances s_1^2 and s_2^2 are compared as $\dfrac{s_1^2}{s_2^2}$, the sampling distribution of the variances is called the **F distribution.**

Characteristics of the F Distribution

1. The values of F cannot be negative, because variances are always positive or zero.
2. The distribution is positively skewed.
3. The mean value of F is approximately equal to 1.
4. The F distribution is a family of curves based on the degrees of freedom of the variance of the numerator and the degrees of freedom of the variance of the denominator.

Figure 9–10 shows the shapes of several curves for the F distribution.

Figure 9–10

The F Family of Curves

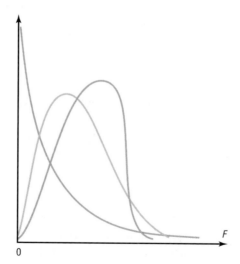

Formula for the F Test

$$F = \frac{s_1^2}{s_2^2}$$

where the larger of the two variances is placed in the numerator regardless of the subscripts. (See note on page 514.)

The F test has two terms for the degrees of freedom: that of the numerator, $n_1 - 1$, and that of the denominator, $n_2 - 1$, where n_1 is the sample size from which the larger variance was obtained.

When you are finding the *F* test value, *the larger of the variances is placed in the numerator of the F formula;* this is not necessarily the variance of the larger of the two sample sizes.

Table H in Appendix C gives the *F* critical values for $\alpha = 0.005, 0.01, 0.025, 0.05$, and 0.10 (each α value involves a separate table in Table H). These are one-tailed values; if a two-tailed test is being conducted, then the $\alpha/2$ value must be used. For example, if a two-tailed test with $\alpha = 0.05$ is being conducted, then the $0.05/2 = 0.025$ table of Table H should be used.

Example 9–12

Find the critical value for a right-tailed *F* test when $\alpha = 0.05$, the degrees of freedom for the numerator (abbreviated d.f.N.) are 15, and the degrees of freedom for the denominator (d.f.D.) are 21.

Solution

Since this test is right-tailed with $\alpha = 0.05$, use the 0.05 table. The d.f.N. is listed across the top, and the d.f.D. is listed in the left column. The critical value is found where the row and column intersect in the table. In this case, it is 2.18. See Figure 9–11.

Figure 9–11

Finding the Critical Value in Table H for Example 9–12

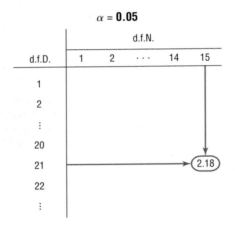

As noted previously, when the *F* test is used, the larger variance is always placed in the numerator of the formula. When you are conducting a two-tailed test, α is split; and even though there are two values, only the right tail is used. The reason is that the *F* test value is always greater than or equal to 1.

Example 9–13

Find the critical value for a two-tailed *F* test with $\alpha = 0.05$ when the sample size from which the variance for the numerator was obtained was 21 and the sample size from which the variance for the denominator was obtained was 12.

Solution

Since this is a two-tailed test with $\alpha = 0.05$, the $0.05/2 = 0.025$ table must be used. Here, d.f.N. $= 21 - 1 = 20$, and d.f.D. $= 12 - 1 = 11$; hence, the critical value is 3.23. See Figure 9–12.

Figure 9–12

Finding the Critical Value in Table H for Example 9–13

$\alpha = 0.025$

When the degree of freedom values cannot be found in the table, the closest value on the smaller side should be used. For example, if d.f.N. = 14, this value is between the given table values of 12 and 15; therefore, 12 should be used, to be on the safe side.

When you are testing the equality of two variances, these hypotheses are used:

Right-tailed	**Left-tailed**	**Two-tailed**
$H_0: \sigma_1^2 = \sigma_2^2$	$H_0: \sigma_1^2 = \sigma_2^2$	$H_0: \sigma_1^2 = \sigma_2^2$
$H_1: \sigma_1^2 > \sigma_2^2$	$H_1: \sigma_1^2 < \sigma_2^2$	$H_1: \sigma_1^2 \neq \sigma_2^2$

There are four key points to keep in mind when you are using the F test.

Notes for the Use of the F Test

1. The larger variance should always be placed in the numerator of the formula regardless of the subscripts. (See note on page 514.)

$$F = \frac{s_1^2}{s_2^2}$$

2. For a two-tailed test, the α value must be divided by 2 and the critical value placed on the right side of the F curve.
3. If the standard deviations instead of the variances are given in the problem, they must be squared for the formula for the F test.
4. When the degrees of freedom cannot be found in Table H, the closest value on the smaller side should be used.

Assumptions for Testing the Difference Between Two Variances

1. The populations from which the samples were obtained must be normally distributed. (*Note:* The test should not be used when the distributions depart from normality.)
2. The samples must be independent of each other.

Remember also that in tests of hypotheses using the traditional method, these five steps should be taken:

Step 1 State the hypotheses and identify the claim.

Step 2 Find the critical value.

Unusual Stat

Of all U.S. births, 2% are twins.

Step 3   Compute the test value.

Step 4   Make the decision.

Step 5   Summarize the results.

Example 9–14

Heart Rates of Smokers

A medical researcher wishes to see whether the variance of the heart rates (in beats per minute) of smokers is different from the variance of heart rates of people who do not smoke. Two samples are selected, and the data are as shown. Using $\alpha = 0.05$, is there enough evidence to support the claim?

Smokers	Nonsmokers
$n_1 = 26$	$n_2 = 18$
$s_1^2 = 36$	$s_2^2 = 10$

Solution

Step 1   State the hypotheses and identify the claim.

$$H_0: \sigma_1^2 = \sigma_2^2 \qquad \text{and} \qquad H_1: \sigma_1^2 \neq \sigma_2^2 \text{ (claim)}$$

Step 2   Find the critical value. Use the 0.025 table in Table H since $\alpha = 0.05$ and this is a two-tailed test. Here, d.f.N. $= 26 - 1 = 25$, and d.f.D. $= 18 - 1 = 17$. The critical value is 2.56 (d.f.N. $= 24$ was used). See Figure 9–13.

Figure 9–13

Critical Value for
Example 9–14

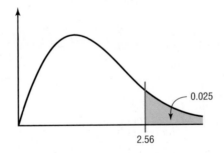

Step 3   Compute the test value.

$$F = \frac{s_1^2}{s_2^2} = \frac{36}{10} = 3.6$$

Step 4   Make the decision. Reject the null hypothesis, since $3.6 > 2.56$.

Step 5   Summarize the results. There is enough evidence to support the claim that the variance of the heart rates of smokers and nonsmokers is different.

Example 9–15

Waiting Time to See a Doctor

The standard deviation of the average waiting time to see a doctor for non-life-threatening problems in the emergency room at an urban hospital is 32 minutes. At a second hospital, the standard deviation is 28 minutes. If a sample of 16 patients was used in the first case and 18 in the second case, is there enough evidence to conclude that the standard deviation of the waiting times in the first hospital is greater than the standard deviation of the waiting times in the second hospital?

Solution

Step 1   State the hypotheses and identify the claim.

$$H_0: \sigma_1^2 = \sigma_2^2 \quad \text{and} \quad H_1: \sigma_1^2 > \sigma_2^2 \text{ (claim)}$$

Step 2   Find the critical value. Here, d.f.N. $= 16 - 1 = 15$, and d.f.D. $= 18 - 1 = 17$. From the 0.01 table, the critical value is 3.31.

Step 3   Compute the test value.

$$F = \frac{s_1^2}{s_2^2} = \frac{32^2}{28^2} = 1.31$$

Step 4   Do not reject the null hypothesis since $1.31 < 3.31$.

Step 5   Summarize the results. There is not enough evidence to support the claim that the standard deviation of the waiting times of the first hospital is greater than the standard deviation of the waiting times of the second hospital.

Finding P-values for the F test statistic is somewhat more complicated since it requires looking through all the F tables (Table H in Appendix C) using the specific d.f.N. and d.f.D. values. For example, suppose that a certain test has $F = 3.58$, d.f.N. $= 5$, and d.f.D. $= 10$. To find the P-value interval for $F = 3.58$, you must first find the corresponding F values for d.f.N. $= 5$ and d.f.D. $= 10$ for α equal to 0.005 on page 648, 0.01 on page 649, 0.025 on page 650, 0.05 on page 651, and 0.10 on page 652 in Table H. Then make a table as shown.

α	0.10	0.05	0.025	0.01	0.005
F	2.52	3.33	4.24	5.64	6.87
Reference page	652	651	650	649	648

Now locate the two F values that the test value 3.58 falls between. In this case, 3.58 falls between 3.33 and 4.24, corresponding to 0.05 and 0.025. Hence, the P-value for a right-tailed test for $F = 3.58$ falls between 0.025 and 0.05 (that is, $0.025 < P\text{-value} < 0.05$). For a right-tailed test, then, you would reject the null hypothesis at $\alpha = 0.05$ but not at $\alpha = 0.01$. The P-value obtained from a calculator is 0.0408. Remember that for a two-tailed test the values found in Table H for α must be doubled. In this case, $0.05 < P\text{-value} < 0.10$ for $F = 3.58$.

Once you understand the concept, you can dispense with making a table as shown and find the P-value directly from Table H.

Example 9–16   **Airport Passengers**

The CEO of an airport hypothesizes that the variance in the number of passengers for American airports is greater than the variance in the number of passengers for foreign airports. At $\alpha = 0.10$, is there enough evidence to support the hypothesis? The data in millions of passengers per year are shown for selected airports. Use the P-value method. Assume the variable is normally distributed.

American airports		Foreign airports	
36.8	73.5	60.7	51.2
72.4	61.2	42.7	38.6
60.5	40.1		

Source: Airports Council International.

Solution

Step 1 State the hypotheses and identify the claim.

$$H_0: \sigma_1^2 = \sigma_2^2 \qquad \text{and} \qquad H_1: \sigma_1^2 > \sigma_2^2 \text{ (claim)}$$

Step 2 Compute the test value. Using the formula in Chapter 3 or a calculator, find the variance for each group.

$$s_1^2 = 246.38 \qquad \text{and} \qquad s_2^2 = 95.87$$

Substitute in the formula and solve.

$$F = \frac{s_1^2}{s_2^2} = \frac{246.38}{95.87} = 2.57$$

Step 3 Find the P-value in Table H, using d.f.N. $= 5$ and d.f.D. $= 3$.

α	0.10	0.05	0.025	0.01	0.005
F	5.31	9.01	14.88	28.24	45.39

Since 2.57 is less than 5.31, the P-value is greater than 0.10. (The P-value obtained from a calculator is 0.234.)

Step 4 Make the decision. The decision is to not reject the null hypothesis since P-value > 0.10.

Step 5 Summarize the results. There is not enough evidence to support the claim that the variance in the number of passengers for American airports is greater than the variance in the number of passengers for foreign airports.

If the exact degrees of freedom are not specified in Table H, the closest smaller value should be used. For example, if $\alpha = 0.05$ (right-tailed test), d.f.N. $= 18$, and d.f.D. $= 20$, use the column d.f.N. $= 15$ and the row d.f.D. $= 20$ to get $F = 2.20$.

Note: It is not absolutely necessary to place the larger variance in the numerator when you are performing the F test. Critical values for left-tailed hypotheses tests can be found by interchanging the degrees of freedom and taking the reciprocal of the value found in Table H.

Also, you should use caution when performing the F test since the data can run contrary to the hypotheses on rare occasions. For example, if the hypotheses are $H_0: \sigma_1^2 \leq \sigma_2^2$ (written $H_0: \sigma_1^2 = \sigma_2^2$) and $H_1: \sigma_1^2 > \sigma_2^2$, but if $s_1^2 < s_2^2$, then the F test should not be performed and you would not reject the null hypothesis.

Applying the Concepts **9–5**

Variability and Automatic Transmissions

Assume the following data values are from the June 1996 issue of *Automotive Magazine*. An article compared various parameters of U.S.- and Japanese-made sports cars. This report centers on the price of an optional automatic transmission. Which country has the greater variability in the price of automatic transmissions? Input the data and answer the following questions.

Japanese cars		**U.S. cars**	
Nissan 300ZX	$1940	Dodge Stealth	$2363
Mazda RX7	1810	Saturn	1230
Mazda MX6	1871	Mercury Cougar	1332
Nissan NX	1822	Ford Probe	932
Mazda Miata	1920	Eagle Talon	1790
Honda Prelude	1730	Chevy Lumina	1833

1. What is the null hypothesis?
2. What test statistic is used to test for any significant differences in the variances?

3. Is there a significant difference in the variability in the prices between the Japanese cars and the U.S. cars?

4. What effect does a small sample size have on the standard deviations?

5. What degrees of freedom are used for the statistical test?

6. Could two sets of data have significantly different variances without having significantly different means?

See page 526 for the answers.

Exercises 9–5

1. When one is computing the F test value, what condition is placed on the variance that is in the numerator?

2. Why is the critical region always on the right side in the use of the F test?

3. What are the two different degrees of freedom associated with the F distribution?

4. What are the characteristics of the F distribution?

5. Using Table H, find the critical value for each.

   a. Sample 1: $s_1^2 = 128$, $n_1 = 23$
      Sample 2: $s_2^2 = 162$, $n_2 = 16$
      Two-tailed, $\alpha = 0.01$
   b. Sample 1: $s_1^2 = 37$, $n_1 = 14$
      Sample 2: $s_2^2 = 89$, $n_2 = 25$
      Right-tailed, $\alpha = 0.01$
   c. Sample 1: $s_1^2 = 232$, $n_1 = 30$
      Sample 2: $s_2^2 = 387$, $n_2 = 46$
      Two-tailed, $\alpha = 0.05$
   d. Sample 1: $s_1^2 = 164$, $n_1 = 21$
      Sample 2: $s_2^2 = 53$, $n_2 = 17$
      Two-tailed, $\alpha = 0.10$
   e. Sample 1: $s_1^2 = 92.8$, $n_1 = 11$
      Sample 2: $s_2^2 = 43.6$, $n_2 = 11$
      Right-tailed, $\alpha = 0.05$

6. (ans) Using Table H, find the P-value interval for each F test value.

   a. $F = 2.97$, d.f.N. = 9, d.f.D. = 14, right-tailed
   b. $F = 3.32$, d.f.N. = 6, d.f.D. = 12, two-tailed
   c. $F = 2.28$, d.f.N. = 12, d.f.D. = 20, right-tailed
   d. $F = 3.51$, d.f.N. = 12, d.f.D. = 21, right-tailed
   e. $F = 4.07$, d.f.N. = 6, d.f.D. = 10, two-tailed
   f. $F = 1.65$, d.f.N. = 19, d.f.D. = 28, right-tailed
   g. $F = 1.77$, d.f.N. = 28, d.f.D. = 28, right-tailed
   h. $F = 7.29$, d.f.N. = 5, d.f.D. = 8, two-tailed

For Exercises 7 through 20, perform the following steps. Assume that all variables are normally distributed.

   a. State the hypotheses and identify the claim.
   b. Find the critical value.
   c. Compute the test value.
   d. Make the decision.
   e. Summarize the results.

Use the traditional method of hypothesis testing unless otherwise specified.

7. **Fiction Bestsellers** The standard deviation for the number of weeks 15 *New York Times* hardcover fiction books spent on their bestseller list is 6.17 weeks. The standard deviation for the 15 *New York Times* hardcover nonfiction list is 13.12 weeks. At $\alpha = 0.10$, can we conclude that there is a difference in the variances?

Source: *The New York Times.*

8. **Costs of Paper Shredders and Calculators** The prices (in dollars) are shown below for a random selection of lightweight paper shredders and for printing calculators. At the 0.10 level of significance, can it be concluded that the variance in price differs between the two types of office machines? Use the P-value method.

Paper shredders				Calculators			
75	115	118	287	110	140	165	90
250	300	50		230	97	269	

9. **Tax-Exempt Properties** A tax collector wishes to see if the variances of the values of the tax-exempt properties are different for two large cities. The values of the tax-exempt properties for two samples are shown. The data are given in millions of dollars. At $\alpha = 0.05$, is there enough evidence to support the tax collector's claim that the variances are different?

City A				City B			
113	22	14	8	82	11	5	15
25	23	23	30	295	50	12	9
44	11	19	7	12	68	81	2
31	19	5	2	20	16	4	5

10. **Noise Levels in Hospitals** In the hospital study cited in Exercise 19 in Exercise set 7–1, it was found that the standard deviation of the sound levels from 20 areas designated as "casualty doors" was 4.1 dBA and the standard deviation of 24 areas designated as operating theaters was 7.5 dBA. At $\alpha = 0.05$, can you substantiate the claim that there is a difference in the standard deviations?

Source: M. Bayo, A. Garcia, and A. Garcia, "Noise Levels in an Urban Hospital and Workers' Subjective Responses," *Archives of Environmental Health.*

11. Calories in Ice Cream The numbers of calories contained in $\frac{1}{2}$-cup servings of randomly selected flavors of ice cream from two national brands are listed here. At the 0.05 level of significance, is there sufficient evidence to conclude that the variance in the number of calories differs between the two brands?

Brand A		Brand B	
330	300	280	310
310	350	300	370
270	380	250	300
310	300	290	310

Source: *The Doctor's Pocket Calorie, Fat and Carbohydrate Counter.*

12. Turnpike and Expressway Travel A researcher wishes to see if the variance in the number of vehicles passing through the tollbooths during a fiscal year on the Pennsylvania Turnpike is different from the variance in the number of vehicles passing through the tollbooths on the expressways in Pennsylvania during the same year. The data are shown. At $\alpha = 0.05$, can it be concluded that the variances are different?

PA Turnpike	PA expressways
3,694,560	2,774,251
719,934	204,369
3,768,285	456,123
1,838,271	1,068,107
3,358,175	3,534,092
6,718,905	235,752
3,469,431	499,043
4,420,553	2,016,046
920,264	253,956
1,005,469	826,710
1,112,722	133,619
2,855,109	3,453,745

Source: *Pittsburgh Post-Gazette.*

13. Population and Area Cities were randomly selected from the list of the 50 largest cities in the United States (based on population). The areas of each in square miles are indicated below. Is there sufficient evidence to conclude that the variance in area is greater for eastern cities than for western cities at $\alpha = 0.05$? At $\alpha = 0.01$?

Eastern		Western	
Atlanta, GA	132	Albuquerque, NM	181
Columbus, OH	210	Denver, CO	155
Louisville, KY	385	Fresno, CA	104
New York, NY	303	Las Vegas, NV	113
Philadelphia, PA	135	Portland, OR	134
Washington, DC	61	Seattle, WA	84
Charlotte, NC	242		

Source: *New York Times Almanac.*

14. Carbohydrates in Candy The number of grams of carbohydrates contained in 1-ounce servings of randomly selected chocolate and nonchocolate candy is listed here. Is there sufficient evidence to conclude that the carbohydrate content varies between chocolate and nonchocolate candy? Use $\alpha = 0.10$.

Chocolate	29	25	17	36	41	25	32	29
	38	34	24	27	29			
Nonchocolate	41	41	37	29	30	38	39	10
	29	55	29					

Source: *The Doctor's Pocket Calorie, Fat and Carbohydrate Counter.*

15. Tuition Costs for Medical School The yearly tuition costs in dollars for random samples of medical schools that specialize in research and in primary care are listed. At $\alpha = 0.05$, can it be concluded that a difference between the variances of the two groups exists?

Research			Primary care		
30,897	34,280	31,943	26,068	21,044	30,897
34,294	31,275	29,590	34,208	20,877	29,691
20,618	20,500	29,310	33,783	33,065	35,000
21,274			27,297		

Source: *U.S. News & World Report Best Graduate Schools.*

16. County Size in Indiana and Iowa A researcher wishes to see if the variance of the areas in square miles for counties in Indiana is less than the variance of the areas for counties in Iowa. A random sample of counties is selected, and the data are shown. At $\alpha = 0.01$, can it be concluded that the variance of the areas for counties in Indiana is less than the variance of the areas for counties in Iowa?

Indiana				Iowa			
406	393	396	485	640	580	431	416
431	430	369	408	443	569	779	381
305	215	489	293	717	568	714	731
373	148	306	509	571	577	503	501
560	384	320	407	568	434	615	402

Source: *The World Almanac and Book of Facts.*

17. Heights of Tall Buildings Test the claim that the variance of heights of tall buildings in Denver is equal to the variance in heights of tall buildings in Detroit at $\alpha = 0.10$. The data are given in feet.

Denver			Detroit		
714	698	544	620	472	430
504	438	408	562	448	420
404			534	436	

Source: *The World Almanac and Book of Facts.*

18. Elementary School Teachers' Salaries A researcher claims that the variation in the salaries of elementary school teachers is greater than the variation in the salaries of secondary school teachers. A sample of the salaries of 30 elementary school teachers has a variance of $8324, and a sample of the salaries of 30 secondary school teachers has a variance of $2862. At $\alpha = 0.05$, can the researcher conclude that the variation in the elementary school teachers' salaries is greater than the variation in the secondary teachers' salaries? Use the P-value method.

Men			Women		
11.9	10.4	12.6	10.6	10.2	8.8
12.3	11.1	14.7	9.6	9.5	9.5
9.2	10.8	12.9	10.1	11.2	9.3
11.2	11.7	13.3	9.4	10.3	9.5
13.8	12.8	14.5	9.8	10.3	11.0

 19. Weights of Running Shoes The weights in ounces of a sample of running shoes for men and women are shown. Calculate the variances for each sample, and test the claim that the variances are equal at $\alpha = 0.05$. Use the P-value method.

 20. Daily Stock Prices Two portfolios were randomly assembled from the New York Stock Exchange, and the daily stock prices are shown below. At the 0.05 level of significance, can it be concluded that a difference in variance in price exists between the two portfolios?

Portfolio A	36.44	44.21	12.21	59.60	55.44	39.42	51.29	48.68	41.59	19.49
Portfolio B	32.69	47.25	49.35	36.17	63.04	17.74	4.23	34.98	37.02	31.48

Source: *Washington Observer-Reporter.*

Technology *Step by Step*

MINITAB
Step by Step

Test for the Difference Between Two Variances

For Example 9–16, test the hypothesis that the variance in the number of passengers for American and foreign airports is different. Use the P-value approach.

American airports	Foreign airports
36.8	60.7
72.4	42.7
60.5	51.2
73.5	38.6
61.2	
40.1	

1. Enter the data into two columns of MINITAB.
2. Name the columns American and Foreign.
   a) Select **Stat>Basic Statistics>2-Variances.**

b) Click the button for Samples in different columns.

c) Click in the text box for First, then double-click C1 American.

d) Double-click C2 Foreign, then click on [Options]. The dialog box is shown. Change the confidence level to **90** and type an appropriate title. In this dialog, we cannot specify a left- or right-tailed test.

3. Click [OK] twice. A graph window will open that includes a small window that says $F = 2.57$ and the P-value is 0.437. Divide this two-tailed P-value by 2 for a one-tailed test.

There is not enough evidence in the sample to conclude there is greater variance in the number of passengers in American airports compared to foreign airports.

TI-83 Plus or TI-84 Plus
Step by Step

Hypothesis Test for the Difference Between Two Variances (Data)

1. Enter the data values into L_1 and L_2.
2. Press **STAT** and move the cursor to TESTS.
3. Press **D (ALPHA X^{-1})** for 2-SampFTest.   (The TI-84 uses E)
4. Move the cursor to Data and press **ENTER**.
5. Type in the appropriate values.
6. Move the cursor to the appropriate alternative hypothesis and press **ENTER**.
7. Move the cursor to Calculate and press **ENTER**.

Hypothesis Test for the Difference Between Two Variances (Statistics)

1. Press **STAT** and move the cursor to TESTS.
2. Press **D (ALPHA X^{-1})** for 2-SampFTest.   (The TI-84 uses E)
3. Move the cursor to Stats and press **ENTER**.
4. Type in the appropriate values.
5. Move the cursor to the appropriate alternative hypothesis and press **ENTER**.
6. Move the cursor to Calculate and press **ENTER**.

Excel
Step by Step

F Test for the Difference Between Two Variances

Excel has a two-sample F test included in the Data Analysis Add-in. To perform an F test for the difference between the variances of two populations, given two independent samples, do this:

1. Enter the first sample data set into column A.
2. Enter the second sample data set into column B.
3. Select the Data tab from the toolbar. Then select Data Analysis.
4. In the Analysis Tools box, select F-test: Two-sample for Variances.
5. Type the ranges for the data in columns A and B.
6. Specify the confidence level Alpha.
7. Specify a location for the output, and click [OK].

Example XL9–4

At $\alpha = 0.05$, test the hypothesis that the two population variances are equal, using the sample data provided here.

Set A	63	73	80	60	86	83	70	72	82
Set B	86	93	64	82	81	75	88	63	63

The results appear in the table that Excel generates, shown here. For this example, the output shows that the null hypothesis cannot be rejected at an α level of 0.05.

F-Test Two-Sample for Variances		
	Variable 1	Variable 2
Mean	74.33333333	77.22222222
Variance	82.75	132.9444444
Observations	9	9
df	8	8
F	0.622440451	
P(F<=f) one-tail	0.258814151	
F Critical one-tail	0.290858004	

Summary

Many times researchers are interested in comparing two parameters such as two means, two proportions, or two variances. When both population standard deviations are known, the z test can be used to compare two means. If both population standard deviations are not known, the sample standard deviations can be used, but the t test is used to compare two means. A z test can be used to compare two proportions. Finally, two variances can be compared using an F test.

Important Terms

dependent samples 487

F distribution 509

F test 509

independent samples 480

pooled estimate of the variance 482

Important Formulas

Formula for the z test for comparing two means from independent populations; σ_1 and σ_2 are known:

$$z = \frac{(\overline{X}_1 - \overline{X}_2) - (\mu_1 - \mu_2)}{\sqrt{\dfrac{\sigma_1^2}{n_1} + \dfrac{\sigma_2^2}{n_2}}}$$

Formula for the confidence interval for difference of two means when σ_1 and σ_2 are known:

$$(\overline{X}_1 - \overline{X}_2) - z_{\alpha/2}\sqrt{\frac{\sigma_1^2}{n_1} + \frac{\sigma_2^2}{n_2}} < \mu_1 - \mu_2$$
$$< (\overline{X}_1 - \overline{X}_2) + z_{\alpha/2}\sqrt{\frac{\sigma_1^2}{n_1} + \frac{\sigma_2^2}{n_2}}$$

Formula for the t test for comparing two means (independent samples, variances not equal), σ_1 and σ_2 are unknown:

$$t = \frac{(\overline{X}_1 - \overline{X}_2) - (\mu_1 - \mu_2)}{\sqrt{\dfrac{s_1^2}{n_1} + \dfrac{s_2^2}{n_2}}}$$

and d.f. = the smaller of $n_1 - 1$ or $n_2 - 1$.

Formula for the confidence interval for the difference of two means (independent samples, variances unequal), σ_1 and σ_2 are unknown:

$$(\overline{X}_1 - \overline{X}_2) - t_{\alpha/2}\sqrt{\frac{s_1^2}{n_1} + \frac{s_2^2}{n_2}} < \mu_1 - \mu_2$$
$$< (\overline{X}_1 - \overline{X}_2) + t_{\alpha/2}\sqrt{\frac{s_1^2}{n_1} + \frac{s_2^2}{n_2}}$$

and d.f. = smaller of $n_1 - 1$ and $n_2 - 2$.

Formula for the t test for comparing two means from dependent samples:

$$t = \frac{\overline{D} - \mu_D}{s_D/\sqrt{n}}$$

where $\overline{D}$ is the mean of the differences

$$\overline{D} = \frac{\Sigma D}{n}$$

and s_D is the standard deviation of the differences

$$s_D = \sqrt{\frac{n\Sigma D^2 - (\Sigma D)^2}{n(n-1)}}$$

Formula for confidence interval for the mean of the difference for dependent samples:

$$\bar{D} - t_{\alpha/2}\frac{s_D}{\sqrt{n}} < \mu_D < \bar{D} + t_{\alpha/2}\frac{s_D}{\sqrt{n}}$$

and d.f. $= n - 1$.

Formula for the z test for comparing two proportions:

$$z = \frac{(\hat{p}_1 - \hat{p}_2) - (p_1 - p_2)}{\sqrt{\bar{p}\,\bar{q}\left(\dfrac{1}{n_1} + \dfrac{1}{n_2}\right)}}$$

where

$$\bar{p} = \frac{X_1 + X_2}{n_1 + n_2} \qquad \hat{p}_1 = \frac{X_1}{n_1}$$

$$\bar{q} = 1 - \bar{p} \qquad \hat{p}_2 = \frac{X_2}{n_2}$$

Formula for confidence interval for the difference of two proportions:

$$(\hat{p}_1 - \hat{p}_2) - z_{\alpha/2}\sqrt{\frac{\hat{p}_1\hat{q}_1}{n_1} + \frac{\hat{p}_2\hat{q}_2}{n_2}} < p_1 - p_2$$

$$< (\hat{p}_1 - \hat{p}_2) + z_{\alpha/2}\sqrt{\frac{\hat{p}_1\hat{q}_1}{n_1} + \frac{\hat{p}_2\hat{q}_2}{n_2}}$$

Formula for the F test for comparing two variances:

$$F = \frac{s_1^2}{s_2^2} \qquad \begin{aligned} &\text{d.f.N.} = n_1 - 1 \\ &\text{d.f.D.} = n_2 - 1 \end{aligned}$$

Review Exercises

For each exercise, perform these steps. Assume that all variables are normally or approximately normally distributed.

   a. State the hypotheses and identify the claim.
   b. Find the critical value(s).
   c. Compute the test value.
   d. Make the decision.
   e. Summarize the results.

Use the traditional method of hypothesis testing unless otherwise specified.

 1. Driving for Pleasure Two groups of drivers are surveyed to see how many miles per week they drive for pleasure trips. The data are shown. At $\alpha = 0.01$, can it be concluded that single drivers do more driving for pleasure trips on average than married drivers? Assume $\sigma_1 = 16.7$ and $\sigma_2 = 16.1$.

Single drivers					Married drivers				
106	110	115	121	132	97	104	138	102	115
119	97	118	122	135	133	120	119	136	96
110	117	116	138	142	139	108	117	145	114
115	114	103	98	99	140	136	113	113	150
108	117	152	147	117	101	114	116	113	135
154	86	115	116	104	115	109	147	106	88
107	133	138	142	140	113	119	99	108	105

  2. Average Earnings of College Graduates The average yearly earnings of male college graduates (with at least a bachelor's degree) are $58,500 for men aged 25 to 34. The average yearly earnings of female college graduates with the same qualifications are $49,339. Based on the results below, can it be concluded that there is a difference in mean earnings between male and female college graduates? Use the 0.01 level of significance.

	Male	Female
Sample mean	$59,235	$52,487
Population standard deviation	8,945	10,125
Sample size	40	35

Source: *New York Times Almanac.*

  3. Communication Times According to the Bureau of Labor Statistics' American Time Use Survey (ATUS), married persons spend an average of 8 minutes per day on phone calls, mail, and e-mail, while single persons spend an average of 14 minutes per day on these same tasks. Based on the following information, is there sufficient evidence to conclude that single persons spend, on average, a greater time each day communicating? Use the 0.05 level of significance.

	Single	Married
Sample size	26	20
Sample mean	16.7 minutes	12.5 minutes
Sample variance	8.41	10.24

Source: *Time* magazine.

 4. Average Temperatures The average temperatures for a 25-day period for Birmingham, Alabama, and Chicago, Illinois, are shown. Based on the samples, at $\alpha = 0.10$, can it be concluded that it is warmer in Birmingham?

Birmingham					Chicago				
78	82	68	67	68	70	74	73	60	77
75	73	75	64	68	71	72	71	74	76
62	73	77	78	79	71	80	65	70	83
74	72	73	78	68	67	76	75	62	65
73	79	82	71	66	66	65	77	66	64

5. **Teachers' Salaries** A sample of 15 teachers from Rhode Island has an average salary of $35,270, with a standard deviation of $3256. A sample of 30 teachers from New York has an average salary of $29,512, with a standard deviation of $1432. Is there a significant difference in teachers' salaries between the two states? Use $\alpha = 0.02$. Find the 98% confidence interval for the difference of the two means.

6. **Soft Drinks in School** The data show the amounts (in thousands of dollars) of the contracts for soft drinks in local school districts. At $\alpha = 0.10$ can it be concluded that there is a difference in the averages? Use the *P*-value method. Give a reason why the result would be of concern to a cafeteria manager.

Pepsi						Coca-Cola		
46	120	80	500	100	59	420	285	57

Source: Local school districts.

7. **High and Low Temperatures** March is a month of variable weather in the Northeast. The chart below records the actual high and low temperatures for a selection of days in March from the weather report for Pittsburgh, Pennsylvania. At the 0.01 level of significance, is there sufficient evidence to conclude that there is more than a 10° difference between average highs and lows?

Maximum	44	46	46	36	34	36	57	62	73	53
Minimum	27	34	24	19	19	26	33	57	46	26

Source: www.wunderground.com

8. **Automobile Part Production** In an effort to increase production of an automobile part, the factory manager decides to play music in the manufacturing area. Eight workers are selected, and the number of items each produced for a specific day is recorded. After one week of music, the same workers are monitored again. The data are given in the table. At $\alpha = 0.05$, can the manager conclude that the music has increased production?

Worker	1	2	3	4	5	6	7	8
Before	6	8	10	9	5	12	9	7
After	10	12	9	12	8	13	8	10

9. **Foggy Days** St. Petersburg, Russia, has 207 foggy days out of 365 days while Stockholm, Sweden, has 166 foggy days out of 365. At $\alpha = 0.02$, can it be concluded that the proportions of foggy days for the two cities are different? Find the 98% confidence interval for the difference of the two proportions.

Source: Jack Williams, *USA TODAY.*

10. **Adopted Pets** According to the 2005–2006 National Pet Owners Survey, only 16% of pet dogs were adopted from an animal shelter and 15% of pet cats were adopted. To test this difference in proportions of adopted pets, a survey was taken in a local region. Is there sufficient evidence to conclude that there is a difference in proportions? Use $\alpha = 0.05$.

	Dogs	Cats
Number	180	200
Adopted	36	30

Source: www.hsus.org

11. **Noise Levels in Hospitals** In the hospital study cited in Exercise 19 in Exercise set 8–1, the standard deviation of the noise levels of the 11 intensive care units was 4.1 dBA, and the standard deviation of the noise levels of 24 nonmedical care areas, such as kitchens and machine rooms, was 13.2 dBA. At $\alpha = 0.10$, is there a significant difference between the standard deviations of these two areas?

Source: M. Bayo, A. Garcia, and A. Garcia, "Noise Levels in an Urban Hospital and Workers' Subjective Responses," *Archives of Environmental Health.*

12. **Heights of World Famous Cathedrals** The heights (in feet) for a random sample of world famous cathedrals are listed below. In addition, the heights for a sample of the tallest buildings in the world are listed. Is there sufficient evidence at $\alpha = 0.05$ to conclude a difference in the variances in height between the two groups?

Cathedrals	72	114	157	56	83	108	90	151	
Tallest buildings	452	442	415	391	355	344	310	302	209

Source: www.infoplease.com

Statistics Today

To Vaccinate or Not to Vaccinate? Small or Large?—Revisited

Using a *z* test to compare two proportions, the researchers found that the proportion of residents in smaller nursing homes who were vaccinated (80.8%) was statistically greater than that of residents in large nursing homes who were vaccinated (68.7%). Using statistical methods presented in later chapters, they also found that the larger size of the nursing home and the lower frequency of vaccination were significant predictions of influenza outbreaks in nursing homes.

Data Analysis

The Data Bank is found in Appendix D, or on the World Wide Web by following links from www.mhhe.com/bluman/

1. From the Data Bank, select a variable and compare the mean of the variable for a random sample of at least 30 men with the mean of the variable for the random sample of at least 30 women. Use a z test.

2. Repeat the experiment in Exercise 1, using a different variable and two samples of size 15. Compare the means by using a t test.

3. Compare the proportion of men who are smokers with the proportion of women who are smokers. Use the data in the Data Bank. Choose random samples of size 30 or more. Use the z test for proportions.

4. Select two samples of 20 values from the data in Data Set IV in Appendix D. Test the hypothesis that the mean heights of the buildings are equal.

5. Using the same data obtained in Exercise 4, test the hypothesis that the variances are equal.

Chapter Quiz

Determine whether each statement is true or false. If the statement is false, explain why.

1. When you are testing the difference between two means for small samples, it is not important to distinguish whether the samples are independent of each other.

2. If the same diet is given to two groups of randomly selected individuals, the samples are considered to be dependent.

3. When computing the F test value, you always place the larger variance in the numerator of the fraction.

4. Tests for variances are always two-tailed.

Select the best answer.

5. To test the equality of two variances, you would use a(n) _____ test.
   a. z   c. Chi-square
   b. t   d. F

6. To test the equality of two proportions, you would use a(n) _____ test.
   a. z   c. Chi-square
   b. t   d. F

7. The mean value of the F is approximately equal to
   a. 0   c. 1
   b. 0.5   d. It cannot be determined.

8. What test can be used to test the difference between two sample means when the population variances are known?
   a. z   c. Chi-square
   b. t   d. F

Complete these statements with the best answer.

9. If you hypothesize that there is no difference between means, this is represented as H_0: _____.

10. When you are testing the difference between two means, the _____ test is used when the population variances are not known.

11. When the t test is used for testing the equality of two means, the populations must be _____.

12. The values of F cannot be _____.

13. The formula for the F test for variances is _____.

For each of these problems, perform the following steps.

   a. State the hypotheses and identify the claim.
   b. Find the critical value(s).
   c. Compute the test value.
   d. Make the decision.
   e. Summarize the results.

Use the traditional method of hypothesis testing unless otherwise specified.

14. **Cholesterol Levels** A researcher wishes to see if there is a difference in the cholesterol levels of two groups of men. A random sample of 30 men between the ages of 25 and 40 is selected and tested. The average level is 223. A second sample of 25 men between the ages of 41 and 56 is selected and tested. The average of this group is 229. The population standard deviation for both groups is 6. At $\alpha = 0.01$, is there a difference in the cholesterol levels between the two groups? Find the 99% confidence interval for the difference of the two means.

15. **Apartment Rental Fees** The data shown are the rental fees (in dollars) for two random samples of apartments in a large city. At $\alpha = 0.10$, can it be concluded that the average rental fee for apartments in the East is greater than the average rental fee in the West? Assume $\sigma_1 = 119$ and $\sigma_2 = 103$.

East					West				
495	390	540	445	420	525	400	310	375	750
410	550	499	500	550	390	795	554	450	370
389	350	450	530	350	385	395	425	500	550
375	690	325	350	799	380	400	450	365	425
475	295	350	485	625	375	360	425	400	475
275	450	440	425	675	400	475	430	410	450
625	390	485	550	650	425	450	620	500	400
685	385	450	550	425	295	350	300	360	400

Source: *Pittsburgh Post-Gazette*.

16. Prices of Low-Calorie Foods The average price of a sample of 12 bottles of diet salad dressing taken from different stores is \$1.43. The standard deviation is \$0.09. The average price of a sample of 16 low-calorie frozen desserts is \$1.03. The standard deviation is \$0.10. At $\alpha = 0.01$, is there a significant difference in price? Find the 99% confidence interval of the difference in the means.

17. Jet Ski Accidents The data shown represent the number of accidents people had when using jet skis and other types of wet bikes. At $\alpha = 0.05$, can it be concluded that the average number of accidents per year has increased from one period to the next?

1987–1991			1992–1996		
376	650	844	1650	2236	3002
1162	1513		4028	4010	

Source: *USA TODAY*.

18. Salaries of Chemists A sample of 12 chemists from Washington state shows an average salary of \$39,420 with a standard deviation of \$1659, while a sample of 26 chemists from New Mexico has an average salary of \$30,215 with a standard deviation of \$4116. Is there a significant difference between the two states in chemists' salaries at $\alpha = 0.02$? Find the 98% confidence interval of the difference in the means.

19. Family Incomes The average income of 15 families who reside in a large metropolitan East Coast city is \$62,456. The standard deviation is \$9652. The average income of 11 families who reside in a rural area of the Midwest is \$60,213, with a standard deviation of \$2009. At $\alpha = 0.05$, can it be concluded that the families who live in the cities have a higher income than those who live in the rural areas? Use the *P*-value method.

20. Mathematical Skills In an effort to improve the mathematical skills of 10 students, a teacher provides a weekly 1-hour tutoring session for the students. A pretest is given before the sessions, and a posttest is given after. The results are shown here. At $\alpha = 0.01$, can it be concluded that the sessions help to improve the students' mathematical skills?

Student	1	2	3	4	5	6	7	8	9	10
Pretest	82	76	91	62	81	67	71	69	80	85
Posttest	88	80	98	80	80	73	74	78	85	93

21. Egg Production To increase egg production, a farmer decided to increase the amount of time the lights in his hen house were on. Ten hens were selected, and the number of eggs each produced was recorded. After one week of lengthened light time, the same hens were monitored again. The data are given here. At $\alpha = 0.05$, can it be concluded that the increased light time increased egg production?

Hen	1	2	3	4	5	6	7	8	9	10
Before	4	3	8	7	6	4	9	7	6	5
After	6	5	9	7	4	5	10	6	9	6

22. Factory Worker Literacy Rates In a sample of 80 workers from a factory in city A, it was found that 5% were unable to read, while in a sample of 50 workers in city B, 8% were unable to read. Can it be concluded that there is a difference in the proportions of nonreaders in the two cities? Use $\alpha = 0.10$. Find the 90% confidence interval for the difference of the two proportions.

23. Male Head of Household A recent survey of 200 households showed that 8 had a single male as the head of household. Forty years ago, a survey of 200 households showed that 6 had a single male as the head of household. At $\alpha = 0.05$, can it be concluded that the proportion has changed? Find the 95% confidence interval of the difference of the two proportions. Does the confidence interval contain 0? Why is this important to know?

Source: Based on data from the U.S. Census Bureau.

24. Money Spent on Road Repair A politician wishes to compare the variances of the amount of money spent for road repair in two different counties. The data are given here. At $\alpha = 0.05$, is there a significant difference in the variances of the amounts spent in the two counties? Use the *P*-value method.

County A	County B
$s_1 = \$11,596$	$s_2 = \$14,837$
$n_1 = 15$	$n_2 = 18$

25. Heights of Basketball Players A researcher wants to compare the variances of the heights (in inches) of four-year college basketball players with those of players in junior colleges. A sample of 30 players from each type of school is selected, and the variances of the heights for each type are 2.43 and 3.15, respectively. At $\alpha = 0.10$, is there a significant difference between the variances of the heights in the two types of schools?

Critical Thinking Challenges

1. The study cited in the article entitled "Only the Timid Die Young" stated that "Timid rats were 60% more likely to die at any given time than were their outgoing brothers." Based on the results, answer the following questions.

   a. Why were rats used in the study?

   b. What are the variables in the study?

   c. Why were infants included in the article?

   d. What is wrong with extrapolating the results to humans?

   e. Suggest some ways humans might be used in a study of this type.

ONLY THE TIMID DIE YOUNG

DO OVERACTIVE STRESS HORMONES DAMAGE HEALTH?

ABOUT 15 OUT OF 100 CHILDREN ARE BORN SHY, BUT ONLY THREE WILL BE SHY AS ADULTS.

FEARFUL TYPES MAY MEET THEIR maker sooner, at least among rats. Researchers have for the first time connected a personality trait—fear of novelty—to an early death.

Sonia Cavigelli and Martha McClintock, psychologists at the University of Chicago, presented unfamiliar bowls, tunnels and bricks to a group of young male rats. Those hesitant to explore the mystery objects were classified as "neophobic."

The researchers found that the neophobic rats produced high levels of stress hormones, called glucocorticoids—typically involved in the fight-or-flight stress response—when faced with strange situations. Those rats continued to have high levels of the hormones at random times throughout their lives, indicating that timidity is a fixed and stable trait. The team then set out to examine the cumulative effects of this personality trait on the rats' health.

Timid rats were 60 percent more likely to die at any given time than were their outgoing brothers. The causes of death were similar for both groups. "One hypothesis as to why the neophobic rats died earlier is that the stress hormones negatively affected their immune system," Cavigelli says. Neophobes died, on average, three months before their rat brothers, a significant gap, considering that most rats lived only two years.

Shyness—the human equivalent of neophobia—can be detected in infants as young as 14 months. Shy people also produce more stress hormones than "average," or thrill-seeking humans. But introverts don't necessarily stay shy for life, as rats apparently do. Jerome Kagan, a professor of psychology at Harvard University, has found that while 15 out of every 100 children will be born with a shy temperament, only three will appear shy as adults. None, however, will be extroverts.

Extrapolating from the doomed fate of neophobic rats to their human counterparts is difficult. "But it means that something as simple as a personality trait could have physiological consequences," Cavigelli says.

—*Carlin Flora*

Reprinted with permission from *Psychology Today*, Copyright © 2004, Sussex Publishers, Inc.

2. Based on the study presented in the article entitled "Sleeping Brain, Not at Rest," answer these questions.

   a. What were the variables used in the study?

   b. How were they measured?

   c. Suggest a statistical test that might have been used to arrive at the conclusion.

   d. Based on the results, what would you suggest for students preparing for an exam?

SLEEPING BRAIN, NOT AT REST

Regions of the brain that have spent the day learning sleep more heavily at night.

In a study published in the journal *Nature*, Giulio Tononi, a psychiatrist at the University of Wisconsin–Madison, had subjects perform a simple point-and-click task with a computer adjusted so that its cursor didn't track in the right direction. Afterward, the subjects' brain waves were recorded while they slept, then examined for "slow wave" activity, a kind of deep sleep.

Compared with people who'd completed the same task with normal cursors, Tononi's subjects showed elevated slow wave activity in brain areas associated with spatial orientation, indicating that their brains were adjusting to the day's learning by making cellular-level changes. In the morning, Tononi's subjects performed their tasks better than they had before going to sleep.

—*Richard A. Love*

Reprinted with permission from *Psychology Today,* Copyright © 2004, Sussex Publishers, Inc.

Data Projects

Use a significance level of 0.05 for all tests below.

1. **Business and Finance** Use the data collected in data project 1 of Chapter 2 to complete this problem. Test the claim that the mean earnings per share for Dow Jones stocks are greater than for NASDAQ stocks.

2. **Sports and Leisure** Use the data collected in data project 2 of Chapter 7 regarding home runs for this problem. Test the claim that the mean number of home runs hit by the American League sluggers is the same as the mean for the National League.

3. **Technology** Use the cell phone data collected for data project 2 in Chapter 8 to complete this problem. Test the claim that the mean length for outgoing calls is the same as that for incoming calls. Test the claim that the standard deviation for outgoing calls is more than that for incoming calls.

4. **Health and Wellness** Use the data regarding BMI that were collected in data project 6 of Chapter 7 to complete this problem. Test the claim that the mean BMI for males is the same as that for females. Test the claim that the standard deviation for males is the same as that for females.

5. **Politics and Economics** Use data from the last Presidential election to categorize the 50 states as "red" or "blue" based on who was supported for President in that state, the Democratic or Republican candidate. Use the data collected in data project 5 of Chapter 2 regarding income. Test the claim that the mean incomes for red states and blue states are equal.

6. **Your Class** Use the data collected in data project 6 of Chapter 2 regarding heart rates. Test the claim that the heart rates after exercise are more variable than the heart rates before exercise.

Answers to Applying the Concepts

Section 9–1   Home Runs

1. The population is all home runs hit by major league baseball players.

2. A cluster sample was used.

3. Answers will vary. While this sample is not representative of all major league baseball players per se, it does allow us to compare the leaders in each league.

4. $H_0: \mu_1 = \mu_2$ and $H_1: \mu_1 \neq \mu_2$

5. Answers will vary. Possible answers include the 0.05 and 0.01 significance levels.

6. We will use the z test for the difference in means.

7. Our test statistic is $z = \dfrac{44.75 - 42.88}{\sqrt{\dfrac{8.8^2}{40} + \dfrac{7.8^2}{40}}} = 1.01$, and our

P-value is 0.3124.

8. We fail to reject the null hypothesis.

9. There is not enough evidence to conclude that there is a difference in the number of home runs hit by National League versus American League baseball players.

10. Answers will vary. One possible answer is that since we do not have a random sample of data from each league, we cannot answer the original question asked.

11. Answers will vary. One possible answer is that we could get a random sample of data from each league from a recent season.

Section 9–2   Too Long on the Telephone

1. These samples are independent.

2. There were $56 + 2 = 58$ people in the study.

3. We compare the P-value of 0.06317 to the significance level to check if the null hypothesis should be rejected.

4. The P-value of 0.06317 also gives the probability of a type I error.

5. The F value of 3.07849 is the result of dividing the two sample variances.

6. Since two critical values are shown, we know that a two-tailed test was done.

7. Since the P-value of 0.06317 is greater than the significance value of 0.05, we fail to reject the null hypothesis and find that we do not have enough evidence to conclude that there is a difference in the lengths of telephone calls made by employees in the two divisions of the company.

8. If the significance level had been 0.10, we would have rejected the null hypothesis, since the P-value would have been less than the significance level.

Section 9–3   Air Quality

1. The purpose of the study is to determine if the air quality in the United States has changed over the past 2 years.

2. These are dependent samples, since we have two readings from each of 10 metropolitan areas.

3. The hypotheses we will test are $H_0: \mu_D = 0$ and $H_1: \mu_D \neq 0$.

4. We will use the 0.05 significance level and critical values of $t = \pm 2.262$.

5. We will use the t test for dependent samples.

6. There are $10 - 1 = 9$ degrees of freedom.

7. Our test statistic is $t = \dfrac{-6.7 - 0}{11.27/\sqrt{10}} = -1.879$. We fail to reject the null hypothesis and find that there is not enough evidence to conclude that the air quality in the United States has changed over the past 2 years.

8. No, we could not use an independent means test since we have two readings from each metropolitan area.

9. Answers will vary. One possible answer is that there are other measures of air quality that we could have examined to answer the question.

Section 9–4   Smoking and Education

1. Our hypotheses are $H_0: p_1 = p_2$ and $H_1: p_1 \neq p_2$.

2. At the 0.05 significance level, our critical values are $z = \pm 1.96$.

3. We will use the z test for the difference between proportions.

4. To complete the statistical test, we would need the sample sizes.

5. Knowing the sample sizes were 1000, we can now complete the test.

6. Our test statistic is $z = \dfrac{0.323 - 0.145}{\sqrt{(0.234)(0.766)\left(\frac{1}{1000} + \frac{1}{1000}\right)}} =$ 9.40, and our P-value is very close to zero. We reject the null hypothesis and find that there is enough evidence to conclude that there is a difference in the proportions of high school graduates and college graduates who smoke.

Section 9–5   Variability and Automatic Transmissions

1. The null hypothesis is that the variances are the same: $H_0: \sigma_1^2 = \sigma_2^2$ ($H_1: \sigma_1^2 \neq \sigma_2^2$).

2. We will use an F test.

3. The value of the test statistic is $F = \dfrac{s_1^2}{s_2^2} = \dfrac{514.8^2}{77.7^2} = 43.92$, and the P-value is 0.0008. There is a significant difference in the variability of the prices between the two countries.

4. Small sample sizes are highly impacted by outliers.

5. The degrees of freedom for the numerator and denominator are both 5.

6. Yes, two sets of data can center on the same mean but have very different standard deviations.

Hypothesis-Testing Summary 1

1. Comparison of a sample mean with a specific population mean.

Example: $H_0: \mu = 100$

a. Use the *z* test when σ is known:

$$z = \frac{\bar{X} - \mu}{\sigma/\sqrt{n}}$$

b. Use the *t* test when σ is unknown:

$$t = \frac{\bar{X} - \mu}{s/\sqrt{n}} \qquad \text{with d.f.} = n - 1$$

2. Comparison of a sample variance or standard deviation with a specific population variance or standard deviation.

Example: $H_0: \sigma^2 = 225$

Use the chi-square test:

$$\chi^2 = \frac{(n-1)s^2}{\sigma^2} \qquad \text{with d.f.} = n - 1$$

3. Comparison of two sample means.

Example: $H_0: \mu_1 = \mu_2$

a. Use the *z* test when the population variances are known:

$$z = \frac{(\bar{X}_1 - \bar{X}_2) - (\mu_1 - \mu_2)}{\sqrt{\dfrac{\sigma_1^2}{n_1} + \dfrac{\sigma_2^2}{n_2}}}$$

b. Use the *t* test for independent samples when the population variances are unknown and assume the sample variances are unequal:

$$t = \frac{(\bar{X}_1 - \bar{X}_2) - (\mu_1 - \mu_2)}{\sqrt{\dfrac{s_1^2}{n_1} + \dfrac{s_2^2}{n_2}}}$$

with d.f. = the smaller of $n_1 - 1$ or $n_2 - 1$.

c. Use the *t* test for means for dependent samples:

Example: $H_0: \mu_D = 0$

$$t = \frac{\bar{D} - \mu_D}{s_D/\sqrt{n}} \qquad \text{with d.f.} = n - 1$$

where n = number of pairs.

4. Comparison of a sample proportion with a specific population proportion.

Example: $H_0: p = 0.32$

Use the *z* test:

$$z = \frac{X - \mu}{\sigma} \qquad \text{or} \qquad z = \frac{\hat{p} - p}{\sqrt{pq/n}}$$

5. Comparison of two sample proportions.

Example: $H_0: p_1 = p_2$

Use the *z* test:

$$z = \frac{(\hat{p}_1 - \hat{p}_2) - (p_1 - p_2)}{\sqrt{\bar{p}\bar{q}\left(\dfrac{1}{n_1} + \dfrac{1}{n_2}\right)}}$$

where

$$\bar{p} = \frac{X_1 + X_2}{n_1 + n_2} \qquad \hat{p}_1 = \frac{X_1}{n_1}$$

$$\bar{q} = 1 - \bar{p} \qquad \hat{p}_2 = \frac{X_2}{n_2}$$

6. Comparison of two sample variances or standard deviations.

Example: $H_0: \sigma_1^2 = \sigma_2^2$

Use the *F* test:

$$F = \frac{s_1^2}{s_2^2}$$

where

s_1^2 = larger variance   d.f.N. = $n_1 - 1$
s_2^2 = smaller variance   d.f.D. = $n_2 - 1$

Correlation and Regression

Objectives

After completing this chapter, you should be able to

1. Draw a scatter plot for a set of ordered pairs.
2. Compute the correlation coefficient.
3. Test the hypothesis $H_0: \rho = 0$.
4. Compute the equation of the regression line.
5. Compute the coefficient of determination.
6. Compute the standard error of the estimate.
7. Find a prediction interval.

Outline

Do Dust Storms Affect Respiratory Health?

Southeast Washington state has a long history of seasonal dust storms. Several researchers decided to see what effect, if any, these storms had on the respiratory health of the people living in the area. They undertook (among other things) to see if there was a relationship between the amount of dust and sand particles in the air when the storms occur and the number of hospital emergency room visits for respiratory disorders at three community hospitals in southeast Washington. Using methods of correlation and regression, which are explained in this chapter, they were able to determine the effect of these dust storms on local residents. See Statistics Today—Revisited at the end of the chapter.

Source: B. Hefflin, B. Jalaludin, N. Cobb, C. Johnson, L. Jecha, and R. Etzel, "Surveillance for Dust Storms and Respiratory Diseases in Washington State, 1991," *Archives of Environmental Health* 49, no. 3 (May–June 1994), pp. 170–74. Reprinted with permission of the Helen Dwight Reid Education Foundation. Published by Heldref Publications, 1319 18th St. N.W., Washington, D.C. 20036-1802. Copyright 1994.

Introduction

In Chapters 7 and 8, two areas of inferential statistics—confidence intervals and hypothesis testing—were explained. Another area of inferential statistics involves determining whether a relationship exists between two or more numerical or quantitative variables. For example, a businessperson may want to know whether the volume of sales for a given month is related to the amount of advertising the firm does that month. Educators are interested in determining whether the number of hours a student studies is related to the student's score on a particular exam. Medical researchers are interested in questions such as, Is caffeine related to heart damage? or Is there a relationship between a person's age and his or her blood pressure? A zoologist may want to know whether the birth weight of a certain animal is related to its life span. These are only a few of the many questions that can be answered by using the techniques of correlation and regression analysis. **Correlation** is a statistical method used to determine whether a relationship between variables exists. **Regression** is a statistical method used to describe the nature of the relationship between variables, that is, positive or negative, linear or nonlinear.

The purpose of this chapter is to answer these questions statistically:

1. Are two or more variables related?
2. If so, what is the strength of the relationship?
3. What type of relationship exists?
4. What kind of predictions can be made from the relationship?

To answer the first two questions, statisticians use a numerical measure to determine whether two or more variables are related and to determine the strength of the relationship between or among the variables. This measure is called a *correlation coefficient.* For example, there are many variables that contribute to heart disease, among them lack of exercise, smoking, heredity, age, stress, and diet. Of these variables, some are more important than others; therefore, a physician who wants to help a patient must know which factors are most important.

To answer the third question, you must ascertain what type of relationship exists. There are two types of relationships: *simple* and *multiple*. In a **simple relationship,** there are two variables—an **independent variable,** also called an explanatory variable or a predictor variable, and a **dependent variable,** also called a response variable. A simple relationship analysis is called *simple regression,* and there is one independent variable that is used to predict the dependent variable. For example, a manager may wish to see whether the number of years the salespeople have been working for the company has anything to do with the amount of sales they make. This type of study involves a simple relationship, since there are only two variables—years of experience and amount of sales.

In a **multiple relationship,** called *multiple regression,* two or more independent variables are used to predict one dependent variable. For example, an educator may wish to investigate the relationship between a student's success in college and factors such as the number of hours devoted to studying, the student's GPA, and the student's high school background. This type of study involves several variables.

Simple relationships can also be positive or negative. A **positive relationship** exists when both variables increase or decrease at the same time. For instance, a person's height and weight are related; and the relationship is positive, since the taller a person is, generally, the more the person weighs. In a **negative relationship,** as one variable increases, the other variable decreases, and vice versa. For example, if you measure the strength of people over 60 years of age, you will find that as age increases, strength generally decreases. The word *generally* is used here because there are exceptions.

Finally, the fourth question asks what type of predictions can be made. Predictions are made in all areas and daily. Examples include weather forecasting, stock market analyses, sales predictions, crop predictions, gasoline price predictions, and sports predictions. Some predictions are more accurate than others, due to the strength of the relationship. That is, the stronger the relationship is between variables, the more accurate the prediction is.

Paired data and scatter plots were explained in Section 2–4; however, a brief review is included here.

10–1   Correlation

Objective 1

Draw a scatter plot for a set of ordered pairs.

In simple correlation and regression studies, the researcher collects data on two numerical or quantitative variables to see whether a relationship exists between the variables. For example, if a researcher wishes to see whether there is a relationship between number of hours of study and test scores on an exam, she must select a random sample of students, determine the hours each studied, and obtain their grades on the exam. A table can be made for the data, as shown here.

Student	Hours of study x	Grade y (%)
A	6	82
B	2	63
C	1	57
D	5	88
E	2	68
F	3	75

As stated previously, the two variables for this study are called the independent variable and the dependent variable. The independent variable is the variable in regression that can be controlled or manipulated. In this case, the number of hours of study is the independent variable and is designated as the x variable. The dependent variable is the variable in regression that cannot be controlled or manipulated. The grade the student received on the exam is the dependent variable, designated as the y variable. The reason for this distinction between the variables is that you assume that the grade the student earns *depends* on the number of hours the student studied. Also, you assume that, to some extent, the student can regulate or *control* the number of hours he or she studies for the exam.

The determination of the x and y variables is not always clear-cut and is sometimes an arbitrary decision. For example, if a researcher studies the effects of age on a person's blood pressure, the researcher can generally assume that age affects blood pressure. Hence, the variable *age* can be called the *independent variable,* and the variable *blood pressure* can be called the *dependent variable.* On the other hand, if a researcher is studying the attitudes of husbands on a certain issue and the attitudes of their wives on the same issue, it is difficult to say which variable is the independent variable and which is the dependent variable. In this study, the researcher can arbitrarily designate the variables as independent and dependent.

The independent and dependent variables can be plotted on a graph called a *scatter plot.* The independent variable x is plotted on the horizontal axis, and the dependent variable y is plotted on the vertical axis.

> A **scatter plot** is a graph of the ordered pairs (x, y) of numbers consisting of the independent variable x and the dependent variable y.

The scatter plot is a visual way to describe the nature of the relationship between the independent and dependent variables. The scales of the variables can be different, and the coordinates of the axes are determined by the smallest and largest data values of the variables.

The procedure for drawing a scatter plot is shown in Examples 10–1.

Example 10–1

Car Rental Companies

Construct a scatter plot for the data shown for car rental companies in the United States for a recent year.

Company	Cars (in ten thousands)	Revenue (in billions)
A	63.0	$7.0
B	29.0	3.9
C	20.8	2.1
D	19.1	2.8
E	13.4	1.4
F	8.5	1.5

Source: *Auto Rental News.*

Solution

Step 1 Draw and label the x and y axes.

Step 2 Plot each point on the graph, as shown in Figure 10–1.

Figure 10–1

Scatter Plot for Example 10–1

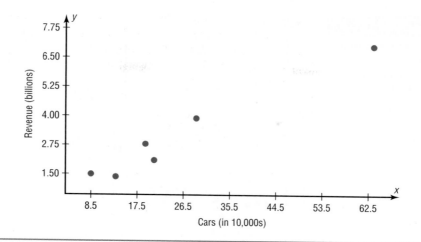

Correlation

Objective 2

Compute the correlation coefficient.

As stated in the Introduction, statisticians use a measure called the *correlation coefficient* to determine the strength of the linear relationship between two variables. There are several types of correlation coefficients. The one explained in this section is called the **Pearson product moment correlation coefficient (PPMC),** named after statistician Karl Pearson, who pioneered the research in this area.

The **correlation coefficient** computed from the sample data measures the strength and direction of a linear relationship between two variables. The symbol for the sample correlation coefficient is *r*. The symbol for the population correlation coefficient is ρ (Greek letter rho).

The *range of the correlation coefficient* is from -1 to $+1$. If there is a *strong positive linear relationship* between the variables, the value of *r* will be close to $+1$. If there is a *strong negative linear relationship* between the variables, the value of *r* will be close to -1. When there is no linear relationship between the variables or only a weak relationship, the value of *r* will be close to 0. See Figure 10–2.

The graphs in Figure 10–3 show the relationship between the correlation coefficients and their corresponding scatter plots. Notice that as the value of the correlation coefficient increases from 0 to $+1$ (parts *a*, *b*, and *c*), data values become closer to an increasingly stronger relationship. As the value of the correlation coefficient decreases from 0 to -1 (parts *d*, *e*, and *f*), the data values also become closer to a straight line. Again this suggests a stronger relationship.

There are several ways to compute the value of the correlation coefficient. One method is to use the formula shown on the next page.

Figure 10–2

Range of Values for the Correlation Coefficient

Figure 10–3

Relationship Between the Correlation Coefficient and the Scatter Plot

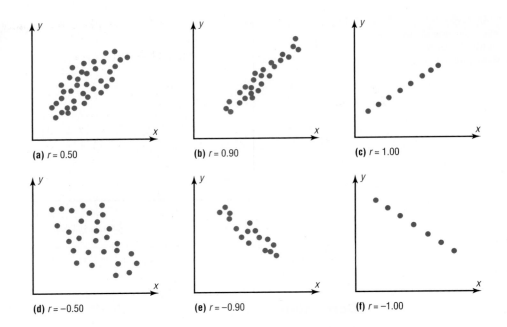

(a) $r = 0.50$ (b) $r = 0.90$ (c) $r = 1.00$

(d) $r = -0.50$ (e) $r = -0.90$ (f) $r = -1.00$

Formula for the Correlation Coefficient r

$$r = \frac{n(\Sigma xy) - (\Sigma x)(\Sigma y)}{\sqrt{[n(\Sigma x^2) - (\Sigma x)^2][n(\Sigma y^2) - (\Sigma y)^2]}}$$

where n is the number of data pairs.

Rounding Rule for the Correlation Coefficient   Round the value of r to three decimal places.

The formula looks somewhat complicated, but using a table to compute the values, as shown in Example 10–2, makes it somewhat easier to determine the value of r.

There are no units associated with r, and the value of r will remain unchanged if the x and y values are switched.

Example 10–2

Car Rental Companies

Compute the correlation coefficient for the data in Example 10–1.

Solution

Step 1   Make a table as shown here.

Company	Cars x (in ten thousands)	Income y (in billions)	xy	x^2	y^2
A	63.0	7.0			
B	29.0	3.9			
C	20.8	2.1			
D	19.1	2.8			
E	13.4	1.4			
F	8.5	1.5			

Step 2 Find the values of xy, x^2, and y^2 and place these values in the corresponding columns of the table.

The completed table is shown.

Company	Cars x (in 10,000s)	Income y (in billions)	xy	x^2	y^2
A	63.0	7.0	441.00	3969.00	49.00
B	29.0	3.9	113.10	841.00	15.21
C	20.8	2.1	43.68	432.64	4.41
D	19.1	2.8	53.48	364.81	7.84
E	13.4	1.4	18.76	179.56	1.96
F	8.5	1.5	2.75	72.25	2.25
	$\Sigma x = 153.8$	$\Sigma y = 18.7$	$\Sigma xy = 682.77$	$\Sigma x^2 = 5859.26$	$\Sigma y^2 = 80.67$

Step 3 Substitute in the formula and solve for r.

$$r = \frac{n(\Sigma xy) - (\Sigma x)(\Sigma y)}{\sqrt{[n(\Sigma x^2) - (\Sigma x)^2][n(\Sigma y^2) - (\Sigma y)^2]}}$$

$$= \frac{(6)(682.77) - (153.8)(18.7)}{\sqrt{[(6)(5859.26) - (153.8)^2][(6)(80.67) - (18.7)^2]}} = 0.982$$

The correlation coefficient suggests a strong relationship between the number of cars a rental agency has and its annual income.

Correlation and Causation   Researchers must understand the nature of the linear relationship between the independent variable x and the dependent variable y. When a hypothesis test indicates that a significant linear relationship exists between the variables, researchers must consider the possibilities outlined next.

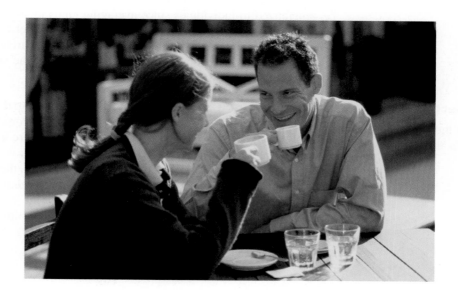

Possible Relationships Between Variables

When the null hypothesis has been rejected for a specific α value, any of the following five possibilities can exist.

1. *There is a direct cause-and-effect relationship between the variables.* That is, x causes y. For example, water causes plants to grow, poison causes death, and heat causes ice to melt.

2. *There is a reverse cause-and-effect relationship between the variables.* That is, y causes x. For example, suppose a researcher believes excessive coffee consumption causes nervousness, but the researcher fails to consider that the reverse situation may occur. That is, it may be that an extremely nervous person craves coffee to calm his or her nerves.

3. *The relationship between the variables may be caused by a third variable.* For example, if a statistician correlated the number of deaths due to drowning and the number of cans of soft drink consumed daily during the summer, he or she would probably find a significant relationship. However, the soft drink is not necessarily responsible for the deaths, since both variables may be related to heat and humidity.

4. *There may be a complexity of interrelationships among many variables.* For example, a researcher may find a significant relationship between students' high school grades and college grades. But there probably are many other variables involved, such as IQ, hours of study, influence of parents, motivation, age, and instructors.

5. *The relationship may be coincidental.* For example, a researcher may be able to find a significant relationship between the increase in the number of people who are exercising and the increase in the number of people who are committing crimes. But common sense dictates that any relationship between these two values must be due to coincidence.

When two variables are highly correlated, item 3 in the box states that there exists a possibility that the correlation is due to a third variable. If this is the case and the third variable is unknown to the researcher or not accounted for in the study, it is called a **lurking variable.** An attempt should be made by the researcher to identify such variables and to use methods to control their influence.

It is important to restate the fact that even if the correlation between two variables is high, it does not necessarily mean causation. There are other possibilities, such as lurking variables or just a coincidental relationship. See the Speaking of Statistics article on page 540.

Also, you should be cautious when the data for one or both of the variables involve averages rather than individual data. It is not wrong to use averages, but the results cannot be generalized to individuals since averaging tends to smooth out the variability among individual data values. The result could be a higher correlation than actually exists.

Thus, when the null hypothesis is rejected, the researcher must consider all possibilities and select the appropriate one as determined by the study. Remember, correlation does not necessarily imply causation.

Objective **3**

Test the hypothesis H_0: $\rho = 0$.

The Significance of the Correlation Coefficient   This section requires coverage of Chapter 8. As stated before, the range of the correlation coefficient is between -1 and $+1$. When the value of r is near $+1$ or -1, there is a strong linear relationship. When the value of r is near 0, the linear relationship is weak or nonexistent. Since the value of r is computed from data obtained from samples, there are two possibilities when r is not equal to zero: either the value of r is high enough to conclude that there is a significant linear relationship between the variables, or the value of r is due to chance.

To make this decision, you use a hypothesis-testing procedure. The traditional method is similar to the one used in previous chapters.

Step 1   State the hypotheses.

Step 2   Find the critical values.

Step 3 Compute the test value.

Step 4 Make the decision.

Step 5 Summarize the results.

The population correlation coefficient is computed from taking all possible (x, y) pairs; it is designated by the Greek letter ρ (rho). The sample correlation coefficient can then be used as an estimator of ρ if the following assumptions are valid.

1. The variables x and y are *linearly* related.
2. The variables are *random* variables.
3. The two variables have a *bivariate normal distribution*.

A biviarate normal distribution means that for the pairs of (x, y) data values, the corresponding y values have a bell-shaped distribution for any given x value, and the x values for any given y value have a bell-shaped distribution.

> Formally defined, the **population correlation coefficient** ρ is the correlation computed by using all possible pairs of data values (x, y) taken from a population.

In hypothesis testing, one of these is true:

$H_0: \rho = 0$ This null hypothesis means that there is no correlation between the x and y variables in the population.

$H_1: \rho \neq 0$ This alternative hypothesis means that there is a significant correlation between the variables in the population.

When the null hypothesis is rejected at a specific level, it means that there is a significant difference between the value of r and 0. When the null hypothesis is not rejected, it means that the value of r is not significantly different from 0 (zero) and is probably due to chance.

Several methods can be used to test the significance of the correlation coefficient. Three methods will be shown in this section. The first uses the t test.

Formula for the t Test for the Correlation Coefficient

$$t = r\sqrt{\frac{n-2}{1-r^2}}$$

with degrees of freedom equal to $n - 2$.

Although hypothesis tests can be one-tailed, most hypotheses involving the correlation coefficient are two-tailed. Recall that ρ represents the population correlation coefficient. Also, if there is no linear relationship, the value of the correlation coefficient will be 0. Hence, the hypotheses will be

$$H_0: \rho = 0 \qquad \text{and} \qquad H_1: \rho \neq 0$$

You do not have to identify the claim here, since the question will always be whether there is a significant linear relationship between the variables.

The two-tailed critical values are used. These values are found in Table F in Appendix C. Also, when you are testing the significance of a correlation coefficient, both variables x and y must come from normally distributed populations.

Example 10–3

Test the significance of the correlation coefficient found in Example 10–2. Use $\alpha = 0.05$ and $r = 0.982$.

Solution

Step 1   State the hypotheses.

$$H_0: \rho = 0 \quad \text{and} \quad H_1: \rho \neq 0$$

Step 2   Find the critical values. Since $\alpha = 0.05$ and there are $6 - 2 = 4$ degrees of freedom, the critical values obtained from Table F are ± 2.776, as shown in Figure 10–4.

Figure 10–4

Critical Values for Example 10–3

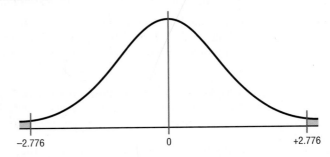

Step 3   Compute the test value.

$$t = r\sqrt{\frac{n - 2}{1 - r^2}} = 0.982\sqrt{\frac{6 - 2}{1 - (0.982)^2}} = 10.4$$

Step 4   Make the decision. Reject the null hypothesis, since the test value falls in the critical region, as shown in Figure 10–5.

Figure 10–5

Test Value for Example 10–3

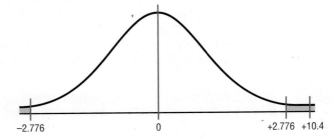

Step 5   Summarize the results. There is a significant relationship between the number of cars a rental agency owns and its annual income.

The second method that can be used to test the significance of r is the P-value method. The method is the same as that shown in Chapters 8 and 9. It uses the following steps.

Step 1   State the hypotheses.

Step 2   Find the test value. (In this case, use the t test.)

Step 3   Find the P-value. (In this case, use Table F.)

Step 4   Make the decision.

Step 5   Summarize the results.

Consider an example where $t = 4.059$ and d.f. $= 4$. Using Table F with d.f. $= 4$ and the row Two tails, the value 4.059 falls between 3.747 and 4.604; hence, $0.01 < P\text{-value} < 0.02$. (The P-value obtained from a calculator is 0.015.) That is, the P-value falls between 0.01 and 0.02. The decision, then, is to reject the null hypothesis since $P\text{-value} < 0.05$.

The third method of testing the significance of r is to use Table I in Appendix C. This table shows the values of the correlation coefficient that are significant for a specific α level and a specific number of degrees of freedom. For example, for 7 degrees of freedom and $\alpha = 0.05$, the table gives a critical value of 0.666. Any value of r greater than $+0.666$ or less than -0.666 will be significant, and the null hypothesis will be rejected. See Figure 10–6. When Table I is used, you need not compute the t test value. Table I is for two-tailed tests only.

Figure 10–6

Finding the Critical Value from Table I

Example 10–4

Using Table I, test the significance of the correlation coefficient $r = 0.067$ at $\alpha = 0.01$ when the sample size is 9.

Solution

$$H_0: \rho = 0 \quad \text{and} \quad H_1: \rho \neq 0$$

Since the sample size is 9, there are 7 degrees of freedom. When $\alpha = 0.01$ and with 7 degrees of freedom, the value obtained from Table I is 0.798. For a significant relationship, a value of r greater than $+0.798$ or less than -0.798 is needed. Since $r = 0.067$, the null hypothesis is not rejected. Hence, there is not enough evidence to say that there is a significant linear relationship between the variables. See Figure 10–7.

Figure 10–7

Rejection and Nonrejection Regions for Example 10–4

Applying the Concepts 10–1

Stopping Distances

In a study on speed control, it was found that the main reasons for regulations were to make traffic flow more efficient and to minimize the risk of danger. An area that was focused on in the study was the distance required to completely stop a vehicle at various speeds. Use the following table to answer the questions.

MPH	Braking distance (feet)
20	20
30	45
40	81
50	133
60	205
80	411

Assume MPH is going to be used to predict stopping distance.

1. Which of the two variables is the independent variable?

2. Which is the dependent variable?

3. What type of variable is the independent variable?

4. What type of variable is the dependent variable?

5. Construct a scatter plot for the data.

6. Is there a linear relationship between the two variables?

7. Redraw the scatter plot, and change the distances between the independent-variable numbers. Does the relationship look different?

8. Is the relationship positive or negative?

9. Can braking distance be accurately predicted from MPH?

10. List some other variables that affect braking distance.

11. Compute the value of r.

12. Is r significant at $\alpha = 0.05$?

See page 569 for the answers.

Coffee Not Disease Culprit, Study Says

NEW YORK (AP)—Two new studies suggest that coffee drinking, even up to 5½ cups per day, does not increase the risk of heart disease, and other studies that claim to have found increased risks might have missed the true culprits, a researcher says.

"It might not be the coffee cup in one hand, it might be the cigarette or coffee roll in the other," said Dr. Peter W. F. Wilson, the author of one of the new studies.

He noted in a telephone interview Thursday that many coffee drinkers, particularly heavy coffee drinkers, are smokers. And one of the new studies found that coffee drinkers had excess fat in their diets.

The findings of the new studies conflict sharply with a study reported in November 1985 by Johns Hopkins University scientists in Baltimore.

The Hopkins scientists found that coffee drinkers who consumed five or more cups of coffee per day had three times the heart-disease risk of non-coffee drinkers.

The reason for the discrepancy appears to be that many of the coffee drinkers in the Hopkins study also smoked—and it was the smoking that increased their heart-disease risk, said Wilson.

Wilson, director of laboratories for the Framingham Heart Study in Framingham, Mass., said Thursday at a conference sponsored by the American Heart Association in Charleston, S.C., that he had examined the coffee intake of 3,937 participants in the Framingham study during 1956–66 and an additional 2,277 during the years 1972–1982.

In contrast to the subjects in the Hopkins study, most of these coffee drinkers consumed two or three cups per day, Wilson said. Only 10 percent drank six or more cups per day.

He then looked at blood cholesterol levels and heart and blood vessel disease in the two groups. "We ran these analyses for coronary heart disease, heart attack, sudden death and stroke and in absolutely every analysis, we found no link with coffee," Wilson said.

He found that coffee consumption was linked to a significant decrease in total blood cholesterol in men, and to a moderate increase in total cholesterol in women.

Source: Reprinted with permission of the Associated Press.

Exercises 10–1

1. What is meant by the statement that two variables are related?

2. How is a linear relationship between two variables measured in statistics? Explain.

3. What is the symbol for the sample correlation coefficient? The population correlation coefficient?

4. What is the range of values for the correlation coefficient?

5. What is meant when the relationship between the two variables is called positive? Negative?

6. Give examples of two variables that are positively correlated and two that are negatively correlated.

7. Give an example of a correlation study, and identify the independent and dependent variables.

8. What is the diagram of the independent and dependent variables called? Why is drawing this diagram important?

9. What is the name of the correlation coefficient used in this section?

10. What statistical test is used to test the significance of the correlation coefficient?

11. When two variables are correlated, can the researcher be sure that one variable causes the other? Why or why not?

For Exercises 12 through 27, perform the following steps.

   a. Draw the scatter plot for the variables.
   b. Compute the value of the correlation coefficient.
   c. State the hypotheses.
   d. Test the significance of the correlation coefficient at $\alpha = 0.05$, using Table I.
   e. Give a brief explanation of the type of relationship.

12. Broadway Productions A researcher wants to see if there is a relationship between the number of new productions on Broadway in any given year and the attendance for the season. The data below were recorded for a selected number of years. Based on these data, can you conclude a relationship between the number of new productions in a season and the attendance?

No. of new productions	54	67	60	54	61	60	50	37
Attendance (millions)	7.4	8.2	7.1	8.8	9.6	11	8.4	7.4

(The information in this exercise will be used for Exercise 12 in Section 10–2.)

Source: *World Almanac.*

13. Commercial Movie Releases The yearly data have been published showing the number of releases for each of the commercial movie studios and the gross receipts for those studios thus far. Based on these data, can it be concluded that there is a relationship between the number of releases and the gross receipts?

No. of releases x	361	270	306	22	35	10	8	12	21
Gross receipts y (million $)	3844	1962	1371	1064	334	241	188	154	125

(The information in this exercise will be used for Exercises 13 and 36 in Section 10–2 and Exercises 15 and 19 in Section 10–3.)

Source: www.showbizdata.com

14. Forest Fires and Acres Burned An environmentalist wants to determine the relationships between the numbers (in thousands) of forest fires over the year and the number (in hundred thousands) of acres burned. The data for 8 recent years are shown. Describe the relationship.

Number of fires x	72	69	58	47	84	62	57	45
Number of acres burned y	62	42	19	26	51	15	30	15

Source: National Interagency Fire Center.

(The information in this exercise will be used for Exercise 14 in Section 10–2 and Exercises 16 and 20 in Section 10–3.)

15. Alumni Contributions The director of an alumni association for a small college wants to determine whether there is any type of relationship between the amount of an alumnus's contribution (in dollars) and the years the alumnus has been out of school. The data follow. (The information is used for Exercises 15, 36, and 37 in Section 10–2 and Exercises 17 and 21 in Section 10–3.)

Years x	1	5	3	10	7	6
Contribution y	500	100	300	50	75	80

16. State Debt and Per Capita Tax An economics student wishes to see if there is a relationship between the amount of state debt per capita and the amount of tax per capita at the state level. Based on the following data, can she or he conclude that per capita state debt and per capita state taxes are related? Both amounts are in dollars and represent five randomly selected states. (The information in this exercise will be used for Exercises 16 and 37 in Section 10–2 and Exercises 18 and 22 in Section 10–3.)

Per capita debt x	1924	907	1445	1608	661
Per capita tax y	1685	1838	1734	1842	1317

Source: *World Almanac.*

17. Larceny and Vandalism A criminology student wishes to see if there is a relationship between the number of larceny crimes and the number of vandalism crimes on college campuses in southwestern Pennsylvania. The data are shown. Is there a relationship between the two types of crimes?

Number of larceny crimes x	24	6	16	64	10	25	35
Number of vandalism crimes y	21	3	6	15	21	61	20

(The information in this exercise will be used for Exercise 17 of Section 10–2.)

18. Pass Attempts A football fan wishes to see how the number of pass attempts (not completions) relates to the number of yards gained for quarterbacks in past NFL season playoff games. The data are shown for five quarterbacks. Describe the relationships.

Pass attempts x	116	90	82	108	92
Yards gained y	1001	823	851	873	839

(The information in this exercise will be used for Exercises 18 and 38 in Section 10–2.)

19. Egg Production Recent agricultural data showed the number of eggs produced and the price received per dozen for a given year. Based on the following data for a random selection of states, can it be concluded that a relationship exists between the number of eggs produced and the price per dozen? (The information in this exercise will be used for Exercise 19 in Section 10–2.)

No. of eggs (millions) x	957	1332	1163	1865	119	273
Price per dozen (dollars) y	0.770	0.697	0.617	0.652	1.080	1.420

Source: *World Almanac.*

20. Emergency Calls and Temperature An emergency service wishes to see whether a relationship exists between the outside temperature and the number of emergency calls it receives for a 7-hour period. The data are shown. (The information in this exercise will be used for Exercises 20 and 38 in Section 10–2.)

Temperature x	68	74	82	88	93	99	101
No. of calls y	7	4	8	10	11	9	13

21. Distribution of Population in U.S. Cities A random sample of U.S. cities is selected to determine if there is a relationship between the population (in thousands) of people under 5 years of age and the population (in thousands) of those 65 years of age and older. The data for the

sample are shown here. (The information in this exercise will be used for Exercises 21 and 36 in Section 10–2.)

Under 5 x	178	27	878	314	322	143
65 and over y	361	72	1496	501	585	207

Source: *New York Times Almanac.*

22. Apartment Rents The results of a survey of the average monthly rents (in dollars) for existing one-bedroom and three-bedroom apartments in randomly selected metropolitan areas are shown below. Determine if there is a significant relationship between the rents. (The information in this exercise will be used for Exercise 22 in Section 10–2.)

One BR	553	578	891	773	812	509
Three BR	1017	916	1577	1234	1403	857

Source: *New York Times Almanac.*

23. Average Temperature and Precipitation The average normal daily temperature (in degrees Fahrenheit) and the corresponding average monthly precipitation (in inches) for the month of June are shown here for seven randomly selected cities in the United States. Determine if there is a relationship between the two variables. (The information in this exercise will be used for Exercise 23 in Section 10–2.)

Avg. daily temp. x	86	81	83	89	80	74	64
Avg. mo. precip. y	3.4	1.8	3.5	3.6	3.7	1.5	0.2

Source: *New York Times Almanac.*

24. Hall of Fame Pitchers A random sample of Hall of Fame pitchers' career wins and their total number of strikeouts is shown next. Is there a relationship between the variables? (The information in this exercise will be used for Exercise 24 in Section 10–2.)

Wins x	329	150	236	300	284	207
Strikeouts y	4136	1155	1956	2266	3192	1277

Wins x	247	314	273	324
Strikeouts y	1068	3534	1987	3574

Source: *New York Times Almanac.*

25. Calories and Cholesterol The number of calories and the number of milligrams of cholesterol for a random sample of fast-food chicken sandwiches from seven restaurants are shown here. Is there a relationship between the variables? (The information in this exercise will be used in Exercise 25 in Section 10–2.)

Calories x	390	535	720	300	430	500	440
Cholesterol y	43	45	80	50	55	52	60

Source: *The Doctor's Pocket Calorie, Fat, and Carbohydrate Counter.*

26. Tall Buildings An architect wants to determine the relationship between the heights (in feet) of a building and the number of stories in the building. The data for a sample of 10 buildings in Pittsburgh are shown. Explain the relationship.

Stories x	64	54	40	31	45	38	42	41	37	40
Height y	841	725	635	616	615	582	535	520	511	485

Source: *World Almanac Book of Facts.*

(The information in this exercise will be used for Exercise 26 of Section 10–2.)

27. Hospital Beds A hospital administrator wants to see if there is a relationship between the number of licensed beds and the number of staffed beds in local hospitals. The data for a specific day are shown. Describe the relationship.

Licensed beds x	144	32	175	185	208	100	169
Staffed beds y	112	32	162	141	103	80	118

Source: *Pittsburgh Tribune-Review.*

(The information in this exercise will be used for Exercise 28 of this section and Exercise 27 in Section 10–2.)

Extending the Concepts

28. One of the formulas for computing r is

$$r = \frac{\Sigma(x - \bar{x})(y - \bar{y})}{(n - 1)(s_x)(s_y)}$$

Using the data in Exercise 27, compute r with this formula. Compare the results.

 29. Compute r for the data set shown. Explain the reason for this value of r. Now, interchange the values of x and y and compute r again. Compare this value with the previous one. Explain the results of the comparison.

x	1	2	3	4	5
y	3	5	7	9	11

 30. Compute r for the following data and test the hypothesis H_0: $\rho = 0$. Draw the scatter plot; then explain the results.

x	−3	−2	−1	0	1	2	3
y	9	4	1	0	1	4	9

10–2   Regression

Objective **4**

Compute the equation of the regression line.

In studying relationships between two variables, collect the data and then construct a scatter plot. The purpose of the scatter plot, as indicated previously, is to determine the nature of the relationship. The possibilities include a positive linear relationship, a negative linear relationship, a curvilinear relationship, or no discernible relationship. After the scatter plot is drawn, the next steps are to compute the value of the correlation coefficient and to test the significance of the relationship. If the value of the correlation coefficient is significant, the next step is to determine the equation of the **regression line,** which is the data's line of best fit. (*Note:* Determining the regression line when r is not significant and then making predictions using the regression line are meaningless.) The purpose of the regression line is to enable the researcher to see the trend and make predictions on the basis of the data.

Line of Best Fit

Figure 10–8 shows a scatter plot for the data of two variables. It shows that several lines can be drawn on the graph near the points. Given a scatter plot, you must be able to draw the *line of best fit. Best fit* means that the sum of the squares of the vertical distances from each point to the line is at a minimum. The reason you need a line of best fit is that the values of y will be predicted from the values of x; hence, the closer the points are to the line, the better the fit and the prediction will be. See Figure 10–9. When r is positive, the line slopes upward and to the right. When r is negative, the line slopes downward from left to right.

Figure 10–8

Scatter Plot with Three
Lines Fit to the Data

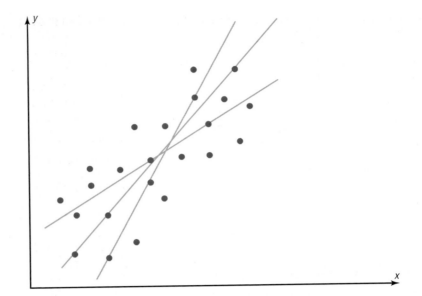

Figure 10–9

Line of Best Fit for a
Set of Data Points

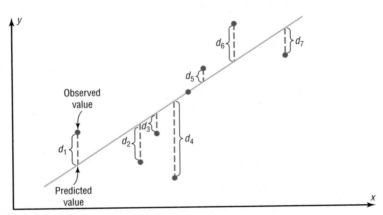

Determination of the Regression Line Equation

Historical Notes

Francis Galton drew
the line of best fit
visually. An assistant
of Karl Pearson's
named G. Yule
devised the
mathematical
solution using the
least-squares
method, employing
a mathematical
technique developed
by Adrien-Marie
Legendre about
100 years earlier.

In algebra, the equation of a line is usually given as $y = mx + b$, where m is the slope of the line and b is the y intercept. (Students who need an algebraic review of the properties of a line should refer to Appendix A, Section A–3, before studying this section.) In statistics, the equation of the regression line is written as $y' = a + bx$, where a is the y' intercept and b is the slope of the line. See Figure 10–10.

There are several methods for finding the equation of the regression line. Two formulas are given here. *These formulas use the same values that are used in computing the value of the correlation coefficient.* The mathematical development of these formulas is beyond the scope of this book.

Formulas for the Regression Line $y' = a + bx$

$$a = \frac{(\Sigma y)(\Sigma x^2) - (\Sigma x)(\Sigma xy)}{n(\Sigma x^2) - (\Sigma x)^2}$$

$$b = \frac{n(\Sigma xy) - (\Sigma x)(\Sigma y)}{n(\Sigma x^2) - (\Sigma x)^2}$$

where a is the y' intercept and b is the slope of the line.

Figure 10–10

A Line as Represented in Algebra and in Statistics

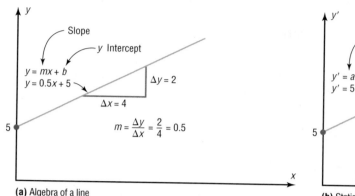

(a) Algebra of a line

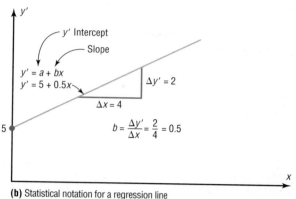

(b) Statistical notation for a regression line

Rounding Rule for the Intercept and Slope Round the values of a and b to three decimal places.

Example 10–5 **Car Rental Companies**

Find the equation of the regression line for the data in Example 10–4, and graph the line on the scatter plot of the data.

Solution

The values needed for the equation are $n = 6$, $\Sigma x = 153.8$, $\Sigma y = 18.7$, $\Sigma xy = 682.77$, and $\Sigma x^2 = 5859.26$. Substituting in the formulas, you get

$$a = \frac{(\Sigma y)(\Sigma x^2) - (\Sigma x)(\Sigma xy)}{n(\Sigma x^2) - (\Sigma x)^2} = \frac{(18.7)(5859.26) - (153.8)(682.77)}{(6)(5859.26) - (153.8)^2} = 0.396$$

$$b = \frac{n(\Sigma xy) - (\Sigma x)(\Sigma y)}{n(\Sigma x^2) - (\Sigma x)^2} = \frac{6(682.77) - (153.8)(18.7)}{(6)(5859.26) - (153.8)^2} = 0.106$$

Hence, the equation of the regression line $y' = a + bx$ is

$$y' = 0.396 + 0.106x$$

To graph the line, select any two points for x and find the corresponding values for y. Use any x values between 10 and 60. For example, let $x = 15$. Substitute in the equation and find the corresponding y' value.

$$y' = 0.396$$
$$= 0.396 + 0.106(15)$$
$$= 1.986$$

Let $x = 40$; then

$$y' = 0.396 + 0.106x$$
$$= 0.396 + 0.106(40)$$
$$= 4.636$$

Figure 10–11

Regression Line for Example 10–5

Historical Note

In 1795, Adrien-Marie Legendre (1752–1833) measured the meridian arc on the earth's surface from Barcelona, Spain, to Dunkirk, England. This measure was used as the basis for the measure of the meter. Legendre developed the least-squares method around the year 1805.

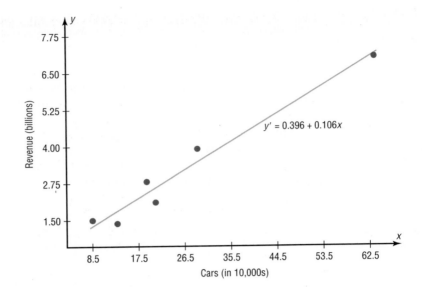

Then plot the two points (15, 1.986) and (40, 4.636) and draw a line connecting the two points. See Figure 10–11.

Note: When you draw the regression line, it is sometimes necessary to *truncate* the graph (see Chapter 2). This is done when the distance between the origin and the first labeled coordinate on the x axis is not the same as the distance between the rest of the labeled x coordinates or the distance between the origin and the first labeled y' coordinate is not the same as the distance between the other labeled y' coordinates. When the x axis or the y axis has been truncated, do not use the y' intercept value to graph the line. When you graph the regression line, always select x values between the smallest x data value and the largest x data value.

The sign of the correlation coefficient and the sign of the slope of the regression line will always be the same. That is, if r is positive, then b will be positive; if r is negative, then b will be negative. The reason is that the numerators of the formulas are the same and determine the signs of r and b, and the denominators are always positive. The regression line will always pass through the point whose x coordinate is the mean of the x values and whose y coordinate is the mean of the y values, that is, $(\bar{x}, \bar{y})$.

The regression line can be used to make predictions for the dependent variable. The method for making predictions is shown in Example 10–6.

Example 10–6

Car Rental Companies

Use the equation of the regression line to predict the income of a car rental agency that has 200,000 automobiles.

Solution

Since the x values are in 10,000s, divide 200,000 by 10,000 to get 20, and then substitute 20 for x in the equation.

$$y' = 0.396 + 0.106x$$
$$= 0.396 + 0.106(20)$$
$$= 2.516$$

Hence, when a rental agency has 200,000 automobiles, its revenue will be approximately $2.516 billion.

The value obtained in Example 10–6 is a point prediction, and with point predictions, no degree of accuracy or confidence can be determined. More information on prediction is given in Section 10–3.

The magnitude of the change in one variable when the other variable changes exactly 1 unit is called a **marginal change.** The value of slope b of the regression line equation represents the marginal change. For example, in Example 10–5 the slope of the regression line is 0.106, which means for each increase of 10,000 cars, the value of y changes 0.106 unit ($106 million) on average.

When r is not significantly different from 0, the best predictor of y is the mean of the data values of y. For valid predictions, the value of the correlation coefficient must be significant. Also, two other assumptions must be met.

Assumptions for Valid Predictions in Regression

1. For any specific value of the independent variable x, the value of the dependent variable y must be normally distributed about the regression line. See Figure 10–12(a).
2. The standard deviation of each of the dependent variables must be the same for each value of the independent variable. See Figure 10–12(b).

Figure 10–12

Assumptions for Predictions

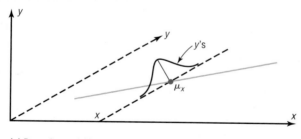

(a) Dependent variable y normally distributed

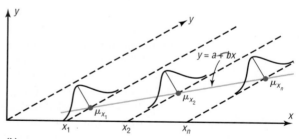

(b) $\sigma_1 = \sigma_2 = \cdots = \sigma_n$

Extrapolation, or making predictions beyond the bounds of the data, must be interpreted cautiously. For example, in 1979, some experts predicted that the United States would run out of oil by the year 2003. This prediction was based on the current consumption and on known oil reserves at that time. However, since then, the automobile industry has produced many new fuel-efficient vehicles. Also, there are many as yet undiscovered oil fields. Finally, science may someday discover a way to run a car on something as unlikely but as common as peanut oil. In addition, the price of a gallon of gasoline was predicted to reach $10 a few years later. Fortunately this has not come to pass. *Remember that when predictions are made, they are based on present conditions or on the premise that present trends will continue.* This assumption may or may not prove true in the future.

The steps for finding the value of the correlation coefficient and the regression line equation are summarized in this Procedure Table:

Procedure Table

Finding the Correlation Coefficient and the Regression Line Equation

Step 1   Make a table, as shown in step 2.

Step 2   Find the values of xy, x^2, and y^2. Place them in the appropriate columns and sum each column.

x	y	xy	x^2	y^2
.	.	.	.	.
.	.	.	.	.
.	.	.	.	.
$\Sigma x =$	$\Sigma y =$	$\Sigma xy =$	$\Sigma x^2 =$	$\Sigma y^2 =$

Step 3   Substitute in the formula to find the value of r.

$$r = \frac{n(\Sigma xy) - (\Sigma x)(\Sigma y)}{\sqrt{[n(\Sigma x^2) - (\Sigma x)^2][n(\Sigma y^2) - (\Sigma y)^2]}}$$

Step 4   When r is significant, substitute in the formulas to find the values of a and b for the regression line equation $y' = a + bx$.

$$a = \frac{(\Sigma y)(\Sigma x^2) - (\Sigma x)(\Sigma xy)}{n(\Sigma x^2) - (\Sigma x)^2} \qquad b = \frac{n(\Sigma xy) - (\Sigma x)(\Sigma y)}{n(\Sigma x^2) - (\Sigma x)^2}$$

A scatter plot should be checked for outliers. An outlier is a point that seems out of place when compared with the other points (see Chapter 3). Some of these points can affect the equation of the regression line. When this happens, the points are called **influential points** or **influential observations.**

When a point on the scatter plot appears to be an outlier, it should be checked to see if it is an influential point. An influential point tends to "pull" the regression line toward the point itself. To check for an influential point, the regression line should be graphed with the point included in the data set. Then a second regression line should be graphed that excludes the point from the data set. If the position of the second line is changed considerably, the point is said to be an influential point. Points that are outliers in the x direction tend to be influential points.

Researchers should use their judgment as to whether to include influential observations in the final analysis of the data. If the researcher feels that the observation is not necessary, then it should be excluded so that it does not influence the results of the study. However, if the researcher feels that it is necessary, then he or she may want to obtain additional data values whose x values are near the x value of the influential point and then include them in the study.

"Explain that to me."

Source: Reprinted with special permission of King Features Syndicate.

Applying the Concepts **10–2**

Stopping Distances Revisited

In a study on speed and braking distance, researchers looked for a method to estimate how fast a person was traveling before an accident by measuring the length of the skid marks. An area that was focused on in the study was the distance required to completely stop a vehicle at various speeds. Use the following table to answer the questions.

MPH	Braking distance (feet)
20	20
30	45
40	81
50	133
60	205
80	411

Assume MPH is going to be used to predict stopping distance.

1. Find the linear regression equation.
2. What does the slope tell you about MPH and the braking distance? How about the y intercept?
3. Find the braking distance when MPH = 45.
4. Find the braking distance when MPH = 100.
5. Comment on predicting beyond the given data values.

See page 569 for the answers.

Exercises 10–2

1. What two things should be done before one performs a regression analysis?

2. What are the assumptions for regression analysis?

3. What is the general form for the regression line used in statistics?

4. What is the symbol for the slope? For the y intercept?

5. What is meant by the *line of best fit?*

6. When all the points fall on the regression line, what is the value of the correlation coefficient?

7. What is the relationship between the sign of the correlation coefficient and the sign of the slope of the regression line?

8. As the value of the correlation coefficient increases from 0 to 1, or decreases from 0 to −1, how do the points of the scatter plot fit the regression line?

9. How is the value of the correlation coefficient related to the accuracy of the predicted value for a specific value of x?

10. If the value of r is not significant, what can be said about the regression line?

11. When the value of r is not significant, what value should be used to predict y?

For Exercises 12 through 27, use the same data as for the corresponding exercises in Section 10–1. For each exercise, find the equation of the regression line and find the y' value for the specified x value. Remember that no regression should be done when r is not significant.

12. **Broadway Productions** New Broadway productions and seasonal attendance are as follows.

No. of new productions	54	67	62	54	61	60	50	37
Attendance (million)	7.4	8.2	7.1	8.8	9.6	11	8.4	7.4

Find y' when $x = 48$ new productions.

13. **Commercial Movie Releases** New movie releases per studio and gross receipts are as follows:

No. of releases	361	270	306	22	35	10	8	12	21
Gross receipts (million $)	3844	1962	1371	1064	334	241	188	154	125

Find y' when $x = 200$ new releases.

14. **Forest Fires and Acres Burned** Number of fires and number of acres burned are as follows:

Fires x	72	69	58	47	84	62	57	45
Acres y	62	41	19	26	51	15	30	15

Find y' when $x = 60$.

15. Years and contribution data are as follows:

Years x	1	5	3	10	7	6
Contribution y, \$	500	100	300	50	75	80

Find y' when $x = 4$ years.

16. **State Debt and Per Capita Taxes** Data for per capita state debt and per capita state tax are as follows:

Per capita debt	1924	907	1445	1608	661
Per capita tax	1685	1838	1734	1842	1317

Find y' when $x = \$1500$ in per capita debt.

17. **Larceny and Vandalism** Larceny crimes and vandalism crimes are as follows:

Larceny x	24	6	16	64	10	25	35
Vandalism y	21	3	6	15	21	61	20

Find y' when $x = 40$.

18. **Pass Attempts** Data for pass attempts and yards gained are as follows:

Attempts x	116	90	82	108	92
Yards y	1001	823	851	873	837

Find y' when $x = 95$.

19. **Egg Production** Number of eggs and price per dozen are shown.

No. of eggs (million)	957	1332	1163	1865	119	273
Price per dozen (\$)	0.770	0.697	0.617	0.652	1.080	1.420

Find y' when $x = 1600$ million eggs.

20. **Emergency Calls and Temperature** Temperature in degrees Fahrenheit and number of emergency calls are shown.

Temperature x	68	74	82	88	93	99	101
No. of calls y	7	4	8	10	11	9	13

Find y' when $x = 80°F$.

21. **Distribution of Population in U.S. Cities** Number (in thousands) of people under 5 years old and people 65 and over living in six randomly selected cities in the United States are shown.

Under 5 x	178	27	878	314	322	143
65 and older y	361	72	1496	501	585	207

Find y' when $x = 200$ thousand.

22. **Apartment Rents** Data for one-bedroom apartment rent and three-bedroom apartment rent are as follows:

One BR	553	578	891	773	812	509
Three BR	1017	916	1577	1234	1403	857

Find y' when $x = \$700$ per month.

23. **Average Temperature and Precipitation** Temperatures (in degrees Fahrenheit) and precipitation (in inches) are as follows:

Avg. daily temp. x	86	81	83	89	80	74	64
Avg. mo. precip. y	3.4	1.8	3.5	3.6	3.7	1.5	0.2

Find y' when $x = 70°F$.

24. **Hall of Fame Pitchers** Wins and strikeouts for Hall of Fame pitchers data are as follows:

Wins x	329	150	236	300	284	207
Strikeouts y	4136	1155	1956	2266	3192	1277
Wins x	247	314	273	324		
Strikeouts y	1068	3534	1987	3574		

Find y' when $x = 260$ wins.

25. **Calories and Cholesterol** Calories and cholesterol are as follows:

Calories x	390	535	720	300	430	500	440
Cholesterol y	43	45	80	50	55	52	60

Find y' when $x = 600$ calories.

26. **Tall Buildings** Stories and heights of buildings data follow:

Stories x	64	54	40	31	45	38	42	41	37	40
Heights y	841	725	635	616	615	582	535	520	511	485

Find y' when $x = 44$.

27. **Hospital Beds** Licensed beds and staffed beds data follow:

Licensed beds x	144	32	175	185	208	100	169
Staffed beds y	112	32	162	141	103	80	118

Find y' when $x = 44$.

For Exercises 28 through 33, do a complete regression analysis by performing these steps.

    a. Draw a scatter plot.

    b. Compute the correlation coefficient.

    c. State the hypotheses.

    d. Test the hypotheses at $\alpha = 0.05$. Use Table I.

    e. Determine the regression line equation.

    f. Plot the regression line on the scatter plot.

    g. Summarize the results.

28. **Fireworks and Injuries** These data were obtained for the years 1993 through 1998 and indicate the

number of fireworks (in millions) used and the related injuries. Predict the number of injuries if 100 million fireworks are used during a given year.

Fireworks in use x	67.6	87.1	117	115	118	113
Related injuries y	12,100	12,600	12,500	10,900	7800	7000

Source: National Council of Fireworks Safety, American Pyrotechnic Assoc.

29. Farm Acreage Is there a relationship between the number of farms in a state and the acreage per farm? A random selection of states across the country, both eastern and western, produced the following results. Can a relationship between these two variables be concluded?

No. of farms (thousands) x	77	52	20.8	49	28	58.2
Acreage per farm y	347	173	173	218	246	132

Source: World Almanac.

30. SAT Scores Educational researchers desired to find out if a relationship exists between the average SAT verbal score and the average SAT mathematical score. Several states were randomly selected, and their SAT average scores are recorded below. Is there sufficient evidence to conclude a relationship between the two scores?

Verbal x	526	504	594	585	503	589
Math y	530	522	606	588	517	589

Source: World Almanac.

31. Coal Production These data were obtained from a sample of counties in southwestern Pennsylvania and indicate the number (in thousands) of tons of bituminous coal produced in each county and the number of employees working in coal production in each county. Predict the number of employees needed to produce 500 thousand tons of coal. The data are given here.

Tons x	227	5410	5328	147	729
No. of employees y	110	731	1031	20	118

Tons x	8095	635	6157
No. of employees y	1162	103	752

32. Television Viewers A television executive selects 10 television shows and compares the average number of viewers the show had last year with the average number of viewers this year. The data (in millions) are shown. Describe the relationship.

Viewers last year x	26.6	17.85	20.3	16.8	20.8
Viewers this year y	28.9	19.2	26.4	13.7	20.2
Viewers last year x	16.7	19.1	18.9	16.0	15.8
Viewers this year y	18.8	25.0	21.0	16.8	15.3

Source: Nielson Media Research.

33. Absences and Final Grades An educator wants to see how the number of absences for a student in her class affects the student's final grade. The data obtained from a sample are shown.

No. of absences x	10	12	2	0	8	5
Final grade y	70	65	96	94	75	82

For Exercises 34 and 35, do a complete regression analysis and test the significance of r at $\alpha = 0.05$, using the P-value method.

34. Father's and Son's Weights A physician wishes to know whether there is a relationship between a father's weight (in pounds) and his newborn son's weight (in pounds). The data are given here.

Father's weight x	176	160	187	210	196	142	205	215
Son's weight y	6.6	8.2	9.2	7.1	8.8	9.3	7.4	8.6

35. Age and Net Worth Is a person's age related to his or her net worth? A sample of 10 billionaires is selected, and the person's age and net worth are compared. The data are given here.

Age x	56	39	42	60	84	37	68	66	73	55
Net worth (billion $) y	18	14	12	14	11	10	10	7	7	5

Source: The Associated Press.

Extending the Concepts

36. For Exercises 13, 15, and 21 in Section 10–1, find the mean of the x and y variables. Then substitute the mean of the x variable into the corresponding regression line equations found in Exercises 13, 15, and 21 in this section and find y'. Compare the value of y' with $\bar{y}$ for each exercise. Generalize the results.

37. The y intercept value a can also be found by using the equation

$$a = \bar{y} - b\bar{x}$$

Verify this result by using the data in Exercises 15 and 16 of Sections 10–1 and 10–2.

38. The value of the correlation coefficient can also be found by using the formula

$$r = \frac{bs_x}{s_y}$$

where s_x is the standard deviation of the x values and s_y is the standard deviation of the y values. Verify this result for Exercises 18 and 20 of Section 10–1.

Technology *Step by Step*

MINITAB
Step by Step

Create a Scatter Plot

1. These instructions use the following data:

x	6	2	15	9	12	5	8
y	82	86	43	74	58	90	78

Enter the data into three columns. The subject column is optional (see step 6b).

2. Name the columns **C1 Subject, C2 Age,** and **C3 Pressure.**

3. Select **Graph>Scatterplot,** then select Simple and click [OK].

4. Double-click on C3 Pressure for the [Y] variable and C2 Age for the predictor [X] variable.

5. Click [Data View]. The Data Display should be Symbols. If not, click the option box to select it. Click [OK].

6. Click [Labels].

   a) Type **Pressure vs. Age** in the text box for Titles/Footnotes, then type **Your Name** in the box for Subtitle 1.

   b) *Optional:* Click the tab for Data Labels, then click the option to Use labels from column.

   c) Select C1 Subject.

7. Click [OK] twice.

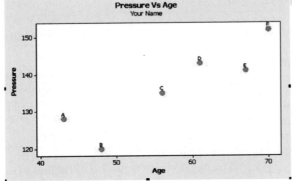

Calculate the Correlation Coefficient

8. Select **Stat>Basic Statistics>Correlation.**

9. Double-click C3 Pressure, then double-click C2 Age. The box for Display p-values should be checked.

10. Click [OK]. The correlation coefficient will be displayed in the session window, $r = +0.897$ with a P-value of 0.015.

Determine the Equation of the Least-Squares Regression Line

11. Select **Stat>Regression>Regression.**

12. Double-click Pressure in the variable list to select it for the Response variable Y.

13. Double-click C2 Age in the variable list to select it for the Predictors variable X.

14. Click on [Storage], then check the boxes for Residuals and Fits.

15. Click [OK] twice.

The session window will contain the regression analysis as shown.

In the worksheet two new columns will be added with the fitted values and residuals. Summary: The scatter plot and correlation coefficient confirm a strong positive linear correlation between pressure and age. The null hypothesis would be rejected at a significance level of 0.015. The equation of the regression equation is pressure = 81.0 + 0.964 (age).

↓	C1-T	C2	C3	C4	C5
	Subject	Age	Pressure	RESI1	FITS1
1	A	43	128	5.48353	122.516
2	B	48	120	-7.33838	127.338
3	C	56	135	-0.05343	135.053
4	D	61	143	3.12467	139.875
5	E	67	141	-4.66162	145.662
6	F	70	152	3.44524	148.555

Regression Analysis: Pressure versus Age

The regression equation is
Pressure = 81.0 + 0.964 Age

Predictor	Coef	SE Coef	T	P
Constant	81.05	13.88	5.84	0.004
Age	0.9644	0.2381	4.05	0.015

S = 5.641   R-Sq = 80.4%   R-Sq (adj) = 75.5%

Analysis of Variance

Source	DF	SS	MS	F	P
Regression	1	522.21	522.21	16.41	0.015
Residual Error	4	127.29	31.82		
Total	5	649.50			

TI-83 Plus or TI-84 Plus
Step by Step

Correlation and Regression

To graph a scatter plot:

1. Enter the x values in L_1 and the y values in L_2.

2. Make sure the Window values are appropriate. Select an Xmin slightly less than the smallest x data value and an Xmax slightly larger than the largest x data value. Do the same for Ymin and Ymax. Also, you may need to change the Xscl and Yscl values, depending on the data.

3. Press **2nd [STAT PLOT] 1** for Plot 1. The other y functions should be turned off.

4. Move the cursor to On and press **ENTER** on the Plot 1 menu.

5. Move the cursor to the graphic that looks like a scatter plot next to Type (first graph), and press **ENTER**. Make sure the X list is L_1, and the Y list is L_2.

6. Press **GRAPH**.

Example TI10–1

Draw a scatter plot for the following data.

x	43	48	56	61	67	70
y	128	120	135	143	141	152

The input and output screens are shown.

Input	Input	Output

To find the equation of the regression line:

1. Press **STAT** and move the cursor to Calc.

2. Press **8** for LinReg(a+bx) then **ENTER.** The values for a and b will be displayed.

In order to have the calculator compute and display the correlation coefficient and coefficient of determination as well as the equation of the line, you must set the diagnostics display mode to on. Follow these steps:

1. Press **2nd [CATALOG].**

2. Use the arrow keys to scroll down to DiagnosticOn.

3. Press **ENTER** to copy the command to the home screen.

4. Press **ENTER** to execute the command.

You will have to do this only once. Diagnostic display mode will remain on until you perform a similar set of steps to turn it off.

Example TI10–2

Find the equation of the regression line for the data in Example TI10–1. The input and output screens are shown.

Input	Output
	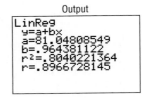

The equation of the regression line is $y' = 81.04808549 + 0.964381122x$.

To plot the regression line on the scatter plot:

1. Press **Y=** and **CLEAR** to clear any previous equations.

2. Press **VARS** and then **5** for Statistics.

3. Move the cursor to EQ and press **1** for RegEQ. The line will be in the Y= screen.

4. Press **GRAPH.**

Example TI10–3

Draw the regression line found in Example TI10–2 on the scatter plot.

The output screens are shown.

Output	Output

To test the significance of b and ρ:

1. Press **STAT** and move the cursor to TESTS.
2. Press **E (ALPHA SIN)** for LinRegTTest. Make sure the Xlist is L_1, the Ylist is L_2, and the Freq is 1.   (Use F for TI-84)
3. Select the appropriate alternative hypothesis.
4. Move the cursor to Calculate and press **ENTER**.

Example TI10–4

Test the hypothesis H_0: $\rho = 0$ for the data in Example TI 10–1. Use $\alpha = 0.05$.

Input	Output	Output

In this case, the t test value is 4.050983638. The P-value is 0.0154631742, which is significant. The decision is to reject the null hypothesis at $\alpha = 0.05$, since $0.0154631742 < 0.05$; $r = 0.8966728145$, $r^2 = 0.8040221364$.

There are two other ways to store the equation for the regression line in Y_1 for graphing.

1. Type Y_1 after the LinReg(a+bx) command.
2. Type Y_1 in the RegEQ: spot in the LinRegTTest.

To get Y_1 do this:

Press **VARS** for variables, move cursor to Y-VARS, press **1** for Function, press **1** for Y_1.

Excel
Step by Step

Scatter Plots

Creating a scatter plot is straightforward when you use the Chart Wizard.

1. You must have at least two columns of data to use the Scatter Plot option.
2. Highlight the data to be plotted. Select the Insert tab from the toolbar. Then select the Scatter chart and the first type (Scatter with only markers).
3. By left-clicking anywhere on the chart, you automatically bring up the Chart Tools group on the toolbar. The Chart Tools menu includes three additional tabs for editing your chart: Design, Layout, and Format.
4. You can add titles to your chart and to the axes by selecting the Layout tab, then selecting the appropriate option from the Labels group.

Correlation Coefficient

The CORREL function in Excel returns the correlation coefficient without regression analysis.

1. Enter the data in columns A and B.
2. Select a blank cell, and then select the Formulas tab from the toolbar.
3. Select Insert Function ![fx icon] icon from the toolbar.
4. Select the Statistical function category and select the CORREL function.
5. Enter the data range **A1:AN,** where **N** is the number of sample data pairs for the first variable in Array1. Enter the data range **B1:BN** for the second variable in Array2, and then click [OK].

Correlation and Regression

This procedure will allow you to calculate the Pearson product moment correlation coefficient without performing a regression analysis.

1. Enter the data from Example 10–2 in a new worksheet. Enter the seven values for the numbers of absences in column A and the corresponding final grades in column B.

2. Select Data from the toolbar. Then select Data Analysis. Under Analysis Tools, select Correlation.

3. In the Correlation dialog box, type **A1:B6** for the Input Range and check the Grouped By: Columns option.

4. Under Output options, select Output Range, and type **D2.** Then click [OK].

This procedure will allow you to conduct a regression analysis and compute the correlation coefficient. Use the data from Example 10–2.

1. Select the Data tab on the toolbar, then **Data Analysis>Regression.**

2. In the Regression dialog box, type **B1:B6** in the Input Y Range and type **A1:A6** in the Input X Range.

3. Under Output options, select Output Range, and type **D6.** Then click [OK].

Note: To see all of the decimal places for the statistics in the Summary Output, expand the width of columns D to L.

1. Highlight columns D through L.

2. Select the Home tab, and then select Format Autofit Column Width.

SUMMARY OUTPUT

Regression Statistics	
Multiple R	0.896672815
R Square	0.804022136
Adjusted R Square	0.75502767
Standard Error	5.641090817
Observations	6

ANOVA

	df	SS	MS	F	Significance F
Regression	1	522.2123776	522.2123776	16.41046844	0.015463174
Residual	4	127.2876224	31.82190561		
Total	5	649.5			

	Coefficients	Standard Error	t Stat	P-value	Lower 95%	Upper 95%	Lower 95.0%	Upper 95.0%
Intercept	81.04808549	13.88088081	5.838828717	0.004289034	42.50858191	119.5875891	42.50858191	119.5875891
X Variable 1	0.964381122	0.238060977	4.050983638	0.015463174	0.303417888	1.625344356	0.303417888	1.625344356

10–3 Coefficient of Determination and Standard Error of the Estimate

The previous sections stated that if the correlation coefficient is significant, the equation of the regression line can be determined. Also, for various values of the independent variable *x*, the corresponding values of the dependent variable *y* can be predicted. Several other measures are associated with the correlation and regression techniques. They include the coefficient of determination, the standard error of the estimate, and the prediction interval. But before these concepts can be explained, the different types of variation associated with the regression model must be defined.

Types of Variation for the Regression Model

 Consider the following hypothetical regression model.

x	1	2	3	4	5
y	10	8	12	16	20

The equation of the regression line is $y' = 4.8 + 2.8x$, and $r = 0.919$. The sample y values are 10, 8, 12, 16, and 20. The predicted values, designated by y', for each x can be found by substituting each x value into the regression equation and finding y'. For example, when $x = 1$,

$$y' = 4.8 + 2.8x = 4.8 + (2.8)(1) = 7.6$$

Now, for each x, there is an observed y value and a predicted y' value; for example, when $x = 1$, $y = 10$, and $y' = 7.6$. Recall that the closer the observed values are to the predicted values, the better the fit is and the closer r is to $+1$ or -1.

The *total variation* $\Sigma(y - \bar{y})^2$ is the sum of the squares of the vertical distances each point is from the mean. The total variation can be divided into two parts: that which is attributed to the relationship of x and y and that which is due to chance. The variation obtained from the relationship (i.e., from the predicted y' values) is $\Sigma(y' - \bar{y})^2$ and is called the *explained variation*. Most of the variations can be explained by the relationship. The closer the value r is to $+1$ or -1, the better the points fit the line and the closer $\Sigma(y' - \bar{y})^2$ is to $\Sigma(y - \bar{y})^2$. In fact, if all points fall on the regression line, $\Sigma(y' - \bar{y})^2$ will equal $\Sigma(y - \bar{y})^2$, since y' is equal to y in each case.

On the other hand, the variation due to chance, found by $\Sigma(y - y')^2$, is called the *unexplained variation*. This variation cannot be attributed to the relationship. When the unexplained variation is small, the value of r is close to $+1$ or -1. If all points fall on the regression line, the unexplained variation $\Sigma(y - y')^2$ will be 0. Hence, the *total variation* is equal to the sum of the explained variation and the unexplained variation. That is,

$$\Sigma(y - \bar{y})^2 = \Sigma(y' - \bar{y})^2 + \Sigma(y - y')^2$$

These values are shown in Figure 10–13. For a single point, the differences are called *deviations*. For the hypothetical regression model given earlier, for $x = 1$ and $y = 10$, you get $y' = 7.6$ and $\bar{y} = 13.2$.

The procedure for finding the three types of variation is illustrated next.

Step 1 Find the predicted y' values.

For $x = 1$ $y' = 4.8 + 2.8x = 4.8 + (2.8)(1) = 7.6$

For $x = 2$ $y' = 4.8 + (2.8)(2) = 10.4$

For $x = 3$ $y' = 4.8 + (2.8)(3) = 13.2$

For $x = 4$ $y' = 4.8 + (2.8)(4) = 16.0$

For $x = 5$ $y' = 4.8 + (2.8)(5) = 18.8$

Figure 10–13

Deviations for the Regression Equation

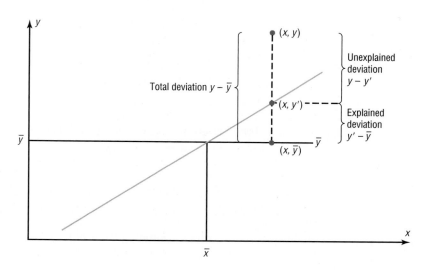

Hence, the values for this example are as follows:

x	y	y'
1	10	7.6
2	8	10.4
3	12	13.2
4	16	16.0
5	20	18.8

Step 2 Find the mean of the y values.

$$\bar{y} = \frac{10 + 8 + 12 + 16 + 20}{5} = 13.2$$

Step 3 Find the total variation $\Sigma(y - \bar{y})^2$.

$$(10 - 13.2)^2 = 10.24$$
$$(8 - 13.2)^2 = 27.04$$
$$(12 - 13.2)^2 = 1.44$$
$$(16 - 13.2)^2 = 7.84$$
$$(20 - 13.2)^2 = \underline{46.24}$$
$$\Sigma(y - \bar{y})^2 = 92.8$$

Step 4 Find the explained variation $\Sigma(y' - \bar{y})^2$.

$$(7.6 - 13.2)^2 = 31.36$$
$$(10.4 - 13.2)^2 = 7.84$$
$$(13.2 - 13.2)^2 = 0.00$$
$$(16 - 13.2)^2 = 7.84$$
$$(18.8 - 13.2)^2 = \underline{31.36}$$
$$\Sigma(y' - \bar{y})^2 = 78.4$$

Step 5 Find the unexplained variation $\Sigma(y - y')^2$.

$$(10 - 7.6)^2 = 5.76$$
$$(8 - 10.4)^2 = 5.76$$
$$(12 - 13.2)^2 = 1.44$$
$$(16 - 16)^2 = 0.00$$
$$(20 - 18.8)^2 = \underline{1.44}$$
$$\Sigma(y - y')^2 = 14.4$$

Notice that

Total variation = Explained variation + Unexplained variation
$$92.8 = 78.4 + 14.4$$

Note: The values $(y - y')$ are called *residuals*. A **residual** is the difference between the actual value of y and the predicted value y' for a given x value. The mean of the residuals is always zero. As stated previously, the regression line determined by the formulas in Section 10–2 is the line that best fits the points of the scatter plot. The sum of the squares of the residuals computed by using the regression line is the smallest possible value. For this reason, a regression line is also called a **least-squares line.**

Coefficient of Determination

The *coefficient of determination* is the ratio of the explained variation to the total variation and is denoted by r^2. That is,

$$r^2 = \frac{\text{explained variation}}{\text{total variation}}$$

For the example, $r^2 = 78.4/92.8 = 0.845$. The term r^2 is usually expressed as a percentage. So in this case, 84.5% of the total variation is explained by the regression line using the independent variable.

Another way to arrive at the value for r^2 is to square the correlation coefficient. In this case, $r = 0.919$ and $r^2 = 0.845$, which is the same value found by using the variation ratio.

> The **coefficient of determination** is a measure of the variation of the dependent variable that is explained by the regression line and the independent variable. The symbol for the coefficient of determination is r^2.

Of course, it is usually easier to find the coefficient of determination by squaring r and converting it to a percentage. Therefore, if $r = 0.90$, then $r^2 = 0.81$, which is equivalent to 81%. This result means that 81% of the variation in the dependent variable is accounted for by the variations in the independent variable. The rest of the variation, 0.19, or 19%, is unexplained. This value is called the *coefficient of nondetermination* and is found by subtracting the coefficient of determination from 1. As the value of r approaches 0, r^2 decreases more rapidly. For example, if $r = 0.6$, then $r^2 = 0.36$, which means that only 36% of the variation in the dependent variable can be attributed to the variation in the independent variable.

> **Coefficient of Nondetermination**
>
> $$1.00 - r^2$$

Standard Error of the Estimate

When a y' value is predicted for a specific x value, the prediction is a point prediction. However, a prediction interval about the y' value can be constructed, just as a confidence interval was constructed for an estimate of the population mean. The prediction interval uses a statistic called the *standard error of the estimate*.

> The **standard error of the estimate,** denoted by s_{est}, is the standard deviation of the observed y values about the predicted y' values. The formula for the standard error of the estimate is
>
> $$s_{est} = \sqrt{\frac{\Sigma(y - y')^2}{n - 2}}$$

The standard error of the estimate is similar to the standard deviation, but the mean is not used. As can be seen from the formula, the standard error of the estimate is the square root of the unexplained variation—that is, the variation due to the difference of the observed values and the expected values—divided by $n - 2$. So the closer the observed values are to the predicted values, the smaller the standard error of the estimate will be.

Example 10–7 shows how to compute the standard error of the estimate.

| Example 10–7 | Copy Machine Maintenance Costs |

A researcher collects the following data and determines that there is a significant relationship between the age of a copy machine and its monthly maintenance cost. The regression equation is $y' = 55.57 + 8.13x$. Find the standard error of the estimate.

Machine	Age x (years)	Monthly cost y
A	1	$ 62
B	2	78
C	3	70
D	4	90
E	4	93
F	6	103

Solution

Step 1 Make a table, as shown.

x	y	y'	$y - y'$	$(y - y')^2$
1	62			
2	78			
3	70			
4	90			
4	93			
6	103			

Step 2 Using the regression line equation $y' = 55.57 + 8.13x$, compute the predicted values y' for each x and place the results in the column labeled y'.

$x = 1$ $\quad y' = 55.57 + (8.13)(1) = \quad 63.70$

$x = 2$ $\quad y' = 55.57 + (8.13)(2) = \quad 71.83$

$x = 3$ $\quad y' = 55.57 + (8.13)(3) = \quad 79.96$

$x = 4$ $\quad y' = 55.57 + (8.13)(4) = \quad 88.09$

$x = 6$ $\quad y' = 55.57 + (8.13)(6) = 104.35$

Step 3 For each y, subtract y' and place the answer in the column labeled $y - y'$.

$62 - 63.70 = -1.70 \qquad 90 - \quad 88.09 = \quad 1.91$

$78 - 71.83 = \quad 6.17 \qquad 93 - \quad 88.09 = \quad 4.91$

$70 - 79.96 = -9.96 \qquad 103 - 104.35 = -1.35$

Step 4 Square the numbers found in step 3 and place the squares in the column labeled $(y - y')^2$.

Step 5 Find the sum of the numbers in the last column. The completed table is shown.

x	y	y'	$y - y'$	$(y - y')^2$
1	62	63.70	−1.70	2.89
2	78	71.83	6.17	38.0689
3	70	79.96	−9.96	99.2016
4	90	88.09	1.91	3.6481
4	93	88.09	4.91	24.1081
6	103	104.35	−1.35	1.8225
				169.7392

Step 6 Substitute in the formula and find s_{est}.

$$s_{est} = \sqrt{\frac{\Sigma(y - y')^2}{n - 2}} = \sqrt{\frac{169.7392}{6 - 2}} = 6.51$$

In this case, the standard deviation of observed values about the predicted values is 6.51.

The standard error of the estimate can also be found by using the formula

$$s_{est} = \sqrt{\frac{\Sigma y^2 - a\,\Sigma y - b\,\Sigma xy}{n - 2}}$$

Example 10–8

Find the standard error of the estimate for the data for Example 10–7 by using the preceding formula. The equation of the regression line is $y' = 55.57 + 8.13x$.

Solution

Step 1 Make a table.

Step 2 Find the product of x and y values, and place the results in the third column.

Step 3 Square the y values, and place the results in the fourth column.

Step 4 Find the sums of the second, third, and fourth columns. The completed table is shown here.

x	y	xy	y^2
1	62	62	3,844
2	78	156	6,084
3	70	210	4,900
4	90	360	8,100
4	93	372	8,649
6	103	618	10,609
	$\Sigma y = 496$	$\Sigma xy = 1778$	$\Sigma y^2 = 42{,}186$

Step 5 From the regression equation $y' = 55.57 + 8.13x$, $a = 55.57$, and $b = 8.13$.

Step 6 Substitute in the formula and solve for s_{est}.

$$s_{est} = \sqrt{\frac{\Sigma y^2 - a\,\Sigma y - b\,\Sigma xy}{n - 2}}$$

$$= \sqrt{\frac{42{,}186 - (55.57)(496) - (8.13)(1778)}{6 - 2}} = 6.48$$

This value is close to the value found in Example 10–7. The difference is due to rounding.

Objective 7

Find a prediction interval.

Prediction Interval

The standard error of the estimate can be used for constructing a **prediction interval** (similar to a confidence interval) about a y' value.

When a specific value x is substituted into the regression equation, the y' that you get is a point estimate for y. For example, if the regression line equation for the age of a machine and the monthly maintenance cost is $y' = 55.57 + 8.13x$ (Example 10–7), then the predicted maintenance cost for a 3-year-old machine would be $y' = 55.57 + 8.13(3)$, or \$79.96. Since this is a point estimate, you have no idea how accurate it is. But you can construct a prediction interval about the estimate. By selecting an α value, you can achieve a $(1 - \alpha) \cdot 100\%$ confidence that the interval contains the actual mean of the y values that correspond to the given value of x.

The reason is that there are possible sources of prediction errors in finding the regression line equation. One source occurs when finding the standard error of the estimate s_{est}. Two others are errors made in estimating the slope and the y' intercept, since the equation of the regression line will change somewhat if different random samples are used when calculating the equation.

Formula for the Prediction Interval about a Value y'

$$y' - t_{\alpha/2}s_{est}\sqrt{1 + \frac{1}{n} + \frac{n(x - \overline{X})^2}{n\,\Sigma x^2 - (\Sigma x)^2}} < y < y' + t_{\alpha/2}s_{est}\sqrt{1 + \frac{1}{n} + \frac{n(x - \overline{X})^2}{n\,\Sigma x^2 - (\Sigma x)^2}}$$

with d.f. $= n - 2$.

Example 10–9

For the data in Example 10–7, find the 95% prediction interval for the monthly maintenance cost of a machine that is 3 years old.

Solution

Step 1 Find Σx, Σx^2, and $\overline{X}$.

$$\Sigma x = 20 \qquad \Sigma x^2 = 82 \qquad \overline{X} = \frac{20}{6} = 3.3$$

Step 2 Find y' for $x = 3$.

$$y' = 55.57 + 8.13x$$
$$= 55.57 + 8.13(3) = 79.96$$

Step 3 Find s_{est}.

$$s_{est} = 6.48$$

as shown in Example 10–8.

Step 4 Substitute in the formula and solve: $t_{\alpha/2} = 2.776$, d.f. $= 6 - 2 = 4$ for 95%.

$$y' - t_{\alpha/2}s_{est}\sqrt{1 + \frac{1}{n} + \frac{n(x - \overline{X})^2}{n\,\Sigma x^2 - (\Sigma x)^2}} < y < y'$$

$$+ t_{\alpha/2}s_{est}\sqrt{1 + \frac{1}{n} + \frac{n(x - \overline{X})^2}{n\,\Sigma x^2 - (\Sigma x)^2}}$$

$$79.96 - (2.776)(6.48)\sqrt{1 + \frac{1}{6} + \frac{6(3 - 3.3)^2}{6(82) - (20)^2}} < y < 79.96$$

$$+ (2.776)(6.48)\sqrt{1 + \frac{1}{6} + \frac{6(3 - 3.3)^2}{6(82) - (20)^2}}$$

$$79.96 - (2.776)(6.48)(1.08) < y < 79.96 + (2.776)(6.48)(1.08)$$
$$79.96 - 19.43 < y < 79.96 + 19.43$$
$$60.53 < y < 99.39$$

Hence, you can be 95% confident that the interval $60.53 < y < 99.39$ contains the actual value of y.

Applying the Concepts **10–3**

Interpreting Simple Linear Regression

Answer the questions about the following computer-generated information.

Linear correlation coefficient $r = 0.794556$
Coefficient of determination = 0.631319
Standard error of estimate = 12.9668
Explained variation = 5182.41
Unexplained variation = 3026.49
Total variation = 8208.90
Equation of regression line $y' = 0.725983X + 16.5523$
Level of significance = 0.1
Test statistic = 0.794556
Critical value = 0.378419

1. Are both variables moving in the same direction?
2. Which number measures the distances from the prediction line to the actual values?
3. Which number is the slope of the regression line?
4. Which number is the *y* intercept of the regression line?
5. Which number can be found in a table?
6. Which number is the allowable risk of making a type I error?
7. Which number measures the variation explained by the regression?
8. Which number measures the scatter of points about the regression line?
9. What is the null hypothesis?
10. Which number is compared to the critical value to see if the null hypothesis should be rejected?
11. Should the null hypothesis be rejected?

See pages 569 and 570 for the answers.

Exercises 10–3

1. What is meant by the *explained variation?* How is it computed?

2. What is meant by the *unexplained variation?* How is it computed?

3. What is meant by the *total variation?* How is it computed?

4. Define the coefficient of determination.

5. How is the coefficient of determination found?

6. Define the coefficient of nondetermination.

7. How is the coefficient of nondetermination found?

For Exercises 8 through 13, find the coefficients of determination and nondetermination and explain the meaning of each.

8. $r = 0.80$

9. $r = 0.75$

10. $r = 0.35$

11. $r = 0.42$

12. $r = 0.18$

13. $r = 0.91$

14. Define the standard error of the estimate for regression. When can the standard error of the estimate be used to construct a prediction interval about a value y'?

15. Compute the standard error of the estimate for Exercise 13 in Section 10–1. The regression line equation was found in Exercise 13 in Section 10–2.

16. Compute the standard error of the estimate for Exercise 14 in Section 10–1. The regression line equation was found in Exercise 14 in Section 10–2.

17. Compute the standard error of the estimate for Exercise 15 in Section 10–1. The regression line equation was found in Exercise 15 in Section 10–2.

18. Compute the standard error of the estimate for Exercise 16 in Section 10–1. The regression line equation was found in Exercise 16 in Section 10–2.

19. For the data in Exercises 13 in Sections 10–1 and 10–2 and 15 in Section 10–3, find the 90% prediction interval when $x = 200$ new releases.

20. For the data in Exercises 14 in Sections 10–1 and 10–2 and 16 in Section 10–3, find the 95% prediction interval when $x = 60$.

21. For the data in Exercises 15 in Sections 10–1 and 10–2 and 17 in Section 10–3, find the 90% prediction interval when $x = 4$ years.

22. For the data in Exercises 16 in Sections 10–1 and 10–2 and 18 in Section 10–3, find the 98% prediction interval when $x = 47$ years.

Summary

Many relationships among variables exist in the real world. One way to determine whether a relationship exists is to use the statistical techniques known as correlation and regression. The strength and direction of a linear relationship are measured by the value of the correlation coefficient. It can assume values between and including +1 and −1. The closer the value of the correlation coefficient is to +1 or −1, the stronger the linear relationship is between the variables. A value of +1 or −1 indicates a perfect linear relationship. A positive relationship between two variables means that for small values of the independent variable, the values of the dependent variable will be small, and that for large values of the independent variable, the values of the dependent variable will be large. A negative relationship between two variables means that for small values of the independent variable, the values of the dependent variable will be large, and that for large values of the independent variable, the values of the dependent variable will be small.

Relationships can be linear or curvilinear. To determine the shape, you draw a scatter plot of the variables. If the relationship is linear, the data can be approximated by a straight line, called the *regression line,* or the *line of best fit.* The closer the value of *r* is to +1 or −1, the more closely the points will fit the line.

In addition, relationships can be multiple. That is, there can be two or more independent variables and one dependent variable. A coefficient of correlation and a regression equation can be found for multiple relationships, just as they can be found for simple relationships.

The coefficient of determination is a better indicator of the strength of a relationship than the correlation coefficient. It is better because it identifies the percentage of variation of the dependent variable that is directly attributable to the variation of the independent variable. The coefficient of determination is obtained by squaring the correlation coefficient and converting the result to a percentage.

Another statistic used in correlation and regression is the standard error of the estimate, which is an estimate of the standard deviation of the *y* values about the predicted *y′* values. The standard error of the estimate can be used to construct a prediction interval about a specific value point estimate *y′* of the mean of the *y* values for a given value of *x*.

Finally, remember that a significant relationship between two variables does not necessarily mean that one variable is a direct cause of the other variable. In some cases this is true, but other possibilities that should be considered include a complex relationship involving other (perhaps unknown) variables, a third variable interacting with both variables, or a relationship due solely to chance.

"At this point in my report, I'll ask all of you to follow me to the conference room directly below us!"

Source: Cartoon by Bradford Veley, Marquette, Michigan. Reprinted with permission.

Important Terms

coefficient of
determination 559

correlation 530

correlation coefficient 533

dependent variable 531

extrapolation 547

independent variable 531

influential point or
observation 548

least-squares line 558

lurking variable 536

marginal change 547

multiple relationship 531

negative relationship 531

Pearson product moment
correlation coefficient 533

population correlation
coefficient 537

positive relationship 531

prediction interval 561

regression 530

regression line 543

residual 558

scatter plot 532

simple relationship 531

standard error of the
estimate 559

Important Formulas

Formula for the correlation coefficient:

$$r = \frac{n(\Sigma xy) - (\Sigma x)(\Sigma y)}{\sqrt{[n(\Sigma x^2) - (\Sigma x)^2][n(\Sigma y^2) - (\Sigma y)^2]}}$$

Formula for the t test for the correlation coefficient:

$$t = r\sqrt{\frac{n-2}{1-r^2}} \qquad \text{d.f.} = n - 2$$

The regression line equation:

$$y' = a + bx$$

where

$$a = \frac{(\Sigma y)(\Sigma x^2) - (\Sigma x)(\Sigma xy)}{n(\Sigma x^2) - (\Sigma x)^2}$$

$$b = \frac{n(\Sigma xy) - (\Sigma x)(\Sigma y)}{n(\Sigma x^2) - (\Sigma x)^2}$$

Formula for the standard error of the estimate:

$$s_{est} = \sqrt{\frac{\Sigma(y - y')^2}{n-2}}$$

or

$$s_{est} = \sqrt{\frac{\Sigma y^2 - a\,\Sigma y - b\,\Sigma xy}{n-2}}$$

Formula for the prediction interval for a value y':

$$y' - t_{\alpha/2}s_{est}\sqrt{1 + \frac{1}{n} + \frac{n(x - \bar{X})^2}{n\,\Sigma x^2 - (\Sigma x)^2}} < y$$

$$< y' + t_{\alpha/2}s_{est}\sqrt{1 + \frac{1}{n} + \frac{n(x - \bar{X})^2}{n\,\Sigma x^2 - (\Sigma x)^2}}$$

$$\text{d.f.} = n - 2$$

Review Exercises

**For Exercises 1 through 7, do a complete regression
analysis by performing the following steps.**

   a. Draw the scatter plot.
   b. Compute the value of the correlation coefficient.
   c. Test the significance of the correlation coefficient at
        $\alpha = 0.01$, using Table I.
   d. Determine the regression line equation.
   e. Plot the regression line on the scatter plot.
   f. Predict y' for a specific value of x.

1. Passengers and Airline Fares The U.S. Department
of Transportation Office of Aviation Analysis provides
the weekly average number of passengers per flight
and the average one-way fare in dollars for common
commercial routes. Randomly selected flights are listed
below with the reported data. Is there evidence of a
relationship between these two variables?

Flight	Avg. no. of passengers x	Avg. one-way fare y
Pittsburgh–Washington, DC	310	$236
Chicago–Pittsburgh	1388	105
Cincinnati–New York City	750	339
Denver–Phoenix	3019	96
Denver–Los Angeles	2151	176
Houston–Philadelphia	1104	180

Source: www.fedstats.gov

2. Day Care Centers A researcher wishes to
determine if there is a relationship between the
number of day care centers and the number of group day
care homes for counties in Pennsylvania. If there is a
significant relationship, predict the number of group care
homes a county has if the county has 20 day care centers.

Day care centers x	5	28	37	16	16	48
Group day care homes y	2	7	4	10	6	9

Source: State Department of Public Welfare.

3. Gasoline and Cigarette Taxes A study was done to compare various common taxes levied by each of the states. Two specific taxes, tax on gasoline and tax on cigarettes, are recorded here for a random selection of states. Can it be concluded that there is a significant relationship between the two? Predict the cigarette tax if the tax on gasoline is 18.4¢.

Gas (cents/gal) x	14	20	24	31	27.8	30.8	23.5
Cig. ($/pack) y	0.60	1.41	1.53	2.46	1.70	2.00	1.51

Source: www.articles.moneycentral.msn.com

4. Driver's Age and Accidents A study is conducted to determine the relationship between a driver's age and the number of accidents he or she has over a 1-year period. The data are shown here. (This information will be used for Exercise 8.) If there is a significant relationship, predict the number of accidents of a driver who is 28.

Driver's age x	16	24	18	17	23	27	32
No. of accidents y	3	2	5	2	0	1	1

5. Typing Speed and Word Processing A researcher desires to know whether the typing speed of a secretary (in words per minute) is related to the time (in hours) that it takes the secretary to learn to use a new word processing program. The data are shown.

Speed x	48	74	52	79	83	56	85	63	88	74	90	92
Time y	7	4	8	3.5	2	6	2.3	5	2.1	4.5	1.9	1.5

If there is a significant relationship, predict the time it will take the average secretary who has a typing speed of 72 words per minute to learn the word processing program. (This information will be used for Exercises 9 and 11.)

6. Protein and Diastolic Blood Pressure A study was conducted with vegetarians to see whether the number of grams of protein each ate per day was related to diastolic blood pressure. The data are given here. (This information will be used for Exercises 10 and 12.) If there is a significant relationship, predict the diastolic pressure of a vegetarian who consumes 8 grams of protein per day.

Grams x	4	6.5	5	5.5	8	10	9	8.2	10.5
Pressure y	73	79	83	82	84	92	88	86	95

7. Medical Specialties and Gender Although more and more women are becoming physicians each year, it is well known that men outnumber women in many specialties. Randomly selected specialties are listed below with the numbers of male and female physicians in each. Can it be concluded that there is a significant relationship between the two variables? Predict the number of male specialists when there are 2000 female specialists.

Specialty	Female x	Male y
Dermatology	3,482	6,506
Emergency medicine	5,098	20,429
Neurology	2,895	10,088
Pediatric cardiology	459	1,241
Radiology	1,218	7,574
Forensic pathology	181	399
Radiation oncology	968	3,215

Source: *World Almanac.*

8. For Exercise 4, find the standard error of the estimate.

9. For Exercise 5, find the standard error of the estimate.

10. For Exercise 6, find the standard error of the estimate.

11. For Exercise 5, find the 90% prediction interval for time when the speed is 72 words per minute.

12. For Exercise 6, find the 95% prediction interval for pressure when the number of grams is 8.

Statistics Today

Do Dust Storms Affect Respiratory Health?—Revisited

The researchers correlated the dust pollutant levels in the atmosphere and the number of daily emergency room visits for several respiratory disorders, such as bronchitis, sinusitis, asthma, and pneumonia. Using the Pearson correlation coefficient, they found overall a significant but low correlation, $r = 0.13$, for bronchitis visits only. However, they found a much higher correlation value for sinusitis, P-value $= 0.08$, when pollutant levels exceeded maximums set by the Environmental Protection Agency (EPA). In addition, they found statistically significant correlation coefficients $r = 0.94$ for sinusitis visits and $r = 0.74$ for upper-respiratory-tract infection visits 2 days after the dust pollutants exceeded the maximum levels set by the EPA.

Data Analysis

The Data Bank is found in Appendix D, or on the World Wide Web by following links from
www.mhhe.com/bluman/

1. From the Data Bank, choose two variables that might be related: for example, IQ and educational level; age and cholesterol level; exercise and weight; or weight and systolic pressure. Do a complete correlation and regression analysis by performing the following steps. Select a random sample of at least 10 subjects.

   a. Draw a scatter plot.
   b. Compute the correlation coefficient.

c. Test the hypothesis H_0: $\rho = 0$.
d. Find the regression line equation.
e. Summarize the results.

2. Repeat Exercise 1, using samples of values of 10 or more obtained from Data Set V in Appendix D. Let x = the number of suspensions and y = the enrollment size.

3. Repeat Exercise 1, using samples of 10 or more values obtained from Data Set XIII. Let x = the number of beds and y = the number of personnel employed.

Chapter Quiz

Determine whether each statement is true or false. If the statement is false, explain why.

1. A negative relationship between two variables means that for the most part, as the x variable increases, the y variable increases.

2. A correlation coefficient of -1 implies a perfect linear relationship between the variables.

3. Even if the correlation coefficient is high or low, it may not be significant.

4. When the correlation coefficient is significant, you can assume x causes y.

5. It is not possible to have a significant correlation by chance alone.

6. In multiple regression, there are several dependent variables and one independent variable.

Select the best answer.

7. The strength of the relationship between two variables is determined by the value of
   a. r c. x
   b. a d. s_{est}

8. To test the significance of r, a(n) _____ test is used.
   a. t c. χ^2
   b. F d. None of the above

9. The test of significance for r has _____ degrees of freedom.
   a. 1   c. $n-1$
   b. n d. $n-2$

10. The equation of the regression line used in statistics is
    a. $x = a + by$ c. $y' = a + bx$
    b. $y = bx + a$ d. $x = ay + b$

11. The coefficient of determination is
    a. r c. a
    b. r^2 d. b

Complete the following statements with the best answer.

12. A statistical graph of two variables is called a(n) _____.

13. The x variable is called the _____ variable.

14. The range of r is from _____ to _____.

15. The sign of r and _____ will always be the same.

16. The regression line is called the _____.

17. If all the points fall on a straight line, the value of r will be _____ or _____.

For Exercises 18 through 21, do a complete regression analysis.

   a. Draw the scatter plot.
   b. Compute the value of the correlation coefficient.
   c. Test the significance of the correlation coefficient at $\alpha = 0.05$.
   d. Determine the regression line equation.
   e. Plot the regression line on the scatter plot.
   f. Predict y' for a specific value of x.

18. **Prescription Drug Prices** A medical researcher wants to determine the relationship between the price per dose of prescription drugs in the United States and the price of the same dose in Australia. The data are shown. Describe the relationship.

U.S. price x	3.31	3.16	2.27	3.13	2.54	1.98	2.22
Australian price y	1.29	1.75	0.82	0.83	1.32	0.84	0.82

19. Age and Driving Accidents A study is conducted to determine the relationship between a driver's age and the number of accidents he or she has over a 1-year period. The data are shown here. If there is a significant relationship, predict the number of accidents of a driver who is 64.

Driver's age x	63	65	60	62	66	67	59
No. of accidents y	2	3	1	0	3	1	4

20. Age and Cavities A researcher desires to know if the age of a child is related to the number of cavities he or she has. The data are shown here. If there is a significant relationship, predict the number of cavities for a child of 11.

Age of child x	6	8	9	10	12	14
No. of cavities y	2	1	3	4	6	5

21. Fat and Cholesterol A study is conducted with a group of dieters to see if the number of grams of fat each consumes per day is related to cholesterol level. The data are shown here. If there is a significant relationship, predict the cholesterol level of a dieter who consumes 8.5 grams of fat per day.

Fat grams x	6.8	5.5	8.2	10	8.6	9.1	8.6	10.4
Cholesterol level y	183	201	193	283	222	250	190	218

22. For Exercise 20, find the standard error of the estimate.

23. For Exercise 21, find the standard error of the estimate.

24. For Exercise 20, find the 90% prediction interval of the number of cavities for a 7-year-old.

25. For Exercise 21, find the 95% prediction interval of the cholesterol level of a person who consumes 10 grams of fat.

Critical Thinking Challenges

Product Sales When the points in a scatter plot show a curvilinear trend rather than a linear trend, statisticians have methods of fitting curves rather than straight lines to the data, thus obtaining a better fit and a better prediction model. One type of curve that can be used is the logarithmic regression curve. The data shown are the number of items of a new product sold over a period of 15 months at a certain store. Notice that sales rise during the beginning months and then level off later on.

Month x	1	3	6	8	10	12	15
No. of items sold y	10	12	15	19	20	21	21

1. Draw the scatter plot for the data.
2. Find the equation of the regression line.

3. Describe how the line fits the data.

4. Using the log key on your calculator, transform the x values into log x values.

5. Using the log x values instead of the x values, find the equation of a and b for the regression line.

6. Next, plot the curve $y = a + b \log x$ on the graph.

7. Compare the line $y = a + bx$ with the curve $y = a + b \log x$ and decide which one fits the data better.

8. Compute r, using the x and y values; then compute r, using the log x and y values. Which is higher?

9. In your opinion, which (the line or the logarithmic curve) would be a better predictor for the data? Why?

Data Projects

Use a significance level of 0.05 for all tests below.

1. **Business and Finance** Use the stocks in data project 1 of Chapter 2 identified as the Dow Jones Industrials as the sample. For each, note the current price and the amount of the last year's dividends. Are the two variables linearly related? How much variability in amount of dividend is explainable by the price?

2. **Sports and Leisure** For each team in major league baseball note the number of wins the team had last year and the number of home runs by its best home run hitter. Is the number of wins linearly related to the number of home runs hit? How much variability in total wins is explained by home runs hit? Write a regression equation to determine how many wins you would expect a team to have, knowing their top home run output.

3. **Technology** Use the data collected in data project 3 of Chapter 2 for this problem. For the data set note the

length of the song and the year it was released. Is there a linear relationship between the length of a song and the year it was released? Is the sign on the correlation coefficient positive or negative? What does the sign on the coefficient indicate about the relationship?

4. **Health and Wellness** Use a fast-food restaurant to compile your data. For each menu item note its fat grams and its total calories. Is there a linear relationship between the two variables? How much variance in total calories is explained by fat grams? Write a regression equation to determine how many total calories you would expect in an item, knowing its fat grams.

5. **Politics and Economics** For each state find its average SAT Math score, SAT English score, and average household income. Which has the strongest linear relationship, SAT Math and SAT English, SAT Math and income, or SAT English and income?

6. **Your Class** Use the data collected in data project 6 of Chapter 2 regarding heart rates. Is there a linear relationship between the heart rates before and after exercise? How much of the variability in heart rate after exercise is explainable by heart rate before exercise? Write a regression equation to determine what heart rate after exercise you would expect for a person, given the person's heart rate before exercise.

Answers to Applying the Concepts

Section 10–1   Stopping Distances

1. The independent variable is miles per hour (mph).

2. The dependent variable is braking distance (feet).

3. Miles per hour is a continuous quantitative variable.

4. Braking distance is a continuous quantitative variable.

5. A scatter plot of the data is shown.

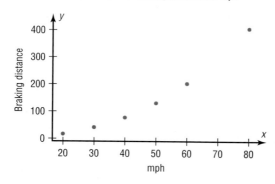

Scatter plot of braking distance vs. mph

6. There might be a linear relationship between the two variables, but there is a bit of a curve in the data.

7. Changing the distances between the mph increments will change the appearance of the relationship.

8. There is a positive relationship between the two variables—higher speeds are associated with longer braking distances.

9. The strong relationship between the two variables suggests that braking distance can be accurately predicted from mph. We might still have some concern about the curve in the data.

10. Answers will vary. Some other variables that might affect braking distance include road conditions, driver response time, and condition of the brakes.

11. The correlation coefficient is $r = 0.966$.

12. The value for $r = 0.966$ is significant at $\alpha = 0.05$. This confirms the strong positive relationship between the variables.

Section 10–2   Stopping Distances Revisited

1. The linear regression equation is
$$y' = -151.90 + 6.4514x$$

2. The slope says that for each additional mile per hour a car is traveling, we expect the stopping distance to increase by 6.45 feet, on average. The y intercept is the braking distance we would expect for a car traveling 0 mph—this is meaningless in this context, but is an important part of the model.

3. $y' = -151.90 + 6.4514(45) = 138.4$ The braking distance for a car traveling 45 mph is approximately 138 feet.

4. $y' = -151.90 + 6.4514(100) = 493.2$ The braking distance for a car traveling 100 mph is approximately 493 feet.

5. It is not appropriate to make predictions of braking distance for speeds outside of the given data values (for example, the 100 mph above) because we know nothing about the relationship between the two variables outside of the range of the data.

Section 10–3   Interpreting Simple Linear Regression

1. Both variables are moving in the same direction. In others words, the two variables are positively

associated. This is so because the correlation coefficient is positive.

2. The unexplained variation of 3026.49 measures the distances from the prediction line to the actual values.

3. The slope of the regression line is 0.725983.

4. The *y* intercept is 16.5523.

5. The critical value of 0.378419 can be found in a table.

6. The allowable risk of making a type I error is 0.10, the level of significance.

7. The variation explained by the regression is 0.631319, or about 63.1%.

8. The average scatter of points about the regression line is 12.9668, the standard error of the estimate.

9. The null hypothesis is that there is no correlation, $H_0: \rho = 0$.

10. We compare the test statistic of 0.794556 to the critical value to see if the null hypothesis should be rejected.

11. Since $0.794556 > 0.378419$, we reject the null hypothesis and find that there is enough evidence to conclude that the correlation is not equal to zero.

11

Chi-Square and Analysis of Variance (ANOVA)

Objectives

After completing this chapter, you should be able to

1 Test a distribution for goodness of fit, using chi-square.

2 Test two variables for independence, using chi-square.

3 Test proportions for homogeneity, using chi-square.

4 Use the ANOVA technique to determine if there is a significant difference among three or more means.

Outline

Statistics and Heredity

An Austrian monk, Gregor Mendel (1822–1884), studied genetics, and his principles are the foundation for modern genetics. Mendel used his spare time to grow a variety of peas at the monastery. One of his many experiments involved crossbreeding peas that had smooth yellow seeds with peas that had wrinkled green seeds. He noticed that the results occurred with regularity. That is, some of the offspring had smooth yellow seeds, some had smooth green seeds, some had wrinkled yellow seeds, and some had wrinkled green seeds. Furthermore, after several experiments, the percentages of each type seemed to remain approximately the same. Mendel formulated his theory based on the assumption of dominant and recessive traits and tried to predict the results. He then crossbred his peas and examined 556 seeds over the next generation.

Finally, he compared the actual results with the theoretical results to see if his theory was correct. To do this, he used a "simple" chi-square test, which is explained in this chapter. See Statistics Today—Revisited at the end of this chapter.

Source: J. Hodges, Jr., D. Krech, and R. Crutchfield, *Stat Lab, An Empirical Introduction to Statistics* (New York: McGraw-Hill, 1975), pp. 228–229. Used with permission.

Introduction

The chi-square distribution was used in Chapters 7 and 8 to find a confidence interval for a variance or standard deviation and to test a hypothesis about a single variance or standard deviation.

It can also be used for tests concerning *frequency distributions,* such as "If a sample of buyers is given a choice of automobile colors, will each color be selected with the same frequency?" The chi-square distribution can be used to test the *independence* of two variables, for example, "Are senators' opinions on gun control independent of party affiliations?" That is, do the Republicans feel one way and the Democrats feel differently, or do they have the same opinion?

The chi-square distribution can be used to test the *homogeneity of proportions.* For example, is the proportion of high school seniors who attend college immediately after graduating the same for the northern, southern, eastern, and western parts of the United States?

The chi-square test can also be used to test the normality of a variable.

In addition to the chi-square test, this chapter also explains another use for the F test. The F test, used to compare two variances shown in Chapter 9, can also be used to compare three or more means. This technique is called *analysis of variance* or *ANOVA.* (*Note:* The F test can also be used to test the equality of two means. But since it is equivalent to the t test in this case, the t test is usually used instead of the F test when there are only two means.) For example, suppose a researcher wishes to see whether the means of the time it takes three groups of students to solve a computer problem using FORTRAN, BASIC, and PASCAL are different. The researcher will use the ANOVA technique for this test. The z and t tests should not be used when three or more means are compared, for reasons given later in this chapter.

11–1

Objective 1

Test a distribution for goodness of fit, using chi-square.

Historical Note

Karl Pearson (1857–1936) first used the chi-square distribution as a goodness-of-fit test for data. He developed many types of descriptive graphs and gave them unusual names such as stigmograms, topograms, stereograms, and radiograms.

Test for Goodness of Fit

In addition to being used to test a single variance, the chi-square statistic can be used to see whether a frequency distribution fits a specific pattern. For example, to meet customer demands, a manufacturer of running shoes may wish to see whether buyers show a preference for a specific style. A traffic engineer may wish to see whether accidents occur more often on some days than on others, so that she can increase police patrols accordingly. An emergency service may want to see whether it receives more calls at certain times of the day than at others, so that it can provide adequate staffing.

When you are testing to see whether a frequency distribution fits a specific pattern, you can use the chi-square **goodness-of-fit test.** For example, suppose as a market analyst you wished to see whether consumers have any preference among five flavors of a new fruit soda. A sample of 100 people provided these data:

Cherry	Strawberry	Orange	Lime	Grape
32	28	16	14	10

If there were no preference, you would expect each flavor to be selected with equal frequency. In this case, the equal frequency is $100/5 = 20$. That is, *approximately* 20 people would select each flavor.

Since the frequencies for each flavor were obtained from a sample, these actual frequencies are called the **observed frequencies.** The frequencies obtained by calculation (as if there were no preference) are called the **expected frequencies.** A completed table for the test is shown.

Frequency	Cherry	Strawberry	Orange	Lime	Grape
Observed	32	28	16	14	10
Expected	20	20	20	20	20

The observed frequencies will almost always differ from the expected frequencies due to sampling error; that is, the values differ from sample to sample. But the question is: Are these differences significant (a preference exists), or are they due to chance? The chi-square goodness-of-fit test will enable the researcher to determine the answer.

Before computing the test value, you must state the hypotheses. The null hypothesis should be a statement indicating that there is no difference or no change. For this example, the hypotheses are as follows:

H_0: Consumers show no preference for flavors of the fruit soda.

H_1: Consumers show a preference.

In the goodness-of-fit test, the degrees of freedom are equal to the number of categories minus 1. For this example, there are five categories (cherry, strawberry, orange, lime, and grape); hence, the degrees of freedom are $5 - 1 = 4$. This is so because the number of subjects in each of the first four categories is free to vary. But in order for the sum to be 100—the total number of subjects—the number of subjects in the last category is fixed.

Formula for the Chi-Square Goodness-of-Fit Test

$$\chi^2 = \sum \frac{(O - E)^2}{E}$$

with degrees of freedom equal to the number of categories minus 1, and where
O = observed frequency
E = expected frequency

Two assumptions are needed for the goodness-of-fit test. These assumptions are given next.

Assumptions for the Chi-Square Goodness-of-Fit Test

1. The data are obtained from a random sample.
2. The expected frequency for each category must be 5 or more.

This test is a right-tailed test, since when the $O - E$ values are squared, the answer will be positive or zero. This formula is explained in Example 11–1.

Example 11–1

Fruit Soda Flavor Preference

Is there enough evidence to reject the claim that there is no preference in the selection of fruit soda flavors, using the data shown previously? Let $\alpha = 0.05$.

Solution

Step 1 State the hypotheses and identify the claim.

H_0: Consumers show no preference for flavors (claim).

H_1: Consumers show a preference.

Step 2 Find the critical value. The degrees of freedom are $5 - 1 = 4$, and $\alpha = 0.05$. Hence, the critical value from Table G in Appendix C is 9.488.

Step 3 Compute the test value by subtracting the expected value from the corresponding observed value, squaring the result and dividing by the expected value, and finding the sum. The expected value for each category is 20, as shown previously.

$$\chi^2 = \sum \frac{(O - E)^2}{E}$$

$$= \frac{(32 - 20)^2}{20} + \frac{(28 - 20)^2}{20} + \frac{(16 - 20)^2}{20} + \frac{(14 - 20)^2}{20} + \frac{(10 - 20)^2}{20}$$

$$= 18.0$$

Step 4   Make the decision. The decision is to reject the null hypothesis, since $18.0 > 9.488$, as shown in Figure 11–1.

Figure 11–1

Critical and Test Values for Example 11–1

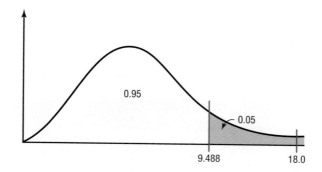

Step 5   Summarize the results. There is enough evidence to reject the claim that consumers show no preference for the flavors.

To get some idea of why this test is called the goodness-of-fit test, examine graphs of the observed values and expected values. See Figure 11–2. From the graphs, you can see whether the observed values and expected values are close together or far apart.

Figure 11–2

Graphs of the Observed and Expected Values for Soda Flavors

When the observed values and expected values are close together, the chi-square test value will be small. Then the decision will be to not reject the null hypothesis—hence, there is "a good fit." See Figure 11–3(a). When the observed values and the expected values are far apart, the chi-square test value will be large. Then the null hypothesis will be rejected—hence, there is "not a good fit." See Figure 11–3(b).

Figure 11–3

Results of the
Goodness-of-Fit Test

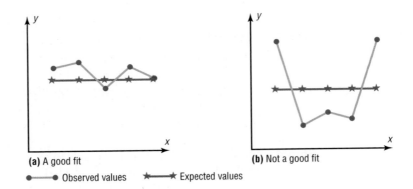

(a) A good fit

(b) Not a good fit

●———● Observed values   ★———★ Expected values

The steps for the chi-square goodness-of-fit test are summarized in this Procedure Table.

Procedure Table

The Chi-Square Goodness-of-Fit Test

Step 1 State the hypotheses and identify the claim.

Step 2 Find the critical value. The test is always right-tailed.

Step 3 Compute the test value.

Find the sum of the $\dfrac{(O - E)^2}{E}$ values.

Step 4 Make the decision.

Step 5 Summarize the results.

When there is perfect agreement between the observed and the expected values, $\chi^2 = 0$. Also, χ^2 can never be negative. Finally, the test is right-tailed because "H_0: Good fit" and "H_1: Not a good fit" mean that χ^2 will be small in the first case and large in the second case.

Example 11–2

Retired Senior Executives Return to Work

The Russel Reynold Association surveyed retired senior executives who had returned to work. They found that after returning to work, 38% were employed by another organization, 32% were self-employed, 23% were either freelancing or consulting, and 7% had formed their own companies. To see if these percentages are consistent with those of Allegheny County residents, a local researcher surveyed 300 retired executives who had returned to work and found that 122 were working for another company, 85 were self-employed, 76 were either freelancing or consulting, and 17 had formed their own companies. At $\alpha = 0.10$, test the claim that the percentages are the same for those people in Allegheny County.

Source: Michael L. Shook and Robert D. Shook, *The Book of Odds.*

Solution

Step 1   State the hypotheses and identify the claim.

H_0: The retired executives who returned to work are distributed as follows: 38% are employed by another organization, 32% are self-employed, 23% are either freelancing or consulting, and 7% have formed their own companies (claim).

H_1: The distribution is not the same as stated in the null hypothesis.

Step 2   Find the critical value. Since $\alpha = 0.10$ and the degrees of freedom are $4 - 1 = 3$, the critical value is 6.251.

Step 3   Compute the test value. The expected values are computed as follows:

$0.38 \times 300 = 114$ $0.23 \times 300 = 69$
$0.32 \times 300 = 96$ $0.07 \times 300 = 21$

$$\chi^2 = \sum \frac{(O - E)^2}{E}$$
$$= \frac{(122 - 114)^2}{114} + \frac{(85 - 96)^2}{96} + \frac{(76 - 69)^2}{69} + \frac{(17 - 21)^2}{21}$$
$$= 3.2939$$

Step 4   Make the decision. Since $3.2939 < 6.251$, the decision is not to reject the null hypothesis. See Figure 11–4.

Figure 11–4

Critical and Test Values
for Example 11–2

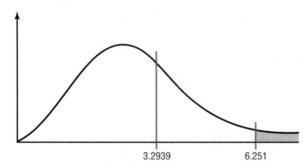

3.2939   6.251

Step 5   Summarize the results. There is not enough evidence to reject the claim. It can be concluded that the percentages are not significantly different from those given in the null hypothesis.

Example 11–3   ### Firearm Deaths

A researcher read that firearm-related deaths for people aged 1 to 18 were distributed as follows: 74% were accidental, 16% were homicides, and 10% were suicides. In her district, there were 68 accidental deaths, 27 homicides, and 5 suicides during the past year. At $\alpha = 0.10$, test the claim that the percentages are equal.

Source: Disease Control and Prevention.

Solution

Step 1   State the hypotheses and identify the claim:

H_0: The deaths due to firearms for people aged 1 through 18 are distributed as follows: 74% accidental, 16% homicides, and 10% suicides (claim).

H_1: The distribution is not the same as stated in the null hypothesis.

Step 2   Find the critical value. Since $\alpha = 0.10$ and the degrees of freedom are $3 - 1 = 2$, the critical value is 4.605.

Step 3   Compute the test value. The expected values are as follows:

$$0.74 \times 100 = 74$$
$$0.16 \times 100 = 16$$
$$0.10 \times 100 = 10$$

$$\chi^2 = \sum \frac{(O - E)^2}{E}$$
$$= \frac{(68 - 74)^2}{74} + \frac{(27 - 16)^2}{16} + \frac{(5 - 10)^2}{10}$$
$$= 10.549$$

Step 4   Reject the null hypothesis, since $10.549 > 4.605$, as shown in Figure 11–5.

Figure 11–5

Critical and Test Values
for Example 11–3

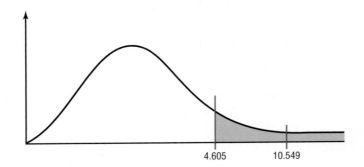

Step 5   Summarize the results. There is enough evidence to reject the claim that the distribution is 74% accidental, 16% homicides, and 10% suicides.

The *P*-value method of hypothesis testing can also be used for the chi-square tests explained in this chapter. The *P*-values for chi-square are found in Table G in Appendix C. The method used to find the *P*-value for a chi-square test value is the same as the method shown in Section 8–5. The *P*-value for $\chi^2 = 3.2939$ with d.f. = 3 (for the data in Example 11–2) is greater than 0.10 since 6.251 is the value in Table G for $\alpha = 0.10$. (The *P*-value obtained from a calculator is 0.348.) Hence *P*-value > 0.10. The decision is to not reject the null hypothesis, which is consistent with the decision made in Example 11–2 using the traditional method of hypothesis testing.

For use of the chi-square goodness-of-fit test, statisticians have determined that the expected frequencies should be at least 5, as stated in the assumptions. The reasoning is as follows: The chi-square distribution is continuous, whereas the goodness-of-fit test is discrete. However, the continuous distribution is a good approximation and can be used when the expected value for each class is at least 5. If an expected frequency of a class is less than 5, then that class can be combined with another class so that the expected frequency is 5 or more.

Test of Normality (Optional)

The chi-square goodness-of-fit test can be used to test a variable to see if it is normally distributed. The null hypotheses are

H_0: The variable is normally distributed.

H_1: The variable is not normally distributed.

The procedure is somewhat complicated. It involves finding the expected frequencies for each class of a frequency distribution by using the standard normal distribution. Then the actual frequencies (i.e., observed frequencies) are compared to the expected frequencies, using the chi-square goodness-of-fit test. If the observed frequencies are close in value to the expected frequencies, the chi-square test value will be small, and the null hypothesis cannot be rejected. In this case, it can be concluded that the variable is approximately normally distributed.

On the other hand, if there is a large difference between the observed frequencies and the expected frequencies, the chi-square test value will be larger, and the null hypothesis can be rejected. In this case, it can be concluded that the variable is not normally distributed. Example 11–4 illustrates the procedure for the chi-square test of normality. To find the areas in the examples, you might want to review Section 6–2.

Example 11–4 shows how to do the calculations.

Example 11–4

Test of Normality

Use chi-square to determine if the variable shown in the frequency distribution is normally distributed. Use $\alpha = 0.05$.

Boundaries	Frequency
89.5–104.5	24
104.5–119.5	62
119.5–134.5	72
134.5–149.5	26
149.5–164.5	12
164.5–179.5	4
	200

Solution

H_0: The variable is normally distributed.

H_1: The variable is not normally distributed.

First find the mean and standard deviation of the variable. Then find the area under the standard normal distribution, using z values and Table E for each class. Find the expected frequencies for each class by multiplying the area by 200. Finally, find the chi-square test value by using the formula $\chi^2 = \sum \dfrac{(O - E)^2}{E}$.

Boundaries	f	X_m	$f \cdot X_m$	$f \cdot X_m^2$
89.5–104.5	24	97	2,328	225,816
104.5–119.5	62	112	6,944	777,728
119.5–134.5	72	127	9,144	1,161,288
134.5–149.5	26	142	3,692	524,264
149.5–164.5	12	157	1,884	295,788
164.5–179.5	4	172	688	118,336
	200		24,680	3,103,220

$$\bar{X} = \frac{24{,}680}{200} = 123.4$$

$$s = \sqrt{\frac{200(3{,}103{,}220) - 24{,}680^2}{200(199)}} = \sqrt{290} = 17.03$$

Unusual Stat

Drinking milk may lower your risk of stroke. A 22-year study of men over 55 found that only 4% of men who drank 16 ounces of milk every day suffered a stroke, compared with 8% of the nonmilk drinkers.

The area to the left of $x = 104.5$ is found as

$$z = \frac{104.5 - 123.4}{17.03} = -1.11$$

The area for $z < -1.11$ is 0.1335.

The area between 104.5 and 119.5 is found as

$$z = \frac{119.5 - 123.4}{17.03} = -0.23$$

The area for $-1.11 < z < -0.23$ is $0.4090 - 0.1335 = 0.2755$.

The area between 119.5 and 134.5 is found as

$$z = \frac{134.5 - 123.4}{17.03} = 0.65$$

The area for $-0.23 < z < 0.65$ is $0.7422 - 0.4090 = 0.3332$.

The area between 134.5 and 149.5 is found as

$$z = \frac{149.5 - 123.4}{17.03} = 1.53$$

The area for $0.65 < z < 1.53$ is $0.9370 - 0.7422 = 0.1948$.

The area between 149.5 and 164.5 is found as

$$z = \frac{164.5 - 123.4}{17.03} = 2.41$$

The area for $1.53 < z < 2.41$ is $0.9920 - 0.9370 = 0.0550$.

The area to the right of $x = 164.5$ is found as

$$z = \frac{164.5 - 123.4}{17.03} = 2.41$$

The area is $1.0000 - 0.9920 = 0.0080$.

The expected frequencies are found by

$$0.1335 \cdot 200 = 26.7$$
$$0.2755 \cdot 200 = 55.1$$
$$0.3332 \cdot 200 = 66.64$$
$$0.1948 \cdot 200 = 38.96$$
$$0.0550 \cdot 200 = 11.0$$
$$0.0080 \cdot 200 = 1.6$$

Note: Since the expected frequency for the last category is less than 5, it can be combined with the previous category.

The χ^2 is found by

O	24	62	72	26	16
E	26.7	55.1	66.64	38.96	12.6

$$\chi^2 = \frac{(24 - 26.7)^2}{26.7} + \frac{(62 - 55.1)^2}{55.1} + \frac{(72 - 66.64)^2}{66.64} + \frac{(26 - 38.96)^2}{38.96}$$
$$+ \frac{(16 - 12.6)^2}{12.6}$$
$$= 6.797$$

The C.V. with d.f. $= 4$ and $\alpha = 0.05$ is 9.488, so the null hypothesis is not rejected. Hence, the distribution can be considered approximately normal.

Applying the Concepts **11–1**

Never the Same Amounts

M&M/Mars, the makers of Skittles candies, states that the flavor blend is 20% for each flavor. Skittles is a combination of lemon, lime, orange, strawberry, and grape flavored candies. The following data list the results of four randomly selected bags of Skittles and their flavor blends. Use the data to answer the questions.

			Flavor		
Bag	**Green**	**Orange**	**Red**	**Purple**	**Yellow**
1	7	20	10	7	14
2	20	5	5	13	17
3	4	16	13	21	4
4	12	9	16	3	17
Total	43	50	44	44	52

1. Are the variables quantitative or qualitative?

2. What type of test can be used to compare the observed values to the expected values?

3. Perform a chi-square test on the total values.

4. What hypotheses did you use?

5. What were the degrees of freedom for the test? What is the critical value?

6. What is your conclusion?

See page 621 for the answers.

Exercises 11–1

1. How does the goodness-of-fit test differ from the chi-square variance test?

2. How are the degrees of freedom computed for the goodness-of-fit test?

3. How are the expected values computed for the goodness-of-fit test?

4. When the expected frequencies are less than 5 for a specific class, what should be done so that you can use the goodness-of-fit test?

For Exercises 5 through 19, perform these steps.

   a. State the hypotheses and identify the claim.

   b. Find the critical value.

   c. Compute the test value.

   d. Make the decision.

   e. Summarize the results.

Use the traditional method of hypothesis testing unless otherwise specified.

5. Home-Schooled Student Activities Students who are home-schooled often attend their local schools to participate in various types of activities such as sports or musical ensembles. According to the government, 82% of home-schoolers receive their education entirely at home, while 12% attend school up to 9 hours per week and 6% spend from 9 to 25 hours per week at school. A survey of 85 students who are home-schooled revealed the following information about where they receive their education.

Entirely at home	Up to 9 hours	9 to 25 hours
50	25	10

At $\alpha = 0.05$, is there sufficient evidence to conclude that the proportions differ from those stated by the government?

Source: www.nces.ed.gov

6. Combatting Midday Drowsiness A researcher wishes to see if the five ways (drinking decaffeinated beverages, taking a nap, going for a walk, eating a sugary snack, other) people use to combat midday drowsiness are equally distributed among office workers. A sample of 60 office workers is selected, and the following data are obtained. At $\alpha = 0.10$ can it be concluded that there is no preference? Why would the results be of interest to an employer?

Method	Beverage	Nap	Walk	Snack	Other
Number	21	16	10	8	5

Source: Based on information from Harris Interactive.

7. In a recent study, the following percentages of U.S. retail car sales based on size were reported: 30.6% small, 45% midsize, 7.3% large, and 17.1% luxury. A recent survey of sales in a particular county indicated that of 100 cars sold, 25 were small, 50 were midsize, 10 were large, and 15 were luxury cars. At the 0.05 level of significance, can it be concluded that the proportions differ from those stated in the report?

Source: *World Almanac.*

8. On-Time Performance by Airlines According to the Bureau of Transportation statistics, on-time performance by the airlines is described as follows:

Action	% of Time
On time	70.8
National Aviation System Delay	8.2
Aircraft Arriving Late	9.0
Other (because of weather and other conditions)	12.0

Records of 200 flights for a major airline company showed that 125 planes were on time, 40 were delayed because of weather, 10 because of a National Aviation System delay, and the rest because of arriving late. At $\alpha = 0.05$, do these results differ from the government's statistics?

Source: www.transtats.bts.gov

9. Genetically Modified Food An ABC News poll asked adults whether they felt genetically modified food was safe to eat. Thirty-five percent felt it was safe, 52% felt it was not safe, and 13% had no opinion. A random sample of 120 adults was asked the same question at a local county fair. Forty people felt that genetically modified food was safe, 60 felt that it was not safe, and 20 had no opinion. At the 0.01 level of significance, is there sufficient evidence to conclude that the proportions differ from those reported in the survey?

Source: ABCNews.com Poll, www.pollingreport.com

10. Blood Types Human blood is grouped into four types: A, B, AB, and O. The percents of Americans with each type are as follows: O, 43%; A, 40%; B, 12%; and AB, 5%. At a recent blood drive at a large university, the donors were classified as shown below. At the 0.05 level of significance, is there sufficient evidence to conclude that the proportions differ from those stated above?

O	A	B	AB
60	65	15	10

Source: www.infoplease.com

11. Credit Union Loans *USA TODAY* reported that 21% of loans granted by credit unions were for home mortgages, 39% were for automobile purchases, 20% were for credit card and other unsecured loans, 12% were for real estate other than home loans, and 8% were for other miscellaneous needs. To see if her credit union customers had similar needs, a manager surveyed a random sample of 100 loans and found that 25 were for home mortgages, 44 for automobile purchases, 19 for credit card and unsecured loans, 8 for real estate other than home loans, and 4 for miscellaneous needs. At $\alpha = 0.05$, is the distribution the same as reported in the newspaper?

Source: *USA TODAY.*

12. Ages of Head Start Program Students The Head Start Program provides a wide range of services to low-income children up to the age of 5 and their families. Its goals are to provide services to improve social and learning skills and to improve health and nutrition status so that the participants can begin school on an equal footing with their more advantaged peers. The distribution of ages for participating children is as follows: 4% five-year-olds, 52% four-year-olds, 34% three-year-olds, and 10% under 3 years. When the program was assessed in a particular region, it was found that of the 200 participants, 20 were 5 years old, 120 were 4 years old, 40 were 3 years old, and 20 were under 3 years. Is there sufficient evidence at $\alpha = 0.05$ that the proportions differ from the program's? Use the *P*-value method.

Source: *New York Times Almanac/*www.fedstats.dhhs.gov

13. Payment Preference A *USA TODAY* Snapshot states that 53% of adult shoppers prefer to pay cash for purchases, 30% use checks, 16% use credit cards, and 1% have no preference. The owner of a large store randomly selected 800 shoppers and asked their payment preferences. The results were that 400 paid cash, 210 paid by check, 170 paid with a credit card, and 20 had no preference. At $\alpha = 0.01$, test the claim that the owner's customers have the same preferences as those surveyed.

Source: *USA TODAY.*

14. Federal Prison Populations The population distribution of federal prisons nationwide by serious offenses is the following: violent offenses, 12.6%; property offenses, 8.5%; drug offenses, 60.2%; public order offenses—weapons, 8.2%; immigration, 4.9%; other, 5.6%. A warden wants to see how his prison compares, so he surveys 500 prisoners and finds 64 are violent offenders, 40 are property offenders, 326 are drug offenders, 42 are public order offenders, 25 are immigration offenders, and 3 have other offenses. Can the warden conclude that the percentages are the same for his prison? Use $\alpha = 0.05$.

15. Internet Users A survey was targeted at determining if educational attainment affected Internet use. Randomly selected shoppers at a busy mall were asked if they used the Internet and their highest level of education attained. The results are listed below. Is there sufficient evidence at the 0.05 level of significance that the proportion of Internet users differs for any of the groups?

Graduated college +	Attended college	Did not attend
44	41	40

Source: www.infoplease.com

 16. Education Level and Health Insurance A researcher wishes to see if the number of adults who do not have health insurance is equally distributed among three categories (less than 12 years of education, 12 years of education, more than 12 years of education). A sample of 60 adults who do not have health insurance is selected, and the results are shown. At $\alpha = 0.05$ can it be concluded that the frequencies are not equal? Use the

P-value method. If the null hypothesis is rejected, give a possible reason for this.

Category	Less than 12 years	12 years	More than 12 years
Frequency	29	20	11

Source: U.S. Census Bureau.

17. Paying for Prescriptions A medical researcher wishes to determine if the way people pay for their medical prescriptions is distributed as follows: 60% personal funds, 25% insurance, 15% Medicare. A sample of 50 people found that 32 paid with their own money, 10 paid using insurance, and 8 paid using Medicare. At $\alpha = 0.05$ is the assumption correct? Use the *P*-value method. What would be an implication of the results?

Source: U.S. Health Care Financing.

Extending the Concepts

18. Tossing Coins Three coins are tossed 72 times, and the number of heads is shown. At $\alpha = 0.05$, test the null hypothesis that the coins are balanced and randomly tossed. (*Hint:* Use the binomial distribution.)

No. of heads	0	1	2	3
Frequency	3	10	17	42

19. State Lottery Numbers Select a three-digit state lottery number over a period of 50 days. Count the number of times each digit, 0 through 9, occurs. Test the claim, at $\alpha = 0.05$, that the digits occur at random.

Technology *Step by Step*

MINITAB
Step by Step

Chi-Square Test for Goodness of Fit

For Example 11–1, is there a preference for flavor of soda? There is no menu command to do this directly. Use the calculator.

1. Enter the observed counts into C1 and the expected counts into C2. Name the columns O and E.

2. Select **Calc>Calculator.**

   a) Type **K1** in the Store result in variable.

   b) In the Expression box type the formula **SUM((O-E)**2/E).**

   c) Click [OK]. The chi-square test statistic will be displayed in the constant K1.

   d) Click the Project Manager icon, then navigate to the Worksheet 1>Constants. K1 is unnamed and equal to 18.

Calculate the *P*-Value

3. Select **Calc>Probability Distributions.**

4. Click on Chi-square.

   a) Click the button for Cumulative probability.

   b) In the box for Degrees of freedom type **4.**

   c) Click the button for Input constant, then click in the text box and select K1 in the variable list.

   d) In the text box, Optional storage type **K2.** This is the area to the left of the test statistic. To calculate the *P*-value, we need the complement—the area to the right.

   e) Select **Calc>Calculator,** then type **K3** for the storage variable and **1 − K2** for the expression.

   f) Click [OK]. In the Project Manager you will see K3 = 0.00121341. This is the *P*-value for the test.

Reject the null hypothesis. There is enough evidence in the sample to conclude there is not 20% of each flavor.

TI-83 Plus or TI-84 Plus
Step by Step

Goodness-of-Fit Test

Example TI11–1

This pertains to Example 11–1 from the text. At the 5% significance level, test the claim that there is no preference in the selection of fruit soda flavors for the data.

Frequency	Cherry	Strawberry	Orange	Lime	Grape
Observed	32	28	16	14	10
Expected	20	20	20	20	20

To calculate the test statistic:

1. Enter the observed frequencies in L_1 and the expected frequencies in L_2.

2. Press **2nd [QUIT]** to return to the home screen.

3. Press **2nd [LIST],** move the cursor to MATH, and press **5** for sum(.

4. Type $(L_1 − L_2)^2/L_2)$, then press **ENTER.**

To calculate the *P*-value:

Press **2nd [DISTR]** then press **7** to get χ^2cdf(.   (Use 8 on the TI-84)

For this *P*-value, the χ^2cdf(command has form χ^2cdf(test statistic, ∞, degrees of freedom).

Use E99 for ∞. Type **2nd [EE]** to get the small E.

For this example use χ^2cdf(18, E99,4):

Since *P*-value = 0.001234098 < 0.05 = significance level, reject H_0 and conclude H_1. Therefore, there is enough evidence to reject the claim that consumers show no preference for soda flavors.

Excel
Step by Step

Chi-Square Goodness-of-Fit Test

Excel does not have a procedure to conduct the goodness-of-fit test. However, you may conduct this test using the MegaStat Add-in available on your CD. If you have not installed this add-in, do so, following the instructions from the Chapter 1 Excel Step by Step.

This example pertains to Example 11–1 from the text.

Example XL11–1

Test the claim that there is no preference for soda flavor. Use a significance level of $\alpha = 0.05$. The table of frequencies is shown below.

Frequency	Cherry	Strawberry	Orange	Lime	Grape
Observed	32	28	16	14	10
Expected	20	20	20	20	20

1. Enter the observed frequencies in row 1 (cells: A1 to E1) of a new worksheet.

2. Enter the expected frequencies in row 2 (cells: A2 to E2).

3. From the toolbar, select Add-Ins, **MegaStat>Chi-Square/Crosstab>Goodness of Fit Test.** *Note:* You may need to open MegaStat from the MegaStat.xls file on your computer's hard drive.

4. In the dialog box, type **A1:E1** for the Observed values and **A2:E2** for the Expected values. Then click [OK].

Goodness-of-Fit Test

Observed	Expected	$O - E$	$(O - E)^2/E$	% of chisq
32	20.000	12.000	7.200	40.00
28	20.000	8.000	3.200	17.78
16	20.000	−4.000	0.800	4.44
14	20.000	−6.000	1.800	10.00
10	20.000	−10.000	5.000	27.78
100	100.000	0.000	18.000	100.00

18.00	chi-square
4	df
0.0012	*P*-value

Since the *P*-value is less than the significance level, the null hypothesis is rejected and thus the claim of no preference is supported.

Chi-Square Test for Normality

Example XL11–2

This example refers to Example 11–4. At the 5% significance level, determine if the variable is normally distributed.

Start with the table of observed and expected values:

Observed	24	62	72	26	16
Expected	26.7	55.1	66.64	38.96	12.6

1. Enter the Observed values in row 1 of a new worksheet.

2. Enter the Expected values in row 2.

Note: You may include labels for the observed and expected values in cells A1 and A2, respectively.

3. Select the Formulas tab, then Insert Function.

4. In the Insert Function dialog box, select the Statistical category and the CHITEST function.

5. Type **B1:F1** for the Actual Range and **B2:F2** for the Expected Range, then click [OK].

The *P*-value of 0.1470 is greater than the significance level of 0.05. So we do not reject the null hypothesis. Thus, the distribution of the variable is approximately normal.

11–2

Tests Using Contingency Tables

When data can be tabulated in table form in terms of frequencies, several types of hypotheses can be tested by using the chi-square test.

Two such tests are the independence of variables test and the homogeneity of proportions test. The test of independence of variables is used to determine whether two variables are independent of or related to each other when a single sample is selected. The test of homogeneity of proportions is used to determine whether the proportions for a variable are equal when several samples are selected from different populations. Both tests use the chi-square distribution and a contingency table, and the test value is found in the same way. The independence test will be explained first.

Objective 2

Test two variables for independence, using chi-square.

Test for Independence

The chi-square **independence test** can be used to test the independence of two variables. For example, suppose a new postoperative procedure is administered to a number of patients in a large hospital. The researcher can ask the question, Do the doctors feel differently about this procedure from the nurses, or do they feel basically the same way? Note that the question is not whether they prefer the procedure but whether there is a difference of opinion between the two groups.

To answer this question, a researcher selects a sample of nurses and doctors and tabulates the data in table form, as shown.

Group	Prefer new procedure	Prefer old procedure	No preference
Nurses	100	80	20
Doctors	50	120	30

As the survey indicates, 100 nurses prefer the new procedure, 80 prefer the old procedure, and 20 have no preference; 50 doctors prefer the new procedure, 120 like the old procedure, and 30 have no preference. Since the main question is whether there is a difference in opinion, the null hypothesis is stated as follows:

H_0: The opinion about the procedure is *independent* of the profession.

The alternative hypothesis is stated as follows:

H_1: The opinion about the procedure is *dependent* on the profession.

If the null hypothesis is not rejected, the test means that both professions feel basically the same way about the procedure and the differences are due to chance. If the null hypothesis is rejected, the test means that one group feels differently about the procedure from the other. Remember that rejection does *not* mean that one group favors the procedure and the other does not. Perhaps both groups favor it or both dislike it, but in different proportions.

To test the null hypothesis by using the chi-square independence test, you must compute the expected frequencies, assuming that the null hypothesis is true. These frequencies are computed by using the observed frequencies given in the table.

When data are arranged in table form for the chi-square independence test, the table is called a **contingency table.** The table is made up of R rows and C columns. The table here has two rows and three columns.

Group	Prefer new procedure	Prefer old procedure	No preference
Nurses	100	80	20
Doctors	50	120	30

Note that row and column headings do not count in determining the number of rows and columns.

A contingency table is designated as an $R \times C$ (rows by columns) table. In this case, $R = 2$ and $C = 3$; hence, this table is a 2×3 contingency table. Each block in the table is called a *cell* and is designated by its row and column position. For example, the cell with a frequency of 80 is designated as $C_{1,2}$, or row 1, column 2. The cells are shown below.

	Column 1	Column 2	Column 3
Row 1	$C_{1,1}$	$C_{1,2}$	$C_{1,3}$
Row 2	$C_{2,1}$	$C_{2,2}$	$C_{2,3}$

The degrees of freedom for any contingency table are (rows $-$ 1) times (columns $-$ 1); that is, d.f. $= (R - 1)(C - 1)$. In this case, $(2 - 1)(3 - 1) = (1)(2) = 2$. The reason for this formula for d.f. is that all the expected values except one are free to vary in each row and in each column.

Using the previous table, you can compute the expected frequencies for each block (or cell), as shown next.

1. Find the sum of each row and each column, and find the grand total, as shown.

Group	Prefer new procedure	Prefer old procedure	No preference	Total
Nurses	100	80	20	Row 1 sum 200
Doctors	+50	+120	+30	Row 2 sum 200
Total	150	200	50	400

Column 1 sum   Column 2 sum   Column 3 sum   Grand total

2. For each cell, multiply the corresponding row sum by the column sum and divide by the grand total, to get the expected value:

$$\text{Expected value} = \frac{\text{row sum} \times \text{column sum}}{\text{grand total}}$$

For example, for $C_{1,2}$, the expected value, denoted by $E_{1,2}$, is (refer to the previous tables)

$$E_{1,2} = \frac{(200)(200)}{400} = 100$$

For each cell, the expected values are computed as follows:

$$E_{1,1} = \frac{(200)(150)}{400} = 75 \qquad E_{1,2} = \frac{(200)(200)}{400} = 100 \qquad E_{1,3} = \frac{(200)(50)}{400} = 25$$

$$E_{2,1} = \frac{(200)(150)}{400} = 75 \qquad E_{2,2} = \frac{(200)(200)}{400} = 100 \qquad E_{2,3} = \frac{(200)(50)}{400} = 25$$

The expected values can now be placed in the corresponding cells along with the observed values, as shown.

Group	Prefer new procedure	Prefer old procedure	No preference	Total
Nurses	100 (75)	80 (100)	20 (25)	200
Doctors	50 (75)	120 (100)	30 (25)	200
Total	150	200	50	400

The rationale for the computation of the expected frequencies for a contingency table uses proportions. For $C_{1,1}$ a total of 150 out of 400 people prefer the new procedure. And since there are 200 nurses, you would expect, if the null hypothesis were true, (150/400)(200), or 75, of the nurses to be in favor of the new procedure.

The formula for the test value for the independence test is the same as the one used for the goodness-of-fit test. It is

$$\chi^2 = \sum \frac{(O - E)^2}{E}$$

For the previous example, compute the $(O - E)^2/E$ values for each cell, and then find the sum.

$$\chi^2 = \sum \frac{(O - E)^2}{E}$$

$$= \frac{(100 - 75)^2}{75} + \frac{(80 - 100)^2}{100} + \frac{(20 - 25)^2}{25} + \frac{(50 - 75)^2}{75}$$

$$+ \frac{(120 - 100)^2}{100} + \frac{(30 - 25)^2}{25}$$

$$= 26.67$$

The final steps are to make the decision and summarize the results. This test is always a right-tailed test, and the degrees of freedom are $(R - 1)(C - 1) = (2 - 1)(3 - 1) = 2$. If $\alpha = 0.05$, the critical value from Table G is 5.991. Hence, the decision is to reject the null hypothesis since $26.67 > 5.991$. See Figure 11–6.

Figure 11–6

Critical and Test Values for the Postoperative Procedures Example

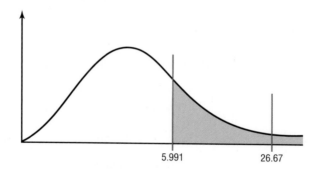

The conclusion is that there is enough evidence to support the claim that opinion is related to (dependent on) profession—that is, that the doctors and nurses differ in their opinions about the procedure.

Examples 11–5 and 11–6 illustrate the procedure for the chi-square test of independence.

Example 11–5

College Education and Place of Residence

A sociologist wishes to see whether the number of years of college a person has completed is related to her or his place of residence. A sample of 88 people is selected and classified as shown.

Location	No college	Four-year degree	Advanced degree	Total
Urban	15	12	8	35
Suburban	8	15	9	32
Rural	6	8	7	21
Total	29	35	24	88

At $\alpha = 0.05$, can the sociologist conclude that a person's location is dependent on the number of years of college?

Solution

Step 1   State the hypotheses and identify the claim.

H_0: A person's place of residence is independent of the number of years of college completed.

H_1: A person's place of residence is dependent on the number of years of college completed (claim).

Step 2   Find the critical value. The critical value is 9.488, since the degrees of freedom are $(3 - 1)(3 - 1) = (2)(2) = 4$.

Step 3   Compute the test value. To compute the test value, first compute the expected values.

$$E_{1,1} = \frac{(35)(29)}{88} = 11.53 \qquad E_{1,2} = \frac{(35)(35)}{88} = 13.92 \qquad E_{1,3} = \frac{(35)(24)}{88} = 9.55$$

$$E_{2,1} = \frac{(32)(29)}{88} = 10.55 \qquad E_{2,2} = \frac{(32)(35)}{88} = 12.73 \qquad E_{2,3} = \frac{(32)(24)}{88} = 8.73$$

$$E_{3,1} = \frac{(21)(29)}{88} = 6.92 \qquad E_{3,2} = \frac{(21)(35)}{88} = 8.35 \qquad E_{3,3} = \frac{(21)(24)}{88} = 5.73$$

The completed table is shown.

Location	No college	Four-year degree	Advanced degree	Total
Urban	15 (11.53)	12 (13.92)	8 (9.55)	35
Suburban	8 (10.55)	15 (12.73)	9 (8.73)	32
Rural	6 (6.92)	8 (8.35)	7 (5.73)	21
Total	29	35	24	88

Then the chi-square test value is

$$\chi^2 = \sum \frac{(O - E)^2}{E}$$

$$= \frac{(15 - 11.53)^2}{11.53} + \frac{(12 - 13.92)^2}{13.92} + \frac{(8 - 9.55)^2}{9.55}$$

$$+ \frac{(8 - 10.55)^2}{10.55} + \frac{(15 - 12.73)^2}{12.73} + \frac{(9 - 8.73)^2}{8.73}$$

$$+ \frac{(6 - 6.92)^2}{6.92} + \frac{(8 - 8.35)^2}{8.35} + \frac{(7 - 5.73)^2}{5.73}$$

$$= 3.01$$

Step 4   Make the decision. The decision is not to reject the null hypothesis since $3.01 < 9.488$. See Figure 11–7.

Figure 11–7

Critical and Test Values for Example 11–5

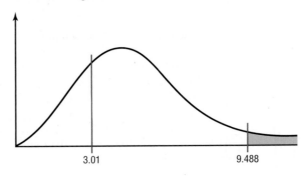

Step 5 Summarize the results. There is not enough evidence to support the claim that a person's place of residence is dependent on the number of years of college completed.

Example 11–6

Alcohol and Gender

A researcher wishes to determine whether there is a relationship between the gender of an individual and the amount of alcohol consumed. A sample of 68 people is selected, and the following data are obtained.

Alcohol consumption

Gender	Low	Moderate	High	Total
Male	10	9	8	27
Female	13	16	12	41
Total	23	25	20	68

At $\alpha = 0.10$, can the researcher conclude that alcohol consumption is related to gender?

Solution

Step 1 State the hypotheses and identify the claim.

H_0: The amount of alcohol that a person consumes is independent of the individual's gender.

H_1: The amount of alcohol that a person consumes is dependent on the individual's gender (claim).

Step 2 Find the critical value. The critical value is 4.605, since the degrees of freedom are $(2 - 1)(3 - 1) = 2$.

Step 3 Compute the test value. First, compute the expected values.

$$E_{1,1} = \frac{(27)(23)}{68} = 9.13 \qquad E_{1,2} = \frac{(27)(25)}{68} = 9.93 \qquad E_{1,3} = \frac{(27)(20)}{68} = 7.94$$

$$E_{2,1} = \frac{(41)(23)}{68} = 13.87 \qquad E_{2,2} = \frac{(41)(25)}{68} = 15.07 \qquad E_{2,3} = \frac{(41)(20)}{68} = 12.06$$

The completed table is shown.

Alcohol consumption

Gender	Low	Moderate	High	Total
Male	10 (9.13)	9 (9.93)	8 (7.94)	27
Female	13 (13.87)	16 (15.07)	12 (12.06)	41
Total	23	25	20	68

Then the test value is

$$\chi^2 = \sum \frac{(O - E)^2}{E}$$
$$= \frac{(10 - 9.13)^2}{9.13} + \frac{(9 - 9.93)^2}{9.93} + \frac{(8 - 7.94)^2}{7.94}$$
$$+ \frac{(13 - 13.87)^2}{13.87} + \frac{(16 - 15.07)^2}{15.07} + \frac{(12 - 12.06)^2}{12.06}$$
$$= 0.283$$

Step 4   Make the decision. The decision is to not reject the null hypothesis, since $0.283 < 4.605$. See Figure 11–8.

Figure 11–8

Critical and Test Values
for Example 11–6

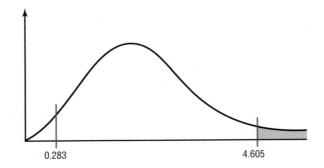

Step 5   Summarize the results. There is not enough evidence to support the claim that the amount of alcohol a person consumes is dependent on the individual's gender.

Objective **3**

Test proportions for
homogeneity, using
chi-square.

Interesting Facts

Water is the most
critical nutrient in your
body. It is needed for
just about everything
that happens. Water is
lost fast: 2 cups daily
is lost just exhaling,
10 cups through
normal waste and
body cooling, and 1
to 2 quarts per hour
running, biking, or
working out.

Test for Homogeneity of Proportions

The second chi-square test that uses a contingency table is called the **homogeneity of proportions test.** In this situation, samples are selected from several different populations, and the researcher is interested in determining whether the proportions of elements that have a common characteristic are the same for each population. The sample sizes are specified in advance, making either the row totals or column totals in the contingency table known before the samples are selected. For example, a researcher may select a sample of 50 freshmen, 50 sophomores, 50 juniors, and 50 seniors and then find the proportion of students who are smokers in each level. The researcher will then compare the proportions for each group to see if they are equal. The hypotheses in this case would be

H_0: $p_1 = p_2 = p_3 = p_4$

H_1: At least one proportion is different from the others.

If the researcher does not reject the null hypothesis, it can be assumed that the proportions are equal and the differences in them are due to chance. Hence, the proportion of students who smoke is the same for grade levels freshmen through senior. When the null hypothesis is rejected, it can be assumed that the proportions are not all equal. The computational procedure is the same as that for the test of independence shown in Example 11–7.

Example 11–7   ## Lost Luggage on Airline Flights

A researcher selected 100 passengers from each of 3 airlines and asked them if the airline had lost their luggage on their last flight. The data are shown in the table. At $\alpha = 0.05$, test the claim that the proportion of passengers from each airline who lost luggage on the flight is the same for each airline.

	Airline 1	Airline 2	Airline 3	Total
Yes	10	7	4	21
No	90	93	96	279
	100	100	100	300

Solution

Step 1 State the hypotheses.

H_0: $p_1 = p_2 = p_3$

H_1: At least one mean differs from the other.

Step 2 Find the critical value. The formula for the degrees of freedom is the same as before: (rows − 1)(columns − 1) = (2 − 1)(3 − 1) = 1(2) = 2. The critical value is 5.991.

Step 3 Compute the test value. First compute the expected values.

$$E_{1,1} = \frac{(21)(100)}{300} = 7 \qquad E_{1,2} = \frac{(21)(100)}{300} = 7 \qquad E_{1,3} = \frac{(21)(100)}{300} = 7$$

$$E_{2,1} = \frac{(279)(100)}{300} = 93 \qquad E_{2,2} = \frac{(279)(100)}{300} = 93 \qquad E_{2,3} = \frac{(279)(100)}{300} = 93$$

The completed table is shown here.

	Airline 1	Airline 2	Airline 3	Total
Yes	10 (7)	7 (7)	4 (7)	21
No	90 (93)	93 (93)	96 (93)	279
	100	100	100	300

$$\chi^2 = \sum \frac{(O - E)^2}{E}$$

$$= \frac{(10 - 7)^2}{7} + \frac{(7 - 7)^2}{7} + \frac{(4 - 7)^2}{7} + \frac{(90 - 93)^2}{93} + \frac{(93 - 93)^2}{93} + \frac{(96 - 93)^2}{93} = 2.765$$

Step 4 Make the decision. Do not reject the null hypothesis since 2.765 < 5.991.

Step 5 Summarize the results. There is not enough evidence to reject the claim that the proportions are equal. Hence it seems that there is no difference in the proportions of the luggage lost by each airline.

When the degrees of freedom for a contingency table are equal to 1—that is, the table is a 2 × 2 table—some statisticians suggest using the *Yates correction for continuity*. The formula for the test is then

$$\chi^2 = \sum \frac{(|O - E| - 0.5)^2}{E}$$

Since the chi-square test is already conservative, most statisticians agree that the Yates correction is not necessary. (See Exercise 33 in Exercises 11–2.)

The steps for the chi-square independence and homogeneity tests are summarized in this Procedure Table.

Procedure Table

The Chi-Square Independence and Homogeneity Tests

Step 1   State the hypotheses and identify the claim.

Step 2   Find the critical value in the right tail. Use Table G.

Step 3   Compute the test value. To compute the test value, first find the expected values. For each cell of the contingency table, use the formula

$$E = \frac{(\text{row sum})(\text{column sum})}{\text{grand total}}$$

to get the expected value. To find the test value, use the formula

$$\chi^2 = \sum \frac{(O - E)^2}{E}$$

Step 4   Make the decision.

Step 5   Summarize the results.

The assumptions for the two chi-square tests are given next.

Assumptions for the Chi-Square Independence and Homogeneity Tests

1. The data are obtained from a random sample.
2. The expected value in each cell must be 5 or more.

If the expected values are not 5 or more, combine categories.

Applying the Concepts 11–2

Satellite Dishes in Restricted Areas

The Senate is expected to vote on a bill to allow the installation of satellite dishes of any size in deed-restricted areas. The House had passed a similar bill. An opinion poll was taken to see if how a person felt about satellite dish restrictions was related to his or her age. A chi-square test was run, creating the following computer-generated information.

Degrees of freedom d.f. = 6
Test statistic $\chi^2 = 61.25$
Critical value C.V. = 12.6
P-value = 0.00
Significance level = 0.05

	18–29	30–49	50–64	65 and up
For	96 (79.5)	96 (79.5)	90 (79.5)	36 (79.5)
Against	201 (204.75)	189 (204.75)	195 (204.75)	234 (204.75)
Don't know	3 (15.75)	15 (15.75)	15 (15.75)	30 (15.75)

1. Which number from the output is compared to the significance level to check if the null hypothesis should be rejected?

2. Which number from the output gives the probability of a type I error that is calculated from your sample data?

3. Was a right-, left-, or two-tailed test run? Why?

4. Can you tell how many rows and columns there were by looking at the degrees of freedom?

5. Does increasing the sample size change the degrees of freedom?

6. What are your conclusions? Look at the observed and expected frequencies in the table to draw some of your own specific conclusions about response and age.

7. What would your conclusions be if the level of significance were initially set at 0.10?

8. Does chi-square tell you which cell's observed and expected frequencies are significantly different?

See pages 621 and 622 for the answers.

Exercises 11–2

1. How is the chi-square independence test similar to the goodness-of-fit test? How is it different?

2. How are the degrees of freedom computed for the independence test?

3. Generally, how would the null and alternative hypotheses be stated for the chi-square independence test?

4. What is the name of the table used in the independence test?

5. How are the expected values computed for each cell in the table?

6. Explain how the chi-square independence test differs from the chi-square homogeneity of proportions test.

7. How are the null and alternative hypotheses stated for the test of homogeneity of proportions?

For Exercises 8 through 31, perform the following steps.

a. State the hypotheses and identify the claim.

b. Find the critical value.

c. Compute the test value.

d. Make the decision.

e. Summarize the results.

Use the traditional method of hypothesis testing unless otherwise specified.

 8. TV and Radio Stations Is there sufficient evidence at the 0.05 level of significance to conclude that a relationship exists between the city and the number of television and radio stations that it has?

	TV stations	Radio stations
Albuquerque, N. Mex.	13	32
Boston, Mass.	12	21
St. Petersburg, Fla.	17	41
Minneapolis, Minn.	7	30
Toledo, Ohio	6	22

Source: *World Almanac.*

9. **Endangered or Threatened Species** Can you conclude a relationship between the class of vertebrate and whether it is endangered or threatened? Use the 0.05 level of significance. Is there a different result for the 0.01 level of significance?

	Mammal	Bird	Reptile	Amphibian	Fish
Endangered	68	76	14	13	76
Threatened	13	15	23	10	61

Source: www.infoplease.com

10. **Women in the Military** This table lists the numbers of officers and enlisted personnel for women in the military. At $\alpha = 0.05$, is there sufficient evidence to conclude that a relationship exists between rank and branch of the Armed Forces?

	Officers	Enlisted
Army	10,791	62,491
Navy	7,816	42,750
Marine Corps	932	9,525
Air Force	11,819	54,344

Source: *New York Times Almanac.*

11. **Composition of State Legislatures** Is the composition of state legislatures in the House of

Representatives related to the specific state?
Use $\alpha = 0.05$.

	Democrats	Republicans
Pennsylvania	100	103
Ohio	39	59
West Virginia	75	25
Maryland	106	35

Source: *New York Times Almanac.*

12. Population and Age Is the size of the population by age related to the state that it's in? Use $\alpha = 0.05$. (Population values are in thousands.)

	Under 5	5–17	18–24	25–44	45–64	65+
Pennsylvania	721	2140	1025	3515	2702	1899
Ohio	740	2104	1065	3359	2487	1501

Source: *New York Times Almanac.*

13. Private Life Occupations of State Legislators It is always interesting to see what occupations legislators hold in private life. Can it be concluded that the session of Congress and the occupations of the legislators are dependent? Use $\alpha = 0.05$.

	109th	108th	107th
Agriculture	5	5	6
Business	30	25	24
Education	12	12	16
Law	58	59	53
Medicine	4	3	3

14. Information Gathering and Educational Background An instructor wishes to see if the way people obtain information is independent of their educational background. A survey of 400 high school and college graduates yielded this information. At $\alpha = 0.05$, test the claim that the way people obtain information is independent of their educational background.

	Television	Newspapers	Other sources
High school	159	90	51
College	27	42	31

Source: *USA TODAY.*

15. Student Majors at Colleges The table below shows the number of students (in thousands) participating in various programs at both two-year and four-year institutions. At $\alpha = 0.05$, can it be concluded that there is a relationship between program of study and type of institution?

	Two-year	Four-year
Agriculture and related sciences	36	52
Criminal justice	210	231
Foreign languages and literature	28	59
Mathematics and statistics	28	63

Source: *Time Almanac.*

16. Organ Transplantation Listed below is information regarding organ transplantation for three different years. Based on these data, is there sufficient evidence at $\alpha = 0.01$ to conclude that a relationship exists between year and type of transplant?

Year	Heart	Kidney/Pancreas	Lung
2003	2056	870	1085
2004	2016	880	1173
2005	2127	903	1408

Source: www.infoplease.com

17. Movie Rental and Age A study is being conducted to determine whether the age of the customer is related to the type of movie he or she rents. A sample of renters gives the data shown here. At $\alpha = 0.10$, is the type of movie selected related to the customer's age?

	Type of movie		
Age	Documentary	Comedy	Mystery
12–20	14	9	8
21–29	15	14	9
30–38	9	21	39
39–47	7	22	17
48 and over	6	38	12

18. Record CDs Sold Are the sales of CDs (in thousands) by genre related to the year in which the sales occurred? Use the 0.05 level of significance.

Year	Classical	Jazz	Soundtracks
2005	15,875	17,139	22,849
2004	18,686	18,794	27,367

Source: *Time Almanac.*

19. Ballpark Snacks and Gender A survey at a ballpark shows this selection of snacks purchased. At $\alpha = 0.10$, is the snack chosen independent of the gender of the consumer?

	Snack		
Gender	Hot dog	Peanuts	Popcorn
Male	12	21	19
Female	13	8	25

20. Effectiveness of New Drug To test the effectiveness of a new drug, a researcher gives one group of individuals the new drug and another group a placebo. The results of the study are shown here. At $\alpha = 0.10$, can the researcher conclude that the drug is effective? Use the *P*-value method.

Medication	Effective	Not effective
Drug	32	9
Placebo	12	18

21. Recreational Reading and Gender A book publisher wishes to determine whether there is a difference in the type of book selected by males and females for recreational reading. A random sample provides the data given here. At $\alpha = 0.05$, test the claim that the type of book selected is independent of the gender of the individual. Use the P-value method.

Gender	Type of book		
	Mystery	**Romance**	**Self-help**
Male	243	201	191
Female	135	149	202

22. Foreign Language Speaking Dorms A local college recently made the news by offering foreign language speaking dorm rooms to its students. When questioned at another school, 50 students from each class responded as shown. At $\alpha = 0.05$, is there sufficient evidence to conclude that the proportions of students favoring foreign language speaking dorms are not the same for each class?

	Freshmen	**Sophomores**	**Juniors**	**Seniors**
Yes (favor)	10	15	20	22
No	40	35	30	28

23. Youth Physical Fitness According to a recent survey, 64% of Americans between the ages of 6 and 17 cannot pass a basic fitness test. A physical education instructor wishes to determine if the percentages of such students in different schools in his school district are the same. He administers a basic fitness test to 120 students in each of four schools. The results are shown here. At $\alpha = 0.05$, test the claim that the proportions who pass the test are equal.

	Southside	**West End**	**East Hills**	**Jefferson**
Passed	49	38	46	34
Failed	71	82	74	86
Total	120	120	120	120

Source: *The Harper's Index Book.*

24. Participation in Market Research Survey An advertising firm has decided to ask 92 customers at each of three local shopping malls if they are willing to take part in a market research survey. According to previous studies, 38% of Americans refuse to take part in such surveys. The results are shown here. At $\alpha = 0.01$, test the claim that the proportions of those who are willing to participate are equal.

	Mall A	**Mall B**	**Mall C**
Will participate	52	45	36
Will not participate	40	47	56
Total	92	92	92

Source: *The Harper's Index Book.*

25. Work Force Distribution A researcher wishes to see if the proportions of workers for each type of job have changed during the last 10 years. A sample of 100 workers is selected, and the results are shown. At $\alpha = 0.05$, test the claim that the proportions have not changed. Can the results be generalized to the population of the United States?

	Services	**Manu-facturing**	**Government**	**Other**
10 years ago	33	13	11	3
Now	18	12	8	2
Total	51	25	19	5

Source: *Pennsylvania Department of Labor and Industry.*

26. Mothers Working Outside the Home According to a recent survey, 59% of Americans aged 8 to 17 would prefer that their mother work outside the home, regardless of what she does now. A school district psychologist decided to select three samples of 60 students each in elementary, middle, and high school to see how the students in her district felt about the issue. At $\alpha = 0.10$, test the claim that the proportions of the students who prefer that their mother have a job are equal.

	Elementary	**Middle**	**High**
Prefers mother work	29	38	51
Prefers mother not work	31	22	9
Total	60	60	60

Source: Daniel Weiss, *100% American.*

27. Volunteer Practices of Students The Bureau of Labor Statistics reported information on volunteers by selected characteristics. They found that 24.4% of the population aged 16 to 24 volunteers a median number of 36 hours per year. A survey of 75 students in each age group revealed the following data on volunteer practices. At $\alpha = 0.05$, can it be concluded that the proportions of volunteers are the same for each group?

	Age				
	18	**19**	**20**	**21**	**22**
Yes (volunteer)	19	18	23	31	13
No	56	57	52	44	62

Source: *Time Almanac.*

28. Fathers in the Delivery Room On average, 79% of American fathers are in the delivery room when their children are born. A physician's assistant surveyed 300 first-time fathers to determine if they had been in the delivery room when their children were born. The results are shown here. At $\alpha = 0.05$, is there enough evidence to reject the claim that the proportions of those who were in the delivery room at the time of birth are the same?

	Hos-pital A	Hos-pital B	Hos-pital C	Hos-pital D
Present	66	60	57	56
Not present	9	15	18	19
Total	75	75	75	75

Source: Daniel Weiss, *100% American.*

 29. Injuries on Monkey Bars A children's playground equipment manufacturer read in a survey that 55% of all U.S. playground injuries occur on the monkey bars. The manufacturer wishes to investigate playground injuries in four different parts of the country to determine if the proportions of accidents on the monkey bars are equal. The results are shown here. At $\alpha = 0.05$, test the claim that the proportions are equal. Use the *P*-value method.

Accidents	North	South	East	West
On monkey bars	15	18	13	16
Not on monkey bars	15	12	17	14
Total	30	30	30	30

Source: Michael D. Shook and Robert L. Shook, *The Book of Odds.*

30. Thanksgiving Travel According to the American Automobile Association, 31 million Americans travel over the Thanksgiving holiday. To determine whether to stay open or not, a national restaurant chain surveyed 125 customers at each of four locations to see if they would be traveling over the holiday. The results are shown here. At $\alpha = 0.10$, test the claim that the proportions of Americans who will travel over the Thanksgiving holiday are equal. Use the *P*-value method.

	Loca-tion A	Loca-tion B	Loca-tion C	Loca-tion D
Will travel	37	52	46	49
Will not travel	88	73	79	76
Total	125	125	125	125

Source: Michael D. Shook and Robert L. Shook, *The Book of Odds.*

 31. Grocery Lists The vice president of a large supermarket chain wished to determine if her customers made a list before going grocery shopping. She surveyed 288 customers in three stores. The results are shown here. At $\alpha = 0.10$, test the claim that the proportions of the customers in the three stores who made a list before going shopping are equal.

	Store A	Store B	Store C
Made list	77	74	68
No list	19	22	28
Total	96	96	96

Source: Daniel Weiss, *100% American.*

Extending the Concepts

32. For a 2 × 2 table, a, b, c, and d are the observed values for each cell, as shown.

a	b
c	d

The chi-square test value can be computed as

$$\chi^2 = \frac{n(ad - bc)^2}{(a + b)(a + c)(c + d)(b + d)}$$

where $n = a + b + c + d$. Compute the χ^2 test value by using the above formula and the formula $\Sigma(O - E)^2/E$, and compare the results for the following table.

12	15
9	23

33. For the contingency table shown in Exercise 32, compute the chi-square test value by using the Yates correction for continuity.

34. When the chi-square test value is significant and there is a relationship between the variables, the strength of this relationship can be measured by using the *contingency coefficient.* The formula for the contingency coefficient is

$$C = \sqrt{\frac{\chi^2}{\chi^2 + n}}$$

where χ^2 is the test value and n is the sum of frequencies of the cells. The contingency coefficient will always be less than 1. Compute the contingency coefficient for Exercises 8 and 20.

Does Color Affect Your Appetite?

It has been suggested that color is related to appetite in humans. For example, if the walls in a restaurant are painted certain colors, it is thought that the customer will eat more food. A study was done at the University of Illinois and the University of Pennsylvania. When people were given six varieties of jellybeans mixed in a bowl or separated by color, they ate about twice as many from the bowl with the mixed jellybeans as from the bowls that were separated by color.

It is thought that when the jellybeans were mixed, people felt that it offered a greater variety of choices, and the variety of choices increased their appetites.

In this case one variable—color—is categorical, and the other variable—amount of jellybeans eaten—is numerical. Could a chi-square goodness-of-fit test be used here? If so, suggest how it could be set up.

Technology *Step by Step*

MINITAB
Step by Step

Tests Using Contingency Tables
Calculate the Chi-Square Test Statistic and *P*-Value

1. Enter the observed frequencies for Example 11–5 into three columns of MINITAB. Name the columns but not the rows. Exclude totals. The complete worksheet is shown.

↓	C1	C2	C3
	NoCollege	Four-year	Advanced
1	15	12	8
2	8	15	9
3	6	8	7

2. Select **Stat>Tables>Chi-Square Test.**

3. Drag the mouse over the three columns in the list.

4. Click [Select]. The three columns will be placed in the Columns box as a sequence, NoCollege through Advanced.

5. Click [OK].

The chi-square test statistic 3.006 has a *P*-value of 0.557. Do not reject the null hypothesis.

There is no relationship between level of education and place of residence.

Chi-Square Test: NoCollege, Four-year, Advanced

```
Expected counts are printed below observed counts
Chi-Square contributions are printed below expected counts

        NoCollege  Four-year  Advanced   Total
   1         15         12          8        35
            11.53      13.92       9.55
             1.041      0.265      0.250

   2          8         15          9        32
            10.55      12.73       8.73
             0.614      0.406      0.009

   3          6          8          7        21
             6.92       8.35       5.73
             0.122      0.015      0.283

Total        29         35         24        88
Chi-Sq = 3.006, DF = 4, P-Value = 0.557
```

Construct a Contingency Table and Calculate the Chi-Square Test Statistic

In Chapter 4 we learned how to construct a contingency table by using gender and smoking status in the Data Bank file described in Appendix D. Are smoking status and gender related? Who is more likely to smoke, men or women?

1. Use **File>Open Worksheet** to open the Data Bank file. Remember do *not* click the file icon.

2. Select **Stat>Tables>Cross Tabulation and Chi-Square.**

3. Double-click Smoking Status for rows and Gender for columns.

4. The Display option for Counts should be checked.

5. Click [Chi-Square].

    a) Check Chi-Square analysis.

    b) Check Expected cell counts.

6. Click [OK] twice.

In the session window the contingency table and the chi-square analysis will be displayed.

Tabulated statistics: SMOKING STATUS, GENDER

```
Rows: SMOKING STATUS    Columns: Gender

               F        M       All

0             25       22        47
           23.50    23.50     47.00

1             18       19        37
           18.50    18.50     37.00

2              7        9        16
            8.00     8.00     16.00

All           50       50       100
           50.00    50.00    100.00
Cell Contents:           Count
                         Expected count

Pearson Chi-Square = 0.469, DF = 2, P-Value = 0.791
```

There is not enough evidence to conclude that smoking is related to gender.

TI-83 Plus or TI-84 Plus
Step by Step

Chi-Square Test for Independence

1. Press **2nd [X^{-1}]** for **MATRIX** and move the cursor to Edit, then press **ENTER.**
2. Enter the number of rows and columns. Then press **ENTER.**
3. Enter the values in the matrix as they appear in the contingency table.
4. Press **STAT** and move the cursor to TESTS. Press **C (ALPHA PRGM)** for χ^2-Test. Make sure the observed matrix is [A] and the expected matrix is [B].
5. Move the cursor to Calculate and press **ENTER.**

Example TI11–2

Using the data shown from Example 11–6, test the claim of independence at $\alpha = 0.10$.

10	9	8
13	16	12

Input	Input	Output

The test value is 0.2808562115. The *P*-value is 0.8689861378. The decision is to not reject the null hypothesis, since this value is greater than 0.10. You can find the expected values by pressing **MATRIX,** moving the cursor to [B], and pressing **ENTER** twice.

Excel
Step by Step

Tests Using Contingency Tables

Excel does not have a procedure to conduct tests using contingency tables without including the expected values. However, you may conduct such tests using the MegaStat Add-in available on your CD. If you have not installed this add-in, do so following the instructions from the Chapter 1 Excel Step by Step.

This example pertains to Example 11–5 from the text.

Example XL11–3

Using a significance level $\alpha = 0.05$, determine whether the number of years of college a person has completed is related to residence.

1. Enter the location variable labels in column A, beginning at cell A2.
2. Enter the categories for the number of years of college in cells B1, C1, and D1, respectively.
3. Enter the observed values in the appropriate block (cell).
4. From the toolbar, select Add-Ins, **MegaStat>Chi-Square/Crosstab>Contingency Table**. *Note:* You may need to open MegaStat from the MegaStat.xls file on your computer's hard drive.
5. In the dialog box, type **A1:D4** for the Input range.
6. Check chi-square from the Output Options.
7. Click [OK].

Chi-Square Contingency Table Test for Independence

	None	4-year	Advanced	Total
Urban	15	12	8	35
Suburban	8	15	9	32
Rural	6	8	7	21
Total	29	35	24	88

```
3.01 chi-square
   4 df
.5569 P-value
```

The results of the test indicate that at the 5% level of significance, there is not enough evidence to conclude that a person's location is dependent on number of years of college.

11–3 Analysis of Variance (ANOVA)

Objective 4

Use the ANOVA technique to determine if there is a significant difference among three or more means.

When an F test is used to test a hypothesis concerning the means of three or more populations, the technique is called **analysis of variance** (commonly abbreviated as **ANOVA**). At first glance, you might think that to compare the means of three or more samples, you can use the t test, comparing two means at a time. But there are several reasons why the t test should not be done.

First, when you are comparing two means at a time, the rest of the means under study are ignored. With the F test, all the means are compared simultaneously. Second, when you are comparing two means at a time and making all pairwise comparisons, the probability of rejecting the null hypothesis when it is true is increased, since the more t tests that are conducted, the greater is the likelihood of getting significant differences by chance alone. Third, the more means there are to compare, the more t tests are needed. For example, for the comparison of 3 means two at a time, 3 t tests are required. For the comparison of 5 means two at a time, 10 tests are required. And for the comparison of 10 means two at a time, 45 tests are required.

Assumptions for the *F* Test for Comparing Three or More Means

1. The populations from which the samples were obtained must be normally or approximately normally distributed.
2. The samples must be independent of one another.
3. The variances of the populations must be equal.

Even though you are comparing three or more means in this use of the F test, *variances* are used in the test instead of means.

With the F test, two different estimates of the population variance are made. The first estimate is called the **between-group variance**, and it involves finding the variance of the means. The second estimate, the **within-group variance**, is made by computing the variance using all the data and is not affected by differences in the means. If there is no difference in the means, the between-group variance estimate will be approximately equal to the within-group variance estimate, and the F test value will be approximately equal to 1. The null hypothesis will not be rejected. However, when the means differ significantly, the between-group variance will be much larger than the within-group variance; the F test value will be significantly greater than 1; and the null hypothesis will be rejected. Since variances are compared, this procedure is called *analysis of variance* (ANOVA).

For a test of the difference among three or more means, the following hypotheses should be used:

H_0: $\mu_1 = \mu_2 = \cdots = \mu_k$

H_1: At least one mean is different from the others.

As stated previously, a significant test value means that there is a high probability that this difference in means is not due to chance, but it does not indicate where the difference lies.

The degrees of freedom for this F test are d.f.N. $= k - 1$, where k is the number of groups, and d.f.D. $= N - k$, where N is the sum of the sample sizes of the groups $N = n_1 + n_2 + \cdots + n_k$. The sample sizes need not be equal. The F test to compare means is always right-tailed.

Examples 11–8 and 11–9 illustrate the computational procedure for the ANOVA technique for comparing three or more means, and the steps are summarized in the Procedure Table shown after the examples.

| Example 11–8 | Lowering Blood Pressure |

A researcher wishes to try three different techniques to lower the blood pressure of individuals diagnosed with high blood pressure. The subjects are randomly assigned to three groups; the first group takes medication, the second group exercises, and the third group follows a special diet. After four weeks, the reduction in each person's blood pressure is recorded. At $\alpha = 0.05$, test the claim that there is no difference among the means. The data are shown.

Medication	Exercise	Diet
10	6	5
12	8	9
9	3	12
15	0	8
13	2	4
$\overline{X}_1 = 11.8$	$\overline{X}_2 = 3.8$	$\overline{X}_3 = 7.6$
$s_1^2 = 5.7$	$s_2^2 = 10.2$	$s_3^2 = 10.3$

Solution

Step 1 State the hypotheses and identify the claim.

H_0: $\mu_1 = \mu_2 = \mu_3$ (claim)

H_1: At least one mean is different from the others.

Step 2 Find the critical value. Since $k = 3$ and $N = 15$,

d.f.N. $= k - 1 = 3 - 1 = 2$

d.f.D. $= N - k = 15 - 3 = 12$

The critical value is 3.89, obtained from Table H in Appendix C with $\alpha = 0.05$.

Step 3 Compute the test value, using the procedure outlined here.

    a. Find the mean and variance of each sample (these values are shown below the data).

    b. Find the grand mean. The *grand mean*, denoted by $\bar{X}_{GM}$, is the mean of all values in the samples.

$$\bar{X}_{GM} = \frac{\Sigma X}{N} = \frac{10 + 12 + 9 + \cdots + 4}{15} = \frac{116}{15} = 7.73$$

When samples are equal in size, find $\bar{X}_{GM}$ by summing the $\bar{X}$'s and dividing by k, where $k =$ the number of groups.

    c. Find the between-group variance, denoted by s_B^2.

$$s_B^2 = \frac{\Sigma n_i(\bar{X}_i - \bar{X}_{GM})^2}{k - 1}$$
$$= \frac{5(11.8 - 7.73)^2 + 5(3.8 - 7.73)^2 + 5(7.6 - 7.73)^2}{3 - 1}$$
$$= \frac{160.13}{2} = 80.07$$

Note: This formula finds the variance among the means by using the sample sizes as weights and considers the differences in the means.

    d. Find the within-group variance, denoted by s_W^2.

$$s_W^2 = \frac{\Sigma(n_i - 1)s_i^2}{\Sigma(n_i - 1)}$$
$$= \frac{(5 - 1)(5.7) + (5 - 1)(10.2) + (5 - 1)(10.3)}{(5 - 1) + (5 - 1) + (5 - 1)}$$
$$= \frac{104.80}{12} = 8.73$$

Note: This formula finds an overall variance by calculating a weighted average of the individual variances. It does not involve using differences of the means.

    e. Find the F test value.

$$F = \frac{s_B^2}{s_W^2} = \frac{80.07}{8.73} = 9.17$$

Step 4 Make the decision. The decision is to reject the null hypothesis, since $9.17 > 3.89$.

Step 5 Summarize the results. There is enough evidence to reject the claim and conclude that at least one mean is different from the others.

Interesting Facts

The weight of 1 cubic foot of wet snow is about 10 pounds while the weight of 1 cubic foot of dry snow is about 3 pounds.

The numerator of the fraction obtained in step 3, part c, of the computational procedure is called the **sum of squares between groups,** denoted by SS_B. The numerator of the fraction obtained in step 3, part d, of the computational procedure is called the **sum of squares within groups,** denoted by SS_W. This statistic is also called the *sum of squares for the error.* SS_B is divided by d.f.N. to obtain the between-group variance. SS_W is divided by $N - k$ to obtain the within-group or error variance. These two variances are sometimes called **mean squares,** denoted by MS_B and MS_W. These terms are used to summarize the analysis of variance and are placed in a summary table, as shown in Table 11–1.

Table 11–1	Analysis of Variance Summary Table			
Source	**Sum of squares**	**d.f.**	**Mean square**	**F**
Between	SS_B	$k - 1$	MS_B	
Within (error)	SS_W	$N - k$	MS_W	
Total				

In the table,

SS_B = sum of squares between groups

SS_W = sum of squares within groups

k = number of groups

$N = n_1 + n_2 + \cdots + n_k$ = sum of sample sizes for groups

$$MS_B = \frac{SS_B}{k - 1}$$

$$MS_W = \frac{SS_W}{N - k}$$

$$F = \frac{MS_B}{MS_W}$$

The totals are obtained by adding the corresponding columns. For Example 11–8, the **ANOVA summary table** is shown in Table 11–2.

Table 11–2	Analysis of Variance Summary Table for Example 11–8			
Source	**Sum of squares**	**d.f.**	**Mean square**	**F**
Between	160.13	2	80.07	9.17
Within (error)	104.80	12	8.73	
Total	264.93	14		

Most computer programs will print out an ANOVA summary table.

Example 11–9

Employees at Toll Road Interchanges

A state employee wishes to see if there is a significant difference in the number of employees at the interchanges of three state toll roads. The data are shown. At $\alpha = 0.05$, can it be concluded that there is a significant difference in the average number of employees at each interchange?

Pennsylvania Turnpike	Greensburg Bypass/ Mon-Fayette Expressway	Beaver Valley Expressway
7	10	1
14	1	12
32	1	1
19	0	9
10	11	1
11	1	11
$\bar{X}_1 = 15.5$	$\bar{X}_2 = 4.0$	$\bar{X}_3 = 5.8$
$s_1^2 = 81.9$	$s_2^2 = 25.6$	$s_3^2 = 29.0$

Source: Pennsylvania Turnpike Commission.

Solution

Step 1 State the hypotheses and identify the claim.

H_0: $\mu_1 = \mu_2 = \mu_3$

H_1: At least one mean is different from the others (claim)

Step 2 Find the critical value. Since $k = 3$, $N = 18$, and $\alpha = 0.05$,

d.f.N. $= k - 1 = 3 - 1 = 2$

d.f.D. $= N - k = 18 - 3 = 15$

The critical value is 3.68.

Step 3 Compute the test value.

a. Find the mean and variance of each sample (these values are shown below the data columns in the example).

b. Find the grand mean.

$$\bar{X}_{GM} = \frac{\Sigma X}{N} = \frac{7 + 14 + 32 + \cdots + 11}{18} = \frac{152}{18} = 8.4$$

c. Find the between-group variance.

$$s_B^2 = \frac{\Sigma n_i(\bar{X}_i - \bar{X}_{GM})^2}{k - 1}$$

$$= \frac{6(15.5 - 8.4)^2 + 6(4 - 8.4)^2 + 6(5.8 - 8.4)^2}{3 - 1}$$

$$= \frac{459.18}{2} = 229.59$$

d. Find the within-group variance.

$$s_W^2 = \frac{\Sigma(n_i - 1)s_i^2}{\Sigma(n_i - 1)}$$

$$= \frac{(6 - 1)(81.9) + (6 - 1)(25.6) + (6 - 1)(29.0)}{(6 - 1) + (6 - 1) + (6 - 1)}$$

$$= \frac{682.5}{15} = 45.5$$

e. Find the *F* test value.

$$F = \frac{s_B^2}{s_W^2} = \frac{229.59}{45.5} = 5.05$$

Step 4　Make the decision. Since $5.05 > 3.68$, the decision is to reject the null hypothesis.

Step 5　Summarize the results. There is enough evidence to support the claim that there is a difference among the means. The ANOVA summary table for this example is shown in Table 11–3.

Table 11–3	Analysis of Variance Summary Table for Example 11-9				
Source	**Sum of squares**	**d.f.**	**Mean square**		**F**
Between	459.18	2	229.59		5.05
Within	682.5	15	45.5		
Total	1141.68	17			

The steps for computing the *F* test value for the ANOVA are summarized in this Procedure Table.

Procedure Table

Finding the *F* Test Value for the Analysis of Variance

Step 1　Find the mean and variance of each sample.

$$(\bar{X}_1, s_1^2), (\bar{X}_2, s_2^2), \ldots, (\bar{X}_k, s_k^2)$$

Step 2　Find the grand mean.

$$\bar{X}_{GM} = \frac{\Sigma X}{N}$$

Step 3　Find the between-group variance.

$$s_B^2 = \frac{\Sigma n_i(\bar{X}_i - \bar{X}_{GM})^2}{k - 1}$$

Step 4　Find the within-group variance.

$$s_W^2 = \frac{\Sigma(n_i - 1)s_i^2}{\Sigma(n_i - 1)}$$

Step 5　Find the *F* test value.

$$F = \frac{s_B^2}{s_W^2}$$

The degrees of freedom are

d.f.N. = $k - 1$

where k is the number of groups, and

d.f.D. = $N - k$

where N is the sum of the sample sizes of the groups

$$N = n_1 + n_2 + \cdots + n_k$$

The P-values for ANOVA are found by using the procedure shown in Section 8–3. For Example 11–9, find the two α values in the tables for the F distribution (Table H), using d.f.N. = 2 and d.f.D. = 15, where $F = 5.05$ falls between. In this case, 5.05 falls between 4.77 and 6.36, corresponding, respectively, to $\alpha = 0.025$ and $\alpha = 0.01$; hence, $0.01 < P$-value < 0.025. Since the P-value is between 0.01 and 0.025 and since P-value < 0.05 (the originally chosen value for α), the decision is to reject the null hypothesis. (The P-value obtained from a calculator is 0.021.)

When the null hypothesis is rejected in ANOVA, it only means that at least one mean is different from the others. In order to locate the difference or differences among the means, it is necessary to use other tests such as the Tukey or the Scheffe test. These tests are beyond the scope of this book.

Applying the Concepts 11–3

Colors That Make You Smarter

The following set of data values was obtained from a study of people's perceptions on whether the color of a person's clothing is related to how intelligent the person looks. The subjects rated the person's intelligence on a scale of 1 to 10. Group 1 subjects were randomly shown people with clothing in shades of blue and gray. Group 2 subjects were randomly shown people with clothing in shades of brown and yellow. Group 3 subjects were randomly shown people with clothing in shades of pink and orange. The results follow.

Group 1	Group 2	Group 3
8	7	4
7	8	9
7	7	6
7	7	7
8	5	9
8	8	8
6	5	5
8	8	8
8	7	7
7	6	5
7	6	4
8	6	5
8	6	4

1. Use ANOVA to test for any significant differences between the means.

2. What is the purpose of this study?

3. Explain why separate t tests are not accepted in this situation.

See page 622 for the answers.

Exercises 11–3

1. What test is used to compare three or more means?

2. State three reasons why multiple t tests cannot be used to compare three or more means.

3. What are the assumptions for ANOVA?

4. Define between-group variance and within-group variance.

5. What is the F test formula for comparing three or more means?

6. State the hypotheses used in the ANOVA test.

7. When there is no significant difference among three or more means, the value of F will be close to what number?

For Exercises 8 through 19, assume that all variables are normally distributed, that the samples are independent, and that the population variances are equal. Also, for each exercise, perform the following steps.

   a. State the hypotheses and identify the claim.
   b. Find the critical value.
   c. Compute the test value.
   d. Make the decision.
   e. Summarize the results, and explain where the differences in the means are.

Use the traditional method of hypothesis testing unless otherwise specified.

8. **Sodium Contents of Foods** The amount of sodium (in milligrams) in one serving for a random sample of three different kinds of foods is listed here. At the 0.05 level of significance, is there sufficient evidence to conclude that a difference in mean sodium amounts exists among condiments, cereals, and desserts?

Condiments	Cereals	Desserts
270	260	100
130	220	180
230	290	250
180	290	250
80	200	300
70	320	360
200	140	300
		160

Source: *The Doctor's Pocket Calorie, Fat, and Carbohydrate Counter.*

9. **Hybrid Vehicles** A study was done before the recent surge in gasoline prices to compare the cost to drive 25 miles for different types of hybrid vehicles. The cost of a gallon of gas at the time of the study was approximately $2.50. Based on the information given below for different models of hybrid cars, trucks, and SUVs, is there sufficient evidence to conclude a difference in the mean cost to drive 25 miles? Use $\alpha = 0.05$.

Hybrid cars	Hybrid SUVs	Hybrid trucks
2.10	2.10	3.62
2.70	2.42	3.43
1.67	2.25	
1.67	2.10	
1.30	2.25	

Source: www.fueleconomy.com

10. **Post Secondary School Enrollments** A random sample of enrollments from public institutions of higher learning (with enrollments under 10,000) is shown. At $\alpha = 0.10$, test the claim that the mean enrollments are the same in all parts of the country.

West	Midwest	Northeast	South
3737	5585	9264	3903
3706	8205	4673	4539
2457	4170	7320	2649
4309	5440	5401	6414
4103	3355	6050	2935
5048	4412	4087	7147
2463	5115	1579	3354
		8739	8669
			2431

Source: *New York Times Almanac.*

11. **Lengths of Suspension Bridges** The lengths (in feet) of a random sample of suspension bridges in the United States, Europe, and Asia are shown. At $\alpha = 0.05$, is there sufficient evidence to conclude that there is a difference in mean lengths?

United States	Europe	Asia
4260	5238	6529
3500	4626	4543
2300	4347	3668
2000	3300	3379
1850		2874

Source: *New York Times Almanac.*

12. **Weight Gain of Athletes** A researcher wishes to see whether there is any difference in the weight gains of athletes following one of three special diets. Athletes are randomly assigned to three groups and placed on the diet for 6 weeks. The weight gains (in pounds) are shown here. At $\alpha = 0.05$, can the researcher conclude that there is a difference in the diets?

Diet A	Diet B	Diet C
3	10	8
6	12	3
7	11	2
4	14	5
	8	
	6	

A computer printout for this problem is shown. Use the P-value method and the information in this printout to test the claim.

Computer Printout for Exercise 12

ANALYSIS OF VARIANCE SOURCE TABLE

Source	df	Sum of Squares	Mean Square	F	P-value
Bet Groups	2	101.095	50.548	7.740	0.00797
W/I Groups	11	71.833	6.530		
Total	13	172.929			

DESCRIPTIVE STATISTICS

Condit	N	Means	St Dev
diet A	4	5.000	1.826
diet B	6	10.167	2.858
diet C	4	4.500	2.646

13. Expenditures per Pupil The per-pupil costs (in thousands of dollars) for cyber charter school tuition for school districts in three areas of southwestern Pennsylvania are shown. At $\alpha = 0.05$, is there a difference in the means? If so, give a possible reason for the difference.

Area I	Area II	Area III
6.2	7.5	5.8
9.3	8.2	6.4
6.8	8.5	5.6
6.1	8.2	7.1
6.7	7.0	3.0
6.9	9.3	3.5

Source: *Tribune-Review.*

14. Ocean Water Temperatures The National Oceanographic Data Center lists water temperatures in degrees Fahrenheit for beaches all around the country. Below are listed selected beach temperatures from the month of February for various coastal areas of the United States. At the 0.05 level of significance, is there sufficient evidence to conclude a difference in mean temperatures?

Southern Pacific	Western Gulf	Eastern Gulf	Southern Atlantic
57	55	70	70
57	58	66	66
60	56	64	73
58	61	58	59
57	60	53	56
56	69	61	55

Source: www.nodc.noaa.gov

15. Number of Farms The numbers (in thousands) of farms per state found in three sections of the country are listed next. Test the claim at $\alpha = 0.05$ that the mean number of farms is the same across these three geographic divisions.

Eastern third	Middle third	Western third
48	95	29
57	52	40
24	64	40
10	64	68
38		

Source: *New York Times Almanac.*

16. Annual Child Care Costs Annual child care costs for infants are considerably higher than for older children. At $\alpha = 0.05$, can you conclude a difference in mean infant day care costs for different regions of the United States? (Annual costs per infant are given in dollars.)

New England	Midwest	Southwest
10,390	9,449	7,644
7,592	6,985	9,691
8,755	6,677	5,996
9,464	5,400	5,386
7,328	8,372	

Source: www.naccrra.org (National Association of Child Care Resources and Referral Agencies: "Breaking the Piggy Bank").

17. Microwave Oven Prices A research organization tested microwave ovens. At $\alpha = 0.10$, is there a significant difference in the average prices of the three types of oven?

Watts		
1000	**900**	**800**
270	240	180
245	135	155
190	160	200
215	230	120
250	250	140
230	200	180
	200	140
	210	130

A computer printout for this exercise is shown. Use the *P*-value method and the information in this printout to test the claim.

Computer Printout for Exercise 17

```
ANALYSIS OF VARIANCE SOURCE TABLE
Source          df      Sum of Squares     Mean Square        F       P-value

Bet Groups       2         21729.735         10864.867       10.118    0.00102
W/I Groups      19         20402.083          1073.794

Total           21         42131.818

DESCRIPTIVE STATISTICS
Condit           N             Means            St Dev

 1000            6           233.333            28.23
  900            8           203.125            39.36
  800            8           155.625            28.21
```

 18. Commute Times Three random samples of times (in minutes) that commuters are stuck in traffic are shown. At $\alpha = 0.05$, is there a difference in the mean times among the three cities? What factor might have influenced the results of the study?

Dallas	Boston	Detroit
59	54	53
62	52	56
58	55	54
63	58	49
61	53	52

Source: Based on information from Texas Transportation Institute.

 19. Average Debt of College Graduates Kiplinger's listed the top 100 public colleges based on many factors. From that list, here is the average debt at graduation for various schools in four selected states. At $\alpha = 0.05$, can it be concluded that the average debt at graduation differs for these four states?

N.Y.	Va.	Calif.	Pa.
14,734	14,524	13,171	18,105
16,000	15,176	14,431	17,051
14,347	12,665	14,689	16,103
14,392	12,591	13,788	22,400
12,500	18,385	15,297	17,976

Source: www.Kiplinger.com

Technology *Step by Step*

MINITAB
Step by Step

One-Way Analysis of Variance (ANOVA)

Which treatment is most effective in lowering cholesterol—medication, diet, or exercise?

1. Enter the data for Example 11–8 into columns of MINITAB.
2. Name the columns **Medication, Exercise,** and **Diet.**
3. Select **Stat>ANOVA>One-Way (Unstacked).**
4. Drag the mouse over the three columns in the list box and then click [Select].
5. Click [OK]. In the session window the ANOVA table will be displayed, showing the test statistic $F = 9.17$ whose *P*-value is 0.004.

One-Way ANOVA: Medication, Exercise, Diet

```
Source   DF      SS      MS      F      P
Factor    2   160.13   80.07   9.17   0.004
Error    12   104.80    8.73
Total    14   264.93
```

```
                                        Individual 95% CIs For Mean
                                        Based on Pooled StDev
Level        N    Mean   StDev     -------+---------+---------+---------+--
Medication   5   11.800  2.387                            (--------*------)
Exercise     5    3.800  3.194     (-------*------)
Diet         5    7.600  3.209             (-------*------)
                                   -------+---------+---------+---------+--
                                     3.5      7.0      10.5      14.0

Pooled StDev = 2.955
```

Reject the null hypothesis. There is enough evidence to conclude that there is a difference between the treatments.

TI-83 Plus or TI-84 Plus
Step by Step

One-Way Analysis of Variance (ANOVA)

1. Enter the data into L_1, L_2, L_3, etc.
2. Press **STAT** and move the cursor to TESTS.
3. Press **F (ALPHA COS)** for ANOVA(.   (Use **H** for the TI-84.)
4. Type each list followed by a comma. End with) and press **ENTER.**

Example TI11–1

Test the claim H_0: $\mu_1 = \mu_2 = \mu_3$ at $\alpha = 0.05$ for these data from Example 11–8.

Medication	Exercise	Diet
10	6	5
12	8	9
9	3	12
15	0	8
13	2	4

Input

Input

Output

Output

The F test value is 9.167938931. The P-value is 0.0038313169, which is significant at $\alpha = 0.05$. The factor variable has

d.f. = 2

SS = 160.133333

MS = 80.0666667

The error has

d.f. = 12

SS = 104.8

MS = 8.73333333

Excel
Step by Step

One-Way Analysis of Variance (ANOVA)

Example XL11–1

1. Enter the data below in columns A, B, and C.

9	8	12
6	7	15
15	12	18
4	3	9
3	5	10

2. From the toolbar, select Data, then Data Analysis.
3. Select Anova: Single Factor under Analysis tools, then [OK].
4. In the Anova: Single Factor dialog box, type **A1:C5** for the Input Range.
5. Check Grouped By: Columns.
6. Type **0.05** for the Alpha level.
7. Under Output options, check Output Range and type **E2**.
8. Click [OK].

The results of the ANOVA are shown below.

Anova: Single Factor

SUMMARY

Groups	Count	Sum	Average	Variance
Column 1	5	37	7.4	23.3
Column 2	5	35	7	11.5
Column 3	5	64	12.8	13.7

ANOVA

Source of Variation	SS	df	MS	F	P-value	F crit
Between Groups	104.9333333	2	52.46666667	3.245360825	0.074707518	3.885293835
Within Groups	194	12	16.16666667			
Total	298.9333333	14				

Summary

Three uses of the chi-square distribution were explained in this chapter. It can be used as a goodness-of-fit test to determine whether the frequencies of a distribution are the same as the hypothesized frequencies. For example, is the number of defective parts produced by a factory the same each day? This test is always a right-tailed test.

The test of independence is used to determine whether two variables are related or are independent. This test uses a contingency table and is always a right-tailed test. An example of its use is a test to determine whether the attitudes of urban residents about the recycling of trash differ from the attitudes of rural residents.

The homogeneity of proportions test is used to determine if several proportions are all equal when samples are selected from different populations.

The F test, as shown in Chapter 9, can be used to compare two sample variances to determine whether they are equal. It can also be used to compare three or more means. When three or more means are compared, the technique is called analysis of variance (ANOVA). The ANOVA technique uses two estimates of the population variance. The between-group variance is the variance of the sample means; the within-group variance is the overall variance of all the values. When there is no significant difference among the means, the two estimates will be approximately equal and the F test value will be close to 1. If there is a significant difference among the means, the between-group variance estimate will be larger than the within-group variance estimate, and a significant test value will result.

Important Terms

analysis of variance (ANOVA) 602

ANOVA summary table 605

between-group variance 603

contingency table 587

expected frequency 573

goodness-of-fit test 573

homogeneity of proportions test 592

independence test 586

mean square 605

observed frequency 573

sum of squares between groups 605

sum of squares within groups 605

within-group variance 603

Important Formulas

Formula for the chi-square test for goodness of fit:

$$\chi^2 = \sum \frac{(O - E)^2}{E}$$

with degrees of freedom equal to the number of categories minus 1 and where

O = observed frequency

E = expected frequency

Formula for the chi-square independence and homogeneity of proportions tests:

$$\chi^2 = \sum \frac{(O - E)^2}{E}$$

with degrees of freedom equal to (rows − 1) times (columns − 1). Formula for the expected value for each cell:

$$E = \frac{(\text{row sum})(\text{column sum})}{\text{grand total}}$$

Formulas for the ANOVA test:

$$\bar{X}_{GM} = \frac{\sum X}{N}$$

$$F = \frac{s_B^2}{s_W^2}$$

where

$$s_B^2 = \frac{\sum n_i(\bar{X}_i - \bar{X}_{GM})^2}{k - 1} \qquad s_W^2 = \frac{\sum (n_i - 1)s_i^2}{\sum (n_i - 1)}$$

d.f.N. = $k - 1$ **$N = n_1 + n_2 + \cdots + n_k$**

d.f.D. = $N - k$ **k = number of groups**

Review Exercises

For Exercises 1 through 17, follow these steps.

a. State the hypotheses and identify the claim.
b. Find the critical value(s).
c. Compute the test value.
d. Make the decision.
e. Summarize the results.

Use the traditional method of hypothesis testing unless otherwise specified.

1. Favorite Shopping Day A storeowner wishes to see if people have a favorite day of the week to shop. A sample of 400 people is selected, and each is asked his or her preference. The data are shown. At $\alpha = 0.05$, test the claim that shoppers have no preference. Give one example of how retail merchants would be able to use the numbers in this study.

Day	Sun.	Mon.	Tues.	Wed.	Thurs.	Fri.	Sat.
Number	28	16	20	26	74	96	140

Source: Based on information from the International Mass Retail Association.

2. Distribution of Colors of M&M's According to the manufacturer, M&M's are produced and distributed in the following proportions: 13% brown, 13% red, 14% yellow, 16% green, 20% orange, and 24% blue. A randomly selected 1.69-ounce bag was opened and it was found to contain the following: 9 brown, 10 red, 11 yellow, 16 green, 5 orange, and 4 blue M&M's. Based on this sample, is there sufficient evidence to conclude that the proportions differ from those stated by the candy company? Use $\alpha = 0.05$.

Source: Mars, Inc.

3. Tire Labeling The federal government has proposed labeling tires by fuel efficiency to save fuel and cut emissions. A survey was taken to see who would use these labels. At $\alpha = 0.10$, is the gender of the individual related to whether or not a person would use these labels? The data from a sample are shown here.

Gender	Yes	No	Undecided
Men	114	30	6
Women	136	16	8

Source: USA TODAY.

4. Gun Sale Denials A police investigator read that the reasons why gun sales to applicants were denied were distributed as follows: criminal history of felonies, 75%; domestic violence conviction, 11%; and drug abuse, fugitive, etc., 14%. A sample of applicants in a large study who were refused sales is obtained and is distributed as follows. At $\alpha = 0.10$, can it be concluded that the distribution is as stated? Do you think the results might be different in a rural area?

Reason	Criminal history	Domestic violence	Drug abuse etc.
Number	120	42	38

Source: Based on FBI statistics.

5. Pension Investments A survey was taken on how a lump-sum pension would be invested by 45-year-olds and 65-year-olds. The data are shown here. At $\alpha = 0.05$, is there a relationship between the age of the investor and the way the money would be invested?

	Large company stock funds	Small company stock funds	International stock funds	CDs or money market funds	Bonds
Age 45	20	10	10	15	45
Age 65	42	24	24	6	24

Source: USA TODAY.

6. Tornadoes According to records from the Storm Prediction Center, the following numbers of tornadoes occurred in the first quarter of each of the years 2003–2006. Is there sufficient evidence to conclude that a relationship exists between the month and year in which the tornadoes occurred? Use $\alpha = 0.05$.

	2006	2005	2004	2003
January	48	33	3	0
February	12	10	9	18
March	113	62	50	43

Source: National Weather Service Storm Prediction Center.

7. Employment of High School Females A guidance counselor wishes to determine if the proportions of high school girls in his school district who have jobs are equal to the national average of 36%. He surveys 80 female students, ages 16 through 18, to determine if they work. The results are shown. At $\alpha = 0.01$, test the claim that the proportions of girls who work are equal. Use the P-value method.

	16-year-olds	17-year-olds	18-year-olds
Work	45	31	38
Don't work	35	49	42
Total	80	80	80

Source: Michael D. Shook and Robert L. Shook, The Book of Odds.

8. Risk of Injury The risk of injury is higher for males compared to females (57% versus 43%). A hospital emergency room supervisor wishes to determine if the proportions of injuries to males in his

Statistics Today

Statistics and Heredity–Revisited

Using probability, Mendel predicted the following:

| | Smooth | | Wrinkled | |
	Yellow	Green	Yellow	Green
Expected	0.5625	0.1875	0.1875	0.0625

The observed results were these:

| | Smooth | | Wrinkled | |
	Yellow	Green	Yellow	Green
Observed	0.5666	0.1942	0.1816	0.0556

Using chi-square tests on the data, Mendel found that his predictions were accurate in most cases (i.e., a good fit), thus supporting his theory. He reported many highly successful experiments. Mendel's genetic theory is simple but useful in predicting the results of hybridization.

A Fly in the Ointment
Although Mendel's theory is basically correct, an English statistician named R. A. Fisher examined Mendel's data some 50 years later. He found that the observed (actual) results agreed too closely with the expected (theoretical) results and concluded that the data had in some way been falsified. The results were too good to be true. Several explanations have been proposed, ranging from deliberate misinterpretation to an assistant's error, but no one can be sure how this happened.

---

hospital are the same for each of four months. He surveys 100 injuries treated in his ER for each month. The results are shown here. At $\alpha = 0.05$, can he reject the claim that the proportions of injuries for males are equal for each of the four months?

	May	June	July	August
Male	51	47	58	63
Female	49	53	42	37
Total	100	100	100	100

Source: Michael D. Shook and Robert L. Shook, *The Book of Odds.*

9. Health Insurance Across the United States in general 15.7% of Americans are without health insurance. Two hundred persons were polled in each of the five states listed. Is there sufficient evidence to conclude that the proportions of Americans without health insurance differ by state? Use $\alpha = 0.10$ and the *P*-value method.

	Va.	Ill.	Washington, D.C.	Wyo.	Tex.
Have (insurance)	171	171	170	168	152
Do not have	29	29	30	32	48

Source: *Time Almanac.*

10. A researcher surveyed 50 randomly selected males and 50 randomly selected females to see how they paid their bills. The data are shown. At $\alpha = 0.01$, test the claim that the proportions are not equal. What might be a reason for the difference, if one exists?

Type of payment	Checks	Electronically	In person
Males	27	15	8
Females	22	19	9
Total	49	34	17

Source: Based on information from Gallup.

11. Lengths of Various Types of Bridges The data represent the lengths in feet of three types of bridges in the United States. At $\alpha = 0.01$, test the claim that there is no significant difference in the means of the lengths of the types of bridges.

Simple truss	Segmented concrete	Continuous plate
745	820	630
716	750	573
700	790	525
650	674	510
647	660	480
625	640	460
608	636	451
598	620	450
550	520	450
545	450	425
534	392	420
528	370	360

Source: *World Almanac and Book of Facts.*

12. Number of State Parks The numbers of state parks found in selected states in three different regions of the country are listed below. At $\alpha = 0.05$ can it be concluded that the average number of state parks differs by region?

South	West	New England
51	28	94
64	44	72
35	24	14
24	31	52
47	40	

Source: *Time Almanac.*

13. Carbohydrates in Cereals The number of carbohydrates per serving in randomly selected cereals from three manufacturers is shown. At the 0.05 level of significance, is there sufficient evidence to conclude a difference in the average number of carbohydrates?

Manufacturer 1	Manufacturer 2	Manufacturer 3
25	23	24
26	44	39
24	24	28
26	24	25
26	36	23
41	27	32
26	25	
43		

Source: *The Doctor's Pocket Calorie, Fat, and Carbohydrate Counter.*

14. Grams of Fat per Serving of Pizza The number of grams of fat per serving for three different kinds of pizza from several manufacturers is listed below. At the 0.01 level of significance, is there sufficient evidence that a difference exists in mean fat content?

Cheese	Pepperoni	Supreme/Deluxe
18	20	16
11	17	27
19	15	17
20	18	17
16	23	12
21	23	27
16	21	20

Source: *The Doctor's Pocket Calorie, Fat, and Carbohydrate Counter.*

15. Iron Content of Foods and Drinks The iron content in three different types of food is shown. At the 0.10 level of significance, is there sufficient evidence to conclude that a difference in mean iron content exists

for meats and fish, breakfast cereals, and nutritional high-protein drinks?

Meats and fish	Breakfast cereals	Nutritional drinks
3.4	8	3.6
2.5	2	3.6
5.5	1.5	4.5
5.3	3.8	5.5
2.5	3.8	2.7
1.3	6.8	3.6
2.7	1.5	6.3
	4.5	

Source: *The Doctor's Pocket Calorie, Fat, and Carbohydrate Counter.*

16. Temperatures in January The average January high temperatures (in degrees Fahrenheit) for selected tourist cities on different continents are listed below. Is there sufficient evidence to conclude a difference in mean temperatures for the three areas? Use the 0.05 level of significance.

Europe	Central and South America	Asia
41	87	89
38	75	35
36	66	83
56	84	67
50	75	48

Source: *Time Almanac.*

17. School Incidents Involving Police Calls A researcher wishes to see if there is a difference in the average number of times local police were called in school incidents. Samples of school districts were selected, and the numbers of incidents for a specific year were reported. At $\alpha = 0.05$, is there a difference in the means? If so, suggest a reason for the difference.

County A	County B	County C	County D
13	16	15	11
11	33	12	31
2	12	19	3
	2	2	
	2		

Source: *U.S. Department of Education.*

Data Analysis

The Data Bank is located in Appendix D, or on the World Wide Web by following links from
www.mhhe.com/bluman

1. Select a sample of 40 individuals from the Data Bank. Use the chi-square goodness-of-fit test to see if the marital status of individuals is equally distributed.

2. Use the chi-square test of independence to test the hypothesis that smoking is independent of gender. Use a sample of at least 75 people.

3. Using the data from Data Set X in Appendix D, classify the data as 1–3, 4–6, 7–9, etc. Use the chi-square goodness-of-fit test to see if the number of times each ball is drawn is equally distributed.

4. From the Data Bank, select a random sample of subjects, and test the hypothesis that the mean cholesterol levels of the nonsmokers, less-than-one-pack-a-day smokers, and one-pack-plus smokers are equal. Use an ANOVA test. Summarize the results.

Chapter Quiz

Determine whether each statement is true or false. If the statement is false, explain why.

1. The chi-square test of independence is always two-tailed.

2. The test values for the chi-square goodness-of-fit test and the independence test are computed by using the same formula.

3. When the null hypothesis is rejected in the goodness-of-fit test, it means there is close agreement between the observed and expected frequencies.

4. In analysis of variance, the null hypothesis should be rejected only when there is a significant difference among all pairs of means.

5. The F test does not use the concept of degrees of freedom.

6. When the F test value is close to 1, the null hypothesis should be rejected.

Select the best answer.

7. The values of the chi-square variable cannot be

   a. Positive
   b. 0
   c. Negative
   d. None of the above

8. The null hypothesis for the chi-square test of independence is that the variables are

   a. Dependent
   b. Independent
   c. Related
   d. Always 0

9. The degrees of freedom for the goodness-of-fit test are

   a. 0
   b. 1
   c. Sample size − 1
   d. Number of categories − 1

10. The analysis of variance uses the _____ test.

    a. z
    b. t
    c. χ^2
    d. F

11. The null hypothesis in the ANOVA is that all the means are _____.

    a. Equal
    b. Unequal
    c. Variable
    d. None of the above

12. When one conducts an F test, _____ estimates of the population variance are compared.

    a. Two
    b. Three
    c. Any number of
    d. No

Complete these statements with the best answer.

13. The degrees of freedom for a 4×3 contingency table are _____.

14. An important assumption for the chi-square test is that the observations must be _____.

15. The chi-square goodness-of-fit test is always _____ tailed.

16. In the chi-square independence test, the expected frequency for each class must always be _____.

17. When three or more means are compared, one uses the _____ technique.

For Exercises 18 through 31, follow these steps.

   a. State the hypotheses and identify the claim.
   b. Find the critical value.
   c. Compute the test value.
   d. Make the decision.
   e. Summarize the results.

Use the traditional method of hypothesis testing unless otherwise specified.

18. **Job Loss Reasons** A survey of why people lost their jobs produced the following results. At $\alpha = 0.05$, test the claim that the number of responses is equally distributed. Do you think the results might be different if the study were done 10 years ago?

Reason	Company closing	Position abolished	Insufficient work
Number	26	18	28

Source: Based on information from U.S. Department of Labor.

19. **Consumption of Takeout Foods** A food service manager read that the place where people consumed takeout food is distributed as follows: home, 53%; car, 19%; work, 14%; other, 14%. A survey of 300 individuals showed the following results. At $\alpha = 0.01$, can it be concluded that the distribution is as stated? Where would a fast-food restaurant want to target its advertisements?

Place	Home	Car	Work	Other
Number	142	57	51	50

Source: Beef Industry Council.

20. **Television Viewing** A survey found that 62% of the respondents stated that they never watched the home shopping channels on cable television, 23% stated that they watched the channels rarely, 11% stated that they watched them occasionally, and 4% stated that they watched them frequently. A group of 200 college students was surveyed, and 105 stated that they never watched the home shopping channels, 72 stated that they watched them rarely, 13 stated that they watched them occasionally, and 10 stated that they watched them

frequently. At $\alpha = 0.05$, can it be concluded that the college students differ in their preference for the home shopping channels?

Source: Based on information obtained from *USA TODAY* Snapshots.

21. **Ways to Get to Work** The 2000 Census indicated the following percentages for means of commuting to work for workers over 15 years of age.

Alone	75.7
Carpooling	12.2
Public	4.7
Walked	2.9
Other	1.2
Worked at home	3.3

A random sample of workers found that 320 drove alone, 100 carpooled, 30 used public transportation, 20 walked, 10 used other forms of transportation, and 20 worked at home. Is there sufficient evidence to conclude that the proportions of workers using each type of transportation differ from those in the Census report? Use $\alpha = 0.05$.

Source: Census Bureau, *Washington Observer-Reporter.*

22. **Favorite Ice Cream Flavor** A survey of women and men asked what their favorite ice cream flavor was. The results are shown. At $\alpha = 0.05$, can it be concluded that the favorite flavor is independent of gender?

		Flavor		
	Vanilla	**Chocolate**	**Strawberry**	**Other**
Women	62	36	10	2
Men	49	37	5	9

 23. **Types of Pizzas Purchased** A pizza shop owner wishes to determine if the type of pizza a person selects is related to the age of the individual. The data obtained from a sample are shown here. At $\alpha = 0.10$, is the age of the purchaser related to the type of pizza ordered? Use the *P*-value method.

		Type of pizza		
Age	**Plain**	**Pepperoni**	**Mushroom**	**Double cheese**
10–19	12	21	39	71
20–29	18	76	52	87
30–39	24	50	40	47
40–49	52	30	12	28

24. **Pennant Colors Purchased** A survey at a ballpark shows the following selection of pennants sold to fans. The data are presented here. At $\alpha = 0.10$, is the color of the pennant purchased independent of the gender of the individual?

	Blue	**Yellow**	**Red**
Men	519	659	876
Women	487	702	787

25. **Tax Credit Refunds** In a survey of children ages 8 through 11, these data were obtained as to what their parents should do with the money from a $400 tax credit.

	Keep it for themselves	**Give it to their children**	**Don't know**
Girls	162	132	6
Boys	147	147	6

At $\alpha = 0.10$, is there a relationship between the feelings of the children and the gender of the children?

Source: Based on information from *USA TODAY* Snapshot.

26. **Employment Satisfaction** A survey of 60 men and 60 women asked if they would be happy spending the rest of their careers with their present employers. The results are shown. At $\alpha = 0.10$, can it be concluded that the proportions are equal? If they are not equal, give a possible reason for the difference.

	Yes	**No**	**Undecided**
Men	40	15	5
Women	36	9	15
Total	76	24	20

Source: Based on information from a Maritz Poll.

27. **Voters in Presidential Elections** In a recent Presidential election, a sample of the percentage of voters who voted is shown. At $\alpha = 0.05$, is there a difference in the mean percentage of voters who voted?

Northeast	**Southeast**	**Northwest**	**Southwest**
65.3	54.8	60.5	42.3
59.9	61.8	61.0	61.2
66.9	49.6	74.0	54.7
64.2	58.6	61.4	56.7

Source: Committee for the Study of the American Electorate.

28. **Ages of Late-Night TV Talk Show Viewers** A media researcher wishes to see if there is a difference in the ages of viewers of three late-night television talk shows. Three samples of viewers are selected, and the ages of the viewers are shown. At $\alpha = 0.01$, is there a difference in the means of the ages of the viewers? Why is the average age of a viewer important to a television show writer?

David Letterman	**Jay Leno**	**Conan O'Brien**
53	48	40
46	51	36
48	57	35
42	46	42
35	38	39

Source: Based on information from Nielsen Media Research.

29. **Prices of Athletic Shoes** Prices (in dollars) of men's, women's, and children's athletic shoes are shown. At the 0.05 level of significance, can it be concluded that there is a difference in mean price?

Women's	Men's	Children's
59	65	40
36	70	45
44	66	40
49	59	56
48	48	46
50	70	36

30. Birth Weights The birth weights of randomly selected newborns at three area hospitals are shown. Using the 0.10 level of significance, test the claim that the mean weights are equal.

Hospital A	Hospital B	Hospital C
7 lb 12 oz	9 lb 6 oz	8 lb 6 oz
8 lb 3 oz	5 lb 9 oz	9 lb 5 oz
11 lb 6 oz	6 lb 8 oz	7 lb 13 oz
6 lb 10 oz	8 lb 9 oz	8 lb 2 oz
7 lb 3 oz	10 lb 5 oz	9 lb 2 oz
8 lb 2 oz	7 lb 6 oz	6 lb 5 oz

31. Alumni Gift Solicitation Several students volunteered for an alumni phone-a-thon to solicit alumni gifts. The number of calls made by randomly selected students from each class is listed. At $\alpha = 0.05$, is there sufficient evidence to conclude a difference in means?

Freshmen	Sophomores	Juniors	Seniors
25	17	20	20
29	25	24	25
32	20	25	26
15	26	30	32
18	30	15	19
26	28	18	20
35			

Critical Thinking Challenges

1. **Random Digits** Use your calculator or the MINITAB random number generator to generate 100 two-digit random numbers. Make a grouped frequency distribution, using the chi-square goodness-of-fit test to see if the distribution is random. To do this, use an expected frequency of 10 for each class. Can it be concluded that the distribution is random? Explain.

2. **Lottery Numbers** Simulate the state lottery by using your calculator or MINITAB to generate 100 three-digit random numbers. Group these numbers 100–199,

200–299, etc. Use the chi-square goodness-of-fit test to see if the numbers are random. The expected frequency for each class should be 10. Explain why.

3. Purchase a bag of M&M's candy and count the number of pieces of each color. Using the information as your sample, state a hypothesis for the distribution of colors, and compare your hypothesis to H_0: The distribution of colors of M&M's candy is 13% brown, 13% red, 14% yellow, 16% green, 20% orange, and 24% blue.

Data Projects

Use a significance level of 0.05 for all tests below.

1. **Business and Finance** Many of the companies that produce multicolored candy will include on their website information about the production percentages for the various colors. Select a favorite multicolored candy. Find out what percentage of each color is produced. Open up a bag of the candy, noting how many of each color are in the bag (be careful to count them before you eat them). Is the bag distributed as expected based on the production percentages? If no production percentages can be found, test to see if the colors are uniformly distributed.

2. **Sports and Leisure** Use a local (or favorite) basketball, football, baseball, and hockey team as the data set. For the most recently completed season, note the teams' home record for wins and losses. Test to see whether home field advantage is independent of sport.

3. **Technology** Use the data collected in data project 3 of Chapter 2 regarding song genres. Do the data indicate that songs are uniformly distributed among the genres?

4. **Health and Wellness** Research the percentages of each blood type that the Red Cross states are in the population. Now use your class as a sample. For each student note the blood type. Is the distribution of blood types in your class as expected based on the Red Cross percentages?

5. **Politics and Economics** Research the distribution (by percent) of registered Republicans, Democrats, and Independents in your state. Use your class as a sample. For each student, note the party affiliation. Is the distribution as expected based on the percentages for your state? What might be problematic about using your class as a sample for this exercise?

6. **Your Class** Conduct a classroom poll to determine which of the following sports each student likes best: baseball, football, basketball, hockey, or NASCAR. Also, note the gender of the individual. Is preference for sport independent of gender?

Use a significance level of 0.05 for all tests below.

7. **Business and Finance** Select 10 stocks at random from the Dow Jones Industrials, the NASDAQ, and the S&P 500. For each, note the gain or loss in the last quarter. Use analysis of variance to test the claim that stocks from all three groups have had equal performance.

8. **Sports and Leisure** Use total earnings data for movies that were released in the previous year. Sort them by rating (G, PG, PG13, and R). Is the mean revenue for movies the same regardless of rating?

9. **Technology** Use the data collected in data project 3 of Chapter 2 regarding song lengths. Consider only three genres. For example, use rock, alternative, and hip hop/rap. Conduct an analysis of variance to determine if the mean song lengths for the genres are the same.

10. **Health and Wellness** Select 10 cereals from each of the following categories: cereal targeted at children, cereal targeted at dieters, and cereal that fits neither of the previous categories. For each cereal note its calories per cup (this may require some computation since serving sizes vary for cereals). Use analysis of variance to test the claim that the calorie content of these different types of cereals is the same.

Answers to Applying the Concepts

Section 11–1 Never the Same Amounts

1. The variables are quantitative.

2. We can use a chi-square goodness-of-fit test.

3. There are a total of 233 candies, so we would expect 46.6 of each color. Our test statistic is $\chi^2 = 1.442$.

4. H_0: The colors are equally distributed.
   H_1: The colors are not equally distributed.

5. There are $5 - 1 = 4$ degrees of freedom for the test. The critical value depends on the choice of significance level. At the 0.05 significance level, the critical value is 9.488.

6. Since $1.442 < 9.488$, we fail to reject the null hypothesis. There is not enough evidence to conclude that the colors are not equally distributed.

Section 11–2 Satellite Dishes in Restricted Areas

1. We compare the P-value to the significance level of 0.05 to check if the null hypothesis should be rejected.

2. The P-value gives the probability of a type I error.

3. This is a right-tailed test, since chi-square tests of independence are always right-tailed.

4. You cannot tell how many rows and columns there were just by looking at the degrees of freedom.

5. Increasing the sample size does not increase the degrees of freedom, since the degrees of freedom are based on the number of rows and columns.

6. We will reject the null hypothesis. There are a number of cells where the observed and expected frequencies are quite different.

7. If the significance level were initially set at 0.10, we would still reject the null hypothesis.

8. No, the chi-square value does not tell us which cells have observed and expected frequencies that are very different.

Section 11–3   Colors That Make You Smarter

1. The ANOVA produces a test statistic of $F = 3.06$, with a P-value of 0.059. We would fail to reject the null hypothesis and find that there is not enough evidence to conclude that the color of a person's clothing is related to people's perceptions of how intelligent the person looks.

2. Answers will vary. One possible answer is that the purpose of the study was to determine if the color of a person's clothing is related to people's perceptions of how intelligent the person looks.

3. We would have to perform three separate t tests, which would inflate the error rate.

Hypothesis-Testing Summary 2

7. Test of the significance of the correlation coefficient.

Example: $H_0: \rho = 0$

Use a t test:

$$t = r\sqrt{\frac{n-2}{1-r^2}} \quad \text{with} \quad \text{d.f.} = n - 2$$

8. Comparison of a sample distribution with a specific population.

Example: H_0: There is no difference between the two distributions.

Use the chi-square goodness-of-fit test:

$$\chi^2 = \sum \frac{(O-E)^2}{E} \quad \text{with d.f.}$$
$$= \text{no. of categories} - 1$$

9. Comparison of the independence of two variables.

Example: H_0: Variable A is independent of variable B.

Use the chi-square independence test:

$$\chi^2 = \sum \frac{(O-E)^2}{E} \quad \text{with d.f.}$$
$$= (R-1)(C-1)$$

10. Test for homogeneity of proportions.

Example: $H_0: p_1 = p_2 = p_3$

Use the chi-square test:

$$\chi^2 = \sum \frac{(O-E)^2}{E} \quad \text{with d.f.}$$
$$= (R-1)(C-1)$$

11. Comparison of three or more sample means.

Example: $H_0: \mu_1 = \mu_2 = \mu_3$

Use the analysis of variance test:

$$F = \frac{s_B^2}{s_W^2}$$

where

$$s_B^2 = \frac{\sum n_i(\bar{X}_i - \bar{X}_{GM})^2}{k-1}$$

$$s_W^2 = \frac{\sum (n_i - 1)s_i^2}{\sum (n_i - 1)}$$

d.f.N. $= k - 1$ $N = n_1 + n_2 + \cdots + n_k$

d.f.D. $= N - k$ $k = $ number of groups

Appendix A

Algebra Review

A–1 Factorials

Definition and Properties of Factorials

The notation called factorial notation is used in probability. *Factorial notation* uses the exclamation point and involves multiplication. For example,

$$5! = 5 \cdot 4 \cdot 3 \cdot 2 \cdot 1 = 120$$
$$4! = 4 \cdot 3 \cdot 2 \cdot 1 = 24$$
$$3! = 3 \cdot 2 \cdot 1 = 6$$
$$2! = 2 \cdot 1 = 2$$
$$1! = 1$$

In general, a factorial is evaluated as follows:

$$n! = n(n - 1)(n - 2) \cdots 3 \cdot 2 \cdot 1$$

Note that the factorial is the product of n factors, with the number decreased by 1 for each factor.

One property of factorial notation is that it can be stopped at any point by using the exclamation point. For example,

$5! = 5 \cdot 4!$	since	$4! = 4 \cdot 3 \cdot 2 \cdot 1$
$\quad = 5 \cdot 4 \cdot 3!$	since	$3! = 3 \cdot 2 \cdot 1$
$\quad = 5 \cdot 4 \cdot 3 \cdot 2!$	since	$2! = 2 \cdot 1$
$\quad = 5 \cdot 4 \cdot 3 \cdot 2 \cdot 1$		

Thus,
$$n! = n(n - 1)!$$
$$\quad = n(n - 1)(n - 2)!$$
$$\quad = n(n - 1)(n - 2)(n - 3)! \quad \text{etc.}$$

Another property of factorials is

$$0! = 1$$

This fact is needed for formulas.

Operations with Factorials

Factorials cannot be added or subtracted directly. They must be multiplied out. Then the products can be added or subtracted.

Example A–1

Evaluate $3! + 4!$.

Solution

$$3! + 4! = (3 \cdot 2 \cdot 1) + (4 \cdot 3 \cdot 2 \cdot 1)$$
$$= 6 + 24 = 30$$

Note: $3! + 4! \neq 7!$, since $7! = 5040$.

Example A–2

Evaluate $5! - 3!$.

Solution

$$5! - 3! = (5 \cdot 4 \cdot 3 \cdot 2 \cdot 1) - (3 \cdot 2 \cdot 1)$$
$$= 120 - 6 = 114$$

Note: $5! - 3! \neq 2!$, since $2! = 2$.

Factorials cannot be multiplied directly. Again, you must multiply them out and then multiply the products.

Example A–3

Evaluate $3! \cdot 2!$.

Solution

$$3! \cdot 2! = (3 \cdot 2 \cdot 1) \cdot (2 \cdot 1) = 6 \cdot 2 = 12$$

Note: $3! \cdot 2! \neq 6!$, since $6! = 720$.

Finally, factorials cannot be divided directly unless they are equal.

Example A–4

Evaluate $6! \div 3!$.

Solution

$$\frac{6!}{3!} = \frac{6 \cdot 5 \cdot 4 \cdot 3 \cdot 2 \cdot 1}{3 \cdot 2 \cdot 1} = \frac{720}{6} = 120$$

Note: $\quad \dfrac{6!}{3!} \neq 2! \quad$ since $\quad 2! = 2$

But $\quad \dfrac{3!}{3!} = \dfrac{3 \cdot 2 \cdot 1}{3 \cdot 2 \cdot 1} = \dfrac{6}{6} = 1$

In division, you can take some shortcuts, as shown:

$$\frac{6!}{3!} = \frac{6 \cdot 5 \cdot 4 \cdot 3!}{3!} \qquad \text{and} \qquad \frac{3!}{3!} = 1$$
$$= 6 \cdot 5 \cdot 4 = 120$$

$$\frac{8!}{6!} = \frac{8 \cdot 7 \cdot 6!}{6!} \qquad \text{and} \qquad \frac{6!}{6!} = 1$$
$$= 8 \cdot 7 = 56$$

Another shortcut that can be used with factorials is cancellation, after factors have been expanded. For example,

$$\frac{7!}{(4!)(3!)} = \frac{7 \cdot 6 \cdot 5 \cdot 4!}{3 \cdot 2 \cdot 1 \cdot 4!}$$

Now cancel both instances of 4!. Then cancel the $3 \cdot 2$ in the denominator with the 6 in the numerator.

$$\frac{7 \cdot \overset{1}{\cancel{6}} \cdot 5 \cdot \overset{1}{\cancel{4!}}}{\underset{1}{\cancel{3}} \cdot \underset{1}{2} \cdot 1 \cdot \underset{1}{\cancel{4!}}} = 7 \cdot 5 = 35$$

Example A–5
Evaluate $10! \div (6!)(4!)$.

Solution

$$\frac{10!}{(6!)(4!)} = \frac{10 \cdot \overset{3}{\cancel{9}} \cdot 8 \cdot 7 \cdot \overset{1}{\cancel{6!}}}{\underset{1}{\cancel{4}} \cdot \underset{1}{\cancel{3}} \cdot \underset{1}{2} \cdot 1 \cdot \underset{1}{\cancel{6!}}} = 10 \cdot 3 \cdot 7 = 210$$

Exercises
Evaluate each expression.

A–1. 9!

A–2. 7!

A–3. 5!

A–4. 0!

A–5. 1!

A–6. 3!

A–7. $\frac{12!}{9!}$

A–8. $\frac{10!}{2!}$

A–9. $\frac{5!}{3!}$

A–10. $\frac{11!}{7!}$

A–11. $\frac{9!}{(4!)(5!)}$

A–12. $\frac{10!}{(7!)(3!)}$

A–13. $\frac{8!}{(4!)(4!)}$

A–14. $\frac{15!}{(12!)(3!)}$

A–15. $\frac{10!}{(10!)(0!)}$

A–16. $\frac{5!}{(3!)(2!)(1!)}$

A–17. $\frac{8!}{(3!)(3!)(2!)}$

A–18. $\frac{11!}{(7!)(2!)(2!)}$

A–19. $\frac{10!}{(3!)(2!)(5!)}$

A–20. $\frac{6!}{(2!)(2!)(2!)}$

A–2   Summation Notation

In mathematics, the symbol Σ (Greek capital letter sigma) means to add or find the sum. For example, ΣX means to add the numbers represented by the variable X. Thus, when X represents 5, 8, 2, 4, and 6, then ΣX means $5 + 8 + 2 + 4 + 6 = 25$.

Sometimes, a subscript notation is used, such as

$$\sum_{i=1}^{5} X_i$$

This notation means to find the sum of five numbers represented by X, as shown:

$$\sum_{i=1}^{5} X_i = X_1 + X_2 + X_3 + X_4 + X_5$$

When the number of values is not known, the unknown number can be represented by n, such as

$$\sum_{i=1}^{n} X_i = X_1 + X_2 + X_3 + \cdots + X_n$$

There are several important types of summation used in statistics. The notation ΣX^2 means to square each value before summing. For example, if the values of the X's are 2, 8, 6, 1, and 4, then

$$\Sigma X^2 = 2^2 + 8^2 + 6^2 + 1^2 + 4^2$$
$$= 4 + 64 + 36 + 1 + 16 = 121$$

The notation $(\Sigma X)^2$ means to find the sum of X's and then square the answer. For instance, if the values for X are 2, 8, 6, 1, and 4, then

$$(\Sigma X)^2 = (2 + 8 + 6 + 1 + 4)^2$$
$$= (21)^2 = 441$$

Another important use of summation notation is in finding the mean (shown in Section 3–1). The mean $\overline{X}$ is defined as

$$\overline{X} = \frac{\Sigma X}{n}$$

For example, to find the mean of 12, 8, 7, 3, and 10, use the formula and substitute the values, as shown:

$$\overline{X} = \frac{\Sigma X}{n} = \frac{12 + 8 + 7 + 3 + 10}{5} = \frac{40}{5} = 8$$

The notation $\Sigma(X - \bar{X})^2$ means to perform the following steps.

STEP 1 Find the mean.

STEP 2 Subtract the mean from each value.

STEP 3 Square the answers.

STEP 4 Find the sum.

Example A–6

Find the value of $\Sigma(X - \bar{X})^2$ for the values 12, 8, 7, 3, and 10 of X.

Solution

STEP 1 Find the mean.

$$\bar{X} = \frac{12 + 8 + 7 + 3 + 10}{5} = \frac{40}{5} = 8$$

STEP 2 Subtract the mean from each value.

$$12 - 8 = 4 \qquad 7 - 8 = -1 \qquad 10 - 8 = 2$$
$$8 - 8 = 0 \qquad 3 - 8 = -5$$

STEP 3 Square the answers.

$$4^2 = 16 \qquad (-1)^2 = 1 \qquad 2^2 = 4$$
$$0^2 = 0 \qquad (-5)^2 = 25$$

STEP 4 Find the sum.

$$16 + 0 + 1 + 25 + 4 = 46$$

Example A–7

Find $\Sigma(X - \bar{X})^2$ for the following values of X: 5, 7, 2, 1, 3, 6.

Solution

Find the mean.

$$\bar{X} = \frac{5 + 7 + 2 + 1 + 3 + 6}{6} = \frac{24}{6} = 4$$

Then the steps in Example A–6 can be shortened as follows:

$$\begin{aligned} \Sigma(X - \bar{X})^2 &= (5 - 4)^2 + (7 - 4)^2 + (2 - 4)^2 \\ &\quad + (1 - 4)^2 + (3 - 4)^2 + (6 - 4)^2 \\ &= 1^2 + 3^2 + (-2)^2 + (-3)^2 \\ &\quad + (-1)^2 + 2^2 \\ &= 1 + 9 + 4 + 9 + 1 + 4 = 28 \end{aligned}$$

Exercises

For each set of values, find ΣX, ΣX^2, $(\Sigma X)^2$, and $\Sigma(X - \bar{X})^2$.

A–21. 9, 17, 32, 16, 8, 2, 9, 7, 3, 18

A–22. 4, 12, 9, 13, 0, 6, 2, 10

A–23. 5, 12, 8, 3, 4

A–24. 6, 2, 18, 30, 31, 42, 16, 5

A–25. 80, 76, 42, 53, 77

A–26. 123, 132, 216, 98, 146, 114

A–27. 53, 72, 81, 42, 63, 71, 73, 85, 98, 55

A–28. 43, 32, 116, 98, 120

A–29. 12, 52, 36, 81, 63, 74

A–30. -9, -12, 18, 0, -2, -15

A–3   The Line

The following figure shows the *rectangular coordinate system*, or *Cartesian plane*. This figure consists of two axes: the horizontal axis, called the x axis, and the vertical axis, called the y axis. Each axis has numerical scales. The point of intersection of the axes is called the *origin*.

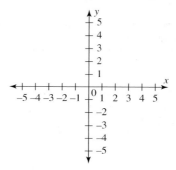

Points can be graphed by using coordinates. For example, the notation for point $P(3, 2)$ means that the x coordinate is 3 and the y coordinate is 2. Hence, P is located at the intersection of $x = 3$ and $y = 2$, as shown.

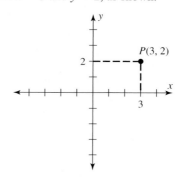

Other points, such as $Q(-5, 2)$, $R(4, 1)$, and $S(-3, -4)$, can be plotted, as shown in the next figure.

When a point lies on the y axis, the x coordinate is 0, as in $(0, 6)(0, -3)$, etc. When a point lies on the x axis, the y coordinate is 0, as in $(6, 0)(-8, 0)$, etc., as shown at the top of the next page.

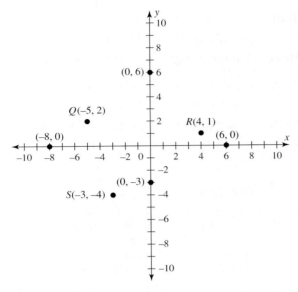

The slopes of lines can be positive, negative, or zero. A line going uphill from left to right has a positive slope. A line going downhill from left to right has a negative slope. And a line that is horizontal has a slope of zero.

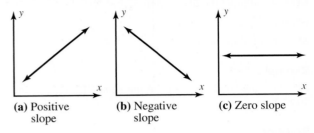

(a) Positive slope   **(b)** Negative slope   **(c)** Zero slope

A point b where the line crosses the x axis is called the *x intercept* and has the coordinates $(b, 0)$. A point a where the line crosses the y axis is called the *y intercept* and has the coordinates $(0, a)$.

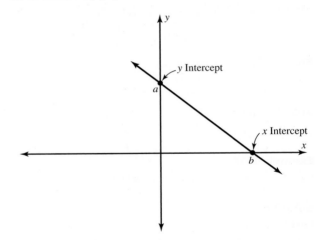

Two points determine a line. There are two properties of a line: its slope and its equation. The *slope m* of a line is determined by the ratio of the rise (called Δy) to the run (Δx).

$$m = \frac{\text{rise}}{\text{run}} = \frac{\Delta y}{\Delta x}$$

For example, the slope of the line shown below is $\frac{3}{2}$, or 1.5, since the height Δy is 3 units and the run Δx is 2 units.

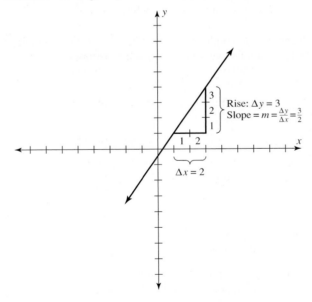

Every line has a unique equation of the form $y = a + bx$. For example, the equations

$$y = 5 + 3x$$
$$y = 8.6 + 3.2x$$
$$y = 5.2 - 6.1x$$

all represent different, unique lines. The number represented by a is the y intercept point; the number represented by b is the slope. The line whose equation is $y = 3 + 2x$ has a y intercept at 3 and a slope of 2, or $\frac{2}{1}$. This line can be shown as in the following graph.

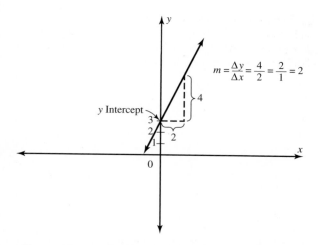

If two points are known, then the graph of the line can be plotted. For example, to find the graph of a line passing through the points $P(2, 1)$ and $Q(3, 5)$, plot the points and connect them as shown below.

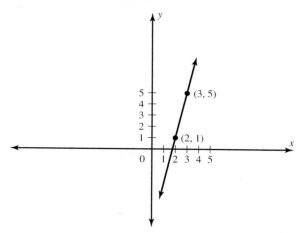

Given the equation of a line, you can graph the line by finding two points and then plotting them.

Example A–8

Plot the graph of the line whose equation is $y = 3 + 2x$.

Solution

Select any number as an x value, and substitute it in the equation to get the corresponding y value. Let $x = 0$.

Then

$$y = 3 + 2x = 3 + 2(0) = 3$$

Hence, when $x = 0$, then $y = 3$, and the line passes through the point $(0, 3)$.

Now select any other value of x, say, $x = 2$.

$$y = 3 + 2x = 3 + 2(2) = 7$$

Hence, a second point is $(2, 7)$. Then plot the points and graph the line.

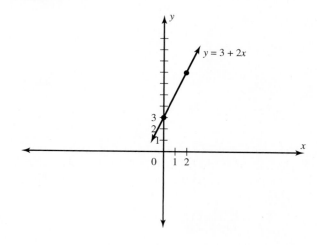

Exercises

Plot the line passing through each set of points.

A–31. $P(3, 2), Q(1, 6)$ **A–34.** $P(-1, -2), Q(-7, 8)$

A–32. $P(0, 5), Q(8, 0)$ **A–35.** $P(6, 3), Q(10, 3)$

A–33. $P(-2, 4), Q(3, 6)$

Find at least two points on each line, and then graph the line containing these points.

A–36. $y = 5 + 2x$ **A–39.** $y = -2 - 2x$

A–37. $y = -1 + x$ **A–40.** $y = 4 - 3x$

A–38. $y = 3 + 4x$

Appendix B-1

Writing the Research Report

After conducting a statistical study, a researcher must write a final report explaining how the study was conducted and giving the results. The formats of research reports, theses, and dissertations vary from school to school; however, they tend to follow the general format explained here.

Front Materials

The front materials typically include the following items:

Title page
Copyright page
Acknowledgments
Table of contents
Table of appendixes
List of tables
List of figures

Chapter 1: Nature and Background of the Study

This chapter should introduce the reader to the nature of the study and present some discussion on the background. It should contain the following information:

Introduction
Statement of the problem
Background of the problem
Rationale for the study
Research questions and/or hypotheses
Assumptions, limitations, and delimitations
Definitions of terms

Chapter 2: Review of Literature

This chapter should explain what has been done in previous research related to the study. It should contain the following information:

Prior research
Related literature

Chapter 3: Methodology

This chapter should explain how the study was conducted. It should contain the following information:

Development of questionnaires, tests, survey instruments, etc.
Definition of the population
Sampling methods used
How the data were collected
Research design used
Statistical tests that will be used to analyze the data

Chapter 4: Analysis of Data

This chapter should explain the results of the statistical analysis of the data. It should state whether the null hypothesis should be rejected. Any statistical tables used to analyze the data should be included here.

Chapter 5: Summary, Conclusions, and Recommendations

This chapter summarizes the results of the study and explains any conclusions that have resulted from the statistical analysis of the data. The researchers should cite and explain any shortcomings of the study. Recommendations obtained from the study should be included here, and further studies should be suggested.

Alternate Approach to the Standard Normal Distribution

The following procedure may be used to replace the cumulative area to the left procedure shown in Section 6–1. This method determines areas from the mean where $z = 0$.

Finding Areas Under the Standard Normal Distribution

For the solution of problems using the standard normal distribution, a four-step procedure may be used with the use of the Procedure Table shown.

STEP 1 Sketch the normal curve and label.

STEP 2 Shade the area desired.

STEP 3 Find the figure that matches the shaded area from the following procedure table.

STEP 4 Follow the directions given in the appropriate block of the procedure table to get the desired area.

Note: Table B–1 gives the area between 0 and any z score to the right of 0, and all areas are positive.

There are seven basic types of problems and all seven are summarized in the Procedure Table, with appropriate examples.

Procedure Table

Examples

1. Between 0 and any z score:
Look up the z score in the table to get the area.

B–3–1: Find the area between $z = 0$ and $z = 1.23$.

Look up area from $z = 0$ to $z = 1.23$ on Table B–1, as shown below.

The area between $z = 0$ and $z = 1.23$ is 0.3907.

2. In any tail:
   a. Look up the z score to get the area.
   b. Subtract the area from 0.5000.

B–3–2: Find the area to the left of $z = -2.37$.

Look up area from $z = 0$ to $z = 2.37$ on Table B–1, as shown below.

The area from $z = 0$ to $z = 2.37$ is the same as the area from $z = 0$ to $z = -2.37$.
Therefore, the area to the left of $z = -2.37 = 0.5000 - 0.4911 = 0.0089$.

3. Between two z scores on the same side of the mean:
   a. Look up both z scores to get the areas.
   b. Subtract the smaller area from the larger area.

B–3–3: Find the area between $z = 1.23$ and $z = 2.37$.

Look up areas for $z = 0$ to $z = 1.23$ and $z = 0$ to $z = 2.37$, as shown in B–3–1 and B–3–2, respectively.

The area between $z = 1.23$ and $z = 2.37 = 0.4911 - 0.3907 = 0.1004$.

4. Between two z scores on opposite sides of the mean:
   a. Look up both z scores to get the areas.
   b. Add the areas.

B–3–4: Find the area between $z = -1.23$ and $z = 2.37$.

Look up areas for $z = 0$ to $z = 1.23$ and $z = 0$ to $z = 2.37$, as shown in B–3–1 and B–3–2, respectively.

The area between $z = -1.23$ and $z = 2.37 = 0.3907 + 0.4911 = 0.8818$.

5. To the left of any z score, where z is greater than the mean:

   a. Look up the z score to get the area.

   b. Add 0.5000 to the area.

B-3-5: Find the area to the left of z = 2.37.

Look up area for z = 2.37, as shown in B-3-2.

The area to the left of z = 0 is 0.5000.

The area to the left of z = 2.37 = 0.4911 + 0.5000 = 0.9911.

6. To the right of any z score, where z is less than the mean:

   a. Look up the area in the table to get the area.

   b. Add 0.5000 to the area.

B-3-6: Find the area to the right of z = −2.37.

Look up area for z = 2.37, as shown in B-3-2.

The area to the right of z = 0 is 0.5000.

The area to the right of z = −2.37 = 0.4911 + 0.5000 = 0.9911.

7. In any two tails:

   a. Look up the z scores in the table to get the areas.

   b. Subtract both areas from 0.5000.

   c. Add the answers.

B-3-7: Find the area to the left of z = −1.23 and to the right of z = 2.37.

Look up areas for z = 0 to z = 1.23 and z = 0 to z = 2.37, as shown in B-3-1 and B-3-2, respectively.

Area to the left of z = −1.23 = 0.5000 − 0.3907 = 0.1093.

Area to the right of z = 2.37 = 0.5000 − 0.4911 = 0.0089.

The area to the left of z = −1.23 and to the right of z = 2.37 = 0.1093 + 0.0089 = 0.1182.

Table B-1	The Standard Normal Distribution

z	.00	.01	.02	.03	.04	.05	.06	.07	.08	.09
0.0	.0000	.0040	.0080	.0120	.0160	.0199	.0239	.0279	.0319	.0359
0.1	.0398	.0438	.0478	.0517	.0557	.0596	.0636	.0675	.0714	.0753
0.2	.0793	.0832	.0871	.0910	.0948	.0987	.1026	.1064	.1103	.1141
0.3	.1179	.1217	.1255	.1293	.1331	.1368	.1406	.1443	.1480	.1517
0.4	.1554	.1591	.1628	.1664	.1700	.1736	.1772	.1808	.1844	.1879
0.5	.1915	.1950	.1985	.2019	.2054	.2088	.2123	.2157	.2190	.2224
0.6	.2257	.2291	.2324	.2357	.2389	.2422	.2454	.2486	.2517	.2549
0.7	.2580	.2611	.2642	.2673	.2704	.2734	.2764	.2794	.2823	.2852
0.8	.2881	.2910	.2939	.2967	.2995	.3023	.3051	.3078	.3106	.3133
0.9	.3159	.3186	.3212	.3238	.3264	.3289	.3315	.3340	.3365	.3389
1.0	.3413	.3438	.3461	.3485	.3508	.3531	.3554	.3577	.3599	.3621
1.1	.3643	.3665	.3686	.3708	.3729	.3749	.3770	.3790	.3810	.3830
1.2	.3849	.3869	.3888	.3907	.3925	.3944	.3962	.3980	.3997	.4015
1.3	.4032	.4049	.4066	.4082	.4099	.4115	.4131	.4147	.4162	.4177
1.4	.4192	.4207	.4222	.4236	.4251	.4265	.4279	.4292	.4306	.4319
1.5	.4332	.4345	.4357	.4370	.4382	.4394	.4406	.4418	.4429	.4441
1.6	.4452	.4463	.4474	.4484	.4495	.4505	.4515	.4525	.4535	.4545
1.7	.4554	.4564	.4573	.4582	.4591	.4599	.4608	.4616	.4625	.4633
1.8	.4641	.4649	.4656	.4664	.4671	.4678	.4686	.4693	.4699	.4706
1.9	.4713	.4719	.4726	.4732	.4738	.4744	.4750	.4756	.4761	.4767
2.0	.4772	.4778	.4783	.4788	.4793	.4798	.4803	.4808	.4812	.4817
2.1	.4821	.4826	.4830	.4834	.4838	.4842	.4846	.4850	.4854	.4857
2.2	.4861	.4864	.4868	.4871	.4875	.4878	.4881	.4884	.4887	.4890
2.3	.4893	.4896	.4898	.4901	.4904	.4906	.4909	.4911	.4913	.4916
2.4	.4918	.4920	.4922	.4925	.4927	.4929	.4931	.4932	.4934	.4936
2.5	.4938	.4940	.4941	.4943	.4945	.4946	.4948	.4949	.4951	.4952
2.6	.4953	.4955	.4956	.4957	.4959	.4960	.4961	.4962	.4963	.4964
2.7	.4965	.4966	.4967	.4968	.4969	.4970	.4971	.4972	.4973	.4974
2.8	.4974	.4975	.4976	.4977	.4977	.4978	.4979	.4979	.4980	.4981
2.9	.4981	.4982	.4982	.4983	.4984	.4984	.4985	.4985	.4986	.4986
3.0	.4987	.4987	.4987	.4988	.4988	.4989	.4989	.4989	.4990	.4990
3.1	.4990	.4991	.4991	.4991	.4992	.4992	.4992	.4992	.4993	.4993
3.2	.4993	.4993	.4994	.4994	.4994	.4994	.4994	.4995	.4995	.4995
3.3	.4995	.4995	.4995	.4996	.4996	.4996	.4996	.4996	.4996	.4997
3.4	.4997	.4997	.4997	.4997	.4997	.4997	.4997	.4997	.4997	.4998

For z values greater than 3.49, use 0.4999.

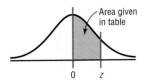

Area given in table

0   z

Appendix C

Tables

Table A	Factorials
n	$n!$
0	1
1	1
2	2
3	6
4	24
5	120
6	720
7	5,040
8	40,320
9	362,880
10	3,628,800
11	39,916,800
12	479,001,600
13	6,227,020,800
14	87,178,291,200
15	1,307,674,368,000
16	20,922,789,888,000
17	355,687,428,096,000
18	6,402,373,705,728,000
19	121,645,100,408,832,000
20	2,432,902,008,176,640,000

| Table B | The Binomial Distribution |

		p										
n	x	0.05	0.1	0.2	0.3	0.4	0.5	0.6	0.7	0.8	0.9	0.95
2	0	0.902	0.810	0.640	0.490	0.360	0.250	0.160	0.090	0.040	0.010	0.002
	1	0.095	0.180	0.320	0.420	0.480	0.500	0.480	0.420	0.320	0.180	0.095
	2	0.002	0.010	0.040	0.090	0.160	0.250	0.360	0.490	0.640	0.810	0.902
3	0	0.857	0.729	0.512	0.343	0.216	0.125	0.064	0.027	0.008	0.001	
	1	0.135	0.243	0.384	0.441	0.432	0.375	0.288	0.189	0.096	0.027	0.007
	2	0.007	0.027	0.096	0.189	0.288	0.375	0.432	0.441	0.384	0.243	0.135
	3		0.001	0.008	0.027	0.064	0.125	0.216	0.343	0.512	0.729	0.857
4	0	0.815	0.656	0.410	0.240	0.130	0.062	0.026	0.008	0.002		
	1	0.171	0.292	0.410	0.412	0.346	0.250	0.154	0.076	0.026	0.004	
	2	0.014	0.049	0.154	0.265	0.346	0.375	0.346	0.265	0.154	0.049	0.014
	3		0.004	0.026	0.076	0.154	0.250	0.346	0.412	0.410	0.292	0.171
	4			0.002	0.008	0.026	0.062	0.130	0.240	0.410	0.656	0.815
5	0	0.774	0.590	0.328	0.168	0.078	0.031	0.010	0.002			
	1	0.204	0.328	0.410	0.360	0.259	0.156	0.077	0.028	0.006		
	2	0.021	0.073	0.205	0.309	0.346	0.312	0.230	0.132	0.051	0.008	0.001
	3	0.001	0.008	0.051	0.132	0.230	0.312	0.346	0.309	0.205	0.073	0.021
	4			0.006	0.028	0.077	0.156	0.259	0.360	0.410	0.328	0.204
	5				0.002	0.010	0.031	0.078	0.168	0.328	0.590	0.774
6	0	0.735	0.531	0.262	0.118	0.047	0.016	0.004	0.001			
	1	0.232	0.354	0.393	0.303	0.187	0.094	0.037	0.010	0.002		
	2	0.031	0.098	0.246	0.324	0.311	0.234	0.138	0.060	0.015	0.001	
	3	0.002	0.015	0.082	0.185	0.276	0.312	0.276	0.185	0.082	0.015	0.002
	4		0.001	0.015	0.060	0.138	0.234	0.311	0.324	0.246	0.098	0.031
	5			0.002	0.010	0.037	0.094	0.187	0.303	0.393	0.354	0.232
	6				0.001	0.004	0.016	0.047	0.118	0.262	0.531	0.735
7	0	0.698	0.478	0.210	0.082	0.028	0.008	0.002				
	1	0.257	0.372	0.367	0.247	0.131	0.055	0.017	0.004			
	2	0.041	0.124	0.275	0.318	0.261	0.164	0.077	0.025	0.004		
	3	0.004	0.023	0.115	0.227	0.290	0.273	0.194	0.097	0.029	0.003	
	4		0.003	0.029	0.097	0.194	0.273	0.290	0.227	0.115	0.023	0.004
	5			0.004	0.025	0.077	0.164	0.261	0.318	0.275	0.124	0.041
	6				0.004	0.017	0.055	0.131	0.247	0.367	0.372	0.257
	7					0.002	0.008	0.028	0.082	0.210	0.478	0.698
8	0	0.663	0.430	0.168	0.058	0.017	0.004	0.001				
	1	0.279	0.383	0.336	0.198	0.090	0.031	0.008	0.001			
	2	0.051	0.149	0.294	0.296	0.209	0.109	0.041	0.010	0.001		
	3	0.005	0.033	0.147	0.254	0.279	0.219	0.124	0.047	0.009		
	4		0.005	0.046	0.136	0.232	0.273	0.232	0.136	0.046	0.005	
	5			0.009	0.047	0.124	0.219	0.279	0.254	0.147	0.033	0.005
	6			0.001	0.010	0.041	0.109	0.209	0.296	0.294	0.149	0.051
	7				0.001	0.008	0.031	0.090	0.198	0.336	0.383	0.279
	8					0.001	0.004	0.017	0.058	0.168	0.430	0.663

Table B (continued)

n	x	0.05	0.1	0.2	0.3	0.4	0.5	0.6	0.7	0.8	0.9	0.95
9	0	0.630	0.387	0.134	0.040	0.010	0.002					
	1	0.299	0.387	0.302	0.156	0.060	0.018	0.004				
	2	0.063	0.172	0.302	0.267	0.161	0.070	0.021	0.004			
	3	0.008	0.045	0.176	0.267	0.251	0.164	0.074	0.021	0.003		
	4	0.001	0.007	0.066	0.172	0.251	0.246	0.167	0.074	0.017	0.001	
	5		0.001	0.017	0.074	0.167	0.246	0.251	0.172	0.066	0.007	0.001
	6			0.003	0.021	0.074	0.164	0.251	0.267	0.176	0.045	0.008
	7				0.004	0.021	0.070	0.161	0.267	0.302	0.172	0.063
	8					0.004	0.018	0.060	0.156	0.302	0.387	0.299
	9						0.002	0.010	0.040	0.134	0.387	0.630
10	0	0.599	0.349	0.107	0.028	0.006	0.001					
	1	0.315	0.387	0.268	0.121	0.040	0.010	0.002				
	2	0.075	0.194	0.302	0.233	0.121	0.044	0.011	0.001			
	3	0.010	0.057	0.201	0.267	0.215	0.117	0.042	0.009	0.001		
	4	0.001	0.011	0.088	0.200	0.251	0.205	0.111	0.037	0.006		
	5		0.001	0.026	0.103	0.201	0.246	0.201	0.103	0.026	0.001	
	6			0.006	0.037	0.111	0.205	0.251	0.200	0.088	0.011	0.001
	7			0.001	0.009	0.042	0.117	0.215	0.267	0.201	0.057	0.010
	8				0.001	0.011	0.044	0.121	0.233	0.302	0.194	0.075
	9					0.002	0.010	0.040	0.121	0.268	0.387	0.315
	10						0.001	0.006	0.028	0.107	0.349	0.599
11	0	0.569	0.314	0.086	0.020	0.004						
	1	0.329	0.384	0.236	0.093	0.027	0.005	0.001				
	2	0.087	0.213	0.295	0.200	0.089	0.027	0.005	0.001			
	3	0.014	0.071	0.221	0.257	0.177	0.081	0.023	0.004			
	4	0.001	0.016	0.111	0.220	0.236	0.161	0.070	0.017	0.002		
	5		0.002	0.039	0.132	0.221	0.226	0.147	0.057	0.010		
	6			0.010	0.057	0.147	0.226	0.221	0.132	0.039	0.002	
	7			0.002	0.017	0.070	0.161	0.236	0.220	0.111	0.016	0.001
	8				0.004	0.023	0.081	0.177	0.257	0.221	0.071	0.014
	9				0.001	0.005	0.027	0.089	0.200	0.295	0.213	0.087
	10					0.001	0.005	0.027	0.093	0.236	0.384	0.329
	11							0.004	0.020	0.086	0.314	0.569
12	0	0.540	0.282	0.069	0.014	0.002						
	1	0.341	0.377	0.206	0.071	0.017	0.003					
	2	0.099	0.230	0.283	0.168	0.064	0.016	0.002				
	3	0.017	0.085	0.236	0.240	0.142	0.054	0.012	0.001			
	4	0.002	0.021	0.133	0.231	0.213	0.121	0.042	0.008	0.001		
	5		0.004	0.053	0.158	0.227	0.193	0.101	0.029	0.003		
	6			0.016	0.079	0.177	0.226	0.177	0.079	0.016		
	7			0.003	0.029	0.101	0.193	0.227	0.158	0.053	0.004	
	8			0.001	0.008	0.042	0.121	0.213	0.231	0.133	0.021	0.002
	9				0.001	0.012	0.054	0.142	0.240	0.236	0.085	0.017
	10					0.002	0.016	0.064	0.168	0.283	0.230	0.099
	11						0.003	0.017	0.071	0.206	0.377	0.341
	12							0.002	0.014	0.069	0.282	0.540

Table B   (continued)

n	x	0.05	0.1	0.2	0.3	0.4	0.5	0.6	0.7	0.8	0.9	0.95
13	0	0.513	0.254	0.055	0.010	0.001						
	1	0.351	0.367	0.179	0.054	0.011	0.002					
	2	0.111	0.245	0.268	0.139	0.045	0.010	0.001				
	3	0.021	0.100	0.246	0.218	0.111	0.035	0.006	0.001			
	4	0.003	0.028	0.154	0.234	0.184	0.087	0.024	0.003			
	5		0.006	0.069	0.180	0.221	0.157	0.066	0.014	0.001		
	6		0.001	0.023	0.103	0.197	0.209	0.131	0.044	0.006		
	7			0.006	0.044	0.131	0.209	0.197	0.103	0.023	0.001	
	8			0.001	0.014	0.066	0.157	0.221	0.180	0.069	0.006	
	9				0.003	0.024	0.087	0.184	0.234	0.154	0.028	0.003
	10				0.001	0.006	0.035	0.111	0.218	0.246	0.100	0.021
	11					0.001	0.010	0.045	0.139	0.268	0.245	0.111
	12						0.002	0.011	0.054	0.179	0.367	0.351
	13							0.001	0.010	0.055	0.254	0.513
14	0	0.488	0.229	0.044	0.007	0.001						
	1	0.359	0.356	0.154	0.041	0.007	0.001					
	2	0.123	0.257	0.250	0.113	0.032	0.006	0.001				
	3	0.026	0.114	0.250	0.194	0.085	0.022	0.003				
	4	0.004	0.035	0.172	0.229	0.155	0.061	0.014	0.001			
	5		0.008	0.086	0.196	0.207	0.122	0.041	0.007			
	6		0.001	0.032	0.126	0.207	0.183	0.092	0.023	0.002		
	7			0.009	0.062	0.157	0.209	0.157	0.062	0.009		
	8			0.002	0.023	0.092	0.183	0.207	0.126	0.032	0.001	
	9				0.007	0.041	0.122	0.207	0.196	0.086	0.008	
	10				0.001	0.014	0.061	0.155	0.229	0.172	0.035	0.004
	11					0.003	0.022	0.085	0.194	0.250	0.114	0.026
	12					0.001	0.006	0.032	0.113	0.250	0.257	0.123
	13						0.001	0.007	0.041	0.154	0.356	0.359
	14							0.001	0.007	0.044	0.229	0.488
15	0	0.463	0.206	0.035	0.005							
	1	0.366	0.343	0.132	0.031	0.005						
	2	0.135	0.267	0.231	0.092	0.022	0.003					
	3	0.031	0.129	0.250	0.170	0.063	0.014	0.002				
	4	0.005	0.043	0.188	0.219	0.127	0.042	0.007	0.001			
	5	0.001	0.010	0.103	0.206	0.186	0.092	0.024	0.003			
	6		0.002	0.043	0.147	0.207	0.153	0.061	0.012	0.001		
	7			0.014	0.081	0.177	0.196	0.118	0.035	0.003		
	8			0.003	0.035	0.118	0.196	0.177	0.081	0.014		
	9			0.001	0.012	0.061	0.153	0.207	0.147	0.043	0.002	
	10				0.003	0.024	0.092	0.186	0.206	0.103	0.010	0.001
	11				0.001	0.007	0.042	0.127	0.219	0.188	0.043	0.005
	12					0.002	0.014	0.063	0.170	0.250	0.129	0.031
	13						0.003	0.022	0.092	0.231	0.267	0.135
	14							0.005	0.031	0.132	0.343	0.366
	15							0.005	0.035	0.206	0.463	

Table B		(continued)									

							p					
n	x	**0.05**	**0.1**	**0.2**	**0.3**	**0.4**	**0.5**	**0.6**	**0.7**	**0.8**	**0.9**	**0.95**
16	0	0.440	0.185	0.028	0.003							
	1	0.371	0.329	0.113	0.023	0.003						
	2	0.146	0.275	0.211	0.073	0.015	0.002					
	3	0.036	0.142	0.246	0.146	0.047	0.009	0.001				
	4	0.006	0.051	0.200	0.204	0.101	0.028	0.004				
	5	0.001	0.014	0.120	0.210	0.162	0.067	0.014	0.001			
	6		0.003	0.055	0.165	0.198	0.122	0.039	0.006			
	7			0.020	0.101	0.189	0.175	0.084	0.019	0.001		
	8			0.006	0.049	0.142	0.196	0.142	0.049	0.006		
	9			0.001	0.019	0.084	0.175	0.189	0.101	0.020		
	10				0.006	0.039	0.122	0.198	0.165	0.055	0.003	
	11				0.001	0.014	0.067	0.162	0.210	0.120	0.014	0.001
	12					0.004	0.028	0.101	0.204	0.200	0.051	0.006
	13					0.001	0.009	0.047	0.146	0.246	0.142	0.036
	14						0.002	0.015	0.073	0.211	0.275	0.146
	15							0.003	0.023	0.113	0.329	0.371
	16								0.003	0.028	0.185	0.440
17	0	0.418	0.167	0.023	0.002							
	1	0.374	0.315	0.096	0.017	0.002						
	2	0.158	0.280	0.191	0.058	0.010	0.001					
	3	0.041	0.156	0.239	0.125	0.034	0.005					
	4	0.008	0.060	0.209	0.187	0.080	0.018	0.002				
	5	0.001	0.017	0.136	0.208	0.138	0.047	0.008	0.001			
	6		0.004	0.068	0.178	0.184	0.094	0.024	0.003			
	7		0.001	0.027	0.120	0.193	0.148	0.057	0.009			
	8			0.008	0.064	0.161	0.185	0.107	0.028	0.002		
	9			0.002	0.028	0.107	0.185	0.161	0.064	0.008		
	10				0.009	0.057	0.148	0.193	0.120	0.027	0.001	
	11				0.003	0.024	0.094	0.184	0.178	0.068	0.004	
	12				0.001	0.008	0.047	0.138	0.208	0.136	0.017	0.001
	13					0.002	0.018	0.080	0.187	0.209	0.060	0.008
	14						0.005	0.034	0.125	0.239	0.156	0.041
	15						0.001	0.010	0.058	0.191	0.280	0.158
	16							0.002	0.017	0.096	0.315	0.374
	17								0.002	0.023	0.167	0.418

Table B　(continued)

n	x	p 0.05	0.1	0.2	0.3	0.4	0.5	0.6	0.7	0.8	0.9	0.95
18	0	0.397	0.150	0.018	0.002							
	1	0.376	0.300	0.081	0.013	0.001						
	2	0.168	0.284	0.172	0.046	0.007	0.001					
	3	0.047	0.168	0.230	0.105	0.025	0.003					
	4	0.009	0.168	0.215	0.168	0.061	0.012	0.001				
	5	0.001	0.070	0.151	0.202	0.115	0.033	0.004				
	6		0.022	0.082	0.187	0.166	0.071	0.015	0.001			
	7		0.005	0.035	0.138	0.189	0.121	0.037	0.005			
	8		0.001	0.012	0.081	0.173	0.167	0.077	0.015	0.001		
	9			0.003	0.039	0.128	0.185	0.128	0.039	0.003		
	10			0.001	0.015	0.077	0.167	0.173	0.081	0.012		
	11				0.005	0.037	0.121	0.189	0.138	0.035	0.001	
	12				0.001	0.015	0.071	0.166	0.187	0.082	0.005	
	13					0.004	0.033	0.115	0.202	0.151	0.022	0.001
	14					0.001	0.012	0.061	0.168	0.215	0.070	0.009
	15						0.003	0.025	0.105	0.230	0.168	0.047
	16						0.001	0.007	0.046	0.172	0.284	0.168
	17							0.001	0.013	0.081	0.300	0.376
	18								0.002	0.018	0.150	0.397
19	0	0.377	0.135	0.014	0.001							
	1	0.377	0.285	0.068	0.009	0.001						
	2	0.179	0.285	0.154	0.036	0.005						
	3	0.053	0.180	0.218	0.087	0.017	0.002					
	4	0.011	0.080	0.218	0.149	0.047	0.007	0.001				
	5	0.002	0.027	0.164	0.192	0.093	0.022	0.002				
	6		0.007	0.095	0.192	0.145	0.052	0.008	0.001			
	7		0.001	0.044	0.153	0.180	0.096	0.024	0.002			
	8			0.017	0.098	0.180	0.144	0.053	0.008			
	9			0.005	0.051	0.146	0.176	0.098	0.022	0.001		
	10			0.001	0.022	0.098	0.176	0.146	0.051	0.005		
	11				0.008	0.053	0.144	0.180	0.098	0.071		
	12				0.002	0.024	0.096	0.180	0.153	0.044	0.001	
	13				0.001	0.008	0.052	0.145	0.192	0.095	0.007	
	14					0.002	0.022	0.093	0.192	0.164	0.027	0.002
	15					0.001	0.007	0.047	0.149	0.218	0.080	0.011
	16						0.002	0.017	0.087	0.218	0.180	0.053
	17							0.005	0.036	0.154	0.285	0.179
	18							0.001	0.009	0.068	0.285	0.377
	19								0.001	0.014	0.135	0.377

Table B	(concluded)										
							p					
n	x	0.05	0.1	0.2	0.3	0.4	0.5	0.6	0.7	0.8	0.9	0.95
20	0	0.358	0.122	0.012	0.001							
	1	0.377	0.270	0.058	0.007							
	2	0.189	0.285	0.137	0.028	0.003						
	3	0.060	0.190	0.205	0.072	0.012	0.001					
	4	0.013	0.090	0.218	0.130	0.035	0.005					
	5	0.002	0.032	0.175	0.179	0.075	0.015	0.001				
	6		0.009	0.109	0.192	0.124	0.037	0.005				
	7		0.002	0.055	0.164	0.166	0.074	0.015	0.001			
	8			0.022	0.114	0.180	0.120	0.035	0.004			
	9			0.007	0.065	0.160	0.160	0.071	0.012			
	10			0.002	0.031	0.117	0.176	0.117	0.031	0.002		
	11				0.012	0.071	0.160	0.160	0.065	0.007		
	12				0.004	0.035	0.120	0.180	0.114	0.022		
	13				0.001	0.015	0.074	0.166	0.164	0.055	0.002	
	14					0.005	0.037	0.124	0.192	0.109	0.009	
	15					0.001	0.015	0.075	0.179	0.175	0.032	0.002
	16						0.005	0.035	0.130	0.218	0.090	0.013
	17						0.001	0.012	0.072	0.205	0.190	0.060
	18							0.003	0.028	0.137	0.285	0.189
	19								0.007	0.058	0.270	0.377
	20								0.001	0.012	0.122	0.358

Note: All values of 0.0005 or less are omitted.

Source: John E. Freund, *Modern Elementary Statistics,* 8th ed., © 1992. Reprinted by permission of Prentice-Hall, Inc., Upper Saddle River, N.J.

Table C   Permutations and Combinations

This table contains the number of permutations of n objects taking r at a time or $_nP_r$

n \ r	0	1	2	3	4	5	6	7	8	9	10
0	1										
1	1	1									
2	1	2	2								
3	1	3	6	6							
4	1	4	12	24	24						
5	1	5	20	60	120	120					
6	1	6	30	120	360	720	720				
7	1	7	42	210	840	2,520	5,040	5,040			
8	1	8	56	336	1,680	6,720	20,160	40,320	40,320		
9	1	9	72	504	3,024	15,120	60,480	181,440	362,880	362,880	
10	1	10	90	720	5,040	30,240	151,200	604,800	1,814,400	3,628,800	3,628,800

This table contains the number of combinations of n objects taking r at a time or $_nC_r$

n \ r	0	1	2	3	4	5	6	7	8	9	10
1	1	1									
2	1	2	1								
3	1	3	3	1							
4	1	4	6	4	1						
5	1	5	10	10	5	1					
6	1	6	15	20	15	6	1				
7	1	7	21	35	35	21	7	1			
8	1	8	28	56	70	56	28	8	1		
9	1	9	36	84	126	126	84	36	9	1	
10	1	10	45	120	210	252	210	120	45	10	1

To find the value of $_nP_r$ or $_nC_r$, locate n in the left column and r in the top row. The answer is found where the row and column intersect in the table.

Examples: $_4P_3 = 24$ $_5C_2 = 10$

Table D   Random Numbers

10480	15011	01536	02011	81647	91646	67179	14194	62590	36207	20969	99570	91291	90700
22368	46573	25595	85393	30995	89198	27982	53402	93965	34095	52666	19174	39615	99505
24130	48360	22527	97265	76393	64809	15179	24830	49340	32081	30680	19655	63348	58629
42167	93093	06243	61680	07856	16376	39440	53537	71341	57004	00849	74917	97758	16379
37570	39975	81837	16656	06121	91782	60468	81305	49684	60672	14110	06927	01263	54613
77921	06907	11008	42751	27756	53498	18602	70659	90655	15053	21916	81825	44394	42880
99562	72905	56420	69994	98872	31016	71194	18738	44013	48840	63213	21069	10634	12952
96301	91977	05463	07972	18876	20922	94595	56869	69014	60045	18425	84903	42508	32307
89579	14342	63661	10281	17453	18103	57740	84378	25331	12566	58678	44947	05584	56941
85475	36857	43342	53988	53060	59533	38867	62300	08158	17983	16439	11458	18593	64952
28918	69578	88231	33276	70997	79936	56865	05859	90106	31595	01547	85590	91610	78188
63553	40961	48235	03427	49626	69445	18663	72695	52180	20847	12234	90511	33703	90322
09429	93969	52636	92737	88974	33488	36320	17617	30015	08272	84115	27156	30613	74952
10365	61129	87529	85689	48237	52267	67689	93394	01511	26358	85104	20285	29975	89868
07119	97336	71048	08178	77233	13916	47564	81056	97735	85977	29372	74461	28551	90707
51085	12765	51821	51259	77452	16308	60756	92144	49442	53900	70960	63990	75601	40719
02368	21382	52404	60268	89368	19885	55322	44819	01188	65255	64835	44919	05944	55157
01011	54092	33362	94904	31273	04146	18594	29852	71585	85030	51132	01915	92747	64951
52162	53916	46369	58586	23216	14513	83149	98736	23495	64350	94738	17752	35156	35749
07056	97628	33787	09998	42698	06691	76988	13602	51851	46104	88916	19509	25625	58104
48663	91245	85828	14346	09172	30168	90229	04734	59193	22178	30421	61666	99904	32812
54164	58492	22421	74103	47070	25306	76468	26384	58151	06646	21524	15227	96909	44592
32639	32363	05597	24200	13363	38005	94342	28728	35806	06912	17012	64161	18296	22851
29334	27001	87637	87308	58731	00256	45834	15398	46557	41135	10367	07684	36188	18510
02488	33062	28834	07351	19731	92420	60952	61280	50001	67658	32586	86679	50720	94953
81525	72295	04839	96423	24878	82651	66566	14778	76797	14780	13300	87074	79666	95725
29676	20591	68086	26432	46901	20849	89768	81536	86645	12659	92259	57102	80428	25280
00742	57392	39064	66432	84673	40027	32832	61362	98947	96067	64760	64584	96096	98253
05366	04213	25669	26422	44407	44048	37937	63904	45766	66134	75470	66520	34693	90449
91921	26418	64117	94305	26766	25940	39972	22209	71500	64568	91402	42416	07844	69618
00582	04711	87917	77341	42206	35126	74087	99547	81817	42607	43808	76655	62028	76630
00725	69884	62797	56170	86324	88072	76222	36086	84637	93161	76038	65855	77919	88006
69011	65797	95876	55293	18988	27354	26575	08625	40801	59920	29841	80150	12777	48501
25976	57948	29888	88604	67917	48708	18912	82271	65424	69774	33611	54262	85963	03547
09763	83473	73577	12908	30883	18317	28290	35797	05998	41688	34952	37888	38917	88050
91567	42595	27958	30134	04024	86385	29880	99730	55536	84855	29080	09250	79656	73211
17955	56349	90999	49127	20044	59931	06115	20542	18059	02008	73708	83517	36103	42791
46503	18584	18845	49618	02304	51038	20655	58727	28168	15475	56942	53389	20562	87338
92157	89634	94824	78171	84610	82834	09922	25417	44137	48413	25555	21246	35509	20468
14577	62765	35605	81263	39667	47358	56873	56307	61607	49518	89656	20103	77490	18062
98427	07523	33362	64270	01638	92477	66969	98420	04880	45585	46565	04102	46880	45709
34914	63976	88720	82765	34476	17032	87589	40836	32427	70002	70663	88863	77775	69348
70060	28277	39475	46473	23219	53416	94970	25832	69975	94884	19661	72828	00102	66794
53976	54914	06990	67245	68350	82948	11398	42878	80287	88267	47363	46634	06541	97809
76072	29515	40980	07391	58745	25774	22987	80059	39911	96189	41151	14222	60697	59583
90725	52210	83974	29992	65831	38857	50490	83765	55657	14361	31720	57375	56228	41546
64364	67412	33339	31926	14883	24413	59744	92351	97473	89286	35931	04110	23726	51900
08962	00358	31662	25388	61642	34072	81249	35648	56891	69352	48373	45578	78547	81788
95012	68379	93526	70765	10593	04542	76463	54328	02349	17247	28865	14777	62730	92277
15664	10493	20492	38391	91132	21999	59516	81652	27195	48223	46751	22923	32261	85653

Reprinted with permission from W. H. Beyer, *Handbook of Tables for Probability and Statistics,* 2nd ed. Copyright CRC Press, Boca Raton, Fla., 1986.

| Table E | The Standard Normal Distribution |

Cumulative Standard Normal Distribution

z	.00	.01	.02	.03	.04	.05	.06	.07	.08	.09
−3.4	.0003	.0003	.0003	.0003	.0003	.0003	.0003	.0003	.0003	.0002
−3.3	.0005	.0005	.0005	.0004	.0004	.0004	.0004	.0004	.0004	.0003
−3.2	.0007	.0007	.0006	.0006	.0006	.0006	.0006	.0005	.0005	.0005
−3.1	.0010	.0009	.0009	.0009	.0008	.0008	.0008	.0008	.0007	.0007
−3.0	.0013	.0013	.0013	.0012	.0012	.0011	.0011	.0011	.0010	.0010
−2.9	.0019	.0018	.0018	.0017	.0016	.0016	.0015	.0015	.0014	.0014
−2.8	.0026	.0025	.0024	.0023	.0023	.0022	.0021	.0021	.0020	.0019
−2.7	.0035	.0034	.0033	.0032	.0031	.0030	.0029	.0028	.0027	.0026
−2.6	.0047	.0045	.0044	.0043	.0041	.0040	.0039	.0038	.0037	.0036
−2.5	.0062	.0060	.0059	.0057	.0055	.0054	.0052	.0051	.0049	.0048
−2.4	.0082	.0080	.0078	.0075	.0073	.0071	.0069	.0068	.0066	.0064
−2.3	.0107	.0104	.0102	.0099	.0096	.0094	.0091	.0089	.0087	.0084
−2.2	.0139	.0136	.0132	.0129	.0125	.0122	.0119	.0116	.0113	.0110
−2.1	.0179	.0174	.0170	.0166	.0162	.0158	.0154	.0150	.0146	.0143
−2.0	.0228	.0222	.0217	.0212	.0207	.0202	.0197	.0192	.0188	.0183
−1.9	.0287	.0281	.0274	.0268	.0262	.0256	.0250	.0244	.0239	.0233
−1.8	.0359	.0351	.0344	.0336	.0329	.0322	.0314	.0307	.0301	.0294
−1.7	.0446	.0436	.0427	.0418	.0409	.0401	.0392	.0384	.0375	.0367
−1.6	.0548	.0537	.0526	.0516	.0505	.0495	.0485	.0475	.0465	.0455
−1.5	.0668	.0655	.0643	.0630	.0618	.0606	.0594	.0582	.0571	.0559
−1.4	.0808	.0793	.0778	.0764	.0749	.0735	.0721	.0708	.0694	.0681
−1.3	.0968	.0951	.0934	.0918	.0901	.0885	.0869	.0853	.0838	.0823
−1.2	.1151	.1131	.1112	.1093	.1075	.1056	.1038	.1020	.1003	.0985
−1.1	.1357	.1335	.1314	.1292	.1271	.1251	.1230	.1210	.1190	.1170
−1.0	.1587	.1562	.1539	.1515	.1492	.1469	.1446	.1423	.1401	.1379
−0.9	.1841	.1814	.1788	.1762	.1736	.1711	.1685	.1660	.1635	.1611
−0.8	.2119	.2090	.2061	.2033	.2005	.1977	.1949	.1922	.1894	.1867
−0.7	.2420	.2389	.2358	.2327	.2296	.2266	.2236	.2206	.2177	.2148
−0.6	.2743	.2709	.2676	.2643	.2611	.2578	.2546	.2514	.2483	.2451
−0.5	.3085	.3050	.3015	.2981	.2946	.2912	.2877	.2843	.2810	.2776
−0.4	.3446	.3409	.3372	.3336	.3300	.3264	.3228	.3192	.3156	.3121
−0.3	.3821	.3783	.3745	.3707	.3669	.3632	.3594	.3557	.3520	.3483
−0.2	.4207	.4168	.4129	.4090	.4052	.4013	.3974	.3936	.3897	.3859
−0.1	.4602	.4562	.4522	.4483	.4443	.4404	.4364	.4325	.4286	.4247
−0.0	.5000	.4960	.4920	.4880	.4840	.4801	.4761	.4721	.4681	.4641

For z values less than −3.49, use 0.0001.

Table E (*continued*)

Cumulative Standard Normal Distribution

z	.00	.01	.02	.03	.04	.05	.06	.07	.08	.09
0.0	.5000	.5040	.5080	.5120	.5160	.5199	.5239	.5279	.5319	.5359
0.1	.5398	.5438	.5478	.5517	.5557	.5596	.5636	.5675	.5714	.5753
0.2	.5793	.5832	.5871	.5910	.5948	.5987	.6026	.6064	.6103	.6141
0.3	.6179	.6217	.6255	.6293	.6331	.6368	.6406	.6443	.6480	.6517
0.4	.6554	.6591	.6628	.6664	.6700	.6736	.6772	.6808	.6844	.6879
0.5	.6915	.6950	.6985	.7019	.7054	.7088	.7123	.7157	.7190	.7224
0.6	.7257	.7291	.7324	.7357	.7389	.7422	.7454	.7486	.7517	.7549
0.7	.7580	.7611	.7642	.7673	.7704	.7734	.7764	.7794	.7823	.7852
0.8	.7881	.7910	.7939	.7967	.7995	.8023	.8051	.8078	.8106	.8133
0.9	.8159	.8186	.8212	.8238	.8264	.8289	.8315	.8340	.8365	.8389
1.0	.8413	.8438	.8461	.8485	.8508	.8531	.8554	.8577	.8599	.8621
1.1	.8643	.8665	.8686	.8708	.8729	.8749	.8770	.8790	.8810	.8830
1.2	.8849	.8869	.8888	.8907	.8925	.8944	.8962	.8980	.8997	.9015
1.3	.9032	.9049	.9066	.9082	.9099	.9115	.9131	.9147	.9162	.9177
1.4	.9192	.9207	.9222	.9236	.9251	.9265	.9279	.9292	.9306	.9319
1.5	.9332	.9345	.9357	.9370	.9382	.9394	.9406	.9418	.9429	.9441
1.6	.9452	.9463	.9474	.9484	.9495	.9505	.9515	.9525	.9535	.9545
1.7	.9554	.9564	.9573	.9582	.9591	.9599	.9608	.9616	.9625	.9633
1.8	.9641	.9649	.9656	.9664	.9671	.9678	.9686	.9693	.9699	.9706
1.9	.9713	.9719	.9726	.9732	.9738	.9744	.9750	.9756	.9761	.9767
2.0	.9772	.9778	.9783	.9788	.9793	.9798	.9803	.9808	.9812	.9817
2.1	.9821	.9826	.9830	.9834	.9838	.9842	.9846	.9850	.9854	.9857
2.2	.9861	.9864	.9868	.9871	.9875	.9878	.9881	.9884	.9887	.9890
2.3	.9893	.9896	.9898	.9901	.9904	.9906	.9909	.9911	.9913	.9916
2.4	.9918	.9920	.9922	.9925	.9927	.9929	.9931	.9932	.9934	.9936
2.5	.9938	.9940	.9941	.9943	.9945	.9946	.9948	.9949	.9951	.9952
2.6	.9953	.9955	.9956	.9957	.9959	.9960	.9961	.9962	.9963	.9964
2.7	.9965	.9966	.9967	.9968	.9969	.9970	.9971	.9972	.9973	.9974
2.8	.9974	.9975	.9976	.9977	.9977	.9978	.9979	.9979	.9980	.9981
2.9	.9981	.9982	.9982	.9983	.9984	.9984	.9985	.9985	.9986	.9986
3.0	.9987	.9987	.9987	.9988	.9988	.9989	.9989	.9989	.9990	.9990
3.1	.9990	.9991	.9991	.9991	.9992	.9992	.9992	.9992	.9993	.9993
3.2	.9993	.9993	.9994	.9994	.9994	.9994	.9994	.9995	.9995	.9995
3.3	.9995	.9995	.9995	.9996	.9996	.9996	.9996	.9996	.9996	.9997
3.4	.9997	.9997	.9997	.9997	.9997	.9997	.9997	.9997	.9997	.9998

For z values greater than 3.49, use 0.9999.

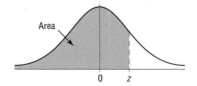

Table F	The *t* Distribution					
	Confidence intervals	**80%**	**90%**	**95%**	**98%**	**99%**
	One tail, α	**0.10**	**0.05**	**0.025**	**0.01**	**0.005**
d.f.	**Two tails, α**	**0.20**	**0.10**	**0.05**	**0.02**	**0.01**
1		3.078	6.314	12.706	31.821	63.657
2		1.886	2.920	4.303	6.965	9.925
3		1.638	2.353	3.182	4.541	5.841
4		1.533	2.132	2.776	3.747	4.604
5		1.476	2.015	2.571	3.365	4.032
6		1.440	1.943	2.447	3.143	3.707
7		1.415	1.895	2.365	2.998	3.499
8		1.397	1.860	2.306	2.896	3.355
9		1.383	1.833	2.262	2.821	3.250
10		1.372	1.812	2.228	2.764	3.169
11		1.363	1.796	2.201	2.718	3.106
12		1.356	1.782	2.179	2.681	3.055
13		1.350	1.771	2.160	2.650	3.012
14		1.345	1.761	2.145	2.624	2.977
15		1.341	1.753	2.131	2.602	2.947
16		1.337	1.746	2.120	2.583	2.921
17		1.333	1.740	2.110	2.567	2.898
18		1.330	1.734	2.101	2.552	2.878
19		1.328	1.729	2.093	2.539	2.861
20		1.325	1.725	2.086	2.528	2.845
21		1.323	1.721	2.080	2.518	2.831
22		1.321	1.717	2.074	2.508	2.819
23		1.319	1.714	2.069	2.500	2.807
24		1.318	1.711	2.064	2.492	2.797
25		1.316	1.708	2.060	2.485	2.787
26		1.315	1.706	2.056	2.479	2.779
27		1.314	1.703	2.052	2.473	2.771
28		1.313	1.701	2.048	2.467	2.763
29		1.311	1.699	2.045	2.462	2.756
30		1.310	1.697	2.042	2.457	2.750
32		1.309	1.694	2.037	2.449	2.738
34		1.307	1.691	2.032	2.441	2.728
36		1.306	1.688	2.028	2.434	2.719
38		1.304	1.686	2.024	2.429	2.712
40		1.303	1.684	2.021	2.423	2.704
45		1.301	1.679	2.014	2.412	2.690
50		1.299	1.676	2.009	2.403	2.678
55		1.297	1.673	2.004	2.396	2.668
60		1.296	1.671	2.000	2.390	2.660
65		1.295	1.669	1.997	2.385	2.654
70		1.294	1.667	1.994	2.381	2.648
75		1.293	1.665	1.992	2.377	2.643
80		1.292	1.664	1.990	2.374	2.639
90		1.291	1.662	1.987	2.368	2.632
100		1.290	1.660	1.984	2.364	2.626
500		1.283	1.648	1.965	2.334	2.586
1000		1.282	1.646	1.962	2.330	2.581
(z) ∞		1.282[a]	1.645[b]	1.960	2.326[c]	2.576[d]

[a]This value has been rounded to 1.28 in the textbook.
[b]This value has been rounded to 1.65 in the textbook.
[c]This value has been rounded to 2.33 in the textbook.
[d]This value has been rounded to 2.58 in the textbook.

Source: Adapted from W. H. Beyer, *Handbook of Tables for Probability and Statistics,* 2nd ed., CRC Press, Boca Raton, Fla., 1986. Reprinted with permission.

Table G	The Chi-Square Distribution									
Degrees of freedom	\multicolumn{10}{c}{α}									
	0.995	**0.99**	**0.975**	**0.95**	**0.90**	**0.10**	**0.05**	**0.025**	**0.01**	**0.005**
1	—	—	0.001	0.004	0.016	2.706	3.841	5.024	6.635	7.879
2	0.010	0.020	0.051	0.103	0.211	4.605	5.991	7.378	9.210	10.597
3	0.072	0.115	0.216	0.352	0.584	6.251	7.815	9.348	11.345	12.838
4	0.207	0.297	0.484	0.711	1.064	7.779	9.488	11.143	13.277	14.860
5	0.412	0.554	0.831	1.145	1.610	9.236	11.071	12.833	15.086	16.750
6	0.676	0.872	1.237	1.635	2.204	10.645	12.592	14.449	16.812	18.548
7	0.989	1.239	1.690	2.167	2.833	12.017	14.067	16.013	18.475	20.278
8	1.344	1.646	2.180	2.733	3.490	13.362	15.507	17.535	20.090	21.955
9	1.735	2.088	2.700	3.325	4.168	14.684	16.919	19.023	21.666	23.589
10	2.156	2.558	3.247	3.940	4.865	15.987	18.307	20.483	23.209	25.188
11	2.603	3.053	3.816	4.575	5.578	17.275	19.675	21.920	24.725	26.757
12	3.074	3.571	4.404	5.226	6.304	18.549	21.026	23.337	26.217	28.299
13	3.565	4.107	5.009	5.892	7.042	19.812	22.362	24.736	27.688	29.819
14	4.075	4.660	5.629	6.571	7.790	21.064	23.685	26.119	29.141	31.319
15	4.601	5.229	6.262	7.261	8.547	22.307	24.996	27.488	30.578	32.801
16	5.142	5.812	6.908	7.962	9.312	23.542	26.296	28.845	32.000	34.267
17	5.697	6.408	7.564	8.672	10.085	24.769	27.587	30.191	33.409	35.718
18	6.265	7.015	8.231	9.390	10.865	25.989	28.869	31.526	34.805	37.156
19	6.844	7.633	8.907	10.117	11.651	27.204	30.144	32.852	36.191	38.582
20	7.434	8.260	9.591	10.851	12.443	28.412	31.410	34.170	37.566	39.997
21	8.034	8.897	10.283	11.591	13.240	29.615	32.671	35.479	38.932	41.401
22	8.643	9.542	10.982	12.338	14.042	30.813	33.924	36.781	40.289	42.796
23	9.262	10.196	11.689	13.091	14.848	32.007	35.172	38.076	41.638	44.181
24	9.886	10.856	12.401	13.848	15.659	33.196	36.415	39.364	42.980	45.559
25	10.520	11.524	13.120	14.611	16.473	34.382	37.652	40.646	44.314	46.928
26	11.160	12.198	13.844	15.379	17.292	35.563	38.885	41.923	45.642	48.290
27	11.808	12.879	14.573	16.151	18.114	36.741	40.113	43.194	46.963	49.645
28	12.461	13.565	15.308	16.928	18.939	37.916	41.337	44.461	48.278	50.993
29	13.121	14.257	16.047	17.708	19.768	39.087	42.557	45.722	49.588	52.336
30	13.787	14.954	16.791	18.493	20.599	40.256	43.773	46.979	50.892	53.672
40	20.707	22.164	24.433	26.509	29.051	51.805	55.758	59.342	63.691	66.766
50	27.991	29.707	32.357	34.764	37.689	63.167	67.505	71.420	76.154	79.490
60	35.534	37.485	40.482	43.188	46.459	74.397	79.082	83.298	88.379	91.952
70	43.275	45.442	48.758	51.739	55.329	85.527	90.531	95.023	100.425	104.215
80	51.172	53.540	57.153	60.391	64.278	96.578	101.879	106.629	112.329	116.321
90	59.196	61.754	65.647	69.126	73.291	107.565	113.145	118.136	124.116	128.299
100	67.328	70.065	74.222	77.929	82.358	118.498	124.342	129.561	135.807	140.169

Source: Donald B. Owen, *Handbook of Statistics Tables,* The Chi-Square Distribution Table, © 1962 by Addison-Wesley Publishing Company, Inc. Copyright renewal © 1990. Reprinted by permission of Pearson Education, Inc.

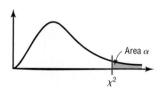

Table H The F Distribution

α = 0.005

									d.f.N.: degrees of freedom, numerator										
d.f.D.: degrees of freedom, denominator	1	2	3	4	5	6	7	8	9	10	12	15	20	24	30	40	60	120	∞
1	16,211	20,000	21,615	22,500	23,056	23,437	23,715	23,925	24,091	24,224	24,426	24,630	24,836	24,940	25,044	25,148	25,253	25,359	25,465
2	198.5	199.0	199.2	199.2	199.3	199.3	199.4	199.4	199.4	199.4	199.4	199.4	199.4	199.5	199.5	199.5	199.5	199.5	199.5
3	55.55	49.80	47.47	46.19	45.39	44.84	44.43	44.13	43.88	43.69	43.39	43.08	42.78	42.62	42.47	42.31	42.15	41.99	41.83
4	31.33	26.28	24.26	23.15	22.46	21.97	21.62	21.35	21.14	20.97	20.70	20.44	20.17	20.03	19.89	19.75	19.61	19.47	19.32
5	22.78	18.31	16.53	15.56	14.94	14.51	14.20	13.96	13.77	13.62	13.38	13.15	12.90	12.78	12.66	12.53	12.40	12.27	12.14
6	18.63	14.54	12.92	12.03	11.46	11.07	10.79	10.57	10.39	10.25	10.03	9.81	9.59	9.47	9.36	9.24	9.12	9.00	8.88
7	16.24	12.40	10.88	10.05	9.52	9.16	8.89	8.68	8.51	8.38	8.18	7.97	7.75	7.65	7.53	7.42	7.31	7.19	7.08
8	14.69	11.04	9.60	8.81	8.30	7.95	7.69	7.50	7.34	7.21	7.01	6.81	6.61	6.50	6.40	6.29	6.18	6.06	5.95
9	13.61	10.11	8.72	7.96	7.47	7.13	6.88	6.69	6.54	6.42	6.23	6.03	5.83	5.73	5.62	5.52	5.41	5.30	5.19
10	12.83	9.43	8.08	7.34	6.87	6.54	6.30	6.12	5.97	5.85	5.66	5.47	5.27	5.17	5.07	4.97	4.86	4.75	4.64
11	12.23	8.91	7.60	6.88	6.42	6.10	5.86	5.68	5.54	5.42	5.24	5.05	4.86	4.76	4.65	4.55	4.44	4.34	4.23
12	11.75	8.51	7.23	6.52	6.07	5.76	5.52	5.35	5.20	5.09	4.91	4.72	4.53	4.43	4.33	4.23	4.12	4.01	3.90
13	11.37	8.19	6.93	6.23	5.79	5.48	5.25	5.08	4.94	4.82	4.64	4.46	4.27	4.17	4.07	3.97	3.87	3.76	3.65
14	11.06	7.92	6.68	6.00	5.56	5.26	5.03	4.86	4.72	4.60	4.43	4.25	4.06	3.96	3.86	3.76	3.66	3.55	3.44
15	10.80	7.70	6.48	5.80	5.37	5.07	4.85	4.67	4.54	4.42	4.25	4.07	3.88	3.79	3.69	3.58	3.48	3.37	3.26
16	10.58	7.51	6.30	5.64	5.21	4.91	4.69	4.52	4.38	4.27	4.10	3.92	3.73	3.64	3.54	3.44	3.33	3.22	3.11
17	10.38	7.35	6.16	5.50	5.07	4.78	4.56	4.39	4.25	4.14	3.97	3.79	3.61	3.51	3.41	3.31	3.21	3.10	2.98
18	10.22	7.21	6.03	5.37	4.96	4.66	4.44	4.28	4.14	4.03	3.86	3.68	3.50	3.40	3.30	3.20	3.10	2.99	2.87
19	10.07	7.09	5.92	5.27	4.85	4.56	4.34	4.18	4.04	3.93	3.76	3.59	3.40	3.31	3.21	3.11	3.00	2.89	2.78
20	9.94	6.99	5.82	5.17	4.76	4.47	4.26	4.09	3.96	3.85	3.68	3.50	3.32	3.22	3.12	3.02	2.92	2.81	2.69
21	9.83	6.89	5.73	5.09	4.68	4.39	4.18	4.01	3.88	3.77	3.60	3.43	3.24	3.15	3.05	2.95	2.84	2.73	2.61
22	9.73	6.81	5.65	5.02	4.61	4.32	4.11	3.94	3.81	3.70	3.54	3.36	3.18	3.08	2.98	2.88	2.77	2.66	2.55
23	9.63	6.73	5.58	4.95	4.54	4.26	4.05	3.88	3.75	3.64	3.47	3.30	3.12	3.02	2.92	2.82	2.71	2.60	2.48
24	9.55	6.66	5.52	4.89	4.49	4.20	3.99	3.83	3.69	3.59	3.42	3.25	3.06	2.97	2.87	2.77	2.66	2.55	2.43
25	9.48	6.60	5.46	4.84	4.43	4.15	3.94	3.78	3.64	3.54	3.37	3.20	3.01	2.92	2.82	2.72	2.61	2.50	2.38
26	9.41	6.54	5.41	4.79	4.38	4.10	3.89	3.73	3.60	3.49	3.33	3.15	2.97	2.87	2.77	2.67	2.56	2.45	2.33
27	9.34	6.49	5.36	4.74	4.34	4.06	3.85	3.69	3.56	3.45	3.28	3.11	2.93	2.83	2.73	2.63	2.52	2.41	2.29
28	9.28	6.44	5.32	4.70	4.30	4.02	3.81	3.65	3.52	3.41	3.25	3.07	2.89	2.79	2.69	2.59	2.48	2.37	2.25
29	9.23	6.40	5.28	4.66	4.26	3.98	3.77	3.61	3.48	3.38	3.21	3.04	2.86	2.76	2.66	2.56	2.45	2.33	2.21
30	9.18	6.35	5.24	4.62	4.23	3.95	3.74	3.58	3.45	3.34	3.18	3.01	2.82	2.73	2.63	2.52	2.42	2.30	2.18
40	8.83	6.07	4.98	4.37	3.99	3.71	3.51	3.35	3.22	3.12	2.95	2.78	2.60	2.50	2.40	2.30	2.18	2.06	1.93
60	8.49	5.79	4.73	4.14	3.76	3.49	3.29	3.13	3.01	2.90	2.74	2.57	2.39	2.29	2.19	2.08	1.96	1.83	1.69
120	8.18	5.54	4.50	3.92	3.55	3.28	3.09	2.93	2.81	2.71	2.54	2.37	2.19	2.09	1.98	1.87	1.75	1.61	1.43
∞	7.88	5.30	4.28	3.72	3.35	3.09	2.90	2.74	2.62	2.52	2.36	2.19	2.00	1.90	1.79	1.67	1.53	1.36	1.00

Table H *(continued)*

$\alpha = 0.01$

d.f.N.: degrees of freedom, numerator

d.f.D.: degrees of freedom, denominator	1	2	3	4	5	6	7	8	9	10	12	15	20	24	30	40	60	120	∞
1	4052	4999.5	5403	5625	5764	5859	5928	5982	6022	6056	6106	6157	6209	6235	6261	6287	6313	6339	6366
2	98.50	99.00	99.17	99.25	99.30	99.33	99.36	99.37	99.39	99.40	99.42	99.43	99.45	99.46	99.47	99.47	99.48	99.49	99.50
3	34.12	30.82	29.46	28.71	28.24	27.91	27.67	27.49	27.35	27.23	27.05	26.87	26.69	26.60	26.50	26.41	26.32	26.22	26.13
4	21.20	18.00	16.69	15.98	15.52	15.21	14.98	14.80	14.66	14.55	14.37	14.20	14.02	13.93	13.84	13.75	13.65	13.56	13.46
5	16.26	13.27	12.06	11.39	10.97	10.67	10.46	10.29	10.16	10.05	9.89	9.72	9.55	9.47	9.38	9.29	9.20	9.11	9.02
6	13.75	10.92	9.78	9.15	8.75	8.47	8.26	8.10	7.98	7.87	7.72	7.56	7.40	7.31	7.23	7.14	7.06	6.97	6.88
7	12.25	9.55	8.45	7.85	7.46	7.19	6.99	6.84	6.72	6.62	6.47	6.31	6.16	6.07	5.99	5.91	5.82	5.74	5.65
8	11.26	8.65	7.59	7.01	6.63	6.37	6.18	6.03	5.91	5.81	5.67	5.52	5.36	5.28	5.20	5.12	5.03	4.95	4.86
9	10.56	8.02	6.99	6.42	6.06	5.80	5.61	5.47	5.35	5.26	5.11	4.96	4.81	4.73	4.65	4.57	4.48	4.40	4.31
10	10.04	7.56	6.55	5.99	5.64	5.39	5.20	5.06	4.94	4.85	4.71	4.56	4.41	4.33	4.25	4.17	4.08	4.00	3.91
11	9.65	7.21	6.22	5.67	5.32	5.07	4.89	4.74	4.63	4.54	4.40	4.25	4.10	4.02	3.94	3.86	3.78	3.69	3.60
12	9.33	6.93	5.95	5.41	5.06	4.82	4.64	4.50	4.39	4.30	4.16	4.01	3.86	3.78	3.70	3.62	3.54	3.45	3.36
13	9.07	6.70	5.74	5.21	4.86	4.62	4.44	4.30	4.19	4.10	3.96	3.82	3.66	3.59	3.51	3.43	3.34	3.25	3.17
14	8.86	6.51	5.56	5.04	4.69	4.46	4.28	4.14	4.03	3.94	3.80	3.66	3.51	3.43	3.35	3.27	3.18	3.09	3.00
15	8.68	6.36	5.42	4.89	4.56	4.32	4.14	4.00	3.89	3.80	3.67	3.52	3.37	3.29	3.21	3.13	3.05	2.96	2.87
16	8.53	6.23	5.29	4.77	4.44	4.20	4.03	3.89	3.78	3.69	3.55	3.41	3.26	3.18	3.10	3.02	2.93	2.84	2.75
17	8.40	6.11	5.18	4.67	4.34	4.10	3.93	3.79	3.68	3.59	3.46	3.31	3.16	3.08	3.00	2.92	2.83	2.75	2.65
18	8.29	6.01	5.09	4.58	4.25	4.01	3.84	3.71	3.60	3.51	3.37	3.23	3.08	3.00	2.92	2.84	2.75	2.66	2.57
19	8.18	5.93	5.01	4.50	4.17	3.94	3.77	3.63	3.52	3.43	3.30	3.15	3.00	2.92	2.84	2.76	2.67	2.58	2.49
20	8.10	5.85	4.94	4.43	4.10	3.87	3.70	3.56	3.46	3.37	3.23	3.09	2.94	2.86	2.78	2.69	2.61	2.52	2.42
21	8.02	5.78	4.87	4.37	4.04	3.81	3.64	3.51	3.40	3.31	3.17	3.03	2.88	2.80	2.72	2.64	2.55	2.46	2.36
22	7.95	5.72	4.82	4.31	3.99	3.76	3.59	3.45	3.35	3.26	3.12	2.98	2.83	2.75	2.67	2.58	2.50	2.40	2.31
23	7.88	5.66	4.76	4.26	3.94	3.71	3.54	3.41	3.30	3.21	3.07	2.93	2.78	2.70	2.62	2.54	2.45	2.35	2.26
24	7.82	5.61	4.72	4.22	3.90	3.67	3.50	3.36	3.26	3.17	3.03	2.89	2.74	2.66	2.58	2.49	2.40	2.31	2.21
25	7.77	5.57	4.68	4.18	3.85	3.63	3.46	3.32	3.22	3.13	2.99	2.85	2.70	2.62	2.54	2.45	2.36	2.27	2.17
26	7.72	5.53	4.64	4.14	3.82	3.59	3.42	3.29	3.18	3.09	2.96	2.81	2.66	2.58	2.50	2.42	2.33	2.23	2.13
27	7.68	5.49	4.60	4.11	3.78	3.56	3.39	3.26	3.15	3.06	2.93	2.78	2.63	2.55	2.47	2.38	2.29	2.20	2.10
28	7.64	5.45	4.57	4.07	3.75	3.53	3.36	3.23	3.12	3.03	2.90	2.75	2.60	2.52	2.44	2.35	2.26	2.17	2.06
29	7.60	5.42	4.54	4.04	3.73	3.50	3.33	3.20	3.09	3.00	2.87	2.73	2.57	2.49	2.41	2.33	2.23	2.14	2.03
30	7.56	5.39	4.51	4.02	3.70	3.47	3.30	3.17	3.07	2.98	2.84	2.70	2.55	2.47	2.39	2.30	2.21	2.11	2.01
40	7.31	5.18	4.31	3.83	3.51	3.29	3.12	2.99	2.89	2.80	2.66	2.52	2.37	2.29	2.20	2.11	2.02	1.92	1.80
60	7.08	4.98	4.13	3.65	3.34	3.12	2.95	2.82	2.72	2.63	2.50	2.35	2.20	2.12	2.03	1.94	1.84	1.73	1.60
120	6.85	4.79	3.95	3.48	3.17	2.96	2.79	2.66	2.56	2.47	2.34	2.19	2.03	1.95	1.86	1.76	1.66	1.53	1.38
∞	6.63	4.61	3.78	3.32	3.02	2.80	2.64	2.51	2.41	2.32	2.18	2.04	1.88	1.79	1.70	1.59	1.47	1.32	1.00

Table H (continued)

α = 0.025

d.f.N.: degrees of freedom, numerator

d.f.D.: degrees of freedom, denominator	1	2	3	4	5	6	7	8	9	10	12	15	20	24	30	40	60	120	∞
1	647.8	799.5	864.2	899.6	921.8	937.1	948.2	956.7	963.3	968.6	976.7	984.9	993.1	997.2	1001	1006	1010	1014	1018
2	38.51	39.00	39.17	39.25	39.30	39.33	39.36	39.37	39.39	39.40	39.41	39.43	39.45	39.46	39.46	39.47	39.48	39.49	39.50
3	17.44	16.04	15.44	15.10	14.88	14.73	14.62	14.54	14.47	14.42	14.34	14.25	14.17	14.12	14.08	14.04	13.99	13.95	13.90
4	12.22	10.65	9.98	9.60	9.36	9.20	9.07	8.98	8.90	8.84	8.75	8.66	8.56	8.51	8.46	8.41	8.36	8.31	8.26
5	10.01	8.43	7.76	7.39	7.15	6.98	6.85	6.76	6.68	6.62	6.52	6.43	6.33	6.28	6.23	6.18	6.12	6.07	6.02
6	8.81	7.26	6.60	6.23	5.99	5.82	5.70	5.60	5.52	5.46	5.37	5.27	5.17	5.12	5.07	5.01	4.96	4.90	4.85
7	8.07	6.54	5.89	5.52	5.29	5.12	4.99	4.90	4.82	4.76	4.67	4.57	4.47	4.42	4.36	4.31	4.25	4.20	4.14
8	7.57	6.06	5.42	5.05	4.82	4.65	4.53	4.43	4.36	4.30	4.20	4.10	4.00	3.95	3.89	3.84	3.78	3.73	3.67
9	7.21	5.71	5.08	4.72	4.48	4.32	4.20	4.10	4.03	3.96	3.87	3.77	3.67	3.61	3.56	3.51	3.45	3.39	3.33
10	6.94	5.46	4.83	4.47	4.24	4.07	3.95	3.85	3.78	3.72	3.62	3.52	3.42	3.37	3.31	3.26	3.20	3.14	3.08
11	6.72	5.26	4.63	4.28	4.04	3.88	3.76	3.66	3.59	3.53	3.43	3.33	3.23	3.17	3.12	3.06	3.00	2.94	2.88
12	6.55	5.10	4.47	4.12	3.89	3.73	3.61	3.51	3.44	3.37	3.28	3.18	3.07	3.02	2.96	2.91	2.85	2.79	2.72
13	6.41	4.97	4.35	4.00	3.77	3.60	3.48	3.39	3.31	3.25	3.15	3.05	2.95	2.89	2.84	2.78	2.72	2.66	2.60
14	6.30	4.86	4.24	3.89	3.66	3.50	3.38	3.29	3.21	3.15	3.05	2.95	2.84	2.79	2.73	2.67	2.61	2.55	2.49
15	6.20	4.77	4.15	3.80	3.58	3.41	3.29	3.20	3.12	3.06	2.96	2.86	2.76	2.70	2.64	2.59	2.52	2.46	2.40
16	6.12	4.69	4.08	3.73	3.50	3.34	3.22	3.12	3.05	2.99	2.89	2.79	2.68	2.63	2.57	2.51	2.45	2.38	2.32
17	6.04	4.62	4.01	3.66	3.44	3.28	3.16	3.06	2.98	2.92	2.82	2.72	2.62	2.56	2.50	2.44	2.38	2.32	2.25
18	5.98	4.56	3.95	3.61	3.38	3.22	3.10	3.01	2.93	2.87	2.77	2.67	2.56	2.50	2.44	2.38	2.32	2.26	2.19
19	5.92	4.51	3.90	3.56	3.33	3.17	3.05	2.96	2.88	2.82	2.72	2.62	2.51	2.45	2.39	2.33	2.27	2.20	2.13
20	5.87	4.46	3.86	3.51	3.29	3.13	3.01	2.91	2.84	2.77	2.68	2.57	2.46	2.41	2.35	2.29	2.22	2.16	2.09
21	5.83	4.42	3.82	3.48	3.25	3.09	2.97	2.87	2.80	2.73	2.64	2.53	2.42	2.37	2.31	2.25	2.18	2.11	2.04
22	5.79	4.38	3.78	3.44	3.22	3.05	2.93	2.84	2.76	2.70	2.60	2.50	2.39	2.33	2.27	2.21	2.14	2.08	2.00
23	5.75	4.35	3.75	3.41	3.18	3.02	2.90	2.81	2.73	2.67	2.57	2.47	2.36	2.30	2.24	2.18	2.11	2.04	1.97
24	5.72	4.32	3.72	3.38	3.15	2.99	2.87	2.78	2.70	2.64	2.54	2.44	2.33	2.27	2.21	2.15	2.08	2.01	1.94
25	5.69	4.29	3.69	3.35	3.13	2.97	2.85	2.75	2.68	2.61	2.51	2.41	2.30	2.24	2.18	2.12	2.05	1.98	1.91
26	5.66	4.27	3.67	3.33	3.10	2.94	2.82	2.73	2.65	2.59	2.49	2.39	2.28	2.22	2.16	2.09	2.03	1.95	1.88
27	5.63	4.24	3.65	3.31	3.08	2.92	2.80	2.71	2.63	2.57	2.47	2.36	2.25	2.19	2.13	2.07	2.00	1.93	1.85
28	5.61	4.22	3.63	3.29	3.06	2.90	2.78	2.69	2.61	2.55	2.45	2.34	2.23	2.17	2.11	2.05	1.98	1.91	1.83
29	5.59	4.20	3.61	3.27	3.04	2.88	2.76	2.67	2.59	2.53	2.43	2.32	2.21	2.15	2.09	2.03	1.96	1.89	1.81
30	5.57	4.18	3.59	3.25	3.03	2.87	2.75	2.65	2.57	2.51	2.41	2.31	2.20	2.14	2.07	2.01	1.94	1.87	1.79
40	5.42	4.05	3.46	3.13	2.90	2.74	2.62	2.53	2.45	2.39	2.29	2.18	2.07	2.01	1.94	1.88	1.80	1.72	1.64
60	5.29	3.93	3.34	3.01	2.79	2.63	2.51	2.41	2.33	2.27	2.17	2.06	1.94	1.88	1.82	1.74	1.67	1.58	1.48
120	5.15	3.80	3.23	2.89	2.67	2.52	2.39	2.30	2.22	2.16	2.05	1.94	1.82	1.76	1.69	1.61	1.53	1.43	1.31
∞	5.02	3.69	3.12	2.79	2.57	2.41	2.29	2.19	2.11	2.05	1.94	1.83	1.71	1.64	1.57	1.48	1.39	1.27	1.00

Table H (continued)

$\alpha = 0.05$

d.f.D.: degrees of freedom, denominator	\multicolumn{19}{c}{d.f.N.: degrees of freedom, numerator}

d.f.D.	1	2	3	4	5	6	7	8	9	10	12	15	20	24	30	40	60	120	∞
1	161.4	199.5	215.7	224.6	230.2	234.0	236.8	238.9	240.5	241.9	243.9	245.9	248.0	249.1	250.1	251.1	252.2	253.3	254.3
2	18.51	19.00	19.16	19.25	19.30	19.33	19.35	19.37	19.38	19.40	19.41	19.43	19.45	19.45	19.46	19.47	19.48	19.49	19.50
3	10.13	9.55	9.28	9.12	9.01	8.94	8.89	8.85	8.81	8.79	8.74	8.70	8.66	8.64	8.62	8.59	8.57	8.55	8.53
4	7.71	6.94	6.59	6.39	6.26	6.16	6.09	6.04	6.00	5.96	5.91	5.86	5.80	5.77	5.75	5.72	5.69	5.66	5.63
5	6.61	5.79	5.41	5.19	5.05	4.95	4.88	4.82	4.77	4.74	4.68	4.62	4.56	4.53	4.50	4.46	4.43	4.40	4.36
6	5.99	5.14	4.76	4.53	4.39	4.28	4.21	4.15	4.10	4.06	4.00	3.94	3.87	3.84	3.81	3.77	3.74	3.70	3.67
7	5.59	4.74	4.35	4.12	3.97	3.87	3.79	3.73	3.68	3.64	3.57	3.51	3.44	3.41	3.38	3.34	3.30	3.27	3.23
8	5.32	4.46	4.07	3.84	3.69	3.58	3.50	3.44	3.39	3.35	3.28	3.22	3.15	3.12	3.08	3.04	3.01	2.97	2.93
9	5.12	4.26	3.86	3.63	3.48	3.37	3.29	3.23	3.18	3.14	3.07	3.01	2.94	2.90	2.86	2.83	2.79	2.75	2.71
10	4.96	4.10	3.71	3.48	3.33	3.22	3.14	3.07	3.02	2.98	2.91	2.85	2.77	2.74	2.70	2.66	2.62	2.58	2.54
11	4.84	3.98	3.59	3.36	3.20	3.09	3.01	2.95	2.90	2.85	2.79	2.72	2.65	2.61	2.57	2.53	2.49	2.45	2.40
12	4.75	3.89	3.49	3.26	3.11	3.00	2.91	2.85	2.80	2.75	2.69	2.62	2.54	2.51	2.47	2.43	2.38	2.34	2.30
13	4.67	3.81	3.41	3.18	3.03	2.92	2.83	2.77	2.71	2.67	2.60	2.53	2.46	2.42	2.38	2.34	2.30	2.25	2.21
14	4.60	3.74	3.34	3.11	2.96	2.85	2.76	2.70	2.65	2.60	2.53	2.46	2.39	2.35	2.31	2.27	2.22	2.18	2.13
15	4.54	3.68	3.29	3.06	2.90	2.79	2.71	2.64	2.59	2.54	2.48	2.40	2.33	2.29	2.25	2.20	2.16	2.11	2.07
16	4.49	3.63	3.24	3.01	2.85	2.74	2.66	2.59	2.54	2.49	2.42	2.35	2.28	2.24	2.19	2.15	2.11	2.06	2.01
17	4.45	3.59	3.20	2.96	2.81	2.70	2.61	2.55	2.49	2.45	2.38	2.31	2.23	2.19	2.15	2.10	2.06	2.01	1.96
18	4.41	3.55	3.16	2.93	2.77	2.66	2.58	2.51	2.46	2.41	2.34	2.27	2.19	2.15	2.11	2.06	2.02	1.97	1.92
19	4.38	3.52	3.13	2.90	2.74	2.63	2.54	2.48	2.42	2.38	2.31	2.23	2.16	2.11	2.07	2.03	1.98	1.93	1.88
20	4.35	3.49	3.10	2.87	2.71	2.60	2.51	2.45	2.39	2.35	2.28	2.20	2.12	2.08	2.04	1.99	1.95	1.90	1.84
21	4.32	3.47	3.07	2.84	2.68	2.57	2.49	2.42	2.37	2.32	2.25	2.18	2.10	2.05	2.01	1.96	1.92	1.87	1.81
22	4.30	3.44	3.05	2.82	2.66	2.55	2.46	2.40	2.34	2.30	2.23	2.15	2.07	2.03	1.98	1.94	1.89	1.84	1.78
23	4.28	3.42	3.03	2.80	2.64	2.53	2.44	2.37	2.32	2.27	2.20	2.13	2.05	2.01	1.96	1.91	1.86	1.81	1.76
24	4.26	3.40	3.01	2.78	2.62	2.51	2.42	2.36	2.30	2.25	2.18	2.11	2.03	1.98	1.94	1.89	1.84	1.79	1.73
25	4.24	3.39	2.99	2.76	2.60	2.49	2.40	2.34	2.28	2.24	2.16	2.09	2.01	1.96	1.92	1.87	1.82	1.77	1.71
26	4.23	3.37	2.98	2.74	2.59	2.47	2.39	2.32	2.27	2.22	2.15	2.07	1.99	1.95	1.90	1.85	1.80	1.75	1.69
27	4.21	3.35	2.96	2.73	2.57	2.46	2.37	2.31	2.25	2.20	2.13	2.06	1.97	1.93	1.88	1.84	1.79	1.73	1.67
28	4.20	3.34	2.95	2.71	2.56	2.45	2.36	2.29	2.24	2.19	2.12	2.04	1.96	1.91	1.87	1.82	1.77	1.71	1.65
29	4.18	3.33	2.93	2.70	2.55	2.43	2.35	2.28	2.22	2.18	2.10	2.03	1.94	1.90	1.85	1.81	1.75	1.70	1.64
30	4.17	3.32	2.92	2.69	2.53	2.42	2.33	2.27	2.21	2.16	2.09	2.01	1.93	1.89	1.84	1.79	1.74	1.68	1.62
40	4.08	3.23	2.84	2.61	2.45	2.34	2.25	2.18	2.12	2.08	2.00	1.92	1.84	1.79	1.74	1.69	1.64	1.58	1.51
60	4.00	3.15	2.76	2.53	2.37	2.25	2.17	2.10	2.04	1.99	1.92	1.84	1.75	1.70	1.65	1.59	1.53	1.47	1.39
120	3.92	3.07	2.68	2.45	2.29	2.17	2.09	2.02	1.96	1.91	1.83	1.75	1.66	1.61	1.55	1.50	1.43	1.35	1.25
∞	3.84	3.00	2.60	2.37	2.21	2.10	2.01	1.94	1.88	1.83	1.75	1.67	1.57	1.52	1.46	1.39	1.32	1.22	1.00

Table H *(concluded)*

α = 0.10

d.f.N.: degrees of freedom, numerator

d.f.D.: degrees of freedom, denominator	1	2	3	4	5	6	7	8	9	10	12	15	20	24	30	40	60	120	∞
1	39.86	49.50	53.59	55.83	57.24	58.20	58.91	59.44	59.86	60.19	60.71	61.22	61.74	62.00	62.26	62.53	62.79	63.06	63.33
2	8.53	9.00	9.16	9.24	9.29	9.33	9.35	9.37	9.38	9.39	9.41	9.42	9.44	9.45	9.46	9.47	9.47	9.48	9.49
3	5.54	5.46	5.39	5.34	5.31	5.28	5.27	5.25	5.24	5.23	5.22	5.20	5.18	5.18	5.17	5.16	5.15	5.14	5.13
4	4.54	4.32	4.19	4.11	4.05	4.01	3.98	3.95	3.94	3.92	3.90	3.87	3.84	3.83	3.82	3.80	3.79	3.78	3.76
5	4.06	3.78	3.62	3.52	3.45	3.40	3.37	3.34	3.32	3.30	3.27	3.24	3.21	3.19	3.17	3.16	3.14	3.12	3.10
6	3.78	3.46	3.29	3.18	3.11	3.05	3.01	2.98	2.96	2.94	2.90	2.87	2.84	2.82	2.80	2.78	2.76	2.74	2.72
7	3.59	3.26	3.07	2.96	2.88	2.83	2.78	2.75	2.72	2.70	2.67	2.63	2.59	2.58	2.56	2.54	2.51	2.49	2.47
8	3.46	3.11	2.92	2.81	2.73	2.67	2.62	2.59	2.56	2.54	2.50	2.46	2.42	2.40	2.38	2.36	2.34	2.32	2.29
9	3.36	3.01	2.81	2.69	2.61	2.55	2.51	2.47	2.44	2.42	2.38	2.34	2.30	2.28	2.25	2.23	2.21	2.18	2.16
10	3.29	2.92	2.73	2.61	2.52	2.46	2.41	2.38	2.35	2.32	2.28	2.24	2.20	2.18	2.16	2.13	2.11	2.08	2.06
11	3.23	2.86	2.66	2.54	2.45	2.39	2.34	2.30	2.27	2.25	2.21	2.17	2.12	2.10	2.08	2.05	2.03	2.00	1.97
12	3.18	2.81	2.61	2.48	2.39	2.33	2.28	2.24	2.21	2.19	2.15	2.10	2.06	2.04	2.01	1.99	1.96	1.93	1.90
13	3.14	2.76	2.56	2.43	2.35	2.28	2.23	2.20	2.16	2.14	2.10	2.05	2.01	1.98	1.96	1.93	1.90	1.88	1.85
14	3.10	2.73	2.52	2.39	2.31	2.24	2.19	2.15	2.12	2.10	2.05	2.01	1.96	1.94	1.91	1.89	1.86	1.83	1.80
15	3.07	2.70	2.49	2.36	2.27	2.21	2.16	2.12	2.09	2.06	2.02	1.97	1.92	1.90	1.87	1.85	1.82	1.79	1.76
16	3.05	2.67	2.46	2.33	2.24	2.18	2.13	2.09	2.06	2.03	1.99	1.94	1.89	1.87	1.84	1.81	1.78	1.75	1.72
17	3.03	2.64	2.44	2.31	2.22	2.15	2.10	2.06	2.03	2.00	1.96	1.91	1.86	1.84	1.81	1.78	1.75	1.72	1.69
18	3.01	2.62	2.42	2.29	2.20	2.13	2.08	2.04	2.00	1.98	1.93	1.89	1.84	1.81	1.78	1.75	1.72	1.69	1.66
19	2.99	2.61	2.40	2.27	2.18	2.11	2.06	2.02	1.98	1.96	1.91	1.86	1.81	1.79	1.76	1.73	1.70	1.67	1.63
20	2.97	2.59	2.38	2.25	2.16	2.09	2.04	2.00	1.96	1.94	1.89	1.84	1.79	1.77	1.74	1.71	1.68	1.64	1.61
21	2.96	2.57	2.36	2.23	2.14	2.08	2.02	1.98	1.95	1.92	1.87	1.83	1.78	1.75	1.72	1.69	1.66	1.62	1.59
22	2.95	2.56	2.35	2.22	2.13	2.06	2.01	1.97	1.93	1.90	1.86	1.81	1.76	1.73	1.70	1.67	1.64	1.60	1.57
23	2.94	2.55	2.34	2.21	2.11	2.05	1.99	1.95	1.92	1.89	1.84	1.80	1.74	1.72	1.69	1.66	1.62	1.59	1.55
24	2.93	2.54	2.33	2.19	2.10	2.04	1.98	1.94	1.91	1.88	1.83	1.78	1.73	1.70	1.67	1.64	1.61	1.57	1.53
25	2.92	2.53	2.32	2.18	2.09	2.02	1.97	1.93	1.89	1.87	1.82	1.77	1.72	1.69	1.66	1.63	1.59	1.56	1.52
26	2.91	2.52	2.31	2.17	2.08	2.01	1.96	1.92	1.88	1.86	1.81	1.76	1.71	1.68	1.65	1.61	1.58	1.54	1.50
27	2.90	2.51	2.30	2.17	2.07	2.00	1.95	1.91	1.87	1.85	1.80	1.75	1.70	1.67	1.64	1.60	1.57	1.53	1.49
28	2.89	2.50	2.29	2.16	2.06	2.00	1.94	1.90	1.87	1.84	1.79	1.74	1.69	1.66	1.63	1.59	1.56	1.52	1.48
29	2.89	2.50	2.28	2.15	2.06	1.99	1.93	1.89	1.86	1.83	1.78	1.73	1.68	1.65	1.62	1.58	1.55	1.51	1.47
30	2.88	2.49	2.28	2.14	2.05	1.98	1.93	1.88	1.85	1.82	1.77	1.72	1.67	1.64	1.61	1.57	1.54	1.50	1.46
40	2.84	2.44	2.23	2.09	2.00	1.93	1.87	1.83	1.79	1.76	1.71	1.66	1.61	1.57	1.54	1.51	1.47	1.42	1.38
60	2.79	2.39	2.18	2.04	1.95	1.87	1.82	1.77	1.74	1.71	1.66	1.60	1.54	1.51	1.48	1.44	1.40	1.35	1.29
120	2.75	2.35	2.13	1.99	1.90	1.82	1.77	1.72	1.68	1.65	1.60	1.55	1.48	1.45	1.41	1.37	1.32	1.26	1.19
∞	2.71	2.30	2.08	1.94	1.85	1.77	1.72	1.67	1.63	1.60	1.55	1.49	1.42	1.38	1.34	1.30	1.24	1.17	1.00

From M. Merrington and C. M. Thompson (1943). Table of Percentage Points of the Inverted Beta (*F*) Distribution. *Biometrika 33*, pp. 74–87. Reprinted with permission from Biometrika.

| Table I | Critical Values for the PPMC |

Reject H_0: $\rho = 0$ if the absolute value of r is greater than the value given in the table. The values are for a two-tailed test; d.f. $= n - 2$.

d.f.	$\alpha = 0.05$	$\alpha = 0.01$
1	0.999	0.999
2	0.950	0.999
3	0.878	0.959
4	0.811	0.917
5	0.754	0.875
6	0.707	0.834
7	0.666	0.798
8	0.632	0.765
9	0.602	0.735
10	0.576	0.708
11	0.553	0.684
12	0.532	0.661
13	0.514	0.641
14	0.497	0.623
15	0.482	0.606
16	0.468	0.590
17	0.456	0.575
18	0.444	0.561
19	0.433	0.549
20	0.423	0.537
25	0.381	0.487
30	0.349	0.449
35	0.325	0.418
40	0.304	0.393
45	0.288	0.372
50	0.273	0.354
60	0.250	0.325
70	0.232	0.302
80	0.217	0.283
90	0.205	0.267
100	0.195	0.254

Source: From *Biometrika Tables for Statisticians,* vol. 1 (1962), p. 138.
Reprinted with permission.

Appendix D

Data Bank

Data Bank Values

This list explains the values given for the categories in the Data Bank.

1. "Age" is given in years.

2. "Educational level" values are defined as follows:

   0 = no high school degree   2 = college graduate

   1 = high school graduate   3 = graduate degree

3. "Smoking status" values are defined as follows:

   0 = does not smoke

   1 = smokes less than one pack per day

   2 = smokes one or more than one pack per day

4. "Exercise" values are defined as follows:

   0 = none   2 = moderate

   1 = light   3 = heavy

5. "Weight" is given in pounds.

6. "Serum cholesterol" is given in milligram percent (mg%).

7. "Systolic pressure" is given in millimeters of mercury (mm Hg).

8. "IQ" is given in standard IQ test score values.

9. "Sodium" is given in milliequivalents per liter (mEq/1).

10. "Gender" is listed as male (M) or female (F).

11. "Marital status" values are defined as follows:

    M = married   S = single

    W = widowed   D = divorced

Data Bank

ID number	Age	Educational level	Smoking status	Exercise	Weight	Serum cholesterol	Systolic pressure	IQ	Sodium	Gender	Marital status
01	27	2	1	1	120	193	126	118	136	F	M
02	18	1	0	1	145	210	120	105	137	M	S
03	32	2	0	0	118	196	128	115	135	F	M
04	24	2	0	1	162	208	129	108	142	M	M
05	19	1	2	0	106	188	119	106	133	F	S
06	56	1	0	0	143	206	136	111	138	F	W
07	65	1	2	0	160	240	131	99	140	M	W
08	36	2	1	0	215	215	163	106	151	M	D
09	43	1	0	1	127	201	132	111	134	F	M
10	47	1	1	1	132	215	138	109	135	F	D

Data Bank *(continued)*

ID number	Age	Educational level	Smoking status	Exercise	Weight	Serum cholesterol	Systolic pressure	IQ	Sodium	Gender	Marital status
11	48	3	1	2	196	199	148	115	146	M	D
12	25	2	2	3	109	210	115	114	141	F	S
13	63	0	1	0	170	242	149	101	152	F	D
14	37	2	0	3	187	193	142	109	144	M	M
15	40	0	1	1	234	208	156	98	147	M	M
16	25	1	2	1	199	253	135	103	148	M	S
17	72	0	0	0	143	288	156	103	145	F	M
18	56	1	1	0	156	164	153	99	144	F	D
19	37	2	0	2	142	214	122	110	135	M	M
20	41	1	1	1	123	220	142	108	134	F	M
21	33	2	1	1	165	194	122	112	137	M	S
22	52	1	0	1	157	205	119	106	134	M	D
23	44	2	0	1	121	223	135	116	133	F	M
24	53	1	0	0	131	199	133	121	136	F	M
25	19	1	0	3	128	206	118	122	132	M	S
26	25	1	0	0	143	200	118	103	135	M	M
27	31	2	1	1	152	204	120	119	136	M	M
28	28	2	0	0	119	203	118	116	138	F	M
29	23	1	0	0	111	240	120	105	135	F	S
30	47	2	1	0	149	199	132	123	136	F	M
31	47	2	1	0	179	235	131	113	139	M	M
32	59	1	2	0	206	260	151	99	143	M	W
33	36	2	1	0	191	201	148	118	145	M	D
34	59	0	1	1	156	235	142	100	132	F	W
35	35	1	0	0	122	232	131	106	135	F	M
36	29	2	0	2	175	195	129	121	148	M	M
37	43	3	0	3	194	211	138	129	146	M	M
38	44	1	2	0	132	240	130	109	132	F	S
39	63	2	2	1	188	255	156	121	145	M	M
40	36	2	1	1	125	220	126	117	140	F	S
41	21	1	0	1	109	206	114	102	136	F	M
42	31	2	0	2	112	201	116	123	133	F	M
43	57	1	1	1	167	213	141	103	143	M	W
44	20	1	2	3	101	194	110	111	125	F	S
45	24	2	1	3	106	188	113	114	127	F	D
46	42	1	0	1	148	206	136	107	140	M	S
47	55	1	0	0	170	257	152	106	130	F	M
48	23	0	0	1	152	204	116	95	142	M	M
49	32	2	0	0	191	210	132	115	147	M	M
50	28	1	0	1	148	222	135	100	135	M	M
51	67	0	0	0	160	250	141	116	146	F	W
52	22	1	1	1	109	220	121	103	144	F	M
53	19	1	1	1	131	231	117	112	133	M	S
54	25	2	0	2	153	212	121	119	149	M	D
55	41	3	2	2	165	236	130	131	152	M	M

Data Bank *(concluded)*

ID number	Age	Educational level	Smoking status	Exercise	Weight	Serum cholesterol	Systolic pressure	IQ	Sodium	Gender	Marital status
56	24	2	0	3	112	205	118	100	132	F	S
57	32	2	0	1	115	187	115	109	136	F	S
58	50	3	0	1	173	203	136	126	146	M	M
59	32	2	1	0	186	248	119	122	149	M	M
60	26	2	0	1	181	207	123	121	142	M	S
61	36	1	1	0	112	188	117	98	135	F	D
62	40	1	1	0	130	201	121	105	136	F	D
63	19	1	1	1	132	237	115	111	137	M	S
64	37	2	0	2	179	228	141	127	141	F	M
65	65	3	2	1	212	220	158	129	148	M	M
66	21	1	2	2	99	191	117	103	131	F	S
67	25	2	2	1	128	195	120	121	131	F	S
68	68	0	0	0	167	210	142	98	140	M	W
69	18	1	1	2	121	198	123	113	136	F	S
70	26	0	1	1	163	235	128	99	140	M	M
71	45	1	1	1	185	229	125	101	143	M	M
72	44	3	0	0	130	215	128	128	137	F	M
73	50	1	0	0	142	232	135	104	138	F	M
74	63	0	0	0	166	271	143	103	147	F	W
75	48	1	0	3	163	203	131	103	144	M	M
76	27	2	0	3	147	186	118	114	134	M	M
77	31	3	1	1	152	228	116	126	138	M	D
78	28	2	0	2	112	197	120	123	133	F	M
79	36	2	1	2	190	226	123	121	147	M	M
80	43	3	2	0	179	252	127	131	145	M	D
81	21	1	0	1	117	185	116	105	137	F	S
82	32	2	1	0	125	193	123	119	135	F	M
83	29	2	1	0	123	192	131	116	131	F	D
84	49	2	2	1	185	190	129	127	144	M	M
85	24	1	1	1	133	237	121	114	129	M	M
86	36	2	0	2	163	195	115	119	139	M	M
87	34	1	2	0	135	199	133	117	135	F	M
88	36	0	0	1	142	216	138	88	137	F	M
89	29	1	1	1	155	214	120	98	135	M	S
90	42	0	0	2	169	201	123	96	137	M	D
91	41	1	1	1	136	214	133	102	141	F	D
92	29	1	1	0	112	205	120	102	130	F	M
93	43	1	1	0	185	208	127	100	143	M	M
94	61	1	2	0	173	248	142	101	141	M	M
95	21	1	1	3	106	210	111	105	131	F	S
96	56	0	0	0	149	232	142	103	141	F	M
97	63	0	1	0	192	193	163	95	147	M	M
98	74	1	0	0	162	247	151	99	151	F	W
99	35	2	0	1	151	251	147	113	145	F	M
100	28	2	0	3	161	199	129	116	138	M	M

Data Set I   Record Temperatures

Record high temperatures by state in degrees Fahrenheit

112	100	128	120	134
118	106	110	115	109
112	100	118	117	116
118	121	114	114	105
109	107	112	114	115
118	117	118	125	106
110	122	108	110	121
113	120	119	111	104
111	120	113	120	117
105	110	118	112	114

Record low temperatures by state in degrees Fahrenheit

−27	−80	−40	−29	−45
−61	−32	−17	−66	−2
−17	12	−60	−36	−36
−47	−40	−37	−16	−48
−40	−35	−51	−60	−19
−40	−70	−47	−50	−47
−39	−50	−52	−34	−60
−19	−27	−54	−42	−25
−50	−58	−32	−23	−69
	−30	−48	−37	−55

Source: Reprinted with permission from the *World Almanac and Book of Facts.* Copyright © K-III Reference Corporation. All rights reserved.

Data Set II   Identity Theft Complaints

The data values show the number of complaints of identity theft for 50 selected cities in the year 2002.

2609	1202	2730	483	655
626	393	1268	279	663
817	1165	551	2654	592
128	189	424	585	78
1836	154	248	239	5888
574	75	226	28	205
176	372	84	229	15
148	117	22	211	31
77	41	200	35	30
88	20	84	465	136

Source: Federal Trade Commission.

Data Set III   Length of Major North American Rivers

729	610	325	392	524
1459	450	465	605	330
950	906	329	290	1000
600	1450	862	532	890
407	525	720	1243	850
649	730	352	390	420
710	340	693	306	250
470	724	332	259	2340
560	1060	774	332	3710

Data Set III   Length of Major North American Rivers   *(continued)*

2315	2540	618	1171	460
431	800	605	410	1310
500	790	531	981	460
926	375	1290	1210	1310
383	380	300	310	411
1900	434	420	545	569
425	800	865	380	445
538	1038	424	350	377
540	659	652	314	360
301	512	500	313	610
360	430	682	886	447
338	485	625	722	525
800	309	435		

Source: Reprinted with permission from the *World Almanac and Book of Facts.* Copyright © K-III Reference Corporation. All rights reserved.

Data Set IV   Heights (in Feet) of 80 Tallest Buildings in New York City

1250	861	1046	952	552
915	778	856	850	927
729	745	757	752	814
750	697	743	739	750
700	670	716	707	730
682	648	687	687	705
650	634	664	674	685
640	628	630	653	673
625	620	628	645	650
615	592	620	630	630
595	580	614	618	629
587	575	590	609	615
575	572	580	588	603
574	563	575	577	587
565	555	562	570	576
557	570	555	561	574

Heights (in Feet) of 25 Tallest Buildings in Calgary, Alberta

689	530	460	410
645	525	449	410
645	507	441	408
626	500	435	407
608	469	435	
580	468	432	
530	463	420	

Source: Reprinted with permission from the *World Almanac and Book of Facts.* Copyright © K-III Reference Corporation. All rights reserved.

Data Set V   School Suspensions

The data values show the number of suspensions and the number of students enrolled in 40 local school districts in southwestern Pennsylvania.

Suspensions	Enrollment	Suspensions	Enrollment
37	1316	63	1588
29	1337	500	6046
106	4904	5	3610
47	5301	117	4329
51	1380	13	1908
46	1670	8	1341
65	3446	71	5582
223	1010	57	1869
10	795	16	1697
60	2094	60	2269
15	926	51	2307
198	1950	48	1564
56	3005	20	4147
72	4575	80	3182
110	4329	43	2982
6	3238	15	3313
37	3064	187	6090
26	2638	182	4874
140	4949	76	8286
39	3354	37	539
42	3547		

Source: U.S. Department of Education, *Pittsburgh Tribune-Review.*

Data Set VI   Acreage of U.S. National Parks, in Thousands of Acres

41	66	233	775	169
36	338	223	46	64
183	4724	61	1449	7075
1013	3225	1181	308	77
520	77	27	217	5
539	3575	650	462	1670
2574	106	52	52	236
505	913	94	75	265
402	196	70	13	132
28	7656	2220	760	143

Source: The Universal Almanac.

Data Set VII   Acreage Owned by 35 Municipalities in Southwestern Pennsylvania

384	44	62	218	250
198	60	306	105	600
10	38	87	227	340
48	70	58	223	3700
22	78	165	150	160
130	120	100	234	1200
4200	402	180	200	200

Source: Pittsburgh Tribune-Review.

Data Set VIII   Oceans of the World

Ocean	Area (thousands of square miles)	Maximum depth (feet)
Arctic	5,400	17,881
Caribbean Sea	1,063	25,197
Mediterranean Sea	967	16,470
Norwegian Sea	597	13,189
Gulf of Mexico	596	14,370
Hudson Bay	475	850
Greenland Sea	465	15,899
North Sea	222	2,170
Black Sea	178	7,360
Baltic Sea	163	1,440
Atlantic Ocean	31,830	30,246
South China Sea	1,331	18,241
Sea of Okhotsk	610	11,063
Bering Sea	876	13,750
Sea of Japan	389	12,280
East China Sea	290	9,126
Yellow Sea	161	300
Pacific Ocean	63,800	36,200
Arabian Sea	1,492	19,029
Bay of Bengal	839	17,251
Red Sea	169	7,370
Indian Ocean	28,360	24,442

Source: The Universal Almanac.

Data Set IX   Commuter and Rapid Rail Systems in the United States

System	Stations	Miles	Vehicles operated
Long Island RR	134	638.2	947
N.Y. Metro North	108	535.9	702
New Jersey Transit	158	926.0	582
Chicago RTA	117	417.0	358
Chicago & NW Transit	62	309.4	277
Boston Amtrak/MBTA	101	529.8	291
Chicago, Burlington, Northern	27	75.0	139
NW Indiana CTD	18	134.8	39
New York City TA	469	492.9	4923
Washington Metro Area TA	70	162.1	534
Metro Boston TA	53	76.7	368
Chicago TA	137	191.0	924
Philadelphia SEPTA	76	75.8	300
San Francisco BART	34	142.0	415
Metro Atlantic RTA	29	67.0	136
New York PATH	13	28.6	282
Miami/Dade Co TA	21	42.2	82
Baltimore MTA	12	26.6	48
Philadelphia PATCO	13	31.5	102
Cleveland RTA	18	38.2	30
New York, Staten Island RT	22	28.6	36

Source: The Universal Almanac.

Data Set X   Keystone Jackpot Analysis*

Ball	Times drawn	Ball	Times drawn	Ball	Times drawn
1	11	12	10	23	7
2	5	13	11	24	8
3	10	14	5	25	13
4	11	15	8	26	11
5	7	16	14	27	7
6	13	17	8	28	10
7	8	18	11	29	11
8	10	19	10	30	5
9	16	20	7	31	7
10	12	21	11	32	8
11	10	22	6	33	11

*Times each number has been selected in the regular drawings of the Pennsylvania Lottery.

Source: Copyright *Pittsburgh Post-Gazette,* all rights reserved. Reprinted with permission.

Data Set XI   Pages in Statistics Books

The data values represent the number of pages found in statistics textbooks.

616	578	569	511	468
493	564	801	483	847
525	881	757	272	703
741	556	500	668	967
608	465	739	669	651
495	613	774	274	542
739	488	601	727	556
589	724	731	662	680
589	435	742	567	574
733	576	526	443	478
586	282			

Source: Allan G. Bluman.

Data Set XII   Fifty Top Grossing Movies–2000

The data values represent the gross income in millions of dollars for the 50 top movies for the year 2000.

253.4	123.3	90.2	61.3	57.3
215.4	122.8	90.0	61.3	57.2
186.7	117.6	89.1	60.9	56.9
182.6	115.8	77.1	60.8	56.0
161.3	113.7	73.2	60.6	53.3
157.3	113.3	71.2	60.1	53.3
157.0	109.7	70.3	60.0	51.9
155.4	106.8	69.7	59.1	50.9
137.7	101.6	68.5	58.3	50.8
126.6	90.6	68.4	58.1	50.2

Source: Reprinted with permission from the *World Almanac and Book of Facts.* Copyright © K-III Reference Corporation. All rights reserved.

Data Set XIII   Hospital Data*

Number	Number of beds	Admissions	Payroll ($000)	Personnel
1	235	6,559	18,190	722
2	205	6,237	17,603	692
3	371	8,915	27,278	1,187
4	342	8,659	26,722	1,156
5	61	1,779	5,187	237
6	55	2,261	7,519	247
7	109	2,102	5,817	245
8	74	2,065	5,418	223
9	74	3,204	7,614	326
10	137	2,638	7,862	362
11	428	18,168	70,518	2,461
12	260	12,821	40,780	1,422
13	159	4,176	11,376	465
14	142	3,952	11,057	450
15	45	1,179	3,370	145
16	42	1,402	4,119	211
17	92	1,539	3,520	158
18	28	503	1,172	72
19	56	1,780	4,892	195
20	68	2,072	6,161	243
21	206	9,868	30,995	1,142
22	93	3,642	7,912	305
23	68	1,558	3,929	180
24	330	7,611	33,377	1,116
25	127	4,716	13,966	498
26	87	2,432	6,322	240
27	577	19,973	60,934	1,822
28	310	11,055	31,362	981
29	49	1,775	3,987	180
30	449	17,929	53,240	1,899
31	530	15,423	50,127	1,669
32	498	15,176	49,375	1,549
33	60	565	5,527	251
34	350	11,793	34,133	1,207
35	381	13,133	49,641	1,731
36	585	22,762	71,232	2,608
37	286	8,749	28,645	1,194
38	151	2,607	12,737	377
39	98	2,518	10,731	352
40	53	1,848	4,791	185
41	142	3,658	11,051	421
42	73	3,393	9,712	385
43	624	20,410	72,630	2,326
44	78	1,107	4,946	139
45	85	2,114	4,522	221

(continued)

Data Set XIII Hospital Data* (continued)

Number	Number of beds	Admissions	Payroll ($000)	Personnel
46	120	3,435	11,479	417
47	84	1,768	4,360	184
48	667	22,375	74,810	2,461
49	36	1,008	2,311	131
50	598	21,259	113,972	4,010
51	1,021	40,879	165,917	6,264
52	233	4,467	22,572	558
53	205	4,162	21,766	527
54	80	469	8,254	280
55	350	7,676	58,341	1,525
56	290	7,499	57,298	1,502
57	890	31,812	134,752	3,933
58	880	31,703	133,836	3,914
59	67	2,020	8,533	280
60	317	14,595	68,264	2,772
61	123	4,225	12,161	504
62	285	7,562	25,930	952
63	51	1,932	6,412	472
64	34	1,591	4,393	205
65	194	5,111	19,367	753
66	191	6,729	21,889	946
67	227	5,862	18,285	731
68	172	5,509	17,222	680
69	285	9,855	27,848	1,180
70	230	7,619	29,147	1,216
71	206	7,368	28,592	1,185
72	102	3,255	9,214	359
73	76	1,409	3,302	198
74	540	396	22,327	788
75	110	3,170	9,756	409
76	142	4,984	13,550	552
77	380	335	11,675	543
78	256	8,749	23,132	907
79	235	8,676	22,849	883
80	580	1,967	33,004	1,059
81	86	2,477	7,507	309
82	102	2,200	6,894	225
83	190	6,375	17,283	618
84	85	3,506	8,854	380
85	42	1,516	3,525	166
86	60	1,573	15,608	236
87	485	16,676	51,348	1,559
88	455	16,285	50,786	1,537
89	266	9,134	26,145	939
90	107	3,497	10,255	431
91	122	5,013	17,092	589

Data Set XIII Hospital Data* (continued)

Number	Number of beds	Admissions	Payroll ($000)	Personnel
92	36	519	1,526	80
93	34	615	1,342	74
94	37	1,123	2,712	123
95	100	2,478	6,448	265
96	65	2,252	5,955	237
97	58	1,649	4,144	203
98	55	2,049	3,515	152
99	109	1,816	4,163	194
100	64	1,719	3,696	167
101	73	1,682	5,581	240
102	52	1,644	5,291	222
103	326	10,207	29,031	1,074
104	268	10,182	28,108	1,030
105	49	1,365	4,461	215
106	52	763	2,615	125
107	106	4,629	10,549	456
108	73	2,579	6,533	240
109	163	201	5,015	260
110	32	34	2,880	124
111	385	14,553	52,572	1,724
112	95	3,267	9,928	366
113	339	12,021	54,163	1,607
114	50	1,548	3,278	156
115	55	1,274	2,822	162
116	278	6,323	15,697	722
117	298	11,736	40,610	1,606
118	136	2,099	7,136	255
119	97	1,831	6,448	222
120	369	12,378	35,879	1,312
121	288	10,807	29,972	1,263
122	262	10,394	29,408	1,237
123	94	2,143	7,593	323
124	98	3,465	9,376	371
125	136	2,768	7,412	390
126	70	824	4,741	208
127	35	883	2,505	142
128	52	1,279	3,212	158

*This information was obtained from a sample of hospitals in a selected state. The hospitals are identified by number instead of name.

Glossary

alpha the probability of a type I error, represented by the Greek letter α

alternative hypothesis a statistical hypothesis that states a difference between a parameter and a specific value or states that there is a difference between two parameters

analysis of variance (ANOVA) a statistical technique used to test a hypothesis concerning the means of three or more populations

ANOVA summary table the table used to summarize the results of an ANOVA test

bar graph a graph that shows the data using vertical or horizontal bars to represent the frequencies of the data

beta the probability of a type II error, represented by the Greek letter β

between-group variance a variance estimate using the means of the groups or between the groups in an F test

bimodal a data set with two modes

binomial distribution the outcomes of a binomial experiment and the corresponding probabilities of these outcomes

binomial experiment a probability experiment in which each trial has only two outcomes, there are a fixed number of trials, the outcomes of the trials are independent, and the probability of success remains the same for each trial

boxplot a graph used to represent a data set when the data set contains a small number of values

categorical frequency distribution a frequency distribution used when the data are categorical (nominal)

central limit theorem a theorem that states that as the sample size increases, the shape of the distribution of the sample means taken from the population with mean μ and standard deviation σ will approach a normal distribution; the distribution will have a mean μ and a standard deviation $\sigma/\sqrt{n}$

Chebyshev's theorem a theorem that states that the proportion of values from a data set that fall within

k standard deviations of the mean will be at least $1 - 1/k^2$, where k is a number greater than 1

chi-square distribution a probability distribution obtained from the values of $(n-1)s^2/\sigma^2$ when random samples are selected from a normally distributed population whose variance is σ^2

class quantitative or qualitative category used to classify data

class boundaries the upper and lower values of a class for a grouped frequency distribution whose values have one additional decimal place more than the data and end in the digit 5

class midpoint a value for a class in a frequency distribution obtained by adding the lower and upper class boundaries (or the lower and upper class limits) and dividing by 2

class width the difference between the upper class boundary and the lower class boundary for a class in a frequency distribution

classical probability the type of probability that uses sample spaces to determine the numerical probability that an event will happen

cluster sample a sample obtained by selecting a preexisting or natural group, called a cluster, and using the members in the cluster for the sample

coefficient of determination a measure of the variation of the dependent variable that is explained by the regression line and the independent variable; the ratio of the explained variation to the total variation

coefficient of variation the standard deviation divided by the mean; the result is expressed as a percentage

combination a selection of objects without regard to order

complement of an event the set of outcomes in the sample space that are not among the outcomes of the event itself

compound event an event that consists of two or more outcomes or simple events

conditional probability the probability that an event B occurs after an event A has already occurred

confidence interval a specific interval estimate of a parameter determined by using data obtained from a sample and the specific confidence level of the estimate

confidence level the probability that a parameter lies within the specified interval estimate of the parameter

confounding variable a variable that influences the outcome variable but cannot be separated from the other variables that influence the outcome variable

consistent estimator an estimator whose value approaches the value of the parameter estimated as the sample size increases

contingency table data arranged in table form for the chi-square independence test, with R rows and C columns

continuous variable a variable that can assume all values between any two specific values; a variable obtained by measuring

control group a group in an experimental study that is not given any special treatment

convenience sample sample of subjects used because they are convenient and available

correction for continuity a correction employed when a continuous distribution is used to approximate a discrete distribution

correlation a statistical method used to determine whether a linear relationship exists between variables

correlation coefficient a statistic or parameter that measures the strength and direction of a linear relationship between two variables

critical or **rejection region** the range of values of the test value that indicates that there is a significant difference and the null hypothesis should be rejected in a hypothesis test

critical value (C.V.) a value that separates the critical region from the noncritical region in a hypothesis test

cumulative frequency the sum of the frequencies accumulated up to the upper boundary of a class in a frequency distribution

cumulative frequency distribution a frequency distribution using cumulative frequencies for the data

data measurements or observations for a variable

data array a data set that has been ordered

data set a collection of data values

data value or **datum** a value in a data set

decile a location measure of a data value; it divides the distribution into 10 groups

degrees of freedom the number of values that are free to vary after a sample statistic has been computed; used when a distribution (such as the t distribution) consists of a family of curves

dependent events events for which the outcome or occurrence of the first event affects the outcome or occurrence of the second event in such a way that the probability is changed

dependent samples samples in which the subjects are paired or matched in some way; i.e., the samples are related

dependent variable a variable in correlation and regression analysis that cannot be controlled or manipulated

descriptive statistics a branch of statistics that consists of the collection, organization, summarization, and presentation of data

discrete probability distribution a distribution of values a random variable can assume and their corresponding probabilities

discrete variable a variable that assumes values that can be counted

empirical probability the type of probability that uses frequency distributions based on observations to determine numerical probabilities of events

empirical rule a rule that states that when a distribution is bell-shaped (normal), approximately 68% of the data values will fall within 1 standard deviation of the mean; approximately 95% of the data values will fall within 2 standard deviations of the mean; and approximately 99.7% of the data values will fall within 3 standard deviations of the mean

equally likely events the events in the sample space that have the same probability of occurring

estimation the process of estimating the value of a parameter from information obtained from a sample

estimator a statistic used to estimate a parameter

event outcome of a probability experiment

expected frequency the frequency obtained by calculation (as if there were no preference) and used in the chi-square test

expected value the theoretical average of a variable that has a probability distribution

experimental study a study in which the researcher manipulates one of the variables and tries to determine how the manipulation influences other variables

explanatory variable a variable that is being manipulated by the researcher to see if it affects the outcome variable

exploratory data analysis the act of analyzing data to determine what information can be obtained by using stem and leaf plots, medians, interquartile ranges, and boxplots

extrapolation use of the equation for the regression line to predict y' for a value of x which is beyond the range of the data values of x

F distribution the sampling distribution of the variances when two independent samples are selected from two normally distributed populations in which the variances are equal and the variances s_1^2 and s_2^2 are compared as $s_1^2 \div s_2^2$

F test a statistical test used to compare two variances or three or more means

finite population correction factor a correction factor used to correct the standard error of the mean when the sample size is greater than 5% of the population size

five-number summary five specific values for a data set that consist of the lowest and highest values, Q_1 and Q_3, and the median

frequency the number of values in a specific class of a frequency distribution

frequency distribution an organization of raw data in table form, using classes and frequencies

frequency polygon a graph that displays the data by using lines that connect points plotted for the frequencies at the midpoints of the classes

fundamental counting rule rule that is used to determine the total number of possibilities in a sequence of events

goodness-of-fit test a chi-square test used to see whether a frequency distribution fits a specific pattern

grouped frequency distribution a distribution used when the range is large and classes of several units in width are needed

Hawthorne effect an effect on an outcome variable caused by the fact that subjects of the study know that they are participating in the study

histogram a graph that displays the data by using vertical bars of various heights to represent the frequencies of a distribution

homogeneity of proportions test a test used to determine the equality of three or more proportions

hypothesis testing a decision-making process for evaluating claims about a population

independence test a chi-square test used to test the independence of two variables when data are tabulated in table form in terms of frequencies

independent events events for which the probability of the first occurring does not affect the probability of the second occurring

independent samples samples that are not related

independent variable a variable in correlation and regression analysis that can be controlled or manipulated

inferential statistics a branch of statistics that consists of generalizing from samples to populations, performing hypothesis testing, determining relationships among variables, and making predictions

influential point or **observation** an observation which when removed from the data values would markedly change the position of the regression line

interquartile range $Q_3 - Q_1$

interval estimate a range of values used to estimate a parameter

interval level of measurement a measurement level that ranks data and in which precise differences between units of measure exist. *See also* nominal, ordinal, and ratio levels of measurement

law of large numbers when a probability experiment is repeated a large number of times, the relative frequency probability of an outcome will approach its theoretical probability

least-squares line another name for the regression line

left-tailed test a test used on a hypothesis when the critical region is on the left side of the distribution

level of significance the maximum probability of committing a type I error in hypothesis testing

lower class limit the lower value of a class in a frequency distribution that has the same decimal place value as the data

lurking variable a variable that influences the relationship between x and y, but was not considered in the study

marginal change the magnitude of the change in the dependent variable when the independent variable changes 1 unit

maximum error of the estimate the maximum likely difference between the point estimate of a parameter and the actual value of the parameter

mean the sum of the values, divided by the total number of values

mean square the variance found by dividing the sum of the squares of a variable by the corresponding degrees of freedom; used in ANOVA

measurement scales a type of classification that tells how variables are categorized, counted, or measured; the four types of scales are nominal, ordinal, interval, and ratio

median the midpoint of a data array

midrange the sum of the lowest and highest data values, divided by 2

modal class the class with the largest frequency

mode the value that occurs most often in a data set

multimodal a data set with three or more modes

multiple relationship a relationship in which many variables are under study

mutually exclusive events probability events that cannot occur at the same time

negative linear relationship a relationship between variables such that as one variable increases, the other variable decreases, and vice versa

negatively skewed or **left-skewed distribution** a distribution in which the majority of the data values fall to the right of the mean

nominal level of measurement a measurement level that classifies data into mutually exclusive (nonoverlapping) exhaustive categories in which no order or ranking can be imposed on them. *See also* interval, ordinal, and ratio levels of measurement

noncritical or **nonrejection region** the range of values of the test value that indicates that the difference was probably due to chance and the null hypothesis should not be rejected

nonrejection region *see* noncritical region

normal distribution a continuous, symmetric, bell-shaped distribution of a variable

normal quantile plot graphical plot used to determine whether a variable is approximately normally distributed

null hypothesis a statistical hypothesis that states that there is no difference between a parameter and a specific value or that there is no difference between two parameters

observational study a study in which the researcher merely observes what is happening or what has happened in the past and draws conclusions based on these observations

observed frequency the actual frequency value obtained from a sample and used in the chi-square test

ogive a graph that represents the cumulative frequencies for the classes in a frequency distribution

one-tailed test a test that indicates that the null hypothesis should be rejected when the test statistic value is in the critical region on one side of the mean

open-ended distribution a frequency distribution that has no specific beginning value or no specific ending value

ordinal level of measurement a measurement level that classifies data into categories that can be ranked; however, precise differences between the ranks do not exist. *See also* interval, nominal, and ratio levels of measurement

outcome the result of a single trial of a probability experiment

outcome variable a variable that is studied to see if it has changed significantly due to the manipulation of the explanatory variable

outlier an extreme value in a data set; it is omitted from a boxplot

parameter a characteristic or measure obtained by using all the data values for a specific population

Pareto chart chart that uses vertical bars to represent frequencies for a categorical variable

Pearson product moment correlation coefficient (PPMCC) a statistic used to determine the strength of a relationship when the variables are normally distributed

Pearson's index of skewness value used to determine the degree of skewness of a variable

percentile a location measure of a data value; it divides the distribution into 100 groups

permutation an arrangement of n objects in a specific order

pie graph a circle that is divided into sections or wedges according to the percentage of frequencies in each category of the distribution

point estimate a specific numerical value estimate of a parameter

pooled estimate of the variance a weighted average of the variance using the two sample variances and their respective degrees of freedom as the weights

population the totality of all subjects possessing certain common characteristics that are being studied

population correlation coefficient the value of the correlation coefficient computed by using all possible pairs of data values (x, y) taken from a population

positive linear relationship a relationship between two variables such that as one variable increases, the other variable increases or as one variable decreases, the other decreases

positively skewed or **right-skewed distribution** a distribution in which the majority of the data values fall to the left of the mean

power of a test the probability of rejecting the null hypothesis when it is false

prediction interval a confidence interval for a predicted value y

probability the chance of an event occurring

probability distribution the values a random variable can assume and the corresponding probabilities of the values

probability experiment a chance process that leads to well-defined results called outcomes

proportion a part of a whole, represented by a fraction, a decimal, or a percentage

P-value the actual probability of getting the sample mean value if the null hypothesis is true

qualitative variable a variable that can be placed into distinct categories, according to some characteristic or attribute

quantiles values that separate the data set into approximately equal groups

quantitative variable a variable that is numerical in nature and that can be ordered or ranked

quartile a location measure of a data value; it divides the distribution into four groups

quasi-experimental study a study that uses intact groups rather than random assignment of subjects to groups

random sample a sample obtained by using random or chance methods; a sample for which every member of the population has an equal chance of being selected

random variable a variable whose values are determined by chance

range the highest data value minus the lowest data value

range rule of thumb dividing the range by 4, given an approximation of the standard deviation

ratio level of measurement a measurement level that possesses all the characteristics of interval measurement and a true zero; it also has true ratios between different units of measure. *See also* interval, nominal, and ordinal levels of measurement

raw data data collected in original form

regression a statistical method used to describe the nature of the relationship between variables, that is, a positive or negative, linear or nonlinear relationship

regression line the line of best fit of the data

rejection region *see* critical region

relative frequency graph a graph using proportions instead of raw data as frequencies

relatively efficient estimator an estimator that has the smallest variance from among all the statistics that can be used to estimate a parameter

research hypothesis another name for the alternate hypothesis

residual the difference between the actual value of y and the predicted value y' for a specific value of x

resistant statistic a statistic that is not affected by an extremely skewed distribution

right-tailed test a test used on a hypothesis when the critical region is on the right side of the distribution

sample a group of subjects selected from the population

sample space the set of all possible outcomes of a probability experiment

sampling distribution of sample means a distribution obtained by using the means computed from random samples taken from a population

sampling error the difference between the sample measure and the corresponding population measure due to the fact that the sample is not a perfect representation of the population

scatter plot a graph of the independent and dependent variables in regression and correlation analysis

simple event an outcome that results from a single trial of a probability experiment

simple relationship a relationship in which only two variables are under study

standard deviation the square root of the variance

standard error of the estimate the standard deviation of the observed y values about the predicted y' values in regression and correlation analysis

standard error of the mean the standard deviation of the sample means for samples taken from the same population

standard normal distribution a normal distribution for which the mean is equal to 0 and the standard deviation is equal to 1

standard score the difference between a data value and the mean, divided by the standard deviation

statistic a characteristic or measure obtained by using the data values from a sample

statistical hypothesis a conjecture about a population parameter, which may or may not be true

statistical test a test that uses data obtained from a sample to make a decision about whether the null hypothesis should be rejected

statistics the science of conducting studies to collect, organize, summarize, analyze, and draw conclusions from data

stem and leaf plot a data plot that uses part of a data value as the stem and part of the data value as the leaf to form groups or classes

stratified sample a sample obtained by dividing the population into subgroups, called strata, according to various homogeneous characteristics and then selecting members from each stratum

subjective probability the type of probability that uses a probability value based on an educated guess or estimate, employing opinions and inexact information

sum of squares between groups a statistic computed in the numerator of the fraction used to find the between-group variance in ANOVA

sum of squares within groups a statistic computed in the numerator of the fraction used to find the within-group variance in ANOVA

symmetric distribution a distribution in which the data values are uniformly distributed about the mean

systematic sample a sample obtained by numbering each element in the population and then selecting every kth number from the population to be included in the sample

t distribution a family of bell-shaped curves based on degrees of freedom, similar to the standard normal distribution with the exception that the variance is greater than 1; used when you are testing small samples and when the population standard deviation is unknown *t* **test** a statistical test for the mean of a population, used when the population is normally distributed and the population standard deviation is unknown

test value the numerical value obtained from a statistical test, computed from (observed value − expected value) ÷ standard error

time series graph a graph that represents data that occur over a specific time

tree diagram a device used to list all possibilities of a sequence of events in a systematic way

two-tailed test a test that indicates that the null hypothesis should be rejected when the test value is in either of the two critical regions

type I error the error that occurs if you reject the null hypothesis when it is true

type II error the error that occurs if you do not reject the null hypothesis when it is false

unbiased estimator the expected value or the mean of the estimates obtained from samples of a given size is equal to the parameter being estimated

ungrouped frequency distribution a distribution that uses individual data and has a small range of data

uniform distribution a distribution whose values are evenly distributed over its range

unimodal a data set or distribution with a single mode

upper class limit the upper value of a class in a frequency distribution that has the same decimal place value as the data

variable a characteristic or attribute that can assume different values

variance the average of the squares of the distance that each value is from the mean

Venn diagram a diagram used as a pictorial representative for a probability concept or rule

weighted mean the mean found by multiplying each value by its corresponding weight and dividing by the sum of the weights

within-group variance a variance estimate using all the sample data for an *F* test; it is not affected by differences in the means

z **distribution** *see* standard normal distribution

z **score** *see* standard score

z **test** a statistical test for means and proportions of a population, used when the population is normally distributed and the population standard deviation is known

z **value** same as *z* score

Glossary of Symbols

a	y intercept of a line
α	Probability of a type I error
b	Slope of a line
β	Probability of a type II error
C	Column frequency
cf	Cumulative frequency
$_nC_r$	Number of combinations of n objects taking r objects at a time
C.V.	Critical value
CVar	Coefficient of variation
D	Difference; decile
$\overline{D}$	Mean of the differences
d.f.	Degrees of freedom
d.f.N.	Degrees of freedom, numerator
d.f.D.	Degrees of freedom, denominator
E	Event; expected frequency; maximum error of estimate
$\overline{E}$	Complement of an event
e	Euler's constant ≈ 2.7183
$E(X)$	Expected value
f	Frequency
F	F test value; failure
MD	Median
MR	Midrange
MS_B	Mean square between groups
MS_W	Mean square within groups (error)
n	Sample size
N	Population size
$n(E)$	Number of ways E can occur
$n(S)$	Number of outcomes in the sample space
O	Observed frequency
P	Percentile; probability
p	Probability; population proportion
$\hat{p}$	Sample proportion
$\overline{p}$	Weighted estimate of p
$P(B|A)$	Conditional probability
$P(E)$	Probability of an event E
$P(\overline{E})$	Probability of the complement of E
$_nP_r$	Number of permutations of n objects taking r objects at a time
π	Pi ≈ 3.14
Q	Quartile
q	$1 - p$; test value for Tukey test

$\hat{q}$	$1 - \hat{p}$
$\overline{q}$	$1 - \overline{p}$
R	Range
GM	Geometric mean
H_0	Null hypothesis
H_1	Alternative hypothesis
HM	Harmonic mean
k	Number of samples
s_D	Standard deviation of the differences
s_{est}	Standard error of estimate
SS_B	Sum of squares between groups
SS_W	Sum of squares within groups
s_B^2	Between-group variance
s_W^2	Within-group variance
t	t test value
$t_{\alpha/2}$	Two-tailed t critical value
μ	Population mean
μ_D	Mean of the population differences
$\mu_{\overline{X}}$	Mean of the sample means
w	Class width; weight
r	Sample correlation coefficient
r^2	Coefficient of determination
ρ	Population correlation coefficient
S	Sample space; success
s	Sample standard deviation
s^2	Sample variance
σ	Population standard deviation
σ^2	Population variance
$\sigma_{\overline{X}}$	Standard error of the mean
Σ	Summation notation
X	Data value; number of successes for a binomial distribution
$\overline{X}$	Sample mean
x	Independent variable in regression
$\overline{X}_{\text{GM}}$	Grand mean
X_m	Midpoint of a class
χ^2	Chi-square
y	Dependent variable in regression
y'	Predicted y value
z	z test value or z score
$z_{\alpha/2}$	Two-tailed z critical value
$!$	Factorial

Bibliography

Aczel, Amir D. *Complete Business Statistics,* 3rd ed. Chicago: Irwin, 1996.

Beyer, William H. *CRC Handbook of Tables for Probability and Statistics,* 2nd ed. Boca Raton, Fla.: CRC Press, 1986.

Brase, Charles, and Corrinne P. Brase. *Understanding Statistics,* 5th ed. Lexington, Mass.: D.C. Heath, 1995.

Chao, Lincoln L. *Introduction to Statistics.* Monterey, Calif.: Brooks/Cole, 1980.

Daniel, Wayne W., and James C. Terrell. *Business Statistics,* 4th ed. Boston: Houghton Mifflin, 1986.

Edwards, Allan L. *An Introduction to Linear Regression and Correlation,* 2nd ed. New York: Freeman, 1984.

Eves, Howard. *An Introduction to the History of Mathematics,* 3rd ed. New York: Holt, Rinehart and Winston, 1969.

Famighetti, Robert, ed. *The World Almanac and Book of Facts 1996.* New York: Pharos Books, 1995.

Freund, John E., and Gary Simon. *Statistics—A First Course,* 6th ed. Englewood Cliffs, N.J.: Prentice-Hall, 1995.

Gibson, Henry R. *Elementary Statistics.* Dubuque, Iowa: Wm. C. Brown Publishers, 1994.

Glass, Gene V., and Kenneth D. Hopkins. *Statistical Methods in Education and Psychology,* 2nd ed. Englewood Cliffs, N.J.: Prentice-Hall, 1984.

Guilford, J. P. *Fundamental Statistics in Psychology and Education,* 4th ed. New York: McGraw-Hill, 1965.

Haack, Dennis G. *Statistical Literacy: A Guide to Interpretation.* Boston: Duxbury Press, 1979.

Hartwig, Frederick, with Brian Dearing. *Exploratory Data Analysis.* Newbury Park, Calif.: Sage Publications, 1979.

Henry, Gary T. *Graphing Data: Techniques for Display and Analysis.* Thousand Oaks, Calif.: Sage Publications, 1995.

Isaac, Stephen, and William B. Michael. *Handbook in Research and Evaluation,* 2nd ed. San Diego: EdITS, 1990.

Johnson, Robert. *Elementary Statistics,* 6th ed. Boston: PWS–Kent, 1992.

Kachigan, Sam Kash. *Statistical Analysis.* New York: Radius Press, 1986.

Khazanie, Ramakant. *Elementary Statistics in a World of Applications,* 3rd ed. Glenview, Ill.: Scott, Foresman, 1990.

Kuzma, Jan W. *Basic Statistics for the Health Sciences.* Mountain View, Calif.: Mayfield, 1984.

Lapham, Lewis H., Michael Pollan, and Eric Ethridge. *The Harper's Index Book.* New York: Henry Holt, 1987.

Lipschultz, Seymour. *Schaum's Outline of Theory and Problems of Probability.* New York: McGraw-Hill, 1968.

Marascuilo, Leonard A., and Maryellen McSweeney. *Nonparametric and Distribution-Free Methods for the Social Sciences.* Monterey, Calif.: Brooks/Cole, 1977.

Marzillier, Leon F. *Elementary Statistics.* Dubuque, Iowa: Wm. C. Brown Publishers, 1990.

Mason, Robert D., Douglas A. Lind, and William G. Marchal. *Statistics: An Introduction.* New York: Harcourt Brace Jovanovich, 1988.

MINITAB. *MINITAB Reference Manual.* State College, Pa.: MINITAB, Inc., 1994.

Minium, Edward W. *Statistical Reasoning in Psychology and Education.* New York: Wiley, 1970.

Moore, David S. *The Basic Practice of Statistics.* New York: W. H. Freeman and Co., 1995.

Moore, David S., and George P. McCabe. *Introduction to the Practice of Statistics,* 3rd ed. New York: W. H. Freeman, 1999.

Newmark, Joseph. *Statistics and Probability in Modern Life.* New York: Saunders, 1988.

Pagano, Robert R. *Understanding Statistics,* 3rd ed. New York: West, 1990.

Phillips, John L., Jr. *How to Think about Statistics.* New York: Freeman, 1988.

Reinhardt, Howard E., and Don O. Loftsgaarden. *Elementary Probability and Statistical Reasoning.* Lexington, Mass.: Heath, 1977.

Roscoe, John T. *Fundamental Research Statistics for the Behavioral Sciences,* 2nd ed. New York: Holt, Rinehart and Winston, 1975.

Rossman, Allan J. *Workshop Statistics, Discovery with Data.* New York: Springer, 1996.

Runyon, Richard P., and Audrey Haber. *Fundamentals of Behavioral Statistics,* 6th ed. New York: Random House, 1988.

Shulte, Albert P., 1981 yearbook editor, and James R. Smart, general yearbook editor. *Teaching Statistics and Probability, 1981 Yearbook.* Reston, Va.: National Council of Teachers of Mathematics, 1981.

Smith, Gary. *Statistical Reasoning.* Boston: Allyn and Bacon, 1985.

Spiegel, Murray R. *Schaum's Outline of Theory and Problems of Statistics.* New York: McGraw-Hill, 1961.

Texas Instruments. *TI-83 Graphing Calculator Guidebook.* Temple, Tex.: Texas Instruments, 1996.

Triola, Mario G. *Elementary Statistics,* 7th ed. Reading, Mass.: Addison-Wesley, 1998.

Wardrop, Robert L. *Statistics: Learning in the Presence of Variation.* Dubuque, Iowa: Wm. C. Brown Publishers, 1995.

Warwick, Donald P., and Charles A. Lininger. *The Sample Survey: Theory and Practice.* New York: McGraw-Hill, 1975.

Weiss, Daniel Evan. *100% American.* New York: Poseidon Press, 1988.

Williams, Jack. *The USA Today Weather Almanac 1995.* New York: Vintage Books, 1994.

Wright, John W., ed. *The Universal Almanac 1995.* Kansas City, Mo.: Andrews & McMeel, 1994.

Photo Credits

Chapter 1

Openers: © Getty RF; p. 2: © Getty RF; p. 10: © Banana Stock Ltd RF.

Chapter 2

Opener: © Corbis RF; p. 36: © Corbis RF; p. 81: © Getty RF.

Chapter 3

Opener: © Comstock/Jupiter Images RF; p. 112: © Getty RF; p. 113: © Image 100 RF; p. 117: © Getty RF.

Chapter 4

Opener: © Corbis RF; p. 190: © Getty RF; p. 238: © The McGraw-Hill Companies, Inc./Evelyn Jo Hebert, photographer; p. 245: © Corbis RF; p. 248: © Corbis RF.

Chapter 5

Opener: © Alamy RF; p. 260: © Fotosearch RF; p. 264: © Brand X/Punchstock RF; p. 278: © Getty RF.

Chapter 6

Opener: Library of Congress; p. 298: © Corbis RF; p. 316: © Corbis RF.

Chapter 7

Opener: USDA; p. 354: © Corbis RF; p. 379: © Brand X Pictures/Getty RF; p. 384: © Corbis RF.

Chapter 8

Opener: © Dr. Parvinder Sethi; p. 398: © PhotoDisc/ Punchstock RF; p. 431: © Jupiter Images/Imagesource RF; p. 456: © Getty RF.

Chapter 9

Openers: © SuperStock RF; p. 468: © Corbis RF; p. 495: © Antonio Reeve/Photo Researchers; p. 503: © Comstcok/PictureQuest RF.

Chapter 10

Opener: © Getty RF; p. 530, 535: © Getty RF.

Chapter 11

Opener: © Comstock RF; p. 572, 599: © Getty RF; p. 620: © The McGraw-Hill Companies, Inc./Jill Braaten, photographer.

Selected Answers*

Chapter 1

Review Exercises

1. Descriptive statistics describe the data set. Inferential statistics use the data to draw conclusions about the population.

3. Answers will vary.

5. Samples are used to save time and money when the population is large and when the units must be destroyed to gain information.

7. a. Ratio   f. Ordinal
   b. Ordinal   g. Ratio
   c. Ratio   h. Ratio
   d. Interval   i. Nominal
   e. Ratio   j. Ratio

9. a. Discrete   e. Discrete
   b. Continuous   f. Discrete
   c. Continuous   g. Continuous
   d. Continuous

11. Random, systematic, stratified, cluster

13. Answers will vary.

15. Answers will vary.

17. a. Experimental   c. Observational
    b. Observational   d. Experimental

19. Possible answers:
    a. Workplace of subjects, smoking habits, etc.
    b. Gender, age, etc.
    c. Diet, type of job, etc.
    d. Exercise, heredity, age, etc.

21. The only time claims can be proved is when the entire population is used.

23. Since the results are not typical, the advertisers selected only a few people for whom the weight loss product worked extremely well.

25. "74% more calories" than what? No comparison group is stated.

27. What is meant by "24 hours of acid control"?

29. Possible answer: It could be the amount of caffeine in the coffee or tea. It could have been the brewing method.

31. Answers will vary.

Chapter Quiz

1. True   2. False
3. False   4. False
5. False   6. True
7. False   8. c
9. b   10. d
11. a   12. c
13. a   14. Descriptive, inferential
15. Gambling, insurance   16. Population
17. Sample
18. a. Saves time   c. Use when population is infinite
    b. Saves money
19. a. Random   c. Cluster
    b. Systematic   d. Stratified
20. Quasi-experimental   21. Random
22. a. Descriptive   d. Inferential
    b. Inferential   e. Inferential
    c. Descriptive

*Answers may vary due to rounding or use of technology.

Note: These answers to odd-numbered and selected even-numbered exercises include *all* quiz answers.

23. *a.* Nominal   *d.* Interval
    b. Ratio   *e.* Ratio
    c. Ordinal

24. *a.* Continuous   *d.* Continuous
    b. Discrete   *e.* Discrete
    c. Continuous

25. *a.* 47.5–48.5 seconds
    b. 0.555–0.565 centimeter
    c. 9.05–9.15 quarts
    d. 13.65–13.75 pounds
    e. 6.5–7.5 feet

Chapter 2

Exercises 2–1

1. To organize data in a meaningful way, to determine the shape of the distribution, to facilitate computational procedures for statistics, to make it easier to draw charts and graphs, to make comparisons among different sets of data

3. *a.* 11.5–18.5; 15; 7
    b. 55.5–74.5; 65; 19
    c. 694.5–705.5; 700; 11
    d. 13.55–14.75; 14.15; 1.2
    e. 2.145–3.935; 3.04; 1.79

5. *a.* Class width is not uniform.
    b. Class limits overlap, and class width is not uniform.
    c. A class has been omitted.
    d. Class width is not uniform.

7.

Class	Tally	Frequency	Percent
A	////	4	10
M	卌 卌 卌 卌 卌 ///	28	70
H	卌 /	6	15
S	//	2	5
		40	100

9.

Limits	Boundaries	f
165–185	164.5–185.5	4
186–206	185.5–206.5	6
207–227	206.5–227.5	15
228–248	227.5–248.5	13
249–269	248.5–269.5	9
270–290	269.5–290.5	1
291–311	290.5–311.5	1
312–332	311.5–332.5	1
		50

A peak occurs in class 207–227 (206.5–227.5). There are no gaps in the distribution, and there is one value in each of the three highest classes.

	cf
Less than 164.5	0
Less than 185.5	4
Less than 206.5	10
Less than 227.5	25
Less than 248.5	38
Less than 269.5	47
Less than 290.5	48
Less than 311.5	49
Less than 332.5	50

11.

Limits	Boundaries	f
746–752	745.5–752.5	4
753–759	752.5–759.5	6
760–766	759.5–766.5	8
767–773	766.5–773.5	9
774–780	773.5–780.5	3
		30

	cf
Less than 745.5	0
Less than 752.5	4
Less than 759.5	10
Less than 766.5	18
Less than 773.5	27
Less than 780.5	30

13.

Limits	Boundaries	f
27–33	26.5–33.5	7
34–40	33.5–40.5	14
41–47	40.5–47.5	15
48–54	47.5–54.5	11
55–61	54.5–61.5	3
62–68	61.5–68.5	3
69–75	68.5–75.5	2
		55

	cf
Less than 26.5	0
Less than 33.5	7
Less than 40.5	21
Less than 47.5	36
Less than 54.5	47
Less than 61.5	50
Less than 68.5	53
Less than 75.5	55

15.

Limits	Boundaries	f
6–132	5.5–132.5	16
133–259	132.5–259.5	3
260–386	259.5–386.5	0
387–513	386.5–513.5	0
514–640	513.5–640.5	1
		20

The lowest class has the most data values, 16, and the next class has 3 values. There is one extremely large data value, 632, and it is in the last class, 514–640 (513.5–640.5).

	cf
Less than 5.5	0
Less than 132.5	16
Less than 259.5	19
Less than 386.5	19
Less than 513.5	19
Less than 640.5	20

17.

Limits	Boundaries	f
150–1,276	149.5–1,276.5	2
1,277–2,403	1,276.5–2,403.5	2
2,404–3,530	2,403.5–3,530.5	5
3,531–4,657	3,530.5–4,657.5	8
4,658–5,784	4,657.5–5,784.5	7
5,785–6,911	5,784.5–6,911.5	3
6,912–8,038	6,911.5–8,038.5	7
8,039–9,165	8,038.5–9,165.5	3
9,166–10,292	9,165.5–10,292.5	3
10,293–11,419	10,292.5–11,419.5	2
		42

	cf
Less than 149.5	0
Less than 1,276.5	2
Less than 2,403.5	4
Less than 3,530.5	9
Less than 4,657.5	17
Less than 5,784.5	24
Less than 6,911.5	27
Less than 8,038.5	34
Less than 9,165.5	37
Less than 10,292.5	40
Less than 11,419.5	42

19. The percents sum to 101. They should sum to 100% unless rounding was used.

Exercises 2–2

1. Eighty applicants do not need to enroll in the developmental programs.

3.

Limits	Boundaries	f
3–45	2.5–45.5	19
46–88	45.5–88.5	19
89–131	88.5–131.5	10
132–174	131.5–174.5	1
175–217	174.5–217.5	0
218–260	217.5–260.5	1
		50

	cf
Less than 2.5	0
Less than 45.5	19
Less than 88.5	38
Less than 131.5	48
Less than 174.5	49
Less than 217.5	49
Less than 260.5	50

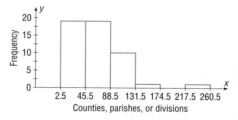

The distribution is positively skewed.

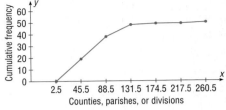

Counties, parishes, or divisions

5.

7.

Limits	Boundaries	f(1998)	f(2003)
0–22	−0.5–22.5	18	26
23–45	22.5–45.5	7	1
46–68	45.5–68.5	3	0
69–91	68.5–91.5	1	1
92–114	91.5–114.5	1	0
115–137	114.5–137.5	0	1
138–160	137.5–160.5	0	1
		30	30

Both distributions are positively skewed, but the data are somewhat more spread out in the first three classes in 1998 than in 2003, and there are two large data values in the 2003 data.

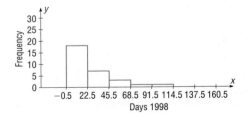

Days 1998

9.

Limits	Boundaries	f
83.1–90.0	83.05–90.05	3
90.1–97.0	90.05–97.05	5
97.1–104.0	97.05–104.05	6
104.1–111.0	104.05–111.05	7
111.1–118.0	111.05–118.05	3
118.1–125.0	118.05–125.05	1
		25

	cf
Less than 83.05	0
Less than 90.05	3
Less than 97.05	8
Less than 104.05	14
Less than 111.05	21
Less than 118.05	24
Less than 125.05	25

Days 2003

11. The peak is in the first class, and then the histogram is rather uniform after the first class. Most of the parks have less than 101.5 thousand acres as compared with any other class of values.

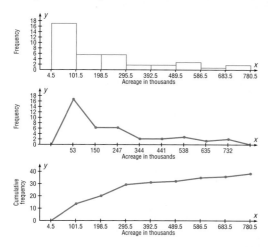

13. The proportion of applicants who need to enroll in the developmental program is about 0.26.

15.

Class boundaries	rf
79.5–108.5	0.17
108.5–137.5	0.28
137.5–166.5	0.04
166.5–195.5	0.20
195.5–224.5	0.22
224.5–253.5	0.04
253.5–282.5	0.04
	0.99

	crf
Less than 79.5	0.00
Less than 108.5	0.17
Less than 137.5	0.45
Less than 166.5	0.49
Less than 195.5	0.69
Less than 224.5	0.91
Less than 253.5	0.95
Less than 282.5	0.99*

*Due to rounding.

The histogram has two peaks.

17.

Class boundaries	rf
−0.5–27.5	0.63
27.5–55.5	0.20
55.5–83.5	0.07
83.5–111.5	0.00
111.5–139.5	0.00
139.5–167.5	0.10
167.5–195.5	0.00
	100.00

	crf
Less than −0.5	0.00
Less than 27.5	0.63
Less than 55.5	0.83
Less than 83.5	0.90
Less than 111.5	0.90
Less than 139.5	0.90
Less than 167.5	1.00

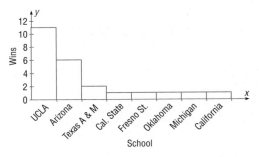

Exercises 2–3

1.

	f
UCLA	11
Texas A & M	2
Cal. State Fullerton	1
Arizona	6
Fresno State	1
Oklahoma	1
California	1
Michigan	1
	24

19. *a.*

Limits	Boundaries	Midpoints	*f*
22–24	21.5–24.5	23	1
25–27	24.5–27.5	26	3
28–30	27.5–30.5	29	0
31–33	30.5–33.5	32	6
34–36	33.5–36.5	35	5
37–39	36.5–39.5	38	3
40–42	39.5–42.5	41	2

	cf
Less than 21.5	0
Less than 24.5	1
Less than 27.5	4
Less than 30.5	4
Less than 33.5	10
Less than 36.5	15
Less than 39.5	18
Less than 42.5	20

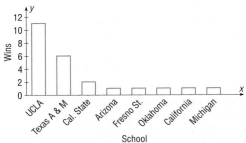

3. The best place to market products would be to the home users.

5.

7.

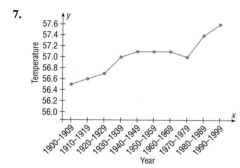

9. The sample used was not representative of the general voting population.

11.

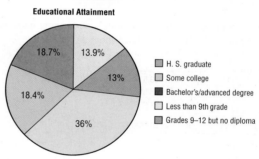

13. The pie graph better represents the data since we are looking at parts of a whole.

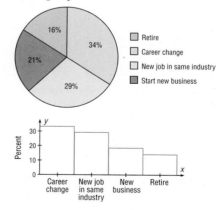

15. The distribution is somewhat symmetric and unimodal and has a peak in the 50s.

```
4 | 2 3
4 | 6 6 7 8 9 9
5 | 0 1 1 1 1 2 2 4 4 4 4 4
5 | 5 5 5 5 6 6 6 7 7 7 7 8
6 | 0 1 1 1 2 4 4
6 | 5 8 9
```

17.

Variety 1		Variety 2
2	1	3 8
3 0	2	5
9 8 8 5 2	3	6 8
3 3 1	4	1 2 5 5
9 9 8 5 3 3 2 1 0	5	0 3 5 5 6 7 9
	6	2 2

The distributions are somewhat similar in their shapes; however, the variation of the data for variety 2 is slightly larger than the variation of the data for variety 1.

19. Answers will vary.

21. Production of both veal and lamb is decreasing with the exception of 1990, where both show an increase.

23.

25. The values on the y axis start at 3.5. Also there are no data values shown for the years 2004 through 2011.

Exercises 2–4

1. Scatter plot or scatter diagram.

3. Two variables are positively related when the values for the y variable increase as the values of the x variable increase.

5. There appears to be a positive linear relationship between the height of a building and the number of stories contained in the building.

7. There appears to be a positive linear relationship between a person's monthly income and the amount a person spends on recreation each month.

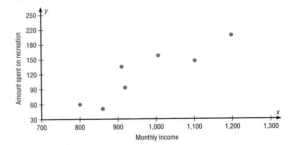

9. There appears to be a positive linear relationship between a student's final exam score in Stat 101 and Stat 102.

11. There appears to be no linear relationship between the number of tournaments and the earnings of LPGA golfers.

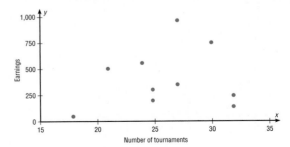

13. There appears to be a negative linear relationship between the number of absences a student has and his or her final grade in a course.

Review Exercises

1.

Class	f
Newspaper	10
Television	16
Radio	12
Internet	12
	50

3.

Class	f
Baseballs	4
Golf balls	5
Tennis balls	6
Soccer balls	5
Footballs	5
	25

5.

Class	f
11	1
12	2
13	2
14	2
15	1
16	2
17	4
18	2
19	2
20	1
21	0
22	1
	20

	cf
Less than 10.5	0
Less than 11.5	1
Less than 12.5	3
Less than 13.5	5
Less than 14.5	7
Less than 15.5	8
Less than 16.5	10
Less than 17.5	14
Less than 18.5	16
Less than 19.5	18
Less than 20.5	19
Less than 21.5	19
Less than 22.5	20

7.

Class limits	Class boundaries	f
15–19	14.5–19.5	3
20–24	19.5–24.5	18
25–29	24.5–29.5	18
30–34	29.5–34.5	8
35–39	34.5–39.5	3
		50

	cf
Less than 14.5	0
Less than 19.5	3
Less than 24.5	21
Less than 29.5	39
Less than 34.5	47
Less than 39.5	50

9.

Class limits	Class boundaries	f
170–188	169.5–188.5	11
189–207	188.5–207.5	9
208–226	207.5–226.5	4
227–245	226.5–245.5	5
246–264	245.5–264.5	0
265–283	264.5–283.5	0
284–302	283.5–302.5	0
303–321	302.5–321.5	1
		30

	cf
Less than 169.5	0
Less than 188.5	11
Less than 207.5	20
Less than 226.5	24
Less than 245.5	29
Less than 264.5	29
Less than 283.5	29
Less than 302.5	29
Less than 321.5	30

11.

Limits	Boundaries	rf
51–59	50.5–59.5	0.125
60–68	59.5–68.5	0.300
69–77	68.5–77.5	0.275
78–86	77.5–86.5	0.200
87–95	86.5–95.5	0.050
96–104	95.5–104.5	0.050
		1.000

	crf
Less than 50.5	0.000
Less than 59.5	0.125
Less than 68.5	0.425
Less than 77.5	0.700
Less than 86.5	0.900
Less than 95.5	0.950
Less than 104.5	1.000

13.

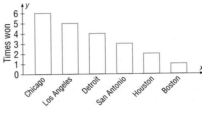

15. Over time the wage has increased.

17. About the same number of people watched the first and second debates in 1992 and 1996. After that more people watched the first debate than watched the second debate.

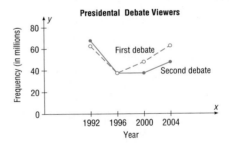

19. Results of Survey Asking If People Would Like to Spend the Rest of Their Careers with Their Present Employer

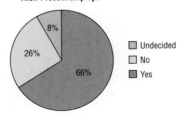

21.

```
10 | 2 8 8
11 | 3
12 |
13 |
14 | 2 4
15 |
16 |
17 | 6 6 6
18 | 4 9
19 | 2
20 | 5 9
21 | 0
```

23. There appears to be a positive linear relationship between the number of viewers (in millions) and the ratings of the 15 television programs.

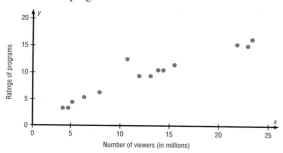

Chapter Quiz

1. False
2. False
3. False
4. True
5. True
6. False
7. False
8. *c*
9. *c*
10. *b*
11. *b*
12. Categorical, ungrouped, grouped
13. 5, 20
14. Categorical
15. Time series
16. Stem and leaf plot
17. Vertical or *y*

18.

Class	*f*
H	6
A	5
M	6
C	8
	25

19.

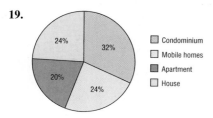

☐	Condominium
☐	Mobile homes
■	Apartment
☐	House

32%, 24%, 20%, 24%

20.

Class boundaries	*f*
0.5–1.5	1
1.5–2.5	5
2.5–3.5	3
3.5–4.5	4
4.5–5.5	2
5.5–6.5	6
6.5–7.5	2
7.5–8.5	3
8.5–9.5	4
	30

	cf
Less than 0.5	0
Less than 1.5	1
Less than 2.5	6
Less than 3.5	9
Less than 4.5	13
Less than 5.5	15
Less than 6.5	21
Less than 7.5	23
Less than 8.5	26
Less than 9.5	30

21.

22.

Class limits	*f*	Class boundaries
27–90	13	26.5–90.5
91–154	2	90.5–154.5
155–218	0	154.5–218.5
219–282	5	218.5–282.5
283–346	0	282.5–346.5
347–410	2	346.5–410.5
411–474	0	410.5–474.5
475–538	1	474.5–538.5
539–602	2	538.5–602.5
	25	

23. The distribution is positively skewed with one more than one-half of the data values in the lowest class.

Number of Murders in 25 Selected Cities

Number of Murders in 25 Selected Cities

Number of Murders in 25 Selected Cities

24.

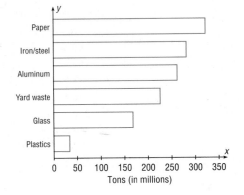

25. The fatalities decreased in 1999 and then increased the next two years.

Fatal Railroad Trespasser Casualties

26.

1	5 9
2	6 8
3	1 5 8 8 9
4	1 7 8
5	3 3 4
6	2 3 7 8
7	6 9
8	6 8 9
9	8

27. There appears to be a positive linear relationship between the number of miles traveled and the sales of a sales representative (in hundreds of dollars).

Chapter 3

Exercises 3–1

1. *a.* 3.724   *b.* 3.73   *c.* 3.74 and 3.70   *d.* 3.715

3. *a.* 68.1   *b.* 68   *c.* 42, 62, 64, 66, 72, 74
   d. 64.5

5. *a.* 9422.2 *b.* 8988   *c.* 7552, 12,568, 8632
   d. 9434. Claim seems a little high.

7. *a.* 6.63   *b.* 6.45   *c.* 5.4, 6.2, 6.4, 7.2
   d. 6.7; answers will vary.

9. *a.* 5678.9 *b.* 5342.5 *c.* 4450 *d.* 5781.5
   The distribution is skewed to the right.

11. 2004:
   a. 8421.2 *b.* 8197   *c.* No mode   *d.* 9984.5
   1990:
   a. 9810   *b.* 9214.5   *c.* No mode   *d.* 13345.5
   Based on these data, it appears that the population is
   declining.

13. *a.* 17.68   *b.* 2.48–7.48 and 17.51–22.51.
Group mean
is less.

15. *a.* 6.5   *b.* 0.8–4.4. Probably not—data are
"top heavy."

17. *a.* 26.7   *b.* 24.2–28.6

19. *a.* 33.8   *b.* 27–33

21. *a.* 23.7   *b.* 21.5–24.5

23. 44.8; 40.5–47.5

25. *a.* 1804.6 *b.* 1013–1345

27. 2.896

29. $545,666.67

31. 82.7

33. *a.* Median   *c.* Mode   *e.* Mode
    b. Mean   *d.* Mode   *f.* Mean

35. Both could be true since one may be using the mean for
the average salary and the other may be using the mode
for the average.

37. 6

39. *a.* 36 mph   *b.* 30.77 mph   *c.* $16.67

41. 5.48

Exercises 3–2

1. The square root of the variance is the standard deviation.

3. σ^2; σ

5. When the sample size is less than 30, the formula for the
variance of the sample will underestimate the population
variance.

7. 48; 254.7; 15.9 (rounded to 16)   The data vary widely.

9.

	Temp. (°F)	Precip. (inches)
Range	32	4
Variance	147.6	1.89
Standard deviation	12.15	1.373
CVar	27.6%	52.2%

The precipitations are more variable.

11. Houston: $\overline{X} = 55.8$, $s = 8.88$, CVar = 15.91%;
Pittsburgh: $\overline{X} = 41.5$, $s = 9.42$, CVar = 22.7%.
Pittsburgh is more variable.

13. $s \approx R/4$ so $s \approx 5$ years.

15. 2004: $R = 9881$, $s^2 = 9,373,909.1$, $s = 3061.7$;
1990: $R = 17,155$, $s^2 = 16,301,960.35$, $s = 4037.6$.
The data for 1990 are more variable.

17. 11,263; 7,436,475.003; 2727.0

19. 133.6; 11.6

21. 27,941.46; 167.2

23. 211.2; 14.5

25. 211.2; 14.5; no, the variability of the lifetimes of the
batteries is quite large.

27. 11.7; 3.4

29. United States: $\overline{X} = 3386.6$, $s = 693.9$, CVar = 20.49%;
World: $\overline{X} = 4997.8$, $s = 803.2$, CVar = 16.07%.
World is more variable.

31. 23.1%; 12.9%; age is more variable.

33. *a.* 96%   *b.* 93.75%

35. Between 164 and 316 calories

37. Between 385 and 895 pounds

39. 86%

41. 16%

43. All the data values fall within 2 standard deviations
of the mean.

45. 56%; 75%; 84%; 88.89%; 92%

47. 4.36

49. It must be an incorrect data value, since it is beyond the
range using the formula $s\sqrt{n-1}$.

Exercises 3–3

1. A z score tells how many standard deviations the data
value is above or below the mean.

3. A percentile is a relative measurement of position; a
percentage is an absolute measure of the part to the total.

5. $Q_1 = P_{25}$; $Q_2 = P_{50}$; $Q_3 = P_{75}$

7. $D_1 = P_{10}$; $D_2 = P_{20}$; $D_3 = P_{30}$; etc.

9. Canada -0.40, Italy 1.47, United States -1.91

11. *a.* 0.75 *b.* -1.25 *c.* 2.25 *d.* -2 *e.* -0.5

13. Neither; $z = 1.5$ for each

15. *a.* -0.93 *b.* -0.85 *c.* -1.4; score in part b is highest

17. *a.* 24th *b.* 67th *c.* 48th *d.* 88th

19. *a.* 234 *b.* 251 *c.* 263 *d.* 274 *e.* 284

21. *a.* 13th *b.* 40th *c.* 54th *d.* 76th *e.* 92nd

23. 597

25. 47

27. 2.1

29. 12

31. *a.* 12; 20.5; 32; 22; 20   *b.* 62; 94; 99; 80.5; 37

Exercises 3–4

1. 6, 8, 19, 32, 54; 24

3. 188, 192, 339, 437, 589; 245

5. 14.6, 15.05, 16.3, 19, 19.8; 3.95

7. 11, 3, 8, 5, 9, 4

9. 95, 55, 70, 65, 90, 25

11.

13. No. It is not symmetric.

15. Based on the median, the data are left-skewed. Based on the lines, the data are right-skewed.

17. *a.* May: 391.7   *b.* 2003: 289.8

c.

Review Exercises

1. $\overline{X} = 79.6$, MD $= 79$, mode $= 84$, MR $= 97$, $R = 138$, $s^2 = 1259.3$, $s = 35.5$

3. *a.* 7.3   *b.* 7–9   *c.* 10.0   *d.* 3.2

5. *a.* 55.5   *b.* 57.5–72.5   *c.* 566.1   *d.* 23.8

7. 1.1

9. 6

11. Magazine variance: 0.214; year variance: 0.417; years are more variable.

13. *a.*

b. 50, 53, 55
c. 10th; 26th; 78th

15. $0.26–$0.38

17. 56%

19. 88.89%

21. The range is much larger.

23. 23.7−35.7

Chapter Quiz

1. True   **2.** True
3. False   **4.** False
5. False   **6.** False
7. False   **8.** False
9. False   **10.** *c*
11. *c*   **12.** *a* and *b*
13. *b*   **14.** *d*
15. *b*   **16.** Statistic
17. Parameters, statistics   **18.** Standard deviation
19. σ **20.** Midrange
21. Positively   **22.** Outlier

23. *a.* 15.3   *c.* 15, 16, and 17   *e.* 6   *g.* 1.9
    b. 15.5   *d.* 15   *f.* 3.61

24. *a.* 6.4   *b.* 6–8   *c.* 11.6   *d.* 3.4

25. *a.* 51.4   *b.* 35.5–50.5   *c.* 451.5   *d.* 21.2

26. *a.* 8.2   *b.* 7–9   *c.* 21.6   *d.* 4.6

27. 1.6   **28.** 4.5

29. 0.33; 0.162; newspapers   **30.** 0.3125; 0.229; brands

31. −0.75; −1.67; science

32. *a.* 0.5   *b.* 1.6   *c.* 15, *c* is highest

33. *a.* 56.25; 43.75; 81.25; 31.25; 93.75; 18.75; 6.25; 68.75
    b. 0.9
    c.

34. *a.*

b. 47; 55; 64
c. 56th, 6th, 99th percentiles

35. The cost of prebuy gas is much less than that of the return without filling gas. The variability of the return without filling gas is larger than the variability of the prebuy gas.

36. 16%, 97.5%

Chapter 4

Exercises 4–1

1. A probability experiment is a chance process that leads to well-defined outcomes.

3. An outcome is the result of a single trial of a probability experiment, but an event can consist of more than one outcome.

5. The range of values is 0 to 1 inclusive.

7. 0

9. 0.80   Since the probability that it won't rain is 80%, you could leave your umbrella at home and be fairly safe.

11. *a.* Empirical   *d.* Classical   *f.* Empirical
     b. Classical   *e.* Empirical   *g.* Subjective
     c. Empirical

13. *a.* $\frac{5}{36}$ *b.* $\frac{1}{6}$ *c.* $\frac{2}{9}$ *d.* $\frac{1}{6}$ *e.* $\frac{1}{6}$

15. *a.* 0.1   *b.* 0.2   *c.* 0.8

17. *a.* 0.43   *b.* 0.52   *c.* 0.17

19. *a.* 0.04   *b.* 0.52   *c.* 0.4

21. *a.* $\frac{1}{8}$ *b.* $\frac{1}{4}$ *c.* $\frac{3}{4}$ *d.* $\frac{3}{4}$

23. $\frac{1}{9}$

25. *a.* $\frac{9}{19}$ *b.* $\frac{9}{38}$ *c.* $\frac{5}{38}$

     d. The event in part *a* is most likely to occur since it has the highest probability of occurring.

27. 0.662

29. *a.* Sample space

	1	2	3	4	5	6
1	1	2	3	4	5	6
2	2	4	6	8	10	12
3	3	6	9	12	15	18
4	4	8	12	16	20	24
5	5	10	15	20	25	30
6	6	12	18	24	30	36

b. $\frac{5}{12}$ *c.* $\frac{17}{36}$

31.

33.

35.

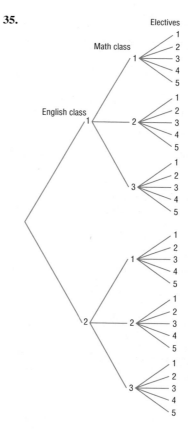

37. *a.* 0.08   *b.* 0.01   *c.* 0.35   *d.* 0.36

39. The statement is probably not based on empirical probability, and is probably not true.

41. Answers will vary.

43. *a.* 1:5, 5:1   *d.* 1:1, 1:1   *g.* 1:1, 1:1
  b. 1:1, 1:1   *e.* 1:12, 12:1
  c. 1:3, 3:1   *f.* 1:3, 3:1

Exercises 4–2

1. Two events are mutually exclusive if they cannot occur at the same time (i.e., they have no outcomes in common). Examples will vary.

3. *a.* 0.707   *b.* 0.589   *c.* 0.011   *d.* 0.731

5. $\frac{11}{19}$

7. *a.* $\frac{7}{25}$ *b.* $\frac{3}{8}$ *c.* $\frac{17}{100}$
  d. The event in part *b* has the highest probability so it is most likely to occur.

9. 0.55

11. *a.* $\frac{6}{7}$ *b.* $\frac{4}{7}$ *c.* 1

13. *a.* 0.058   *b.* 0.942   *c.* 0.335

15. *a.* 0.056   *b.* 0.004   *c.* 0.076

17. *a.* $\frac{14}{31}$ *b.* $\frac{23}{31}$ *c.* $\frac{19}{31}$

19. *a.* $\frac{1}{15}$ *b.* $\frac{1}{3}$ *c.* $\frac{5}{6}$ *d.* $\frac{5}{6}$ *e.* $\frac{1}{3}$

21. *a.* $\frac{5}{12}$ *b.* $\frac{1}{8}$ *c.* $\frac{2}{3}$ *d.* $\frac{23}{24}$

23. *a.* $\frac{3}{13}$ *b.* $\frac{3}{4}$ *c.* $\frac{19}{52}$ *d.* $\frac{7}{13}$ *e.* $\frac{15}{26}$

25. 0.318

27. 0.06

29. 0.30

Exercises 4–3

1. *a.* Independent   *e.* Independent
  b. Dependent   *f.* Dependent
  c. Dependent   *g.* Dependent
  d. Dependent   *h.* Independent

3. *a.* 0.009   *b.* 0.226

5. 0.373; the event is unlikely to occur since the probability is less than 0.5.

7. *a.* 0.0954   *b.* 0.9046   *c.* 0.1601

9. 0.5139

11. *a.* 0.807   *b.* 0.194

13. *a.* 0.0197   *b.* 0.611

15. $\frac{243}{1024}$

17. $\frac{5}{28}$

19. 0.210; the event is unlikely to occur since the probability is less than 0.50.

21. 0.116   **23.** 0.03

25. $\frac{49}{72}$ **27.** 0.1157

29. 89%   **31.** 70%

33. *a.* 0.7143   *b.* 0.4348   *c.* 0.1558

35. *a.* 0.498   *b.* 0.109
  c. No. $P(\text{path}|\text{female}) \neq P(\text{path})$

37. *a.* 0.1717   *b.* 0.8283

39. 0.574

41. 0.9869

43. $\frac{14{,}498}{20{,}825}$

45. *a.* 0.332   *b.* 0.668

47. $\frac{31}{32}$

49. 0.721; the event is likely to occur since the probability is about 72%.

51. $\frac{7}{8}$

53. No, since $P(A \cap B) = 0$ and does not equal $P(A) \cdot P(B)$.

55. Enrollment and meeting with DW and meeting with MH are dependent. Since meeting with MH has a low probability and meeting with LP has no effect, all students, if possible, should meet with DW.

Exercises 4–4

1. 100,000; 30,240   **3.** 5040

5. 40,320   **7.** 5040

9. 1000; 72   **11.** 600

13. *a.* 40,320   *c.* 1   *e.* 2520   *g.* 60   *i.* 120
  b. 3,628,800   *d.* 1   *f.* 11,880   *h.* 1   *j.* 30

15. 24   **17.** 7315

19. 840   **21.** 151,200

23. 5,527,200   **25.** 495; 11,880

27. *a.* 10   *c.* 35   *e.* 15   *g.* 1   *i.* 66
  b. 56   *d.* 15   *f.* 1   *h.* 36   *j.* 4

29. 120   **31.** 210

33. 15,504   **35.** 43,758; 12,870

37. 495; 210; 420   **39.** 475

41. 2970

43. $_7C_2$ is 21 combinations + 7 double tiles = 28

45. 330   **47.** 194,040

49. 125,970   **51.** 1,860,480

53. 136   **55.** 120

57. 200   **59.** 336

61. 2; 6; $(n - 1)!$

63. *a.* 4   *b.* 36   *c.* 624   *d.* 3744

Exercises 4–5

1. $\frac{11}{221}$

3. a. $\frac{4}{35}$ b. $\frac{1}{35}$ c. $\frac{12}{35}$ d. $\frac{18}{35}$

5. a. 0.129   b. 0.107   c. 0.015

7. $\frac{1}{1225}$

9. a. 0.120   b. 0.296   c. 0.182

11. a. 0.3216   b. 0.1637   c. 0.5146
    d. It probably got lost in the wash!

13. $\frac{5}{72}$ 15. $\frac{1}{60}$

17. 0.727

Review Exercises

1. a. 0.167   b. 0.667   c. 0.5

3. a. 0.7   b. 0.5

5. $\frac{17}{30}$ 7. 0.19

9. 0.98

11. a. 0.0001   b. 0.402   c. 0.598

13. a. $\frac{2}{17}$ b. $\frac{11}{850}$ c. $\frac{1}{5525}$

15. a. 0.603   b. 0.340   c. 0.324   d. 0.379

17. 0.4   19. 0.51

21. 57.3%

23. a. $\frac{19}{44}$ b. $\frac{1}{4}$

25. 0.718

27. 175,760,000; 78,624,000; 88,583,040

29. 350   31. 45

33. 100! (Answers may vary regarding calculator.)

35. 495   37. 15,504

39. 175,760,000; 0.0000114

41. 0.097

43.

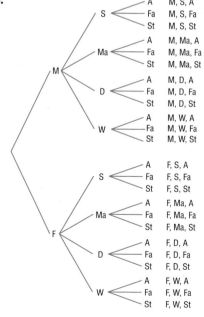

Chapter Quiz

1. False   2. False
3. True   4. False
5. False   6. False
7. True   8. False
9. b   10. b and d
11. d   12. b
13. c   14. b
15. d   16. b
17. b   18. Sample space
19. 0, 1   20. 0
21. 1   22. Mutually exclusive
23. a. $\frac{1}{13}$ b. $\frac{1}{13}$ c. $\frac{4}{13}$
24. a. $\frac{1}{4}$ b. $\frac{4}{13}$ c. $\frac{1}{52}$ d. $\frac{1}{13}$ e. $\frac{1}{2}$
25. a. $\frac{12}{31}$ b. $\frac{12}{31}$ c. $\frac{27}{31}$ d. $\frac{24}{31}$
26. a. $\frac{11}{36}$ b. $\frac{5}{18}$ c. $\frac{11}{36}$ d. $\frac{1}{3}$ e. 0   f. $\frac{11}{12}$
27. 0.68   28. 0.002
29. a. $\frac{253}{9996}$ b. $\frac{33}{66,640}$ c. 0
30. 0.54   31. 0.53
32. 0.81   33. 0.056
34. a. $\frac{1}{2}$ b. $\frac{3}{7}$
35. 0.99   36. 0.518
37. 0.9999886   38. 2646
39. 40,320   40. 1365
41. 1,188,137,600; 710,424,000
42. 720   43. 33,554,432
44. 56   45. $\frac{1}{4}$
46. $\frac{3}{14}$ 47. $\frac{12}{55}$
48.

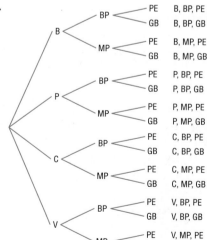

Chapter 5

Exercises 5–1

1. A random variable is a variable whose values are determined by chance. Examples will vary.

3. The number of commercials a radio station plays during each hour. The number of times a student uses his or her calculator during a mathematics exam. The number of leaves on a specific type of tree.

5. A probability distribution is a distribution that consists of the values a random variable can assume along with the corresponding probabilities of these values.

7. No; probabilities cannot be negative and the sum of the probabilities is not 1.

9. Yes

11. No, the probability values cannot be greater than 1.

13. Discrete

15. Continuous

17. Discrete

19.

X	0	1	2	3
P(X)	$\frac{6}{15}$	$\frac{5}{15}$	$\frac{3}{15}$	$\frac{1}{15}$

21.

X	2	3	5	7
P(X)	0.35	0.41	0.15	0.09

23.

X	1	2	3	4	5	6
P(X)	$\frac{1}{2}$	$\frac{1}{6}$	$\frac{1}{12}$	$\frac{1}{12}$	$\frac{1}{12}$	$\frac{1}{12}$

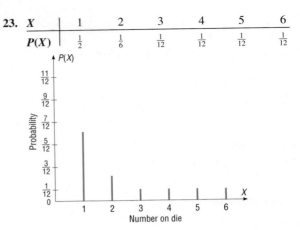

25.

X	2	3	4	5
P(X)	0.01	0.34	0.62	0.03

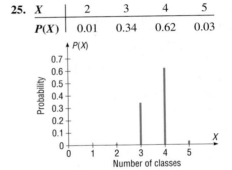

27.

X	1	5	10	20
P(X)	$\frac{3}{11}$	$\frac{2}{11}$	$\frac{5}{11}$	$\frac{1}{11}$

29.

X	1	2	3	4
P(X)	$\frac{1}{4}$	$\frac{1}{4}$	$\frac{3}{8}$	$\frac{1}{8}$

31.

X	1	2	3
P(X)	$\frac{1}{6}$	$\frac{1}{3}$	$\frac{1}{2}$

Yes

33.

X	3	4	7
$P(X)$	$\frac{3}{6}$	$\frac{4}{6}$	$\frac{7}{6}$

No, the sum of probabilities is greater than 1.

35.

X	1	2	4
$P(X)$	$\frac{1}{7}$	$\frac{2}{7}$	$\frac{4}{7}$

Yes

Exercises 5–2

1. 0.2; 0.3; 0.6; 2

3. 1.3, 0.9, 1. No, on average, each person has about 1 credit card.

5. 5.4; 2.94; 1.71; 0.027

7. 6.6; 1.3; 1.1

9. 9.4; 5.24; 2.289; 0.25

11. $260

13. $0.83

15. −$1.00

17. −$0.50, −$0.52

19. $4.00

21. 10.5

23. Answers will vary.

25. Answers will vary.

Exercises 5–3

1. *a.* Yes   *c.* Yes   *e.* No   *g.* Yes   *i.* No
  b. Yes   *d.* No   *f.* Yes   *h.* Yes   *j.* Yes

3. *a.* 0.0005   *c.* 0.342   *e.* 0.173
  b. 0.131   *d.* 0.007

5. 0.021; no, it's only about a 2% chance.

7. *a.* 0.124   *b.* 0.912   *c.* 0.017

9. 0.071

11. *a.* 0.346   *b.* 0.913   *c.* 0.663   *d.* 0.683

13. *a.* 0.242   *b.* 0.547   *c.* 0.306

15. 8; 7.9; 2.8

17. 9; 8.73; 2.95

19. 210; 165.9; 12.9

21. 0.199

23. 0.559

25. 0.177

27. 0.246

29.

X	0	1	2	3
$P(X)$	0.125	0.375	0.375	0.125

Review Exercises

1. Yes

3. No; the sum of the probabilities is greater than 1.

5. *a.* 0.35   *b.* 1.55; 1.8075; 1.3444

7.

9. 15.2; 1.6; 1.3

11. 24.2; 1.5; 1.2

13. $2.15

15. *a.* 0.008   *b.* 0.724   *c.* 0.0002   *d.* 0.276

17. 135; 33.8; 5.8

19. 0.886

21. 0.190

Chapter Quiz

1. True

2. False

3. False

4. True

5. chance

6. $n \cdot p$

7. 1

8. *c*

9. *c*

10. *d*

11. No, since $\Sigma P(X) > 1$

12. Yes

13. Yes

14. Yes

15.

16.

X	0	1	2	3	4
$P(X)$	0.02	0.3	0.48	0.13	0.07

17. 2.0; 1.3; 1.1

18. 32.2; 1.1; 1.0

19. 5.2

20. $9.65

21. 0.124

22. *a.* 0.075   *b.* 0.872   *c.* 0.125

23. 240; 48; 6.9

24. 9; 7.9; 2.8

Chapter 6
Exercises 6–1

1. The characteristics of the normal distribution are as follows:
  a. It is bell-shaped.
  b. It is symmetric about the mean.
  c. Its mean, median, and mode are equal.
  d. It is continuous.
  e. It never touches the *x* axis.
  f. The area under the curve is equal to 1.
  g. It is unimodal.

3. 1, or 100%

5. 68%; 95%; 99.7%

7. 0.2734

9. 0.4808

11. 0.4090

13. 0.0764

15. 0.1094

17. 0.0258

19. 0.0442

21. 0.9826

23. 0.5987

25. 0.3574

27. 0.2486

29. 0.4418

31. 0.0023

33. 0.1131

35. 0.9522 (TI: 0.9521)

37. 0.0706 (TI: 0.0707)

39. 0.9222

41. $z = -1.39$ (TI: -1.3885)

43. $z = -2.08$ (TI: -2.0792)

45. -1.26 (TI: -1.2602)

47. *a.* -2.28 (TI: -2.2801)
  b. -0.92 (TI: -0.91995)
  c. -0.27 (TI: -0.26995)

49. *a.* $z = +1.96$ and $z = -1.96$ (TI: ± 1.95996)
  b. $z = +1.65$ and $z = -1.65$, approximately (TI: ± 1.64485)
  c. $z = +2.58$ and $z = -2.58$, approximately (TI: ± 2.57583)

51. 0.6827; 0.9545; 0.9973; they are very close.

53. 2.10

55. -1.45 and 0.11

57. $y = \dfrac{e^{-X^2/2}}{\sqrt{2\pi}}$

Exercises 6–2

1. 0.0022

3. *a.* 0.2005 (TI: 0.2007)   *b.* 0.4315 (TI: 0.4316)

5. *a.* 0.3023   *b.* 0.0062

7. *a.* 0.3557 (TI: 0.3547)
  b. 0.8389 (TI: 0.8391)

9. 0.0262; 0.0001; Would want to know why it had only been driven less than 6000 miles (TI: 0.0260; 0.0002)

11. *a.* 0.9803 (TI: 0.9801)
  b. 0.2514 (TI: 0.2511)
  c. 0.3434 (TI: 0.3430)

13. *a.* 0.9699 (TI: 0.9696)   *b.* 0.8264 (TI: 0.8257)
  c. Use the range rule of thumb. The range is about $4 \times 16 = 64$ minutes.

15. *a.* 0.3281   *b.* 0.4002   *c.* Not usually

17. $\$5518.25 < \mu < \$7465.75$; yes (TI: $\$5513.98 < \mu < \$7470.02$)

19. The maximum size is 1927.76 square feet; the minimum size is 1692.24 square feet. (TI: 1927.90 maximum, 1692.10 minimum)

21. 0.006; $821

23. The maximum price is $9222, and the minimum price is $7290. (TI: $7288.14 minimum, $9223.86 maximum)

25. 6.7; 4.05 (TI: for 10%, 6.657; for 30%, 4.040)

27. $18,840.48 (TI: $18,869.48)

29. 18.6 months

31. *a.* $\mu = 120, \sigma = 20$ *b.* $\mu = 15, \sigma = 2.5$
  c. $\mu = 30, \sigma = 5$

33. There are several mathematics tests that can be used.

35. 1.05

37. $\mu = 45, \sigma = 1.34$

39. Not normal

41. Not normal

Exercises 6–3

1. The distribution is called the sampling distribution of sample means.

3. The mean of the sample means is equal to the population mean.

5. The distribution will be approximately normal when the sample size is large.

7. $z = \dfrac{\bar{X} - \mu}{\sigma/\sqrt{n}}$

9. *a.* 0.0026 (TI: 0.0026)
  b. 0.8212 (TI: 0.8201)
  c. 0.1787 (TI: 0.1799)

11. 0.1112; no, since the average weight of the group is within 2 standard deviations (standard errors) of the mean. (TI: 0.1113)

13. 0.0427; 0.9572 (TI: 0.0423; 0.9577)

15. *a.* 0.3859 (TI: 0.3875)   *b.* 0.1841 (TI: 0.1831)
    c. Individual values are more variable than means.

17. 0.4176 (TI: 0.4199)

19. 0.1254 (TI: 0.12769)

21. *a.* 0.3446   *b.* 0.0023
    c. Yes, since it is within 1 standard deviation of the mean.
    d. Very unlikely

23. *a.* 0.3707 (TI: 0.3694)   *b.* 0.0475 (TI: 0.04779)

25. 0.0174   No—the central limit theorem applies.

27. 0.0143

29. $\sigma_{\bar{X}} = 1.5, n = 25$

Exercises 6–4

1. When *p* is approximately 0.5, as *n* increases, the shape of the binomial distribution becomes similar to that of the normal distribution. The conditions are that $n \cdot p$ and $n \cdot q$ are both ≥ 5. The correction is necessary because the normal distribution is continuous and the binomial distribution is discrete.

3. *a.* Yes   *c.* No   *e.* Yes
   b. No   *d.* Yes   *f.* No

5. 0.166

7. 0.0301 (TI: 0.0304)

9. 0.6664 (TI: 0.6681)

11. 0.9871 (TI: 0.9873)

13. 0.9951; yes (TI: 0.9950)

15. *a.* $n \geq 50$ *c.* $n \geq 10$ *e.* $n \geq 50$
    b. $n \geq 17$ *d.* $n \geq 25$

Review Exercises

1. *a.* 0.4744   *e.* 0.2139   *h.* 0.9131
   b. 0.1443   *f.* 0.8284   *i.* 0.0183
   c. 0.0590   *g.* 0.0233   *j.* 0.9535
   d. 0.8329 (TI: 0.8330)

3. 0.1131; $4872 and $5676
   (TI: $4869.31 minimum, $5678.69 maximum)

5. 40.13%; 12.92% (TI: 13.03%)

7. *a.* 0.7054 (TI: 0.7057)   *b.* 0.8869 (TI: 0.8868)

9. *a.* 0.0143 (TI: 0.0142)   *b.* 0.9641

11. 0.0023; yes, since the probability is less than 1%.

13. 0.7123; 0.9999 (TI: 0.7139; 0.9999)

15. 0.0465

17. Not normal

Chapter Quiz

1. False   2. True
3. True   4. True
5. False   6. False
7. *a*   8. *a*
9. *b*   10. *b*
11. *c*   12. 0.5
13. Sampling error
14. The population mean
15. Standard error of the mean
16. 5   17. 5%
18. *a.* 0.4332   *d.* 0.1029   *g.* 0.0401   *j.* 0.9131
    b. 0.3944   *e.* 0.2912   *h.* 0.8997
    c. 0.0344   *f.* 0.8284   *i.* 0.017
19. *a.* 0.4846   *d.* 0.0188   *g.* 0.0089   *j.* 0.8461
    b. 0.4693   *e.* 0.7461   *h.* 0.9582
    c. 0.9334   *f.* 0.0384   *i.* 0.9788
20. *a.* 0.7734   *b.* 0.0516   *c.* 0.3837
    d. Any rainfall above 65 inches could be considered an extremely wet year since this value is 2 standard deviations above the mean.
21. *a.* 0.0668   *b.* 0.0228   *c.* 0.4649   *d.* 0.0934
22. *a.* 0.4525   *b.* 0.3707   *c.* 0.3707   *d.* 0.019
23. *a.* 0.0013   *b.* 0.5   *c.* 0.0081   *d.* 0.5511
24. *a.* 0.0037   *b.* 0.0228   *c.* 0.5   *d.* 0.3232
25. 8.804 centimeters
26. 121.24 is the lowest acceptable score.
27. 0.015   28. 0.9738
29. 0.0495; no   30. 0.0630
31. 0.8577   32. 0.0495
33. Not normal
34. Approximately normal

Chapter 7

Exercises 7–1

1. A point estimate of a parameter specifies a particular value, such as $\mu = 87$; an interval estimate specifies a range of values for the parameter, such as $84 < \mu < 90$. The advantage of an interval estimate is that a specific confidence level (say 95%) can be selected, and one can be 95% confident that the interval contains the parameter that is being estimated.

3. The maximum error of estimate is the likely range of values to the right or left of the statistic which may contain the parameter.

5. A good estimator should be unbiased, consistent, and relatively efficient.

7. For one to be able to determine sample size, the maximum error of estimate and the degree of confidence must be specified and the population standard deviation must be known.

9. *a.* 2.58   *c.* 1.96   *e.* 1.88
    b. 2.33   *d.* 1.65

11. *a.* 82   *b.* $77 < \mu < 87$
    c. $75 < \mu < 89$ (TI: $75.5 < \mu < 88.5$)
    d. The 99% confidence interval is larger because the confidence level is larger.

13. $1.72 < \mu < 1.88$; lower

15. $145{,}030 < \mu < 154{,}970$

17. $4913 < \mu < 5087$; 4000 hours does not seem reasonable since it is outside the interval.

19. $59.5 < \mu < 62.9$

21. 114

23. 139 cookies

25. 240 exams

Exercises 7–2

1. The characteristics of the *t* distribution are: It is bell-shaped, it is symmetric about the mean, and it never touches the *x* axis. The mean, median, and mode are equal to 0 and are located at the center of the distribution. The variance is greater than 1. The *t* distribution is a family of curves based on degrees of freedom. As a sample size increases, the *t* distribution approaches the standard normal distribution.

3. The *t* distribution should be used when σ is unknown and $n < 30$.

5. $15 < \mu < 17$

7. $\overline{X} = 33.4$; $s = 28.7$; $21.2 < \mu < 45.6$; the point estimate is 33.4, and it is close to 32. Also, the interval does indeed contain $\mu = 32$. The data value 132 is unusually large (an outlier). The mean may not be the best estimate in this case.

9. $266 < \mu < 286$; it is highly unlikely.

11. $13.5 < \mu < 15.1$; about 30 minutes.

13. $17.87 < \mu < 20.53$. Assume normal distribution; it's higher.

15. $109 < \mu < 121$

17. $32.0 < \mu < 70.9$. Assume normal distribution.

19. Answers will vary.

21. $\overline{X} = 2.175$; $s = 0.585$; $\mu > \$1.95$ means one can be 95% confident that the mean revenue is greater than \$1.95; $\mu < \$2.40$ means one can be 95% confident that the mean revenue is less than \$2.40.

Exercises 7–3

1. *a.* 0.5, 0.5   *c.* 0.46, 0.54   *e.* 0.45, 0.55
    b. 0.45, 0.55   *d.* 0.58, 0.42

3. $0.365 < p < 0.415$

5. $0.092 < p < 0.153$; 11% is contained in the confidence interval.

7. $0.797 < p < 0.883$

9. $0.596 < p < 0.704$

11. $0.286 < p < 0.562$. It would not be considered somewhat larger since 0.52 is in the interval.

13. $0.419 < p < 0.481$

15. *a.* 3121   *b.* 4161

17. 801 homes; 1068 homes

19. 1089   **21.** 95%

Exercises 7–4

1. Chi-square

3. *a.* 3.816; 21.920   *d.* 0.412; 16.750
    b. 10.117; 30.144   *e.* 26.509; 55.758
    c. 13.844; 41.923

5. $56.6 < \sigma^2 < 236.3$; $7.5 < \sigma < 15.4$

7. Use $\sigma = r \div 4$
    $1{,}593{,}756 < \sigma^2 < 16{,}537{,}507$; $1262.4 < \sigma < 4066.6$;
    $8{,}469{,}845 < \sigma^2 < 87{,}886{,}811$; $2910.3 < \sigma < 9374.8$

9. $604 < \sigma^2 < 5837$; $24.6 < \sigma < 76.4$

11. $4.1 < \sigma < 7.1$

13. $16 < \sigma < 20$

Review Exercises

1. $13.99 < \mu < 25.27$ (or $14 < \mu < 25$)
    (TI: $14.005 < \mu < 25.255$)

3. 7.5; $7.46 < \mu < 7.54$

5. $25 < \mu < 31$

7. 28

9. $0.434 < p < 0.660$; yes, it looks as if up to 66% of the people are dissatisfied.

11. 460

13. $0.218 < \sigma < 0.435$. Yes. It seems that there is a large standard deviation.

15. $5.1 < \sigma^2 < 18.3$

Chapter Quiz

1. True   **2.** True

3. False   **4.** True

5. *b*   **6.** *a*

7. *b*

8. Unbiased, consistent, relatively efficient

9. Maximum error of estimate

10. Point   **11.** 90; 95; 99

12. $23.45; $22.79 $< \mu <$ $24.11

13. $44.80; $43.15 $< \mu <$ $46.45

14. 4150; 3954 $< \mu <$ 4346

15. 45.7 $< \mu <$ 51.5

16. 418 $< \mu <$ 458   **17.** 26 $< \mu <$ 36

18. 180   **19.** 25

20. 0.604 $< p <$ 0.810   **21.** 0.295 $< p <$ 0.425

22. 0.342 $< p <$ 0.547   **23.** 545

24. 7 $< \sigma <$ 13

25. 30.9 $< \sigma^2 <$ 78.2   **26.** 1.8 $< \sigma <$ 3.2
    5.6 $< \sigma <$ 8.8

Chapter 8

Exercises 8–1

Note: For Chapters 8–13, specific *P*-values are given in parentheses after the *P*-value intervals. When the specific *P*-value is extremely small, it is not given.

1. The null hypothesis states that there is no difference between a parameter and a specific value or that there is no difference between two parameters. The alternative hypothesis states that there is a specific difference between a parameter and a specific value or that there is a difference between two parameters. Examples will vary.

3. A statistical test uses the data obtained from a sample to make a decision about whether the null hypothesis should be rejected.

5. The critical region is the range of values of the test statistic that indicates that there is a significant difference and the null hypothesis should be rejected. The noncritical region is the range of values of the test statistic that indicates that the difference was probably due to chance and the null hypothesis should not be rejected.

7. α, β

9. A one-tailed test should be used when a specific direction, such as greater than or less than, is being hypothesized; when no direction is specified, a two-tailed test should be used.

11. Hypotheses can be proved true only when the entire population is used to compute the test statistic. In most cases, this is impossible.

13. *a.* $H_0: \mu = 24.6$ and $H_1: \mu \neq 24.6$
    b. $H_0: \mu = \$51,497$ and $H_1: \mu \neq \$51,497$
    c. $H_0: \mu = 25.4$ and $H_1: \mu > 25.4$
    d. $H_0: \mu = 88$ and $H_1: \mu < 88$
    e. $H_0: \mu = 70$ and $H_1: \mu < 70$
    f. $H_0: \mu = \$79.95$ and $H_1: \mu \neq \$79.95$
    g. $H_0: \mu = 8.2$ and $H_1: \mu \neq 8.2$

Exercises 8–2

1. $H_0: \mu = 5000$; $H_1: \mu > 5000$ (claim); C.V. = 1.65; test statistic $z = 4.53$; reject H_0. There is sufficient evidence at $\alpha = 0.05$ to conclude that the mean is greater than 5000 steps.

3. $H_0: \mu = \$24$ billion and $H_1: \mu > \$24$ billion (claim); C.V. = 1.65; $z = 1.85$; reject. There is enough evidence to support the claim that the average revenue is greater than $24 billion.

5. $H_0: \mu = 1468$; $H_1: \mu \neq 1468$ (claim); C.V. = ± 2.58; $z = 2.03$; do not reject H_0. There is insufficient evidence at $\alpha = 0.01$ to conclude that the mean health care expenditure differs from $1468.

   $H_0: \mu = 1468$; $H_1: \mu \neq 1468$; C.V. = ± 1.96; test statistic $z = 2.03$; reject H_0. There is sufficient evidence at $\alpha = 0.05$ to conclude that the mean differs from $1468.

7. $H_0: \mu = 29$ and $H_1: \mu \neq 29$ (claim); C.V. = ± 1.96; $z = 0.944$; do not reject. There is not enough evidence to say that the average height differs from 29 inches.

9. $H_0: \mu = 26,025$; $H_1: \mu > 26,025$ (claim); C.V. = 1.65; $z = 1.92$; reject H_0. There is sufficient evidence to conclude that the cost has increased.

11. $H_0: \mu = 500$; $H_1: \mu \neq 500$ (claim); C.V. = ± 2.58; $z = -4.04$; reject H_0. There is sufficient evidence to conclude that the mean differs from 500.

13. $H_0: \mu = 60.35$; $H_1: \mu < 60.35$ (claim); C.V. = -1.65; $z = -4.82$; reject H_0. There is sufficient evidence to conclude that the state senators are younger.

15. *a.* Do not reject.   *d.* Reject.
    b. Reject.   *e.* Reject.
    c. Do not reject.

17. $H_0: \mu = 264$ and $H_1: \mu < 264$ (claim); $z = -2.53$; *P*-value = 0.0057; reject. There is enough evidence to support the claim that the average stopping distance is less than 264 ft. (TI: *P*-value = 0.0056)

19. $H_0: \mu = 546$ and $H_1: \mu < 546$ (claim); $z = -2.4$; *P*-value = 0.008. Yes, it can be concluded that the number of calories burned is less than originally thought. (TI: *P*-value = 0.0082)

21. $H_0: \mu = 444$; $H_1: \mu \neq 444$; $z = -1.70$; *P*-value = 0.0892; do not reject H_0. There is insufficient evidence at $\alpha = 0.05$ to conclude that the average size differs from 444 acres. (TI: *P*-value = 0.0886)

23. $H_0: \mu = 30,000$ (claim) and $H_1: \mu \neq 30,000$; $z = 1.71$; *P*-value = 0.0872; reject. There is enough evidence to reject the claim that the customers are adhering to the recommendation. Yes, the 0.10 level is appropriate. (TI: *P*-value = 0.0868)

25. $H_0: \mu = 10$ and $H_1: \mu < 10$ (claim); $z = -8.67$; *P*-value < 0.0001; since *P*-value < 0.05, reject. Yes, there is enough evidence to support the claim that the average number of days missed per year is less than 10. (TI: *P*-value = 0)

27. H_0: $\mu = 8.65$ (claim) and H_1: $\mu \neq 8.65$; C.V. $= \pm 1.96$; $z = -1.35$; do not reject. Yes; there is not enough evidence to reject the claim that the average hourly wage of the employees is \$8.65.

Exercises 8–3

1. It is bell-shaped, it is symmetric about the mean, and it never touches the x axis. The mean, median, and mode are all equal to 0, and they are located at the center of the distribution. The t distribution differs from the standard normal distribution in that it is a family of curves and the variance is greater than 1; and as the degrees of freedom increase, the t distribution approaches the standard normal distribution.

3. *a.* $+1.833$ *c.* -3.365 *e.* ± 2.145 *g.* ± 2.771
    b. ± 1.740 *d.* $+2.306$ *f.* -2.819 *h.* ± 2.583

5. H_0: $\mu = 179$; H_1: $\mu \neq 179$ (claim); C.V. $= \pm 3.250$; d.f. $= 9$; $t = 3.162$; do not reject H_0. There is insufficient evidence to conclude that the mean differs from \$179.

7. H_0: $\mu = 4172$; H_1: $\mu > 4172$ (claim); C.V. $= 1.729$; d.f. $= 19$; $t = 1.091$; do not reject H_0. There is insufficient evidence to conclude that the mean amount is greater than \$4172.

9. H_0: $\mu = 700$ (claim) and H_1: $\mu < 700$; C.V. $= -2.262$; d.f. $= 9$; $t = -2.71$; reject. There is enough evidence to reject the claim that the average height of the buildings is at least 700 feet.

11. H_0: $\mu = \$13,252$ and H_1: $\mu > \$13,252$ (claim); C.V. $= 2.539$; d.f. $= 19$; $t = 2.949$; reject. Yes. There is enough evidence to support the claim that the mean cost has increased.

13. H_0: $\mu = \$54.8$ million and H_1: $\mu > \$54.8$ million (claim); C.V. $= 1.761$; d.f. $= 14$; $t = 3.058$; reject. Yes. There is enough evidence to support the claim that the average cost of an action movie is greater than \$54.8 million.

15. H_0: $\mu = 623$; H_1: $\mu > 623$ (claim); C.V. $= 2.528$; d.f. $= 20$; $t = 1.718$; do not reject H_0. There is insufficient evidence to conclude that the employees are correct; i.e., that the mean is greater than \$623.

17. H_0: $\mu = 5.8$ and H_1: $\mu \neq 5.8$ (claim); d.f. $= 19$; $t = -3.462$; P-value < 0.01; reject. There is enough evidence to support the claim that the mean number of times has changed. (TI: P-value $= 0.0026$)

19. H_0: $\mu = \$15,000$ and H_1: $\mu \neq \$15,000$; d.f. $= 11$; $t = -1.10$; C.V. $= \pm 2.201$; do not reject. There is not enough evidence to conclude that the average stipend differs from \$15,000.

Exercises 8–4

1. Answers will vary.

3. $np \geq 5$ and $nq \geq 5$

5. H_0: $p = 0.686$; H_1: $p \neq 0.686$ (claim); C.V. $= \pm 2.58$; $z = -1.93$; do not reject H_0. There is insufficient evidence to conclude that the proportion differs.

7. H_0: $p = 0.40$ and H_1: $p \neq 0.40$ (claim); C.V. $= \pm 2.58$; $z = -1.07$; do not reject. No. There is not enough evidence to support the claim that the proportion is different from 0.40.

9. H_0: $p = 0.78$ (claim); H_1: $p \neq 0.78$; C.V. $= \pm 1.96$; $z = -2.33$; reject H_0. There is sufficient evidence to conclude that the percentage of professors differs from that proportion stated in the almanac.

11. H_0: $p = 0.54$ (claim) and H_1: $p \neq 0.54$; C.V. $= \pm 1.96$; $z = -0.81$; do not reject. No. There is not enough evidence to reject the claim that 54% of fatal car/truck accidents are caused by driver error.

13. H_0: $p = 0.54$ (claim) and H_1: $p \neq 0.54$; $z = 0.93$; P-value $= 0.3524$; do not reject. There is not enough evidence to reject the claim that the proportion is 0.54. Yes, a healthy snack should be made available for children to eat after school. (TI: P-value $= 0.3511$)

15. H_0: $p = 0.18$ (claim) and H_1: $p \neq 0.18$; $z = -0.60$; P-value $= 0.5486$; since P-value > 0.05, do not reject. There is not enough evidence to reject the claim that 18% of all high school students smoke at least a pack of cigarettes a day. (TI: P-value $= 0.2739$)

17. H_0: $p = 0.67$ and H_1: $p \neq 0.67$ (claim); C.V. $= \pm 1.96$; $z = 3.19$; reject. Yes. There is enough evidence to support the claim that the percentage is not 67%.

19. H_0: $p = 0.576$ and H_1: $p < 0.576$ (claim); C.V. $= -1.65$; $z = -1.26$; do not reject. There is not enough evidence to support the claim that the proportion is less than 0.576.

21. No

23. $z = \dfrac{X - \mu}{\sigma}$

$z = \dfrac{X - np}{\sqrt{npq}}$ since $\mu = np$ and $\sigma = \sqrt{npq}$

$z = \dfrac{X/n - np/n}{\sqrt{npq}/n}$

$z = \dfrac{X/n - np/n}{\sqrt{npq/n^2}}$

$z = \dfrac{\hat{p} - p}{\sqrt{pq/n}}$ since $\hat{p} = X/n$

Exercises 8–5

1. *a.* H_0: $\sigma^2 = 225$ and H_1: $\sigma^2 > 225$; C.V. $= 27.587$; d.f. $= 17$

    b. H_0: $\sigma^2 = 225$ and H_1: $\sigma^2 < 225$; C.V. $= 14.042$; d.f. $= 22$

    c. H_0: $\sigma^2 = 225$ and H_1: $\sigma^2 \neq 225$; C.V. $= 5.629$; 26.119; d.f. $= 14$

d. H_0: $\sigma^2 = 225$ and H_1: $\sigma^2 \neq 225$; C.V. = 2.167; 14.067; d.f. = 7

e. H_0: $\sigma^2 = 225$ and H_1: $\sigma^2 > 225$; C.V. = 32.000; d.f. = 16

f. H_0: $\sigma^2 = 225$ and H_1: $\sigma^2 < 225$; C.V. = 8.907; d.f. = 19

g. H_0: $\sigma^2 = 225$ and H_1: $\sigma^2 \neq 225$; C.V. = 3.074; 28.299; d.f. = 12

h. H_0: $\sigma^2 = 225$ and H_1: $\sigma^2 < 225$; C.V. = 15.308; d.f. = 28

3. H_0: $\sigma = 60$ (claim) and H_1: $\sigma \neq 60$; C.V. = 8.672; 27.587; d.f. = 17; $\chi^2 = 19.707$; do not reject. There is not enough evidence to reject the claim that the standard deviation is 60.

5. H_0: $\sigma = 15$ and H_1: $\sigma < 15$ (claim); C.V. = 4.575; d.f. = 11; $\chi^2 = 9.0425$; do not reject. There is not enough evidence to support the claim that the standard deviation is less than 15.

7. H_0: $\sigma = 1.2$ (claim) and H_1: $\sigma > 1.2$; $\alpha = 0.01$; d.f. = 14; $\chi^2 = 31.5$; P-value < 0.005 (0.0047); since P-value < 0.01, reject. There is enough evidence to reject the claim that the standard deviation is less than or equal to 1.2 minutes.

9. H_0: $\sigma = 20$ and H_1: $\sigma > 20$ (claim); C.V. = 36.191; d.f. = 19; $\chi^2 = 58.5502$; reject. There is enough evidence to support the claim that the standard deviation is greater than 20.

11. H_0: $\sigma = 35$ and H_1: $\sigma < 35$ (claim); C.V. = 3.940; d.f. = 10; $\chi^2 = 8.359$; do not reject. There is not enough evidence to support the claim that the standard deviation is less than 35.

13. H_0: $\sigma^2 = 25$ and H_1: $\sigma^2 > 25$ (claim); C.V. = 22.362; d.f. = 13; $\chi^2 = 23.622$; reject. There is enough evidence to support the claim that the variance is greater than 25.

15. H_0: $\sigma^2 = 0.2704$; H_1: $\sigma^2 > 0.2704$ (claim); C.V. = 30.144; $\chi^2 = 22.670$; do not reject H_0. There is insufficient evidence to conclude that the standard deviation is outside the guidelines.

Exercises 8–6

1. H_0: $\mu = 1800$ (claim) and H_1: $\mu \neq 1800$; C.V. = ± 1.96; $z = 0.47$; $1706.04 < \mu < 1953.96$; do not reject. There is not enough evidence to reject the claim that the average of the sales is $1800.

3. H_0: $\mu = 86$ (claim) and H_1: $\mu \neq 86$; C.V. = ± 2.58; $z = -1.29$; $80.00 < \mu < 88.00$; do not reject. There is not enough evidence to reject the claim that the average monthly maintenance is $86.

5. H_0: $\mu = 19$; H_1: $\mu \neq 19$ (claim); C.V. = ± 2.145; d.f. = 14; $t = 1.37$; do not reject H_0. There is insufficient evidence to conclude that the mean number of hours differs from 19.

95% C.I.: $17.7 < \mu < 24.9$. Because the mean ($\mu = 19$) is in the interval, there is no evidence to support the idea that a difference exists.

Review Exercises

1. H_0: $\mu = 98°$ (claim) and H_1: $\mu \neq 98°$; C.V. = ± 1.96; $z = -2.02$; reject. There is enough evidence to reject the claim that the average high temperature in the United States is 98°.

3. H_0: $\mu = 1229$; H_1: $\mu \neq 1229$ (claim); C.V. = ± 1.96; $z = 1.875$; do not reject H_0. There is insufficient evidence to conclude that the rent differs.

5. H_0: $\mu = 18{,}000$; H_1: $\mu < 18{,}000$ (claim); C.V. = -2.368; d.f. = 90; test statistic $t = -3.58$; reject H_0. There is sufficient evidence to conclude that the mean debt is less than $18,000.

7. H_0: $\mu = 208$; H_1: $\mu > 208$ (claim); C.V. = 2.896; d.f. = 9; $t = 3.13$; reject H_0. There is sufficient evidence that the mean weight is greater than 208 g.

9. H_0: $p = 0.602$ and H_1: $p > 0.602$ (claim); C.V. = 1.65; $z = 1.96$; reject. Yes. There is enough evidence to support the claim that the proportion is greater than 0.602.

11. H_0: $p = 0.65$ (claim) and H_1: $p \neq 0.65$; $z = 1.17$; P-value = 0.242; since P-value > 0.05, do not reject. There is not enough evidence to reject the claim that 65% of teenagers own their own radios. (TI: P-value = 0.2412)

13. H_0: $\mu = 10$ and H_1: $\mu < 10$ (claim); $z = -2.22$; P-value = 0.0132; reject. There is enough evidence to support the claim that the average time is less than 10 minutes.

15. H_0: $\sigma = 4.3$ (claim) and H_1: $\sigma < 4.3$; d.f. = 19; $\chi^2 = 6.95$; $0.005 < P$-value < 0.01 (0.006); since P-value < 0.05, reject. Yes, there is enough evidence to reject the claim that the standard deviation is greater than or equal to 4.3 miles per gallon.

17. H_0: $\sigma^2 = 40$; H_1: $\sigma^2 \neq 40$ (claim); C.V. = 2.700 and 19.023; test statistic $\chi^2 = 9.68$; do not reject H_0. There is insufficient evidence to conclude that the variance in the number of games played differs from 40.

19. H_0: $\mu = 4$ and H_1: $\mu \neq 4$ (claim); C.V. = ± 2.58; $z = 1.49$; $3.85 < \mu < 4.55$; do not reject. There is not enough evidence to support the claim that the growth has changed.

Chapter Quiz

1. True   **2.** True

3. False   **4.** True

5. False   **6.** b

7. d **8.** c

9. b **10.** Type I

11. β **12.** Statistical hypothesis

13. Right   **14.** $n - 1$

15. H_0: $\mu = 28.6$ (claim) and H_1: $\mu \neq 28.6$; $z = 2.15$; C.V. $= \pm 1.96$; reject. There is enough evidence to reject the claim that the average age of the mothers is 28.6 years.

16. H_0: $\mu = \$6500$ (claim) and H_1: $\mu \neq \$6500$; $z = 5.27$; C.V. $= \pm 1.96$; reject. There is enough evidence to reject the agent's claim.

17. H_0: $\mu = 8$ and H_1: $\mu > 8$ (claim); $z = 6$; C.V. $= 1.65$; reject. There is enough evidence to support the claim that the average is greater than 8.

18. H_0: $\mu = 500$ (claim) and H_1: $\mu \neq 500$; d.f. $= 6$; $t = -0.571$; C.V. $= \pm 3.707$; do not reject. There is not enough evidence to reject the claim that the mean is 500.

19. H_0: $\mu = 67$ and H_1: $\mu < 67$ (claim); $t = -3.1568$; P-value < 0.005 (0.003); since P-value < 0.05, reject. There is enough evidence to support the claim that the average height is less than 67 inches.

20. H_0: $\mu = 12.4$ and H_1: $\mu < 12.4$ (claim); $t = -2.324$; C.V. $= -1.345$; reject. There is enough evidence to support the claim that the average is less than the company claimed.

21. H_0: $\mu = 63.5$ and H_1: $\mu > 63.5$ (claim); $t = 0.47075$; P-value > 0.25 (0.322); since P-value > 0.05, do not reject. There is not enough evidence to support the claim that the average is greater than 63.5.

22. H_0: $\mu = 26$ (claim) and H_1: $\mu \neq 26$; $t = -1.5$; C.V. $= \pm 2.492$; do not reject. There is not enough evidence to reject the claim that the average is 26.

23. H_0: $p = 0.39$ (claim) and H_1: $p \neq 0.39$; C.V. $= \pm 1.96$; $z = -0.62$; do not reject. There is not enough evidence to reject the claim that 39% took supplements. The study supports the results of the previous study.

24. H_0: $p = 0.55$ (claim) and H_1: $p < 0.55$; $z = -0.8989$; C.V. $= -1.28$; do not reject. There is not enough evidence to reject the survey's claim.

25. H_0: $p = 0.35$ (claim) and H_1: $p \neq 0.35$; C.V. $= \pm 2.33$; $z = 0.666$; do not reject. There is not enough evidence to reject the claim that the proportion is 35%.

26. H_0: $p = 0.75$ (claim) and H_1: $p \neq 0.75$; $z = 2.6833$; C.V. $= \pm 2.58$; reject. There is enough evidence to reject the claim.

27. P-value $= 0.0323$

28. P-value $= 0.0001$

29. H_0: $\sigma = 6$ and H_1: $\sigma > 6$ (claim); $\chi^2 = 54$; C.V. $= 36.415$; reject. There is enough evidence to support the claim.

30. H_0: $\sigma = 8$ (claim) and H_1: $\sigma \neq 8$; $\chi^2 = 33.2$; C.V. $= 27.991$, 79.490; do not reject. There is not enough evidence to reject the claim that $\sigma = 8$.

31. H_0: $\sigma = 2.3$ and H_1: $\sigma < 2.3$ (claim); $\chi^2 = 13$; C.V. $= 10.117$; do not reject. There is not enough

evidence to support the claim that the standard deviation is less than 2.3.

32. H_0: $\sigma = 9$ (claim) and H_1: $\sigma \neq 9$; $\chi^2 = 13.4$; P-value > 0.20 (0.291); since P-value > 0.05, do not reject. There is not enough evidence to reject the claim that $\sigma = 9$.

33. $28.9 < \mu < 31.2$; no

34. $\$6562.81 < \mu < \$6637.19$; no

Chapter 9

Exercises 9–1

1. Testing a single mean involves comparing a sample mean to a specific value such as $\mu = 100$; testing the difference between two means involves comparing the means of two samples, such as $\mu_1 = \mu_2$.

3. The populations must be independent of each other, and they must be normally distributed; s_1 and s_2 can be used in place of σ_1 and σ_2 when σ_1 and σ_2 are unknown, but a t test must be used.

5. H_0: $\mu_1 = \mu_2$ (claim) and H_1: $\mu_1 \neq \mu_2$; C.V. $= \pm 2.58$; $z = -0.88$; do not reject. There is not enough evidence to reject the claim that the average lengths of the major rivers are the same. (TI: $z = -0.856$)

7. H_0: $\mu_1 = \mu_2$; H_1: $\mu_1 \neq \mu_2$ (claim); C.V. $= \pm 1.96$; $z = -3.65$; reject. There is sufficient evidence at $\alpha = 0.05$ to conclude that the commuting times differ in the winter.

9. H_0: $\mu_1 = \mu_2$; H_1: $\mu_1 > \mu_2$ (claim); C.V. $= 2.33$; $z = 3.75$; reject. There is sufficient evidence at $\alpha = 0.01$ to conclude that the average hospital stay for men is longer.

11. H_0: $\mu_1 = \mu_2$ and H_1: $\mu_1 < \mu_2$ (claim); C.V. $= -1.65$; $z = -2.01$; reject. There is enough evidence to support the claim that the stayers had a higher grade point average.

13. H_0: $\mu_1 = \mu_2$ and H_1: $\mu_1 > \mu_2$ (claim); C.V. $= +2.33$; $z = +1.09$; do not reject. There is not enough evidence to support the claim that colleges spend more money on male sports than they spend on female sports.

15. H_0: $\mu_1 = \mu_2$ and H_1: $\mu_1 \neq \mu_2$ (claim); $z = 1.01$; P-value $= 0.3124$; do not reject. There is not enough evidence to support the claim that there is a difference in self-esteem scores. (TI: P-value $= 0.3131$)

17. $2.8 < \mu_1 - \mu_2 < 6.0$

19. $10.48 < \mu_1 - \mu_2 < 59.52$. The interval provides evidence to reject the claim that there is no difference in mean scores because the interval for the difference is entirely positive. That is, 0 is not in the interval.

21. H_0: $\mu_1 - \mu_2 = 8$ (claim) and H_1: $\mu_1 - \mu_2 > 8$; C.V. $= +1.65$; $z = -0.73$; do not reject. There is not enough evidence to reject the claim that private school students have exam scores that are at most 8 points higher than those of students in public schools.

Exercises 9–2

1. $H_0: \mu_1 = \mu_2$ and $H_1: \mu_1 \neq \mu_2$ (claim); C.V. = ± 2.262; d.f. = 9; $t = -4.02$; reject. There is enough evidence to support the claim that there is a significant difference in the values of the homes based on the appraisers' values. $-\$7967 < \mu_1 - \mu_2 < -\$2229$

3. $H_0: \mu_1 = \mu_2$ (claim) and $H_1: \mu_1 \neq \mu_2$; C.V. = ± 2.145; $t = -1.70$; do not reject. There is not enough evidence to reject the claim that the means are equal.

5. $H_0: \mu_1 = \mu_2$; $H_1: \mu_1 > \mu_2$ (claim); $t = 4.36$; P-value 0.00 (0.00005) $< \alpha$; reject. There is sufficient evidence to conclude that the houses in Whiting are older. (TI: P-value = 0.000055)

7. $H_0: \mu_1 = \mu_2$ and $H_1: \mu_1 \neq \mu_2$ (claim); C.V. = ± 2.821; d.f. = 9; $t = -2.84$; reject. There is enough evidence to support the claim that there is a difference in the average times of the two groups. $-11.96 < \mu_1 - \mu_2 < -0.04$.

9. $H_0: \mu_1 = \mu_2$; $H_1: \mu_1 \neq \mu_2$ (claim); C.V. = ± 2.365; $t = -3.21$; reject. There is sufficient evidence to conclude that fruits and vegetables differ in moisture content.

11. $H_0: \mu_1 = \mu_2$; $H_1: \mu_1 \neq \mu_2$ (claim); C.V. = ± 2.306; $t = 1.17$; do not reject. There is insufficient evidence to conclude a difference in means.

13. $\$1789.70 < \mu_1 - \mu_2 < \$12,425.41$

Exercises 9–3

1. *a.* Dependent   *d.* Dependent
   b. Dependent   *e.* Independent
   c. Independent

3. $H_0: \mu_D = 0$ and $H_1: \mu_D < 0$ (claim); C.V. = -1.397; d.f. = 8; $t = -2.8$; reject. There is enough evidence to support the claim that the seminar increased the number of hours students studied.

5. $H_0: \mu_D = 0$ and $H_1: \mu_D \neq 0$ (claim); C.V. = 2.365; d.f. = 7; $t = 1.6583$; do not reject. There is not enough evidence to support the claim that the means are different.

7. $H_0: \mu_D = 0$ and $H_1: \mu_D > 0$ (claim); C.V. = 2.571; d.f. = 5; $t = 2.24$; do not reject. There is not enough evidence to support the claim that the errors have been reduced.

9. $H_0: \mu_D = 0$ and $H_1: \mu_D \neq 0$ (claim); d.f. = 7; $t = 0.978$; $0.20 < P$-value < 0.50 (0.361). Do not reject since P-value > 0.01. There is not enough evidence to support the claim that there is a difference in the pulse rates. $-3.23 < \mu_D < 5.73$

11. Using the previous problem $\bar{D} = -1.5625$, whereas the mean of the before values is 95.375 and the mean of the after values is 96.9375; hence, $\bar{D} = 95.375 - 96.9375 = -1.5625$.

Exercises 9–4

1a. *a.* $\hat{p} = \frac{34}{48}, \hat{q} = \frac{14}{48}$ *d.* $\hat{p} = \frac{6}{24}, \hat{q} = \frac{18}{24}$
   b. $\hat{p} = \frac{28}{75}, \hat{q} = \frac{47}{75}$ *e.* $\hat{p} = \frac{12}{144}, \hat{q} = \frac{132}{144}$
   c. $\hat{p} = \frac{50}{100}, \hat{q} = \frac{50}{100}$

1b. *a.* 16   *b.* 4   *c.* 48
   d. 104   *e.* 30

3. $\hat{p}_1 = 0.327$; $\hat{p}_2 = 0.4$; $\bar{p} = 0.363$; $\bar{q} = 0.637$; $H_0: p_1 = p_2$; $H_1: p_1 \neq p_2$ (claim); C.V. = ± 2.58; $z = -1.867$; do not reject. There is insufficient evidence to conclude a difference. (TI: $z = -1.867$)

5. $\hat{p}_1 = 0.747$; $\hat{p}_2 = 0.75$; $\bar{p} = 0.749$; $\bar{q} = 0.251$; $H_0: p_1 = p_2$ and $H_1: p_1 \neq p_2$ (claim); C.V. = ± 1.96; $z = -0.07$; do not reject. There is not enough evidence to support the claim that the proportions are not equal.

7. $\hat{p}_1 = 0.83$; $\hat{p}_2 = 0.75$; $\bar{p} = 0.79$; $\bar{q} = 0.21$; $H_0: p_1 = p_2$ (claim) and $H_1: p_1 \neq p_2$; C.V. = ± 1.96; $z = 1.39$; do not reject. There is not enough evidence to reject the claim that the proportions are equal. $-0.032 < p_1 - p_2 < 0.192$

9. $\hat{p}_1 = 0.55$; $\hat{p}_2 = 0.45$; $\bar{p} = 0.497$; $\bar{q} = 0.503$; $H_0: p_1 = p_2$ and $H_1: p_1 \neq p_2$ (claim); C.V. = ± 2.58; $z = 1.302$; do not reject. There is not enough evidence to support the claim that the proportions are different. $-0.097 < p_1 - p_2 < 0.297$

11. $\hat{p}_1 = 0.347$; $\hat{p}_2 = 0.433$; $\bar{p} = 0.385$; $\bar{q} = 0.615$; $H_0: p_1 = p_2$ and $H_1: p_1 \neq p_2$ (claim); C.V. = ± 1.96; $z = -1.03$; do not reject. There is not enough evidence to say that the proportion of dog owners has changed $(-0.252 < p_1 - p_2 < 0.079)$. Yes, the confidence interval contains 0. This is another way to conclude that there is no difference in the proportions.

13. $\hat{p}_1 = 0.25$; $\hat{p}_2 = 0.31$; $\bar{p} = 0.286$; $\bar{q} = 0.714$; $H_0: p_1 = p_2$ and $H_1: p_1 \neq p_2$ (claim); C.V. = ± 2.58; $z = -1.45$; do not reject. There is not enough evidence to support the claim that the proportions are different. $-0.165 < p_1 - p_2 < 0.045$

15. $0.077 < p_1 - p_2 < 0.323$

17. $\hat{p}_1 = 0.33$; $\hat{p}_2 = 0.27$; $\bar{p} = 0.3$; $\bar{q} = 0.7$; $H_0: p_1 = p_2$; $H_1: p_1 > p_2$ (claim); C.V. = 1.645; $z = 1.60$; do not reject. There is insufficient evidence to conclude the percentage of never married men is more.

19. $-0.0631 < p_1 - p_2 < 0.0667$. It does agree with the *Almanac* statistics stating a difference of -0.042 since -0.042 is contained in the interval.

Exercises 9–5

1. The variance in the numerator should be the larger of the two variances.

3. One degree of freedom is used for the variance associated with the numerator, and one is used for the variance associated with the denominator.

5. *a.* d.f.N. = 15, d.f.D. = 22; C.V. = 3.36
   b. d.f.N. = 24, d.f.D. = 13; C.V. = 3.59
   c. d.f.N. = 45, d.f.D. = 29; C.V. = 2.03
   d. d.f.N. = 20, d.f.D. = 16; C.V. = 2.28
   e. d.f.N. = 10, d.f.D. = 10; C.V. = 2.98

7. H_0: $\sigma_1^2 = \sigma_2^2$ and H_1: $\sigma_1^2 \neq \sigma_2^2$ (claim); C.V. = 2.53; d.f.N. = 14; d.f.D. = 14; F = 4.52; reject. There is enough evidence to support the claim that there is a difference in the variances.

9. H_0: $\sigma_1^2 = \sigma_2^2$ and H_1: $\sigma_1^2 \neq \sigma_2^2$ (claim); C.V. = 2.86; d.f.N. = 15; d.f.D. = 15; F = 7.85; reject. There is enough evidence to support the claim that the variances are different. Since both data sets vary greatly from normality, the results are suspect.

11. H_0: $\sigma_1^2 = \sigma_2^2$ and H_1: $\sigma_1^2 \neq \sigma_2^2$ (claim); C.V. = 4.99; d.f.N. = 7; d.f.D. = 7; F = 1; do not reject. There is not enough evidence to support the claim that there is a difference in the variances.

13. H_0: $\sigma_1^2 = \sigma_2^2$; H_1: $\sigma_1^2 > \sigma_2^2$ (claim); C.V. = 4.950; F = 9.801; reject. There is sufficient evidence at α = 0.05 to conclude that the variance in area is greater for Eastern cities. C.V. = 10.67; do not reject. There is insufficient evidence to conclude the variance is greater.

15. H_0: $\sigma_1^2 = \sigma_2^2$ and H_1: $\sigma_1^2 \neq \sigma_2^2$ (claim); C.V. = 4.03; d.f.N. = 9; d.f.D. = 9; F = 1.1026; do not reject. There is not enough evidence to support the claim that the variances are not equal.

17. H_0: $\sigma_1^2 = \sigma_2^2$ (claim) and H_1: $\sigma_1^2 \neq \sigma_2^2$; C.V. = 3.87; d.f.N. = 6; d.f.D. = 7; F = 3.18; do not reject. There is not enough evidence to reject the claim that the variances of the heights are equal.

19. H_0: $\sigma_1^2 = \sigma_2^2$ (claim) and H_1: $\sigma_1^2 \neq \sigma_2^2$; F = 5.32; d.f.N. = 14; d.f.D. = 14; P-value < 0.01 (0.004); reject. There is enough evidence to reject the claim that the variances of the weights are equal.

Review Exercises

1. H_0: $\mu_1 = \mu_2$ and H_1: $\mu_1 > \mu_2$ (claim); C.V. = 2.33; z = 0.59; do not reject. There is not enough evidence to support the claim that single drivers do more pleasure driving than married drivers.

3. H_0: $\mu_1 = \mu_2$; H_1: $\mu_1 > \mu_2$ (claim); C.V. = 1.729; t = 4.595; reject. There is sufficient evidence to conclude that single persons spend a greater time communicating.

5. H_0: $\mu_1 = \mu_2$ and H_1: $\mu_1 \neq \mu_2$ (claim); C.V. = ±2.624; d.f. = 14; t = 6.54; reject. Yes, there is enough evidence to support the claim that there is a difference in the teachers' salaries. $3494.80 < \mu_1 - \mu_2 < \$8021.20$

7. H_0: $\mu_D = 10$; H_1: $\mu_D > 10$ (claim); C.V. = 2.821; t = 3.249; reject. There is sufficient evidence to conclude that the difference in temperature is greater than 10 degrees.

9. H_0: $p_1 = p_2$ and H_1: $p_1 \neq p_2$ (claim); C.V. = ±2.33; z = 3.03; reject. There is enough evidence to support the claim that the proportions of foggy days are different. $0.027 < p_1 - p_2 < 0.198$

11. H_0: $\sigma_1 = \sigma_2$ and H_1: $\sigma_1 \neq \sigma_2$ (claim); C.V. = 2.77; α = 0.10; d.f.N. = 23; d.f.D. = 10; F = 10.365; reject. There is enough evidence to support the claim that there is a difference in the standard deviations.

Chapter Quiz

1. False   **2.** False

3. True   **4.** False

5. *d*   **6.** *a*

7. *c*   **8.** *a*

9. $\mu_1 = \mu_2$ **10.** *t*

11. Normal   **12.** Negative

13. $\dfrac{s_1^2}{s_2^2}$

14. H_0: $\mu_1 = \mu_2$ and H_1: $\mu \neq \mu_2$ (claim); z = −3.69; C.V. = ±2.58; reject. There is enough evidence to support the claim that there is a difference in the cholesterol levels of the two groups. $-10.2 < \mu_1 - \mu_2 < -1.8$

15. H_0: $\mu_1 = \mu_2$ and H_1: $\mu > \mu_2$ (claim); C.V. = 1.28; z = 1.60; reject. There is enough evidence to support the claim that the average rental fees for the apartments in the East are greater than the average rental fees for the apartments in the West.

16. H_0: $\mu_1 = \mu_2$ and H_1: $\mu_1 \neq \mu_2$ (claim); t = 10.922; C.V. = ±2.779; reject. There is enough evidence to support the claim that the average prices are different. $0.298 < \mu_1 - \mu_2 < 0.502$

17. H_0: $\mu_1 = \mu_2$ and H_1: $\mu_1 < \mu_2$ (claim); C.V. = −1.860; d.f. = 8; t = −4.05; reject. There is enough evidence to support the claim that accidents have increased.

18. H_0: $\mu_1 = \mu_2$ and H_1: $\mu_1 \neq \mu_2$ (claim); t = 9.807; C.V. = ±2.718; reject. There is enough evidence to support the claim that the salaries are different. $6653 < \mu_1 - \mu_2 < \$11{,}757$

19. H_0: $\mu_1 = \mu_2$ and H_1: $\mu_1 > \mu_2$ (claim); d.f. = 10; t = 0.874; 0.10 < P-value < 0.25 (0.198); do not reject since P-value > 0.05. There is not enough evidence to support the claim that the incomes of city residents are greater than the incomes of rural residents.

20. H_0: $\mu_D = 0$ and H_1: $\mu_D < 0$ (claim); t = −2.44; C.V. = −2.821; do not reject. There is not enough evidence to support the claim that the sessions improved math skills.

21. H_0: $\mu_D = 0$ and H_1: $\mu_D < 0$ (claim); $t = -2.02$; C.V. $= -1.833$; reject. There is enough evidence to support the claim that egg production was increased.

22. H_0: $p_1 = p_2$ and H_1: $p_1 \neq p_2$ (claim); $z = -0.69$; C.V. $= \pm 1.65$; do not reject. There is not enough evidence to support the claim that the proportions are different. $-0.105 < p_1 - p_2 < 0.045$

23. H_0: $p_1 = p_2$ and H_1: $p_1 \neq p_2$ (claim); C.V. $= \pm 1.96$; $z = 0.544$; do not reject. There is not enough evidence to support the claim that the proportions have changed. $-0.026 < p_1 - p_2 < 0.0460$. Yes, the confidence interval contains 0; hence, the null hypothesis is not rejected.

24. H_0: $\sigma_1^2 = \sigma_2^2$ and H_1: $\sigma_1^2 \neq \sigma_2^2$ (claim); $F = 1.637$; d.f.N. $= 17$; d.f.D. $= 14$; P-value > 0.20 (0.357). Do not reject since P-value > 0.05. There is not enough evidence to support the claim that the variances are different.

25. H_0: $\sigma_1^2 = \sigma_2^2$ and H_1: $\sigma_1^2 \neq \sigma_2^2$ (claim); $F = 1.296$; C.V. $= 1.90$; do not reject. There is not enough evidence to support the claim that the variances are different.

Chapter 10

Exercises 10–1

1. Two variables are related wh between them

3.

5.

7.

9. P

11. Th
rela

13. H_0: .066; reject. There .... conclude that a significant relatio. ....etween the number of releases and gross receipts.

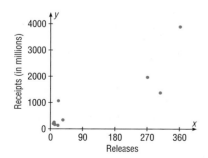

15. H_0: $\rho = 0$; H_1: $\rho \neq 0$; $r = -0.883$; C.V. $= \pm 0.811$; reject. There is a significant relationship between the number of years a person has been out of school and his or her contribution.

Years vs. Contributions

17. H_0: $\rho = 0$; H_1: $\rho \neq 0$; $r = 0.104$; C.V. $= \pm 0.754$; do not reject. There is no significant linear relationship between the number of larceny crimes and the number of vandalism crimes committed on college campuses in southwestern Pennsylvania.

Larceny and Vandalism

H_0: $\rho = 0$; H_1: $\rho \neq 0$; $r = -0.833$; C.V. $= \pm 0.811$; eject. There is sufficient evidence to conclude a lationship exists between the number of eggs produced d the price per dozen.

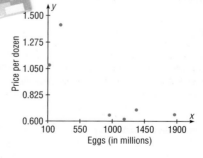

21. H_0: $\rho = 0$; H_1: $\rho \neq 0$; $r = 0.997$; C.V. $= \pm 0.811$; reject. There is a significant linear relationship between the number of people under age 5 and the number of people who are age 65 and older in the U.S. cities.

23. H_0: $\rho = 0$; H_1: $\rho \neq 0$; $r = 0.883$; C.V. $= \pm 0.754$; reject. There is a significant linear relationship between the average daily temperature and the average monthly precipitation.

25. H_0: $\rho = 0$; H_1: $\rho \neq 0$; $r = 0.725$; C.V. $= \pm 0.754$; do not reject. There is no significant linear relationship between the number of calories and the cholesterol content of fast-food chicken sandwiches.

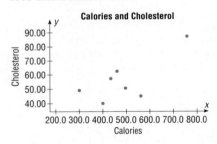

27. H_0: $\rho = 0$; H_1: $\rho \neq 0$; $r = 0.831$; C.V. $= \pm 0.754$; reject. There is a significant linear relationship between the number of licensed beds in a hospital and the number of staffed beds.

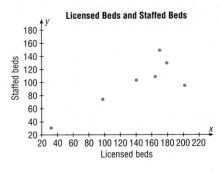

29. $r = 1.00$: All values fall in a straight line. $r = 1.00$: The value of r between x and y is the same when x and y are interchanged.

Exercises 10–2

1. A scatter plot should be drawn, and the value of the correlation coefficient should be tested to see whether it is significant.

3. $y' = a + bx$

5. It is the line that is drawn through the points on the scatter plot such that the sum of the squares of the vertical distances from each point to the line is a minimum.

7. When r is positive, b will be positive. When r is negative, b will be negative.

9. The closer r is to $+1$ or -1, the more accurate the predicted value will be.

11. When r is not significant, the mean of the y values should be used to predict y.

13. $y' = 181.661 + 7.319x$; $y' = 1645.5$ (million \$)

15. $y' = 453.176 - 50.439x$; 251.42

17. Since r is not significant, no regression should be done.

19. $y' = 1.252 - 0.000398x$; $y' = 0.615$ per dozen

21. $y' = 14.165 + 1.685x$; 351

23. $y' = -8.994 + 0.1448x$; 1.1

25. Since r is not significant, no regression should be done.

27. $y' = 22.659 + 0.582x$; 48.267

29. H_0: $\rho = 0$; H_1: $\rho \neq 0$; $r = 0.429$; C.V. $= \pm 0.811$; do not reject. There is insufficient evidence to conclude a relationship exists between number of farms and acreage.

31. H_0: $\rho = 0$; H_1: $\rho \neq 0$; $r = 0.970$; C.V. = ± 0.707; reject; $y' = 34.852 + 0.140x$; when $x = 500$, $y' = 104.9$. There is a significant relationship between the tons of coal produced and the number of employees.

Tons of Coal and Number of Employees

$y' = 34.852 + 0.140x$

33. H_0: $\rho = 0$; H_1: $\rho \neq 0$; $r = -0.981$; C.V. = ± 0.811; reject. There is a significant relationship between the number of absences and the final grade; $y' = 96.784 - 2.668x$.

Absences and Final Grades

$y' = 96.784 - 2.668x$

35. H_0: $\rho = 0$; H_1: $\rho \neq 0$; $r = -0.265$; P-value > 0.05 (0.459); do not reject. There is no significant linear relationship between the ages of billionaires and their net worth. No regression should be done.

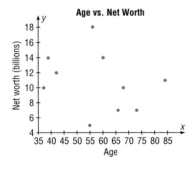

Age vs. Net Worth

37. 453.173; regression should not be done

Exercises 10–3

1. Explained variation is the variation due to the relationship. It is computed by $\Sigma(y' - \bar{y})^2$.

3. Total variation is the sum of the squares of the vertical distances of the points from the mean. It is computed by $\Sigma(y - \bar{y})^2$.

5. The coefficient of determination is found by squaring the value of the correlation coefficient.

7. The coefficient of nondetermination is found by subtracting r^2 from 1.

9. $R^2 = 0.5625$; 56.25% of the variation of y is due to the variation of x; 43.75% is due to chance.

11. $R^2 = 0.1764$; 17.64% of the variation of y is due to the variation of x; 82.36% is due to chance.

13. $R^2 = 0.8281$; 82.81% of the variation of y is due to the variation of x; 17.19% is due to chance.

15. 629.4862

17. 94.22*

19. $365.80 < y' < 2925.04$*

21. $30.46 < y < 472.38$*

*Answers may vary due to rounding.

Review Exercises

1. H_0: $\rho = 0$; H_1: $\rho \neq 0$; $r = -0.686$; C.V. = ± 0.917; do not reject. There is insufficient evidence to conclude that a relationship exists between number of passengers and one-way fare cost.

3. H_0: $\rho = 0$; H_1: $\rho \neq 0$; $r = 0.950$; C.V. = ± 0.875; reject. There is sufficient evidence to conclude a relationship exists between gas tax and cigarette tax. $y' = -0.567 + 0.089x$; $y' = 1.07$

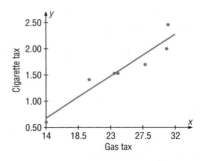

5. $H_0: \rho = 0$; $H_1: \rho \neq 0$; $r = -0.974$; C.V. $= \pm 0.708$; d.f. $= 10$; reject. There is a significant relationship between speed and time; $y' = 14.086 - 0.137x$; $y' = 4.222$.

Typing Speeds vs. Learning Times

$y' = 14.086 - 0.137x$

7. $H_0: \rho = 0$; $H_1: \rho \neq 0$; $r = 0.907$; C.V. $= \pm 0.875$; reject. There is sufficient evidence to conclude a relationship exists between the numbers of female physicians and male physicians in a given field. $y' = 102.846 + 3.408x$; $y' = 6919$

9. 0.468^* (TI value 0.513)

11. $3.34 < y < 5.10^*$

*Answers may vary due to rounding.

Chapter Quiz

1. False

2. True

3. True

4. False

5. False

6. False

7. *a*

8. *a*

9. *d*

10. *c*

11. *b*

12. Scatter plot

13. Independent

14. $-1, +1$

15. *b*

16. Line of best fit

17. $+1, -1$

18. $H_0: \rho = 0$; $H_1: \rho \neq 0$; $r = 0.600$; C.V. $= \pm 0.754$; do not reject. There is no significant linear relationship between the price of the same drugs in the United States and in Australia. No regression should be done.

Price Comparison of Drugs

19. $H_0: \rho = 0$; $H_1: \rho \neq 0$; $r = -0.078$; C.V. $= \pm 0.754$; do not reject. No regression should be done.

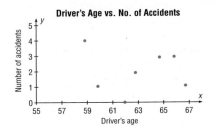

Driver's Age vs. No. of Accidents

20. $H_0: \rho = 0$; $H_1: \rho \neq 0$; $r = 0.842$; C.V. $= \pm 0.811$; reject. $y' = -1.918 + 0.551x$; 4.14 or 4.

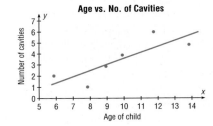

Age vs. No. of Cavities

21. $H_0: \rho = 0$; $H_1: \rho \neq 0$; $r = 0.602$; C.V. $= \pm 0.707$; do not reject. No regression should be done.

Fat vs. Cholesterol

22. 1.129*

23. 29.5* For calculation purposes only. No regression should be done.

24. $0 < y < 5$*

25. 217.5 (average of y' values is used since there is no significant relationship)

*These answers may vary due to the method of calculation or rounding.

Chapter 11

Exercises 11–1

1. The variance test compares a sample variance with a hypothesized population variance; the goodness-of-fit test compares a distribution obtained from a sample with a hypothesized distribution.

3. The expected values are computed on the basis of what the null hypothesis states about the distribution.

5. H_0: 82% of home-schooled students receive their education entirely at home, 12% attend school up to 9 hours per week, and 6% spend from 9 to 25 hours per week at school. H_1: The proportions differ from those stated in the null hypothesis (claim). C.V. = 5.991; χ^2 = 31.75; reject. There is sufficient evidence to conclude that the proportions differ from those stated by the government.

7. H_0: 30.6% of automobiles sold were small, 45% were midsize, 7.3% were large, and 17.1% were luxury size. H_1: The proportions differ from the ones stated in the null hypothesis (claim). C.V. = 7.815; χ^2 = 2.837; do not reject. There is insufficient evidence to conclude that the proportions differ from those stated in the report.

9. H_0: 35% feel that genetically modified food is safe to eat, 52% feel that genetically modified food is not safe to eat, and 13% have no opinion. H_1: The distribution is not the same as stated in the null hypothesis (claim). C.V. = 9.210; d.f. = 2; χ^2 = 1.4286; do not reject. There is not enough evidence to support the claim that the proportions are different from those reported in the survey.

11. H_0: The types of loans are distributed as follows: 21% for home mortgages, 39% for automobile purchases, 20% for credit card, 12% for real estate, and 8% for miscellaneous (claim). H_1: The distribution is different from that stated in the null hypothesis. C.V. = 9.488; d.f. = 4; χ^2 = 4.786; do not reject. There is not enough evidence to reject the claim that the distribution is the same as reported in the newspaper.

13. H_0: The methods of payments of adult shoppers for purchases are distributed as follows: 53% pay cash, 30% use checks, 16% use credit cards, and 1% have no preference (claim). H_1: The distribution is not the same as stated in the null hypothesis. C.V. = 11.345; d.f. = 3; χ^2 = 36.8897; reject. There is enough evidence to reject the claim that the distribution at the large store is the same as in the survey.

15. H_0: The proportion of Internet users is the same for the groups. H_1: The proportion of Internet users is not the same for the groups (claim). C.V. = 5.991; χ^2 = 0.208; do not reject. There is insufficient evidence to conclude that the proportions differ.

17. H_0: The distribution of the ways people pay for their prescriptions is as follows: 60% used personal funds, 25% used insurance, and 15% used Medicare (claim). H_1: The distribution is not the same as stated in the null hypothesis. The d.f. = 2; α = 0.05; χ^2 = 0.667; do not reject since P-value > 0.05. There is not enough evidence to reject the claim that the distribution is the same as stated in the null hypothesis. An implication of the results is that the majority of people are using their own money to pay for medications. Maybe the medication should be less expensive to help out these people. (TI: P-value = 0.7164)

19. Answers will vary.

Exercises 11–2

1. The independence test and the goodness-of-fit test both use the same formula for computing the test value. However, the independence test uses a contingency table, whereas the goodness-of-fit test does not.

3. H_0: The variables are independent (or not related). H_1: The variables are dependent (or related).

5. The expected values are computed as (row total × column total) ÷ grand total.

7. H_0: $p_1 = p_2 = p_3 = p_4 = \cdots = p_n$. H_1: At least one proportion is different from the others.

9. H_0: The number of endangered species is independent of the number of threatened species. H_1: The number of endangered species is dependent upon the number of threatened species (claim). C.V. = 9.488; χ^2 = 45.315; reject. There is sufficient evidence to conclude a relationship. The result is not different at α = 0.01.

11. H_0: The composition of the legislature (House of Representatives) is independent of the state. H_1: The composition of the legislature is dependent upon the state (claim). C.V. = 7.815; d.f. = 3; χ^2 = 48.7521; reject. There is enough evidence to support the claim that the composition of the legislature is dependent upon the state.

13. H_0: The occupation of legislators is independent of the Congressional sessions. H_1: The occupation of U.S. legislators is dependent upon the Congressional session (claim). C.V. = 15.507; χ^2 = 2.035; do not reject. There is insufficient evidence to conclude dependence.

15. H_0: The program of study of a student is independent of the type of institution. H_1: The program of study of a student is dependent upon the type of institution (claim). C.V. = 7.815; χ^2 = 13.702; reject. There is sufficient evidence to conclude that there is a relationship between program of study and type of institution.

17. H_0: The type of video rented is independent of the person's age. H_1: The type of video rented is dependent on the person's age (claim). C.V. = 13.362; d.f. = 8; χ^2 = 46.733; reject. Yes, there is enough evidence to support the claim that the type of movie selected is related to the age of the customer.

19. H_0: The type of snack purchased is independent of the gender of the consumer (claim). H_1: The type of snack purchased is dependent upon the gender of the consumer. C.V. = 4.605; d.f. = 2; χ^2 = 6.342; reject. There is enough evidence to reject the claim that the type of snack is independent of the gender of the consumer.

21. H_0: The type of book purchased by an individual is independent of the gender of the individual (claim). H_1: The type of book purchased by an individual is dependent on the gender of the individual. The d.f. = 2; α = 0.05; χ^2 = 19.43; P-value < 0.05; reject since P-value < 0.05. There is enough evidence to reject the claim that the type of book purchased by an individual is independent of the gender of the individual. (TI: P-value = 0.00006)

23. H_0: $p_1 = p_2 = p_3 = p_4$ (claim). H_1: At least one proportion is different. C.V. = 7.815; d.f. = 3; χ^2 = 5.317; do not reject. There is not enough evidence to reject the claim that the proportions are equal.

25. H_0: $p_1 = p_2 = p_3 = p_4$ (claim). H_1: At least one of the proportions is different from the others. C.V. = 7.815; d.f. = 3; χ^2 = 1.172; do not reject. There is not enough evidence to reject the claim that the proportions are equal. Since the survey was done in Pennsylvania, it is doubtful that it can be generalized to the population of the United States.

27. H_0: $p_1 = p_2 = p_3 = p_4 = p_5$. H_1: At least one proportion is different. C.V. = 9.488; χ^2 = 12.028; reject. There is sufficient evidence to conclude that the proportions differ.

29. H_0: $p_1 = p_2 = p_3 = p_4$ (claim). H_1: At least one proportion is different. The d.f. = 3; χ^2 = 1.734; α = 0.05; P-value > 0.10 (0.629); do not reject since P-value > 0.05. There is not enough evidence to reject the claim that the proportions are equal. (TI: P-value = 0.6291)

31. H_0: $p_1 = p_2 = p_3$ (claim). H_1: At least one proportion is different. C.V. = 4.605; d.f. = 2; χ^2 = 2.401; do not reject. There is not enough evidence to reject the claim that the proportions are equal.

33. χ^2 = 1.075

Exercises 11–3

1. The analysis of variance using the F test can be employed to compare three or more means.

3. The populations from which the samples were obtained must be normally distributed. The samples must be independent of each other. The variances of the populations must be equal.

5. $F = \dfrac{S_B^2}{S_W^2}$

7. 1

9. H_0: $\mu_1 = \mu_2 = \mu_3$. H_1: At least one of the means differs from the others. C.V. = 4.26; d.f.N. = 2; d.f.D. = 9; F = 14.149; reject. There is sufficient evidence to conclude at least one mean is different from the others.

11. H_0: $\mu_1 = \mu_2 = \mu_3$. H_1: At least one mean is different from the others (claim). C.V. = 3.98; α = 0.05; d.f.N. = 2; d.f.D. = 11; F = 2.7313; do not reject. There is not enough evidence to support the claim that at least one mean is different from the others.

13. H_0: $\mu_1 = \mu_2 = \mu_3$. H_1: At least one mean is different from the others (claim). C.V. = 3.68; α = 0.05; d.f.N. = 2; d.f.D. = 15; F = 8.14; reject. There is enough evidence to support the claim that at least one mean is different from the others.

15. H_0: $\mu_1 = \mu_2 = \mu_3$ (claim). H_1: At least one mean is different from the others. C.V. = 4.10; α = 0.05; d.f.N. = 2; d.f.D. = 10; F = 3.9487; do not reject. There is not enough evidence to reject the claim that the means are equal.

17. H_0: $\mu_1 = \mu_2 = \mu_3$. H_1: At least one mean is different from the others (claim). F = 10.118; P-value = 0.00102; reject. There is enough evidence to conclude that at least one mean is different from the others.

Review Exercises

1. H_0: People show no preference for the day of the week that they do their shopping (claim). H_1: People show a preference for the day of the week that they do their shopping. C.V. = 12.592; d.f. = 6; χ^2 = 237.15; reject. There is enough evidence to reject the claim that shoppers have no preference for the day of the week that they do their shopping. Retail merchants should probably plan for more shoppers on Fridays and Saturdays than they will have on the other days of the week.

3. H_0: Opinion is independent of gender. H_1: Opinion is dependent on gender (claim). C.V. = 4.605; d.f. = 2; χ^2 = 6.163; reject. There is enough evidence to support the claim that opinion is dependent on gender.

5. H_0: The type of investment is independent of the age of the investor. H_1: The type of investment is dependent on the age of the investor (claim). C.V. = 9.488; d.f. = 4; χ^2 = 28.0; reject. There is enough evidence to support the claim that the type of investment is dependent on the age of the investor.

7. H_0: $p_1 = p_2 = p_3$ (claim). H_1: At least one proportion is different. χ^2 = 4.912; d.f. = 2; α = 0.01; 0.05 < P-value < 0.10 (0.086); do not reject since P-value > 0.01. There is not enough evidence to reject the claim that the proportions are equal.

9. H_0: $p_1 = p_2 = p_3 = p_4 = p_5$. H_1: At least one proportion is different. χ^2 = 9.487; P-value = 0.05 < 0.10; reject. There is sufficient evidence to conclude that the proportions are not all the same.

11. $H_0: \mu_1 = \mu_2 = \mu_3$ (claim). H_1: At least one mean is different from the others. C.V. = 5.39; d.f.N. = 2; d.f.D. = 33; $\alpha = 0.01$; $F = 6.94$; reject. There is sufficient evidence to conclude that at least one mean is different from the others.

13. $H_0: \mu_1 = \mu_2 = \mu_3$. H_1: At least one mean is different from the others (claim). C.V. = 3.55; $\alpha = 0.05$; d.f.N. = 2; d.f.D. = 18; $F = 0.0408$; do not reject. There is not enough evidence to support the claim that at least one mean is different from the others.

15. $H_0: \mu_1 = \mu_2 = \mu_3$. H_1: At least one mean is different from the others (claim). C.V. = 2.61; $\alpha = 0.10$; d.f.N. = 2; d.f.D. = 19; $F = 0.4876$; do not reject. There is not enough evidence to support the claim that at least one mean is different from the others.

17. $H_0: \mu_1 = \mu_2 = \mu_3 = \mu_4$. H_1: At least one mean is different from the others (claim). C.V. = 3.59; $\alpha = 0.05$; d.f.N. = 3; d.f.D. = 11; $F = 0.182$; do not reject. There is not enough evidence to support the claim that at least one mean is different from the others.

Chapter Quiz

1. False

2. True

3. False

4. False

5. False

6. False

7. c

8. b

9. d

10. d

11. a

12. a

13. 6

14. Independent

15. Right

16. At least five

17. ANOVA

18. H_0: The reasons why people lost their jobs are equally distributed (claim). H_1: The reasons why people lost their jobs are not equally distributed. C.V. = 5.991; d.f. = $\chi^2 = 2.334$; do not reject. There is not enough evidence to reject the claim that the reasons why people lost their jobs are equally distributed. The results could have been different 10 years ago since different factors of the economy existed then.

19. H_0: Takeout food is consumed according to the following distribution: 53% at home, 19% in the car, 14% at work, and 14% at other places (claim). H_1: The distribution is different from that stated in the null hypothesis. C.V. = 11.345; d.f. = 3; $\chi^2 = 5.271$; do not reject. There is not enough evidence to reject the claim that the distribution is as stated. Fast-food restaurants may want to make their advertisements appeal to those who like to take their food home to eat.

20. H_0: College students show the same preference for shopping channels as those surveyed. H_1: College students show a different preference for shopping channels (claim). C.V. = 7.815; d.f. = 3; $\alpha = 0.05$; $\chi^2 = 21.789$; reject.

There is enough evidence to support the claim that college students show a different preference for shopping channels.

21. H_0: The number of commuters is distributed as follows: 75.7%, alone; 12.2%, carpooling; 4.7%, public transportation; 2.9%, walking; 1.2%, other; and 3.3%, working at home. H_1: The proportion of workers using each type of transportation differs from the stated proportions. C.V. = 11.071; d.f. = 5; $\chi^2 = 41.269$; reject. There is enough evidence to support the claim that the distribution is different from the one stated in the null hypothesis.

22. H_0: Ice cream flavor is independent of the gender of the purchaser (claim). H_1: Ice cream flavor is dependent upon the gender of the purchaser. C.V. = 7.815; d.f. = 3; $\chi^2 = 7.198$; do not reject. There is not enough evidence to reject the claim that ice cream flavor is independent of the gender of the purchaser.

23. H_0: The type of pizza ordered is independent of the age of the individual who purchases it. H_1: The type of pizza ordered is dependent on the age of the individual who purchases it (claim). $\chi^2 = 107.3$; d.f. = 9; $\alpha = 0.10$; P-value < 0.005; reject since P-value < 0.10. There is enough evidence to support the claim that the pizza purchased is related to the age of the purchaser.

24. H_0: The color of the pennant purchased is independent of the gender of the purchaser (claim). H_1: The color of the pennant purchased is dependent on the gender of the purchaser. $\chi^2 = 5.632$; C.V. = 4.605; reject. There is enough evidence to reject the claim that the color of the pennant purchased is independent of the gender of the purchaser.

25. H_0: The opinion of the children on the use of the tax credit is independent of the gender of the children. H_1: The opinion of the children on the use of the tax credit is dependent upon the gender of the children (claim). C.V. = 4.605; d.f. = 2; $\chi^2 = 1.534$; do not reject. There is not enough evidence to support the claim that the opinion of the children on the use of the tax is dependent on their gender.

26. $H_0: p_1 = p_2 = p_3$ (claim). H_1: At least one proportion is different from the others. C.V. = 4.605; d.f. = 2; $\chi^2 = 6.711$; reject. There is enough evidence to reject the claim that the proportions are equal. It seems that more women are undecided about their jobs. Perhaps they want better income or greater chances of advancement.

27. $H_0: \mu_1 = \mu_2 = \mu_3 = \mu_4$. H_1: At least one mean is different from the others (claim). C.V. = 3.49; $\alpha = 0.05$; d.f.N. = 3; d.f.D. = 12; $F = 3.23$; do not reject. There is not enough evidence to support the claim that there is a difference in the means.

28. $H_0: \mu_1 = \mu_2 = \mu_3$. H_1: At least one mean is different from the others (claim). C.V. = 6.93; $\alpha = 0.01$; d.f.N. = 2; d.f.D. = 12; $F = 3.49$. There is not enough evidence to support the claim that at least one mean is different from the others. Writers would want to target their material to the age group of the viewers.

29. H_0: $\mu_1 = \mu_2 = \mu_3$. H_1: At least one mean is different from the others (claim). C.V. = 3.68; $\alpha = 0.05$; d.f.N. = 2; d.f.D. = 15; $F = 10.494$; reject. At least one mean is different from the others.

30. H_0: $\mu_1 = \mu_2 = \mu_3$ (claim). H_1: At least one mean is different from the others. C.V. = 2.70; $\alpha = 0.10$; d.f.N. = 2; d.f.D. = 15; $F = 0.0509$; do not reject. There is not enough evidence to reject the claim that the means are equal.

31. H_0: $\mu_1 = \mu_2 = \mu_3 = \mu_4$. H_1: At least one mean is different from the others (claim). C.V. = 3.07; $\alpha = 0.05$; d.f.N. = 3; d.f.D. = 21; $F = 0.4564$; do not reject. There is not enough evidence to support the claim that at least one mean is different from the others.

Appendix A

A–1. 362,880

A–3. 120

A–5. 1

A–7. 1320

A–9. 20

A–11. 126

A–13. 70

A–15. 1

A–17. 560

A–19. 2520

A–21. 121; 2181; 14,641; 716.9

A–23. 32; 258; 1024; 53.2

A–25. 328; 22,678; 107,584; 1161.2

A–27. 693; 50,511; 480,249; 2486.1

A–29. 318; 20,150; 101,124; 3296

A–31.

A–33.

A–35.

A–37.

A–39.

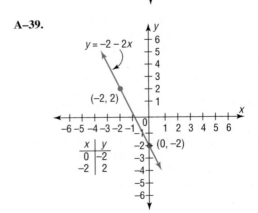

Index